The Basic Dictionary
of Science

The Basic Dictionary
of Science

EDITED IN BASIC ENGLISH

for

THE ORTHOLOGICAL INSTITUTE

by

E. C. GRAHAM, Ph.D.

THE MACMILLAN COMPANY

NEW YORK

First published 1965 by Evans Brothers Limited, London
First American edition 1966

The Macmillan Company, New York
Printed in the United States of America

ABOUT THIS BOOK

The special purpose of this Dictionary is to be of help to those interested in science.

In order to make the senses of the words as clear and simple as possible they have been given in Basic English.[1] This is not to say that the language of the Dictionary will seem at all unnatural. In fact, without reading this statement, most users would be quite unconscious that it was in any way different from full English. The structure of Basic is quite regular, and the Basic words, though limited in number and controlled in sense, are a selection well representative of the word-store of any person of education. The point in using Basic here is that it makes it necessary to get down to the root ideas at the back of any word before attempting to put it into other words—a process the outcome of which, though of special help to persons who have had no or little training in science, is without question of value to anybody, even to science experts themselves.

The Dictionary gives the senses of more than 25,000 words and word-groups taken from all branches of Physics, Chemistry, Biology, Medicine, Psychology, Astronomy, Geology, and Anthropology, as well as from important fields of science in industry, such as Engineering, Aeronautics, and Metallurgy.[2] In addition, a small number of words have been put in which are not special to science, but which are so much a part of its framework that science reading is unable to get far without a knowledge of them.

The general level of selection and detail is about that of first-year university work. Though in the present condition of growth in science, when new discoveries are being made, and new words and senses are coming into the language, at an unparalleled rate, it is impossible for any dictionary to be completely up to the minute, every care has been taken to get in all the important new words which have become current up to the time of printing.

The system of the Dictionary is very simple, and the rules and directions given on pp. ix to xvi will make it all quite clear without further observations. There is, however, one point on which it may be well to say something. Naturally, any science word in the Dictionary may be

---

[1] The word-list of Basic English is a selection of 850 English words chiefly representative of those key ideas into which more complex ones may be broken down, and it is used with the addition of such words as are common to all the important languages at the present-day—among them a number of science words and the names of the chief sciences themselves.

[2] A more detailed view of the fields covered may be got from the list of Science Guides on p. xiii.

used in giving the sense of another; but when a word so used is not Basic, it is put in special print. What is to be noted is that no attempt has been made to do without this use of science words needing to be looked up, or to put any unnatural limit to the number which may be used in any one connection. From this point of view, a science dictionary is quite different from a general dictionary. Every science not only has its key-words, which come into almost everything general which has to be said about it, and in relation to which other words have to be placed, but it has groups of words having such a connection with one another that a knowledge of one is incomplete without a knowledge of the others. It is the business of a dictionary of this sort not only to give the senses of words but to give them in such a way that the reader sees these words in the complex of which they are a part.

The Dictionary was first undertaken as part of the programme made possible by the support given by the Rockefeller Foundation to the Ortho-logical Institute before the war. The earliest form of it was produced in 1938–9 by Dr. H. Stafford Hatfield. Though in the end, when ideas as to the range and level and organization of the Dictionary had become clearer, very little of this first attempt was used, it was of value in getting together a mass of material and in pointing by example to the dangers to be kept clear of and the questions needing decision; and in that sense the present Dictionary may be said to be based on it.

Nothing more was done while the war was on and for some time after, but in 1947 the work was started again with money from the newly-formed Basic English Foundation, and by 1949, after much discussion with men of science in all fields, and the special help of Dr. James Lawrie,[1] who went through the material in detail, the lines on which the book was to be worked out had been more or less fixed. I then became responsible for the detailed organization and for the Basic side of the work, with Mr. William Grubb as my chief helper at the Ortho-logical Institute and Mr. C. L. Boltz (at that time Science Correspondent at the B.B.C.) to oversee the science side. Among the great number of other experts who gave their help at different stages on general or special questions, or in special fields, were, most importantly: Dr. J. A. Lauwerys, Professor of Comparative Education in the University of London and Chairman of the Basic English Foundation; Dr. G. C. Ainsworth of the Commonwealth Mycological Institute at Kew; and the late Dr. G. A. Thomas of Guy's Hospital Medical School.

In 1953 the work was complete, but first the ending of Government support and then the death of C. K. Ogden kept it from getting into print. It was not till 1960 that it was taken up again, and we were then faced by the need for the addition of the great number of new words which had become current in the years between, and for other changes made necessary by the unparalleled expansion of science in those years. In making these additions and changes, I had the help of Mr. Norman Manners, whose work keeps him in touch with new

---

[1] Then Editor of *Chemical Products* and *The Chemical News*.

developments in science on a very wide front, and whose experience and knowledge were of the very greatest value.[1]

I am happy to give credit here to all those who had a hand in getting the Dictionary into its present form, and specially to put on record my great debt to Mr. Boltz and Mr. Manners for the care and interest they took in clearing up complex points so that they might be put in simple English.

This account is itself all in Basic English.

ELSIE C. GRAHAM

[1] Mr. Manners was at that time Chief Press Officer for the *Department of Scientific and Industrial Research*.

RULES AND DIRECTIONS

1. WEIGHT. A mark is put before the part of a word on which the weight comes (**a′brupt**). In words formed from a root word by the addition of an ending, or of another word, and not printed in full (*see* § 11), if the weight is on the root word the mark is put before the joining-sign (as **′-er**, under **bleed**); if the weight is on the ending or the second word, the mark is put after the joining-sign (as **-′mastoid** under **para**). When the weight comes equally on the two parts of a complex word, no mark is used (**air-dry**).

2. If a word has two or more different forms, this is made clear: (a) Sometimes by putting a letter between ( ) as a sign that it may or may not be put in, for example, **Arch(a)ean.** (In such examples the simpler form is more commonly used in America and the other in Britain); (b) Sometimes by giving different possible endings after a '-', as in "**arbo′re-al, -ous,** aa." (which is to say that there are two words, **arboreal** and **arboreous,** having the same sense), or "**anti′ve-nin, -nene, -nine,** nn." (*See* § 4); (c) Sometimes by giving the different forms in full with a ',' or 'or' separating them, as in "**mono′genesis, mon′ogeny,** nn." and "**pale, ′palet** or **′palea,** nn."

3. Forms for more than one which are not regular are put in common print between ( ) straight after the word: "**aphelion** (aphelia)." Sometimes there is a regular form in addition (**apex**, for example, may have **apices** or **apexes**), but this is not noted, as the regular form will be clear when it is come across.

4. The regular English names for the different sorts of words are, in their short forms, put after all listed words to make clear their use in a statement:

n. (noun)	v. (verb)
a. (adjective)	t. (transitive)
adv. (adverb)	i. (intransitive)

   After groups of words, these letters are put twice as a sign for more than one, as "**pan′iculate, ′panicled,** aa.", and "**mi′cell(e), mi′cella,** nn."

5. In the account of the sense or senses of a word, or in listing or making clear any word or word-group formed from it, if the word itself is needed, only its first letter is used (or its first letter twice for more than one). For example, under **anvil** we have:

   a.′bone. The . . . a.-like bone . . .
   and under **alve′olus:**
   alve′olar, a. Having, to do with, aa.

6. PRINT. **Black print** is used for any word or word-group listed for attention, that is, of which the sense is given or is made clear by an

ending etc.—in other words, for any chief word or group of letters at the left of the page, or any word or word-group formed from, or dependent on, one of these and made clear by the rules if not necessarily by a statement of sense. For example:

> **ab′normal,** a. Not normal. **a. psych′ology.** The . . . .

> **′plan(o)-.** With the power of moving about: **′plano-spore,** n., **′plano′zygote,** n.

Sloping print is used for: (a) Words in any language other than English, frequently the Latin group-names of plants and animals, as " *in vitro*, adv." and: "'**psitta′cosis,** n. [Med.] A . . . disease of certain birds, sp. of the order *Psittacideae* . . . "; (b) Words given as examples of the working of a rule, etc., for example, under **a′phaeresis,** "such as *'gainst* for *against*"; (c) The word *'See'* used in pointing to pictures, etc. on other pages.

GREAT LETTERS are used for any word not in the general Basic English word-list which comes into the account given of another one (*see* p. vi.) E.g.: "'**febrile,** a, [Med.] To do with FEVER." All such words are made clear in the Dictionary, and, if they are strange to the reader, will have to be looked up in their places. Even Basic words are printed in this way when they are used in a sense special to some science, of which, though the user of Basic may have a general idea of it, it will be well for him to make certain in detail. For example, SALT, MASS, ACID, WAVE.

7. Words formed from a chief word by different endings, but being of the same sort and having the same sense, are given in a group with aa., nn., etc. after them. But if their sense or use is different to even the smallest degree, they are put separately. For example, under **′febrile,** "'**febricant, febri′facient,** nn., aa. **feb′riferous,** a. **feb′rific,** a."

8. Letters or groups of letters incomplete in themselves, but used for putting at the front of words to make new words of a certain sense, are listed in the same way as words, with examples of the words made from them put after them. When the sense of any of these new words is clear from the senses of its parts, then no account of it is given:

> **bi-.** Two, twice, every two: **-′angular,** a., **-′axial,** a.

If there are two or more forms for the same sense, then they are grouped together like words, e.g. **'mes(o),'** and **'pi′eso-, piezo-.'** But this is only done when their places in the ABC order are very near one another. If not, they are put in separately, as **a-** and **an-.**

9. ORDER. First come all the senses of the chief word; second, all the word-groups of which it is the first word; third, all the words formed from or dependent on it, with the word-groups etc. formed from any new word put straight after it (the new word, however, unlike the chief word, being printed in its full form in all these):

> **'iodine,** n, Chemical . . . . . . **i. value** or **number.** . . . . . . **iodic,** a. To do with, having in it i., . . . **i′odic a′cid.** . . . the reaction of i. . ., **'iodism,** n. [Med.] . . . . . . **i′odo′phil-ic, -ous,** aa. . . . . **i′odo-.**

Take note that if the chief word, or any part or word made from it is used as a joining-form at the front of other words, then this is put last of all, without any statement of sense, as **iodo-** in the example given.

10. WORD-MAKING. New words may be made from a root word by the addition of endings—a process which is not new to the Basic learner. But in this Dictionary, the word used as a chief word is not necessarily a root-word, to which endings are joined. It is a word which is looked on as in some sense a key-word, with which a number of other words, formed from it or having some other clear connection with it, are grouped. It may be the most important word in the group, or the word in the light of which the others are most readily made clear. It may itself have been formed with an ending, so that new words are to be made from it by dropping or changing this, in place of by the simple addition of an ending. For example, from the key-word **adap′tation** we get a′**dapt,** v. t. and a′**daptor,** n. In whatever way a new word is formed, if its connection with the key-word is quite clear no account of its sense is given. But this is never done when there is the smallest danger of any error.

11. GENERAL AND SPECIAL ENDINGS. A complete list of the general English endings of fixed sense used in the Dictionary is given on pp. xiii–xvi, from which the user may readily see the senses of the words formed with them.

Endings special to science, such as **-ectomy,** n. [Med.] and **-cide,** n. [Biol.], are used in the same way, but they are not listed as a group. They are all given separately in the Dictionary and may be looked up in their places.

Words made from a key-word by the simple addition of endings may, if their form and sound are quite regular, not be printed in full, but only pointed to by the ending, with '**-**' in place of the first part.

　　　′**mineral,** n. . . . ′**-ize,** v. t. Make the addition of a m. or mm. to . . .

But if the ending makes any change in where the weight comes, or in any of the letters, or is so short that it might be overlooked, or for any other reason does not give a straightforward picture of the new form, then all the word is printed, as a′**tomic,** a. under ′**atom.**

COMPLEX WORDS. A complete word which is put straight onto the chief word to make a complex word is printed after '**-**' in the same way as the ending (as **-ball** under **eye,** for **eyeball**). But if a complex word is joined by '**-**', then the first letter of the chief word is put before the joining-sign (as ′**e.-cup** under **eye,** for **eye-cup**).

12. SHORT FORMS etc. A guide to the signs used in Chemistry, and guides to short forms for British and European weights and measures, have been put at the end of the book, together with a number of other lists, to do with different sciences, which will be of great help to any user of the Dictionary (see pp. 548–68).

All short forms for other science words and word-groups which have been used, such as '**at. wt.**' (for 'atomic weight'), '**at. no.**' (for 'atomic number'), **'e.m.f.'** (for 'electromotive force'), **'C'** (for 'Centigrade') and so on, are listed in their places and made clear there.

In addition, use has been made of some short forms common in general English, These are:

N., S., E., & **W.** (North, South, East, and West)
Lat. (Latitude)
Long. (Longitude)
sec. (second—of time)
Brit. (British)
Am. (American)
e.g. (for example)
etc. (and so on)
freq. (frequently)
gen. (generally)
i.e. (that is)
opp. ('opposite to' or 'the opposite of')

Then there are two small Latin words of great value in putting things shortly:

non-   Put before other words to give the sense of 'not' where 'un-' would seem strange. E.g. **non-con'ducting,** a. [Elec.].

per   Used in giving rates, in the sense of 'in (or for) every', as "200 km. per hour", "10 shillings per person."

Last, there is the use of 'th' after numbers higher than three when naming order: **4th, 20th,** etc.

13. SCIENCE GUIDES. The names of a number of sciences are used between [ ], and generally in short form, to put before senses which are special to any of them. For example:

'micropyle, n. [Biol.] Very small opening for letting something in or out, sp. [Zoo.] in the skin . . .

This is done only when necessary, however. It is not done if there is only one sense and the account of it makes it quite clear in what science it is used. Where there are special senses in connection with different sciences which have to be kept separate from one another in this way, then the general sense, if any, comes first, as in:

com'ponent, n. Any of the parts, substances etc., making up a more complex thing or substance. [Mech.] Of a given force . . . [Phys., Chem.] In a system of . . . [Astron.] Any of the stars forming . . .

Sometimes the sense of a word formed from a key-word would be quite clear from its ending, but it has, in addition, a special sense in a certain science, or a number of such senses. When this is so, only the special sense or senses are given, starting with the short form 'Sp.,' put before the name of the science needed:

mi'grate, v. t. . . . **mi'gration,** n. Sp.: [Biol]. The change of living-place made regularly . . . [Bot.] The moving of plants by natural processes ... [Phys.-Chem.] The motion of IONS ...; the moving of an ATOM or atoms ....

Here are the short forms used for these science guides:

Acous. (Acoustics)
Anat. (Anatomy)
Anthrop. (Anthropology)
Archaeol. (Archaeology)
Arith. (Arithmetic)
Astron. (Astronomy)
Bact. (Bacteriology)
Biochem. (Biochemistry)
Biogeog. (Biogeography)
Biol. (Biology)
Bot. (Botany)
Chem. (Chemistry)
Cryst. (Crystallography)
Elec. (Electricity)
Engin. (Engineering)
Geog. (Geography)
Geol. (Geology)

Geom. (Geometry)
Mach. (Machinery)
Mag. (Magnetism)
Math. (Mathematics)
Mech. (Mechanics)
Med. (Medicine)
Metal. (Metallurgy)
Meteor. (Meteorology)
Mineral. (Mineralogy)
Palaeont. (Palaeontology)
Philol. (Philology)
Phonet. (Phonetics)
Photog. (Photography)
Phys. (Physics)
Physiol. (Physiology)
Psych. (Psychology)
Zoo. (Zoology)

The names of other sciences, when used, are given in their full form, as: Aeronautics, Astronautics, Optics, Radio, Surveying.

14. THE REGULAR ENDINGS

-able, a.   Able to be acted on in the given way, able to undergo the given process: **autoxidizable, filterable.**

-aceous, a.   Of, to do with, like, having, made up of: **acanthaceous, bulbaceous, scoriaceous, setaceous.**

-age, n.   1. Act, process, condition, or effect of doing or undergoing: **linkage, seepage.**
2. Amount or measure in the given units: **amperage, mileage.**

-al, a.   Of, to do with, like, coming from, produced by: **abdominal, bracteal, catarrhal, fungal, obsessional, rhomboidal.**

-an, 1. a.   Of, to do with, like, having the qualities of: **protozoan.**
    2. n.   Animal etc. of the named group: **crustacean.**

-ant, 1. a.   Doing or being what is named: **suppurant.**
    2. n.   Thing, substance, doing what is named: **oxidant.**

-ar, a.   Of, to do with, like, in the form of: **palmar, rectangular, stipular, scutellar.**

-ary, a.   **-ory: axillary.**

-ate,[1] a.	Having, marked by: **arillate, chelate, craniate, septate.**
-ation, -ition, n.	1. Act or process of doing, condition or degree of undergoing, being, what is named: **sensitization, rectification, supplementation, decomposition.** 2. Effect of, thing produced by, **-ation: magnification.**
-cy, n.	Condition, quality, or degree of being a given thing: **latency.**
-ence, n.	Act or fact of doing or undergoing the given process, or condition of having the given property: **coalescence, arborescence, flatulence, transience.**
-ent, a., n.	**-ant: abducent, fluorescent, repellent.**
-escence, n.	The condition, process, or property of being **-escent: spinulescence.**
-escent, a.	In a condition of becoming, starting to do or be, being to a small degree, what is named: **tumescent, senescent, obsolescent.**
-ial, a.	**-al: archesporial, equatorial.**
-ible, a.	**-able: transmissible.**
-ian, a., n.	**-an: holothurian.**
-ic,[2] 1. a.	Of, to do with, like, being, having, made up of: **achromatinic, biogenetic, bubonic, pancreatic, thoracic, spherulitic.**
2. n.	Person having the given disease, or substance or thing causing the given process: **arthritic, emetic.**
-ical, a.	**-ic: dropsical, meteorological, seismological.**
-iform, a.	Having the given form, in form like thing named: **aculeiform, bursiform, palpiform, stipuliform.**
-ify, v. t. & i.	Make, become, get formed into, what is named: **acidify.**
-ine, a.	Of, to do with, like, having the qualities of, being: **alkaline, corolline, sepaline.**
-ion, n.	1. Act, process, condition, of doing or undergoing what is named: **abduction, extravasation, migration.** 2. Effect of, thing or condition produced by, the given act or process: **bifurcation, infection.**
-ious, a.	**-ous: infectious.**
-ism,[3] n.	Act of doing, condition of being, what is named: **cretinism, eroticism.** 2. System or theory based on, or having some connection with, what is named: **dualism.**
-ist, n.	1. One who does, sp. one who is an expert in, the named process, science etc.: **agronomist, economist, geologist.** 2. A supporter of an **-ism: behaviourist.**
-ity, n.	The condition, property, power, or degree of being what is named: **abnormality, acidity, viscidity.**

---

[1] This ending has two special senses in Chemistry, one as n. and one as v., which see on p. 32.
[2] This ending has a special sense in Chemistry, *see* p. 190.
[3] This ending has a special medical sense, *see* p. 209.

-ive, 1. a.	Causing or having a tendency to a given act, or having the property of or some connection with a given thing: **agglutinative, excretive, expansive, obsessive, verificative.**
2. n.	Thing or substance which is **-ive: abrasive, purgative, contraceptive.**
-ize,[1] **ise,** v. t.	Make undergo a given act or process, or make into, make become, a given thing: **pasteurize, sterilize, immunize.**
-let, n.	A small example or sort of the thing named: **drupelet.**
-less, a.	Without, not having: **flowerless, seedless, sexless.**
-logist, -logy, nn.	**-ologist, -ology: zoölogy, zoölogist.**
-ment, n.	1. Act, process, or condition of acting or being acted on in the given way: **treatment.**
	2. Thing produced by or producing such a condition: **reinforcement.**
-ness, n.	Condition, quality, of being what is named: **aggressiveness.**
-oid, 1. a.	(Somewhat) like, in the form of, forming or formed of: **acanthoid, sepaloid.**
2. n.	Thing etc. which is **-oid: fibroid.**
-ologist, b.	An expert in a given science or theory: **meteorologist, palaeontologist, radiologist, seismologist.**
-ology, n.	Theory or science of: **actinology, vitaminology, serology.**
-ory, 1. a.	To do with, used for, causing, effecting: **copulatory, excretory, excitatory, respiratory.**
2. n.	Substance etc. which is **-ory: vomitory.**
-ose, a.	Formed or made up of, full of, having the qualities of, like: **bulbose, cymose, globose, setose.**
-ous,[2] a.	Of, to do with, formed or made up of, full of, having the form or qualities of, like: **acinous, cartilagenous, fibrous, monotrematous.**
-sion, -tion, nn.	**-ation: intrusion.**
-ulous, a.	With a tendency to be, somewhat: **acidulous.**
-y, 1. a.	Having, full of, having the properties of: **pulpy, rainy, stony, glassy, scurfy.**
2. n.	The condition of being what is pointed to, sp. something of which the name has the ending **-ous: anisomery, epigyny.**

In addition to these, there are the endings forming part of the Basic system, which are freely used:

-ed, a.	1. Having undergone the act or process named: **carbonized, decomposed, staggered, sensitized.**
	2. Having, marked by: **winged.**

---

[1] This ending has a special sense in Chemistry, *see* p. 212.
[2] This ending has a special sense in Chemistry, *see* p. 300.

-er, or, nn.	Person doing, or instrument or apparatus used for doing, what is named: **dilator, discharger, photographer, regulator.**
-ing, 1. a.	In the given act or condition, or used for the purpose of effecting or producing it: **refracting, screening.**
2. n.	The act or fact of, or thing produced by or used for, doing the given act: **soldering, lagging.**
-ly, adv.	In the given way, or from the point of view of, in relation to, a given thing: **abruptly, biologically externally, practically, symmetrically.**

A, Sign for ARGON.

A or **Å** = ÅNGSTROM UNIT(s).

A = ABSOLUTE (of TEMPERATURE).

α, *See* ALPHA.

a-, Not, not having, the opposite of: a′carpellous, a′petalous, a′septate, a′synchronous, a′typical, aa.

ab-, Away from. [Phys.] Put before the names of some electric measuring units to make the name of the ELECTROMAGNETIC C.G.S. unit used for measuring the same thing, as ABAMPERE, ABVOLT, etc. (chiefly U.S.A.).

ab′actinal, a. [Zoo.] Opposite the mouth (of ECHINODERMS).

ab′ampere, n. [Elec.] *See* AB-, = 10 AMPERES.

ab′axial, a. Not on, pointing away from, or [Biol.] on the side of a leaf, muscle, etc., furthest from, the AXIS.

′Abder′halden reaction or **test.** [Med.] A chemical test given to the blood to see if certain ENZYMES are present, used in testing for PREGNANCY and certain diseases.

ab′domen (abdomina), n. The lower hollow part of the body in man and back-boned animals, in which are stomach, INTESTINES, etc.; the back division of the body in insects and other ARTHROPODA. **ab′-dominal,** a. **abdominal pores.** Openings joining COELOM with outside in CYCLOSTOMES and some fish.

ab′duct, v.t. [Physiol.] Get (a part of the body) moved or turned away from the body's middle line. **ab′ducent,** a. **abducent nerve.** Nerve going to muscle by which eyeball is turned out. **ab′duction,** n. **ab′ductor,** n. Any muscle effecting abduction.

′Abel tester, Abel flash-point apparatus. [Chem.] Apparatus for measuring the FLASH POINT of an oil.

aben′teric, a. [Med.] Outside the INTESTINES.

ab′errant, a. [Biol.] Different from the normal. **ab′errancy,** n.

aber′ration, n. [Astron.] The amount by which the direction of a star as seen from the earth seems to be different from its true direction because of the rate of motion of the earth and the rate of motion of light. [Optics] (Amount of) error in IMAGE formed by a LENS or looking-glass caused by its not making rays come together at the right points (*see* SPHERICAL A., CHROMATIC A.). [Physiol.] The going of blood or other body liquid into the wrong place. [Biol.] Any plant, animal, or part which is not normal.

ab′farad, n. [Elec.] *See* AB-, = 10⁹ FARADS.

ab′henry, n. [Elec.] *See* AB-, = 10 HENRYS.

abi′etic acid. [Chem.] A CRYSTALLINE acid, $C_{20}H_{30}O_2$, got from ROSIN.

abio′genesis, n. [Biol.] The producing of living things from unliving material.

ab′jection, n. [Bot.] The sending off of SPORES by the SPOROPHORE of a FUNGUS.

ab′junction, n. [Bot.] ABSTRICTION.

ab′lation, n. [Geol.] The process of taking away, such as the wasting away of ROCK by the operation of water. [Med.] The operation of taking away body TISSUE by cutting etc.

′ablaut, n. [Philol.] VOWEL-change in words formed from a root-word, freq. as sign of a special use, e.g. *get, got.*

ab′luent, a., n. DETERGENT.

′Abney ′level. A special form of CLINOMETER used in SURVEYING.

′Abney colour sensi′tometer. A form of SENSITOMETER used in camera work.

ab′normal, a. Not normal. **a. psy′chology.** The branch of psychology having to do with a. mind-processes, as in the MENTALLY DEFICIENT or INSANE, or those with abnormally high powers of mind, or normal persons under special conditions, such as HYPNOSIS, etc. **abnor′mality,** **ab′normity,** nn.

ab′ohm, n. [Elec.] *See* AB-, = 10⁻⁹ OHMS.

abo′ma-sum, -sus, nn. [Zoo.] Fourth stomach of a RUMINANT (cow, etc.).

ab′oral, a. [Zoo.] Opposite the mouth.

abo′rigenes, n.pl. The earliest men living in a country. **abo′riginal,** a.

a′bortion, n. [Biol.] (Of part of plant or animal) condition of being stopped in normal development; a part in this condition. [Med.] The producing of offspring before it has power of living, sp. not more than 16 weeks after start of development; an offspring so produced. **a′bort,** v.i Become, or give birth to, an a. **a′borti′-facient,** a., n. [Med.] (Substance) causing a, **a′bortive** a. Produced by, causing, or in a condition of a.

a′boulia, n. ABULIA.

a′branchi-ate, -an, -ous, aa. [Zoo.] Not having GILLS.

a′brasion, n. The process of rubbing away a substance, smoothing or damaging it by rubbing; a mark, etc., made by a., sp. [Med.] a wound caused by the a. of the skin by something rough. **a′brasive,** 1.a. 2.n. Substance used for rubbing down or polishing metal, etc. **a′brade,** v.t. Get (thing) smoothed or damaged by rubbing.

′abraum salts. Mixed salts got from the earth at Stassfurt from which the metal K is got.

abre′action, n. [Psychoanalysis] The letting out of secret feelings causing a COMPLEX by talking or acting out the secret or unconscious desires or memories which are at the root of the trouble.

a′brupt, a. [Bot.] Ending suddenly, as if cut off. **a′bruptly,** adv. **a′bruptly ′pinnate.** [Bot.] (Of leaves) PINNATE with no small leaf ending the stem, opp. ODD PINNATE.

′abscess, n. [Med.] A pocket of PUS-producing diseased substance at some point in the body, walled off from the healthy substance round it by LYMPH, caused by BACTERIA.

ab'scissa (abscissae), n. [Math.] *See* CARTESIAN COORDINATES.

ab'scission, n. [Bot.] Any natural process by which two parts become separate, as the separating of a SPORE from a SPOROPHORE.

'absciss 'layer. [Bot.] A thin wall or division between two parts which later become separate, sp. between leaf and stem.

'absolute, a. Viewed independently, not in relation to or as conditioned by any other thing, as *a. space, time, motion* (opp. RELATIVE). [Phys.] Measured or measuring in a. units. [Chem.] Unmixed with any other substance, sp. **a. alcohol** (C_2H_4OH). **a. boiling-point.** CRITICAL TEMPERATURE. **a. hu'midity.** [Meteor.] The number of grammes of water-VAPOUR in 1 m.³ of the air. **a. 'magnitude.** [Astron.] The size a star would seem to be at a distance of 32·6 LIGHT-YEARS. **a. pitch.** (Of a sound) the number of VIBRATIONS in a second. **a. 'pressure.** True PRESSURE of a liquid or gas measured in relation to no pressure at all in units of force per unit AREA. **a. scale (of temperature).** [Phys.] A TEMPERATURE scale based on THERMODYNAMIC arguments and not on the physical behaviour of water or any other substance, of which the starting-point is a. zero and the degrees are equal to those of the Centigrade scale. **a. 'temperature.** TEMPERATURE measured on the a. scale. **a. 'unit.** A measuring unit which may be given in units of LENGTH, MASS, and time, sp. one based on the centimetre, the gramme, and the second, opp. PRACTICAL (*see* AB-). **a. 'zero.** [Phys.] The TEMPERATURE at which a substance would in theory be without any motion of its MOLECULES or ATOMS and so quite without heat, −273°C. -ly adv.

ab'sorb, v.t. (Of a thing or substance) take into itself (another thing or substance) as the absorbing of water by a sponge, or [Med.] of food by the body, or [Chem.] of a SOLUTE by a SOLVENT. [Phys.] Have the effect of keeping (a motion) from going further, not turning it back or letting it through, as the absorbing of shocks by the springs of an automobile or of sound-waves or ELECTROMAGNETIC waves, such as light or radio waves, by certain substances, etc.; take up (ENERGY) by changing it into some other form. ab'sorbe'facient, n., a. [Chem., Med.] (Substance) causing or helping the process of absorbing. ab'sorbent, n., a. (Substance) having the property of absorbing. ab'sorptive, a. Absorbent. 'absorp'tivity, n. Property or power of absorbing.

ab'sorpti'ometer, n. [Chem.] Instrument for measuring the degree to which gases are ABSORBED by liquids.

ab'sorption, n. The process of ABSORBING or being absorbed. **a. band or line.** [Phys.] Dark band or line in the a. spectrum of a substance representative of rays undergoing a. in that substance. **a. coeff'icient.** [Chem.] Amount of gas taken up under normal conditions by a fixed unit amount of a liquid (1 c.c.—Bunsen, 1 gm.—Kehnen, 100 c.c.—Raoult). [Phys.] A. factor; in PLASMA PHYSICS, the amount of the loss of ENERGY undergone by the wave in going a unit distance. **a. edge.** The WAVELENGTH at which there is a sudden change in the a. spectrum of X-RAYS. **a. 'factor.** The number giving the RATIO of the amount of light or other ENERGY undergoing a. by a given substance to the amount going into it. **a. 'spectrum.** [Phys., Chem.] (The system of a. bands or lines seen in) the SPECTRUM formed by white light when it is sent through a given substance in which certain rays undergo a. **a. tubes.** [Chem.] Pipe-like vessels full of some solid for the a. of liquid or gas in some chemical process.

'abstract, 1.a. To do with ideas viewed in themselves, without relation to material things, with general ideas as separated from special facts or examples, or with thought and theory as opp. physical facts. 2.n. A short outline of the chief points in a book, paper, etc.

ab'striction, n. [Bot.] The forming of SPORES by the growth of division-walls across the SPOROPHORE, cutting off one bit after another.

ab'terminal, a. Going from the end to the middle, said of electric currents going through a muscle.

a'bulia, n. [Med.] Loss of power of making a decision.

ab'volt, n. [Elec.] *See* AB-, $= 10^{-8}$ VOLTS.

a'byss, n. Deepest part of sea. **a'byssal, a'bysmal,** aa. [Biol.] Living in the a. [Geol.] PLUTONIC. **abysso-.**

Ac, Sign for ACTINIUM.

A.C. = ALTERNATING CURRENT.

a'calyculate, a. [Bot.] Having no CALYX (or, infrequently, no CALYCLE); free from the calyx, as some STAMENS.

aca'naceous, a. [Bot.] Having sharp points.

a'cantha (acanthae), n. [Biol.] A sharp point. **acan'thaceous, a'canthous,** aa. **a'canthoid, a'cantho-.**

a'capnia, n. [Med.] Condition in which no or not enough CO_2 is present in the blood.

Aca'rina, n.pl. [Zoo.] An important CLASS of small ARACHNIDS of wide distribution, in which there is no clear division between CEPHALOTHORAX and ABDOMEN, freq. PARASITES, some causing special diseases of man, animals, or plants, chief representatives MITES and TICKS. **aca′riasis,** n. [Med.] Condition of being attacked by A. or disease caused by this. **a′caricide,** n. Substance causing destruction of A. **′acarid,** n. One of the A.

a′carpellous, a. [Bot.] Having no CARPELS.

a′carpous, a. [Bot.] Producing no fruit.

a′caulous, -ine, -ose, aa. [Bot.] Having no true stem, or only a very short one under the earth.

accele′ration, n. Change, sp. increase, in the rate of a motion, process, or reaction; any change in the rate and/or direction of a VELOCITY. [Mech.] Rate of a. of motion in a certain direction, normally measured as unit of distance per unit of time per unit of time. [Biol.] The development of changes of form earlier and earlier in offspring of a family of plants or animals. [Astron.] The day-to-day a. of the seeming motion of a FIXED STAR in comparison with that of sun; (of PLANET) a. of motion in going from APHELION to PERIHELION; (of moon) increase in MEAN rate of motion; (of TIDE) amount by which time of high water becomes earlier than the MEAN time in the 2nd and 4th QUARTERS of the moon. **ac′celerate,** v.t. and i. **ac′celerator,** n. Chemical substance, apparatus in engine, etc., causing a. [Phys.] Apparatus for giving great KINETIC ENERGY to CHARGED PARTICLES, such as ELECTRONS, HELIUM IONS, by ACCELERATING them to a very high rate of motion, used in NUCLEAR PHYSICS—for example, a CYCLO-TRON **′acceler′ometer,** n. **ac′celerograph,** n. **a. of ′gravity.** Rate of a. of the free fall of a body to the earth (980·6 cm./sec./sec. in Lat. 45°).

′accent, n. Sloping mark or marks placed at the right-hand top side of a letter in mathematics to make clear different values, as in *a′*, *a″*, or used with a number as representative of feet (′) and inches (″), or minutes (′) and seconds (″) of time or angle. [Phonet.] A quality given to one division of a word, or one word of a group, in talking, to make it more marked than the rest, or the way in which this is done, for example by saying it with more force, making it louder or longer, giving it a different PITCH, or producing some or all of these effects together; a mark put before or after an accented syllable in writing or print; a mark put over, under, etc., a letter, gen. a VOWEL, in writing or print to make clear that it has here some special sound. 2.v.t. [Phonet.] Put an a. mark against a letter, etc.; say with an a.

ac′ceptor, n. [Chem.] That substance in an INDUCED REACTION which does not undergo reaction with the INDUCTOR. [Radio] A CIRCUIT so TUNED to a certain in-coming wave or SIGNAL as to give the greatest possible current.

access′orius, n. [Zoo.] A muscle helping the operation of another.

ac′cessory, n., a. (Thing) present in addition to, helping, forming a small part of, the thing named. **a. cell.** [Bot.] A special CELL present with a GUARD-CELL in a STOMA, but different from it in structure. **a. ′chromosome.** [Zoo.] SEX CHROMOSOME. **a. (food) factor.** [Zoo.] VITAMIN. **a. fruit.** [Bot.] PSEUDOCARP. **a. gland.** [Zoo.] Any of certain GLANDS in connection with the male sex-parts in ARTHROPODA, sp. insects, producing a substance which becomes mixed with the SPERMATOZOA. **a. tone.** [Acous.] HARMONIC.

′accidence, n. [Philol.] (Rules having to do with) form-changes of words as a sign of different relations.

accli′mation, n. [Biol.] The adjustment of a plant or aninal to the different conditions of weather, etc. in a new country. **a. ′fever.** [Med.] Any of a number of diseases, gen. FEVERS, caused in man or animals on first coming to a different, sp. a TROPICAL, country, by some INFECTION general in those parts against which the blood of new-comers is not armed. **′acclimate,** v.t. and i. (Make) become used to the weather, etc., conditions of a new living-place. **′acclimated,** a.

ac′climati′zation, n. ACCLIMATION. [Chem.] The process by which certain SOLS undergo less COAGULATION when an ELECTRO-LYTE is put into them by slow degrees than when the same amount is put in at a greater rate. **acc′limatize,** v.t. and i. (Make) undergo a.

ac′commodation, n. [Zoo.] The automatic adjustment of the FOCAL LENGTH of the eye to different distances in seeing. **ac′commodate,** v.t. and i. (Make) undergo a.

ac′crescent, a. [Bot.] Getting greater in size after flowering, said sp. of CALYX. **ac′-crescence,** n.

ac′cretion, n. Growth, slow increase in size, sp. by addition of new parts or substance to outside; substance etc. forming such addition. [Med.] The growth together of parts naturally separate, as fingers.

accultu′ration, n. The process by which the arts and behaviour of one nation become like those of another near to it.

ac′cumbent, a. [Bot.] Touching something, sp. of COTYLEDONS having edges against RADICLE.

ac′cumulator, n. [Phys.] Any apparatus by which power, for example water-power, is stored. [Elec.] A STORAGE CELL or BATTERY.

′accurate, a. EXACT. **′accuracy,** n. Property of being a.

a′centric, a. [Biol.] Not placed at, ranged

round, or having parts ranged round, a middle point. [Zoo.] Not to do with or starting from a NERVE CENTRE; ACEN-TROUS.

a'centrous, a. [Zoo.] Having a NOTOCHORD all through existence without development of CENTRA.

-aceous, a. To do with, of, like.

a'cephalous, a. [Bot.] With OVARY not ending in a STIGMA. [Zoo.] Without a head. **a'cephalo-.**

'acerate, 'acerose, 'acerous, aa. [Bot.] Needle-like in form.

a'cerv-ate, -ative, -uline, aa. [Biol.] In the form of a small mass, massed together.

a'cervulus (acervuli), n. [Bot.] (In FUNGI) a well-marked group of CONIDIOPHORES. **a. 'cerebri.** BRAIN SAND.

ace'tabulum (acetabula), n. [Zoo.] Cup-like hollow in PELVIC GIRDLE, into which top of leg bone goes.

'acet'aldehyde, n. CH₃CHO. A liquid with a strong fruit-like smell and no colour produced by the reaction of O with ETHYL ALCOHOL and widely used in the making of ORGANIC substances.

'acet'amide, n. [Chem.] CH₃NOCH₂, a white solid in the form of needle-like CRYSTALS, the AMIDE of ACETIC ACID. (*See* p. 556.)

a'cetic acid. [Chem.] CH₃COOH, a CORROS-IVE liquid with a sharp smell and no colour produced by the reaction of O with ACETALDEHYDE, used, for example, in making CELLULOSE ACETATE. **'acetate, n.** Any SALT of a.a.

'acetone, n. [Chem.] The simplest KETONE, CH₃COCH₃. **aceto'n(a)emia, n.** [Med.] Diseased condition in which a. bodies are present in the blood. **aceto'nuria, n.** [Med.] Diseased condition in which a. bodies are present in the URINE. **a. body.** [Biochem., Med.] Any of a group of a.-like substances present in the blood etc. as the effect of incomplete METABOLISM, for example in the disease of DIABETES.

a'cetyl, a. [Chem.] Having the group CH₃CO-.

a'cetyl 'choline, n. [Biochem.] The substance (CH₃)₃.N.OH.CH₂.CH₂.O.CO.CH₃, produced at nerve-endings for taking impulses on to other nerves or to muscles, and causing increased working of the PARASYMPATHETIC nerves when put into the body.

a'cetylene, n. [Chem.] HC:CH, a gas without colour got chiefly by the reaction of water with CaC₂, used in the chemical industry and for lighting, having the property of burning with a very bright white flame.

ache, 1.n. [Med.] A pain which goes on, gen. a DIFFUSE one over a part, as opp. a violent, sudden pain or one which seems to be sharply limited to a point. 2.v.i.

Be experiencing, be the seat of, an a.

a'chene, n. [Bot.] Small, dry, thin-coated, one-seeded fruit, not bursting open.

A'cheulean, a., n. (Of) the 3rd division of the PALAEOLITHIC stage in man's history.

a'chilary, a. [Bot.] Having no lip.

A'chilles tendon. [Zoo.] TENDON from muscles in back of lower leg, fixed to bone at back of foot.

a'chlamydate, a. (Zoo.) (Of MOLLUSCS, etc.) without MANTLE.

Achla'mydeae, n.pl. [Bot.] A division of the ARCHICLAMYDEAE having no PETALS and no SEPALS.

achla'mydeous, a. [Bot.] Having no PERI-ANTH.

achlor'hydria, n. [Med.] Condition in which not enough HCl is produced in stomach.

achloro'phyllous, a. [Bot.] Without CHLORO-PHYLL.

a'cholia, n. [Med.] Condition in which not enough BILE is produced.

a'chondrite, n. [Geol.] A stone-like METEOR-ITE having no CHONDRULES.

achro'globin, n. [Zoo.] A RESPIRATORY PIGMENT without colour present in some UROCHORDA and MOLLUSCA.

a'chroiocy'thaemia, n. [Med.] Disease in which the red blood-CELLS have less than the right amount of HAEMOGLOBIN.

achro'masi-a, -e, nn. [Biol.] The loss of CHROMATIN from a CELL NUCLEUS, seen from its not becoming coloured by STAIN.

achro'matic, a. [Optics] (Almost completely) free from colour; (in the science of colour) without HUE, that is, grey, white, or black; (of instrument or substance) letting light through without separating it into rays of different colour. [Biol.] Not readily coloured by chemicals. **a. lens.** One made up of glasses of different forms and materials, so that the CHROMATIC ABERRATION of one is almost completely overcome by the effect of the other(s).

a'chromatin, n. [Biochem.] The base-substance of the CELL NUCLEUS, not coloured by chemicals. **a'chroma'tinic, a.**

a'chromic, a. Having, producing, no colour.

a'cicula (aciculae), n. Needle-like part of animal or plant. [Cryst.] Thin sharp-pointed CRYSTAL. **a'cicular, a.** Having form of needle; having sharp points. **a'ciculate, -d, aa.** Having aa.; marked with thin lines as if by needle.

'acid, 1.n. Chemical substance having in it H able to be exchanged for metal or metal-like BASE, forming a SALT, and which gives up H IONS when put in water (*see* pH-VALUE), in other words, a complex substance having a tendency to give up PROTONS. 2.a. Having a. properties; (of SOLUTIONS) having pH < 7·0. [Geol.] Acidic. **a. dye.** [Chem.] Any of a great group of DYES whose colouring properties

4

come from a. groups present in them, used chiefly for colouring animal materials such as wool and silk. **a. an'hydride.** A. from which one or more MOLECULES of water have been taken. **a. egg.** Egg-like vessel for storing a. **a. number** or **value.** (Of an oil or fat) number of mg. of KOH needed for destruction of a. in 1 gm. **a. 'radical.** A MOLECULE of an a. without its acidic hydrogen; RADICAL of which the HYDROXIDE is an a. **a.** or **a'cidic rock** [Geol.] One having in it more than 66% of SiO₂. **a. salt.** One in which H of a. is only part exchanged. **a. tide.** [Med.] Time or condition of increased acidity of body liquids and URINE caused by a. GASTRIC JUICE not being produced. **a.-fast,** a. [Bact.] Not acted on by a. when coloured by chemicals. **a'cidic,** a. A.-forming. [Geol.] Having much SiO₂. **a'cidic 'hydrogen.** That part of the H in an a. whose place may be taken by metal, etc. **a'cidify,** v.t. and i. **aci'dimeter,** n. Any apparatus or testing SOLUTION used for the purpose of acidimetry. **aci'dimetry,** n. [Chem.] The measuring of the amount of a. present in a SOLUTION, sp. by TITRATION. **a'cidity,** n. **aci'dosis,** n. [Med.] Condition in which there is over-much a. in the blood. **a'cidulate,** v.t. Make acidulous. **a'cidulous,** a. Somewhat a.

a'cidophil, a. [Zoo.] (Of CELLS, etc.) Readily coloured by acid STAINS.

acie'ration, n. Process of changing iron into steel. **'acierate,** v.t.

a'ciniform, a. [Bot.] Berry-like in form.

'acinus (acini), n. [Bot.] Berry, sp. separate berry of a fruit made up of small berries; a seed of a berry. [Anat.] Any of small round masses of CELLS producing the special liquid in a RACEMOSE GLAND. **'acinous,** a.

a'clinic line [Phys.] Line near the EQUATOR joining those points on the earth at which there is no MAGNETIC DIP.

A'coelo'mata, n.pl. [Zoo.] Division of TRIPLOBLASTIC METAZOA in which there is no COELOM and which are not METAMERIC. **a'coelom-ate, -ous,** aa. Having no COELOM.

a'c(o)elous, a. [Zoo.] Having VERTEBRAE with flat CENTRA; having no stomach or digestion apparatus; having no COELOM.

a'condyl-ose, -ous, aa. [Bot.] Having no JOINTS.

a'cone, a. (Of insect eye) having no liquid in CONE CELLS.

a'contium (acontia), n. [Zoo.] Any of the thread-like parts pushed out of the body of certain ANTHOZOA when in danger.

acoty'ledon, n. Plant without COTYLEDONS. **'-ous,** a.

a'coumeter, n. AUDIOMETER.

a'coustic, a. To do with sound or the ear. **a. absorp'tivity.** [Phys.] The sound ENERGY

taken up by a body ÷ the sound energy falling on it. **a. ca'pacitance, a. im'pedance, a. re'sistance, a. re'actance.** A. ANALOGUES of electric CAPACITANCE, etc. **a. dis'persion.** The change in the rate of motion of a sound-wave with any change in its FREQUENCY. **a. interfer'ometer.** An instrument for making physical observations on STANDING WAVES. **a. ohm.** The unit of a. resistance, etc. **a. radi'ation 'pressure.** An unchanging PRESSURE put on a SURFACE by an a. wave. **a. radi'ometer.** An instrument for measuring a. radiation pressure. **a. re'fraction.** The process by which the direction of a sound-wave is changed as the effect of changes in its rate of motion in the MEDIUM from point to point. **a. satu'ration.** (Of a sound-producing instrument) the degree to which it has an effect on hearing in competition with other sounds going on at the same time. **a. 'scattering.** The unregular REFLECTION, REFRACTION, or DIFFRACTION of sound in a number of different directions. **a'coustics,** 1.n. The science of sound, how it is produced and transported and the effects caused by it, 2.n.pl. The special conditions controlling sound-effects in a building such as a theatre.

a'cquired, a. [Biol., Psych.] Not being an INHERITED part or necessary development of the structure or powers of a living thing, but produced by experience, learning, some special operation, or as the effect of special conditions in the process of growth, etc. **a. 'character.** A quality so produced. **a. imm'unity.** [Biol., Med.] An IMMUNITY produced in some way in a plant or animal which is not common to all its sort.

A'crania, n.pl. [Zoo.] CEPHALOCHORDA.

a'crania, n. [Med.] Condition of being without part or all of the SKULL at birth.

'acre, n. British unit of land measure, = 4840 YARDS² or 4047 m².

'acrid, a. Having a biting or burning taste or smell.

'acr(o)-. To do with, at, the end or point of something, sp. Biol.

'acroblast, n. [Zoo.] The part of a SPERMATID forming the ACROSOME.

acro'carp-ous, -ic, aa. Having fruit at end of stem, sp. of MUSCI.

'acrocyst, n. [Zoo.] Bag in which eggs are formed in some COELENTERATA.

'acrodont, n. [Zoo.] Having teeth united to supporting bone, not fixed in ALVEOLI.

acrodrome, a'crodromous, aa. (Of a leaf) having the chief VEINS meeting at the leaf-point.

a'crogamous, a. [Bot.] Having the egg-apparatus at point of EMBRYO-SAC. **a'crogamy,** n.

5

'acrogen, n. [Bot.] Any plant of the highest sorts of CRYPTOGAMS, the ARCHE-GONIATAE.

acro'megaly, n. Disease in which hands, feet, head, and chest become increasingly greater than normal, caused by over-working of PITUITARY after normal growth is complete

a'crometer, n. [Phys.] HYDROMETER for oils.

a'cromion, n. [Zoo.] The arched outer end of the SPINE of the SCAPULA. a'cromial, a.

a'cronyc(h)al, a. [Astron.] Taking place at nightfall, said of the coming into view, or going out of view, of a star.

a'eropetal suc'cession. [Bot.] Development of side branches, flowers of group, etc., in such order that the youngest is nearest the end of the stem.

acro'phobia, n. [Med.] Unnatural fear of being in high places.

acro'scopic, a. [Bot.] Facing in the direction of the APEX.

'acrosome, n. [Zoo.] The structure at the end of the head of a SPERMATOZOON. acrosomal, a.

'acrospore, n. [Bot.] SPORE at end of HYPHA.

A.C.T.H. = ADRENO-CORTICOTROPHIC HOR-MONE.

ac'tinal, a. [Zoo.] To do with that part of RADIO-SYMMETRICAL animal from which the arms go out, and where the mouth is.

actinen'chyma, n. [Bot.] Plant substance made up chiefly of starlike CELLS.

Ac'tini'aria, n.pl. [Zoo.] An ORDER of ANTHOZOA having separate existence and with no hard supporting structure, gen. living under the edge of the sea fixed to some solid thing by an expansion at the base of the thick pipe-like body. ac'tin'arian, n., a.

ac'tinian, n., a. [Zoo.] (Animal) of or like the ACTINIARIA.

actinidone series. [Chem.] A range of RADIOACTIVE metal ELEMENTS of great weight and increasing ATOMIC NUMBERS, starting with Ac and ending with the element of at. no. 103, looked on as like the LANTHANIDE SERIES.

'actinism, n. The property of light or other rays (seen sp. in those of very short WAVE-LENGTH) by which chemical changes are produced. ac'tinic, a. actinic rays. Those having marked a. a'ctin'ology, n.

ac'tinium, n. Chemical ELEMENT, at. no. 89, at. wt. 227·2, sign Ac, a RADIOACTIVE substance with a HALF-LIFE of 13·5 years.

'actino. 1. [Phys., Chem.] To do with AC-TINISM: 'a.-chemistry, n. 2. [Zoo.] Having ray-structure.

'actino'carp-ous, -ic, aa. [Bot.] Having flowers and fruit raying from one point.

ac'tinograph, n. Instrument used in camera work as guide to timing, based on chemical power of sunlight under different conditions.

'actinoid, a. [Zoo.] In the form of a star.

ac'tinologue, n. [Zoo.] Any part of an ACTINOMERE which is like a part in an-other actinomere.

ac'tinomere, n. Any of the ray divisions making up body of a RADIO-SYMMETRICAL animal.

acti'nometer, n. Apparatus for measuring heat, or chemical power, of sun or other light rays.

'actino'morphic, a. [Biol.] RADIOSYM-METRICAL, star-like. 'actino'morphism, n.

'actinomy'cosis, n. Disease of cows, sheep, pigs, sometimes taken by man, caused by a FUNGUS and marked by the pro-ducing of hard masses round the mouth.

'actinon, n. [Chem.] An ISOTOPE of RADON, a short-living gas of great weight forming part of the URANIUM-ACTINIUM RADIO-ACTIVE SERIES, sign An.

ac'tinophone, n. Apparatus for producing sound as the effect of ACTINIC RAYS.

'Actin'opoda, n.pl. [Zoo.] A group of SAR-CODINA made up of all those, such as RADIOLARIANS, which have raying PSEU-DOPODIA.

'Actin'opter'ygii, n.pl. [Zoo.] The group of fish, sometimes rated as a CLASS of back-boned animals, sometimes as a SUB-CLASS of PISCES, sometimes as a division of the OSTEICHTHYES, taking in all fish which have a framework of bone but DIPNOI and CROSSOPTERYGII.

'actinost, n. [Zoo.] Any of the small bones supporting the rays of the side-FINS in fish.

'actino'trichium (actinotrichia), n. [Zoo.] In fish, any of the stiff thread-like parts at the outer end of the FIN-rays.

Actinozoa, n.pl. ANTHOZOA.

'action, n. A condition of acting such as the motion of a clock, gun, or other machine when in operation. [Phys.] ENERGY × time. a. current. Electric current pro-duced in the operation of a muscle, nerve, etc. a. time. REACTION TIME.

'active, n. In a condition, or having the power, of acting, working, or causing or undergoing chemical change, sp. acting readily; (of persons, etc.) not given to resting much. [Phys., Chem.] (Of a substance) having OPTICAL ACTIVITY (gen. optically a.). a. imm'unity. [Med.] An IMMUNITY against a given disease effected by an animal's power of produc-ing ANTIBODIES. a. 'immuni'zation. [Med.] IMMUNIZATION by putting dead or feeble disease-BACTERIA etc. in an animal's blood so as to get it producing ANTIBODIES as a reaction. a. 'principle [Med.] That substance in a COMPOUND or mixed substance which is responsible for its medical effect, as opp. the substance or substances with which it is mixed only to get it into the right form for use. activate, v.t. Make a., sp.: [Chem.] get (C or CHARCOAL) changed into activated carbon; [Phys.] get the ENERGY of (ATOMS or MOLECULES) increased so as to give them more powers of reaction; make (a substance) RADIOACTIVE; [Biochem.] get (an ENZYME) freed from a complex substance so that it has its effect in causing a reaction; get (SLUDGE) changed into activated sludge. 'activated, a. a. or 'activated carbon. [Chem.] C, sp. CHARCOAL, which has been put through a special process of heating, driving off HYDROCARBONS and greatly increasing its powers of ABSORPTION and ADSORPTION, used in different industries for taking up desired or undesired gases, and in GAS-MASKS. 'activated sludge. SLUDGE in which the growth of BACTERIA causing the destruction of bad-smelling and disease-causing material has been greatly increased by blowing air through it, and which is then mixed with other sludge to get the bacteria working in that. acti'vation, n. 'activator, n. Substance activating another. ac'tivity, n.

'actor, n. [Chem.] In an INDUCED REACTION, that substance which undergoes reaction with the INDUCTOR as well as with the ACCEPTOR.

a'culeus (aculei), n. [Biol.] Sharp or hair-like outgrowth, as on stem of plant or wing of some insects; STING. a'culeate, a. a'culeiform, a.

a'cuminate, a. [Bot.] (Sp. of ends of leaves) with in-curving edges narrowing to a thin point. acumi'nation, n. (See p. 223.)

'acu'puncture, 1.n. [Med.] The act of putting a needle through the skin at a key point to let out liquid, put a stop to pain by STIMULATING a nerve, etc., used against certain diseases, for example SCIATICA.

a'cute, a. [Med.] (Of a disease) in process of undergoing, or of a sort which undergoes, quick development, opp. CHRONIC; (of condition) strongly marked, very bad. [Bot.] (Sp. of leaf-ends or bases) coming to a point, but not a specially long or sharp point. [Geom.] (Of an angle) less than 90°. a'cutely, adv.

a'cuti'foliate, a. [Bot.] Having sharply pointed leaves.

a'cuti'lobate, a. [Bot.] Having sharply pointed LOBES.

a'cyclic, a. [Chem.] ALIPHATIC. [Bot.] Having flower-parts grouped in a SPIRAL. [Phys.] Unchanging, having one value only, not PERIODIC; not turning round.

'acyl (group), n. [Chem.] Any ORGANIC ACID RADICAL.

a'dactyl, -e, -ous, aa. [Zoo.] Having no fingers or toes.

'adamanti'noma, n. [Med.] A diseased growth on the JAW produced from the ENAMEL-producing substance of a tooth.

'Adam's 'apple. [Zoo.] In PRIMATES, the rounded PROJECTION in the front of the neck, specially marked in males, caused by the point of the THYROID CARTILAGE.

adap'tation, n. [Physiol., Psych.] Automatic adjustment of sense-instrument to conditions, as of eye to degree of light. [Biol.] The slow change of living forms by which their adjustment to their living conditions is made. a'dapt, v.t. and i. Put or come into adjustment with conditions or with some purpose etc.

a'dapt-er, -or, nn. [Mach., Elec.] Bit of apparatus used for making a connection between other parts or an adjustment of some instrument to a special purpose or condition.

ad'axial, a. Turned in direction of AXIS.

add, v.t. and i. Put (something) with (a. it to) some other thing as an increase of some sort, or put (things) together so as to give them a united effect, though not necessarily by uniting them physically or chemically. [Math.) Get the number or amount formed of (two or more given numbers or amounts) or get (one number or amount) united to (another) so as to make a new number etc., formed of the two. add'ition, 1.n. 2.a. [Chem.] ADDITIVE. add'itional, a. Further, added to some other thing, being an addition. add'itionally, adv.

'addict, n. [Med.] Person who has become used to taking some DRUG and is unable to do without it. ad'dicted, a. Having become an a. in relation to something. ad'diction, n. Condition of being addicted (to).

'Addison's disease. Disease in which there is slow destruction of the SUPRARENAL GLAND, marked by wasting and skin turning brown, and gen. causing death.

'additive, 1.a. To do with, produced by addition; being an addition. 2.n. A substance mixed with another to give it some desired property, for example, colour, taste, smooth touch, without having any effect on its special physical or chemical structure or operation. a. 'compound. [Chem.] A COMPOUND formed by the addition of an ATOM or group of atoms to a MOLECULE. a. 'primary. [Optics, Psych.] PHYSIOLOGICAL PRIMARY. a. 'property. A property of a complex substance whose value is given by the addition of its values for the parts of which the substance is made up.

ad'duct, v.t. [Physiol.] Make come in the direction of the middle line of the body. ad'duction, n. ad'ductor, n. Muscle effecting adduction; (in BIVALVES) muscle by which SHELL is shut.

ade'ciduate, a. [Bot.] Not DECIDUOUS.

adelo'morphic, a. [Biol.] Having no fidex form.

a'delphous, a. [Bot.] Having STAMENS united by their stems. -a'delphous. Having the given number of groups of united stamens, as *monadelphous* (1), *diadelphous* (2).

ade'nitis, n. [Med.] INFLAMMATION of GLANDS.

'adeno-. To do with a GLAND or glands: ade'nography, n. ade'nopathy, n.

'adenocarci'noma, n. [Med.] CARCINOMA with GLAND structure.

'adenoid, 1.a. GLAND-like. 2.n. [Med.] Overgrowth of GLAND-tissue at back of nose (gen. aa.) ade'noidal, a.

ade'noma, n. [Med.] Overgrowth of GLAND-CELLS, gland-like growth, not in itself serious.

'adenomy'oma, n. [Med.] MYOMA with GLAND structure.

'adeno'phyllous, a. Having leaves with GLANDS.

'adequate, a. Enough in amount or effect for its purpose. a. 'stimulus. [Psych.] The sort of stimulus normally causing a given instrument of sense, etc., to give the reaction for which it is designed, its natural stimulus, for example air-waves are the a. stimulus of hearing.

ad'hesion, n. The process of becoming, or the condition of being, fixed to some other thing, sp. by a sticky substance, or as the effect of being sticky. [Med.] The uniting of SURFACES normally separate by the development of new TISSUE as the effect of INFLAMMATION; such tissue. [Bot.] The uniting in growth of parts normally forming separate groups. [Phys.] Any force of attraction keeping two touching bodies together, for example, that between two MAGNETIC bodies or between an automobile TYRE and the road when slowing or stopping. ad'here, v.i. Be, become, fixed to another thing, or fixed together, by a. ad'hesive, 1.a., Sp. sticky. 2.n. A sticky substance used for causing a. ad'hesive plaster. [Med.] A bit of material coated on one side with an adhesive, used for putting over a wound or keeping other dressings in place.

adia'batic, a. [Phys.] Taking place without loss or increase of heat.

adiac'tinic, a. [Phys., Chem.] Not letting ACTINIC rays through.

adia'thermancy, n. [Phys.] Property of not letting heat waves through.

adipo'cellulose, n. [Chem.] CELLULOSE with a great amount of SUBERIN in it, as cork.

adipo'cere, n. Wax-like substance produced by chemical change in dead animal fat or muscle which has been long under the earth or in water.

'adipose, a., n. (Having to do with) animal fat. a. 'tissue. That part of animal body in which fat is stored. adi'pos-is, -ity, nn. [Med.] Condition of being over-fat, FATTY DEGENERATION. adi'poso'genital,

a. *See* FROHLICH'S SYNDROME.

'adit, n. Side way cut through earth, gen. almost level with sky-line, into some part of mine, for going in and out, letting air through, etc.

'aditus, n. [Anat.] An opening into a hollow place.

'ad'jacent, a. Placed touching or near with no other thing between. [Chem.] VICINAL. [Geom.] (Of angles) having one arm or one plane in common.

'adjective, n., a. [Chem.] (DYE) needing a MORDANT.

ad'juvant, n., a. [Med.] (Substance, process, etc.) used for helping the effect of another.

ad'mittance, n. [Elec.] 1 ÷ IMPEDANCE.

'adnate, a. [Biol.] United in growth from birth, sp. of unlike parts. [Zoo.] United in growth to a stem by one side, as ZOÖIDS of CORALS. ad'nation, n.

ado'lescence, n. Stage, process of development of boy or girl from PUBERTY to full growth, ado'lescent a., n.

ad'oral, a. [Zoo.] Near the mouth.

ad'radius (adradii), n. [Zoo.] In COELEN-TERATA, any RADIUS coming between a PERRADIUS and an INTERRADIUS.

ad'rectal, a. [Zoo.] Near the RECTUM.

ad'renal, a. [Zoo.] SUPRARENAL.

ad'renalin(e), n. [Biochem.] A HORMONE, $C_9H_{13}NO_3$, produced by the inner part of the SUPRARENAL GLANDS, which has the effect of increasing the BLOOD PRESSURE and the heart rate when present in a greater amount than normal, as it is at times of very strong feeling, such as great fear.

'adre'nergic, a. [Zoo.] (To do with those nerves) producing an ADRENALINE-like substance at the nerve-endings when a NERVE-IMPULSE gets there.

adreno-corticotrophic hormone. [Biochem., Med.] A substance produced by the PITUITARY GLAND which has the effect of causing CORTISONE to be produced by the ADRENAL GLAND, commonly named by the first letters of its name, A.C.T.H.

ad'sorption, n. [Phys.-Chem.] The taking on by the SURFACE of a substance of MOLE-CULES or ATOMS from a substance touching it, for example the forming of a coat of the SOLUTE on the surface of a solid put into a SOLUTION. ad'sorb, v.t. Take on by a. ad'sorbent, ad'sorptive, aa., nn.

a'dult, n., a. (Person, animal, or plant) which has come to its full growth.

ad'vanced, a [Phonet.] Said with tongue far forward.

ad'vantage, n. [Mech.] Relation between force acting on and force given by any apparatus.

ad'vection, n. [Meteor.] HORIZONTAL motion of air masses as cause of changes in weather, sp. heat.

adven'titia, n. [Zoo.] Outside coat of a blood-vessel or other ORGAN.

adven'titious, a. [Biol.] (Of parts) produced in a position or in a way other than the normal or chief one, as **a. bud** (any but an AXILLARY BUD), **a. embryo** (one formed from a cell other than the female GAMETE), **a. root** (sp. one coming from point not under earth); ADVENTIVE. [Med.] Not a necessary development, got by chance, as disease. [Anat.] Of an ADVENTITIA. **a. membrane.** A MEMBRANE joining parts not normally joined, or of a quality different from normal, as in a CICATRIX.

ad'ventive, a. [Bot.] Not being or having become natural to a place, said of plants taken from other places.

ae'cidium, 'aecium, nn. [Bot.] Cup-like SORUS of the UREDINALES. **ae'cidiospore, 'aeciospore,** nn. SPORE formed in an a.

'aed(o)e'agus, n. In insects, male sex-part designed for putting into female.

-(a)emia, n. [Med.] Blood, condition of the blood, used sp. in naming diseases, as ANAEMIA. **-aemic,** a.

A'ëneolithic, a., n. (Of) the stage in man's history between the NEOLITHIC and the BRONZE AGE, when stone and copper instruments were in use.

ae'olian, a. [Geol.] Formed, transported, etc. by the wind. **a. rocks.** ROCKS formed of materials put down by the wind.

ae'olopile, n. Early apparatus giving example of steam power, in form of a metal vessel turned round and round by force of steam coming through small outlets and meeting air outside.

ae'olo'tropic, a. [Phys.] Having different physical properties, such as power of letting heat or light through, in different directions, opp. ISOTROPIC. **'aeo'lotropy,** n.

aerate, v.t. Put gas, gen. CO_2, into (a liquid), as *aerated water*; let air to or into, e.g. earth or water.

aeren'chyma, n. A special sort of breathing TISSUE, seen in some water plants, having great spaces between CELLS.

'aerial, a. Of, to do with, living in, the air. **a. con'ductor, a. wire.** Radio ANTENNA. **a. per'spective.** The art of giving the effect of distance in a picture by the use of colour, shade, etc. **a. root.** [Bot.] Any root coming from a part of a plant which is not bedded in earth, as the root of an EPIPHYTE fixing it to another plant, or those coming from the stem of some CLIMBERS, sometimes, in addition to giving support, doing the work of a leaf in food-getting, or, in PARASITIC plants, of a SUCKER.

aero-. Air or gas (*see* AIR-): **aer'ography,** n.

'aerobe, aero'biont, nn. [Biol.] Any living thing, sp. any of certain BACTERIA, needing O for its existence. **ae'robic,** a.

aero'bioscope, n. Apparatus for measuring number of BACTERIA in air.

aerobi'osis, n. Existence of living things in air or O.

aerocyst, n. [Bot.] Any of the air-vessels in brown ALGAE.

aero'dynamic, a. To do with the motion of air and other gases, **-s,** n. Science of gases in motion, sp. of the forces acting on bodies moving through air.

'aerofoil, n. Any flat or curved part of airplane, such as wing, designed to make use of AERODYNAMIC force as a help to its motion.

aero'hydrous, a. (Of MINERAL) having water in small hollows.

'aerolite, 'aerolith, nn. [Geol.] METEORITE formed chiefly of stone.

ae'rology, n. Science of the air, sp. of the higher air.

aerome'chanics, n. Science of air at rest and in motion.

ae'rometer, n. Apparatus for measuring weight of air or other gases.

aero'nautics, n. Science of flight in airships or airplanes.

'aerophone, n. Name given to a number of different instruments, no longer in use, for producing or hearing sounds.

'aerophyte, n. EPIPHYTE.

'aeroplane, n. Airplane.

aero'plankton, n. [Biol.] The small living things (seeds, BACTERIA) in the air.

'aeroscope, n. Apparatus for getting dust, BACTERIA, SPORES, etc., out of the air for test purposes.

'aero'siderite, n. [Geol.] METEORITE made of iron.

'aerosi'derolite, n. [Geol.] METEORITE made of stone and iron.

'aerosol, n. [Chem.] A COLLOIDAL SOLUTION in which the substance in which the other is DISPERSED is a gas, for example, mist.

'aerosphere, n. ATMOSPHERE.

'aerostat, n. [Zoo.] AIR-SAC. [Phys.] Any machine for flight using gas of less weight than air to keep it up. **aero'static, -al,** a. To do with aa. or aerostatics. **aero'statics,** n. Science of the behaviour of gases in relation to solid bodies supported by them.

aero'taxis, n. [Biol.] The effect of O in increasing or stopping growth of BACTERIA; TAXIS in reaction to O, as in the motions of swimming plants conditioned by the amount of O in the water round them.

'aero'tonometer, n. [Med.] Instrument for measuring TENSION of gases in the blood.

aero'tropism, n. [Biol.] TROPISM in reaction to gases, sp. O, as seen in changes in the direction of growth of roots, etc. **aero'tropic,** a.

'aeschy'nomenous, a. [Bot.] Having very delicate reactions, as leaves of certain plants.

'aesthacyte, n. Sense-CELL of simplest animals.

aes'thesia, n. [Physiol.] Power or condition of feeling.

aesthesi'ometer, n. Instrument measuring how delicate sense of touch is.

'aestival, a. To do with summer.

aesti'vation, n. [Zoo.] Sleep-like, unmoving condition caused by heat of summer. [Bot.] The way parts of a flower are grouped in the BUD. 'aestivate, v.i. [Zoo.] Go through summer in condition of a.

ae'thalium (aethalia), n. Flat FRUIT-BODY in some MYXOMYCETES, formed by joining of PLASMODIA.

'aether, n. [Phys.] ETHER.

aeti'ology, n. Science of the causes of disease. aetio'logical, a.

A.F.=AUDIOFREQUENCY.

'affect, n. [Psych.] The degree of pleasure or its opposite colouring any feeling such as love, hate. af'fective, a. To do with feelings such as fear, love, etc.

'afferent, a. [Zoo.] Taking something from an outer to an inner part of the body, sp. of nerves taking impulses to the brain, etc., opp. EFFERENT.

af'finity, n. [Chem.] Chemical attraction, the force uniting ATOMS into MOLECULES. [Biol.] Like structure seen in different SPECIES making clear their development from the same forms.

'affluent, n. A river going into a greater river.

'afflux, n. [Med.] Motion of liquid to, or amount of liquid moving to, certain places, as an a. of blood to the head.

af'forest, v.t. Get (stretch of country) thickly planted with trees.

'affricate, n. [Phonet.] Sound starting with a PLOSIVE and ending in a FRICATIVE, as tsh. af'fricative, a., n.

afla'gellar, a. [Biol.] Without FLAGELLA.

'afterbirth, n. [Med.] The PLACENTA, etc., which comes away from the mother after birth of baby.

'afterblow, n. In the BASIC BESSEMER PROCESS of steel-making, the keeping on of the blowing after C is all burned away.

'afterburning, n. [Engin.] The slow burning of gas in engine after EXPLOSION has taken place; the burning of FUEL put into the JET-pipe of a TURBO-JET engine for the purpose of getting a greater forward push by burning it with the unburned air.

'afterdamp, n. The gas present in a coal mine after EXPLOSION and making breathing impossible, chiefly CO_2 and N.

'afterflow, n. The change in form of a solid which takes place after the force acting on it has come to a stop.

'afterglow, n. Any light still present after what it comes from has gone out or out of view, as light in sky after sundown. [Phys.] Light given out by gas after electric current has been sent through it; in PLASMA PHYSICS, the short DECAY of a PLASMA after the power has been turned off.

'after-'image, n. [Psych.] Sense-effect going on after cause has come to an end, sp. picture seen when eyes are shut after looking very fixedly at something (see COMPLEMENTARY, POSITIVE, and NEGATIVE).

'aftermath, n. Second growth of grass cut from the same field, etc., in one summer.

'afterpain, n. [Med.] Pains coming after birth of baby, caused by UTERUS getting smaller.

'after-sen'sation, n. [Psych.] AFTER-IMAGE.

'aftershaft, n. Small feather or feather-like growth on hollow part of stem of feather.

Ag, Sign for silver.

'agamete, n. In PROTOZOA, offspring produced by division and undergoing complete development without sex process.

a'gamic, a. Without sex; producing offspring by other than sex process, as by division, BUDDING, or by female without help of male.

a'gamo'genesis, aga'mogony, 'agamy, nn. Any form of AGAMIC producing of offspring.

'agamous, a. To do with plants which do not have true flowers or seeds.

'agar(-'agar), n. Jelly got from certain red ALGAE, used [Med.] as an APERIENT, and [Biol.] for CULTURES; any of the plants from which a. is made.

'agaric, n. [Bot.] Any of certain FUNGI having an umbrella-like top with GILLS on the under side.

a'gastric, a. [Zoo.] Having no stomach or like ORGAN for digestion of food.

'agate, n. [Mineral.] A form of QUARTZ marked with bands of colour.

age, n. The time for which anything has been in existence, how old it is; a long space of time in the earth's history, marked by special conditions, sp. [Archaeol.], one of the stages in man's development (for example, the Stone A.), and [Geol.], time in which a FORMATION is put down. 2.v.i. and t. (Let) undergo change, loss or increase of quality, in becoming older, as effect of time; make same changes come about in (a thing) as would be produced by time. a.-'hardening. [Metal.] A change in the physical structure of a metal, causing it to become harder and stronger, which comes about in certain mixed metals some time after HEAT TREATMENT or COLD WORKING if they are kept at rest till their inner adjustments are made. 'ageing, n., a. Sp., a.-hardening.

agen'esia, a'genesis, nn. [Med.] Fact or condition of incomplete development.

'agent, n. Substance (having power of) acting chemically on others, producing reaction.

ag'glomerate, 1.a. [Bot.] Massed but not united. 2.n. Mass of sharp bits of stone of all sizes sent out by VOLCANO and united by heat. -d, a. A.

agglomer'ation, n. A number of things massed together, a loose mass; the process of becoming or the condition of being massed together. [Acous.] The uniting of small PARTICLES hanging in a gas or liquid into greater masses by the operation of sound waves.

ag'gluti'nation, n. [Chem., Med.] The massing together of PARTICLES or CELLS present in a liquid, as the a. of red blood-cells when blood of different groups is mixed, the a. of BACTERIA under certain conditions. [Zoo.] The massing together of some PROTOZOA, etc. [Med.] Process by which edges of wounds come together and are united. [Philol.] The uniting of simpler words into complex ones whose parts undergo little or no change in sense or form. a. test. [Med.] Any test given to blood which is based on the a. of blood or BACTERIA if certain conditions are present, for example WIDAL'S TEST.

ag'glutinate, 1.v.t. and i. (Make) undergo a. 2.a. [Bot.] United into mass by sticky substance, said sp. of POLLEN. [Philol.] Marked by a. ag'glutinative, a. agglutinative language. One forming words by a., sp. the a. of root-words and words of operation, as opp. INFLECTION. ag'glutinant, n. Sticky substance uniting POLLEN, etc.

ag'glutinin, n. [Biochem.] Any ANTIBODY substance causing the AGGLUTINATION of blood, BACTERIA, etc.

agglu'tinogen, n. [Biochem.] Any substance in blood or BACTERIA etc., in reaction to which an AGGLUTININ is formed and by the reaction of which with this agglutinin AGGLUTINATION is caused.

'aggregate, 1.a. [Anat.] Formed into groups, as a. glands. [Bot.] Massed together into a solid head, as a. flowers. [Zoo.] United into a group or solid mass, as certain COMPOUND ANIMALS. [Geol.] Formed of CRYSTALS or bits of stone of one or more sorts. 2.n. An a. mass, sp. [Geol.] a. fruit. Fruit formed from a number of separate CARPELS grouped together.

aggre'gation, n. [Biol.] Number of plants or animals forming a unit within a larger group. [Bot.] Process going on in CELLS of plants living on animal substances.

ag'gressin, n. [Med.] A substance produced by disease BACTERIA in the body of an animal attacked by them and increasing their damaging effect, probably by stopping the operation of the body's instruments for overcoming them, for example, the LEUCOCYTES.

agg'ressive, a. [Zoo., Psych.] Given to attacking other animals, putting them to death or driving them from their food or living-places, or to pushing oneself forward, pushing others and their rights out of the way; used or designed for purposes of attack, to do with attacking or the quality of being a. a. 'mimicry, a. re'semblance. [Zoo.] The development by an animal, sp. an insect, of colouring, etc., like that of things round it to keep it from being readily seen by the animals it has designs on. agg'ression, n. A. behaviour, an act of attacking. '-ness, n. 'aggress'ivity, n. Sp. [Bot.], the degree to which a PARASITE has the power and tendency to do damage to the plant or animal on which it is living.

agi'tation, n. A violent and unregular motion. 'agitate, v.t. Put into a condition of a. 'agitator, n. Name given in different industries to machines for mixing liquid or other substances, or producing some other desired effect, by violent shaking, moving round and round, etc.

a'glossate, a. [Zoo.] Having no tongue. a'glossia, n. Condition of being a.

'agnate, a. Having relation by blood through father, sp. by males only; coming from same male in family tree.

Ag'natha, n.pl. [Zoo.] SUB-PHYLUM, or in some systems, CLASS, of back-boned animals taking in all those without JAWS, all of them being fish-like animals living in water and having no, or only one PAIR of, FINS, of which most sorts have long gone out of existence, CYCLOSTOMATA being the only present-day representatives.

ag'nath(o'stomat)ous, aa. Having no bones supporting mouth, as CYCLOSTOMATA.

ag'nosis, n. [Med.] Loss of the power of seeing what things are through the senses, of making use of sense DATA, sp. loss of any memory of things of which one has common experience.

a'gonic, a. Not making an angle. a. line. Line on map joining places at which MAGNETIC needle keeps true North.

'agonist, n. Muscle which has another muscle (ANTAGONIST) acting against it.

'agora'phobia, n. [Med.] Fear of open spaces.

A.G.R. = ADVANCED GAS-COOLED REACTOR.

a'granulocy'tosis, n. Diseased condition in which there are no, or almost no, GRANULOCYTES in the blood.

a'graphia, n. [Med.] Form of APHASIA marked by loss of power of writing.

a'gronomy, 'agro'nomics, nn. Science of the use of land for growth of food produce. agro'nomic, a. a'gronomist, n.

agros'tology, n. Science of grasses.

'aileron, n. Small wing fixed to back of wing of airplane, and controlled by the driver, used chiefly for balancing the 'plane from side to side in flight.

air, n. The mixed gas of which the earth's ATMOSPHERE is formed, made up chiefly of N and O with increasingly small amounts of A, CO_2, Kr, Xe, Ne, and He.

air-. Air or gas, see AERO-.

air 'bearings. [Mach.] BEARINGS which are LUBRICATED by having air forced or pulled onto them.

'air-bladder, n. [Zoo.] SAC full of air in certain fishes formed by outgrowth from ALIMENTARY CANAL.

air con'denser. In steam-engines, etc., apparatus for turning steam to water by use of air to take away heat.

'air-con'ditioning, n. A process of cleaning, drying, heating, etc., air before letting it into a building. 'air-conditioned, a. (Of a building) having an a.-c. apparatus.

'air-cooled, a. (Of an engine, machine, etc.) kept from getting over-heated by a current of air going through it, sometimes naturally as the effect of its structure, sometimes sent through it by a special apparatus. 'air-'cooling, n. The process of taking heat from anything by a current of cold air.

'aircraft, n. Any machine for journeying through the air, such as an AIRPLANE OR AIRSHIP.

air-dry, 1.a. So dry as to give off no more liquid to the air. 2.v.t. and i. Make or become dry in the air under normal conditions. a.-d. zone [Geol. etc.] The top coat of earth, in which the spaces are quickly drained of water after rain and the grains are more or less dried by EVAPORATION, the degree being dependent on the amount of water in the air.

'air-lock, n. Stopping of motion of liquid in pipe caused by air having got into it.

'airplane, n. A machine for transport through the air which is of greater weight than air and dependent for its support on the reaction of wing-like planes to the force of the air through which it is moved.

'air-pocket, n. Strong down-current of air causing sudden drop of airplane; air in pipe, etc., causing AIR-LOCK.

'air-pump, n. Any apparatus used for pumping air out of or into a vessel or shut space, for forcing it through an apparatus, etc., or, in general, for taking or sending it from one place to another.

air-sac, n. In birds, any of the hollow air-vessels in the body having a connection with the breathing apparatus and helping breathing and flight; any of the like parts with a like purpose in insects.

'-airscrew, n. A SCREW PROPELLER designed to be used in air for driving an airplane.

'airship, n. A machine for transport through

the air which is of less weight than and supported by the air, having some apparatus for driving it and controlling its direction.

'air-slaked, a. (Of LIME) having undergone reaction with water from the air ($CaO + H_2O = Ca(OH)_2$).

air ther'mometer. THERMOMETER based on changes in the space taken up by, or the PRESSURE produced by, a fixed amount of air at different degrees of heat.

'Airy experiment. Test for ABERRATION of light from stars by use of liquid in TELESCOPE.

'Airy points. [Mech.] The points at which it is best for a rod to be supported HORIZONTALLY to overcome as far as possible the tendency for it to become bent.

Al, Sign for aluminium.

'ala (alae), n. Wing-like part on flower, fruit, bone, etc. 'alae 'cordis. In insects, MEMBRANES supporting heart. '-ry, a. Formed like, to do with, a wing.

'alabaster, n. A natural form of GYPSUM, white or delicately coloured, somewhat TRANSLUCENT, readily cut; sorts of natural $CaCO_3$ having like qualities.

a'lalia, n. [Med.] Loss of power of talking, caused by loss of control of muscles needed.

'alar, a. [Biol.] Wing-like, winged; of the SHOULDER.

'alate, -d, aa. [Biol.] Having wings; (of shells) having a wide lip.

al'bedo, n. [Astron., Optics] Relation between amount of light sent back from a dark or unpolished SURFACE and amount falling on it, measuring its power of REFLECTION.

al'bescent, a. Getting white; almost but not quite white.

al'bino, n. Person, animal, or plant without normal colouring substance in all or part of it, such persons having a milk-white skin and very light hair and eyes. 'albinism, n.

'albite, n. [Mineral.] A FELDSPAR made up chiefly of $NaAlSi_3O_8$, gen. with some K and $CaCO_3$, very commonly forming part of IGNEOUS ROCKS.

al'bumen, n. [Zoo.] Material round yolk of egg in higher animals, commonly named the 'white'. [Bot.] ENDOSPERM. al'buminous, a.

al'bumin, n. [Biochem.] Any of a group of simple PROTEINS, SOLUBLE in water, forming an important part of the blood and of other animal and plant substances. '-oid, a. albumi'nimeter, n. Instrument for measuring amount of a. in a liquid. albuminosis, n. [Med.] Condition in which there is overmuch a. in the blood. '-ous, a. albumi'nuria, n. [Med.] Condition in which a. is present in URINE.

al'buminoid, n. [Biochem.] SCLEROPROTEIN.

'albumose, n. Any of certain forms of PROTEIN coming from the ALBUMINS.
albumo'suria, n. Disease in which aa. are present in URINE.
al'burnum, n. The soft, not completely formed, young wood of a plant stem, ringing the hard, true wood in the middle.
'alchemy, n. Chemical science of early times, of which the chief purpose was to make gold out of common metals.
'alcogel, n. [Chem.] GEL formed by an ALCOSOL.
'alcohol, n. [Chem.] Any substance having the structure of a HYDROCARBON but with OH in place of one H ATOM, sp. C₅H₄OH (*ethyl a.*). alco'holic, 1.a. 2.n. Person in a condition of alcoholism. alcoholic fermen'tation. [Bot., Biochem.] The producing of a. from sugar and STARCH by YEASTS. '-ism, n. Diseased condition caused by taking overmuch alcoholic drink. '-ometry, n. Process of measuring amounts of a. in liquids. '-ometer, n.
'alcosol, n. SOLUTION of a COLLOID in ALCOHOL.
aldeba'ranium, n. THULIUM.
'aldehyde, n. [Chem.] Any substance in which the group CHO is united with a HYDROCARBON group, sp. ACETALDEHYDE.
'aldrey, n. [Metal.] An ALLOY of Al and Mg having in it about 5% Mg.
a'lecithal, a. (Of eggs) having no YOLK.
a'leurone, n. PROTEIN material present in very small grains in seeds of a great number of plants.
a'lexia, n. [Med.] Loss of the power of reading language caused by damage to the brain.
a'lexin, n. [Biochem., Med.] COMPLEMENT.
a'lexi-'pharmic, -'teric, nn., aa. [Med.] (Substance) acting against poison.
'Algae, n.pl. [Bot.] Group of very simple plants, without true stems or leaves, gen. living in water, forming one of the chief divisions of THALLOPHYTA, and of which the most noted groups are: *brown A.* (PHAEOPHYCEAE), *red A.* (RHODOPHYCEAE), *blue-green A.* (CYANOPHYCEAE), *green A.* (CHLOROPHYCEAE), and DI-ATOMS. 'alga (algae), n. Any plant of the A. 'algal, a. algal 'fungi. [Bot.] PHYCOMYCETES. algal 'layer, algal zone. [Bot.] The part of a LICHEN made up of algae when these are ranged in a clearly marked division of the plant-body between masses of FUNGAL HYPHAE. 'algoid, a.
'algebra, n. [Math.] The science of the general properties of numbers, using letters, etc., as representative of them, and covering a much wider field than arithmetic. alge'braic, a. algebraic addition. The addition of numbers, etc., having the signs + or − in front of them,

covering the processes in arithmetic of addition and SUBTRACTION, for example the addition of −10 to +6 giving the number −4. algebraic sum. A number or amount got by algebraic addition.
'algia, n. [Med.] Pain. -algic, a.
'algin, n. ALGINIC ACID.
'alginate, n. [Chem.] Any SALT of ALGINIC ACID.
al'ginic acid. [Chem.] A jelly-like acid made up of C, H, and O, got from certain sea ALGAE and used in making EMULSIONS, jellies, PLASTICS, paper, etc.
al'gology, n. Science of ALGAE.
Al'gonkian, a., n. [Geol.] PROTEROZOIC.
ali'cyclic, a. [Chem.] Having a ring structure, but formed from an ALIPHATIC one.
'alidade, n. An instrument used in mapping land in SURVEYING, made up of a flat rule with small upright SIGHTS at the two ends so that, resting on the paper, it may be got in line with anything whose direction has to be marked on the map.
'alienist, n. Expert on diseases of the mind.
'aliform, a. Wing-like in form.
a'lignment, n. The putting of things in straight lines; line(s) so formed.
ali'mentary, a. To do with food or digestion. a. ca'nal. [Zoo.] The complete structure of pipes, etc., through which food goes from mouth to anus.
ali'phatic, a. [Chem.] Said of ORGANIC substances with open chains of C ATOMS, that is, of all those formed of C in which no rings are present, as opp. AROMATIC.
'aliquot part. [Math.] A number which goes into another number a number of times with nothing over, as 2 is an a.p. of 8.
ali'sphenoid, -al, aa. [Zoo.] To do with wings of the SPHENOID bone.
'alitrunk, n. In insects, the THORAX, or the last two rings of it, on which are the wings.
alka'laemia, n. [Med.] Condition in which blood is over-ALKALINE.
'alkali, n. [Chem.] Substance which is a strong BASE, and gives OH IONS in water. a. metals. The MONOVALENT metals Li, Na, K, Rb, and Cs. alka'limeter, n. Instrument measuring ALKALINITY. 'alkaline, a. alkaline earth. Ca(OH)₂, or Ba(OH)₂, or Sr(OH)₂. alkaline earth metals. The DIVALENT metals Ca, Sr, Ba, Ra (with which are sometimes grouped Be and Mg). alka'linity, n. Degree to which substance is alkaline, property of being alkaline.
'alkaloid, n. [Chem.] Any of a group of complex natural substances with N in a ring structure, generally poisons, some used medically.
al'kene, n. [Chem.] OLEFINE.
'alkyl, n. [Chem.] A group formed when one ATOM of H is taken from a PARAFFIN,

that is, any group of the general form C_nH_{2n+1}. **a.'radical.** A.

allan'tois, n. [Zoo.] Bag-like outgrowth of the ALIMENTARY CANAL in EMBRYOS of all AMNIOTES, the stem of which is in the UMBILICAL cord. **allan'toic, allan'toid,** aa.

'allele, n. ALLELOMORPH.

al'lelomorph, n. [Biol.] One or other of two GENES which have the same positions in HOMOLOGOUS CHROMOSOMES of two uniting GAMETES, come together in the process of MEIOSIS, and have opposite effects on the same branch of development (for example, size or colour), producing opposite qualities in mixed offspring in agreement with MENDEL'S LAW; the quality produced by an a. **al'lelo-'morphic,** a., **al'lelo'morphism,** n.

al'lelo'plastic, a. Said of GRAFTING from one animal to another when the animals are of different sorts or families.

al'lelotrope, n. [Chem.] One or other of two ISOMERS which are so readily changed into one another that they are normally present together in a certain balance. **alle'lotropism,** n.

'Allen's law. [Zoo.] The general rule of observation that the feet, ears, and tails of MAMMALS of the same sort, or like sorts, have a tendency to be shorter in colder parts of the earth.

'allergy, al'lergia, nn. [Med.] (Tendency to) strong special reaction by person's body against certain foods, substances breathed in from the air, etc., in however small amounts; increase in body's reaction to certain ORGANISMS or substances, sp. PROTEINS, caused by one INOCULATION with them and seen when they are put into it again. **al'lergic,** a.

'allo-. Different (from normal, etc.); of different sort(s). [Chem.] Being an ISOMER, near relation, or special form, of what is named: **'-caf'feine,** n.

'allochro'matic crystal. CRYSTAL having PHOTOCONDUCTIVITY caused by very small PARTICLES in it.

all'och'thonous, a. Coming from outside; not natural to place, animal, etc., said sp. [Geol.] of coal-beds formed of transported material, and [Ecol.] as opp. AUTOCHTHONOUS.

'allo'isomerism, n. [Chem.] STEREOISOMERISM.

al'lomeric, a. [Chem.] Different in chemical structure, but having same CRYSTAL form. **al'lomerism,** n.

allo'morphic, a. [Chem.] The same in chemical structure, but different in CRYSTAL form. **'allomorph,** n. Any of the a. forms of one substance. **allo'morphism,** n.

al'lopathy, n. [Med.] System of attacking disease with substances whose effects are unlike those of the disease, opp. HOMOEOPATHY.

'allope'lagic, a. [Zoo.] Living in the sea anywhere from near the top to far down, seemingly independent of heat and cold.

'allosome, n. [Biol.] Any CHROMOSOME of a special sort, as a sex-chromosome.

allo'thogen-ic, -ous, a. [Geol.] Formed in, or of materials transported from, some place other than the present position, sp. of CLASTIC ROCKS.

allo'toxin, n. [Med.] Substance formed by the body, and acting against poisons produced by BACTERIA.

all'otrio'morphic, a. [Geol.] XENOMORPHIC. **all'otriomorph,** n.

allo'trophic, a. (Of plants) dependent for food on ready-made plant substance, opp. AUTOTROPHIC.

al'lotropy, n. The existence of a chemical ELEMENT in two or more different forms, as grey and white tin, **allo'tropic,** a. **'allotrope,** n. Any of two or more forms of one ELEMENT.

'alloy, n. Substance made up of two or more metals, or of a metal mixed with other material.

al'luvion, n. [Geol.] Wash of river against its edge; overrunning of land by river.

al'luvium, n. Earth, sand, etc., taken by river from land and put down later, forming level beds. **al'luvial,** a.

'almu'cantar, n. [Astron.] A circle ringing the sky parallel to the HORIZON at any given distance from it, on which all stars which are equally high have their place, forming part of a system of such circles used in astronomy for mapping the positions of the stars; a special TELESCOPE used for measuring the distances of stars from the horizon.

'alpha(-), n. The Greek letter α, used, with β, γ, etc., before names as a sign of a special property, structure, or sort, sp. for naming: [Chem.] Certain ATOMS in complex substances which are exchanged for atoms of other substances, and the substances formed by such exchanges (**a. de'rivatives**); one of two or more ISOMERS as 'α-Fe(OH)$_3$'; [Astron.] The. brightest star of a CONSTELLATION, as *Alpha* (or α) *Boötis* = ARCTURUS. **a. 'particle.** [Phys., Chem.] He NUCLEUS with POSITIVE CHARGE given off by a RADIOACTIVE substance. **a. ray.** Ray formed of a. particles.

'alpine, 1.a. To do with, living in, high mountains. 2.n. Any plant natural to mountain tops or the far north.

al'pigenous, a. [Biol.] (of plant or animal) having undergone EVOLUTION in, natural to, high mountains or the far North.

al'tazimuth, n. [Astron.] Instrument like a THEODOLITE for measuring at one and the same time the ALTITUDE and AZIMUTH of a sky body.

al'ternate, a. [Bot.] (Of leaves) placed one by one on the stem in a line twisting round it from end to end, not opp. one another. **a. host.** One or the other of the 2 unlike HOSTS of a HETEROECIOUS PARASITE.

'alternate, 1.v.i. (Of two or more things or events) take place, be ranged, in turn, in a regular order over and over; undergo a change from one condition, value, direction, etc., to another and back again, sp. in a regular rhythm. 2.v.t. Make a., put in an ALTERNATE order. **'alternating,** a. **alternating 'cleavage.** [Zoo.] SPIRAL CLEAVAGE. **alternating 'current.** [Elec.] An electric current changing regularly from one direction to the opposite. **alternating person'ality** [Psych.] MULTIPLE PERSONALITY. **alter'nation,** n. **alternation of 'generations.** Process by which two (or more) GENERATIONS are needed for the complete REPRODUCTION of a plant or animal, the offspring produced by it being of a form different from itself, from which, in a different way, the first form is again produced—gen. sex-produced offspring alternating with offspring not sex-produced. **'alternator,** n. Electric machine producing alternating current.

'al'ternative, 1.a. Which may be done, had, etc., in place of some other thing, being one of two (or, loosely, more) things possible in place of one another but not together. 2.n. One or other of two a. things; the chance of selection between two a. things.

'altigraph, n. ALTIMETER with recording apparatus.

al'timeter, n. Instrument for measuring ALTITUDE, sp. BAROGRAPH scaled for this purpose for use in airplane.

'altitude, n. Distance up at right angles to a given HORIZONTAL plane, as sea-level, measured by line or angle. [Astron.] The a. of X is XOA where O is the centre of the CELESTIAL SPHERE and A is the point nearest to X in which the plane through X, O, and the ZENITH is cut by the CELESTIAL HORIZON.

alto'cumulus, n. [Meteor.] Cloud structure formed of white or grey clouds, in part shaded, frequently ranged in lines.

alto'stratus, n. [Meteor.] Cloud structure formed of one dark unbroken stretch at low level.

'altrices, n.pl. Any birds of which the young are very feeble and have need of care for a long time.

'aludel, n. UDELL.

'alula (alulae), n. [Zoo.] Small, thinly feathered outgrowth on wing of bird; a small part separated off from back edge of wing-base in certain insects.

'alum, n. The substance $KAl(SO_4)_2.12H_2O$ (POTASSIUM ALUMINIUM SULPHATE), forming 8-sided CRYSTALS without colour, a strong ASTRINGENT, used medically, in DYEING as a MORDANT, and in other industries; any of a group of salts of like form and structure having other metals of equal uniting power taking the place of the K and the Al, as $KCr(SO_4)_2.12H_2O$. **'-stone,** n. ALUNITE.

a'lumina, n. [Chem.] Al_2O_3 (ALUMINIUM TRIOXIDE), present naturally in the earth as CORUNDUM.

alu'minium, a'luminum, nn. Chemical ELEMENT, at. no. 13, at. wt. 29·96, sign Al, a silver white metal noted for its small DENSITY.

a'lumino'ferric, 1.a. Of Al and iron, 2.n. $Al_2(SO_3)$ mixed with salt of iron.

a'lumino'thermy, n. [Chem.] Process of separating metals from O united with them by mixing them with powdered Al and firing a mass of powdered Al and Na_2O_2 (*sodium peroxide*) placed over them, producing great heat and strong reaction in which the O is freed from the metal and united with the Al. **a'lumino'thermic,** a.

'alunite, n. A MINERAL made up of K_2SO_4, $Al_2(SO_4)_3$, and $Al(OH)_2$, from which ALUM is produced.

'alveola (alveolae), n. [Biol.] A small hollow in a SURFACE, as a PORE of FUNGUS, **'-r,** a. Marked by aa.

'alveolus (alveoli), n. [Biol.] A small hole or pocket, such as that in which a tooth is fixed; a small group of CELLS round a hollow space in LUNGS; any of the cells in bees' wax; an ALVEOLA. **aa.** [Phonet.] Alveolar arch. **'alve'olar,** 1.a. Having, to do with, aa. or parts of the mouth in which teeth are rooted. [Phonet.] Said with tongue touching or near the alveolar arch. **alveolar arch** or **ridge,** The part of the mouth at back of the top front teeth. 2.n. [Phonet.] An a. CONSONANT, as the English *t*. **alveolar 'theory.** [Zoo.] The theory that PROTOPLASM is made up of CELLS formed of a skin of a more solid substance with liquid substances inside it. **'alveolo-.** Sp. of the aa. of the mouth.

a'malgam, n. [Chem.] Substance formed of Hg mixed with one or more other metals. **a'malgamate,** v.t. and i. Get, become, united into an a. **a'malga'mation,** n. **amalgamation process.** Process by which gold and silver are got free from their ORES by crushing these and acting on them with Hg.

amas'thenic, a. Causing light-rays to come together to one point.

'amatol, n. EXPLOSIVE made up of NH_4NO_3 and T.N.T.

amaur'osis, n. [Med.] Loss of power to see caused by damage to nerve controlling eye or other cause outside the eye itself.

'amber, n. [Mineral.] Yellow to brown FOSSIL RESIN got sp. round the Baltic

Sea, strongly electric when rubbed.
'ambi- = AMPHI-: -'lateral, a.
ambi'dextrous, a. Able to make use of left
and right hands equally. ambi'dexter, n.
A. person.
'ambient, a. Being that which is all round
something, in which a thing is, as the
a. TEMPERATURE, that is, the temperature of the air etc. round a thing.
ambi'genous, a. [Bot.] Having outer flower
leaves different from inner ones.
ambi'polar, a. Working in opp. directions
at same time, as electric current in gas in
ELECTROLYTIC CELL.
ambi'valent, a. [Psych.] Having at the
same time opp. feelings for the same
person or thing, as love and hate. ambi'valence, n.
ambo'ceptor, n. [Immunol.] One of the
bodies which is part of Ehrlich's SIDE-
CHAIN THEORY.
am'brosia, n. A sort of FUNGUS present
inside branches etc. which is used as
food and looked after for this purpose by
some BORING COLEOPTERA; BEEBREAD.
ambu'lacrum (ambulacra), n. Any of the
ray-divisions on which the TUBE-FEET
of animal such as starfish are placed.
ambu'lacral, a. ambulacral groove. [Zoo.]
In ECHINODERMS such as starfish, the
hollow down the middle of the under side
of a ray housing the two lines of TUBE
FEET, the edges of which may be pulled
together, shutting the tube-feet in, when
the animal is attacked.
a'meloblast, n. [Zoo.] ENAMEL CELL.
amenor'rhoea, n. [Med.] The stopping of
MENSTRUATION from other than normal
causes.
a'ment, n. [Bot.] Flowering part of plant in
the form of hanging stem thickly
covered with very small flowers without
stems. amen'taceous, a.
a'mentia, n. [Med.] Condition of being
feeble-minded, from birth, or as effect of
damage or disease. 'ament, n. Person in
this condition.
a'meri'cium, n. Chemical ELEMENT, at. no.
95, sign Am, one of the TRANSURANIC
elements.
'amethyst, n. [Mineral.] Sort of QUARTZ of a
red-blue colour having in it small amounts
of Mn, Al, and Fl.
A'mici prism. [Optics] PRISM made of two
sorts of glass, causing division of white
light into colours, but not changing
direction of light rays.
a'micron, n. [Phys., Chem.] Body so small
that it is not seen in ULTRAMICROSCOPE
i.e. less than 1×10^{-7} cm.
'amide, n. [Chem.] Any of those chemical
substances formed when the OH of the
group CO.OH gives place to NH_2.
a'mido(-). a. Of, having the group
$CO.NH_2$.

'amine, n. [Chem.] Any of a group of
chemical substances formed by exchanging one, two, or three of the H ATOMS of
AMMONIA (NH_3) for one, two, or three
HYDROCARBON groups—named from the
number of atoms changed, primary aa.
(1), secondary aa. (2), and tertiary aa. (3).
a'mino(-), a. [Chem.] Having in it, formed
of, the group NH_2. a. acid. Any of a
group of substances such as those
present in PROTEINS whose structure is
that of an ORGANIC acid but with one or
more ATOMS of the H in a HYDROCARBON
group exchanged for an a. group or
groups.
ami'tosis, n. [Biol.] CELL division in which
there is simple division of NUCLEUS without CHROMOSOMES separating out. ami-
'totic, a.
'ammeter, n. Instrument measuring electric
current by pointer on scale.
'ammine, n. [Chem.] Any of the INORGANIC
substances produced by the addition of
one or more NH_3 MOLECULES to a
molecule of a SALT or like complex substance.
'ammonal, n. EXPLOSIVE made up of
T.N.T., NH_4NO_3, and powdered Al.
am'monia, n. NH_3, an ALKALINE gas with
no colour and very biting smell, readily
going into SOLUTION in water.
'ammonite, n. [Geol.] (FOSSIL of) any of
sorts of CEPHALOPOD, sp. that with SHELL
twisted into a flat round, common in
MESOZOIC time. ammoni'tiferous, a.
Having in it aa. or parts of them.
am'monium, n. [Chem.] The group NH_4,
whose behaviour in complex substances
is much like that of an ALKALI METAL. a.
hydroxide. NH_4OH, substance formed
when NH_3 goes into SOLUTION in water,
or such solution.
am'nesia, n. [Med.] Loss of memory.
'amnion, n. [Zoo.] Thin skin forming bag in
which EMBRYOS of higher animals go
through their development. 'amniote, a.,
n. (Of) any animal undergoing development in a. amni'otic, a. amniotic fluid.
Liquid in a.
A'moeba, n. [Zoo.] A GENUS of PROTOZOA,
very small and simple water-animals
made up of a mass of half-liquid PROTO-
PLASM of which the form is all the time
changing and putting out wide, rounded,
arm-like parts for the purpose of overrunning food or changing the place of
the animal by moving the rest of its
substance into the new arm. a'moeba
(amoebae or amoebas), n. Any animal
of the A. a'moebic, a. amoebic 'dysentery.
Disease caused by amoebae in INTESTINES.
a'moeboid, a. Sp. moving from place to
place by changing its form, as an amoeba.
a'morphous, a. [Biol.] With no clearly
marked form and little organization, as

beings at a low level of development. [Chem., Crystal.] Not having CRYSTAL-LINE structure. [Geol.] Without division into STRATA, etc.

a′mortisseur, n. [Elec.] DAMPER. **a.** winding. A.

amp. = AMPERE.

′ampere, n. The common unit of electric current, = the current by which, when it is sent through a SOLUTION of $AgNO_3$, silver is produced at the rate of ·001118 gms. per sec., amounting to 0·1 × the c.g.s. unit or **absolute a.** (ABAMPERE). ′a.-′balance, n. KELVIN BALANCE. ′a.-hour, n. A unit of amount of ELECTRICITY based on current and time, being that produced by a current of 1 a. in 1 hour (or by a current of 2 aa. in half an hour, etc.), used for measuring the output of an ACCUMULATOR. **a. turn.** The MAGNETO-MOTIVE FORCE produced round one turn of a SPIRAL of wire through which is going a current of 1 a. ′amperage, n. The value in aa. of an electric current.

Am′perian whorl *or* current. Electric current said by Ampère to be going round every ATOM of a MAGNETIC substance.

Ampère′s rule. [Elec.] Rule for getting the direction of a MAGNETIC FIELD produced by an electric current, which says that if a man is pictured as swimming with the current facing a MAGNETIC NEEDLE, the NORTH POLE of the needle will be turned to his left.

′amphe′rotoky, n. AMPHITOKY.

′amphi-. Two, of two sorts, on two sides, etc.: -′sexual, a.

′amphiar′throsis, n. [Anat.] Connection between bones, etc., which makes possible a very limited degree of motion in relation to one another.

′amphi′aster, n. [Biol.] The two star-like bodies, together with the part joining them, formed in MITOSIS. ′amphi′astral, a.

Am′phibia, n.pl. CLASS of cold-blooded, back-boned animals with apparatus for living on land and in water and looked on as between fishes and REPTILES, freq. AMPHIBIOTIC, without AMNION and gen. egg-producing. am′ph′ibian, l.n. [Zoo.] Any animal of the A. [Bot.] Amphibious plant. [Mach.] Airplane or automobile designed for use on land or water. 2.a. Of the A.; amphibious. am′phibious, a. Living, designed for use, on land and in water.

′amphibi′otic, a. [Zoo.] Living in water in early stage(s) of development, but on land at full growth.

amphi′blastic, a. (Of egg) undergoing complete division but into unequal parts.

′amphibole, n. [Mineral.] Any of a group of dark-coloured CRYSTALLINE SILICATES forming part of a great number of ROCKS, e.g. HORNBLENDE. amphi′bolic, a.

amphi′bolic, a. [Zoo.] Having power of turning back or forward, as outer toe of certain birds.

amphi′carp-ic, -ous, aa. [Bot.] Producing fruit of two sorts.

amphi′coelous, a. [Zoo.] (Of VERTEBRAE) having the two ends hollowed in.

′Amphi′oxus, n. [Zoo.] The chief GENUS of CEPHALOCHORDA, small TRANSLUCENT sea-animals somewhat fish-like in form but worm-like in behaviour, living in the sand of the sea-bed near the land. **amphi-oxus,** b. An animal of this group.

′amphi′pathic, a. [Chem.] Said of an ION of which one end is pulled to water and the other end is pushed away.

amphip′neust-ic, -ous, aa. [Zoo.] Having air-breathing and water-breathing apparatus all through existence; (of the LARVAE of certain flies) having breathing-hole at front and at back.

Am′phipoda, n.pl. [Zoo.] An order of small CRUSTACEA having flat bodies, without hard covers—some water animals, some living in earth, and some PARASITIC.

amphi′podous, a. [Zoo.] Having legs for walking and other legs for swimming.

′amphispore, n. [Bot.] SPORE produced by some RUSTS in very dry conditions and acting as a RESTING SPORE.

′amphi′stylic, a. [Zoo.] Having top JAW joined to HYOID ARCH at back but in front to CRANIUM, as some fish. ′amphi-′styly, n.

′amphitene, a., n. [Biol.] (Of or being) that stage of MEIOSIS in which HOMOLOGOUS CHROMOSOMES in the form of thin threads come together in two′s.

′amphi′toky, n. [Zoo.] PARTHENOGENESIS in which male and female offspring are produced.

amphi′tric-ate, -ous, aa. [Biol.] Having FLAGELLA at the two ends of the CELL (said sp. of BACTERIA).

am′phitrocha, n. [Zoo.] A free-swimming ANNELID LARVA, with two complete CILIA rings.

amphi′trop-ous, al, aa. [Bot.] Having OVULE upside down, with connection near middle of one side.

ampholyte, n. [Chem.] AMPHOTERIC substance.

ampho′teric, a. [Chem.] Having with strong acids the reaction of a BASE, and with strong bases the reaction of an acid.

am′plexicaul, -ine, aa. (Of leaves) with base going round stem.

′amplify, v.t. [Optics] Make field of view of instrument such as MICROSCOPE greater. [Phys.] Make increase in electric current or VOLTAGE by development of more power than is given; give greater range or VOLUME to sound. amplifi′cation, n. ′amplifier, n. [Optics] LENS put at the back of an OBJECTIVE to a. the field of view. [Radio] An apparatus, gen. a system of THERMIONIC VALVES, for increasing a RADIOFREQUENCY or AUDIOFREQUENCY current.

'amplitude, n. [Phys.] Distance between the middle and outer positions, or between the two outer positions, of a body in VIBRATION; greatest + or − value of an ALTERNATING current etc., or amount by which this is greater than the MEAN. [Astron.] The ARC of the HORIZON between true east or west and the VERTICAL CIRCLE through a star; arc of horizon between MAGNETIC east or west and such circle.

'ampoule, n. Small glass vessel designed to take measured amount of medical substance and then be shut by heating, etc., to be broken open when needed.

am'pulla, n. [Zoo.] Any small bag-like structure, sp. those seen in ear of back-boned animals, in milk-GLANDS, and at base of TUBE-FEET. [Bot.] Like structures on underwater parts of certain plants. -r, -ry, aa.

ampul'lace-al, -ous, aa. [Biol.] Like a round-bodied bottle in form.

'ampu'tation, n. [Med.] The cutting off of some outer part of body, as arm, leg, ear. 'amputate, v.t.

a.m.u. = ATOMIC MASS UNIT.

a'mygdala, n. [Zoo.] A TONSIL; one or other of the two small round out-growths on the lower side of the CEREBELLUM.

a'mygdaloid, n. [Geol.] ROCK in which while still liquid small hollows were formed by the expansion of steam and later became full of other MINERALS, sp. SiO₂. a. 'nucleus. [Anat.] Small mass of grey substance in the TEMPORAL LOBE of the brain.

a'mygdale, n. [Geol.] Any of the bits of stone formed in the hollows in AMYGDALOID.

'amyl, a., n. [Chem.] (Having) the OPEN-CHAIN group –C₅H₁₁.

amy'laceous, a. To do with, like, STARCH.

'amylase, n. [Biochem.] Any AMYLOLYTIC ENZYME.

amylo-. STARCH.

'amyloid, 1.a. STARCH-like. 2.n. [Chem.] Substance formed by acting on CELLULOSE with H₂SO₄; GUM-like substance in some seeds. [Med.] Starch-like substance formed in KIDNEYS, etc., in certain diseases.

amy'lolysis, n. [Biol.] The changing of STARCH into sugars, sp. as process of digestion. amylo'lytic, a.

'amylo'plast, -id, nn. [Bot.] STARCH-forming LEUCOPLAST.

amy'lopsin, n. [Biochem.] The AMYLASE produced by the PANCREAS.

'amylose, n. [Chem.] Any of the CRYSTALLINE substances of the sugar group produced from STARCH. [Bot.] STARCH or other CARBOHYDRATE used by plant.

a'mylum, n. [Chem.] STARCH. a. grain, a. granule. [Bot.] Any of the a. bodies made by LEUCOPLASTS.

An, Sign for ACTINON.

an-. Not, the opposite of (the form taken by a- when put before VOWELS):—-'amniote, n.; -amni'otic, -'androus, -'anthous, -'astig'matic, -'euploid, -'hysteric, -iso-'meric, aa.

'ana-. Up, back, again; greatly, overmuch.

ana'batic, a. [Meteor.] (Of winds) caused by the moving up of heated air, as the daytime MOUNTAIN WINDS and VALLEY WINDS.

a'nabolism, n. The chemical changes in living beings effecting the building up of complex substances from simpler ones and the storing of ENERGY.

ana'camptic, a. To do with, causing, caused by, REFLECTION of sound waves.

a'naclasis, n. [Med.] The moving of an arm or leg at a JOINT by force.

ana'clastic, a. To do with, causing, caused by, REFRACTION of light.

ana'clinal, a. [Geol.] (Of river, etc.) going in direction opp. slope of STRATA.

ana'dromous, a. [Zoo.] (Of fish) going up rivers from the sea at certain times for sex-connection.

a'n(a)emia, n. Disease in which blood has not enough ERYTHROCYTES, or erythrocytes do not have enough HAEMOGLOBIN. a'n(a)emic, a.

a'naerobe, anae'robiont, nn. Plant-form, sp. one of certain BACTERIA, to which free O is unnecessary or poison. anae'robic, a. a'naerobiosis, n. Existence without air or free O. a'naerobi'otic, a.

an(a)es'thesia, n. [Med.] (Of part of body) loss of power of feeling (local a.) or (of person) unconscious condition (general a.), sp. produced for purpose of operation, etc. an(a)es'thetic, n., a. (Chemical substance) producing a. a'n(a)esthetist, n. Person who gives anaesthetic in operation, etc. a'n(a)estheti'zation, n. a'n(a)esthetize, v.t. Put in condition of a.

'anaki'nesis, n. Chemical process in living substance by which some MOLECULES get increased ENERGY. 'anaki'netic, a. 'anaki'netomer, -e, n. Such MOLECULE.

'anal, a. [Zoo.] Of, near, the ANUS. a. fin. A FIN on the lower side of the body of a fish near the tail and sometimes united with the tail fin.

analem'matic 'sundial. Apparatus giving time of day and true North and South by position of shade made by sun.

anal'gesia, n. [Med.] Condition of not feeling pain. anal'gesic, n., a. (Anything) taking away pain more or less completely.

'analogue, n. A parallel, anything having like properties, uses, or effects, to another thing, playing a like part in a different system, etc. [Biol.] Part of animal or plant having same purpose as some part in another animal or plant, but with a different structure and development; SPECIES in one group like in some ways to species in another group. [Chem.] One ELEMENT is the a. of another when they are in the same group of the PERIODIC SYSTEM. **a. 'com'puter.** That one of the 2 sorts of COMPUTER (the other being a DIGITAL COMPUTER) in which the representative used for every VARIABLE is some physical QUANTITY, such as electric current, so that addition, SUB-TRACTION, and even MULTIPLICATION and other MATHEMATICAL processes may be done by the addition and so on of the currents. **a'nalogous, a. a'nalogy,** n.

'analyser, n. Apparatus which does ANALY-SIS, sp. [Optics] part of POLARIMETER by which change in position of PLANE OF POLARIZATION is measured.

a'nalysis (analyses), n. The separating of anything complex into its parts with a view to the discovery of its structure, etc., as the a. by chemical processes of a com-plex substance, the a. in Physics of light and other rays. **'analy-se, -ze,** v.t. Make a. of. **'analyst,** n. An expert in a., sp. chemical a. **ana'lytic, -al,** aa. **analytical balance.** Delicate apparatus for measur-ing weight used in chemical a. **analytic language.** An INFLECTIONAL language in which development has been away from the inflectional system to the use of separate words for making relations and complex ideas clear.

ana'morphota lens or **ob'jective.** In motion pictures, a LENS used in some WIDE-SCREEN PROCESSES, (a) in the CAMERA to COMPRESS the picture from side to side on the FILM, and (b) in the PROJECTOR to get this stretched out again on the SCREEN to its right size and form.

ana'morphism, n. [Geol.] Complex process of change undergone by ROCKS in lower parts of earth as effect of heat, water, and weight of material over them.

'anamor'phosis, n. [Biol.] EVOLUTION from a simpler to a more complex form by degrees. [Optics] Picture so made that it gives true view of thing only when looked at through special instrument, etc.

'anaphase, n. [Biol.] Stage in MITOSIS or MEIOSIS in which halves of CHROMOSOMES take up positions to make NUCLEI of new CELLS.

anapho'resis, n. [Chem.] Motion of small bits of solid material in SUSPENSION in a liquid in the direction of the ANODE when an electric current is sent through.

anaphy'laxis, n. [Med.] The condition pro-duced in UNSTRIATED muscle by a PRO-TEIN taken into the system, causing it to give a greatly increased reaction when-ever the same protein is taken in again.

'anaphy'lactic, a. Of, to do with, being in a condition of, a. **anaphy'lactic shock.** The shock to the system, freq. causing a serious condition, caused by the strong or violent reaction of the unstriated muscles to a protein to which they have become anaphylactic.

ana'plasis, n. [Med.] Change of living CELLS back to simpler form, as in some diseased growths. **ana'plastic, a.**

an'apsid, a. [Zoo.] (Of the SKULL of a REPTILE) completely roofed over, with no openings on the upper side but those in connection with the eyes, nose, and ears.

'anap'tyxis, n. [Phonet.] Sound-change made by putting in a VOWEL sound between two CONSONANTS coming to-gether, as in saying 'Henery' for 'Henry'.

ana'sarca, n. [Med.] Forming of over-much liquid in skin and parts under it, causing unhealthy expansion. **ana'sarcous, a.**

ana'seismic, a. (Of earth shocks) having up and down motion.

'anastate, n. [Biochem.] Any substance formed from simpler ones as a step to forming very complex substance such as PROTOPLASM.

a'nasto'mosis, n. [Biol.] The forming of a network system of connections between blood-vessels, nerves, leaf-VEINS, etc., so that other ways through are possible if one is stopped. [Med.] Connection be-tween blood-vessels, etc., made by operation. **a'nastomose,** v.i. and t. Have or make network connection or a.

an'astral, a. [Biol.] (Of MITOSIS) in which no ASTERS are formed.

ana'texis, n. [Geol.] Process by which ROCKS deep in the earth are again made liquid by heat of gases coming from lower levels.

a'natomy, n. Science of the structure of plants or animals, sp. man; art of cut-ting up animals and plants for purpose of learning their structure; the special structure of any animal, plant or part.

ana'tropous, a. [Bot.] (Of an OVULE) bent over in growth so that the MICROPYLE is near to the base of the FUNICLE, with the body of the ovule having become united to the funicle.

'ancestor, n. [Biol.] SPECIES or other group of earlier times in relation to later one which is a development from it; person in the past from whom a family line has come down.

anchieu'tectic, a. [Geol.] Formed of MINERALS in a roughly EUTECTIC relation.

an'chylo-. [Med.] Growth together of parts.

'anchy'losis, n. [Med.] The loss of power of motion in a JOINT as effect of uniting of bones or growth of hard substance between them. [Zoo.] The uniting of two or more bones or stiff parts into one. **'anchylose,** v.t. and i. Be cause of, or undergo a.

'anc(h)ylosto'miasis, n. Disease caused by HOOKWORMS living in small INTESTINE.

'anda'lusite, n. [Geol.] ROCK made of Al$_2$SiO$_5$ produced by the effect of heat on CLAY rocks.

'andesine, n. [Mineral.] PLAGIOCLASE with more Na than Ca.

'andesite, n. [Geol.] A small-grained IGNEOUS ROCK, normally a LAVA, with PLAGIOCLASE as the chief FELDSPAR. (*see* p. 192).

andro'ecium, n. [Bot.] The STAMENS of a flower or male parts of a MOSS taken as a group.

'androgen, n. [Zoo.] Any of the HORMONES having to do with the development and operation of male properties and powers in back-boned animals.

andro'genous, a. [Bot.] Producing males only.

'androgyne, n. Plant producing separate male and female flowers on same stem. andro'gyn-ous, -al, aa. andro'gynism, an'drogyny, nn.

andro'gynary, a. [Bot.] Having PETAL-like STAMENS qnd PISTILS.

andro'petalous, a. [Bot.] Having STAMENS changed into PETALS.

an'drosterone, n. [Biochem.] One of the ANDROGENS.

-'androus, a. [Bot.] having the number or sort of STAMENS named: mon'androus.

a'nemia, anes'thesia, etc. *See* ANAEMIA, ANAESTHESIA.

a'nemograph, n. [Meteor.] A recording ANEMOMETER.

ane'mometer, n. [Meteor.] Instrument for measuring force or rate of motion of wind. ane'mometry, n. anemo'metric, -al, aa.

'aneroid (barometer). Instrument measuring the PRESSURE of the ATMOSPHERE by its effect on a thin metal box out of which most of the air has been pumped.

a'neuria, n. [Med.] Loss of nerve power.

'aneurin, n. [Biochem.] THIAMIN.

'aneur-ism, -ysm, n. [Med.] Great expansion of blood-vessel into bag-like form, caused by disease of vessel wall.

angien'chyma, n. [Bot.] The sort of TISSUE forming vessels.

an'gina, n. [Med.] Any INFLAMMATION of throat, with tendency to sudden attacks of loss of power to take breath. a. 'pectoris. Strong and sudden attack of pain in lower part of chest, caused by narrowing of the vessels taking blood to the heart.

angi'oma, n. Diseased growth made up of blood-vessels which have undergone expansion.

angi'opathy, n. Disease of blood-vessels.

'Angio'spermae, n.pl. The greatest DIVISION of seed-plants, taking in all flowering plants, in which the development of seeds takes place in a shut seed-vessel. 'angio-

sperm, n. Any plant of the A. 'angio-'spermous, a.

'angio'sporous, a. [Bot.] Having SPORES in a spore-vessel.

'angle, n. [Geom.] The amount by which one of two meeting lines or planes would have to be turned to put it in the same position as the other, measured in DEGREES or in RADIANS. (*See* SOLID A.)

angle of 'contact. [Phys.] The angle which the SURFACE of a liquid makes with the vessel in which it is, or with any solid cutting the surface.

angle of de'pression. (Of a seen thing) the angle under the HORIZONTAL made at the eye or an instrument by a straight line from it to the thing.

angle of dip. [Phys.] MAGNETIC DIP.

angle of ele'vation. (Of a seen thing) the angle over the HORIZONTAL made at the eye or an instrument by a straight line from it to the thing.

angle of 'incidence. [Phys., Optics] The angle which any straight line, or anything in the form of a straight line (sp. [Optics] a ray of light), meeting a SURFACE, makes with a line at right angles to the surface at the point of meeting.

angle of 'polarization. [Optics] That ANGLE OF INCIDENCE of a light-ray on a SURFACE from which it undergoes REFLECTION which gives the greatest amount of PLANE POLARIZATION of the ray after reflection.

angle of re'flection. [Phys., Optics] The angle made by a ray after REFLECTION from a SURFACE with a line at right angles to the surface at the point of reflection.

angle of re'fraction. [Phys., Optics] The angle made by a ray after REFRACTION into a body with a line at right angles to the SURFACE of the body at the point of refraction.

'Angström unit. Unit used in measuring the WAVE-LENGTHS of light and other rays, 10^{-8} cm.

An'guillidae, n.pl. [Zoo.] The commonest FAMILY of APODES, important as food fish, marked by having very small SCALES bedded in the skin and noted for the mass journeying of the young up rivers from the sea to go through a long development in inland waters, and their journeying back to certain parts of the sea to BREED when their sex-development is complete.

'angular, a. Having, forming, an angle or angles, sp. having sharp angles or a great number of them; of or measured by an angle, as a. distance. a. dis'placement. [Phys.] (Of a moving body) the angle turned through by a body moving about a given AXIS, or by the straight line joining a moving body to a fixed point. a. mo'mentum. [Phys.] (Of a thing

having a. motion) the MOMENT OF
INERTIA, the a. velocity. **a. motion.** The
motion of a body turning or moving about
a fixed AXIS. **a. processes.** [Anat.] The
out-growths of bone over the eyes. **a.
vein.** VEIN going down side of top part
of nose and across face. **a. velocity.**
[Phys.] The rate of a. displacement.

angu'lar(e), n. [Zoo.] A MEMBRANE BONE on
the lower edge of the lower JAW in most
back-boned animals other than MAMMALS.

'**angulate, -d,** aa. [Bot.] Having angles, as
a. leaves.

'**angusti-,** Narrow: -'foliate, -'rostrate,
-'septate, aa.

an'hedron, n. [Crystal.] Body having the
inner structure of a CRYSTAL but not its
regular form. **an'hedral,** a.

an'hydride, n. Substance produced by
taking water away chemically from
another substance, sp. from acids.

an'hydrite, n. [Mineral.] ANHYDROUS $CaSO_4$.

an'hydrous, a. Chemically free from water,
sp. from WATER OF CRYSTALLIZATION.

'**aniline,** n. An oil-like, AROMATIC liquid,
$C_6H_5NH_2$, got from coal, used in making
DYES and medical substances.

'**animal,** n. Living being which takes in O
and gives off CO_2 all the time and has a
system for the digestion of food in the
form of plant or animal substance,
being without the power of building up
its food from simpler chemicals, and
which gen. has some power of free
motion. **a. 'kingdom.** [Biol.] The group of
living things made up of all aa., the
highest group in the system of grouping
in Zoology, of which the chief divisions
are SUB-KINGDOMS (see p. 562).

animal 'charcoal. CHARCOAL made from
animal substances such as bone, used for
taking colour out of materials.

ani'malcule, ani'malculus, nn. Any very
small living thing, animal or free-moving
plant, sp. of sorts living in water.

animal pole. [Zoo.] That half of a fertile
OVUM in which, or point in this about
which, division goes on at greatest rate.

animal starch. [Chem.] GLYCOGEN.

A'nimi'kean, a., n. [Geol.] (Of) an important system of PROTEROZOIC ROCKS in
North America.

'**animism,** n. Belief that all natural, material
things are conscious beings.

'**anion,** n. [Phys., Chem.] ATOM, or complex
of atoms, having NEGATIVE electric
CHARGE, moving to ANODE in gas or liquid.

'**anio'notropy,** n. IONOTROPY of an ANION.

a'niso'carp-ous, -ic, aa. [Bot.] Having
smaller number of CARPELS than of other
flower-parts.

a'niso'dactylous, a. [Zoo.] Having unequal
or unequally spaced toes, sp. of birds
with 3 toes turned forward and one
turned back.

a'nisoga'mete, n. [Biol.] Sex-CELL uniting
with one of opposite sex which is markedly different in form or sp. size. **ani'so-
gamy,** n. The uniting of aa. **ani'sogamous,**
a.

ani'somerous, a. Not having same number
of parts in every ring of flower-parts.
a'niso'mery, n.

a'niso'metric, a. [Phys.] Not measuring the
same in all directions, said sp. of CRYSTALS.

a'niso'phyllous, a. Having leaves of different
sizes or forms on same stem. **a'nisophylly,**
n.

aniso'stemonous, a. [Bot.] Not having same
number of STAMENS as of PETALS and
SEPALS.

aniso'trop-ic, -al, -ous, aa. [Phys., Chem.]
Having different physical properties in
different directions. [Zoo.] (Of eggs)
having a fixed AXIS. [Bot.] Having one-
sided reaction to STIMULI. **'aniso'tropy,** n.

'**ankle,** n. [Anat.] JOINT between foot and
leg. **a. jerk,** [Med.] Sudden, automatic
motion of foot down, as reaction to
stretching of leg or blow on ACHILLES'
TENDON, a sign of HYSTERIA when
strongly marked.

ankylo-, anky'losis. ANCHYLO-, ANCHYLOSIS.

'**anlage,** n. [Biol.] The group of CELLS marking the start of the development of some
part or structure in an EMBRYO, that is,
such part or structure in its earliest form.

an'neal, v.t. Make soft by heating to a high
degree and then let get cold slowly, sp.
glass and metals which have been worked
when cold, to make them less readily
cracked.

An'nelida, n.pl. A PHYLUM of METAZOA in
which are grouped animals without back-
bones having SEGMENTED BODIES but no
legs. '**annelid,** n., a. (Any animal) of the A.

annihi'lation radiation. [Phys.] RADIATION
produced by the meeting and destruction
of an ELECTRON and a POSITRON.

'**annual,** n., a. (Plant) living through only
one year's growth. **a. rings.** Rings seen
in stem of tree, etc., representative of one
year's growth of wood.

'**annual 'parallax.** [Astron.] The a.p. of a
star is the angle whose SINE is $\frac{a}{d}$, where a
is the distance of the earth from the sun
and d of the star from the sun.

'**annular,** a. See ANNULUS.

'**Annu'lata,** n. ANNELIDA.

'**annulate,** a. ANNULAR; circled with rings
of colour. [Zoo.] Made up of ring-like
divisions.

annulus, n. [Biol.] Ring-like part, sp. ring of
TISSUE round the stem of an AGARIC
FRUIT-BODY after expansion of the
PILEUS. [Astron.] Ring of light seen in
ANNULAR ECLIPSE. '**annular,** a. Of, in the
form of, a ring; ringed or marked with
circles. **annular e'clipse.** ECLIPSE of sun

when the moon is so far away that its shade has round it a thin ring of sunlight.

a′node, n. ELECTRODE by which an electric current goes into a gas or liquid, the + POLE of a vessel through which electric current is sent; that electrode in an ELECTRON DISCHARGE TUBE to which all electrons come. **a. drop** or **fall.** Fall of POTENTIAL at a. **a. rays.** Rays of + IONS sent out from a. of ELECTRON TUBE. **a′nodic,** a.

a′noestru-s, -m, nn. [Zoo.] Time between regular operation of sex-impulses, sp. in females.

ano′etic, a. [Psych.] Not given conscious attention, at the edge of conscious thought.

′anolyte, n. Liquid round ANODE.

anoma′listic month. [Astron.] The time between the moon's being at PERIGEE and coming round to it again, = 27·55 days.

anoma′listic year. [Astron.] The time taken by the earth to go from PERIHELION round to perihelion again, = 365 days, 6 hours, 13 minutes, 53·1 seconds.

a′nomaly, n. [Biol.] Any property, etc., which is not normal or representative. [Astron.] The distance of a PLANET from its PERIHELION measured by the angle between the straight line joining the perihelion to the sun and that joining the sun to the planet (*true a.*); the angle between the APSE LINE and the straight line from a planet moving in an ELLIPTIC ORBIT to the middle of that orbit (*eccentric a.*). **a′nomalous,** a.

′Anoplura, n.pl. An ORDER of small, EXOPTERYGOTE, PARASITIC insects without wings.

anor′ganic, a. INORGANIC.

ano′rexia, n. [Med.] Loss of desire for food.

a′northic, a. (Of CRYSTAL) having unequal OBLIQUE AXES.

an′orthite, n. [Mineral.] A white or grey FELDSPAR formed of $CaAl_2(SiO_4)_2$, very common in IGNEOUS ROCKS.

anox(a)′emia, a′noxia, nn. [Med.] Condition of not having enough O in blood, as when person becomes ill high up on a mountain.

ant-. ANTI-, -′acid, n. -′alkali, n.

an′tagonism, n. The acting against one another in bodies of plants and animals of two or more parts, ORGANISMS, or substances, sp. muscles, MICROORGANISMS, poisons. **an′tagonist,** n. Thing, sp. muscle, acting against another. **antago′nistic,** a. antagonistic symbi′osis. PARASITISM.

′antambu′lacral, a. ABACTINAL.

ant′apex, n. [Astron.] *See* SOLAR ANTAPEX.

′Ant′arctic, a., n. (To do with, being in) the south part of the earth, limited by the A. Circle. **A. Circle.** The PARALLEL OF LATITUDE 23°30′ from the SOUTH POLE.

′ante-. Coming before, in time or place.

′antecedent, 1.a. Coming before, earlier than, some other thing. [Geog.] (Of a river, river-hollow, etc.) formed before the country underwent changes in its level, etc., and still in existence after such changes, though no longer a natural outcome of the structure of the country, opp. CONSEQUENT. 2.n. A. thing, sp. [Arith.] the first number of a RATIO. **a. ′drainage.** [Geol.] System of a.waterways.

′ante′centre, n. Point on earth opposite EPICENTRE.

′ante′natal, a. [Med.] To do with time from start of baby's development up to point of birth.

an′tenna (antennae), n. [Zoo.] Long, thin, gen. JOINTED structure on head of certain animals, such as insects and CRUSTACEANS, used for purpose of touch, feeler. [Radio] Structure of wires by which waves are sent out or taken in. **a. ar′ray.** Radio a. made up of system of equally spaced parallel wires, ranged in a curve so as to have special effect in certain directions. **an′tennary,** a. [Zoo.] **an′tennule,** n. [Zoo.] Small a.

′ante ′partum, a. [Med.] Before birth.

an′terior, a. [Biol.] To do with, near, the head of an animal; VENTRAL, on the underside, or (of man) at the front, of the body; facing out, away from middle line or stem. **a. pi′tuitary.** [Zoo.] *See* PITUITARY. **a. root.** [Zoo.] (Of a nerve) VENTRAL ROOT.

an′thela, n. Feather-like flower of certain grass-like plants.

ant′helion, n. Bright ring seen in sky on cloud or mist opposite sun.

′anther, n. [Bot.] The part of STAMEN producing POLLEN.

′anthe′ridio′phore, n. [Bot.] Special stem supporting ANTHERIDIUM.

′anthe′ridium (antheridia), n. [Bot.] Part in which male sex-CELLS of CRYPTOGAMS undergo development. **′anthe′ridial,** a.

′anthero′zo(ö)id, n. [Bot.] Any of the male sex-CELLS in an ANTHERIDIUM.

′anthocarp, n. [Bot.] A fruit made up of the OVARY and its seeds together with other parts of the flower. **antho′carpous,** a.

antho′cyanin, n. Any of a group of complex GLUCOSIDE colouring-substances in plants and flowers, gen. blue or red-blue, but sometimes red.

an′thodium, n. [Bot.] COMPOUND FLOWER; the INVOLUCRE of an a.

-′anthous, a. Having the sort or number of flowers named, as *mo′nanthous.*

antho′xanthin, n. Any of a group of yellow colouring-substances common in flowers.

Antho′zoa, n.pl. [Zoo.] A CLASS of COELENTERATES in whose development there is no sexed GENERATION, some of which have body-divisions formed by ingrowths from body wall.

'**anthracene,** n. [Chem.] An AROMATIC substance, $C_{14}H_{10}$, a CRYSTALLINE substance having blue FLUORESCENCE, got from COAL TAR and used for making DYES.

'**anthracite,** n. A very hard coal, almost completely made up of C.

'**anthrax,** n. Disease of animals, sometimes given to man, caused by a BACTERIUM and marked by ULCERATION of the skin. **an'thracic,** a.

'**anthropo-.** Man, to do with man.

'**anthropo'centric,** a. Taking man's reactions and behaviour as a guide to those of other animals.

'**anthropo'geography,** n. That branch of Anthropology having to do with the distribution of man over the earth and his relation to his GEOGRAPHICAL condition.

'**Anthro'poidea,** n.pl. [Zoo.] The SUB-ORDER of PRIMATES made up of anthropoid apes, other higher forms of monkeys, and man.

'**anthropoid,** 1.a. Of, to do with, the A.; man-like. 2.n. An anthropoid animal. **anthropoid ape.** Any of the sorts of higher monkeys without tails nearest to man in development.

anthro'pology, n. The general science of man, covering his history, distribution, physical development, forms of society, etc.

'**anthro'pometry,** n. The science of measuring man's body, its parts and powers. '**anthropo'metric(al)** aa.

'**anthro'ponomy,** n. The science of man's behaviour.

'**anthropo'morphism,** n. Taking beings other than man to have minds like that of man. '**anthropo'morph-ic, -ous,** aa.

'**anti-.** Opp. in position or effect, sp. [Med.] (substance, etc.) acting against, having opp. effect to, overcoming substance or condition named: '-'bacterial, a., '-co-'agulant, a., n. -'lysin, n., -ra'chitic, a., n., '-scor'butic, a., n.

'**antibi'otic,** n. a. [Med.] Any of a group of substances produced by living things, sp. by BACTERIA in FUNGI, which have the power of destruction of other MICRO-ORGANISMS, for example, PENICILLIN. 2.a. To do with aa., having such power of destruction.

'**antibody,** n. [Med.] Any substance in the blood, normally present or produced as reaction to attack, acting against certain poisons or the BACTERIA etc. producing them, or against other undesired substance coming into the body.

'**anti'cataly-st, -zer,** nn. [Chem.] CATALYST making chemical reaction slower.

'**anti'cathode,** n. [Phys.] Metal part of X-RAY TUBE where X-rays are produced by CATHODE rays falling on it. [Elec.] The ANODE of an ELECTRON DISCHARGE TUBE.

'**anti'clinal,** a. Sloping in opp. directions.

[Biol.] Undergoing division of CELLS at right angles to the APEX. [Geol.] Of, having, an anticline. **a. fold.** Anticline. '**anticline,** n. [Geol.] FOLD of arch-like form, opp. SYNCLINE.

'**anticli'norium,** n. [Geol.] A number of ANTICLINES and SYNCLINES grouped in the general form of an arch.

'**antico'agulin,** n. [Biochem.] Any substance causing blood coming from the body to keep in a liquid condition.

anti'cryptic color'ation. [Zoo.] AGGRESSIVE MIMICRY in colouring.

'**anti'cyclone,** n. [Meteor.] A stretch of high ATMOSPHERIC PRESSURE over part of the earth, with the pressure greatest in the middle, and winds circling out, opp. CYCLONE. '**anticy'clonic,** a. **anticyclonic storm.** Very strong wind on edge of a.

'**antidote,** n. [Med.] Substance acting against effects of poison.

'**anti'dromous,** a. [Bot.] Having TENDRILS or line of leaf-positions twisting in opp. directions on same plant. '**anti'dromy,** n.

'**anti'enzyme,** n. [Biochem.] ANTIBODY produced in reaction to an ENZYME.

'**anti-'freeze,** n. Any substance of low FREEZING-POINT used in place of, or mixed with, water in the RADIATORS of automobile engines, etc., to keep them from being damaged by the FREEZING of the liquid.

'**anti'friction metal.** Any of a number of ALLOYS used in machines for the purpose of making FRICTION less.

'**antigen,** n. [Med.] Any substance, etc., which when put into the body is the cause of chemical changes forming ANTIBODIES.

'**anti-'knock,** n. Any substance used as, or mixed with, the FUEL in an INTERNAL COMBUSTION ENGINE to overcome DETONATION.

an'tilogous pole. That POLE of a PYRO-ELECTRIC CRYSTAL which becomes NEGATIVE on heating.

'**anti'logarithm,** n. [Math.] The number of which a given number is the LOGARITHM, that is, if $a^n = b$, then the a. of n is b. *See* LOGARITHM.

'**anti'lysin,** n. [Biochem.] Any substance, sp. an ANTIBODY, acting against a LYSIN.

'**antimony,** n. Chemical ELEMENT, at. no. 51, at. wt. 121·76, sign Sb, a silver-white metal. '**antimonic,** a.

'**anti-'neutron,** n. [Phys.] Name given to a PARTICLE causing the destruction of a NEUTRON and at the same time undergoing destruction itself.

'**anti'node,** n. [Phys.] Point of greatest AMPLITUDE of a VIBRATION, half-way between two NODES.

an'tinomy, n. Relation between two laws or statements having opp. senses and seeming to be equally true.

'anti'oxidant, n. [Chem.] Substance acting against OXIDATION, sp. of rubber by air.

'anti'lysin, n. [Biochem.] Any substance, sp. an ANTIBODY, acting against a LYSIN.

'anti-'particle, n. [Phys.] Name given to a group of physical PARTICLES acting against or as opposites of the FUNDAMENTAL PARTICLES, as an ANTI-NEUTRON.

'antipa'thetic, a. Acting against, having a strong reaction against, opposite in effect (*to* some other thing or, of two things, to one another)—said of the body or the mind, or of two chemical substances, etc. **a. symbi'osis,** ANTAGONISTIC SYMBIOSIS. **an'tipathy,** n. The condition of being a., sp. [Psych.] a strong, deep-rooted, natural feeling of disgust or hate against something, for example some sort of animal, which is not based on reason.

'antiperi'odic, n., a. [Med.] (Substance, etc.) acting against PERIODIC attacks of disease.

'anti'peri'stalsis, n. [Zoo.] PERISTALSIS in opp. direction to normal. 'anti'peri'staltic, a.

'anti'petalous, a. [Bot.] Having STAMENS in front of PETALS.

an'tipodal, a. At opp. end(s) of middle line through circle or ball. **a. cell.** [Bot.] Any of 3 unwalled CELLS at end of EMBRYO SAC opp. MICROPYLE, in seed-plants. **a. cone.** [Biol.] In MITOSIS, CONE of rays opp. SPINDLE. **'antipode,** n. [Chem.] ENANTIOMORPH. **an'tipodes,** n.pl. [Geog.] Place, part, a. to another on the earth.

'anti-'proton, n. [Phys.] PARTICLE which is the same as a PROTON but with a NEGATIVE CHARGE.

'anti-'resonance, n. [Phys.] The opposite of RESONANCE, which is present whenever a small change in the FREQUENCY of EXCITATION, up or down, takes place, causing an increase in the reaction.

'anti'septic, n., a. [Med.] (Substance) causing destruction or stopping growth or operation of BACTERIA, used sp. of substances put on the body, on wounds etc., for this purpose, as opp. DISINFECTANT; to do with antisepsis. **'anti-'sepsis,** n. A process; use of ba.

'anti'serum, n. [Med.] SERUM used against a disease.

'anti'squama (antisquamae), n. [Zoo.] In insects, that one of two SQUAMAE which is nearest the ALULA.

'anti-'Stokes line. [Optics] In the RAMAN EFFECT, the ray sent out which is of higher FREQUENCY than the light used.

'anti'thrombin, n. [Biochem.] Substance produced by LIVER which keeps blood from COAGULATION in blood-vessels.

'anti'toxin, n. [Biochem., Med.] Chemical substance produced by the blood of a living animal as reaction to certain poisons, sp. BACTERIA-produced ones, and having power of stopping their operation, made use of in IMMUNOLOGY. **'anti'toxic, a**

'anti-'trade, a., n. (Of) wind blowing high over TRADE WIND, and in opp. direction.

'anti'tropic, a. [Bot.] Twisting like a corkscrew but from left to right.

'anti've-nin, -nene, -nine, nn. Any ANTITOXIN produced by snake poison.

'antler, n. [Zoo.] A horn of an animal of the family CERVIDAE, different from those of other animals, such as the cow, in being formed completely of bone, freq. branching, and dropped and produced again every year.

ant'orbital, a. [Anat.] In front of ORBIT.

'antrum (antra), n. [Zoo.] A hollow, sp. the air-hollow in the MAXILLARY bone at back of nose in higher animals.

A'nura, n.pl. [Zoo.] SALIENTIA. **a'nural,** a'nurous, aa. Of, or like, the A.; having no tail.

a'nuria, n. [Med.] Loss of power to URINATE.

'anus, n. [Zoo.] The opening at the end of the ALIMENTARY CANAL through which waste is sent out of the body.

'anvil, n. A solid mass of metal, gen. iron, commonly in the form of a thick neck curving up from a wide base and supporting a flat top with one end pointed and a rounded under side, on which metal is worked into desired forms by hammering or stamping; a structure of like purpose but more complex form used in present-day physics in the making of new materials under very high PRESSURES and at very high TEMPERATURES. **a. bone.** [Zoo.] The middle, somewhat a.-like bone of the three small bones in the ear of higher animals.

a'orta, n. [Zoo.] Great ARTERY taking blood to all parts of body other than LUNGS. **a'ortic, a. a'ortic arch.** [Zoo.] In fish and the early stages of higher backboned animals, any of the group of blood-vessels, formed in two's opposite one another, branching round from the VENTRAL a., between the GILL-SLITS, to the DORSAL a.

'apatite, n. MINERAL, $3Ca_3(PO_4).CaF_2$, present in different forms in a great number of rocks.

ape, n. [Zoo.] Monkey, sp. one of the great sorts without tail.

a'perient, n., a. [Med.] (Substance) helping clearing of waste from INTESTINES.

a'peri'odic, a. Not PERIODIC. [Phys.] So DAMPED as to put a stop to VIBRATION, said sp. of instrument pointer which goes straight to rest on its reading without first moving from side to side.

'aper'tometer, n. [Optics] Instrument for measuring the APERTURE of a system of LENSES.

'aperture, n. Opening. [Optics] (DIAMETER of) a. letting light into camera, or of the

OBJECTIVE of an instrument such as a TELESCOPE (freq. given as measure of a. angle). **a. angle.** [Optics] The angle between lines joining ends of DIAMETER of LENS to its chief FOCUS.

apex (apices), n. The to some degree pointed top or end of anything, such as leaf; of heart, the lower pointed part; of lung, the narrow top end going into the root of neck. [Geom.] The point of a CONE or PYRAMID, or that angle of a TRIANGLE opposite whatever side is taken as the base. **a. of earth's motion.** Point in sky in the direction of which the earth is moving at a given time. **a. of sun's motion.** SOLAR A.

A'petalae, n.pl., [Bot.] MONOCHLAMYDEAE.

aph-. APO-.

a'ph(a)erisis, n. [Philol.] The dropping of a letter or sound unit from the front of a word, as in *'gainst* for *against*.

Aphan'iptera, n.pl. [Zoo.] An ORDER of ENDOPTERYGOTA, very small, with no wings and great jumping power, PARASITIC on birds and MAMMALS.

'apha'nipterous, a. [Zoo.] Seeming to be without wings.

a'phasia, n. [Med.] Loss of power of using or getting sense of language, caused by some damage to brain or sometimes by shock, etc.

ap'helion (aphelia), n. [Astron.] The point on the line of motion of a body moving round the sun (sp. the earth) at which it is farthest from the sun.

a'phelio'tropic, a. APHOTOTROPIC. **a'phelio-'tropism,** n.

a'phesis, n. [Philol.] Loss by degrees as effect of PHONETIC process of a short VOWEL from the front of a word, as in the development of *esquire* into *squire*.

A'phididae, n.pl. [Zoo.] A FAMILY of HOMOPTERA made up of small insects living on the JUICES of plants, the females generally without wings and some of them producing offspring PATHOGENETIC-ALLY, important for the damage they do by their great numbers and sometimes by causing VIRUS diseases. **'aphid,** n. An insect of the A. **'aphis** (aphides), n. An aphid of the GENUS *Aphis*, specially damaging to fruit trees and garden produce, or, loosely, any aphid.

a'photo'tropism, n. [Biol.] TROPISM away from light. **a'photo'tropic,** a.

'aphro'disiac, n., a. [Med.] (Substance, etc.) causing increase in sex desire.

a'phill-ous, -ose, aa. [Bot.] Having no leaves. **a'phylly,** n.

'apical, a. At, near, or to do with the APEX. **a. cell.** [Bot.] CELL at point of an a. cone, by division of which growth takes place. **a. cone.** VEGETATIVE CONE. **a. growth.** Sp. growth of a HYPHA at point only. **a. plane.** In DIATOMS, plane of middle line.

a'picular, a. APICAL.

a'piculate, a. [Bot.] Ending suddenly in a sharp point, as leaf.

a'pilary, a. [Bot.] (Of COROLLA) having no, or incomplete development of, top lip.

'apioid, n. [Phys.] Form taken by a quickly turning liquid mass acted on only by force of earth's attraction.

'api'ology, n. The science of bees.

'apla'cental, a. Producing, having, no PLACENTA.

'apla'natic, a. [Optics] Having no SPHERICAL ABERRATION. **'aplanat,** n. Special sort of a. LENS.

a'plano-. Without power of motion. **-'gamete,** n. **-'plastid,** **'-spore,** nn. Sp., RESTING SPORE without sex seen in certain ALGAE.

'aplite, n. A small-grained, light-coloured IGNEOUS ROCK produced by the separating of certain materials from a MAGMA and seen as thin bands or walls in igneous rock.

ap'neustic, a. (Of insect LARVAE) having no breathing-openings.

ap'noea, n. [Zoo., Med.] Stopping of breathing-motions caused by too little CO_2 in the blood.

'apo-. Away from, off, separate. [Chem.] Naming a substance formed from, or having some relation to, substance named: **'apoa'conitine,** n.

apo'carp-ous, apocar'pistic, aa. [Bot.] Having CARPELS separate from one another, or only in part united.

'apocentre, n. [Astron.] That point of an ORBIT farthest from the body producing the attraction.

'apochro'matic, a. [Optics] (Of a COMPOUND LENS) so designed as to be as free as possible from CHROMATIC ABERRATION.

a'pocope, n. [Philol., Gram.] The loss or dropping of a letter or sound unit from the end of a word, as in *th'* for *the*.

A'poda, n.pl. [Zoo.] An ORDER of AMPHIBIA made up of worm-like animals which make their way down into the earth or sand near water, and whose chief food is earthworms—the only Amphibia at present in existence which have SCALES, these being deeply bedded in the skin.

apodeme, apo'dema, nn. [Zoo.] In ARTHRO-PODA, any of the CHITINOUS ingrowths from the body-wall forming an inner supporting framework to which the muscles are fixed; in insects, sp. such an ingrowth from the sides of the THORAX.

A'podes, n.pl. [Zoo.] An ORDER of TELEOST fish with snake-like bodies, no separate tail-FIN, no PELVIC FINS, other fins with soft FIN-RAYS, and no or very small SCALES, of which ANGUILLIDAE are the commonest representatives.

'apoga'lacteum, n. [Astron.] Point in motion of sun or star at which it is farthest from the MILKY WAY.

a'pogamy, n. [Bot.] The producing of a SPOROPHYTE by a GAMETOPHYTE without FERTILIZATION in PTERIDOPHYTA.

'apogee, n. [Astron., Astronautics] The point at which any body going round the earth or another star is farthest away from it.

apo'mixis, n. [Biol.] Any form of the producing of offspring by a sexed plant or animal, or by a process seemingly like a sex process, without any sex connection, for example, PARTHENOGENESIS and APOGAMY.

a'pophony, n. [Philol.] ABLAUT. [Phonet.] GRADATION.

a'pophysis, n. [Bot.] In MUSCI or FUNGI, thick part of stem supporting SPORE-vessel. [Zoo.] In VERTEBRA an outgrowth on a bone; in insects, an outgrowth from the inside of the body-wall to which muscle is fixed. [Geol.] Arm-like part stretching from an INTRUSION.

'apoplexy, n. [Med.] Sudden loss of conscious feeling, power of motion, caused by the bursting or stopping up of a blood-vessel in, or in connection with, the brain; condition of any part, such as LUNG, in which blood gets out of blood-vessels.

'apose'matic, a. [Zoo.] (Of structures or colouring) acting as a sign to other animals that the animal so marked is armed with some cruel power of wounding, etc., such as a STING, and so not to be attacked, sp. **a. color'ation. a. 'mimicry.** MIMICRY of things which are unpleasing or a danger, with a view to keeping off attackers.

apo'sepalous, a. [Bot.] POLYSEPALOUS.

a'pospory, n. [Bot.] The producing of GAMETOPHYTES without the SPORE stage, straight from SPOROPHYTES, as by certain MUSCI and FILICALES.

a pos'teri'ori. Of, to do with, reasoning from effect to cause or from experience to rule.

a'postrophe, n. [Bot.] The ranging of CHLOROPLASTS on side walls of leaf CELLS in bright light, opp. EPISTROPHE.

a'pothecaries' measure. The English system of liquid measures used by chemists for medical substances. **apothecaries' weight.** The English system of weights used for medical substances, of which the pound, the ounce, and the grain have the same values as in TROY WEIGHT, but which has different units, the DRACHM and the SCRUPLE, between.

apo'thecium (apothecia), n. ASCOCARP of plate- or cup-like form, as in LICHENS.

Appa'lachian revo'lution. [Geol.] The time of mountain-building earth motions in N. Am. near the end of the PALAEOZOIC PERIOD.

'appar'atus, n. Any instrument, freq.

complex, or system of things, used for making tests, etc., in science work. [Zoo.] Any group or system of parts working together, as *the breathing a.*

ap'parent, a. (Of value, size, position, etc.) open to observation; as it seems to the eye, ear, etc., or to simple observation, as opp. what it truly is, as made clear by observation with instruments, or by reasoning. **a. di'ameter.** [Astron.] The angle based on the DIAMETER of a star, etc., as seen from the middle of the earth. **a. free space.** [Bot.] The part of a plant through which SALTS are freely transported, gen. taken to be all the parts outside the PROTOPLASM. **a. noon.** [Astron.] The time at which the sun is on the OBSERVER'S MERIDIAN, **a. re'sistance.** IMPEDANCE. **a. 'solar day.** [Astron.] The time between an a. noon and the a. noon after it. **a. (solar) time.** The time of day based on the position in which the sun in fact is at that point of time, as opp. that based on the MEAN SUN.

ap'pendage, n. [Bot.] Any outgrowth which seems not to be a necessary part of a plant's structure. [Zoo.] Outgrowth or outside part of animal's body, sp. leg or arm.

'appen'dectomy, n. [Med.] Operation of cutting out VERMIFORM APPENDIX.

'appen'dicial, a. [Anat.] To do with VERMIFORM APPENDIX.

ap'pendi'citis, n. [Med.] INFLAMMATION of VERMIFORM APPENDIX.

'appen'dicular, a. [Zoo.] To do with an APPENDAGE. [Med.] APPENDICIAL.

ap'pendix, n. An addition, sp. a separate division giving further material at the end of a book. [Zoo.] An outgrowth. [Med.] The VERMIFORM A.

apper'ception, n. [Psych.] The act of the mind by which it gets anything of which it is conscious into relation with its store of knowledge.

'Appleton 'layer. STRATUM of the IONO-SPHERE about 230 km. from the earth, by which short radio waves are turned back to earth, important for long-distance radio, freq. named *the F-layer.*

ap'ply, 1.v.t. Put something to or into another thing for the purpose of producing some effect, as a. heat *to* a substance; make use of a rule, a process, and so on in relation to a special example. 2.v.i. (Of a rule, theory, etc.) have relation *to*, be of a sort to be applied *to*, some event, etc. **'applic'ation**, n. **ap'plied**, a. Sp. in relation to use, said of that branch of any science which has to do with it as an instrument of other sciences or of industry, as **a. mathematics**, mathematics as used in working out questions about the behaviour of physical things.

'appo'sition, n. [Bot.] Growth of CELL-wall

by coat over coat of new material.

approxi'mation, n. The process of getting nearer and nearer to the right answer, measure, value, etc., step by step; a value got by a.; a value which is not quite the true one, but near enough to it for some purpose, or as near as it is possible to get. **app'roximate,** 1.v.t. and i. Come near (*to* a true value), be an a. 2.a. (Of a value, etc.) got by a., very near to but not quite the true one. **app'roxi-mately,** adv. Almost.

a pri'ori. Based on, to do with, reasoning from cause to effect or from theory to fact.

a'proctous, a. [Zoo.] Without an ANUS.

'apron, n. [Biol., Mach.] Name given to a number of flat parts in living things or machines, acting as covers, supports, etc. [Geol.] Flat mass of earth put down by water in front of GLACIER.

'apse, 'apsis (apsides), [Astron.] A point in the ORBIT of a body where its distance from the body causing attraction is greatest (*higher a.*) or least (*lower a.*). **apse line.** Line joining higher aa. or lower aa. **'apsidal,** a.

ap'terium (apteria), n. [Zoo.] Any of the uncovered or DOWN-covered spaces between those parts of a bird's skin where the long feathers are rooted. **ap'terial,** a.

'apter-ous, -al, aa. [Zoo.] Without wings. [Bot.] Not having wing-like expansions.

'apte'rygial, a. [Zoo.] Without wings; without FINS.

Ap'tery'gota, n.pl. A group of small insects without wings, which do not undergo METAMORPHOSIS, of very wide distribution. **ap'tery'gotous,** a.

'aqua, n. Name for water used in naming chemical, sp. medical, substances, gen. as sign of SOLUTION. **a. 'fortis.** NITRIC ACID (HNO_3). **a. 'regia.** 3 to 4 parts HYDROCHLORIC ACID SOLUTION (HCl.Aq) mixed with 1 part NITRIC ACID (HNO_3), a yellow liquid having power of taking gold into solution.

'aqualung, n. An apparatus used in underwater swimming by which COMPRESSED air from a vessel fixed to a swimmer's back is automatically breathed in through a mouth-part, so that he has no need of pipes to take air down to him from the top.

'aquama'rine, n. [Mineral.] A sort of BERYL, light blue-green in colour.

A'quarius, n. [Astron.] The 11th SIGN or THE ZODIAC.

'aqueduct, n. [Zoo.] Narrow way or pipe forming connection between parts, sp. [Anat.], in brain, and bones of head and face.

'aqueous, a. To do with, made by, water. [Chem.] Formed in great part of water.

a. 'humour. Liquid in eye between CRYSTALLINE LENS and CORNEA. **a. 'tissue.** [Bot.] Water-storing CELLS. **'aqueo-.** [Geol.] A. and :...-'glacial, a.,-'igneous, a.

'aquiculture, n. The growth by man of things living in water, sp. the care of sea or inland waters with a view to increasing their produce.

a'quiferous, a. [Geol.] Transporting water. **'aquifer,** n. Under-earth bed of sand or other substance which lets water through.

'aquo-'ion, n. [Phys., Chem.] Complex ION having in it one or more water MOLECULES.

A'rachnida, n.pl. [Zoo.] CLASS of ARTHROPODS such as ACARIDS, with 8 legs and no wings or feelers, and gen. having head united with THORAX, chiefly land animals. **a'rachnid,** n., a. (Animal) of the A.

a'rachnoid, 1.a. [Biol.] Formed of, covered with, a loose network of thin, soft hairs. 2.n. [Anat.] A. membrane. **a. 'membrane.** The MEMBRANE covering the brain between the DURA MATER and the PIA MATER.

'aragonite, n. [Mineral.] One of the natural forms of $CaCO_3$.

Aran'eida, n.pl. An ORDER of ARACHNIDS having a short ABDOMEN, gen. without division, two pointed outgrowths in front of the mouth used for sending poison into the bodies of other animals, and an apparatus at the end of the abdomen for making WEBS, in which they take prisoner insects etc. used for food.

'arbalest, n. An apparatus for sending sharp-pointed PROJECTILES with great force, based on the old instruments of war used by archers, and now used for putting to death great fish and so on deep down in the sea where the use of firearms would be impossible.

'arbitrary, a. (Of values, etc.) fixed by decision, not worked out from other values.

'arbor, n. [Mach.] Rod on which wheel, sp. of clock, is turned; any of other special forms of rods.

ar'bore-al, -ous, aa. Living in trees,

arbo'rescent, a. Tree-like in form, structure, or growth, sp. branching. [Mineral.] Having a. grouping of CRYSTALS. **arbo'rescence,** n. SP., an a. structure.

arbori'culture, n. Growth of trees as a science and art. **'arbori'cultural,** a. **'arbori'culturist,** n.

'arbori'zation, n. (Development into) treelike, branching, structure. [Palaeont.] Outline of tree or plant in FOSSIL. [Anat.] Branching outgrowth of nerve CELL. DENDRITE.

'arbor 'vitae. [Anat.] Tree-like structure seen in CEREBELLUM when cut through from top to base.

arc, n. [Geom.] Any part of a curve, for

example, of a circle, between any two separate points. [Phys.] Bridge of light formed by the transporting of ELECTRICITY from one CONDUCTOR to another through an IONIZED gas, for example when two rods of C or of a metal are put in touch and then parted while an electric current is going from one to the other. **a. 'spectrum.** The SPECTRUM of the light given by a substance when it is placed in an electric a. or is one of the POLES of such an a.—representative of its non-IONIZED ATOMS. **a. 'welding.** WELDING in which the heat is produced by an electric a. formed between an electric apparatus and the metal parts to be united. **'a.-lamp.** n. Form of lighting apparatus using electric a. between rods of C mixed with salts of Ca, K, and other metals (*flame a.-l,*), or of copper mixed with Fe_3O_4, TiO_2 or Cr_2O_3 (*magnetite a.-l.*), and producing very bright light.

Ar'ch(a)ean, a. [Geol.] ARCHAEOZOIC or, sometimes, PRE-CAMBRIAN, used sp. of ROCKS of that time.

'arch(a)eo-. [Geol.] Of very early times.

'arch(a)e'ology, n. The science of early buildings and other things made by men in early times, as material for the history of those times.

'Arch(a)eo'zoic, a. To do with earliest division of earth's history in the system of Geology, the time of the first living things (*see* p. 559).

'arche'centrum, n. ARCOCENTRUM.

arche'gonial, a. [Bot.] Of, to do with, an ARCHEGONIUM.

'Arche'goniatae, n.pl. [Bot.] One of the chief groups of plants, having the ARCHEGONIUM as the female ORGAN and undergoing the process of REPRODUCTION by SPOROPHYTE and GAMETOPHYTE in turn, **arche'goniate,** n., a. (Plant) of the A.

'arche'goniophore, n. [Bot.] Stem supporting ARCHEGONIUM.

'arche'gonium (archegonia), n.[Bot.] Female sex-part, bottle-like in form, of BRYOPHYTES, PTERIDOPHYTES, and, in a simpler form, most GYMNOSPERMS.

ar'chenteron, n. [Zoo.] The inner hollow of a GASTRULA from which the ALIMENTARY CANAL is formed.

'arche'spor-e, -ium, nn. [Bot.] CELL or cells from which SPORE MOTHER-CELLS are formed. **'arche'sporial,** a.

'archetype, n. [Biol.] The earliest ANCESTOR of a group of plants or animals; the general structure common to a group of plants or animals and looked on as representative of the earlier, simpler form of which they are all developments.

'archi-. [Biol.] First-formed or first form of, PRIMITIVE.

'Archian'nelida, n.pl. [Zoo.] CLASS of small

sea ANNELIDA having no outer divisions and with nerve-system not completely separate from outer skin.

'archicarp, n. [Bot.] Female sex-part of ASOMYCETES.

'Archicla'mydeae, n.pl. [Bot.] A great division of the DICOTYLEDONS marked by having no PETALS, or petals quite separate from one another.

Archi'medean or **Archi'medes' principle.** Law that a body when completely or in part in a liquid undergoes a loss in weight equal to the weight of the liquid whose place has been taken by the body.

'archi'nephric, a. To do with ARCHINEPHRIDIUM or ARCHINEPHROS.

'archine'phridium, n. [Zoo.] Simple form of NEPHRIDIUM in LARVAE.

'archi'nephros, n. [Zoo.] PRONEPHROS.

'archi'pallium. n. [Zoo.] In back-boned animals, that part of the outer grey substance of the front brain to do with sense of smell.

'archiplasm, 'archoplasm, nn. [Biol.] In MITOSIS, the substance from which ASTERS and SPINDLES are formed.

'arci'centrous, a. ARCOCENTROUS.

'arciform, a. Formed like an arch.

'arco'centrum, n. [Zoo.] CENTRUM of VERTEBRA formed chiefly by development from bases of NEURAL and HAEMAL ARCHES, opp. CHORDACENTRUM. **'arco'centrous,** a.

'arcoplasm, n. ARCHIPLASM.

'Arctic, a., n. (To do with, being in) the north part of the earth, limited by the A. Circle. **A. Circle.** The PARALLEL OF LATITUDE 23° 30' from the NORTH POLE.

arc'togenous, a. [Biol.] (Of a plant or animal) natural to, having undergone its EVOLUTION in, the ARCTIC.

arcu'ale (arcualia), n. [Zoo.] Any of the CARTILAGES from which the NEURAL and HAEMAL ARCHES are formed.

'arcuate, a. Bent or curved in form of arch.

ar'dometer, n. Apparatus measuring TEMPERATURE of highly heated body by light given out by it.

are, n. METRIC square measure (*see* p. 566).

'area, n. The measure of a plane form or of a plane or curved SURFACE given in SQUARE units; a space of two DIMENSIONS. [Anat.] A part of the brain looked on as doing some special work, e.g. the *visual a.* **a. o'paca.** [Zoo.] Unclear part round a. pellucida. **a. pel'lucida.** In eggs of REPTILES and birds, clear middle part in which EMBRYO is formed. **'areal,** a.

are'naceous, a. [Biol.] Living, doing best, in sand; (of SHELL, etc.) formed of sand or like substance. [Geol.] Formed chiefly of sand.

'are'ola, n. [Biol.] Small space limited by lines or cracks, or between network of vessels, etc., e.g. on leaves, insect's wing;

coloured ring round MAMILLA or like part; part of IRIS edging PUPIL of eye.

a'reolar, a. areolar 'tissue. [Zoo.] In back-boned animals, a soft somewhat sponge-like form of CONNECTIVE TISSUE of which the framework is a loose network of white and yellow COLLAGEN threads.

ar'genteous, a. Like silver.

'argen'tiferous, a. Producing or having in it silver.

'argentite, n. [Mineral.] Natural Ag$_2$S, an important ORE of silver.

'argil'laceous, a. CLAY-like. [Geol.] Formed chiefly of CLAY.

ar'gillo-. CLAY (and . . .).

'argol, n. [Chem.] TARTAR.

'argon, n. Chemical ELEMENT, at. no. 18, at. wt. 39·944, sign A, a gas without colour or smell giving no chemical reactions and forming a small part of air.

'Aries, n. [Astron.] The first SIGN OF THE ZODIAC (see FIRST POINT OF A.).

'aril, n. [Bot.] Outer cover of certain seeds, having its development from the FUNICLE. **'-lary,** a. **'-late,** a. **'-lode.** n. A false a., taking its development from the MICROPYLE, **'-loid,** a.

a'rista, n. [Bot.] AWN. [Zoo.] Thin, stiff, pointed outgrowth at end of feeler in some flies. **a'ristate,** a.

'Aristotle's 'lantern. [Zoo.] Framework of hard plates and muscles supporting teeth in ECHINOIDEA.

a'rithmetic, n. That branch of mathematics which has to do with the addition, SUBTRACTION, MULTIPLICATION, and division of numbers. **'arith'metical,** a. arithmetical mean. Of n numbers, the number got by the addition of them and the division of their amount by n. **arithmetical pro'gression.** An ordered group of numbers every one of which is greater than the one before it by the same amount.

'armature, n. [Phys.] In any electric machine or apparatus, the moving part, as (and sp.), in a DYNAMO or electric MOTOR, the part made up of the CONDUCTORS in which the current is produced or through which it is sent, together with the body of MAGNETIC iron, etc., round which these go and the parts supporting it; the metal cover keeping an electric wire from damage; a KEEPER, or any bit of FERROMAGNETIC material put across the POLES of a MAGNET or a number of magnets for any other purpose. **a. 'winding.** In an a., the COILS of wire taking the current and making connections with the TERMINALS of the machine.

'armillary sphere. Old-time apparatus, formed of a ball made up of a number of rings, for giving position and motion of the stars, etc.

aro'matic, a. [Chem.] (Of ORGANIC COM-POUNDS) having a BENZENE RING structure as opp. ALIPHATIC **a. acid.** Any of those ORGANIC ACIDS in which the CARBOXYL group is joined to an ARYL RADICAL.

arrec'tores pi'lorum. [Zoo.] In MAMMALS, small muscles lifting hairs on skin into upright position.

ar'rhythmia, n. [Med.] Any change from normal in the rhythm of the heart.

'arsenic, 1.n. Chemical ELEMENT, at. no. 33, at. wt. 74·91, sign As, commonly a grey, readily broken solid, but having two other forms (ALLOTROPES), yellow a. and black a. 2.a. Having in it a., sp. DIVALENT a., as opp. arsenious. **ar'senical,** a. Of, to do with, having in it a. **'arsenide,** n. Substance formed of a. and a metal. **ar'senious,** a. Having in it a., sp. TRIVALENT a.

ar'sine, n. AsH$_3$, a gas without colour having strong poisoning effect.

ar'terial, a. [Zoo.] Of, to do with, ARTERIES. **a. scle'rosis.** Disease in which walls of ARTERIES become hard.

ar'terio-. Of ARTERIES (and . . .) **'-scle'rosis.** n. **'-'venous,** a.

ar'teriole, n. A small ARTERY.

'artery, n. [Zoo.] Any of the blood-vessels taking blood from heart to other parts of body.

Ar'tesian well. [Geol. etc.] WELL going down to a bed which comes out of the earth at other points higher than the well, so that water draining down through it is forced up through the hole.

ar'thritis, n. [Med.] INFLAMMATION of a JOINT. **a. de'formans.** A. in which some destruction of JOINTS and growth of new bone-material takes place. **ar'thritic,** a., n.

'artho- [Zoo.] JOINT-: **-chon'dritis,** n. **ar'thrography,** n., **ar'thropathy,** n.

'arthro'branch, -ia, nn. [Zoo.] Breathing-apparatus on MEMBRANE joining leg to body in CRUSTACEANS.

ar'throdia, n. [Zoo.] JOINT by which parts are given power of moving over one another but not of turning. **ar'throdial,** a.

Ar'thropoda, n.pl. [Zoo.] A PHYLUM of METAZOA in which are grouped jointed animals without back-bone having jointed legs etc., gen. with hard outer cover, e.g. insects, CRUSTACEANS, ARACHNIDS. **'arthropod,** n., a. (Any) of the A. **ar'thropod-al, -ous,** aa.

ar'throsis, n. [Zoo.] Any sort of join between bones.

'article, n. [Biol.] An ARTICULATED division.

ar'ticular, a. [Zoo.] Of, at, or near JOINT(s). **a. 'capsule.** CAPSULAR LIGAMENT. **a. cartilage.** CARTILAGE covering the meeting faces of the bones at a JOINT. **a. la-'mella.** The hard coat of bone to which an a. cartilage is fixed. **a. 'process.** In higher back-boned animals, any of the four outgrowths from the NEURAL ARCH, two pointing forward and two back, by which a VERTEBRA is locked to the one before and the one after it.

ar'ticu'lare (articularia) n. In most back-boned animals, bone making connection between lower JAW and QUADRATE.

articu'lation, n. [Biol.] Join, joining structure, between bones or other stiff parts of animal, giving them power of motion in relation to one another; join between parts of plant, sp. where these are designed to become separate; the condition of having aa. or of being articulated. **ar'ticulate,** 1.a. (Of animals) formed of side-to-side divisions (like or different) united by aa.; (of body-part or plant) having aa. 2.v.i. Be joined by a(a). **ar'ticulated,** a.

ar'ticulator, n. [Acous.] Apparatus used in telephone, etc., for getting clearer voice effects.

'artifact, n. [Archaeol.] Thing made or worked on by early man as opp. natural thing possibly used by him but not changed for his purpose. [Biol.] Structure or quality in dead TISSUE etc. which is not natural to it, but the effect of some substance etc., used on it for purpose of science work.

'artio'dactyl, n., a. (Animal, such as sheep, pig) having the same number of toes, ranged in the same way, on the two sides of middle line of foot. **'Artio'dactyla,** n.pl. [Zoo.] The ORDER or SUB-ORDER made up of aa. **'-ous,** a.

aryl, a. [Chem.] Having an AROMATIC group with one VALENCY. **'arylate,** v.t. To put one or more a. groups in place of other groups in a substance.

As, Sign for ARSENIC.

as'bestos, n. [Mineral.] Any of a number of natural SILICATES present in ROCKS as plates or masses of thread-like CRYSTALS, elastic enough to be made into very thin material and having property of being unchanged by great heat.

Asca'roidea, n.pl. [Zoo.] A CLASS of the NEMATODA of which some sorts are PARASITES and most sorts have three lips. **'ascarid,** n. Worm of the A.

a'scending 'colon. [Zoo.] See COLON.

as'cending 'latitude. [Astron.] The increasing LATITUDE of a PLANET moving north.

'Ascheim-'Zondek test. [Med.] Test for PREGNANCY based on putting URINE of woman into living animal.

'asci, n.pl. See ASCUS.

'Ascidi'acea, n.pl. [Zoo.] CLASS of URO-CHORDA made up of sea animals, at full growth bag-like in form, with two openings and very simple nerve-system, and gen. fixed, but in earlier stage free, tailed, and CHORDATE. **a'scidian,** a., n. (Of) one of the A. **a. 'tadpole.** Long-tailed LARVA of aa.

as'cidium, n. [Bot.] Bag-like leaf or part.

as'ci-ferous, -gerous, aa. [Bot.] Producing ASCI.

'ascocarp, n. [Bot.] Vessel in which ASCI are produced, the fruit-body of ASCOMY-CETES.

'asco'gonium, n. [Bot.] FERTILIZED part of ARCHICARP.

'Ascoli'chenes, n.pl. [Bot.] The chief group of LICHENS, in which the FUNGUS is one of the ASCOMYCETES.

as'coma, n. [Bot.] Flat round form of ASCOCARP in certain FUNGI.

'Ascomy'cetes, n.pl. [Bot.] One of the chief groups of FUNGI, in which the SPORE-producing body is an ASCUS. **'ascomy'cetous,** a.

a'scorbic acid. VITAMIN C.

'ascospore, n. [Bot.] SPORE formed in an ASCUS.

'ascus (asci), n. [Bot.] Pipe-like CELL in which SPORES are formed in ASCOMY-CETES.

-ase. [Biochem.] Ending used with names of ENZYMES.

a'septic, a. [Med.] Made or kept free from BACTERIA causing disease. **a'sepsis,** n. A. condition; system used in operations, etc., for purpose of asepsis.

a'sexual, a. [Biol.] Having no sex; (of a development) effected, (of plants or animals) producing offspring, by some process other than a sex process.

ash, n. RESIDUE, freq. powder-like, of a substance which has been burned as completely as possible.

'Asiatic cholera. Disease freq. causing death, common in Asia, caused by BACTERIA in INTESTINES.

aso'matophyte, n. [Bot.] Any plant having no CELLS which undergo development into special materials forming a plant body of fixed structure, and no special apparatus for producing offspring, but in which all the cells go on producing others of the same sort so that growth is unlimited, for example a BACTERIUM.

'aspect, n. [Mech.] Position of a plane (e.g. airplane wing) in relation to air, water, etc., through which it is moving, or to current moving past it.

as'pergil'losis, n. Any disease of man or animal caused by a FUNGUS of the GENUS *Aspergillus.*

a'sperm-ia, -atism, nn. [Med.] Loss of power of producing or giving out SEMEN.

'asphalt, as'phaltum, nn. Black, sticky substance, formed chiefly of mixed HYDRO-CARBONS, present naturally in the earth and in certain PETROLEUMS, used on roads, roofs, etc.

a'sphyxia, n. [Med.] Death-like condition caused by need for O in blood, as when breathing is stopped by unnatural causes, **a'sphyxial,** a. **a'sphyxiate,** v.t. Sp.

put to death by causing a. **a′sphyxia-tion,** n.

′aspirate, 1.n. [Phonet.] (Sound said with) sound of breath being let out, as the *h*-sound; letter, etc., representative of an a. **2.**v.t. Say with a. **3.**a. Aspirated.

aspir′ation, n. [Phonet.] The producing of an ASPIRATE sound. [Med.] The act of taking in (one) breath. [Chem., etc.] The act of taking up a gas or liquid by SUC-TION, or of sending it through or out of anything in a slow current, sp. [Med.] the taking of gases or liquids from the body in this way. **′aspirator,** n. [Chem., etc.] An instrument for the a. of gases or liquids.

′aspirin, n. Common name of ACETYL-SALICYLIC acid, a substance used medic-ally against pain and FEVER.

a′splanchnic, a. [Zoo.] Having no ALIMEN-TARY CANAL.

a′sporous, a. [Biol.] Having no true SPORES.

as′say, v.t., n. (Make) chemical test of something, sp. of material taken from a mine, to see if and in what amount a certain substance is present. **′-er,** n. **′-ing,** n.

as′sibi′lation, n. [Philol., Phonet.] The changing of a sound in a word into a SIBILANT, as in saying *-tion* as *-shun.*

as′similate, v.t. and i. Make (something taken in) a part of the self (that is, of the substance or system taking it in), as the body assimilates food, the mind assimi-lates new ideas; make (food, ROCKS, sounds) undergo assimilation in any of the special senses; (of a substance or thing taken in) undergo assimilation, be assimilated. **as′simi′lation,** n. Sp.:— [Bot.] General process by which food is made and used by plant, sp. PHOTOSYN-THESIS. [Zoo.] End-process of turning food into body-substance after digestion, ANABOLISM. [Geol.] The chemical uniting of liquid MAGMA with ROCKS getting into it. [Phonet.] Process by which (the sound of) a letter in a word is changed to take on some quality of another near it, e.g. after the UNVOICED letter *k*, the VOICED letter *d* gets the unvoiced sound of *t*, as in *walked.* **as′similate,** v.t. **as′similative, as′similatory,** aa.

as′soci′ation, n. [Bot.] Number of plants of different sorts, but freq. with one or two greatly outnumbering the rest, seen living regularly together in certain sorts of country and forming a natural group. [Chem.] The joining together into loose complexes of some of the MOLECULES of a liquid or gas. [Psych.] (The forming of) a connection in the mind between ideas which have been experienced together, so that when one of them becomes conscious the other automatically does so. **as′so-ciative,** a. **as′sociate,** v.t. and i. **as′soci-**

′ationism, n. [Psych.] Theory that de-velopment of mind takes place only by a. of ideas got by the senses. **as′soci′ationist,** n. [Psych.].

as′sumption, n. [Phonet.] Addition of a VOWEL-sound between two CONSONANTS.

as′tasia, n. [Med.] Loss of power of putting or keeping self in upright position.

a′static, a. [Phys.] Having no tendency to take up a fixed position, direction. **a. galva′nometer.** A GALVANOMETER with a. needles. **a. needles, a. system.** Two or more MAGNETIC needles so placed that the force of a MAGNETIC FIELD, such as the earth's, is balanced by their united effect, and they have the power of turning freely in any direction.

′astatine, n. Chemical ELEMENT, at. no. 85, sign At, readily changed into other elements, one of the HALOGEN family.

a′stely, n. [Bot.] Condition of having no STELE. **a′stelic,** a.

′aster, n. [Biol.] Star-like body formed in cell in process of MITOSIS. [Zoo.] In sponges, star-like SPICULE. **a. rays.** [Biol.] FIBRES forming the rays of an a.

′asterism, n. [Astron.] A group of stars. [Cryst.] (Property causing) light effect in form of star, seen when rays are acted on by certain CRYSTALS. **as′teriated,** a. Having property of a.

′asteroid. 1.n. [Astron.] PLANETOID. [Zoo.] Any animal of the ASTEROIDEA. **2.**a. [Zoo.] Of, like, an a.

′Astero′idea, n.pl. [Zoo.] A CLASS of ECHINO-DERMS in which the body is flat and star-like in form, having mouth in middle of under side and hollow arms or rays, gen. 5, with digestion pipes running into them and lines of TUBE-FEET on the under side.

as′thenia, n. [Med.] Loss of force in muscles or processes, the condition of being physically feeble. **as′thenic,** a. In the condition of a., feeble, having little force. [Psych.] In Kretschmer's system of PSYCHO-PHYSIOLOGICAL groups, having the physical structure which frequently goes with SCHIZOID tendencies, tall, thin, and long-faced, with narrow hands, etc. (*see* ATHLETIC, PYKNIC). **asthenic feelings,** [Psych.] The sort of feelings, such as sad feeling, loss of hope, etc., which take away the impulse to acting.

′asthma, n. Disease marked by noise and attacks of trouble in breathing, and by cough, caused by sudden narrowing motion of the BRONCHI. **asth′matic,** a., n.

a′stigmatism, n. [Optics] A DEFECT in a curved looking-glass, a LENS, or a system of lenses, such that rays from a point make a line- in place of a point-IMAGE, an effect regularly produced by rays making a great angle with the AXIS of a common lens or curved looking-glass. [Med.] A. in eye, gen. caused by unequal curving of

CORNEA. **'astig'matic,** a. **'astig'mometer,** n. Apparatus measuring degree of **a.**

a'stomatous, a. Not having mouth or sp. [Bot.] STOMATA.

'astomous, a. ASTOMATOUS; (of MUSCI) having seed-vessel bursting open at any point, not having a cover for opening.

'astra'galus, n. [Zoo.] One of the bones nearest leg in group between foot and leg in higher animals, named in man the ANKLE bone.

'astral, a. [Biol.] To do with an ASTER.

a'strictive, n., a. ASTRINGENT.

a'stringent, n., a. [Med.] (Substance) having power of making outer TISSUES such as skin or MUCOUS MEMBRANE tighter, driving blood from them.

'astro-. To do with the stars.

as'trogeny, n. Science of the development of the stars.

as'trography, n. Science of mapping the sky. **'astro'graphic,** a.

as'trology, n. That part of early Astronomy which had to do with the relation of the stars to events among men, and the reading of the future from their positions at a certain time, etc.

as'trometry, n. Branch of Astronomy having to do with measuring the stars, etc., and sp. their positions and motions.

'astronaut, n. Person who goes up into outer space in SPACE-CAPSULE or SPACE-SHIP. **astro'nautics,** n.pl. Science of sending vessels into further space outside the earth's ATMOSPHERE for the purpose of observation or in the hope of getting to other stars. **astro'nautical,** a.

a'stronomy, n. Science of the stars and other bodies in space. **as'tronomer,** n. **astro'nomic(al)',** aa. **astronomical unit.** Unit of distance used in a., 149,504,000 km., sign **A.U. astronomical year.** TROPICAL YEAR.

'astro'physics, n. Science of physical and chemical structure of stars.

'astrosphere, n. [Biol.] CENTROSPHERE; complete ASTER all but CENTROSOME.

asym'metric, a. Having no SYMMETRY. [Zoo.] Of form such that it is not cut into two like halves by any plane. [Bot.] A. in relation to LONGITUDINAL plane; MONOSYMMETRIC. **a. 'carbon 'atom.** [Chem.] ATOM of C. joined to 4 different groups of atoms. **a. 'compound.** [Chem.] One in which grouping of ATOMS in space is not balanced, sp. one having two possible space structures of which one is like the other seen in a looking-glass. **a. system.** [Cryst.] TRICLINIC system. **'-al,** a. **a'symmetry,** n.

'asymptote, n. [Math.] A straight line which gets nearer and nearer to a curved line without ever meeting it. **asymp'totic,** a.

a'syngamy, n. [Bot.] Condition when two flowers are unable to make one another fertile because of development at different times.

a'systole, n. [Med.] Condition of heart whose power of pumping out blood has become feeble.

'atavism. n. [Biol.] Development by off-spring of qualities present in family at an earlier time, but not seen in GENERATION(s) between.

a'tax-ia, -y, nn. [Med.] Any condition of body in which muscles, nerves, are not working normally together, sp. loss of power of controlling motion of legs, etc. **a'taxic,** a.

-ate, n. [Chem.] Salt or ESTER of acid of like name ending in **-ic.**

ate'lectasis, n. [Med.] Condition in which the normal expansion at birth of the air-vessels in the LUNGS takes place only incompletely or not at all; COLLAPSE of lung as effect of disease.

'atelo-. (Having) wrong or uncomplete structure or development of : **-'cardia,** n. **-'cephalous,** a.

ather'oma. n. [Med.] A condition in which the inner coat of the ARTERIES becomes thick and undergoes FATTY DEGENERATION.

'athlete's foot. [Med.] RINGWORM of the foot.

a'thletic, a. [Psych., Med.] In Kretschemer's system of PSYCHO-PHYSIOLOGICAL groups, having the good bone and muscle development and well-balanced body frequently going with SCHIZOPHRENIA (*see* ASTHENIC, PYKNIC).

'athodyd, n. An apparatus for greatly increasing the rate of motion of an airplane by the addition of JET PROPULSION, dependent on the forcing of a high-VELOCITY current of air into a pipe by the forward motion of the plane only, without the help of a pump, and so not coming into operation till the plane is moving at a high rate.

'atlas, n. [Zoo.] The top bone of the backbone, supporting the head. **at'lantal, 'atloid,** aa. **at'lanto-. 'atlo(ido)-.**

'atmograph, n. [Med.] SPIROGRAPH.

at'molysis, n. [Phys., Chem.] Process of separating mixed gases by letting them go through POROUS material, the gas of least weight going through the quickest. **'atmolyse,** v.t.

at'mometer, n. Instrument measuring rate of loss of water from wet SURFACE.

'atmosphere, n. The gas(es) round any body, sp. the Earth; normal PRESSURE of Earth's a. at sea level used as measuring unit, fixed at that of 760 mm. Hg. (=1,013,249 DYNES/cm2). **atmos'pheric,** a. **atmos'pherics,** n.pl. Electric waves sent out by thunder clouds, etc., causing trouble in radio.

atmo'therapy, n. [Med.] Use of ATOMIZED substances in attacking disease in breathing apparatus.

'atoll, n. CORAL island in form of ring, etc., shutting in sea.

'atom, n. The smallest division of an ELEMENT having the properties special to it and able to take part in chemical reaction. **a. (or a'tomic) bomb.** A BOMB whose power of EXPLOSION is dependent on NUCLEAR FISSION. **a. 'smasher.** [Phys.] Common name for ACCELERATOR, CYCLOTRON, etc. **a'tomic, a. atomic ab'sorption co'efficient.** [Phys.] The RATIO of the ABSORPTION COEFFICIENT of an ELEMENT to the number of aa. in unit VOLUME. **atomic 'energy.** NUCLEAR ENERGY. **a'tomic 'frequency 'standard,** [Phys.] A FREQUENCY STANDARD in which the controlling FACTOR is one of the unchanging properties of an ATOM such as CAESIUM. **atomic heat.** The amount of heat needed for increasing the TEMPERATURE of 1 GRAM-ATOM of a substance by 1°C ($=$ at. wt. $\times$ SPECIFIC HEAT). **atomic mass unit.** Unit used for measuring the MASSES of ISOTOPES of ELEMENTS, fixed as $\frac{1}{16}$ of the mass of an a. of the commonest isotope of O, that of at. wt. 16, and equal to 1.66×10^{-24} gm. **atomic number.** Number of an ELEMENT in the list of elements put in the order of the increasing number of CHARGES on their NUCLEI, starting with H as 1. **atomic physics.** The science of the make-up of the a., the properties of the ELEMENTARY PARTICLES of which it is formed, its ENERGY, and the RADIATIONS coming from it. **atomic pile.** NUCLEAR REACTOR. **atomic 'spectrum.** The LINE SPECTRUM produced by an ELEMENT whose aa. are not united into MOLECULES. **atomic theory.** The general theory on which present-day chemistry is based, that all ELEMENTS are made up of aa., of which those of any given element are the same in structure and properties as one another and different in some way from those of other elements, and that chemical reactions are caused by attraction between the aa. of different elements, which become united into the MOLECULES forming complex substances in fixed and simple PROPORTIONS by number. **atomic weight.** Weight of an a. of an ELEMENT measured in relation to that of an a. of O, which is fixed at 16.

'atomize, v.t. Get (liquid) broken up into mist-like form of very small drops. **'atomi'zation,** n. **'atomizer,** n. An instrument for atomizing a liquid (for example, in an oil-engine, or in medical use to send onto a part, as up the nose or onto the wall of the throat, etc.).

'atony, n. [Med.] Loss of power or elastic property, feeble condition, of muscles, etc. **a'tonic, a.** 1. [Med.] 2. [Phonet.] Not VOICED.

atra'biliary capsule or **gland.** SUPRARENAL CAPSULE.

a'tresia, n. [Med.] Condition of having some normal opening in body shut or narrowed. **a'tresic, a'tretic,** aa.

'atriopore, n. [Zoo.] Outlet opening of ATRIUM in AMPHIOXUS.

'atrium, n. Any of certain hollows in animal body, sp.: 1, in UROCHORDA and other sea animals, the bag-like part into which the water from the breathing-apparatus is sent. 2. In higher animals, the chief hollow of an AURICLE of the heart, or the complete AURICULAR SPACE; the hollow of the MIDDLE EAR. **atrio-.**

'atrophy, 1.n. [Med.] The wasting away of a part of the body, or its change into substance of no use. [Biol.] DEGENERATION of a part, sp. as effect of its not being used. 2.v.i. and t. Undergo a.; be cause of a. of. **a'trophic, a.**

'atropine, n. [Chem.] $C_{17}H_{22}NO_3$, an ALKALOID got from plants and used medically, sp. for causing expansion of the PUPIL of the eye.

'atropous, a. ORTHOTROPOUS.

at'tachment, n. Structure or part by which one thing is fixed to another. **a. con'striction.** [Biol.] SPINDLE ATTACHMENT.

at'tenu'ation, n. Process of becoming, or causing to become, smaller, thinner, or sp. less strong, loss of power, said of electric current, radio waves, chemical liquids, disease bodies, etc. **a. factor.** [Phys.] Measure of a. of rays going through a substance, $=$ power of outgoing $\div$ power of ingoing rays. **at'tenuate,** v.t. and i. (Make) undergo a. **attenuated, a.**

at'traction, n. [Phys.] A force acting between material bodies pulling them to one another.

at'traction sphere. [Biol.] CENTROSPHERE.

at'tritus, n. Substance rubbed to powder, sp. as name for plant a. forming part of certain sorts of coal.

'Atwood's machine. A special apparatus for teaching Newton's laws of motion.

at. wt. $=$ ATOMIC WEIGHT.

A.U. $=$ ASTRONOMICAL UNIT.

A.U. or **Å.U.** $=$ ÅNGSTROM UNIT.

Au, Sign for gold.

'audible, n. Able to be sensed by hearing, loud enough to have an effect on hearing.

audi'bility, n. Of sounds, (measure of) power of acting on hearing.

audio-. To do with hearing or AUDIBILITY.

'audio'frequency, n. [Phys.] FREQUENCY of electric waves such that they may be turned into sound-waves having AUDIBILITY.

33

'**audiogram**, n. A GRAPH giving the lowest INTENSITIES at which sounds of different FREQUENCIES have an effect on hearing, used for measuring hearing loss.

audi'ometer, n. [Acous.] An instrument for measuring the power of hearing or the AUDIBILITY of sounds.

'**audiphone**, n. Apparatus for sending sound to nerves of hearing through teeth and bones of head.

au'dition, n. Sense or power of hearing.

'**audit-ory, -ive**, a.a. To do with hearing or ears. **a. a'phasia.** Loss of power of hearing words as such, taking in what is said. **a. ca'nal, a. me'atus.** [Zoo.] One or other of the two pipe-like openings in the ear of higher animals, one from the outside to the TYMPANIC MEMBRANE, the other through which the a. nerve comes from the brain to the inner ear. **a. 'capsule.** [Zoo.] That part of the bone framework of the head in higher animals in which is housed the apparatus of hearing; a. vesicle. **a. 'ossicle.** [Zoo.] Any of the chain of three small bones in the ear of higher animals (*incus, malleus,* and *stapes*) by which the sound-waves coming against the TYMPANIC MEMBRANE are handed on to the INNER EAR. **a. per'spective.** [Psych.] Man's power of sensing a number of sounds produced together as coming from different distances and directions. **a. 'vesicle.** [Zoo.] The bag-like part in the EMBRYOS of higher animals which undergoes development into the inner ear.

'**Auerbach's 'plexus.** In back-boned animals, complex mass of nerves between the two muscle coats of the small INTESTINE.

'**Auger effect.** [Phys.] The freeing of two ELECTRONS from different levels of an ATOM by one X-RAY QUANTUM.

'**augite**, n. [Mineral.] Natural SILICATE of Fe, Mg, and some Al, generally black or dark green, forming part of many BASIC IGNEOUS ROCKS.

'**augment**, n. [Philol.] The addition or making longer of a VOWEL at front of an operation-word as a sign of past time.

'**aura**, n. [Med.] Any special strange feeling, as that of cold air going from body to head, giving sign of a coming attack of EPILEPSY, HYSTERIA, etc.

'**aural**, a. To do with the ear. **a. 'critical band.** [Acous.] That FREQUENCY-band in a CONTINUOUS SPECTRUM of noise which has a sound-power equal to that of a simple, unmixed note in the middle of it and strong enough to be AUDIBLE (but no more) in the full noise. **a. har'monic.** A HARMONIC produced in the hearing apparatus itself.

'**aureole**, n. [Meteor.] The ring of clear space between sun or moon and a HALO; bright ring round sun seen in a clear sky. [Geol.]

CONTACT ZONE.

'**auric**, a. [Chem.] Of, having in it, gold, as **a. acid,** $Au(OH)_3$, **a. oxide,** Au_2O_3.

'**auricle**, n. [Zoo.] The outer ear, of higher animals; the hollow space, or one of the two hollow spaces, in the higher part of the heart, from which blood coming from the VEINS is pumped into the lower part. [Biol.] Part, outgrowth, roughly like an ear in form. **au'ricular,** 1.a. [Zoo.] Of, like, to do with, the AURICLE(S); AUDITORY. 2.n. Any of the small feathers covering the ear of a bird. **au'riculo-.**

'**auricu'laria**, n. [Zoo.] A free-swimming HOLOTHURIAN LARVA with CILIA in one band.

au'riculate, a. [Biol.] Having ears or ear-like parts, sp. of form of leaf.

au'riferous, a. Having gold in it.

'**Aurig'nacian**, a., n. (Of) the 5th division of the PALEOLITHIC stage in man's history.

au'rora au'stralis. A like effect to the AURORA BOREALIS seen in the far South, commonly named *the Southern Lights.*

au'rora bore'alis. Bands and arches of white, red, yellow, and green light seen in sky at night in the far North, possibly caused by some sort of electric rays from the sun, commonly named *the Northern lights.* **au'roral line.** Green line in the SPECTRUM of the a. b.

'**aurous**, a. [Chem.] Of, having in it, MONOVALENT gold, as **a. chloride,** $AuCl$.

auscul'tation, n. [Med.] The noting of sounds produced inside the body, e.g. by the heart, as a way of getting knowledge of its condition.

'**austenite**, n. Solid SOLUTION of C or Fe_2C in iron, forming part of certain specially hard steels, **auste'nitic,** a.

'**Austral**, a. Of, being in, the south part of the earth.

Austra'lasian 'region. [Biogeog.] One of the divisions of the earth based on the sort of animals living in it, taking in Australia, New Zealand, etc., and the islands south and east of WALLACE'S LINE.

'**Australoid**, n., a. (Person) of the RACE group taking in the Australian blacks.

'**autacoid**, n. HORMONE.

aute'cology, n. Science of relation of a separate plant to the things round it.

authi'gen-ic, -ous, aa. [Geol.] (Of ROCK material) having been formed where present, not transported there.

'**autism**, n. [Psych.] Condition in which attention is given only to ideas in the mind, and not to things outside.

'**auto-.** 1. Self, of, caused by, from, to, itself: '**a.-diag'nosis,** n. '**a.-hyp'nosis,** n., '**a.-'ki'netic,** a. 2. Self-moving, like the automobile: '**auto-bus,** n.

'**autoca'talysis**, n. The increasing of the rate of a chemical reaction by a substance produced by the reaction. [Zoo.] Destruction of CELL, etc., as effect of something produced by itself.

'autochrome, n. A form of camera PLATE for taking coloured pictures.

au'tochthonous, a. [Biol.] Natural to place or sort. [Geol.] AUTHIGENIC; not pushed out of place by OVERTHRUST. au'tochthonism, au'tochthony, nn.

auto'clastic, a. [Geol.] (Of ROCKS having broken structure) having undergone crushing in present position, not formed of crushed materials transported there.

'autoclave, n. Thick-walled, airtight vessel used for chemical reactions under pressure and at high degree of heat.

'autocoid, n. AUTACOID.

'auto'collimator, n. [Optics] TELESCOPE with scale inside for reading angle between two points at a distance; COLLIMATOR with self-adjustment to a position at right angles to a plane. [Phys.] Apparatus for automatically keeping ALPHA PARTICLES in a narrow parcel of rays.

'autodecompo'sition, n. Process by which a substance is broken up as the effect of AUTOCATALYSIS.

'autodi'gestion, n. AUTOLYSIS.

'autodyne, n. [Radio] HETERODYNE in which heterodyne current is produced in CIRCUIT taking incoming waves.

auto'ecious, a. [Biol.] (Of PARASITE) going through all the stages of its development on the same plant or animal. [Bot.] AUTOICIOUS.

'autoelec'tronic e'mission. The sending out of ELECTRONS from cold metals in strong electric fields.

'auto'erotism, 'autoe'roticism, nn. [Psych.] Sex-desire, sex-pleasure, produced by self, not in connection with another person. 'autoe'rotic, a.

au'togamy, n. [Bot.] The FERTILIZATION of a flower by POLLEN produced by itself. [Zoo.] Uniting of GAMETES or NUCLEI produced by same CELL.

auto'genesis, au'togeny, nn. [Biol.] Process of increasing in number by division, as body CELLS. autoge'netic, a.

autoge'netic 'drainage. [Geog.] The draining of a stretch of country by rivers, etc., whose directions are conditioned by the present form of the country, not by earlier land-structure.

au'togenous, a. [Biol.] Produced by the self or independently of the regular process. a. 'welding. Process of uniting bits of the same metal without using a joining substance, by heating the touching parts till liquid. a. vac'cine. VACCINE made from BACTERIA taken from the person etc. on whom it is to be used.

'auto'giro, 'auto'gyro, n. Trade-name for airplane lifted and supported in flight by a system of ROTATING planes on a more or less upright AXIS, giving it power of taking off and landing in very limited space.

'autograft, n. GRAFT of part or material taken from the same body. auto'grafting, n. AUTOPLASTY.

auto'graphic, a. (Of instrument) recording automatically.

au'toicious, a. [Bot.] (Of MUSCI, etc.) having male and female ORGANS on same plant.

'autoig'nition, n. The taking fire of a substance without the help of a flame, etc., as in certain sorts of engines.

'autoi'nocu'lation, n. [Med.] The INOCULATION of a person with BACTERIA from his body.

'autoin'toxi'cation, n. [Med.] Poisoning of body by substances produced in it.

'auto-ioni'zation, n. [Chem.] IONIZATION which takes place without outside cause, as effect of inner forces.

au'tolysis, n. [Biochem.] Self-digestion, i.e. the operation on the substance of a CELL, etc., of ENZYMES produced by itself. auto'lytic, a.

auto'matic, a. (Of a machine or process) going on through a certain fixed train of operations without further impulse or control from outside after being started, or coming into operation at some point without any help from outside, as the effect of some train of events in a machine, etc. [Psych.] (Of acts, etc.) done without conscious purpose or control. a. gain (or 'volume) con'trol. [Radio] A CIRCUIT forming part of a radio RECEIVER by which the INTENSITY of output is automatically kept from changing with changes in input, so that the VOLUME of the sound produced is at all times the same. auto'matically, adv.

au'tomatism, n. [Physiol.] Motion, process, in the body which is not dependent on outside cause, as that of the heart; reaction to outside cause which is not controlled by higher NERVE-CENTRES, sp. of sort which at one time was so controlled but has become independent through use. [Psych.] Act(ing) without conscious purpose or control, or, in certain conditions, without the actor's knowledge, as in sleep-walking.

au'tomaton, n. Automatic machine copying behaviour of man or other animal; any apparatus acting as automatic control or in some other way taking the place of a person.

auto'morphic, a. [Cryst.] IDIOMORPHIC.

auto'nomic, a. [Biol.] Independent of outside cause or control, or able to give a reaction independently of other parts of a system. a. (nervous) system. In backboned animals, that part of the nerve system taking NERVE IMPULSES to the UNSTRIATED muscles, the heart, and the GLANDS. auto′nomics, n. The science of copying animal behaviour in MECHANICAL or ELECTRONIC systems, such as COMPUTERS or machines for changing writings from one language into another.

au′tonomous, a. [Biol.] AUTONOMIC; having independent existence, not forming a part or stage of development of some other being. au′tonomy, n. The condition of being a. or autonomic.

auto′pathic, a. [Med.] Dependent on structure or changes of diseased body, not caused from outside.

auto′phagia, au′tophagy, nn. [Med.] The body's use of itself as food when it is without any other. [Zoo.] The use by an animal of part of its body, e.g. when broken or cut off, as food. au′tophagous, a. To do with, marked by, a.; able to get food from birth, as certain birds. au′tophagi, n.pl. Autophagous birds.

′auto′photo′electric, a. [Phys.] To do with Richardson's theory that ELECTRONS sent out by a heated body are made free by rays from the body itself.

auto′phya, n. [Zoo.] The parts of an animal's hard outer covering or inner framework formed of substance produced by itself, as opp. XENOPHYA.

′autophyte, n. [Bot.] An AUTOTROPHIC plant.

auto′plasty, n. [Med.] The GRAFTING of material from the same body onto a damaged part. auto′plastic, a.

′auto′polyploid, n., a. [Biol.] (POLYPLOID) with 4 like groups of CHROMOSOMES.

′autopsy, n. [Med.] Observation, and commonly cutting open, of a dead body for discovery of cause of death, or to get detailed knowledge of effects of disease.

auto′racemi′zation, n. [Chem.] See RACEMIZATION.

′auto′skeleton, n. [Zoo.] SKELETON formed inside animal from substance produced by itself, sp. that of a sponge, opp. PSEUDOSKELETON.

′autosome, n. [Biol.] Any CHROMOSOME other than a sex chromosome.

auto′stylic, a. [Zoo.] Having mouth-bones joined straight to the bones of the head, without connection through HYOID ARCH.

′autosug′gestion, n. [Psych.] The causing of behaviour, condition, in person by suggestions made by his unconscious self, as in self-HYPNOSIS.

auto′syndesis, n. [Biol.] The joining in an AUTOPOLYPLOID of the CHROMOSOMES from the same plant or animal.

au′totomy, n. [Biol.] The division of the body or a part, or the cutting off of a part of an animal, by itself; self-division, as of CELL.

auto′toxin, n. [Med.] Any poison produced in the body by its processes.

′autotrans′former, n. [Elec.] TRANSFORMER having only one WINDING, part of which does the work of a SECONDARY.

′autotransplan′tation, n. AUTOPLASTY.

auto′trophic, a. [Bot.] (Of plant) building up its food from simple chemical substances, not using or not dependent on ready-made plant substances, living or dead. auto′troph-ism, -y, nn.

au′toxi′dation, n. [Chem.] Reaction of substance with O at normal TEMPERATURES, or as effect of simply being put in air; INDUCED REACTION with O. au′toxidize, v.t. au′toxi′dizable, a.

au′tumnal ′equinox. See EQUINOX.

′auxa′nometer, n. Instrument for measuring rate of growth of plants.

au′xiliary, 1.a. Used or designed for giving help, being a supporting addition, not itself the chief thing. 2.n. A. thing; boat having engine or other power in addition to sails. a. cell. [Bot.] Any of certain CELLS in RHODOPHYCEAE which, though not taking part in the sex-process, have some connection with the development of the fruit. a. circles. The two circles whose DIAMETERS are the long and short diameter of an ELLIPSE. aux′ilio-.

au′xilio′meter, a. [Anat.] Helping, or giving a tendency to, motion.

′auximone, n. [Bot.] Any of certain substances which have to be present in the food of plants, though only in very small amounts, for growth, plant VITAMIN.

′auxin, n. [Bot.] Any of a group of substances having a strong effect on the growth of plants, even when present in very small amounts, some of them naturally produced in the plants themselves and acting as HORMONES (for example, the one causing the CELLS to become longer at the growth points), others chemically produced for the purposes of man.

′auxochrome, n. [Chem.] A group of ATOMS which, when put into a coloured substance, makes it into, or gives it greater power as, a DYE.

′auxograph, n. Apparatus recording growth of plants.

au′xometer, n. [Optics] Instrument for measuring the MAGNIFICATION of a system of LENSES.

a.v. = AVOIRDUPOIS.

a′vailable, a. Able to be got, used. a. ′energy. That part of the ENERGY of a body or system which may be changed into work.

a′vascular, a. [Med.] Without blood-vessels.

′average, a., n. (Being, got by working out) an ARITHMETICAL MEAN; representative of a group, as if based on an a. a. life. [Phys.] The time taken for the RADIOACTIVE power of a substance to get to 36·97% of its first value.

Aves, n.pl. The CLASS of back-boned animals made up of birds.

avian, a. Of, to do with, birds.

avicu'larium (avicularia), n. [Zoo.] In POLYZOA, a development of the body-wall having the power of sudden gripping or biting motion. **avicu'larian,** a.

aviculture, n. The care and producing of birds.

avidity, n. [Chem.] Chemical power of an acid or BASE dependent on degree of DISSOCIATION.

avitami'nosis, n. [Med.] Condition caused by need for VITAMINS.

Avo'gadro's law or **hypothesis.** [Chem.] Law that equal VOLUMES of all gases under the same conditions of TEMPERATURE and PRESSURE have the same number of MOLECULES.

Avo'gadro constant or **number.** The number of ATOMS in a GRAM-ATOM of any ELEMENT, or the number of MOLECULES in a GRAM-MOLECULE of any substance ($=6.064 \times 10^{23}$).

avoirdu'pois, a., n. (Of) the British system of weights, based on 1 lb. $=$ 453·59 grams (*see* p. 565).

awn, n. [Bot.] Any of the stiff hairs forming BEARD of grasses, etc.

axial, a. To do with, on, near, in the direction of, the AXIS. **a. 'filament.** [Zoo.] Thread-like part going down middle of PSEUDOPODIUM with rays, or of FLAGELLUM. **a. 'magnifi'cation.** [Optics] Distance between two IMAGE-points near together on the AXIS of an instrument $\div$ the distance between the same points cn the thing of which image is formed. **a. 'ratio.** [Cryst.] Measure of one AXIS of CRYSTAL $\div$ that of another. **a. 'skeleton.** [Zoo.] Bone framework of head and body without arms and legs.

axiate 'pattern. [Biol.] Distribution of parts in relation to a given AXIS.

axil, n. [Bot.] Angle between leaf or branch and stem from which it comes. **a'xillary,** a.

axile, a. [Bot.] Placed on the AXIS. **a. placen'tation.** [Bot.] PLACENTATION in an OVARY formed of a number of CARPELS, in which the edges of the carpels are folded in, forming division-walls meeting and uniting in a round structure in the middle, on which OVULES are produced.

axi'lemma, axo'lemma, nn. [Zoo.] MEDULLARY SHEATH.

a'xilla, n. [Zoo.] The hollow under the arm or front leg at the point where it is joined to the body. **a'xillary,** a.

axillary, a. Of AXIL or AXILLA. **a. bud.** [Bot.] A BUD produced, as is normal for side-branches, in an AXIL.

axiom, n. A statement taken as true for the purpose of basing on it a system of argument or mathematics, a statement about

which there is no question. **axio'matic,** a.

axis (axes), n. Straight line going, or pictured as going, through the middle of a body or system and making a balanced division of its parts, sp. that round which a turning body is turning as on a rod. [Biol.] Line-like structure round which parts are grouped, sp. chief stem or root, or any part supporting branches. [Zoo.] The second VERTEBRA from the head in the neck of higher animals. **a. 'cylinder.** The middle part of a MEDULLATED NERVE-FIBRE. **aa. of a 'crystal.** The straight lines pictured as going through the middle point of a CRYSTAL in relation to which its form and properties (e.g. OPTICAL, elastic) are made clear. **a. of rotation.** [Phys.] A. on which a body is turning.

axle, n. Rod or pin on which a wheel is turned; a.-tree, or part of it on which wheel is fixed. **'a.-tree,** n. Rod joining opposite wheels of carriage, etc.

a'xometer', n. [Optics] Instrument used for discovery of AXIS of OPTICAL system, sp. one used in adjustment of glasses to axes of eyes.

axon, n. [Zoo.] Long, thread-like out-growth of nerve-CELL, transporting impulses away from cell. (*See* NERVE FIBRE.)

axono'metric, a. Said of the PROJECTION of a solid form such as a CUBE onto a flat paper etc. in such a way that three sides, or the top and two sides, are seen.

a'zeotrope, n. [Chem.] Any mixed liquid having a boiling-point lower than that of the liquids of which it is made up. **azeo'tropic,** a. **'aze'otrop-ism, -y,** nn.

azide, n. [Chem.] A substance having in it the group N_3.

A'zilian, a., n. (Of) that stage in man's history at end of PALAEOLITHIC, forming bridge to NEOLITHIC.

azimuth, n. [Astron., Surveying] (Of a star or a line) the angle between the plane of the MERIDIAN and the upright plane going through the star or line and the earth. **a. 'compass.** A MAGNETIC COMPASS having SIGHTS and used in SURVEYING for getting BEARINGS. **azi'muthal,** a. **azimuthal angle.** In SURVEYING, a HORIZONTAL angle. **azimuthal circle.** [Astron.] VERTICAL CIRCLE. **azimuthal 'quantum number.** QUANTUM NUMBER by which ANGULAR MOMENTUM of ELECTRON is fixed.

azo-, a. Having the group –N:N–.

azobacter, a'zotobacter, nn. Any of sorts of BACTERIA common in earth which have power of causing N of air to become united with O.

a'zoic, a. [Geol.] Of the time in earth's history before living things (*see* p. 559).

azole, n. [Chem.] PYRROLE in which one or more N atoms take the place of C.

'azotize, v.t. Get (substance) chemically united with N. azo'tometer, n. Apparatus for measuring amount of N in a substance.

azo'turia, n. [Med.] Condition in which more N than normal is present in URINE.

'azurite, n. [Mineral.] An ORE of copper, $2CuCO_3,Cu(OH)_2$, blue in colour, present in the earth as well-formed CRYSTALS or in masses.

'azygos, n. [Zoo.] AZYGOUS part.

a'zygo-sperm, -spore, nn. [Bot.] SPORE like ZYGOSPORE in structure, but produced from GAMETE without sex process.

'azygous, a. [Zoo.] Not forming one of two like parts, having no sister part. a. vein, One or the other of two VEINS making connection between higher and lower VENAE CAVAE.

B, Sign for: BORON; BAUMÉ.

β, See BETA.

'Babbitt metal. A soft white metal used for the inner parts of BEARINGS.

'Babinet 'compensator. [Phys.] Apparatus for the ANALYSIS of ELLIPTICALLY POLARIZED light.

Ba'binski 'reflex. [Med.] The reaction of stretching the toes wide, which is not normal, when the under side of the foot is touched, a sign of nerve disease.

'bacca (baccae), n. [Bot.] A BERRY, sp. one formed from an INFERIOR OVARY. 'baccate, a. Berry-like, sp. in being a soft mass; producing bb. bac'ciferous, a. 'bacciform, a.

Bacill'ario'phyceae, Bacill'ario'phyta, nn.pl. [Bot.] The group of ALGAE made up of the DIATOMS, sometimes looked on as a CLASS or SUB-CLASS.

'bacillary, ba'cilliform, aa. [Biol.] Having form of a rod; made up of small rods or rod-like bodies.

ba'cillus (bacilli), b. Rod-like BACTERIUM.

back, a. [Phonet.] Said of VOWELS as in 'test', 'nose', 'foot', made with the back of the tongue somewhat high. b. e.m.f. [Elec.] An ELECTROMOTIVE FORCE produced in an electric CELL or CIRCUIT by some special condition and acting in the opposite direction to, that is, against, the normal electromotive force or current. b. 'pressure. PRESSURE acting against a current of liquid or gas; drop in pressure in some part of current.

back, n. [Zoo.] DORSUM.

back, v.i. [Meteor.] (Of wind) go round to a different direction in the opposite way to the hands of a clock, for example, from west to south-west, opp. VEER.

'backcross, n. [Biol.] Offspring produced by a HYBRID and one of the two sorts producing it.

back-fire, n. [Eng.] The firing before the right time of the FUEL in an INTERNAL COMBUSTION ENGINE when being started, causing an EXPLOSION before the PISTON has got to the end of the COMPRESSION STROKE, driving it back. 'backfire. v.i. (Of an engine) undergo a b. f.

'background noise [Acous.] All the INTERFERENCE effects, from whatever cause, taken together, in a system used for producing, DETECTING, measuring, or recording a SIGNAL, for example a radio.

'backlash, n. [Mach.] (Amount of) motion possible to a connection without its moving the part it is designed to put in motion, caused by its being loose or in bad adjustment; any sudden shock or force acting against the smooth operation of a machine caused by a bad adjustment of its parts, or by an over-sudden changing of its motion to the opposite direction, etc.

Bac'teria, n.pl. See BACTERIUM. bac'terial, a. Of, to do with, caused by, B.

bac'tericide, n. Substance etc., causing death of BACTERIA.

bac'teri'ology, n. Science of BACTERIA. bac'terio'logical, a.

bac'terio'lysin, n. [Med.] Any substance produced in the blood by reaction to a BACTERIUM and causing its destruction.

'bacteri'olysis, n. Destruction of BACTERIA.

bac'terio'phage, n. Substance, possibly living, which seems to be dependent on BACTERIA for its existence, and to be cause of their destruction. bac'teri-'ophagy, n. Science, use in medical work, of bb.

bac'terio'static, a. Stopping growth of BACTERIA without causing their destruction.

bac'terium (bacteria), n. [Bot., Med.] Any of a great group of different sorts of very small and simple one-CELLED plants, without PLASTIDS or a clearly-marked NUCLEUS and with a very thin cell-wall of PROTEIN, producing offspring at a great rate by simple division, and present in earth, water, air, and DECAYING or diseased animal and plant material, some of which are PARASITES and among the most important causes of disease. Bac'teria, n.pl. The PHYLUM of THALLOPHYTA made up of the bb.

bac'teri'uria, n. [Med.] Condition in which BACTERIA are present in person's URINE.

'bacteroid, a., n. (Like a) BACTERIUM by

which N is fixed in roots of plants.

'baffle, n. A structure for stopping or changing the direction of sound-waves sp. from a LOUDSPEAKER. **b. plate.** Plate put in way of current of gas or liquid, turning it to one side, or making its motion more regular.

ba'gasse, n. Crushed, dry sugar plant after sugar has been taken out.

'Baily's beads. [Astron.] Bright points seen on edge of moon at start and end of a TOTAL ECLIPSE of sun.

'Bainbridge reflex, n. [Med.] Increase in the heart rate when the PRESSURE of the blood going back to the heart is increased.

'bakelite, n. A trade name for RESIN made from PHENOL and FORMALDEHYDE, a widely used PLASTIC.

'baking 'soda. SODIUM BICARBONATE, NaHCO₃, used in cooking, (See SODA).

'baking 'powder, n. A powder put into cakes, etc., for the purpose of producing gas causing expansion when cooking, made up chiefly of a CARBONATE (gen. NaHCO₃) and some acid substance with which it undergoes a reaction freeing CO₂.

'balance, n. An instrument for measuring the weight of things by balancing them against fixed weights or forces, for example one in which the weights to be balanced are placed on plates hanging from the ends of a rod balanced on its middle point, or one in which the weight to be measured is balanced by the force of a spring and the reading is given by a pointer, etc.; BALANCE WHEELS.

'balancer, n. [Elec.] Apparatus keeping VOLTS unchanged between the different wires of an electric distribution system of more than two wires. [Zoo.] HALTER.

'balance wheel. In a time-keeping instrument, such as a watch, the small toothed wheel turning regularly first one way and then the other by the operation of a spring, and controlling the motion of the ESCAPEMENT.

'balata, n. A rubber-like substance got from a South American tree.

ba'lausta, n. [Bot.] Soft fruit made up of a great number of CELLS and seeds covered by a strong skin.

ba'leen, n. WHALEBONE.

ball-and-socket joint. [Zoo., Engin.] A JOINT in which the round end of one bone or rod goes into a cup-like hollow in the end of another, with power of turning in any direction inside this.

ball 'bearing. [Mach.] A ring of hard steel balls rolling loose in a hollow, collar-like structure put round a turning rod at its point of support in a machine to make its motion freer and smoother by making FRICTION less. 'ball-bearing, a. Having a b.b. or b.bb.

ball clay. [Geol.] A sort of white CLAY which is of special value as POTTER'S CLAY.

bal'listic, a. To do with free motion of bodies moving through the air, etc., as effect of an impulse given by an outside force. **b. galva'nometer.** [Elec.] GALVANOMETER having no DAMPING, so that the pointer goes quickly to its reading and back when a short electric impulse is given to it. **b.'missile.** A military PROJECTILE whose journey is dependent, completely or in part, on the impulse with which it is sent out and the force of GRAVITY acting on its flight. **ballistics,** n. Science of bodies, in b. motion.

ball mill. Apparatus for powdering substances by putting them with stone or metal balls in a turning vessel.

bal'loon, n. A bag-like structure of silk or other soft but strong substance which has been made air-tight and full of air at low PRESSURE, or of some gas of less weight than air, so that it is supported by and goes up in the air; a machine for air transport supported by a b.

ball valve. VALVE formed by metal ball resting on ring in pipe, shutting pipe one way, but opening to let liquid or gas go through the opposite way.

'Balmer 'series. A certain range of lines in the H SPECTRUM.

band, n. [Phys.] A range of waves (light, radio, etc.) near together in FREQUENCY. **b. edge** or **head.** Limiting FREQUENCY of a b. in a SPECTRUM. **b. elimi'nation.** [Radio] The cutting out of a b. of FREQUENCIES. **b. pass 'filter.** Apparatus letting through only waves in one b. **b. 'spectrum.** Sort of SPECTRUM made up of wide bb.

'banket, n. [Mining] A CONGLOMERATE in which there is some gold.

'banner, n. [Bot.] VEXILLUM.

bar, n. [Meteor.] Unit of PRESSURE used for measuring the pressure of the ATMOSPHERE, =10⁶ dynes/cm² at 60°C, or that of 750·076 mm. Hg.

'baraesthesi'ometer, n. [Psych.] Instrument for measuring sense of PRESSURE.

barb, n. [Zoo.] Any of the hair-like outgrowths down the sides of the stem of a feather. [Bot.] Hair ending in a hook.

'barbate, n. [Bot.] Having long stiff hairs.

'barbel, n. Thin finger-like structure with sense of touch, on lips of some fishes.

'barbellate, n. [Bot.] Having short, stiff, hooked hairs.

'barbicel, n. [Zoo.] Any of the very small, hair-like outgrowths, frequently hooked, down the under side of a BARBULA.

'barbi'tal, 'barbitone, nn. [Chem., Med.] A BARBITURATE in the form of a white powder which is used medically for producing an unconscious condition for operations, etc., or for helping sleep.

bar'biturate, n. [Chem., Med.] Any of a

group of ORGANIC COMPOUNDS got from BARBITURIC ACID noted for their sleep-producing powers, HABIT-FORMING and causing death if taken in more than very small amounts.

barbi'turic acid. [Chem.] $CO(NH.CO)_2CH_2$, got by heating MALONIC ACID with UREA and important as the substance from which BARBITURATES are produced.

'barbula, n. [Bot.] Ring of teeth round mouth of the CAPSULE in MUSCI.

'barbule, n. [Zoo.] Any of the hair-like outgrowths down the sides of a BARB.

'Bardach re'action. Test for PROTEINS, in which KI and I with $(CH_3)_2CO$ give yellow needle-like CRYSTALS.

bari'centric, a. CENTROBARIC.

'barium, n. Chemical ELEMENT, at. no. 56, at. wt. 137·7, sign Ba, an ALKALINE EARTH METAL of great weight.

bark, n. The hard outer cover of the stem, branches, and older roots of a tree or tree-like plant.

'Barkhausen effect. Sudden MAGNETIC changes in metal produced by MAGNETIC FIELD changing slowly and regularly.

'Barkhausen-Kurz 'oscillator. [Radio] Apparatus producing very high FREQUENCIES (between 3×10^8 and 15×10^8) with common form of VALVE.

barn, n. In NUCLEAR PHYSICS a unit of CROSS-SECTION $= 10^{-24} cm^2$.

'barograph, n. BAROMETER automatically recording its readings.

ba'rometer, n. Instrument measuring PRESSURE of the earth's ATMOSPHERE. **baro-'metric,** a.

'baropho'resis, n. [Chem.] DIFFUSION of powdered substance in a liquid acted on by outside forces, such as Earth's attraction.

'baroscope, n. Simple sort of instrument giving signs of changes in PRESSURE of the ATMOSPHERE.

'barotaxis, n. [Biol.] TAXIS in reaction to PRESSURE.

baro'thermograph, n. Instrument automatically recording TEMPERATURE and PRESSURE of the ATMOSPHERE.

bar'ranc-a, -o, nn. Deep cut coming from CRATER and down side of VOLCANO.

'barrier reef. Line of CORAL formed in the sea at some distance from, and parallel to, the land.

'barrow, n. TUMULUS.

'barysphere, n. [Geol.] The inner part of the earth, made of material of greater DENSITY than the outer parts.

ba'ryta, n. BARIUM OXIDE, BaO.

ba'rytes, n. [Mineral.] Natural BARIUM SULPHATE, $BaSO_4$.

'basal, a. At or to do with the base. **b. body** B. granule. **b. 'cleavage.** In CRYSTAL crack(ing) parallel to base. **b. 'ganglion,** Zoo.] Any of the masses of nerve sub-.

stance joining the CEREBRUM to other parts of the brain. **b. 'granule.** [Zoo.] A BLEPHAROPLAST at the base of the FLAGELLUM in certain PROTOZOA. **b. leaf.** One produced at base of stem. **b. me'tabolism.** The METABOLISM of an animal which is resting and not taking in food, as measured by the rate at which heat is given off (the **b. meta'bolic rate**). **b. pla'centa.** PLACENTA formed at base of OVARY. **b. plane.** Plane in a CRYSTAL parallel to chief PLANE OF SYMMETRY. **b. plates.** In the process of development of the VERTEBRATE SKULL, a plate of CARTILAGE formed by the joining of the PARACHORDALS. **b. wall.** [Bot.] Wall making division of OÖSPORE in ARCHEGONIATAE into front and back half.

ba'salar, a. Under the base of the wings (of an insect).

ba'sale (ba'salia), n. Division of FIN-RAY of fish nearest body; BASIPTERYGIUM.

'basalt, n. [Geol.] Common dark or black IGNEOUS ROCK (see p. 192).

'basanite, n. [Geol.] An IGNEOUS ROCK, somewhat like BASALT, with OLIVINE in it.

base, n. [Maths.] (Of a LOGARITHM) the number of which the logarithm is the POWER, that is, if $x = y^n$, then n is the logarithm of x "to the base y"; the side opposite the APEX of a CONE or PYRAMID, or, in a TRIANGLE, that side on which the form is looked on as resting.

base, n. [Chem.] The substance forming the greatest part of a mixed or COMPOUND substance, sp. an INACTIVE substance with which an ACTIVE substance is mixed so that it may be used for medical or other purposes; any compound which undergoes a reaction with an acid producing a SALT and water, and which gives –OH (*hydroxyl*) IONS when DISSOLVED in water, in other words, a substance which has a tendency to take on PROTONS. [Biol.] That part of a structure by which it is fixed to the part from which it comes, or which is nearest to that. **b. exchange.** The reaction by which an exchange of metals takes place between certain SALTS in SOLUTION in water and other salts, so that, for example, water with Ca IONS in it running over a SILICATE of Na becomes water with Na ions in it and the silicate is changed to a silicate of Ca—an important process in geology, and used in SOFTENING water. **b. metals.** Metals, such as Cu, Pb, Zn, Sn, which are acted on by common acids or become OXIDIZED when heated in air.

'Basel ana'tomical no'menclature. System for naming parts of body, fixed at Basel, 1895.

'base-'level, n. [Geog.] The lowest level to which land may be cut through or lowered by the operation of rivers, etc., the level at which the hollowing out of a river bed is unable to go deeper.

'basement 'membrane. [Zoo.] Delicate skin forming base of EPITHELIUM.

basi'branchial, a., n. [Zoo.] (To do with) the lower middle part of the bone framework supporting the GILLS.

'basi- 'basio-. At, to do with, a base.

'basic, a. First, deepest, present in greatest amount, most necessary, most important. [Biol.] Of, to do with, at, or near the BASE. [Chem.] Having the properties of a BASE. **b. dye.** Any DYE whose colouring-power comes from a BASE of which it is a SALT, used chiefly for printing designs on cotton or in Biology (see STAIN). **b. rock.** IGNEOUS ROCK with only 45–55% SiO2. **b. salt.** The sort of SALT formed when not all the OXIDE or HYDROXIDE group of a BASE is taken out by reaction with an acid, so that the MOLECULE is a complex of salt and base, as **b. lead 'sulphate,** $2PbSO_4.PbO$. **b. steel process.** Process for changing CAST iron into steel by blowing air through the liquid metal in a vessel coated inside with a BASE (CaO, MgO), driving off the carbon in the form of CO_2, and causing other substances to be united with the coating, so that almost unmixed iron is produced which may then be united with the right amount of C. ba'sicity, n. Quality or condition of being a BASE; (of an acid) the number of its H ATOMS in place of which metal atoms may be put.

basi'cranial, a. [Zoo.] Placed at base of bone structure of head.

basi'chromatin, n. [Biol.] Substance forming network of CELL NUCLEUS, which takes a deep colour when acted on by BASIC DYE.

'basi'cyte, n. [Zoo., Med.] MAST CELL.

Ba'sidiomy'cetes, n.pl. [Bot.] A great CLASS of FUNGI with SEPTATE MYCELIUM, among which are the AGARICS and like forms, some good for food, some poison, and the UREDINALES and USTILA-GINALES.

ba'sidiophore, n. [Bot.] Fruit-body producing BASIDIA.

ba'sidiospore, n. [B.] SPORE on BASIO-PHORE.

ba'sidium (basidia) n. [Bot.] Form of SPORO-PHORE in BASIDIOMYCETES. ba'sidial, a.

basi'dorsal, a. [Zoo.] At base of back.

ba'sigamous, a. [Bot.] Having normal position of egg apparatus and ANTIPODAL CELLS turned round in MEGASPORE, egg being at lower end.

'basilar, a. [Biol.] Near, or having growth from, base. **b. 'membrane.** MEMBRANE of the inner ear to do with the sense of hearing.

ba'silic vein, n. VEIN in top part of arm.

basi'lingual, a. [Zoo.] At base of tongue.

'basioc'cipital, n. In higher back-boned animals, the bone at the base of the CRANIUM straight in front of the chief opening.

ba'sipetal, a. [Bot.] Having order of development from top down, said of flowers or leaf-parts ranged on a common stem.

'basiphil, a. [Zoo.] (Of CELL-structures, etc.) readily coloured by BASIC DYES.

ba'sipodite, n. [Zoo.] The second JOINT of the end part of the APPENDAGES of certain ARTHROPODA.

basi'podium, n. [Zoo.] JOINT between leg and foot or between arm and hand.

'basipte'rygium, n. In BASAL bone or CARTI-LAGE in FIN of fish.

basip'terygoid, n. Outgrowth of BASISPHEN-OID bone in some birds.

basi'sphenoid, a., n. [Zoo.] (To do with) that part of the base of the CRANIUM between BASIOCCIPITAL and PRESPHEN-OID. basisphe'noidal, a.

basi'temporal, a., n. (To do with) one of two MEMBRANE BONES in head of bird, under and uniting with the BASISPHENOID and BASIOCCIPITAL.

'basophil, a. BASIPHIL.

bast, n. [Bot.] PHLOEM; b. fibre. **b. cell.** Any of the long and narrow, thick-walled CELLS of which b. fibre is made up. **b. 'fibre.** A cord-like structure of b. cells forming a strong material used for making cord, floor-coverings, etc., got from the PHLOEM, and sometimes from other parts, of certain trees.

'bastard, 1.n. [Biol.] Offspring of two different sorts of plant or animal. 2.a. Not true or normal, said of a disease, MINERAL, plant, etc. **b. wing.** [Zoo.] That part of a bird's wing supporting three or four short feathers, which is representative of the thumb in man.

'bathic, a. To do with deep levels of sea.

'bathochrome, n. [Chem.] An ATOM or RADICAL which on addition to a substance has the effect of moving its AB-SORPTION SPECTRUM in the direction of the red.

'batholith, 'bathylith, nn. [Geol.] Very great mass of IGNEOUS ROCK which became solid under the earth.

ba'thymeter, n. Instrument for measuring how deep water is. bathy'metric(al), aa. ba'thymetry, n.

'bathyscaphe, n. A later development from the BATHYSCOPE, first tested by Piccard in 1948, in theory able to go down 50,000 feet under the water and having the power of moving about on the sea-bed.

'bathyscope, n. Under-water vessel first designed by Piccard to go deeper than any vessel had been before, for the purpose of observations on the deep-sea bed, having the power of going down and coming up of itself without any chains for lowering and lifting it, but not that of moving about on the sea-bed.

'bathyseism, n. EARTHQUAKE very deep in the earth.

'bathysphere, n. Hollow ball of metal, with windows, which may be let down by chains to sea bed and has room inside for two persons making observations.

ba'trachian, n., a. (Animal) of, to do with, SALIENTIA.

'batswing 'burner. Old form of gas-burner in which gas-flame has form of wing.

'battery, n. A number of like units for producing or using power, working together, as ELECTRIC CELLS, ACCUMULATORS, boilers, stamps.

Baumé scale, n. A scale used on some sorts of HYDROMETER on which 0° is the point to which the instrument goes down in water and 10° the point to which it goes down in a 10% SOLUTION of NaCl at 12·5°C.

'bauxite, n. [Mineral.] Natural $Al_2O_3.2H_2O$, an important ORE of Al.

Ba'veno twin. [Cryst.] TWIN CRYSTAL of special form, almost square.

Be, Sign for BERYLLIUM.

b. d. v. = BREAKDOWN VOLTAGE.

Bé. = BAUMÉ.

beach, n. Land edging sea or inland water, gen. made up of sand or round stones, and freq. covered at HIGH TIDE.

'beacon, n. Light of great power placed on a high point so as to be seen from a great distance, used as a guide for ships or airplanes; see RADIO B.

bead test. Colour test for the discovery of the metals in a substance by the use of a BORAX BEAD.

beak, n. The hard mouth-part of a bird; any like growth in other animals or in a plant.

'beaker, n. Open vessel in form like a straight drinking-glass, but generally with lip, used chiefly in chemistry.

beam, n. [Phys.] A group of rays sent out together in the same direction.

beam 'compass(es). An instrument for making great circles or curves on paper, etc., formed of a wood or metal rod with two points, one for support and one for marking, coming down from it and gripped by collar-like parts by which they may be moved to any desired point on the rod.

beam trap. [Phys.] In a CATHODE RAY TUBE, a bucket-like ELECTRODE into which the ray of ELECTRONS is sent when it is desired to keep it from getting to the SCREEN.

beam width. [Acous.] Of a TRANSDUCER or AERIAL at a given FREQUENCY, the angle between the two directions, one to the left and the other to the right of the BEAM AXIS, at which the ANGULAR

DEVIATION loss has a given value, generally measured in DECIBELS.

beard, n. In animals, special outgrowth of hair, feathers, or threadlike structures, for example, the hairs under chin of goat, the feathers hanging from throat of fowl, the structures on mouth of certain CETACEAE and some fishes, or on GILLS of other sea-animals; like growth in plant, specially the AWN of grain.

'bearing, n. Support keeping a turning rod in position in a machine (gen. bb.). [Astron. etc.] Direction of a point P from a fixed point of observation, O, as given by the angle between a line to the north and another from O to P, for example the b. of P and O is the angle NOP where the direction of ON is to the north.

beat, n. A blow or motion, or the sound produced by it, coming regularly over and over, sp. the motion of the heart or one unit of its motion. [Phys., Acous.] Regular change in power of a sound or other wave-motion, produced when two waves, almost equal in FREQUENCY, are acting together at the same point. 2.vt. Be giving regular blows to (something). 3.v.i. Be producing a b. of any sort. b. 'frequency.[Radio] FREQUENCY of b., sp. in radio apparatus. b. frequency 'oscillator. OSCILLATOR in which the output is a b., gen. at AUDIOFREQUENCY, made from two waves at RADIOFREQUENCY. b. tone. Sound having same FREQUENCY as b. between two wave-trains.

'Bechold 'filter. [Chem.] FILTER for COLLOIDS.

'Bechmann ther'mometer. THERMOMETER with great bulb giving it power of measuring very small changes over a very limited range, which may be changed as needed by the adjustment of the amount of Hg.

'Becke test. [Geol.] A way of making a comparison between the REFRACTIVE INDICES of two substances by the use of a MICROSCOPE.

'Becquerel ef'fect. Electric current produced between two like metals in a liquid when light is sent onto one of them. 'Becquerel rays. The rays (α, β, γ) given out by RADIOACTIVE substances.

bed, n. [Geol.] STRATUM. '-ding, n. [Geol.] STRATIFICATION. bedding plane. The plane of the SURFACE on which a b. is put down, or of the meeting faces of two bb. in a STRATIFIED ROCK.

'beebread, n. The yellow-brown, bitter substance formed from POLLEN and stored up by bees for use, mixed with HONEY, as food.

Beer's law. [Phys., Chem.] Law that the INTENSITY of a ray of light which has gone through a MEDIUM is in INVERSE PROPORTION to the distance covered in the medium.

beg(a)-. [Elec.] Put before names of measures to make the name of a measure 10^9 times as great, for example **beg'ohm** ($= 10^9$ OHMS).

be'haviourism, n. Theory that the science of psychology is limited to observation of physical reactions in persons and animals and that sense-experiences, feelings and thoughts have no place in it. **be'haviorist,** n. **be'havior'istic,** a.

be'heading, n. [Geog.] RIVER CAPTURE.

'belemnite, n. [Geol.] FOSSIL formed like a short straight horn, hollow at the thick end, part of a CEPHALOPOD. **'belemniod,** a.

bel, n. [Phys.] A unit on a LOGARITHMIC scale for the comparison of two levels of power, e.g. if W_1 and W_2 are two power levels the number of bb. between them is $\text{LOG} \dfrac{W_1}{W_2}$, *see* DECIBEL.

'bell-crank 'lever. LEVER whose two arms are at an angle to one another (generally a right angle) with the FULCRUM at their meeting-point.

bell jar. Glass vessel in form somewhat like a bell used as cover for apparatus, sp. on plate of AIRPUMP.

bell metal. Mixed metal made up chiefly of copper with up to 30% of tin and sometimes small amounts of lead and zinc, used for making bells.

'bellows, n. Any instrument or part of a machine by which, as the effect of expansion and CONTRACTION in turn, air is taken in through an opening and then sent out through a pipe-like part, used for blowing a current of air through anything; the soft, folding covering between the LENS and the back of a camera which makes possible the adjustment of the lens to different distances.

'belly, n. [Zoo.] The inner hollow, or the VENTRAL side, of the ABDOMEN in higher animals; of a muscle, etc., the thick, round part.

'belonite, n. [Geol.] Rod-like small CRYSTAL with round or pointed ends.

belt, n. Band of leather, rubber, or other material joined end to end, running over two or more wheels or other turning parts, used for sending on motion, power, transporting goods, and so on. **b. drive.** [Engin.] The handing on of motion from one machine SHAFT to another by a b. going over PULLEYS on the shafts.

'Bence-'Jones 'protein. [Biochem.] A PROTEIN with special properties present sometimes in URINE.

'bending 'moment. [Mech.] The MOMENT at any point in a bent elastic rod which is keeping it bent.

be'nign, be'nignant, aa. [Med.] (Of un-normal growths in the body) not in themselves causing death and generally not forming again after being cut out.

'benthos, n. The living things on the sea-bed.

benz'aldehyde, n. [Chem.] An AROMATIC COMPOUND, C_6H_5CHO, an oil with no colour and with a strong special smell, present naturally in some fruit-stones and produced chemically for a number of uses, such as DYE-making.

'benzene, n. [Chem.] C_6H_6, the 6 C ATOMS forming a ring structure, a liquid without colour, which takes fire very readily and is a SOLVENT for fat, produced chiefly from coal. **b. 'nucleus** or **ring.** The structure seen in the b. MOLECULE in which the 6 C ATOMS are in a ring, with first a DOUBLE BOND and then a SINGLE BOND all round, and the H atoms are joined to the C atom sin the outside (*see* p. 169). **b. sul'phonic acid.** Any of a number of AROMATIC COMPOUNDS having in them the group $-SO_3H$, used in making DYES.

'benzine, n. [Chem.] Mixed low-boiling HYDROCARBONS of the PARAFFIN series.

'benzo-. [Chem.] Having the AROMATIC group C_6H_5-.

ben'zoic 'acid. [Chem.] An AROMATIC COMPOUND, C_6H_5COOH, in the form of thin, white, smooth CRYSTALS, used as an ANTISEPTIC, food PRESERVATIVE, etc.

'benzol, n. [Chem.] BENZENE as it is first produced mixed with small amounts of other substances.

'benzoyl, a. [Chem.] Having or being the AROMATIC group $C_6H_5.CO-$.

'benzyl, a. Having the AROMATIC group $-CH_2.C_6H_5$. **'b. 'alcohol.** [Chem.] $C_6H_5CH_2OH$, an AROMATIC COMPOUND in the form of a liquid without colour. used medically.

'BEPO, n. [Phys.] BRITISH EXPERIMENTAL PILE 0.

'bergschrund, n. [Geol.] The deep crack or cracks frequently formed between a GLACIER and the mountain side.

'beri-'beri, n. Disease caused by living on food having little or no VITAMIN B, and marked by INFLAMMATION of the nerves, causing pain, loss of power in the muscles, and general wasting.

'Berkefeld 'filter, n. Apparatus for freeing water from BACTERIA, in which it is FILTERED through DIATOMACEOUS earth.

ber'kelium, n. Chemical ELEMENT, at. no. 97, sign Bk.

Bern'ouille's 'principle or theorem. [Phys.] In a current of liquid, the amount of ENERGY per unit of MASS is unchanging.

'berry, n. [Bot.] Any SIMPLE FRUIT formed of a thick, soft mass covered with a thin outer skin and having the seeds, generally more than one in number, bedded in the middle of it. [Zoo.] Egg of certain CRUSTACEA.

'beryl, n. [Geol.] Natural BERYLLIUM ALUMINIUM SILICATE in the form of blue, yellow or light red six-sided CRYSTALS.

be'ryllium, n. Chemical ELEMENT, at. no. 4, at. wt. 9·02, sign Be, a steel-like metal of little weight.

Bessemer process. [Metal.] BASIC STEEL PROCESS.

'beta, n. The Greek letter β, used like α, γ, etc., before names as a sign of some special property, structure, or sort, sp. for naming:—[Chem.] one of two or more ISOMERS; [Astron.] the second brightest star of a CONSTELLATION. b. 'factor. In ATOMIC PHYSICS, the RATIO of the KINETIC PRESSURE to the MAGNETIC PRESSURE. b. 'particle. [Phys.] ELECTRON sent out from the NUCLEUS of an ATOM in RADIOACTIVITY, moving at a rate near to that of light. b. ray. Line of b. particles. b. transfor'mation. Change in chemical ELEMENT by the loss of a b. particle.

be'tatron, n. [Phys.] A NUCLEAR ACCELERATOR made up of an ELECTRON DISCHARGE TUBE bent round in a circle between the POLES of an ELECTROMAGNET, BETA RAYS being sent out in the tube and ACCELERATED round and round by the electromagnet till they at last COLLIDE with the ANTI-CATHODE, so producing very high-ENERGY PHOTONS and X-RAYS of great power.

Bett's process. Process for getting lead free from other metals by sending an electric current through a SOLUTION of PbSiF$_6$.

Betz cells. [Anat.] CELLS of great size in the part of the brain to do with motion.

'bevatron, n. [Phys.] An ACCELERATOR of great power, somewhat like the SYNCHROTRON.

B.H.P. = BRAKE HORSE-POWER.

Bi, Sign for BISMUTH.

bi-, Two, twice, every two: '-'angular, '-'axial, a.

'bias, n. [Elec.] POTENTIAL, normally negative (−) given to GRID of VALVE.

bi'carbonate, n. [Chem.] Any ACID SALT of H$_2$CO$_3$ (carbonic acid), sp. SODIUM B.

'biceps, n. [Zoo.] Muscle coming from, rooted at, two points, sp. b. 'flexor 'cubiti, in arm, and b. 'flexor 'cruris, b. 'femoris. in leg.

bi'cipital, a. [Zoo.] Coming from two points, as BICEPS; having to do with a b. muscle. [Bot.] Having a division into two parts at one end. b. groove. Hollow line on top part of HUMERUS. b. ridges. Lips of bicipital groove.

bicol'lateral, a. [Bot.] With XYLEM between two PHLOEM threads.

bi'concave, a. With the two opposite sides curved in, as in a b. LENS.

bi'convex, a. With the two opposite sides curved out.

bi'cornuate, a. Having two horns or horn-like structures.

bi'costate, a. (Of leaves, etc.) having two chief RIBS going from end to end.

bi'crenate, a. (Of leaves) having an edge with waves or rounded teeth which themselves again have a like edge.

bi'cuspid. [Biol.] 1.a. Having, ending in, two sharp points. 2.n. B. tooth. b. valve. The VALVE controlling the motion of the blood between the left AURICLE and the left VENTRICLE of the heart.

bi'cyclic, a. [Biol.] In the form of two circles or [Bot.] WHORLS.

bi'ennial, n., a. (Plant) living for only two years and flowering in the second.

bi'facial, a. [Bot.] DORSIVENTRAL.

'bifid, a. [Biol.] Having two equal LOBES, forked.

bi'filar, a. [Phys.] Made up of, using, two threads of wires. b. sus'pension. The hanging of a body, such as part of an instrument, by two parallel thin threads or wires.

'biflex, a. Having two curves; bent in two directions.

bi'florate, a. Having two flowers.

bi'focal, a. Having two FOCI. [Optics] Formed of two LENSES having different FOCAL distances, as eyeglasses designed for reading etc., and for seeing things at a distance.

'bifurcate, 1.v.t. and i. (Make) undergo forking. 2.a. Forked. bifur'cation, n.

bi'geminal, a. To do with CORPORA BIGEMINA in brain. b. pulse. [Med.] A PULSE of which the BEATS come in twos with a stop after them, caused by an unnormal operation of the heart.

bi'geminate, a. [Biol., Cryst.] Having two groups of two like parts or forms.

bige'neric, a. [Zoo.] Said of offspring of two different GENERA.

bi'labial, a. [Phonet.] said of sounds made with the two lips, as p, m. w.

bi'labiate, a. [Bot.] Having two lips, as COROLLAS of certain flowers.

bi'lateral, a. Having, being on, to do with, two opposite ([Med.] right and left) sides. [Biol.] Having b. symmetry. b. 'symmetry. [Biol.] Condition of being cut into two like and opposite halves by one plane only, as the body of a man is by the middle plane from back to front.

bile, n. [Zoo.] Bitter green or yellow liquid produced by LIVER, helping in digestion of fats.

'bilhar'ziasis, bil'harzi'osis, nn. Disease of man and higher animals, common in Africa, caused by worms of GENUS Bilharzia living in the blood vessels.

'biliary, a. To do with, transporting, BILE. b. 'calculus. GALLSTONE.

'bilious, a. [Med.] Troubled by, or caused by, overmuch BILE being produced.

bili'rubin, n. Red-yellow colouring material in BILE of man and some other animals.

'biliverdin, n. Green colouring material in BILE, formed by uniting of BILIRUBIN with O.

bill, n. [Zoo.] BEAK of a bird, or like mouthpart of certain other animals, sp. CHELONIA.

'billion, n. In British use, 1,000,000 million; in the U.S.A., 1,000 million.

bi'lobate, a. [Biol.] Having two LOBES.

bi'lobular, a. [Biol.] Having two LOBULES.

bi'locular, a. [Biol.] Having two CELLS or divisions.

'bime'tallic, a. Made up of two separate metals. bi'metal, n. B. plate used in THERMOSTATS.

'bimo'lecular, a. To do with two molecules, as b. reaction.

'binary, a. Made up of two things or parts. b. 'fission. [Biol.] Division of a cell into two. b. no'menclature. BINOMIAL NOMENCLATURE. b. star. DOUBLE STAR.

'binate, a. [Bot.] Having growth in twos.

bin'aural, a. To do with having, designed for, two ears.

'binding 'energy, n. [Chem.] The ENERGY needed to get a FUNDAMENTAL PARTICLE away from the system of which it is a part.

'Binet (or 'Binet-'Simon) scale. [Psych.] A scale for measuring a young person's brain-power by tests based on the general level of powers at different AGES, there being a different test for every year from three to twelve. Binet test. Any of the different tests making up the B. s.

bi'nocular, a. To do with the two eyes. bi'noculars, n.pl. An instrument for long-distance seeing formed of two TELESCOPES fixed side by side to be looked through with the two eyes.

bi'nodal, a. Having two NODES.

bi'nomial, a. Made up of, to do with, two TERMS or names. b. no'menclature. System of naming animals and plants by two Latin names, giving GENUS and SPECIES.

'bio-. To do with living things.

'bioan'alysis, n. The measuring of very small amounts of chemical substances by use of BACTERIA, PROTOZOA, or PROTOPHYTA.

'bio-as'say, n. The measuring of power of medical substances by their effects on animals.

bio'chemistry, n. Chemistry of living things. bio'chemical, a.

'bioc(o)e'nosis, bio'c(o)enose, nn. Society of animals and plants living on the same land and more or less dependent on one another. 'bioc(o)e'notic, a.

'bioclima'tology, n. [Biol.] The science of the effects of CLIMATE on plants and animals.

bio'colloid, n. [Chem.] COLLOID got from animals or plants.

'biody'namics, n. The branch of biology which has to do with the working of living bodies, with what goes on in them, opp. the science of their structure.

bio'element, n. Any chemical ELEMENT necessary to the existence of plants or animals.

bio'genesis, bi'ogeny, nn. Theory that living things are only produced by living things. 'bioge'netic, a. 'biogenetic law. RECAPITULATION THEORY.

bio'genous, a. PARASITIC.

'bioge'ography, n. Branch of biology to do with the distribution of plants and animals over the earth.

bio'logics, n.pl. Group of medical substances got from living things, sp. BACTERIA, POLLEN, PROTEIN.

bi'ology, n. Science of living things. bio'logical, a. Of. to do with, b. or living things; (of a form, SPECIES, etc.) marked off from other groups which are little or no different from it in structure by special reactions or behaviour (=PHYSIOLOGICAL). bio'logic(al) (race) 'speciali'zation. PHYSIOLOGICAL (RACE) SPECIALIZATION. bio'logically, adv.

'biolumi'nescence, n. [Biol.] The producing of light by animals and plants, for example fireflies, certain fish and certain FUNGI.

'biome, n. The complete plant-animal society in any place.

'biomech'anics, n. The MECHANICS of living things, sp. of the operation of muscles, such as the motion of a man's foot and ankle in relation to his shoe.

bio'metrics, bi'ometry, nn. Science of STATISTICS as used in connection with plants and animals. bio'metrica(l), aa.

bio'nomic, a. To do with relation between living things and the conditions in which they have their existence. bio'nomics, n. B. science.

-'biont, n. Plant or animal living in some special way given by the first part of the word, as AEROBIONT. -bi'ontic, a. -bi'osis, n.

bi'ophagous, a. [Biol.] Using living things as food.

'bio'physics, n. The physics of living things. bio'physical, a.

'biophyte, n. BIOPHAGOUS plant.

'biopsy, n. [Med.] Observation of bit of substance taken from living body as a test for disease.

'bios, n. VITAMIN-like substance necessary for growth of YEAST.

bi'oscopy, n. [Med.] The testing of a body to see if it is living or not. bio'scopic, a.

bio'statics, n. Science of the structure of

living bodies and the use of their different parts.

'biosyste'matics, n. The science of the CLASSIFICATION of living things.

bi'otic, a. To do with plants and animals. **b. suc'cession.** Change in a plant-animal society caused by changes in outside conditions.

'biotin, n. VITAMIN H.

'biotite, n. [Mineral.] Natural SILICATE of Al, Fe, Mg, K and H.

biotope, n. A part of the earth having the same weather conditions and the same sorts of animals all over it.

bi'parous, a. Giving birth to two offspring at the same time.

bi'partient, a. Undergoing division into two parts or twice.

bi'partite, a. In two parts, sp. [Bot.] with division almost to base, as leaf.

'biped, n. Animal having two feet. **bi'pedal,** a.

bipin'naria, n. Free-swimming LARVA of certain starfish (ASTEROIDEA).

bi'pinnate, a. (Of a leaf) PINNATE, with the divisions again pinnate. (*See* picture page 223.)

bipin'natifid, a. (Of a leaf) PINNATIFID, with the divisions again pinnatifid.

bi'planar, a. Being in two planes.

'biplane, n. Airplane with two planes one over the other.

bi'polar, a. [Elec., Biol.] Having two POLES. **b. e'lectrode.** Metal division between two bodies of liquid, with electric current going through it from one to the other. **bipo'larity,** n.

bi'prism, n. [Optics] PRISM with REFRACTING angle of almost 180 degrees.

bipy'ramidal, a. In the form of two PYRAMIDS placed base to base, as some CRYSTALS. **bi'pyramid,** n.

bi'quartz, n. [Optics] QUARTZ plate cut into two parts turning POLARIZED light opposite ways, used in POLARISCOPE.

bi'radial, a. [Zoo.] Having b. symmetry. **b. 'symmetry,** SYMMETRY which is in part RADIAL and in part LATERAL.

bi'radiate(d), aa. [Zoo.] Having two rays.

bi'ramous, a. [Zoo.] Having two branches.

bi'rectifi'cation, n. [Chem.] Process of measuring the amounts of different substances in a mixed liquid by DISTILLATION.

'bire'fringence, n. [Optics] Division of a ray of light going through a substance into two rays bent at different angles; property or power, seen in most CRYSTALS, of causing b. **birefringent,** a.

biro'tation, n. [Chem.] Change in the OPTICAL ROTATION of SOLUTIONS of some substances, sp. sugars, in time.

birth con'trol. The act or system of keeping offspring from being produced, or limiting the number of births in a family or society, as, for example,

by the use of CONTRACEPTIVES.

birthmark, n. [Med.] Any special mark present on the skin from birth, as a NAEVUS.

birth rate. The number of births for every 100 or 1000 persons in a given society or group in a given time.

bi'sect, v.t. Get cut, make division of, into two equal parts.

bi'septate, a. Having two divisions.

bi'serial, a. Ranged in two lines or groups.

bi'serrate, a. [Bot.] Having a toothed edge with teeth again toothed.

bi'set-ose, ous, aa. [Bot.] Having two stiff hairs.

bi'sexual, a. [Biol.] HERMAPHRODITE. [Psych.] Having male and female qualities, feelings, sex-desires.

'bismuth, n. Chemical ELEMENT, at. no. 83, at. wt. 209·00, sign Bi, a grey-white metal. **b. 'spiral.** Flat COIL of Bi wire used for measuring MAGNETIC FIELDS.

bi'sphenoid, n. CRYSTAL with 4 three-sided faces, two meeting at the top and two at the base in edges at right-angles to one another.

bi'stipul-ar, -ate, aa. [Bot.] Having two STIPULES.

bi'sulphate, n. Substance having in it the group $-HSO_4$.

bi'sulphite, n. Substance having in it the group $-HSO_3$.

bisym'metric(al), aa. SYMMETRICAL about two planes at right-angles to one another.

bitch, n. Female of dog and some like animals.

bi'ternate, a. [Bot.] With three parts which themselves have three parts.

'bittern, n. [Chem.] Waste liquid after salt has been taken out of sea water.

'bitter 'pattern or bands. Structure formed on face of CRYSTAL by MAGNETIC powder.

'bitter-spar, n. DOLOMITE.

'bitumen, n. Any of a number of solid or half-solid substances present in the earth, which are able to be burned, natural OXYGENATED HYDROCARBONS such as NAPHTHA, PETROLEUM, and ASPHALT. **bi'tuminous,** a.

bi'typic, a. [Biol.] (Of GENUS) made up of two SPECIES.

bi'valent, a. [Chem.] Having VALENCY 2. [Biol.] Formed of two, said chiefly of a CHROMOSOME made up of two joined together. 2n. [Biol.] Any of the b. chromosomes formed in MEIOSIS.

'bivalve, a. [Zoo.] Having SHELL in form of two plates opening like a book, as LAMELLIBRANCHIA. [Bot.] Having seed-box of like structure. 2.n. Any b. animal.

bi'variant, a. [Phys., Chem.] Having two DEGREES OF FREEDOM.

bi'vitate, a. [Bot.] Having two oil-pipes, as certain fruits. [Zoo.] Having two lines or bands of colour going from end to end.

black band. [Mineral.] A natural, CLAY-like form of $FeCO_3$, frequently present with coal.

'black' body. [Phys.] Substance taking up all the light or other rays of any FREQUENCY falling on it. **b.-b. radi'ation.** ENERGY sent out by b.-b. at any TEMPERATURE. **b.-b. 'temperature.** Temperature at which a b.-b. would send out the same amount of energy as is sent out by a given body at a given temperature.

black-bulb ther'mometer. THERMOMETER with black bulb and fixed in a space free from air, to keep any loss of heat from taking place, for measuring heat of sun's rays.

'Blackburn pendulum. PENDULUM which may have different times of motion in two directions at right angles.

black damp. Gas in a mine formed of air in which CO_2 has taken the place of O as the effect of an EXPLOSION, etc., causing CHOKING.

'blackhead, n. [Med.] Small mass of fat stopping up opening of fat GLAND and forming black point on skin; INFECTIOUS LIVER disease of certain birds.

black 'manganese. [Mineral.] PYROLUSITE.

'Blackmann reaction. [Bot.] That part of a PHOTOSYNTHESIS reaction in which light takes no part.

black rot. Any of number of plant diseases caused by BACTERIA and FUNGI.

'bladder, n. Bag-like part of animal, having in it air or liquid, sp. the URINE b. **'-worm,** n. The b.-like LARVA of the TAPEWORM.

blade, n. The flat part of a leaf or like flower-part; flat upper part of tongue, for about $\frac{1}{2}$ in. back from the point.

blank de'termination or **ex'periment** or **test.** [Chem.] Test made under all the conditions of a true test, but without the substance to be tested, for the purpose of taking into account any special effects dependent on the quality of other substances used, and so on.

blast, 1. n. Forced current of air used in b. furnace for producing great heat or caused by a very quick expansion of air after an EXPLOSION; the firing or going off of an EXPLOSIVE CHARGE put into ROCK, etc. 2. v. t. Send b. through (material in a b. furnace, etc.); get (ROCK, etc.) broken up by explosion. **b. 'furnace.** SMELTING apparatus using air-b., specially used for smelting iron. **'-ing,** n. [Eng.] Process of getting ROCK broken up by use of EXPLOSIVES forced into holes made in it. [Elec.] Loud unnormal noise in LOUDSPEAKER.

-blast, n. [Biol.] A CELL or group of CELLS forming the first stage in some development, that from which the named sort of cell or material comes.

'blasto-. BUD, GERM, egg, or EMBRYO in early stages.

blasto'carpous, a. [Bot.] Starting growth while still inside seed-vessel cover.

'blastochyle, n. [Zoo.] Liquid in BLASTO-COELE.

'blastocoel(e), n. [Zoo.] Hollow space formed in an OVUM near the end of the process of CLEAVAGE and becoming the hollow inside the BLASTULA.

'blastocolla, n. [Bot.] Sticky substance coating certain BUDS.

'blastocyst, n. [Zoo.] GERMINAL VESICLE; BLASTULA.

'blastoderm, n. The part of an egg YOLK in which division first takes place. **blasto-'dermic,** a. blastodermic 'vesicle. BLAS-TULA.

blasto'genesis, n. [Zoo.] Forming of offspring by BUDDING; theory that qualities are handed on to offspring only by GERM PLASM.

blasto'genic, a. [Zoo.] Present in, to do with, coming from, the GERM PLASM.

'blastogra'nitic, a. [Geol.] Giving signs of earlier GRANITE structure.

blastoki'nesis, n. [Zoo.] Change of place of EMBRYO in certain insect eggs.

'blastomere, n. [Zoo.] One of great CELLS formed in first stages of development of OVUM.

'blastomy'cosis, n. [Med.] A disease of man and animals caused by YEAST-like FUNGI and marked by skin trouble or inner ABSCESSES.

'blastophore, n. [Zoo.] First stage of PLUMULE in birds; offspring-producing body of certain ANTHOZOA; middle part of SPERMATOCYTE mass in worms, which does not undergo development into SPERMATOZOA.

'blastopore, n. [Zoo.] Small opening in a GASTRULA where the outer CELLS are pulled in to undergo development into ENDODERM and MESODERM, sometimes later shutting up, sometimes becoming the opening of the ANUS.

'blastoporphy'ritic, a. [Geol.] Giving signs of earlier PORPHYRITIC structure.

'blastostyle, n. [Zoo.] in HYDROZOA, a ZOOID without mouth or TENTACLES producing GONOPHORES.

'blasto'zooid, n. [Zoo.] LARVA BUD in ASCIDIACEAE, coming before its time; ZOOID produced by BUDDING.

'blastula (blastulae), n. [Zoo.] Early stage of development in the EMBRYO of a number of animals, when the OVUM has undergone division into a mass of CELLS generally taking the form of a hollow ball, the wall of which is one cell thick and without opening. **blastu'lation,** n. The forming of bb.

'Blattnerphone, n. Trade name of an apparatus for recording sound by the

MAGNETIZATION of a steel band.

'B-'layer, n. [Radio] A part of the Earth's ATMOSPHERE, from 10 to 30 km. up, which has a feeble power of REFLECTION and DISPERSION of radio-waves.

bleach, 1.v.t. Take the colour out of (something), sp. make (some natural material, such as cotton) white by a chemical process. 2.n. Any chemical used for bleaching. **'bleaching,** n., a. **'bleaching powder.** Sp. CHLORIDE OF LIME.

bleb, n. [Med.] Small BLISTER full of clear liquid.

bleed, 1.v.i. (Of animals or plants) give out blood or SAP, etc., from a wounded part; (of substance, apparatus, etc.) undergo loss of liquid or gas as if by bleeding. 2.v.t. [Med.] Take some blood from (a person's body) for medical reasons. [Engin.] Take off some steam, gas, or liquid on its way through the pipes of a system, to make use of it for some purpose such as heating boiler, etc. **'-er,** n. Person having HAEMOPHILIA. **'-ing,** a., n.

'blende, n. MINERAL made up of SULPHIDES of certain metals, sp. Zn and Pb.

'blended (or 'blending) in'heritance. [Biol.] Form of HEREDITY in which in some quality the offspring seem to be half-way between the father and mother, and not, as in Mendel's theory, like one or the other only, for example brown skin colour in the offspring of a black mother and a white father.

blenn-, blenno-. To do with, having, MUCUS: **'blennoid,** a., **'blenno'genic,** a.

'blephar(o)-. Eyelid: **blepha'ritis,** n. [Med.]

'blepharoplast, n. [Biol.] A small grain of substance, possibly a CENTROSOME, in a CELL at the base of a CILIUM or FLAGELLUM.

blight, n. Any plant disease stopping growth and causing death of parts other than a ROT; b.-producing insect or FUNGUS.

blind, a. [Med.] Without the power of seeing. **b. spot.** Point on RETINA of eye on which light has no effect, where nerve of seeing comes in.

blink com'parator, blink 'microscope. [Astron.] Instrument by which two pictures which are almost the same are viewed, one with one eye and one with the other, and quickly covered in turn, so that the ways in which they are different are readily seen.

'blister, 1.n. [Med.] Bag-like place full of liquid, clear or mixed with blood, formed on skin as the effect of burning, rubbing, or disease. [Bot.] B.-like place or disease producing such places, on leaves. [Metal., etc.] B.-like place on solid stone or metal caused by the forming or expansion of gas inside the material while it is soft or liquid with heat (sometimes named **b. spot**). 2.v.t. and i. Be cause of, or undergo the forming of bb. **b. steel.** Rough form of steel produced by heating WROUGHT-IRON in C powder.

block, n. A solid mass of material such as stone, wood, or metal, with six roughly plane and right-angled faces, like a brick, sp. as used for some special purpose, for example as a support for material to be worked, as a stop to some motion, or (with a design cut into one face or fixed to it on a metal plate) for printing from. [Mach.] A frame fixed to a support by a hook, band, etc. and housing one or more PULLEY wheels. **b. and tackle.** A PULLEY b. together with the ropes or chains going over the pulley.

block, 1.v.t. Get (an opening, pipe, etc.) stopped up, get (a motion, operation) stopped by getting in its way, etc. 2.n. A condition of being blocked; anything causing this condition, stopping up an opening or getting in the way of a motion.

block tin. Tin (Sn) as generally put on market, in the form of BLOCKS having in it small amounts of Fe, Co, Pb, Sb, As.

'blocking con'denser. Electric CONDENSER used for stopping DIRECT CURRENT and letting through ALTERNATING CURRENT.

'blocking 'layer. [Elec.] The place where a metal and a bad CONDUCTOR are touching (as Cu and Cu_2O) which has the effects of stopping current in one direction, and of producing current when acted on by light.

blood, n. [Zoo.] The liquid going through a net-work of pipes in the bodies of higher animals, transporting O, food and HORMONES, taking away waste material, and helping to keep the temperature at the same level. **b. cell, b. 'corpuscle.** An ERYTHROCYTE or LEUCOCYTE present in the b. **b. clot.** A mass of COAGULATED b., such as is formed when b. comes from a wound, or sometimes inside a b. vessel. **b. count.** [Med.] (The process of getting) the number of the different sorts of b. corpuscles in a given amount of a person's b. **b. dust.** Small drops of fat in the b. **b. group.** Any of the four chief groups, named A, B, AB, and O, into which persons are put in agreement with the different make-up of their blood, the blood of any one group undergoing COAGULATION when mixed with that of a different group, so that only b. of the same group may be used for b. transfusion. **b. islands.** Red parts in middle GERM LAYER of OVA of back-boned animals in process of development, where b. vessels and CELLS are forming. **b. 'plasma.** B. from which all b. corpuscles have been taken, in back-boned animals a clear, uncoloured liquid, different from

b. serum in still having the property of COAGULATING. **b. plate. b. plaque. b. 'platelet.** THROMBOCYTE. **b. poisoning.** [Med.] Any diseased condition of the blood caused by the getting into it of BACTERIA or poison produced by them (see SEPTICAEMIA, TOXAEMIA). **b. 'pressure.** [Med.] The force of the b. on the walls of the b. vessels, which may become increased to the point of danger in old persons or in certain diseases. **b. 'serum.** Liquid part of b. which becomes separate from b. clot as this becomes more solid. **b. test.** Test of b. for disease, b. group, etc. **b. trans'fusion.** [Med.] The operation of putting b. of one person or animal into b.-vessels of another to make up for loss. **'b.-'vessel.** Any of the pipes in an animal's body through which b. goes, a VEIN, ARTERY or CAPILLARY.

bloodstone, n. [Mineral.] A natural form of SiO_2, green with red marks, used as an ornament in rings, etc.

bloom, n. Thin coat of grains of wax material on some fruits and leaves.

'blower, n. Apparatus for producing a current of air or gas.

'blowing 'engine. BLOWER worked by engine, sp. that used for forcing air through BLAST FURNACE.

'blowhole, n. [Zoo.] Breathing-hole at top of head in CETACEAE; hole in ice to which certain sea-animals come for breathing. [Metal.] Small pocket or hole in metal caused by gas formed in it when liquid. [Geol.] Hole in ROCK face through which air is forced by the sea going into greater hole in base.

'blowpipe, n. Pipe-like instrument through which air or other gas is forced, used in Chemistry to send a strong current into fire or gas-flame to give it great heat, in Biology for clearing hollows, and in a special form, in glass-making. **b. an'alysis.** [Chem.] The observation of the b. reaction of a substance with a view to the discovery of its make-up or properties. **b. re'action.** [Chem.] The reaction of a substance to heating in b. flame, which is used for the purpose of noting certain qualities.

'blubber, n. The fat stretching under the skin of certain sea-animals such as CETACEAE, from which oil may be got.

blue 'baby. [Med.] Baby with blue skin caused by heart disease.

blue-green 'algae. CYANOPHYCEAE.

blue mud. [Geog.] A sort of MUD put down on the sea-bed over a great part of the Pacific Ocean, having in it much DECAYED animal and plant material and iron SULPHIDE, which gives it a special dark blue colour.

blue 'timber. Wood disease produced by a FUNGUS, causing wood to become blue.

blue 'vitriol, n. See VITRIOL.

blur 'circle. The circle of light produced on a SCREEN (such as the back of the eye) which is very near to, but not at, the FOCUS of rays from a point.

B.N.A. Short for BASEL ANATOMICAL NOMENCLATURE.

Board of Trade 'Unit. [Elec.] English name for 1 KILOWATT-HOUR or 3.6×10^{13} ERGS.

'Boas test. [Med.] Test for HCl in stomach liquid, using $C_6H_4(OH)_2$ and sugar in alcohol (C_2H_5OH).

bob, n. A weight hanging on end of line or rod, as in PENDULUM.

'body, n. [Phys.] Any separate mass or unit of material substance; any separate sort of material substance. [Zoo.] The complete physical structure of an animal. [Biol., etc.] The chief part of an animal's b., or of any other structure, such as a plant or a machine, not taking in the arms, legs, head or other such outgrowths or additions. **b. 'cavity.** [Zoo.] Space inside b. in which the apparatus of digestion has its place. **b. cell.** [Zoo.] SOMATIC CELL. **b. wall.** [Zoo.] The wall of skin and muscle round the b. cavity.

'body-'cent(e)red, a. Said of a unit of CRYSTAL structure which has an ATOM at its middle point, or of structure made up of such units, sp. one in which the other atoms may be looked on as forming a design of square boxes, with one at every angle in addition to the one in the middle, as in most metals.

bog, n. [Geog.] A stretch of soft, wet land of sponge-like quality, formed chiefly of DECAYING plant material, sp. MUSCI, gen. as the effect of plant growth covering and taking up not very deep inland waters till an almost solid mass is formed. **b. 'butter.** Fat-like substance in PEAT. **b. iron ore.** Soft mass of LIMONITE under water.

Bohr 'atom. See Bohr theory. **Bohr 'theory.** Theory of the ATOM as a NUCLEUS with a POSITIVE CHARGE round which ELECTRONS are moving, together with the QUANTUM THEORY that the motion of the ELECTRONS is possible only in a limited number of ORBITS, the jump of an electron from one orbit to another of lower ENERGY causing the sending out of light of one WAVE-LENGTH only.

boil, v.i. and t. [Phys.] (Of a liquid) be in a condition of dancing motion as the effect of heat, forming bubbles of gas which come to the top and are given off; make (a liquid) b. by heating it, or make (a solid undergo the operation of heat by putting it in boiling liquid. **'-er, n.** [Eng.] An apparatus for producing steam for driving an engine, etc., made up of a system of vessels and pipes in which water is heated and steam forced to the desired outlet. '-ing, a., n. **boiling-point,** n. The TEMPERATURE at which a given liquid boils when open to the air, that is, at which its SATURATED VAPOUR PRESSURE is equal to the pressure of the ATMO-SPHERE, and so dependent on this, which is fixed for normal boiling-points at that of 76 cm. Hg. 'boiling point 'constant. Amount by which boiling point of a liquid is made higher by the addition of one GRAM MOLECULE of a substance to 1,000 g. of the liquid.

boil, n. [Med.] A small but deep INFLAMED outburst on the skin, giving out PUS and having a hard middle part, caused by the attacking of the substance at the root of a hair by a certain STAPHYLOCOCCUS.

'boiling-'water re'actor. [Phys.] A NUCLEAR REACTOR in which boiling water is MODERATOR and COOLANT.

bole, n. [Mineral.] A red or yellow readily broken CLAY, chiefly $Al_2O_3 + MgO + SiO_2 + H_2O$.

Bo'logna 'phosphorus. A light-giving form of BaS, made from $BaSO_4$.

'bolide, n. METEORITE.

'bolograph, b. Automatic record made with BOLOMETER. bolo'graphic, a. bo'lography, n.

bo'lometer, n. [Phys.] Instrument for measuring small amounts of RADIANT ENERGY by change in electric RESISTANCE of black-coated Pt wire placed in the way of the RAYS. bolo'metric, a.

'Boltzmann 'constant. [Phys.] The RATIO of all the ENERGY in a gas to the ABSOLUTE TEMPERATURE.

'bolus, n. Round mass; medical substance formed into b. for giving to animal; mass of food in mouth about to be taken into stomach. b. 'alba. KAOLIN.

bomb, n. A parcel of EXPLOSIVE material designed to go off at a fixed time or on being dropped, sent against something, etc., used in war. [Chem.] Very strong metal vessel, used for chemical reactions, etc., in which development of great force takes place. [Geol.] Round or egg-like mass of solid material sent out by VOLCANO. b. calo'rimeter. Instrument for measuring CALORIFIC VALUE of substances by burning them in a b.

bom'bard, v.t. [Phys.] Send a quick fire of PARTICLES or rays, sp. electric, against; (of particles, etc.) come against in this way.'-ment. n.

bond, n. [Chem.] Unit of force joining two ATOMS together in a MOLECULE (*see* VALENCY BOND).

bone, n. [Zoo.] The very hard CONNECTIVE TISSUE with a great amount of Ca salts in it forming the inner framework of animals such as birds, fish, and MAMMALS; any separate unit of such a b. framework.

b. **ash.** White substance formed when bb. are burned, chiefly b. phosphate. b. 'breccia. [Geol.] Mass of bits of broken b., gen. mixed with earth etc. b. con'duction. The process by which sound is taken to the INNER EAR through the bb. of the head. b. oil. [Chem.] A dark, oil-like liquid with a bad smell, got by the DESTRUCTIVE DISTILLATION of bb. and from which PYRROLE and like substances are produced. b. 'phosphate $Ca_3(PO_4)_2$. b. 'spavin. Growth of new bone on lower part of leg of horse caused by INFLAMMATION. 'bony, a. Formed of b. or b.-like material; having, being supported by, b(b). bony fish. [Zoo.] OSTEICHTHYES. bony' labyrinth. [Zoo.] *See* INNER EAR.

book gill. [Zoo.] GILL in XIPHOSURA, made of delicate leaf-like plates placed one over the other like the leaves of a book.

book lung. Breathing apparatus like BOOK GILL in certain ARACHNIDA.

'booster, n. Pump used for increasing PRESSURE of liquids; instrument or machine put into an electric CIRCUIT for purpose of controlling or changing VOLTAGE; substance used for increasing the force of an EXPLOSION.

'borate, n. A salt got from one of the BORIC ACIDS.

'borax, n. [Chem.] A white CRYSTALLINE SALT, $Na_2B_4O_7.10H_2O$, changing into a clear glass-like solid after being made liquid by heat, produced naturally by EVAPORATION of inland waters in certain parts of the earth, sp. in California and Tibet, used in glass-making and other industries and as an ANTISEPTIC. b. bead. A small mass of b. made liquid by heat and gripped in a twist of wire, used for testing for metals in SALTS because of its property of undergoing reactions with metal salts and freq. taking on a special colour representative of the metal.

'borbo'rygmus, n. [Med.] Noise sometimes made by gases in INTESTINES in the process of digestion.

Bor'deaux 'mixture. $CuSO_4$ and $Ca(OH)_2$ in water, used for destruction of FUNGI attacking plants.

'bordered pit. [Bot.] Thin place, with thick edge, in the wall between two VESSELS or TRACHEIDS, through which liquid goes from one to the other.

bore, v.i. and t. Make a hole through or into some solid substance by a screwing motion of some narrow pointed instrument or (of animals) the use of some special part of the head or mouth; make (a hole), make a hole in (something), in this way. 'borer, n. Sp., any insect or other small animal which makes its way deep into wood, stone, etc., by boring, freq. taking in the material as food.

bore, n. The hollow going through a pipe; the DIAMETER of such a hollow.

bore, n. [Geog.] High wave which goes up certain rivers like a wall of water at certain times, caused by the meeting of a high incoming TIDE with the river current in a narrow river-mouth, so that the sea-water is for a time kept back and massed up.

'**boreal,** a. To do with land in north parts of earth where the AVERAGE TEMPERATURE is not over 18°C. **b.′ forest.** The sort of woods present in b. parts of the earth.

'**boric acid.** [Chem.] Any of the substances HBO_2, H_3BO_3, or $H_2B_4O_7$.

'**boron,** n. Chemical ELEMENT, at. no. 5, at. wt. 10·82, sign B, a substance normally in the form of a brown powder, not a metal. '**boric,** a.

boss, n. [Geol.] BATHOLITH.

'**bosselated,** a. [Zoo.] Covered with little round PROTUBERANCES.

'**botany,** n. Science of plants. **bo′tanic(al),** a. '**botanist,** n. '**botanize,** v.t. and i.

'**bothrium,** n. [Zoo.] SUCKER.

'**botryoid(al),** aa. [Zoo.] '**botryose,** a. [Bot.], [Geol.] Having form of a mass of berries; RACEMOSE.

'**botulism,** n. [Med.] Poisoning caused by food, freq. by tinned food, which has been attacked by the ANAEROBIC BACILLUS *Bacillus botulinus.*

'**bougie,** n. [Med.] Long, thin, readily bent rod used for opening pipes in body which have become narrowed or stopped up.

'**bougie ′decimale.** French unit of light = 1/20 of that given by 1 sq. cm. of Pt at its FREEZING POINT.

'**Bouguer ′formula,** n. FORMULA giving rate of change of earth's attraction as dependent on distance over sea level.

'**bouillon,** n. Liquid (got by boiling beef in water) in which BACTERIA are put for growth.

'**boulder,** n. [Geol.] Great stone (from about 10 cm. up to as much as 300 cm. across) made round by weather and water. **b. clay.** The sort of material transported by a moving mass of ice, made up of CLAY mixed with sand, small stones, and bb.

bound, a. [Chem.] (Of substances) chemically united or kept so united.

bound ′particle. [Phys.] A PARTICLE limited by a force round it which its KINETIC ENERGY is not great enough to overcome.

'**Bourdon gauge.** Instrument for measuring PRESSURE of liquid or gas by its effect on a pipe in the form of a flat COIL, shut at one end, the pipe being forced out of its curve by pressure of gas or liquid let into it.

'**bovine,** a. [Zoo.] Of, to do with, animals of the GENUS *Bos,* such as the cow.

'**bowel,** n. INTESTINE.

'**Bowman's ′capsule.** [Zoo.] In KIDNEY of back-boned animals, the thin-walled hollow at the outer end of a URINIFEROUS TUBULE. '**Bowman's glands.** Branching pipe-like GLANDS in the under part of the skin inside nose.

Boyle's law, n. Law that PRESSURE × VOLUME of a mass of gas kept at the same TEMPERATURE is a fixed amount, that is, the volume gets less (greater) as the pressure gets greater (less)—true of most gases between certain limits of pressure.

b.p. = boiling point.

B.P. = BRITISH PHARMACOPOEIA.

Br, Sign for BROMINE.

'**braccate,** a. [Zoo.] Having feathered legs and feet.

brace, n. [Engin.] STAY.

'**brachial,** a. To do with an arm or arm-like part, like an arm. **b.** '**artery.** The chief ARTERY of the higher part of the arm. **b.** '**plexus.** Complex network of nerves in hollow under arm.

'**brachiate,** a. [Biol.] Branched; (of tree) having widely stretching branches, sp. grouped in twos with every two at right angles to the two before; having or supporting arms.

'**brachi(o)-.** (To do with) arm or arms.

'**Brachi′opoda,** n.pl. [Zoo.] A PHYLUM of sea-animals, gen. with a TWO-VALVED SHELL, living fixed to stones, etc. under the water and having two long, CILIATED, arm-like structures for producing a current taking food into the mouth—a group going back to PALAEOZOIC times, when it had a much greater number of representatives than it has today. '**brachiopod,** n., a. (Animal) of the B.

'**brachium,** n. [Zoo.] Top part of arm or front leg; any of certain arm-like parts of lower animals; any of the bands of white nerve substance in connection with the OPTIC LOBES of the brain.

'**brachy-,** Short.

'**brachy′axis,** n. BRACHYDIAGONAL.

'**brachyce′phalic,** '**brachy′cephalous,** aa. [Anthrop.] Short-headed, having CEPHALIC INDEX of 80 or more, **brachy′-cephaly,** n.

brachy′dactyly, n. Condition in which fingers or toes are much shorter than normal, sp. when fingers have only two joints.

'**brachydi′agonal,** n. (Of CRYSTALS) the shorter DIAGONAL; shorter LATERAL AXIS in ORTHORHOMBIC and TRICLINIC systems.

'**brachy(o)dont,** a. [Zoo.] (Of teeth) with short tops and long roots; having b. teeth, as man.

brachygnathia, n. Condition of having lower bone of mouth shorter than normal.

brachy-'urous, -'ural, aa. [Zoo.] Having small short ABDOMEN turned in under THORAX, by which it is completely covered, said of certain CRUSTACEAE.

'Brackett 'series. [Phys.] Group of INFRA-RED lines in H. SPECTRUM, whose frequencies are some number of times $\left(\dfrac{1}{4^2} - \dfrac{1}{n^2}\right)$, where $n = 5, 6, 7 \ldots$ etc.

bract, n. [Bot.] Leaf having flower or flower-branch coming from angle where it is joined to stem. [Zoo.] Flat leaf-like part on legs of some CRUSTACEA; HYDRO-PHYLLUM. **b. scale.** Small outer scale at base of seed scale in CONE. **'bracteal,** a. **'bracteate,** a. Having bb.

'bracteolate, a. (Of flowers) having bracteoles. **'bracteole,** n. A leaf, generally very small, on stem of flower. **'bracteose,** a. Having many bb.

'brady-. Slow.

brady'cardia, n. [Med.] Slow heart rhythm.

brady'seism-al, -ic, -ical, aa. To do with a slow motion of the outer part of the earth.

Bragg('s) Law. [Crystal.] FORMULA for working out conditions for the greatest REFLECTION of X-RAYS by a CRYSTAL, dependent on the WAVE-LENGTH of the rays, the distance between the planes of the crystal, and the angle between the X-rays and the crystal planes—used for getting knowledge of the structure of the crystal.

brain, n. [Zoo.] The chief GANGLIONIC mass of the CENTRAL NERVOUS SYSTEM, placed in the head, or, in lower animals, in the forward part of the body. **b. sand.** Small grains of Ca, NH₄ and Mg PHOSPHATES present in parts of the brain. **b. stem.** Part of brain joining it to SPINAL CORD.

brake, 1.n. [Mach.] Any sort of apparatus, forming part of a cart, automobile, train, etc. or of any sort of engine or machine, by which its motion may be slowed down or stopped, most commonly ending in a band or grip of some sort acting against the turning of a wheel. 2.v.t. Get (an engine, carriage, etc.) stopped or slowed in its motion by the use of a b. **b. horse-power.** [Eng.] The amount of HORSE-POWER which in fact comes into effect in the operation of an engine or MOTOR, as worked out from the force needed for stopping it by a b. acting on the DRIVING-SHAFT.

branch, n. [Bot.] A stem which is an outgrowth of the chief stem of a plant, or of some stem greater than itself. **b. gap.** An opening in the structure of a STELE where a b. trace goes out. **b. trace.** The VASCULAR material branching out from the STELE to go to the making of a b.

'branchia, n. [Zoo.] GILL. **'branchial,** a. **'branchial arch.** Any of the structures of bone or CARTILAGE supporting GILLS of fishes and AMPHIBIA. **branchial 'basket.** Structure supporting GILLS of CYCLO-STOMATA. **branchial cleft.** Any of the openings between branchial arches through which water taken in at the mouth goes out over GILLS. **branchial pouch.** Bag-like structure on branchial cleft in certain animals.

bran'chicolous, a. [Zoo.] Living as PARASITE on fish GILLS.

branchi'hyal, a., n. (To do with) one of the divisions making up a BRANCHIAL ARCH.

'branching 'ratio. [Phys.] In an ELEMENT having NUCLEAR ISOMERISM, the RATIO between the number of ATOMS undergoing DECAY by the loss of ALPHA PARTICLES and the number undergoing decay by the loss of BETA PARTICLES.

'Branchi'opoda, n.pl. [Zoo.] A SUB-CLASS of CRUSTACEA made up of small water-animals with a great number of flat, leaf-like feet, which are used for breathing as well as for swimming.

branchi'ostegite, n. [Zoo.] Part of SHELL of certain CRUSTACEAE forming GILL cover.

brand, n. [Bot.] FUNGUS producing burned look on leaves.

brasque, n. Paste made by mixing powdered coal with CLAY, sugar, etc., used for coating inside of pots in which substances are to be heated to a high degree.

brass, n. Metal made up of 60–90% Cu, the rest Zn, with sometimes small amounts of other metals.

Braun tube. [Phys.] The first sort of CATHODE RAY TUBE made, having a FLUORESCENT SCREEN at end to which rays come.

'braxy, n. Serious INFECTIONS disease of sheep caused by BACTERIA and attacking stomach and digestion pipes.

braze, v.t. SOLDER (metal) with a substance needing great heat to make soft, generally brass.

breadth, n. Measure of a thing from side to side.

'breakdown, n. [Elec.] Sudden overcoming of INSULATION by electric current when VOLTAGE becomes higher than a certain limit. **b. voltage.** VOLTAGE at or over which a b. takes place.

'breastbone, n. STERNUM.

breathed, a. [Phonet.] Said of sounds such as *f* and *s*, made without motion of VOCAL CORDS.

'breccia, n. [Geol.] ROCK formed chiefly of broken sharp-edged bits of earlier rocks fixed together as a solid mass.

breech, n. BUTTOCKS; short rough wool on b. and back legs of dogs, sheep, and other animals; part of gun at back end of BORE. **b. delivery.** [Med.] The coming of a baby from its mother's body b. first. **b. presen-'tation.** Position of baby in b. delivery.

breed, 1.v.i. and t. [Zoo.] Have young, get offspring produced, said sp. of animals in which this development takes place as the effect of the coming together of a male and a female; have, be producers of (offspring). [Biol.] (Of man) get (plants or animals) produced from others by giving them the right conditions for this purpose, for example making certain that POLLINATION takes place among a growth of desired plants, putting male and female animals of the desired sort and qualities together at the right time, etc. 2.n. A group of animals or plants which have come to have special qualities as the effect of selection by man in breeding, but which keep on handing down these qualities only so long as they breed only with one another, and so do not make a new natural division of the SPECIES. **'breeding,** a., n. Sp., the business of breeding plants or animals for the purpose of producing certain desired qualities or new forms by selection or CROSSING.

breed, v.i. [Phys.] (Of apparatus) make more NUCLEAR material than is used. **'breeder re'actor.** A NUCLEAR REACTOR in which breeding goes on.

'bregma, n. [Anat.] Meeting point of the CORONAL and SAGITTAL SUTURES in the head.

'braphic. a. [Biol.] To do with an early stage of growth.

brevi-. Short: **brevi'foliate,** a., **brevi'lingual,** a.

brevi'pennate, a. [Zoo.] Having short wings without power of flight.

'Brewster's law. Law that the ANGLE OF POLARIZATION of light by a substance is the angle whose tangent is equal to the REFRACTIVE INDEX of the substance.

'brightness, n. The quality of being bright, or the degree to which something is bright. [Psych.] (Of colours) LIGHTNESS. [Optics] (Of a light SOURCE) the LUMINOUS INTENSITY in any direction per unit of PROJECTED AREA, measured by the LAMBERT, the CANDELA, and the STILB per cm.^{2}

Bright's disease. Disease of KIDNEYS, marked by ALBUMEN being present in person's URINE.

'brilliance, 'brilliancy, nn. BRIGHTNESS.

'brimstone, n. Old name for S.

Brin's process. Process for making O by first producing BaO_2 by heating BaO in air, and then causing the BaO_2 to give off O by increased heating.

brine, n. Water having in it a great amount of a SALT, sp. NaCl.

Bri'nell apparatus. Apparatus used in Brinell test. **Bri'nell test.** Way of measuring how hard a metal is by size of the hollow made by a hard steel ball pushed

against it by a certain force. **Brinell 'number, Bri'nell 'hardness.** Outcome of Brinell test given by force in kilograms ÷ size of hollow in square millimetres.

bri'sance, n. Power of destruction of an EXPLOSIVE.

'bristle, n. [Biol.] A short hair or hair-like structure.

'British Ex'perimental Pile O. [Phys.] A great NUCLEAR REACTOR at Harwell, England.

'British 'Pharmaco'poeia. A list of medical substances with details of their use, printed by authority of the British government.

'British 'Thermal 'Unit. Amount of heat needed to make TEMPERATURE of one lb. of water higher by 1°F., =about 252 GRAM-CALORIES.

'brittle, a. (Of a substance, etc.) of such a structure as to be more readily broken than bent, giving way to force by separating before much or any change of form has taken place. **'-ness,** n.

broad, a. [Phonet.] Of VOWELS, OPEN.

broad 'ligament. [Anat.] One or other of the two bands going from sides of UTERUS to sides of PELVIS.

'Broca's area. [Anat.] The part of the brain controlling talking.

brochi'dodromous, bro'chidodrome, a. (Of leaves) having veins turning across themselves like the letter 'l' in writing.

'bromate, n. Substance having in it the group $-BO_3$.

bromide, n. Substance got by uniting one ELEMENT with Br.

'bromine, n. Chemical ELEMENT, at. no. 35, at. wt. 79·916, sign Br, a dark red liquid.

bronchi. See BRONCHUS.

'bronchia, n.pl. [Zoo.] The smaller BRONCHI.

bronchial, a. Of, to do with the BRONCHIA or BRONCHI. **b. tube.** BRONCHUS. **b. 'respi'ration.** [Med.] Breathing marked by BRONCHOPHONY.

bronchi'ectasis, n. [Med.] Expansion of one or more of the greater BRONCHI as effect of walls becoming less strong.

'bronchiole, n. A very small BRONCHUS.

bron'chitis, n. [Med.] INFLAMMATION of BRONCHI, causing cough.

'broncho-, BRONCHIAL (and . . .): **broncho-'pulmonary,** a. **broncho-'tracheal,** a.

bron'chophony, n. [Med.] Increased sound of voice normally coming through STETHOSCOPE when placed over a healthy BRONCHUS, which is a sign of lung disease when noted in other parts of chest.

'broncho-pneu'monia, n. [Med.] Form of PNEUMONIA limited to parts of LUNGS near to BRONCHI.

'bronchoscope, n. [Med.] A pipe-like instrument having a light and a looking-glass for looking into the BRONCHI.

bron'chotomy, n. [Med.] Operation of cutting into the TRACHEA.

'bronchus ('bronchi), n. [Zoo.] Any of the branches of the TRACHEA which take air to LUNGS, sp. one of the two chief branches.

'Bronson re'sistance. [Elec.] High RESISTANCE formed by gas in a vessel with a little RADIOACTIVE substance.

'brontograph, bron'tometer, nn. [Meteor.] Apparatus for recording facts in connection with THUNDERSTORMS.

bronze, n. Metal made up of 70-90% Cu, and the rest Sn; copper mixed with some other metal, for example, Al. **B. Age.** Early stage in history of man, about 3500-100 B.C., when b. was the metal chiefly used.

brood, n. [Zoo.] The offspring of one mother, sp. bird, produced at the same time. **b. bud.** [Bot.] BULBIL; SOREDIUM. **b. cell.** SPORE CELL of ALGAE. **b. 'chamber, b. pouch** .[Zoo.] Space or bag-like structure in the body of an animal in which eggs or young are housed and undergo development.

brown 'Algae [Bot.] PHACOPHYCEAE.

brown coal. LIGNITE.

'Brownian 'motion. Quick irregular motion kept up by very small bits of solid in smoke or in liquid, the effect of blows from MOLECULES of the liquid, etc.

'Bruehl re'ceiver. [Chem.] Air-tight vessel having in it a number of small vessels which may be turned into position to take liquid.

bruise, 1.n. [Med.] CONTUSION. 2.v.t. and i. Make a b. on, undergo bruising. **bruised,** a. **'bruising,**/n.

bruit, n. [Med.] Any sound produced inside the body as noted for medical purposes, sp. one which is a sign of disease.

'Brunner's glands. [Zoo.] Small RACEMOSE GLANDS in DUODENUM.

brush, n. Plate, rod and so on of metal or C forced by spring against metal ring etc., on electric machine, such as a MOTOR or DYNAMO, for purpose of taking current to or away from part in motion. **b. dis-'charge.** Electric DISCHARGE in form of a broken, feather-like light together with an 's-s-s' sound, less strong than that causing a spark.

bry'ology, b. That branch of Botany which has to do with the BRYOPHYTA.

Bryo'phyta, n.pl. [Bot.] A division of ARCHIGONIATAE, made up of MUSCI and HEPATICAE, small, freq. flat, plants, with no true roots or VASCULAR TISSUE and needing free water for their complete development, of which the small SPORE-producing forms are PARASITIC on the GAMETE-producing ones. **'bryophyte,** n. Any plant of the B.

Bryo'zoa, n.pl. [Zoo.] POLYZOA.

B.T.U. = BOARD OF TRADE UNIT.

B.Th.U. = BRITISH THERMAL UNIT.

'bubble, n. Ball of air or gas in liquid, or with thin skin of liquid round it. **'b. 'chamber,** [Phys.] An apparatus in which the way taken by a quickly-moving CHARGED PARTICLE is seen as a line of BUBBLES produced in a liquid (such as liquid PROPANE or, very importantly, liquid H) which is heated far past its normal boiling-point by the sudden taking off of very high PRESSURE —the bubbles being the effect of the loss to the liquid of ENERGY by the particle on its way through, causing increased heating at different points. These bubble-TRACKS may be lighted up and PHOTOGRAPHED, making a record. **b. 'sextant.** SEXTANT in which adjustment is made to edge of b. in level vessel of liquid, in place of to sky-line. **b. tube.** Shut glass pipe with the inside of the top curved, not quite full of ETHER so that a b. of gas is formed, used for testing if thing is level, measuring angle of slope and so on.

'bubo, n. [Med.] LYMPHATIC GLAND in condition of INFLAMMATION and SWELLING, sp. in GROIN. **bu'bonic,** a. **bubonic plague.** An EPIDEMIC disease of rats which is handed on to man, caused by a BACILLUS and marked by bb., causing death in great numbers (see PLAGUE).

'buccal, a. To do with inside of face and mouth. [Phonet.] ORAL.

'buccinator, n. Thin wide muscle at side of face.

'bucco-. BUCCAL (and . . .): -'labial, a., -'lingual, a., -'nasal, a., -pha'ringeal, a.

'Buchner 'funnel. [Chem.] FILTER FUNNEL having inside, before narrowing, a flat plate with holes in it, on which filter paper is put.

buck, n. [Zoo.] Name given to the male of certain animals of which the female is named the 'doe', sp. CERVIDAE.

'Buckley gauge. Instrument measuring very low gas PRESSURES.

bud, n. A stem or branch of a plant in its first stage of development as a small, freq. pointed, outgrowth formed of very young leaves rolled round a growth point; unopened leaf or flower; a b.-like outgrowth of certain plants and simple animals which undergoes development into a new plant or animal; any b.-like structure, as the TASTE BB. of the tongue. 2.v.i. Put out bb. **b. gap.** BRANCH GAP. **b. scale.** A simple form of leaf on outside of b. helping to keep it from becoming dry and from other damage. **b. trace.** BRANCH TRACE. **'budding,** n. Sp. the producing of offspring by budding as opp. simple division or a sex process.

'buffer, n. Elastic apparatus for cushioning the shock caused by two bodies coming together. [Chem.] Any substance having tendency to keep amount of H IONS the same after addition of an acid or BASE. **b. 'action.** Behaviour of a chemical b.

bulb, n. [Bot.] Resting stage of certain plants in the form of a great BUD under the earth, made up of a short, thick stem from which roots go down, with thick leaf bases storing food grouped one over the other all round it and forming a solid ball-like or CONE-like mass. [Zoo., Anat.] A round mass or part, sp. at end of another, for example, end of nerve to do with the sense of heat; (of hair) root; (of the SPINAL CORD) MEDULLA OBLONGATA; (of tooth) soft material in hollow middle part. [Elec.] ELECTRIC LIGHT BULB. -'aceous, a. '-ar, a. To do with the MEDULLA OGLONGATA. **bulb'iferous,** a. '-iform, '-ose, '-ous, '-y, aa.

'bulbil, n. A small BUD having a bulb-like structure, formed on stem of plant and able to undergo. development into new plant when taken off. [Anat.] Small hollow bulb.

'bulbus, n. [Anat.] Bulb. **b. a'ortae, b. ar'teriosus.** In some back-boned animals, an expansion of the AORTA near heart.

bulk 'modulus. [Phys.] In an ELASTIC substance with an equal PRESSURE over

all its SURFACE, the RATIO $\dfrac{pV}{v}$ where

p is the INTENSITY of the STRESS, V is the VOLUME of the body before pressure, and v is the change in volume produced by the stress.

bull, n. Male of certain animals, such as cow.

'bulla, n. [Med.] BLISTER. [Zoo.] A round, hollow, thin-walled outgrowth or expansion of a bone, sp. the TYMPANIC B. **'bullate,** a.

bullet, n. A small round or long mass of metal, gen. lead, for firing from a hand-gun.

bump, v.i. Be boiling in sudden bursts.

'bundle, n. Group of parallel nerves, rays and so on forming a band. [Bot.] FIBRO-VASCULAR B. **bundle of His.** B. of muscles going from upper to lower part of heart and controlling its rhythm.

'bunion, n. [Med.] SWELLING on first joint of great toe caused by INFLAMMATION of BURSA.

'bunodont, a. [Zoo.] Having CUSPS on top of back teeth.

'bunoid, a. [Zoo.] Formed like a low CONE with round top, said of points on top of back teeth.

buno'lophodont, a. (Of teeth) BUNODONT at edge and LOPHODONT in middle; having b. back teeth.

'bunose'lenodont, a. (Having back teeth) of which middle CUSPS are BUNOID and outer ones in form of new moon.

'Bunsen 'burner. Gas burner in form of

straight pipe with holes for letting in air at base, giving light blue flame of great heat. **'Bunsen cell.** Electric CELL with POSITIVE (+) plates of C in HNO_3 and NEGATIVE (−) of Zn in H_2SO_4. **Bunsen coeff'icient.** VOLUME of gas at normal TEMPERATURE and PRESSURE present in unit volume of liquid touching it.

Bunsen pho'tometer. Instrument for comparison of two lights, using paper waxed in one place to let light through, so that if lights are put at opposite sides of it they will be equal when the waxed place is no longer seen. **Bunsen valve.** Short rubber pipe stopped up at one end by glass rod and having a cut down the side opening so as to let out gas or liquid without letting air in.

'buoyancy, n. [Phys.] A body's loss of weight in a liquid or a gas, caused by the lifting force of the liquid or gas and equal to the weight of that measure of it whose place is taken by the body; a body's property, as the effect of a b., of resting completely or in part on the top of a liquid, or keeping up in a gas. **'buoyant,** a. Having the property of b.

bu'rette, n. Glass pipe marked with very small degrees, open at top and narrowing at other end, which may be shut with a STOPCOCK, used for measuring liquid or gas put into or let out of it.

bur(r), n. [Bot.] Seed-vessel covered with stiff, frequently hooked, hairs or sharp points.

'bursa, n. [Zoo.] Small bag or hollow, sp. one with sticky liquid in it placed between moving parts of body, for example between two bones, or between skin and bone, to keep them from rubbing. **'bursiform,** a. **'b. copu'latrix.** Bag-like sex-part in some female animals. **b. semi'nalis.** Bag having SPERMATOZOA in worms.

bur'sitis, n. [Med.] INFLAMMATION of a BURSA.

bus bar, n. A metal rod having a number of screws by which connection may be made to different electric machines or circuits.

bush, bushing, nn. A separate inner or outer coat of special material put in or over a machine-part to make rubbing or other damage less; part used for INSULATION of hole and so on through which a CONDUCTOR taking electric current has to go.

'bushel, n. English measure (*see* p. 545).

bu'tane, n. [Chem.] One or other of two ISOMERIC PARAFFIN gases, C_4H_{10}, of the METHANE SERIES.

butterfly valve. VALVE in form of:—1. a round plate turning about a rod across a pipe; 2. two half-round plates hinged to rod across pipe.

butt-joint, n. [Eng.] Join between two parts meeting edge-to-edge, frequently covered by a band of metal.

'buttock, n. [Zoo.] Cushion of muscle and fat forming back of top part of the back leg.

'buttress-root, n. Root other than chief root, sent out by plant, generally from stem or branch, and acting as a support.

'butyl, n. [Chem.] The OPEN-CHAIN ALKYL RADICAL C_4H_9, got from BUTANE.

bu'tyric 'acid. [Chem.] One or other of two ISOMERIC ACIDS ($C_3H_7CO_2H$), of which the NORMAL one is present in butter and other fats, when free being a thick liquid smelling like butter which, has gone bad (*see* p. 557). **bu'tyric,** a. To do with or, producing b. a., **bu'tyr-, bu'tyro-.** Butyric.

'bypass, n. A way, such as a small pipe, by which liquid, gas, electric current may go round some part in a system and back into the chief pipe, etc., again. **b. con-'denser.** CONDENSER put IN PARALLEL with some part of electric system, for letting through HIGH-FREQUENCY current.

'by-product, n. Material or effect produced by any process in addition to that which is its chief purpose.

'bysmalith, n. [Geol.] An INTRUSION with a FAULT all round it and a round top pushing up earth over it.

'byssus, n. Brush-like group of long strong threads on foot of certain BIVALVE MOLLUSCA, by which animal gets itself fixed to stone, etc. **'byssal,** a. **byss'ifer-ous,** a.

C, Sign for CARBON.
C=CENTIGRADE or Celsius.
C, Sign for: CONCENTRATION; SPECIFIC HEAT of gases at fixed VOLUME (C_v) and at fixed PRESSURE (C_p).
c, Sign for VELOCITY of light in a VACUUM.
Ca, Sign for CALCIUM.

'cable, n. [Elec.] Number of wires twisted together and covered with cloth, rubber, etc., frequently with an outside cover of steel or lead, for transporting electric current.

ca'chexia, n. [Med.] The condition seen in persons having CANCER, marked by a great loss of power, ANAEMIA, wasting away, and a grey colour of the skin.

'cacodyl, n. [Chem.] A liquid, $As_2(C_4)_4$, with no colour and a most disgusting

smell, boiling at 170°C—a substance from which are produced a number of others important in industry and sp. in the making of rubber.

Cac'taceae, n.pl. [Bot.] A FAMILY of flowering plants, chiefly seen in America, designed for living in very dry, warm places, having thick, water-storing stems, and leaf-like branches with SCALES or sharp points in place of leaves.

ca'cuminal, a. [Phonet.] Said of sounds made with point of tongue turned up and back so that underside of point is touching roof of mouth.

ca'daver, n. [Med.] A dead body, sp. one for use in medical school. **ca'daver-ic, -ous,** aa.

'cadmium, n. Chemical ELEMENT. at. no. 48, at. wt. 112·41, sign Cd, a white metal. **c. red line.** The red part of the light given out by Cd gas, used as a STANDARD for the WAVE-LENGTH of light.

ca'ducous, a. [Bot.] (Of parts) falling off the plant early, as some SEPALS at the opening of the flower.

'caecal, a. [Zoo.] To do with the CAECUM.

'caec(o), [Zoo.] CAECAL (and . . .); the CAECUM: **cae'costomy,** n.

'caecum (caeca), n. [Zoo.] Bag-like part at the start of the LARGE INTESTINE, where the SMALL INTESTINE goes into it.

cae'sar-ean(-ian) ope'ration or 'section. [Med.] Operation of cutting woman open to get baby out living, when normal birth is not possible.

'c(a)esium, n. Chemical ELEMENT, at. no. 55, at. wt. 132·91, sign Cs, a soft, silver-white alkali metal—the most ELECTRO-POSITIVE of the elements, giving very ready and strong reactions.

'caespitose, a. [Bot.] Having stems coming from root in groups, as in some sorts of grass.

'caffeine, n. [Chem.] An ALKALOID, $C_8H_{10}N_4O_2$, present in certain plants, sp. in coffee and tea, which has a strong STIMULATING effect on the heart and the producing of URINE, and is used medically.

Caino'zoic, Caeno'zoic, aa., nn. [Geol.] (To do with, being) the latest division in the earth's history, taking in the TERTIARY and the QUATERNARY ERAS (*see* p. 558).

'cairngorm, n. [Mineral.] A natural form of SiO_2, yellow or brown in colour, the more beautifully marked examples of which are sometimes used as jewel-stones.

'caisson, n. [Eng.] Strong, water-tight, box-like structure used in building under-water structures such as the supporting parts of bridges. [Zoo.] Group of muscle FIBRES in earthworm. **c. disease.** [Med.] A disease marked by sharp pains in the nerves, caused by coming over-suddenly from a place where air is COMPRESSED, such as a c., to normal air-PRESSURE, as the effect of which BUBBLES of N are formed in the blood.

cake, v.i. [Chem.] (Of powdered material) become crushed together, united into a solid mass.

calam'iferous, a. [Bot.] Having a hollow stem.

calamine, n. [Mineral.] Natural $ZnSi_2O_7$ $(OH)_2H_2O$ (*hydrous zinc silicate*), or, in Britain, natural $ZnCO_3$ (*zinc carbonate*), used medically as an EMOLLIENT for insect bites and other skin troubles.

cal'caneum, n. [Zoo.] In man and higher back-boned animals, the great bone of the back of the foot, a development of the FIBULARE of lower animals; in birds, an outgrowth of the back upper part of the TARSOMETATARSUS. **cal'caneal,** a. **cal'caneo-.**

'calcar, n. [Bot.] Hollow pointed part at lower end of PETAL or SEPAL. [Zoo.] Any of different pointed outgrowths on legs or wings of animals. **c. 'avis.** [Zoo.] A curved growth on the middle wall of the back part of the two side VENTRICLES of the brain. **'calcarine, cal'cariform,** aa.

cal'careous, a. Made of, having in it, chalk or other COMPOUND of Ca. [Bot.] Having growth on chalk land. **c. 'tufa.** [Geol.] TRAVERTINE.

'calcari'uria, n. [Med.] Condition in which there is more than normal amount of Ca salts in URINE.

'calci-. Of, in relation to, Ca, $CaCO_3$, or other Ca SALTS: **cal'ciferous,** a.

'calcicole, cal'cicolous, a. [Bot.] Living on land with much $CaCO_3$ in it.

cal'ciferol, n. [Biochem.] VITAMIN D_2, the part of the vitamin D complex produced by the effect of sunlight on ERGOSTEROL.

'calcifuge, n. [Bot.] Plant which does not do well on land having in it $CaCO_3$.

'calcify, v.i. and t. Sp. [Biol.] Of plant or animal TISSUES, become or make become hard by producing or taking in Ca SALTS. **calcifi'cation,** n.

cal'cine, v.t. [Chem., Metal.] Make substance into powder or get it free from water or gas, by long heating to a high enough degree. **cal'cinatory,** a. **'calcined,** a. **'calciner,** n. Apparatus for calcination. **calci'nation,** n.

cal'cino, n. Disease of SILKWORMS caused by BACTERIA.

'calcite, n. [Mineral.] Natural CRYSTALLINE $CaCO_3$, widely present in the earth in a number of common forms, for example chalk.

'calcium, n. Chemical ELEMENT, at. no. 20, at. wt. 40·08, sign Ca, a silver-white metal.

'calculate, 1.v.t. Get (a value, time, etc.) worked out by arithmetic, or, more loosely, by reasoning. 2.v.i. Do calculat-

ing. **'calculable,** a. Which may be got by calculation, and so (of effects, etc.) of which one may be certain before they take place. **'calculated,** a. Sp. designed (*to* do something). **calcu'lation,** n. The act of calculating; the train of arithmetic or reasoning used in calculating.

'calculin, n. [Biochem.] Very small grains present in DUODENAL MUCUS, possibly a form of CHOLESTEROL.

'calculus, n. [Med.] Small, hard, stone-like mass of some MINERAL formed in some part of the body, sp. in BILE and URINE. **calculous,** a.

'calculus, [Maths.] A branch of Mathematics having to do with the working out of the rate of change of a FUNCTION in relation to the VARIABLE on which it is dependent (**differential c.**), and with the INVERSE process (**integral c.**)

'Calder Hall, [Phys.] The first great NUCLEAR POWER station on the earth, in Cumberland, England, with a nuclear REACTOR having U metal in Mg. vessels and using CO_2 gas as COOLANT and GRAPHITE as MODERATOR, giving 92 million watts of power from two reactors.

'caldera, n. [Geol.] A CRATER of great size produced sometimes by very violent ERUPTIONS, sometimes by the falling in of the middle part of the VOLCANO.

'calendar, n. [Astron., etc.] Any of the systems of division of time, of which the day is the unit, used by man for everyday purposes, gen. based on the time taken for the earth to go round the sun, but making some adjustment in this to make the arithmetic simpler. (*See* GREGORIAN c., JULIAN c.) **c. month.** A month as fixed for c. purposes, any of the named divisions, gen. 12, of a c. year. **c. year.** A year as fixed for c. purposes, being in present-day Western use a space of 365 days increased every fourth year to 366 days.

'calender, n. Machine, generally with rollers, for making paper, cloth, etc., into thin regular sheets or smoothing it.

calf (calves) n. [Zoo.] A young one of certain animals, sp. cow. **c. ice.** [Geol.] Small masses of ice in sea, etc., broken off from an ICEBERG or from a GLACIER at the edge of the land.

calf (calves), n. [Zoo.] The rounded back part of man's leg between the knee and the foot.

'calibrate, v.t. Get the measure of, or make an adjustment in, the CALIBRE of (a pipe, etc.) from point to point, or the calibration of (an instrument). **'calibrated,** a. (Of an instrument) marked with a scale, sp. with a true scale based on a process of calibration. **'calibration,** n. Sp. the process of making the calibration of an instrument true, by some sort of testing or by comparison from point to point with a very true calibrated instrument of the same sort, used for this purpose; the scale of degrees on an instrument used for measuring certain values. **'calibrator,** n. Instrument for measuring the CALIBRE of a pipe, sp. [Med.] of the URETHRA.

'calibre, 'caliber, nn. The DIAMETER of a round body or hole, sp. of the inside of a pipe.

ca'liche, n. [Mineral.] Natural $NaNO_3$ mixed with from 50% to 80% earth.

cali'fornium, n. Chemical ELEMENT, at. no. 98, a TRANSURANIC element.

'caline, n. [Bot.] One sort of plant HORMONE.

'Callendar-'Griffiths bridge, [Elec.] Form of WHEATSTONE BRIDGE used with RESISTANCE THERMOMETER

'cal(l)ipers, n.pl. Sorts of instrument formed of two legs, sometimes curved and freq. fixed together in a scissors-like way by a screw or spring, used for measuring how thick, wide, long, something is.

'callophane, n. [Phys.] Instrument for measuring FLUORESCENCE, using white light.

cal'losal, a. [Anat.] To do with the CORPUS CALLOSUM. **c. convo'lution.** Fold of the brain curving round CORPUS CALLOSUM. **c. 'fissure.** Deep cut division between c. convolution and CORPUS CALLOSUM.

'callose, 1.n. [Bot.] A hard CARBOHYDRATE present in CALLUS PLATES and certain other CALLOSITIES in plants. 2.a. CALLOUS.

call'osity, n. [Biol., Med.] Place where the outer skin of a plant or animal has become thick and hard as the effect of rubbing, etc.

'callous, a. [Biol.] (Of skin or BARK) having become thick and hard, horn-like.

'callus, n. [Bot.] Soft, thick PARENCHYMA formed over or round a damaged part of a plant; c. plate. [Med.] CALLOSITY; the substance forming the first stage in the development of new bone joining a broken bone. **c. plate.** [Bot.] A cover of CALLOSE formed over a SIEVE-PLATE and keeping it from working.

'calomel, n. [Chem., Med.] MERCURIOUS CHLORIDE (Hg_2Cl_2), a white or yellow-white powder used for producing CORROSIVE SUBLIMATE and medically as an APERIENT.

calor'escence, n. [Phys.] The taking in of RADIATIONS by a body and their changing by it into radiations of shorter WAVELENGTH which are then given out, seen sp. in the giving out of light by a body after being heated by INFRA-RED rays. **'calor'escent,** a.

ca'loric, n. [Phys.] Name given to heat in older physical theory, when it was taken to be a substance.

'calorie, n. [Phys.] Unit of amount of heat, equal to that taken up by 1 gm. of water

in going from 15° to 16°C (the *small c.* or *gram-c.*), or to that taken up by one gm. of water in going from 0°C to 100°C (the *rational c.* or *centuple c.*); $\frac{1}{100}$ of a rational c. (the *mean c.*). **'Calorie,** n. 1000 small cc., named the *kilogram c.*, the *large c.*, or the *kilocalorie*, and used in measuring the ENERGY-producing value of food.

calo'rific, a. Producing heat; to do with heat. **c.'value.** Amount of heat produced by unit weight of a burning substance.

ca'lorifier, n. Apparatus for heating a liquid by sending steam through pipes in the liquid.

calor'imetry, n. The measuring of amounts of heat, **calor'imeter,** n. Any apparatus used for c., gen. measuring an amount of heat by its effect in increasing the TEMPERATURE of a given amount of water or other liquid, or in causing the MELTING of ice (**ice calorimeter**), and so on.

'calorize, v.t. [Metal.] Keep a metal, sp. iron or steel, from damage by OXIDATION by coating it with Al and heating it to from 800°C to 1000°C. **'calo'riser, calor-isator,** nn.

'calutron, n. [Phys.-Chem.] Short name for 'California University CYCLOTRON', the apparatus used for separating URANIUM 235 and uranium 238 from one another.

calx, n. Readily-broken material produced by CALCINATION or burning of a metal or MINERAL.

calyci-. CALYX-: **caly'ciferous,** a., **ca'lyci-form,** a.

calyci'flor-al, -ate, -ous, aa. [Bot.] Having STAMENS and PETALS united to the CALYX.

'calycine, a. [Bot.] To do with the CALYX.

'calycle, ca'lyculus, nn. [Bot.] Ring of small leaves like an outer CALYX round base of calyx. [Zoo.] Any small cup-like structure, sp. that housing a CORAL POLYP. **'calycled,** a. **ca'licular, ca'liculate,** aa.

ca'lypter (ca'lypteres), n. [Zoo.] In two-winged flies, a thin structure 'covering base of wing. **ca'lyptrate,** a.

Ca'liptoblas'tea, n.pl.[Zoo.] LEPTOMEDUSAE. **ca'lypto'blastic,** a.

ca'lyptra, n. [Bot.] Cover over SPORE vessel in some BRYOPHYTA; ROOT CAP.

ca'lyptrogen, n. [Bot.] Group of CELLS at end of root from which the ROOT CAP is formed.

ca'lyptron, n. CALYPTER.

'calyx (calyces), n. [Bot.] The outer ring of flower-parts, made up of SEPALS. [Zoo.] A cup-like part, sp.:--the cup-like part of the URETER where it is joined to the KIDNEY; in some HYDROZOA, the THECA; in CRINOIDEA, the body without the arms and stem. **'calycoid,** a.

cam, n. [Mach.] A PROJECTION on a wheel or a turning SHAFT so formed as to give some desired straight-line motion to another part of the machine. **'-shaft,** n.

SHAFT on which a c. is fixed or of which it is a part.

'cambium, n. [Bot.] Soft TISSUE by which new tissue is produced in trees and tree-like plants, forming a thin coat between the XYLEM and the PHLOEM of stems, branches and roots and making additions to these two tissues. 'cambiform, a.

'Cambrian, a., n. (To do with, formed in) the first PERIOD of the PALAEZOIC (*see* p. 595).

'camera, n. The apparatus used for PHOTO-GRAPHY, of which the chief parts are a LENS, for FOCUSING the light-rays from the thing to be pictured onto the light-SENSITIVE substance, a CARRIER for the plate or FILM coated with this, a light-tight BELLOWS to keep out other light, and a SHUTTER covering the lens when not in use and lifting to let the light in when a picture is being taken.

camera 'lucida. Apparatus for putting on-to MICROSCOPE, etc. by which things looked at through the instrument are seen at the same time in the form of flat pictures on paper so that they may be outlined on it.

'camera ob'scura. [Optics] A dark room in which a picture of things outside it is sent onto a SCREEN through a small opening, gen. having in it a long-FOCUS CONVEX LENS.

cam'paniform, cam'panulate, aa. [Zoo., Bot.] Bell-like or DOME-like in form.

'camphene, n. [Chem.] A CAMPHOR-like TERPENE, $C_{10}H_{16}$, present in a number of ESSENTIAL OILS.

'camphor, n. [Chem.] $C_{10}H_{16}O$, a white TRANSLUCENT substance with a special smell, got naturally from a tree of Japan, used medically and in the making of CELLULOID, etc.

campy'lotrop-al, -ous, aa. [Bot.] (Of an OVULE) having NUCELLUS and its cover so curved that the top is near the base.

'Canada 'balsam, 'Canada 'turpentine. A yellow to green sweet-smelling liquid got from a tree, *Abies balsamea*, of the CONIFERAE, becoming glass-like when solid, and used as an ADHESIVE for optical instruments (because its RE-FRACTIVE INDEX is almost the same as that of the glass generally used for such things) and in making LACQUERS and VARNISHES.

ca'nal, n. [Biol.] A pipe-like vessel or space for storing or transporting liquid, making connection between parts, etc.; narrow opening in edge of SHELL through which animal puts out a breathing-pipe. c. cell. [Bot.] Any of the line of CELLS down the middle of an ARCHEGONIUM, of which the lowest undergoes division into two parts from the greater of which the egg comes, the rest forming the inner part of the neck. c. rays. [Phys.] POSITIVE

RAYS. '-iform, a. 'canalize, v.t. Make a c. or other way through for (a liquid, etc.), sp. [Med.] get wound drained in this way. 'canaliz'ation, n. Sp. [Med.] the development of new cc. to let liquid through, for example, in a mass of half-solid blood stopping up a blood-vessel.

cana'liculus, n. [Zoo.] Very small CANAL, for example, one of those present in bone. cana'licular, a. cana'licular apparatus. GOLGI BODIES cana'liculated, a.

'cancer, n. [Med.] CARCINOMA, '-ous, 'cancroid, aa.

'Cancer, n. [Astron.] The 4th SIGN OF THE ZODIAC. *See* TROPIC.

'cancrum 'oris. [Med.] NOMA.

can'dela, n. [Optics] The unit of LUMINOUS INTENSITY taken up internationally in 1946 to take the place of the INTER-NATIONAL CANDLE, based on the luminous intensity of a BLACK BODY at the FREEZ-ING-POINT of Pt as fixed at 60 cd./cm^2.

cande'lilla wax. [Chem.] A natural hard, yellow or brown wax, becoming liquid at 67–68°C, produced as a coating on certain Mexican SHRUBS and used in making polishes for shoes, floors, etc.

'candle, n. [Optics] INTERNATIONAL CANDLE. 'c.-power, n. LUMINOUS INTENSITY meas-ured in cc. or CANDELAS.

ca'nescent, a. [Bot.] Having a grey-white look because covered with very short hairs.

cane sugar. [Chem.] SUCROSE.

'canine, a. [Zoo.] Of, to do with dogs; to do with, like, c. tooth. c. tooth. Pointed tooth between upper and lower front teeth and side teeth at left and right, in man the third from the middle.

'canker, n. [Bot.] Name of a number of diseases of trees caused by FUNGI. [Vet.] Name given to certain INFLAMMATIONS, ABSCESSES etc., in animals, such as horses, dogs, birds, for example, a form of CHRONIC ECZEMA in a dog's ear.

'cannel coal. Sort of readily-broken coal burning with a bright flame, used for gas-making.

'cannon bone. [Zoo.] Long bone of leg going from the knee or HOCK JOINT to the FETLOCK in UNGULATA; the TARSOMETA-TARSUS in birds.

'cannula, n. [Med.] A pipe of metal, glass, rubber, etc., gen. used with a TROCAR, for putting into a part of the body to send liquid in or get it drained away.

cantilever, n. A long, generally metal, support fixed at one end and free at the other. c. bridge. Bridge resting on cc. arching from upright supports at sides and meeting in middle.

'caoutchouc, n. Unworked rubber.

cap, n. Name given to a number of top parts or covers in different sciences, sp.:—
[Bot.] PILEUS; CALYPTRA. [Zoo.] The top

part of a bird's head from the root of the BEAK in front to the start of the neck at the back. [Meteor.] The cover of cloud resting on the top of a mountain.

ca'pacitance, n. [Elec.] That property of a body or apparatus which is measured by the amount of ELECTRICITY needed for increasing its POTENTIAL by 1 unit. **c. coef'ficient.** C. of one CONDUCTOR of a system, when all others are at POTENTIAL 0.

ca'pacitor, n. [Elec.] CONDENSER.

ca'pacity, n. [Phys.] Measure of the amount of space in a vessel, or shut in by walls; amount of something which a vessel, a substance, a machine and so on is able to take in in given conditions; CAPACITANCE; power output of an electric apparatus, or amount of electric current which may be taken from it.

cap cell. [Bot.] CELL on neck of ARCHE-GONIUM.

ca'pillary, 1.a. [Phys., Biol.] (Of vessels) thin and narrow, hair-like; to do with c. tubes or vessels, or with capillarity. 2.n. [Zoo.] any small thin-walled vessel forming part of network in different parts of the body, sp. any of the hair-like *blood cc.* running through the TISSUES and making connections between the smallest branches of the ARTERIES and those of the VEINS, and through the walls of which O and other substances go from the blood to the tissues and CO_2 etc., from the tissues to the blood. **c. ac'tivity.** [Chem.] SURFACE ACTIVITY. **c. elec'trometer.** [Elec.] Instrument for seeing if very small electric currents are present from the motion of the level of Hg in a c. tube. **c. tube.** Very narrow pipe. **c. zone** [Geol.] The division of the upper earth between the AIR-DRY ZONE and the SATURATED ZONE, where water is kept by capillarity in the natural c. tubes of earth and ROCK substance.

capil'larity, n. [Phys.] The effects which take place where a body of liquid is touching a solid, caused by the attraction of the MOLECULES of the solid for the molecules on the face of the liquid, seen specially in c. tubes or any substance made up of hollow threads, such as rough paper or the stems of plants, where the liquid goes up in the pipes or threads.

'capillator, n. [Chem.] Apparatus for measuring the pH-VALUE by comparison of colours of liquids in thin glass pipes.

capi'tatum, n. [Zoo.] The greatest bone of the WRIST.

ca'pitulum, n. [Anat., Zoo.] Expansion at end of any part (such as feeler, hair); round outgrowth at end of bone, going into hollow in another bone. [Bot.] A RACEMOSE flower-group in which the separate SESSILE flowers are massed together on a round expansion at the end of a SCAPE, with a ring of BRACTS round the mass, which has the look of one flower (*see* picture p. 199).

'capon, n. Male fowl with sex-parts taken away, used in testing sex HORMONES.

'capric 'acid. [Chem.] A FATTY ACID, $C_9H_{19}CO_2H$, present in butter and some oils.

'Capricorn, Capri'cornus, nn. [Astron.] The 11th SIGN OF THE ZODIAC. (*See* TROPIC.)

cap'roic acid. [Chem.] A FATTY ACID present in butter etc. with CAPRIC ACID, $C_5H_{11}CO_2H$ (*see* p. 557).

'capsule, n. [Bot.] Any shut, box-like vessel in which are produced SPORES, sp. the spore-vessel of BRYOPHYTA; in flowering-plants, a dry, DEHISCENT fruit, gen. with a great number of seeds, formed from two or more united CARPELS. [Zoo.] A bag-like or box-like cover for some part, for example, the skin round a VISCUS. [Med.] A small hollow ball or pipe-like structure of some substance such as GELATIN which dissolves in the stomach, inside which bitter, etc., medical substances are put so that they may be taken without disgust. [Astronautics] Vessel having in it instruments for observation, animals, or men, fired into outer space by a ROCKET. **'capsular,** a.

capsular 'ligament. [Zoo.] A bag-like structure of LIGAMENT having in it SYNOVIAL FLUID, completely covering a JOINT between moving bones and fixed to the bones themselves.

'capture, n. The act of taking something to itself, making it a part of itself, as the c. of an ELECTRON from one ATOM by another.

'captive ba'lloon. [Meteor. etc.] A BALLOON fixed to a line so that it may be pulled back when desired.

'caput (capita), n. [Zoo.] Head-like end, or round outgrowth at end, of a part, as bone, muscle.

'caramel, n. [Chem.] The brown, sticky, chemically complex substance, hard and readily broken when cold, formed when common sugar is heated to a higher degree than that at which it becomes liquid, used in cooking for its taste and colour and as a backing for camera plates to overcome HALATION.

'carapace, n. [Zoo.] Hard cover of horn or CHITIN over back of certain animals, as CRUSTACEA.

'carat, n. A unit of weight for jewel stones, fixed internationally in 1932 at 200 mg.; a unit for measuring the degree to which gold is mixed with other metals, completely unmixed gold being fixed at 24 cc.

car'bamic 'acid. [Chem.] An acid, $NH_2.CO.OH$, which has never been got free but of which there are SALTS and ESTERS.

'carbamide, n. [Chem.] UREA.
'carbide, n. [Chem.] Any substance formed of C united with one other ELEMENT.
'carbinol, n. [Chem.] METHYL ALCOHOL, $CH_3.OH$.
'carbo-, CHARCOAL-, CARBON- (C).
carbo'cyclic, a. [Chem.] (Of ORGANIC COMPOUNDS) having a RING structure formed of C ATOMS only.
carbo'hydrate, n. [Chem.] Any of a great group of substances such as are produced in all green plants by PHOTOSYNTHESIS (e.g. sugar, STARCH, CELLULOSE), having the general form $(CH_2O)_x$, which in food are responsible for producing ENERGY.
car'bolic 'acid. [Chem.] PHENOL, C_6H_5OH, with a little water.
'carbon, n. Chemical ELEMENT, at. no. 6, at. wt. 12·01, sign C, a non-metal taking a number of different forms, necessary to all living things and forming part of all living substance, present naturally in the earth as GRAPHITE and DIAMOND and making up the chief part of coal. [Elec.] Stick of hard c. used in ARC-LAMP. **c. black.** C in the form of a soft powder produced by incompletely burning HYDROCARBONS such as MINERAL OILS, and by a gas flame when it comes up against metal, and used in making rubber. **c. brush** [Elec.] See BRUSH. **c. di'oxide.** A gas, CO_2, with no colour and little smell, present in the air, from which it is taken by plants and used in making CARBOHYDRATES, and which is given off by animals in the process of breathing, and produced by the OXIDATION of C. compounds, for example, in the burning of coal and in FERMENTATION. **c. ('filament) lamp.** Electric bulb in which the light-giving part is a thin wire of C. **c. mon'oxide.** A poison gas with no colour and little smell and burning with a bright blue flame, formed when C is heated without much air, present in coal gas etc. **c. steel.** [Metal.] A specially strong hard steel which gets its quality from the fact that it is made up almost completely of iron and C, other substances being present only in small amounts. **c. 'tetra'chloride.** [Chem.] A liquid (CCl_4) with no colour and a strong, somewhat sweet smell, which does not take fire, used as a cleaner for clothing etc. and for putting out fires. **'-'aceous,** a. [Chem.] (Of a substance) having in it natural C or some substance, sp. some animal or plant substance, formed of C. [Geol.] (Of ROCKS) made up chiefly of C produced from plant material, as coal, **car'bonic,** a. **carbonic acid.** H_2CO_3, a not very strong acid formed when c. dioxide goes into SOLUTION in water. **carbonic acid gas.** C. dioxide.

carbo'nado, n. [Mineral.] A black, very hard form of DIAMOND, used in industry for cutting.
'carbonate, n. [Chem.] A SALT or ESTER of CARBONIC ACID, i.e. substance having in it the group $-CO_3$.
carbonate, v.t. and i. [Chem.] (Make) become changed into a CARBONATE by reaction with H_2CO_3 or CO_2; get (water or other liquid) mixed with CO_2. **'carbonated,** a. **carbo'nation,** n.
carbo'niferous, 1.a. Producing or having in it C or coal. **Carbo'niferous,** a., n. [Geol.] (To do with) the last PERIOD but one of the PALAEOZOIC, in which most coal-beds were formed (see p. 559).
'carbonize, v.t. [Chem.] Get (substance) broken up into C and other substances, by heating or burning, or chemical reaction, **'carbonized,** a. **'carboni'zation,** n.
carbo'nometer, n. [Med.] Apparatus measuring amount of CO_2 in blood.
'carbonyl, n. [Chem.] Any of the substances formed by uniting certain metals with CO, such as nickel c., $(Ni(CO)_4)$. **c. group.** The DIVALENT group CO.
carbo'rundum, n. Trade name for SILICON CARBIDE (SiC_2), a very hard substance used for coating the inside of FURNACES, etc., and for GRINDING and polishing metals.
car'boxyl(ic), aa. [Chem.] Having in it the acid group $-COOH$.
'carbuncle, n. [Mineral.] Dark red form of iron aluminium SILICATE, valued as a jewel stone. [Med.] An ABSCESS in the TISSUE under the skin, freq. with more than one opening to the outside, causing great pain and sometimes serious effects on the system, caused by a STAPHYLOCOCCUS.
'carburet-ter, -(t)or, n. [Engin.] Apparatus for getting liquid FUEL mixed with air as it is taken into automobile or other like engine.
carce'rulus, n. [Bot.] A fruit parting when ready into a number of one-seeded divisions (see picture p. 158).
'carcino'genesis, n. [Med.] The development of CARCINOMA. **'carcinoge'netic,** a.
carci'noma (carcinomata), n. [Med.] A MALIGNANT TUMOUR in which the diseased growth is of EPITHELIAL CELLS, for example, in the skin of the INTESTINE; the diseased condition caused by such growths. **'carcino-.**
-cardia, n. [Med., Zoo.] Heart, condition of the heart.
'cardiac, a. Of, to do with, near the heart; at the top part of the stomach. **c. 'impulse.** Force of blow of heart on chest wall. **c. muscle.** The special sort of muscle substance, marked by a network of STRIAE, forming the walls of the heart in

back-boned animals. **c. vein.** Any of the blood-vessels taking the blood back from the c. muscle into the heart.

'**cardinal**, a. Chief, most important. [Zoo.] To do with a CARDO. **c. number.** A number such as 1, 2, 3, etc., used in giving the number of things, as opp. a number such as 'first' or 'second' used in giving their order. **c. points of the 'compass.** [Astron.] North, south, east, and west. **c. points of the ec'liptic.** [Astron.] The two EQUINOC-TIAL and two SOLSTITIAL points. **c. sinus** or **vein.** [Zoo.] Any of four blood-vessels parallel to the backbone of an EMBRYO. **c. 'vowels.** [Phonet.] 16 fixed VOWEL-sounds by comparison with which the vowel-sounds of different languages may be given an account of.

'**cardi(o)-.** [Zoo., Med.] Of, to do with, the heart; '**cardiocen'tesis**, n., **cardi'ology**, n.

cardiogram, n. [Med.] Record made by a CARDIOGRAPH.

'**cardiograph**, n. [Med.] Instrument which makes records on paper of the rhythms of the heart. **cardio'graphic**, a.

cardi'ology, n. [Med.] The science of the heart. **cardio'logical**, a. **cardi'ologist**, n.

cardi'ometer. n. [Med.] Instrument for measuring the size of the heart or the force of its motion. **cardio'metric**, a. **cardi'ometry**, n.

'**cardioscope**, n. [Med.] Instrument for observation of inside of heart.

'**cardo**, n. [Zoo.] HINGE at base of mouth-parts of insects; HINGE between two parts of SHELL.

Car'duceae, n.pl. [Bot.] A great and important FAMILY of seed-plants of the group COMPOSITAE, marked by having flowers which are TUBULAR or tubular and LIGULATE but not ligulate only.

'**Carey 'Foster bridge.** [Elec.] Form of WHEATSTONE BRIDGE for comparison of two almost equal RESISTANCES.

'**caries**, n. [Med.] Disease of bone substance and teeth in which they become soft and go bad. '**carious**, a. **cari'osity**, '**carious-ness**, nn.

ca'rina, n. [Zoo.] Sharp-edged outgrowth on certain bones, for example, the STERNUM of a bird; middle plate on back of some CRUSTACEAE. [Bot.] Boat-like part of certain flowers made up of two PETALS united; sharp-edged line down middle of certain grasses. **ca'rinal**, a. '**carinate**, a. **ca'riniform**, a.

car'nassial, a., n. [Zoo.] (To do with) great cutting tooth, longer than others, of which there are generally four, one top tooth and one lower tooth at the right side and the same at the left, in animals using other animals as food.

car'nelian, n. [Mineral.] A red, TRANSLUCENT form of SiO_2, valued as a jewel stone.

Car'nivora, n.pl. [Zoo.]. An ORDER of MAM-MALS which take meat for food, having teeth formed for cutting and pulling to bits. '**carnivore**, n. One of the C. **car-'nivorous**, a.

'**Carnot 'cycle.** [Phys.] The four stages in the theory of operation of a heat engine which it goes through over and over:—expansion at unchanging TEMPERATURE, expansion without heat being taken in or given out, COMPRESSION at unchanging temperature and compression without heat intake or outgo. **Carnot 'theorems.** [Phys.] (1) No heat-engine working between two TEMPERATURES has a greater EFFICIENCY than a REVERSIBLE HEAT-ENGINE working between these temperatures. (2) The efficiency of a reversible heat-engine working between two temperatures is not dependent on the form of engine or sort of working substance used but only on the temperatures.

'**carnotite**, n. [Mineral.] A VANADATE of U and K from which Ra is got, present in Colorado as a yellow powder or loose mass, gen. mixed with SANDSTONE.

'**carotene**, '**carotin**, nn. [Chem., Biochem.] Any of a group of orange or light red CRYSTALLINE HYDROCARBONS, $C_{40}H_{56}$, present in and giving their colour to certain plants and certain natural oils and fats, producing VITAMINE A when used as food.

ca'rotid, a., n. [Zoo.] (Of, near, or being) one or other of the two great ARTERIES taking blood to the head. **c. 'reflex.** [Med.] Change to slower heart-rate when PRESSURE in a c. is increased.

ca'rotinoid, 1.n. [Biochem.] Any of a group of orange, red, or yellow colouring-substances present in plants and the fat of animals and of like structure to CARO-TENE, for example, carotene itself and XANTHOPHYLL. 2.a. Of, like, the cc. **c. 'pigment.**

-**carp**, n. [Bot.] Fruit.

'**carpal**, 1.n. [Zoo.] Any of the bones (in man, 8) forming the CARPUS. 2.a. Of, to do with, the CARPUS or a c.

'**carpel**, n. [Bot.] The complete structure of OVARY, STYLE, and STIGMA forming the GYNAECIUM, or one of the like units of the gynaecium, of a flower (see p. 151). **car'pellary**, a.

'**carpo-.** [Bot.] Fruit-. [Zoo.] CARPAL.

carpo'gonium (carpogonia), n. [Bot.] In RHODOPHYCEAE, the bottle-like lower part of the female sex-part by which the CYSTOCARP is produced after FERTILIZA-TION: an ASCOGONIUM.

carpo'meta'carpus, n. [Zoo.] The united DISTAL, CARPAL and METACARPAL bones of birds, or the part of the wing supported by these bones. **carpo'meta-'carpal**, a.

'**carpophore**, n. [Bot.] In FUNGI, the stem of

a SPOROCARP; thin end of flower stem supporting CARPELS.

-carpous, a. [Bot.] Having the sort of fruit, or the number of fruits, named.

'carpospore, n. [Bot.] Any of the SPORES produced on a CYSTOCARP.

'carpus, n. [Zoo.] In higher animals, the part of the arm or front leg joining it to the hand or front foot, in man made up of two lines of small bones.

'carrier, n. [Mach.] Box, frame, vessel, or other apparatus in which or by which something, for example, a camera plate, is supported or transported. [Med.] Person or animal in whose body certain disease BACTERIA are present normally, without producing in him the disease but causing him to give it to others. [Chem] ATOM or group of atoms (commonly a CATALYST) by which another atom or group is transported from one substance to another; ACCEPTOR. c. 'frequency. [Radio] The fixed FREQUENCY of a c. wave. c. wave. [Radio] The WAVE-MOTION sent out by a radio apparatus without a stop, by MODULATION of which sound is transported.

Car'tesian co'ordinates. Two lines in the same plane, gen. on squared paper, cutting one another at right angles at a middle point named the *origin*, the upright line being named the *ordinate* and the line at right angles the *abscissa*, in relation to which the position of any point may be given in the form of its distance from the two lines, distances up from the abscissa or to the right of the ordinate being given the sign + and those in the opposite direction the sign −.

'cartilage, n. [Zoo.] Strong, stiff, elastic, somewhat TRANSLUCENT material forming part of the framework of the bodies of back-boned animals, made up of a mass of CHONDRIN with special CELLS, named c. cells, bedded in it, and taking the place of bone in lower animals and the EMBRYOS of higher. c. bone. Bone formed by development from c. as opp. MEMBRANE BONE. carti'laginous, a.

cart'ography, n. The science and art of map-making. cart'ographer, n.

'caruncle, n. [Zoo.] Outgrowth of uncovered FLESH, as on heads of some birds. [Bot.] Outgrowth near base of seed-coat. [Anat., Med.] Any small, soft outgrowth. ca'runculate, a. [Bot.]

ca'runcula lacr'malis. [Anat.] The small, somewhat red CARUNCLE at the inner angle of the eye.

'caryo-, KARYO-.

cary'opsis, n. [Bot.] Small dry fruit with one CELL, as in grasses. (*See* p. 158.)

cas'cade, n. A number of apparatuses (as electric CONDENSERS, CELLS, MOTORS)

placed in connection end to end, so that there is an addition of their effects, or so that liquid goes from one to another.

'case-harden, v.t. Put a hard skin on iron by heating it in C powder then making cold quickly.

'casein, n. [Chem.] PROTEIN produced from milk by the operation of an acid, etc., a yellow solid used in making paints, PLASTICS, etc.

ca'seinogen, n. [Chem.] CASEIN as present in milk, the chief PROTEIN in it.

'caseous, a. [Med.] Like cheese. case'ation, n. Process of becoming c., as TISSUES in certain diseases.

cas'siterite, n. [Mineral.] Natural OXIDE of tin, SnO_2.

cast, 1.n. [Metal.] Metal or other solid material which has been given form by putting it into a MOULD while soft or liquid, to get hard. [Zoo.] Anything put off or out of the body of an animal in a fixed form, as the skin of a snake, the earth which has gone through an earth-worm. [Geol.] FOSSIL formed of earth substance which has got inside the outer cover of a dead animal when its soft inner parts have gone, and has become hard in this form. [Med.] A c. of substance formed in and sent out of some pipe-like structure in the body, for example, the small pipes in the KIDNEY, in certain diseases. 2.v.t. [Metal.] Make c(c). of metal, etc. [Zoo.] Put off or out of body. 3.a. [Metal.] Given form by, having undergone, casting. [Zoo.] Which has been put off, etc., as a snake's skin. c. 'iron. Iron having in it between 2·5% and 4·5% of C in the form of CEMENTITE or GRAPHITE, and given the desired form by casting because readily broken by hammering and so unable to be worked. 'casting, n.

caste, n. [Zoo.] Of certain insects, such as ants, living in societies, any of the different sorts, formed to do different work, making up the group.

'Castner('s) 'process. [Chem.] A process for producing Cl and ALKALINE HYDROXIDES by ELECTROLYSIS of a SOLUTION of NaCl.

'castor oil. An oil, without colour or some-what yellow, got from the seeds of a TROPICAL plant and used as LUBRICANT, medically as a CATHARTIC, and in soap.

cas'trate, v.t. [Zoo., Med.] Take away male sex-parts of (an animal). cas'tration, n. cas'tration complex. [Psychol.] Unconscious fear of loss of sex parts and the reactions produced by this.

cata-, KATA-.

ca'tabolism, n. KATABOLISM. cata'bolic, a.

cata'clastic, a. [Geol.] (Of ROCKS) formed of substance crushed out of normal form. c. rock. BRECCIA.

'cataclysm, n. [Geol.] Sudden and violent

change in outer part of earth. **cata-'clysm-al, -ic,** aa.

'catalase, n. [Chem.] ENZYME by which PEROXIDES are broken up.

'catalep-sy, -sis, nn. [Med.] (Sudden attack of) sleep-like condition in which muscles become stiff and legs and arms keep in any position in which they are put. **cata'leptic,** n., a. (Person) having cataleptic attacks. **cata'leptiform,** a. Like c.

ca'talysis, n. [Chem.] The changing, sp. increasing, of the rate of a chemical reaction by the addition of a substance which itself undergoes no change. **'catalyst, 'catalyser,** nn. Substance causing c. **cata'lytic,** a.

cata'menia, n.pl. [Med.] MENSES.

cata'morphism, n. [Geol.] Chemical and physical changes produced in ROCK by wind and water.

'catapho'resis, n. [Phys.] The process by which very small bits of solid substance in SUSPENSION in a liquid, sp. in COLLOIDAL SOLUTION, are put in motion as the effect of an ELECTRIC FIELD, sp. in motion in the direction of the CATHODE as opp. ANAPHORESIS. [Med.] The process of getting chemical substances into the body through the skin by the use of an electric current.

cata'plasia, n. [Biol.] Process by which CELLS, etc., go back to a simpler form.

'catapult, n. Apparatus for sending airplane quickly into the air by violent push. **c. 'mechanism.** [Bot.] Process or apparatus of seed distribution dependent on sudden shakes given to a long stiff stem when the fruit is moved in the wind.

'cataract, n. [Med.] Diseased condition of LENS of eye in which it becomes clouded all through so that a person is unable to see anything but light and dark. **catar'actous,** a.

ca'tarrh, n. [Med.] INFLAMMATION of a MUCOUS MEMBRANE causing change in quality and amount of liquid produced. **ca'tarrhal,** a.

cata'tonia, n. [Med.] Serious form of DEMENTIA PRAECOX, marked by NEGATIVISM, times of not talking or moving, and, sometimes, CATALEPSY. **cata'tonic,** a.

'catchment 'area or **'basin.** [Geog.] Stretch of country from which rain water is drained into one river.

cate'lectrode, n. [Elec.] CATHODE.

'catenary, I. a. Like a chain, sp. a chain of things. 2.n. [Maths.] The curve formed by a chain supported at its two ends and hanging freely between them (freq. named **c. curve**).

cate'nation, n. Chain-like connection. [Phonet.] Grouping together of sounds. **'catenate, ca'tenulate,** aa. Having c., ranged in chains, sp. [Bot.] of SPORES, etc.

'caterpillar. n. [Zoo.] Worm-like LARVA of a number of insects, sp. LEPIDOPTERA, having six true legs at front and a number of other leg-like parts, short feelers, and strong mouth-parts for biting.

'catgut, n. Cord made from INTESTINES of sheep, used for stitching wounds, etc.

ca'tharsis, n. [Med.] The sending out of waste, etc., from any outlet in the body, sp. the clearing of the BOWELS as effect of medical substance. [Psych.] The clearing up of COMPLEXES and so on by becoming conscious of and talking freely about unconscious or secret thoughts and feelings. **ca'thartic,** 1.a. Sp. producing c. 2.n. Cathartic medical substance.

'catheter, n. [Med.] Thin pipe used for draining liquid or gas from, or sending it into, any part of body, sp. one put into BLADDER to let URINE out. **'catheterize,** v.t. Make use of c. on (part, person). **'catheteri'zation,** n.

cathe'tometer, n. [Phys., etc.] Instrument having TELESCOPE fixed to upright rod with scales marked on it for measuring small distances in an up and down direction. **catheto'metric,** a.

ca'thexis, n. [Psych.] A strong and fixed direction of desire or other feeling to some special thing, idea; the force of such desire or feeling.

'cathode, n. [Phys., Chem., Elec.] The ELECTRODE by which an electric current goes out of an ELECTROLYTE or gas, that is, from which ELECTRONS or NEGATIVE IONS go into it; the electrode from which electrons are sent out in an ELECTRON DISCHARGE TUBE. **c. dark space.** The dark space in front of the c. glow. **c. glow.** Light given out by the c. in a GAS DISCHARGE TUBE. **c. ray.** Ray made up of electrons sent out from the c. when an electric current goes through a gas at low PRESSURE—an effect on which a great number of present-day instruments are based and after which they are named, for example, the c.-ray VOLTMETER. **c.-ray 'furnace.** [Phys.] An apparatus for heating a very small amount of a substance to a very high degree by sending onto it a very strong BEAM of c. rays. **c-ray os'cillograph** or **os'cilloscope.** An OSCILLOGRAPH using a c.-ray tube. **c-ray tube.** Vessel, gen. of glass, in which c. rays are sent against a FLUORESCENT SCREEN so as to make points of light on it, used in the c-ray oscillograph to give pictures of waveforms, and in TELEVISION. **ca'thodic,** a. **ca'thodolumi'nescence, ca'thodo'phosphorescence,** nn. The giving out of light by a substance acted on by c. rays. **ca'thodo'thermoluminescence,** n. The giving out of light by a heated body which has first been acted on by c. rays.

cathod'ography, cath'ography, nn. The

taking of X-ray pictures.

'**cathozyte,** n. [Elec.] In ELECTROLYSIS, that part of the ELECTROLYTE which is nearest the CATHODE.

'**cation,** n. [Phys., Chem.] The ION in an ELECTROLYTE which has a POSITIVE (+) CHARGE, and so goes to the CATHODE. **cati'onic,** a.

'**catkin,** n. [Bot.] AMENT.

cat's whisker. [Radio] The wire touching the CRYSTAL in a CRYSTAL RECTIFIER.

Cau'casian, n., a. [Anthrop.] (Person) of that division of man made up of the chief RACES of Europe, North Africa, and South-West Asia, marked by skins which may be named light or 'white' in comparison with the very dark brown or black, the yellow, or the red skins of other races.

'**cauda,** n. [Zoo.] Tail or thing like tail. '**caudal,** a. Like, to do with, tail. **caudal fin.** Tail of fish. '**caudate,** a. **caudate** '**nucleus.** Mass of grey material in CORPUS STRIATUM.

Cau'data, n.pl. [Zoo.] URODELA.

caul, n. [Physiol.] AMNION.

ca(u)lk, v.t. Make joins (in ship, boiler, or other structure) water-tight by forcing soft material into them, or by hammering the edge of one plate over that of the other and so on.

'**causal,** a. Causing; dependent on, reasoned by, a system of cause and effect; having, taken to have, a cause. **cau'sality,** n. Sp. theory that the condition of a system at any time is a necessary outcome of its condition in the past. **cau'sation,** n. Act of causing; cause. '**causative,** a. Acting as a cause, causing.

caus'algia, n. [Med.] A violent burning pain in the skin when the nerve going to that part is damaged.

caustic, a. [Chem.] Having the property of causing destruction of, burning, living substance, sp. skin of man. **c.** '**alkali.** Caustic potash or caustic soda. **c.** '**potash.** POTASSIUM HYDROXIDE (KOH). **c.** '**soda.** SODIUM HYDROXIDE (NaOH), used in chemistry and in soap-making. (*See* SODA).

caustic, n. [Phys.] C. curve. **c. curve.** A curve to which rays of light are TANGENTIAL after REFLECTION from, or REFRACTION out of, a body SURFACE.

'**cautery,** n. [Med.] Process of burning a wound, etc., with a CAUSTIC chemical or heated iron, etc., for some medical purpose, such as destruction of diseased material; apparatus used for this purpose. '**cauterize,** v.t. Make use of c. on. **cauteri'zation,** n.

cave, n. [Geol.] A room-like hollow in ROCK, with or without an opening to the outer air, for example in a mountain side or at the edge of a river or sea, chiefly caused by the DISSOLVING or washing away of certain sorts of rock by water. **c.** '**dweller.** [Anthrop.] Person of the PALAEOLITHIC PERIOD, when men's living places were cc.

'**Cavendish ex'periment.** [Phys.] The use of a TORSION BALANCE for measuring the attraction between two small masses of lead for the purpose of fixing the GRAVITATIONAL CONSTANT. [Elec.] A test designed by Cavendish to make it clear that all electric CHARGES are on the outside of a charged body.

'**cavern,** n. CAVE. '**cavernous,** a. Sp. [Zoo.] having a hollow or hollows.

cavi'tation, n. [Med.] The forming of hollow places in any structure, sp. in diseased LUNGS. [Eng.] The forming of a space between the back end of a body moving in a liquid and the liquid normally touching it, for example, at the back of the blades of a ship's PROPELLER.

'**cavity,** n. A hollow space inside a body. **c.** **mag'netron.** [Phys.] A form of MAGNETRON for the producing of OSCILLATIONS of very high FREQUENCY, used in RADAR. **c. radi'ation.** [Phys.] BLACK BODY RADIATION. **c.** '**resonator.** [Elec.] A hollow box-like space in which electric OSCILLATIONS are produced by REFLECTION from its walls, used in the c. magnetron and like instruments.

Cb, Sign for COLUMBIUM.

Cd, Sign for CADMIUM.

Ce, Sign for CERIUM.

celestial, a. [Astron.] To do with the sky or bodies seen in it. **c. e'quator.** The circle in which the c. sphere is cut by the plane of the EQUATOR. **c. ho'rizon.** The circle in which the c. sphere is cut by the plane parallel to the HORIZON through the CENTRE of the earth. **c.** '**latitude.** The ANGULAR DISTANCE of a c. body from the ECLIPTIC. **c.** '**longitude.** The ANGULAR DISTANCE of a c. body east on the ECLIPTIC, measured from the VERNAL EQUINOX to the circle going through the POLE of the ecliptic and through the body. **c. me'ridian.** The circle through the ZENITH and the c. poles. **c. poles.** The points in which the c. sphere is cut by the earth's AXIS. **c. sphere.** A SPHERE with the CENTRE of the earth as its centre on which the stars are mapped, that is, without taking into account their true distance from the earth.

'**celestine,** '**celestite,** nn. [Mineral.] Natural $SrSO_4$ (*strontium sulphate*) a white or blue substance from which Sr is got.

cell, n. [Elec.] A vessel or division of a vessel having in it an ELECTROLYTE and two ELECTRODES between which an E.M.F. is produced as the effect of chemical reactions (*see* PRIMARY CELL, STORAGE CELL). [Biol.] Unit of structure of plants and animals, a very small mass of PROTO-

PLASM covered with a PLASMA MEMBRANE or c. wall, and gen. having a NUCLEUS; small, hollow, walled space, for example a division in the OVARY of a plant. **c. division.** [Biol.] Any of the processes by which a c. undergoes division into two or more new cc. (*see* AMITOSIS, MEIOSIS, MITOSIS). **c. 'nucleus.** [Biol.] *See* NUCLEUS. **c. 'organ.** [Biol.] Any part of the substance of a c. having a special structure and some special part in its working or development. **c. 'respir'ation.** *See* RESPIRATION. **c. sap.** [Bot.] The liquid, made up chiefly of SALTS and acids in SOLUTION in water, present inside the VACUOLES of a plant c. [Zoo.] The liquid part of c. substance. **c. 'theory.** [Biol.] The theory that plants and animals are made up of cc. and the substances produced by them, and that all growth and development and the producing of offspring are effected by c. division. **c. wall.** [Biol.] The outer cover of a c., sp. [Bot.] the skin, at first very thin and formed chiefly of PECTINOUS material, but becoming stronger and thicker as time goes on by the addition of CELLULOSE and freq. other materials, covering most plant cc. and giving support to plant substance. **'cellular,** a. Full of small hollows or having a network structure; made up of, having to do with, cc.

'cellulase, n. [Biochem.] ENZYME acting on CELLULOSE, got from certain fruit-stones.

cellu'litis, n. [Med.] INFLAMMATION of CELLULAR TISSUE.

'celluloid, n. [Chem.] Horn-like substance made from NITROCELLULOSE, $C_6H_7O_5$ $(NO_3)_3$, and CAMPHOR, $C_{10}H_{16}O$.

'cellulose, n. [Chem.] The most complex CARBOHYDRATE, forming CELL walls of plants, got from wood, cotton, and other FIBROUS materials and used in making a great number of complex substances, such as C. ACETATES, C. ESTERS, and C. NITRATES, which are important in industry, sp. in the producing of LACQUERS, ARTIFICIAL silks, etc.

'Celsius scale. [Phys.] CENTIGRADE TEMPERATURE scale.

ce'ment, 1.n. A building material, gen. made of powdered LIMESTONE and sand, which is mixed with water to make a paste or liquid, later becoming hard and stone-like, used among other things for joining bodies together; any substance of like properties and uses. [Zoo.] A bone-like substance coating the roots of the teeth of higher animals where there is no ENAMEL. 2.v.t. Get united by or covered with a c. **c. 'layer.** [Zoo.] The c. coating of a tooth.

'cement'ation, n. The process by which a PLASTIC substance becomes hard. [Metal.]

CASE-HARDENING. [Bot.] The uniting of HYPHAE into a solid mass by a sticky substance.

ce'mentite, n. [Metal.] Fe_3C (*iron carbide*) a very hard, BRITTLE substance present in CAST IRON and steel.

ce'mentstone, n. [Mineral.] CALCITE mixed with CLAY.

Cenozoic, a. CAINOZOIC.

'censer 'mechanism. [Bot.] System or apparatus of seed distribution in which seeds are sent out of fruit as the effect of shaking by the wind.

'center, n. CENTRE.

cen'tesis, n. [Med.] The operation of making a small hole in a part with a pointed instrument.

centi-. 100; in the METRIC SYSTEM $\frac{1}{100}$: **'centigram,** n., **'centimetre,** n., **'centiare,** n.

'Centigrade, a. Of, to do with, having, the C. scale. **C. scale.** TEMPERATURE scale on which the FREEZING-POINT of water is at 0° and the boiling point at 100°.

centimetre-gram-second. *See* C.G.S.

'centimetre wave. [Radio] An ELECTROMAGNETIC WAVE whose WAVE-LENGTH is between 1 and 100 cm.

centi'normal, a. [Chem.] Of SOLUTION, $\frac{1}{100}$ as strong as a NORMAL SOLUTION.

'centipoise, n. [Phys.] Unit measure of VISCOSITY $= \frac{1}{100}$ POISE.

'central, a. At, to do with, the CENTRE. **c. ca'nal.** [Zoo.] Very small pipe going from VENTRICLES of brain through grey substance of backbone. **c. cell.** [Bot.] CELL at the base of the ARCHEGONIUM in GYMNOSPERMS from which egg is formed. [Zoo.] Any of the small cells coating the inside of the PEPTIC GLANDS. **c. 'cylinder.** [Bot.] STELE. **c. 'nervous 'system.** [Zoo.] That controlling part of a nerve system which gets IMPULSES from the senses and sends out impulses to the muscles, in back-boned animals the brain and SPINAL CORD. **c. 'vowels.** [Phonet.] VOWELS made with the middle of the tongue somewhat high.

cen'trale (centralia), n. [Zoo.] A bone present in the CARPUS or TARSUS of some animals between the two lines of small bones of which these are commonly made up.

'centre, n. Middle point of anything; meeting-point of a number of like things, as a NERVE c. **c. of 'buoyancy.** [Phys.] (Of a body supported by a liquid or gas) the c. of gravity of the liquid or gas pushed out of place by it. **c. of 'curvature.** [Geom.] (Of a curve) the meeting-point of any two lines at right-angles to it from two CONSECUTIVE points on it, for example, for any part of a circle the c. of the circle. **c. of flo'tation.** The c. of gravity of the water plane of a ship. **c. of 'gravity.** [Phys.] That point in a body or system of bodies at which its weight seems to be acting, that is, the point at which it has to be supported to be balanced. **c. of in'ertia.** C. of gravity. **c. of mass.** [Phys.] That point in a body or system of bodies at which its complete MASS may be taken, for purposes of CALCULATION, to be acting — for bodies under the earth's attraction, this is the same thing as the c. of gravity. **c. of 'motion.** Point of body which is at rest while other points are in motion round it. **c. of oscil'lation.** Point at which the complete mass of a body in OSCILLATION might be present without changing the time of oscillation. **c. of 'ossifi'cation.** [Zoo.] Point at which forming of bone is started. **c. of popu'la-tion.** C. of gravity of persons living in a stretch of country, taking that stretch of country to be a plane and every person to have the same weight. **c. of pro'jec-tion.** Point through which lines are taken to make a picture of anything by PRO-JECTION. **c. of ro'tation of the eye.** [Zoo.] The point about which the eye-ball is moving when it is turned up or down or from side to side. **c. of 'symmetry.** [Crystal.] A point in a CRYSTAL such that all straight lines through this point from one face to the opposite face are cut in two by it, and any point in one half of the crystal is balanced by a point in the other half at the same distance from, and in the same position in relation to, the c. of symmetry.

cen'trifugal, a. Going or sending away from a middle point. [Zoo.] EFFERENT. [Bot.] (Of flower group) having development from middle out and top down, so that the youngest are outside. **c. force.** Sp. [Phys.] The reaction of a body in motion in a curve against an outside force driving it in the direction of a middle point, and equal and opposite to it, by which it keeps its distance from the middle. **c. 'moment or torque.** MOMENT of a c. force or of a group of c. forces taken together.

'centrifuge. n. Apparatus in which a liquid or wet solid is turned round and round at great rate, forcing bits of solid out of the liquid or liquid out of the solid.

'centriole, n. [Biol.] Small body at middle of CENTROSOME which becomes two when MITOSIS is about to take place.

cen'tripetal, a. Going or sending in the direction of a middle point. [Zoo.] AFFERENT. [Bot.] (Of flower group) having development from outside in and base up, so that the youngest flowers are on the inside. **c. force.** Sp. [Phys.] the force acting on a body in motion on a curve, equal and opposite to CENTRIFUGAL FORCE.

centro'baric, a. [Phys.] To do with the CENTRE OF GRAVITY or the process of its discovery.

'centroid, n. CENTRE OF MASS.

centro'lecithal, a. [Zoo.] (Of egg) having YOLK in middle.

'centromere, n. [Biol.] SPINDLE ATTACH-MENT.

'centrosome, n. [Biol.] Very small body having a connection with the NUCLEUS in a number of animal and some plant CELLS, which in the process of MITOSIS is separated, with the NUCLEUS, into two parts, to which the CHROMOSOMES then go.

'centrosphere, n. [Biol.] The middle mass of an ASTER from which the rays go out.

'centrum (centra), n. [Zoo.] The solid mass forming the base of a VERTEBRA, on the under side of the SPINAL CORD.

cen'tuple, a. 100 times (what is named). **c. 'calorie.** See CALORIE.

'century, n. A space of 100 years.

'cephal-, 'cephalo-, [Zoo.]. Head.

ce'phalic, a. [Zoo.] To do with the head. **c. fin.** FIN on head of certain fish. **c. 'index.** [Anthrop.] Number got by division of 100 times the measure of the SKULL at its widest part by its measure at longest part and used in grouping heads into sorts.

'cephali'zation, n. [Zoo.] Development of the forward end of an animal so as to become the chief end, the forming of a head.

'Cephalo'chord(at)a, n.pl. [Zoo.] SUB-PHYLUM of CHORDATA, without a brain or hard framework but with a NOTO-CHORD, present at all stages, going from one end of the body to the other, and having NEPHRIDIA—sea animals living in sand. (See p. 563.)

'Cephal'opoda, n.pl. [Zoo.] A CLASS of swim-ming MOLLUSCA in which there is a strong development of head, eyes, and nerve system, and which generally have TENTACLES with SUCKERS or hooks round the head and freq. no outer SHELL, its place being taken in some sorts by a hard inner supporting plate. **'cephalopod,** n. One of the C. (See p. 564.)

cepha'lometer, n. Instrument for measuring CEPHALIC INDEX. **cepha'lometry,** n.

'cephalo'thorax, n. [Zoo.] The united head and THORAX of ARACHNIDAE and CRUSTACEA.

ce'ramic, a. Made of, to do with, being, pot or other material produced by heating or burning an earth substance such as KAOLIN or certain OXIDES such as BaO. **ce'ramics,** 1.n. The art and science of making c. material. 2.n.pl. Things made of c. material.

'cerato'branchial, a., n. [Zoo.] (Of) middle part of BRANCHIAL arch.

'cerato'hyal, a., n. [Zoo.] (Of) middle part of HYOID ARCH; a c. bone which in man becomes the small horn of the hyoid arch.

'cerato'trichia, n.pl. [Zoo.] Thin threads of horn-like material at edge of FINS in fishes.

'cercal, a. [Zoo.] To do with tail.

cer′caria (cercariae), n. [Zoo.] LARVA of TREMATODA with round or egg-like body and long, strong tail.

′cercus (cerci), n. [Zoo.] One or the other of two JOINTED, feeler-like structures at the end of the body in insects and some other ARTHROPODA.

′cereal, n. [Bot.] Grain-producing grass, grain.

cere′bellum (cerebelli), n. [Zoo.] In back-boned animals, the round division of the brain, at the back and base of the head, to do with the working of the muscles in harmony and with the sense of balance. **cere′bellar,** a.

′cerebral, a. [Zoo.] To do with the CEREBRUM. or brain. **c. ′cortex.** The outer coat of the c. hemispheres, made up of GREY MATTER, in higher back-boned animals, sp. MAMMALS. **c. ′ganglion.** The mass of GANGLIA over the OSEOPHAGUS forming the 'brain' of a number of animals without backbones such as worms and ARTHROPODA. **c. ′hemispheres.** The two halves of the CEREBRUM, right and left. **c. ′vesicle.** Any of the hollows or divisions of the brain of a back-boned animal in early stage of development.

′cerebro-. CEREBRAL: **′cerebro′ganglion,** n.

′cerebro′spinal, a. [Zoo.] To do with the brain and the SPINAL CORD. **c. ′axis.** The brain and SPINAL CHORD. **c. fluid.** The clear liquid present in the spaces inside the brain and SPINAL CORD and between the PIA MATER and the ARACHNOID, produced by the CHOROID PLEXUSES and moving in a slow current down the middle of the spinal cord and up the sides, to be taken in by the VEINS of the brain again, made up of a SOLUTION of blood chemicals such as salt, GLUCOSE, and ALBUMINS.

′cerebrum, n. [Zoo.] In back-boned animals the chief part of the brain, in front of and over the other parts, in man controlling conscious mind processes.

′ceresin(e), n. Yellow or white wax made from OZOKERITE.

′cerium, Chemical element, at. no. 58, at. wt. 140·14, sign Ce, a steel-grey metal, MELTING-point 635°C, one of the RARE EARTHS.

′cernuous, a. [Bot.] Hanging down.

ce′rumen, n. [Zoo.] The wax of the ear. **ce′ruminous,** a. To do with or producing c.

cer′vical, a. [Anat.] To do with the neck.

′Cervidae, n.pl. [Zoo.] A FAMILY of RUMINANTS marked by having ANTLERS in place of the hollow, unbranched horns of other ruminants such as cows, goats, and sheep, made up chiefly of animals noted for their power of running quickly.

′cervix, n. [Zoo.] Neck, sp. the back part; neck or narrow mouth of part of the body. **c. ′uteri,** Neck of WOMB.

′cesium, n. CAESIUM.

Ces′toda, n.pl. [Zoo.] A CLASS of flat PLATYHELMINTHES with no ALIMENTARY CANAL, PARASITES living inside the bodies of other animals. **′cestode,** n., a (Worm) of the C.

Ce′tacea, n.pl. [Zoo.] An ORDER of MAMMALIA, water-living, with no back legs, a marked development of the tail, FINS on back, and nose opening on top of head.

C.G.S. (or **c.g.s.**) **system.** [Phys.] System of c.g.s. units. **c.g.s. ′unit.** Any measuring unit based on the centimetre, the gramme, and the second, for example, a DYNE.

′chadacryst, n. [Crystal.] Small CRYSTAL grains fixed in any position in a different and greater crystal.

′chaeta (chaetae), n. [Zoo.] Any of the short, stiff, hair-like structures seen on the skin of certain worms. **chae′tiferous, chae′tophorous,** aa. **′chaetotaxy,** n. The way in which cc. are grouped.

Chae′topoda, n.pl. [Zoo.] A CLASS of ANNELIDA having CHAETAE on all or most of their divisions, sometimes on PARAPODIA. **′chaetopod,** n., a. (Animal) of, like the C.

chain, n. [Chem.] A number of ATOMS joined together as in a chain, chiefly forming MOLECULES of C compounds, sp. an *open c.*, that is, a c. not joined to make a RING, **c. ′compound.** Substance in which C ATOMS are joined in an open chain.

chain re′action. [Phys., Chem., Psych.] A complex reaction in which one reaction is the cause of a second and the second of a third, and so on, sp. in NUCLEAR FISSION where every fission of an ATOM gives birth to more than one NEUTRON, every one of which is the cause of the fission of another atom.

cha′laza, n. [Zoo.] One or the other of two twisted cords of ALBUMEN joining the YOLK to the skin of a bird's egg. [Bot.] Base of NUCLEUS of OVULE.

chalk, n. [Geol.] A soft, white or near white, small-grained form of LIMESTONE made up chiefly of the SHELLS of small sea animals of the CRETACEOUS PERIOD.

chal′cedony, n. [Mineral.] A natural form of SiO_2 made up of very small CRYSTALS, used for ornament.

cha′lybeate, a. [Geol.] Having in it iron SALTS, said sp. of natural spring water.

′chalybite, n. [Mineral.] SIDERITE.

′chamber, n. Shut-in space. [Chem.] Vessel coated inside with lead in which chemical reaction, sp. that produced in making H_2SO_4, takes place. **c. acid.** H_2SO_4 made in c.

′Chamberland ′filter. One sort of FILTER for BACTERIA, made of pot. **′Chamberland flask.** Glass vessel with side pipe used for growth of BACTERIA.

'chamosite, n. [Mineral.] A natural SILICATE of iron with H_2O, forming OÖLITHS on sea-floor.

'Chance-'Claus 'process. [Chem.] Process for getting back S from waste material.

'chancre, n. [Med.] A hard SWELLING produced in the first stage of SYPHILIS.

'chancroid, n. [Med.] Any VENEREAL ULCER not caused by SYPHILIS.

change of life. MENOPAUSE.

change of state. [Chem.] The change from any of the possible forms of material substance into any of the others, *see* STATE OF MATTER, p. 444.

'channel, n. Pipe, pipe-like hollow, sp. for or made by current of liquid. [Radio] Narrow band of waves wide enough for use by one station.

'channeled 'spectrum. [Phys.] SPECTRUM having INTERFERENCE BANDS, produced by light REFLECTED from two parallel faces.

cha'parral, n. [Geog.] Thick growth of SHRUBS and low trees, covering part of California.

'character, n. [Biol.] Any clearly-marked property, sp. one taken as representative of a certain sort of animal or plant; any clearly-marked property which is handed down to offspring and looked on as the effect of a special GENE or genes. [Psych.] The non-physical qualities of a person, other than reasoning-power, taken together, sp. those which are important in his relations with society—his general make-up of desires, tendencies, tastes, impulses, etc., and his power of control over them. [Philol.] Any sign used in writing or in any form of recording, such as a letter, a number, a picture or form, representative of some unit of language or thought.

character'istic, n., a. (Quality) representative of a thing, or by which it is regularly marked; (sign, etc.) giving a thing's position in a system or its relation to some general law. c. curve. [Radio, etc.] GRAPH giving the relation between the measure of the VOLTAGE on the GRID of a THERMIONIC VALVE and the measure of the voltage of the current in the ANODE CIRCUIT.

'charcoal, n. [Chem.] General name for different forms of C made by strongly heating wood or other plant or animal substances when no air is present, all black or very dark-coloured, and gen. very POROUS.

charge, 1.n. (The amount of) material put into an apparatus or needed for its operation, sp. of firing material put into a gun, of EXPLOSIVE put into anything for blowing it up, or of ELECTRICITY put into a STORAGE BATTERY, etc. [Elec.] That which an ATOM or MOLECULE, or a body formed of such atoms or molecules, is said to have when it has undergone a loss (*positive c.*) or an addition (*negative c.*) of ELECTRONS, giving it the electric properties of attraction for atoms, etc. of opposite c. and REPULSION for those of like c., and of being acted on by forces when placed in an ELECTRIC FIELD; the amount of c., that is, of ELECTRICITY, in a body, measured in ELECTROSTATIC UNITS or in COULOMBS. 2.v.t. Put a c. in or on (something). 'c.-'mass 'ratio. [Elec.] $\frac{e}{m}$ where e is the electric c. on a body and m is its mass. 'charged, a. Having a c. in it. [Elec.] Having an electric c. charging, n., a.

'Charles's law. [Phys.] Law that the VOLUME of a given mass of gas at a fixed PRESSURE is increased by $\frac{1}{273}$ of its volume at 0°C for every increase in TEMPERATURE of 1°C, other name *Gay–Lussac's law*.

chart, n. Map, sp. of the stars or of the sea, for use on ships; GRAPH representative of a range of changing values, such as the curve on paper made by a recording-instrument; paper printed with a scale ready to be put in a recording-instrument.

char'tography, n. Map-making, gen. CARTOGRAPHY.

'chassis (chassis), n. Under-part of automobile with the wheels and works: frame-work of the body of an airplane; supporting parts of a radio apparatus.

'Chatterton's compound. [Chem.] Substance made of rubber and wax mixed, used as electric INSULATOR.

'Chattock gauge. [Phys.] Very delicate form of MANOMETER.

cheek, n. [Zoo.] In MAMMALS, the side of the face under the eye, the wall of the mouth; in other animals and insects, the side parts of the head. c. pouch. Bag-like structure in c. of certain monkeys and other animals, used for keeping food.

Chei'roptera, n.pl. CHIROPTERA.

'chela (chelae) [Zoo.] On certain legs of CRUSTACEA and ARACHNIDAE, a gripping instrument formed by the outgrowth of the end division but one of the leg in such a way that it makes with the end division a scissors-like structure, used like the thumb and first finger of a hand. 'chelate, a. che'liferous, a. 'cheliform, a.

che'licerae, n.pl. [Zoo.] In ARACHNIDAE, the two front outgrowths on the head, which are generally CHELATE.

'Chellean, a., n. [Geol.] (To do with) the earliest division of the PALEOLITHIC.

Che'lonia, n.pl.[Zoo.] An ORDER of REPTILIA with the body housed between an arched top plate and a flat under plate of bone and horn, into which covering the head, tail, and feet may generally be pulled at need, and having a BEAK of horn in place of teeth.

chemical, 1.a. Of, to do with, used in, chemistry. 2.n. Any substance as used in chemistry or produced by a process of chemistry. **c. aff'inity.** The force which keeps ATOMS together in MOLECULES. **c. 'balance.** A very delicate form of BALANCE used for very small amounts of substance such as chemistry has to do with. **c. bond.** VALENCY BOND. **c. change.** A change in which a new substance is formed. **c. 'compound.** A substance made up of two or more ELEMENTS in a fixed RATIO by weight which is not dependent on the way in which it is made. **c. consti'tution.** The number and arrangement of the ATOMS in a chemical compound. **c. 'energy.** The ENERGY produced in a chemical reaction. **c. e'quation.** A statement, using c. symbols and formulae, of what takes place in any chemical reaction, the substances undergoing the reaction being put on the left of the sign ' = ' and those produced by them on the right. **c. equi'librium.** *See* EQUILIBRIUM. **c. e'quivalent.** That weight of a given ELEMENT or RADICAL which takes the place of or may be united with, 1 unit weight of H or 8 unit weights of O. **c. 'formula.** A group of c. symbols and numbers representative of the ATOMS making up the MOLECULE of a complex substance (*see* EMPIRICAL FORMULA, MOLECULAR FORMULA), or of c. symbols and signs representative in addition of the way in which these atoms are grouped and united (*see* GRAPHIC FORMULA, VALENCE FORMULA). **c. re'action.** A process in which some substance is changed into a different one. **c. 'symbol.** A letter or letters used as a sign for an ATOM of the element, e.g. Fe is the sign for iron.

che'migraphy, n. The process of making designs, etc. on metals by acting on them chemically.

'chemilumi'nescence, n. [Chem.] The giving out of light without heat by substances undergoing chemical reaction.

chemi'sorption, n. [Chem.] ADSORPTION in which a chemical reaction takes place between the ADSORBED substance and the face by which it is adsorbed, so that the coating becomes fixed.

'chemistry, n. The science of what substances are made of and of their reactions with one another.

'chemo-. Chemical.

chemo'autrophic, a. [Bot.] CHEMOSYNTHETIC.

chemo'ceptor, n. [Zoo.] CHEMORECEPTOR.

chemoimmu'nology, n. The chemistry of IMMUNOLOGY.

'chemolysis, n. [Chem., Biol.] The DECOMPOSITION of animal and plant substances by chemicals.

'chemonasty, n. [Bot.] The NASTIC MOVEMENT of a plant in reaction to a chemical in the earth, etc. round it.

'chemore'ceptor, n. [Zoo.] Sense-nerve of the sort put in operation by chemical STIMULI, such as those of taste and smell.

che'mosis, n. [Med.] SWELLING of the CONJUNCTIVA.

chemos'mosis, n. [Chem.] The taking place of a chemical reaction through a SEMIPERMEABLE MEMBRANE.

'chemo'synthesis, n. [Bot.] The building up of ORGANIC substances by certain BACTERIA, using ENERGY produced by chemical reaction. **'chemosyn'thetic,** a.

chemo'taxis, n. [Biol.] TAXIS in reaction to chemical effects, as the motion of PROTOZOA in the direction · of dead plant substance. **chemo'tactic,** a.

chemo'therapy, n. [Med.] The use against disease of chemical substances acting as poison to the BACTERIA responsible.

che'motropism, n. [Biol.] TROPISM in reaction to chemical effects, as the turning of a root in the direction of food.

chert, n. [Mineral.] A sort of ROCK chiefly made up of very small CRYSTALS of SiO_2 formed from the framework of certain simple animals such as sponges.

'Cheyne-'Stokes respi'ration or **'breathing.** [Med.] Condition in diseases of the heart, brain or KIDNEYS in which breathing gets quicker and quicker, then comes to a complete stop, and then goes on again after some seconds.

chi'asma (chias'mata), n. [Biol.] Structure formed by the going of one thread-like part, such as nerve, across another; exchange of material between HOMOLOGOUS CHROMOSOMES in MEIOSIS.

'chicken-pox, n. VARICELLA.

'chilblain, n. [Med.] ERYTHEMA PERMIO.

'childbirth, n. [Med.] The process of giving birth to offspring by a woman.

'Chile salt'petre, 'Chile 'nitre. [Chem.] Natural form of SODIUM NITRATE ($NaNO_3$).

chill, 1.v.t. Make suddenly cold, sp. [Chem., Metal.] do this to the outside of a mass of liquid metal so that it becomes hard before the inside. 2.n. [Metal.] A MOULD, gen. of iron, used for chilling liquid metals. [Med.] A condition marked by an inner sense of cold together with a shaking of the body, freq. a sign of the starting of a cold or other disease as the effect of getting very cold or wet, or coming between attacks of FEVER. **c. 'crystals.** [Metal.] The small CRYSTALS formed when a liquid metal comes in touch with a chilling MOULD, caused by very quick FREEZING.

chi'm(a)era, n. [Bot.] Plant which is a

MOSAIC HYBRID or in which TISSUES from two different plants have become mixed by GRAFTING, so that the plant produced may put out, for example, two sorts of leaves on the same branch.

'china clay. KAOLIN.

Chi'roptera, n.pl. [Zoo.] An ORDER of small MAMMALS having wings of MEMBRANE supported by the very long bones of the 'hand' and stretching back to the back legs, sometimes covering the tail—the only mammals with the power of flight, gen. sleeping in the day and coming out at night only, and living on insects or fruit.

chi'ropte'rygium, n. [Zoo.] 5-fingered arm (or leg) of higher back-boned animals.

'chitin, n. [Zoo.] White horn-like substance forming harder part of outer coat of insects and CRUSTACEA, and present in some FUNGI, a complex of H, O, C, and N. '-ous, a.

'chlamydospore, n. [Bot.] In FUNGI, a thick-walled SPORE with the power of acting as a RESTING SPORE, produced without a sex-process by a CELL or HYPHA.

'chloragen (or chloragogen or chloragogue) cells. [Zoo.] Yellow CELLS round ALIMENTARY CANAL of certain worms which have some part in sending out waste material.

'chloral, n. [Chem.] CCl₃.CHO, an oil-like liquid with no colour and a special smell produced by the reaction of Cl with ALCOHOL. c. 'hydrate. CCl₃.CH(OH)₂, a white CRYSTALLINE substance got by uniting c. and water, a strong NARCOTIC.

'chlorate, n. [Chem.] Any SALT of CHLORIC ACID.

'chloric 'acid. [Chem.] HClO₃.

'chloride, n. [Chem.] Substance formed by uniting one ELEMENT with Cl; any SALT of HYDROCHLORIC ACID. c. of lime. A white powder made up chiefly of CaOCl₂, formed by acting on Ca(OH)₂ with Cl gas, used in BLEACHING and as a DISINFECTANT.

'chlorinate, v.t. [Chem.] Put Cl into (a substance), sp. into water to STERILIZE it. 'chlorinated, a.

'chlorine, n. Chemical ELEMENT, at. no. 17, at. wt. 35·475, sign Cl, a green-yellow gas with a strong smell, used as a poison gas in war and for making CHLORIDE OF LIME, etc.

'chlorite, n. [Mineral.] A natural SILICATE of Al, Fe, and Mg.

chloro-. [Biol.] Light green. [Chem.] CHLORINE, united with Cl, as '-benzene. n. C₆H₅Cl.

chloro'cruorin, n. [Zoo.] a green RESPIRATORY PIGMENT in the blood of certain worms.

'chloroform, n. [Chem.] CHCl₃, an uncoloured very VOLATILE liquid of great weight with a strong special smell, used medically as an ANAESTHETIC and in industry as a SOLVENT for fats, oils, rubber, and other substances.

Chloro'phyceae, n.pl. [Bot.] The group of ALGAE whose colouring-substance is unmixed CHLOROPHYLL, ranging from very small one-CELLED forms to more complex forms of band-like or cord-like structure, living in the sea or inland waters, or on land in very wet, shaded places.

'chlorophyll, n. Green colouring substance of plants, made up of two green and two yellow substances, which takes in light in the first stage of PHOTOSYNTHESIS, turning it into the ENERGY which is later used in forming sugars from the CO₂ in the air and water.

'chloroplast, n. [Bot.] Small body with CHLOROPHYLL in it present in plant cells.

chlor'osis, n. [Bot.] An unhealthy condition marked by the turning yellow of parts normally green, the effect of not enough CHLOROPHYLL being formed. [Med.] A form of ANAEMIA seen in young women caused by an unnormally small amount of HAEMOGLOBIN, but not of ERYTHROCYTES, in the blood—readily overcome by taking iron and today no longer common.

'choana (choanae), n. [Zoo.] FUNNEL-like opening. 'choanocyte, n. CELL with funnel-like collar round base of FLAGELLUM. 'choanoid, a.

Choa'nichthyes, n.pl. [Zoo.] The group of fish, sometimes rated as a division of OSTEICHTHYES, sometimes as a separate CLASS, made up of DIPNOI and CROSSOPTERYGII.

choke, v.t. and i. [Med.] Put a stop to the breathing of (an animal) by gripping or stopping up the TRACHEA, or (of a gas, etc.) by getting into the breathing-apparatus where it is unable to be breathed; undergo choking; have a SPASM of the trachea as the effect of choking. c. damp. Any gas produced in mines which is unable to be breathed and is the cause of choking, commonly BLACK DAMP.

choke, n. [Elec.] Number of turns of wire giving great INDUCTANCE and used in A.C. CIRCUITS to make the current smaller. [Eng.] In INTERNAL COMBUSTION ENGINES, a VALVE in the CARBURETTOR by which the air intake may be made less, so as to get more of the FUEL VAPOUR when starting the engine.

chol'(a)emia, n. [Med.] Disease caused by BILE in the blood.

'chol(e)-, 'cholo-. [Med.] BILE.

'cholecys'titis, n. [Med.] INFLAMMATION of the GALL-BLADDER.

'cholera, n. [Med.] An ACUTE disease of

Asia and India, caused by a BACILLUS, which is gen. taken in in drinking water or food, and marked by VOMITING, DIARRHOEA, and CRAMPS, freq. causing death and sometimes becoming EPIDEMIC (specially named *Asiatic c.*). **c. 'morbus.** A condition marked by INFLAMMATION of the MUCOUS MEMBRANE of the stomach and INTESTINES, with effects somewhat like those of Asiatic c. but much less serious, seen in Europe in warm weather.

cho'lestea'toma, n. [Med.] A TUMOUR of the brain or the MIDDLE EAR made up of CHOLESTEROL.

chol'esterol, n. [Chem., Biochem.] A white, wax-like substance, $C_{27}H_{55}OH$, present in all the CELLS of the animal body, sp. nerve and brain cells, and having an important part in the transport of fat and the producing of HORMONES.

'choline, n. [Biochem.] A CRYSTALLINE substance with strong BASIC properties present in plant and animal substances, sp. in BILE and in the brain, gen. as a part of LECITHIN.

cholin'ergic, a. [Zoo.] (Of a NERVE FIBRE) producing ACETYLCHOLINE at its ending when an out-going NERVE IMPULSE gets there.

chondr-, 'chondri-. [Zoo.] (To do with) CARTILAGE.

Chon'drichthyes, n.pl. [Zoo.] In some groupings, one of the chief groups of fish, sometimes looked on as a CLASS, sometimes as a SUB-CLASS, of PISCES, marked by having a framework of more or less hard CARTILAGE in place of true bone, the mouth on the underside of the front end of the body, and PLACOID SCALES.

'chondrifi'cation, n. [Zoo.] The forming of CARTILAGE.

chondrin, n. [Zoo.] The strong, elastic, TRANSLUCENT substance, formed chiefly of GELATIN, which is the framework material of CARTILAGE.

'chondrio-some, -sphere, -mere, -plast, nn. MITOCHONDRIUM. **'chondrio'somal,** a.

'chondrite, n. [Geol.] A METEORITE of stone-like substance with CHONDRULES bedded in it.

chondro-. [Zoo.] CARTILAGE.

'chondroblast, n. [Zoo.] CARTILAGE-producing CELL.

'chondroclast, n. [Zoo.] CARTILAGE CELL with a number of NUCLEI effecting the destruction of CHONDRIN.

chondro'cranium, n. [Zoo.] SKULL when made of CARTILAGE, as in lower backboned animals and the EMBRYOS of higher ones.

chon'droma, n. [Med.] TUMOUR formed of CARTILAGE material.

'chondro'skeleton, n. [Zoo.] The stiff framework of an animal when formed of CARTILAGE; the cartilage parts of the framework of a back-boned animal.

chon'drosteous, a. [Zoo.] Having, to do with, a CHONDROSKELETON.

'chondrule, n. [Min.] Round grain of ENSTATITE or CHRYSOLITE seen bedded in CHONDRITES or in deep sea-bed.

'chonolith, n. [Geol.] Mass of IGNEOUS ROCK not of any common regular size.

chord, n. [Geom.] Straight line joining two points on a curve, for example on a circle.

'chorda (chordae), n. [Zoo.] NOTOCHORD; any cord-like structure, sp. one of the cords joined to valves of heart.

chorda'centrum (chordacentra), n. [Zoo.] CENTRUM formed chiefly from the outer cover of the NOTOCHORD.

Chor'data, n.pl. [Zoo.] A PHYLUM of METAZOA having a NOTOCHORD (at least in early stages), one hollow nerve cord down the middle of the back, and blood pumped to the head by a vessel which in higher groups becomes the heart. (*See* pp. 563–4.)

'chordate, a. [Zoo.] Having a NOTOCHORD.

cho'rea, n. [Med.] Disease of brain in which person keeps moving head, arms, legs etc., without power of control, having some connection with RHEUMATISM in young persons and commonly named *St. Vitus Dance.* **cho're-al, -ic,** aa.

'chorioid coat, 'chorioid 'membrane. [Zoo.] The delicate, VASCULAR, coloured coat coming between the RETINA and the SCLEROTIC COAT in the eye of a back-boned animal.

'chorioid 'plexus. [Zoo.] In higher animals, a delicate comb-like outgrowth from the roof into a VENTRICLE of the brain, made up almost completely of groups of blood-vessels covered with EPITHELIUM, by which CEREBROSPINAL FLUID is produced.

'chorion, n. [Zoo.] The outer coat of an AMNION; the outer skin of an insect's egg.

'Choripetalae, n.pl. [Bot.] POLYPETALAE.

'choroid = CHORIOID.

chre'sard, n. [Bot.] That amount of water in the earth which is of use for plant growth.

'chroma, n. [Optics] In the MUNSELL SYSTEM, the degree of HUE in a colour.

chro'maffin(e), a. [Zoo.] Becoming deeply coloured when acted on by Cr salts, said of certain CELLS.

'chromaphore, n. [Bot.] CHROMATOPHORE.

'chromasie, n. [Biol.] The increasing of CHROMATIN in a NUCLEUS and the forming of a NUCLEOLUS.

'chrom(at)-, chrom(at)o-. Colour.

'chromate, n. [Chem.] Any SALT having in it the group $-CrO_4$.

chro'matic, a. Coloured; to do with colours; able to be coloured by chemicals. [Phys.] Having the colour quality for which the word HUE is used. **c. 'aberration.** [Optics] The ABERRATION of a LENS having a different FOCUS for light of different WAVE-LENGTHS. **c. sphere.** [Bot.] Body formed by the joining of the CHROMO-SOMES after the ANAPHASE. **chroma'ticity. n.** The property of being c. **chromaticity co'ordinates.** The three values, x, y, z, used in the C.I.E. system for giving the chromaticity of a colour.

'chromatid, n. [Biol.] Any of the 4 like divisions of a TETRAD.

'chromatin, n. [Biol.] Substance in CHROMO-SOMES which is readily and deeply coloured by BASIC DYES.

'chromatism, n. [Phys.] CHROMATIC ABER-RATION. [Bot.] Unnormal colour of part of plant normally green.

'chromato'cyte, n. [Zoo.] Colour-CELL.

chroma'tography, n. [Chem.] The ANALYSIS of complex substances by sending them in liquid form slowly through some material such as a mass of chalk, a FILTER PAPER, or any of certain GELS, by which they are separated by ADSORPTION or ABSORPTION at different levels or points, and seen in different colours. **'chromato-'graphic, a.** chromatographic an'alysis. C·

'chromatoid, a. [Biol.] Like CHROMATIN, sp. in the property of being strongly coloured by BASIC DYES.

chro'matophore, n. [Bot.] Coloured PLASTID in plant CELLS. [Zoo.] Colouring cell on skin with property of changing the distribution of its colouring-substance and so changing the colour of the skin.

chro'matoplast(id), n. [Bot.] CHROMOPLAST.

chrome, n. [Chem.] Another word for CHROMIUM, used sp. in naming DYES or other substances used in industry which have chromium in them, such as $Na_2Cr_2O_7$, $K_2Cr_2O_7$, or Cr_2O_3. **c. alum.** $Cr_2(SO_4)_3K_2SO_4.24H_2O$, a dark blue-red CRYSTALLINE substance used in DYEING, printing cotton, and TANNING. **c. iron ore.** [Mineral.] CHROMITE. **-chrome, n.**

'chromic, a. [Chem.] Of, to do with CHRO-MIUM, said sp. of substances in which the chromium is TRIVALENT. **c. acid.** H_2CrO_4, an acid not readily got free but producing a number of CHROMATES.

chro'midium (chromidia), **n.** [Biol.] Small bit of CHROMATIN outside the NUCLEUS.

'chromite, n. [Chem.] Any SALT having in it the group $-CrO_2$. [Mineral.] Natural $FeCr_2O_4$, from which Cr is produced.

'chromium, n. Chemical ELEMENT, at. no. 24, at. wt. 52·01, MELTING-point 1830°C, sign Cr, a grey-white metal.

'chromoblast, n. [Biol.] CELL undergoing development into a CHROMOCYTE.

'chromocyte, n. [Biol.] Any coloured CELL.

'chromogen, n. [Chem.] Any chemical substance which is not itself a DYE but has in it a CHROMOPHORE so that it is readily made into one. [Biochem.] Any chemical in plant or animal substances which becomes coloured when acted on by air. **chromo'genic, a.** Producing colour, as *chromogenic bacteria*.

'chromoi'somerism, n. [Chem.] The property of a chemical substance of having dif-ferent-coloured forms. **'chromoi'somer, n.** Any of the differently coloured forms of a substance having c. **'chromoiso'meric, a.**

'chromomere, n. [Biol.] Any of the grains of which CHROMATIN is formed.

chromo'nema, n. [Biol.] (Any of the) twisted threads in first stage of MITOSIS.

'chromophanes, n.pl. [Zoo.] Small red, yellow, and green drops of oil in RETINA of birds, REPTILES, fishes, etc.

'chromophil(e), n., a. [Biol.] (A substance) readily STAINED. **chromo'philic, a.**

'chromophobe, n., a. [Biol.] (A substance) not readily STAINED. **chromo'phobic, a.**

'chromophore, n. [Chem.] Any of certain groups of ATOMS, such as $-NO_2$, $-N:N-$, $-C:O$, which, when joined with an AUXOCHROME, give a DYE its colouring property. [Phys.] The ATOMIC unit which gives the colour to a coloured substance. **'chromo'phoric, chro'mophorous, aa.**

'chromoplast, n. [Bot.] A coloured PLASTID, sp. one giving red or yellow colour, as opp. CHLOROPLAST.

'chromo'protein, n. [Biochem.] Any sub-stance formed of a PROTEIN united with a colouring-material.

'chromosome, n. [Biol.] Any of the thread-like bodies present in the NUCLEI of living CELLS of which every animal and plant has the same number, special to its sort, in all cells other than sex-cells, and a different number, gen. half, in sex-cells, which become twisted up into short, thick, rod-like bodies, readily coloured by BASIC DYES, in the process of MITOSIS or MEIOSIS. **c. 'complement.** The group of cc. representative of the NUCLEI of any plant or animal. **c. number.** [Biol.] The number of cc. in a NUCLEUS which is fixed for any given sort of plant or animal. **c. set.** All the cc. present in the NUCLEUS of a female sex-cell before FERTILIZATION.

'chromosphere, n. [Astron.] The gas round the PHOTOSPHERE of the sun, seen as a ring of light in a TOTAL ECLIPSE.

'chromous, a. [Chem.] Of, having in it, DIVALENT Cr. **c. acid.** The acid $HCrO_2$ from which CHROMITES are formed.

'chronax-ie, -y, n. [Zoo.] Smallest time needed for producing effect on nerve, etc. by an electric current twice as great as the smallest by which the effect may be produced.

-chrone. Curve.

'chronic, a. [Med.] (Of disease) going on regularly for a long time, changing slowly or not at all, opp. ACUTE.

'chronograph, n. Instrument for measuring stretches of time with smallest possible error.

chro'nology, n. The science of measuring time in units, as in astronomy and geology; the order in time of a group of events. chrono'logical, a. To do with c.; placing events in their order in time.

chro'nometer, n. Clock or other time-keeping instrument of the highest quality, sp. for use at sea.

'chronoscope, n. Instrument for measuring very short times, used, for example, in psychology for measuring the time taken for a reaction.

'chrysalis, n. [Zoo.] PUPA stage of insects; the cover in which the insect goes through this stage.

'chrysolite, n. [Mineral.] OLIVINE, sp. the light yellow, glass-like sort used as a jewel stone.

'chrysophyll, n. [Bot.] Yellow colouring-material in plants, formed from CHLORO-PHYLL.

'chrysoprase, n. [Mineral.] A light green form of CHALCEDONY.

'chrysotile, n. [Geol.] A form of ASBESTOS, chiefly Mg SILICATE.

chyle, n. [Zoo.] In back-boned animals, liquid by which fat and other produce of digestion are taken into the blood from the CHYME. chy'laceous, a. chyli'faction, n. The making of c. chy'liferous, a. chy'lific, a.

chyme, n. [Zoo.] Soft, almost liquid, mass of food in the SMALL INTESTINE after part digestion in the stomach. 'chy'miferous, a. 'chymifi'cation, n. Making of c. from food. 'chymous, a.

cica'tricial 'tissue. [Med.] TISSUE formed to take the place of wounded tissue.

'cicatricle, n. [Bot.] CICATRIX. [Zoo.] Round bit of PROTOPLASM in the yolk of the eggs of birds, snakes, etc., which becomes the EMBRYO.

'cicatrix, n. [Med.] Bit of CICATRICIAL TISSUE joining edges of or covering wound; mark of old wound on skin caused by the CONTRACTION of the c. [Zoo.] Mark where some part has come away. [Bot.] Mark on stem of plant after fall of leaf; mark of old wound on plant; the HILUM of a seed, cica'tricular, a. cica'trisive, cica'trizant, nn., aa. [Med.] (Substance which is) of help in forming cicatricial tissue. 'cicatrize, v.t. and i. [Med.] (Make) get better by forming c. cicatri'zation, n.

-cide, c. [Biol.] Substance, etc. causing the destruction of what is named.

C.I.E.=Commission Internationale de l'Eclairage, a body which in 1931 put

forward a system for naming and measuring colours.

'cilia, 'ciliated, 'ciliary. See CILIUM.

Cili'ophera, n.pl. [Zoo.] A CLASS of PRO-TOZOA which get food and keep in motion by the use of CILIA.

'cilium (cilia). [Zoo.] One of the delicate thread-like outgrowths frequently fixed to CELLS in great numbers, having a quick, whip-like, motion in regular rhythm, used by one-celled animals for swimming, by higher animals to make currents of liquid, as in nose or chest; EYELASH; BARBICEL of feather. 'ciliary, a. Like, to do with, cc.; to do with or naming any of a group of structures in the eye of back-boned animals which have to do with ACCOMMODATION. ciliary body. The ring of substance on the inner face of the CHOROID COAT made up chiefly of the ciliary muscles, and to which the CRYSTALLINE LENS and the IRIS are fixed. 'ciliate(d), aa. Having a line of long hairs on the edge; having cc.

cin'cinnus, n. [Bot.] CYME in which the side branches go out to left and right in turn. cin'cinnal, a.

'cingulum (cingula), n. [Zoo.] Any circling band or collar-like structure, sp.:—in worms, the CLITELLUM: in higher animals, such a structure round the base of the CROWN of a tooth, keeping hard bits of food from cutting the GUM.

'cinnabar, n. [Mineral.] Natural HgS, in the form of red or brown CRYSTALS, from which most Hg is got.

'cipher, n. The sign 0.

circle, n. [Geom.] A curved line meeting itself on which every point is at the same distance from a fixed point inside it, or the plane form limited by such a line. [Astron.] Instrument for the observation of the stars whose measuring scale is in the form of a complete c. c. of 'latitude. PARALLEL OF LATITUDE. c. of 'longitude. A c. on the face of the earth going through the North and South POLES. c. of the sphere. A c. on the face of the earth or [Astron.] the SPHERE, named a great circle when its middle point is the same as that of the earth or sphere, a small circle when it is not.

'circuit, n. [Elec.] The way taken by an electric current, the CONDUCTOR or system of conductors through which it goes (see CLOSED CIRCUIT, OPEN CIRCUIT). c. 'breaker. Automatic apparatus for cutting off electric current when it becomes greater than fixed amount.

'circular, a. Formed like a circle. c. mag-neti'zation. MAGNETIZATION of a piece of material in the form of a CYLINDER in such a way that the lines of force go round it. c. mil. Unit of AREA, being that of a circle 0·001 in. across, used in

measuring wire. **c. polari'zation.** The
POLARIZATION of light in two planes at
right-angles to one another, the light-
waves in one plane being equal to those
in the other in AMPLITUDE and FRE-
QUENCY and one-quarter of a PERIOD in
front of them. **'circularly,** adv. **circularly
'polarized.** Having undergone c. polarization.

'circulate, v.i. Go round and round through
a system of ways, vessels, etc., as the
blood in the body, an electric current,
etc. **circu'lation,** n. Sp. [Zoo.] The unbroken motion of the blood of an animal
from the heart through the blood-vessels
and back to the heart again. **'circulating,** a. **circu'latory,** a. **circu'latory
'system.** [Zoo.] A system of vessels
through which a current of liquid is kept
circulating, sp. that transporting the
blood in higher animals.

'circum-. Going all round: **'-'lunar,** a.

cir'cumference, n. (The measure of) the
line limiting a circle or other plane form
sp. curved. **cir'cumfe'rential,** a. To do
with the c.; going round something, sp.
[Zoo.] of CARTILAGES going round certain
hollows or JOINTS.

cir'cumferentor, n. MAGNETIC COMPASS
fixed facing up, with two opposite arms
in a straight line supporting SIGHTS, used
in SURVEYING, etc..

'circumflex, a. Bent round or in the form of a
∧, said sp. [Zoo.] of certain blood-
vessels and nerves.

cir'cumfluence, n. [Zoo.] The process used
by an animal of taking in food, etc. by
putting out PSEUDOPODIA and overrunning with its substance the space
where the food is, seen in PHAGOCYTES,
AMOEBAE, etc. **cir'cumfluent,** a.

'circum'polar stars. [Astron.] Those stars
which, seen from a given part of the
earth, do not come up or go down, but
are at all times moving round the
CELESTIAL POLE, up in the sky.

'circumvall'ation, n. CIRCUMFLUENCE.

'cirr(h)ate, a. [Biol.] Having a CIRRUS or
cirri.

'cirr(h)ose, a. [Biol.] CIRRATE; like a
TENDRIL, waving or twisting; (of a leaf)
having a long tendril coming from the
point.

cir'rhosis, n. [Med.] Disease in which a
part slowly becomes hard through a
general increase of FIBROUS TISSUE, sp. c.
of the LIVER. **ci'rrhotic,** a.

Cirri'pedia, n.pl. [Zoo.] A SUB-CLASS OF
CRUSTACEA, sea-animals free-swimming
in their young stage but later gen. fixed
to stones, etc., or to the bodies of other
animals on which they are PARASITIC, by
feeler-like structures on the head, having
a body with not very clearly marked
divisions, in part covered by a thick fold

of skin made stiff by hard CALCAREOUS
plates, and legs thickly covered with
stiff hair-like structures, in which they
take smaller animals as in a net.

'cirro-'cumulus, n. [Meteor.] High cloud
grouped in small, round masses

'cirro-'filum, n. [Meteor.] CIRRUS cloud
ranged in parallel threads or bands.

'cirro-'macula, n. [Meteor.] CIRRO-CUMULUS
cloud broken into small bits.

'cirro-'nebula, n. [Meteor.] A very thin
stretch of CIRRUS cloud of no special
design.

'cirro-'stratus, n. [Meteor.] High STRATUS
mist

'cirro-'velum, n. [Meteor.] A complete thin
cover of CIRRUS.

'cirrus ('cirri), n. [Meteor.] White, very
high feather-like clouds sometimes
separate, sometimes ranged in special
designs, formed of ice-CRYSTALS. [Zoo.]
Any of different sorts of long, thin outgrowths. [Bot.] TENDRIL.

'cis-trans i'somerism. [Chem.] ISOMERISM
of a COMPOUND having in it a DOUBLE
BOND in which one form (the **cis-'compound** or **cis-form**) has two like groups
on the same side of the double bond
(that is, in the **cis-**position), and the
other (the **'trans-'compound** or **'trans-
form**) has one on one side and the other
on the other (that is, in the **trans-**
position).

'citrate, n. [Chem.] Any SALT of CITRIC
ACID.

'citric, a. [Chem.] Of, to do with, CITRUS
FRUITS or c. acid. **c. acid.** $C_6H_8O_7$, a
white CRYSTALLINE substance with a very
acid taste present in CITRUS FRUITS.

'citrus fruit. [Bot.] The fruit of any plant of
the orange and citron group, a BACCA of
some size with a number of divisions,
much liquid in the soft mass, and a thick
and strong but not hard outer skin of
sponge-like structure.

'civics, n. That branch of POLITICAL
SCIENCE which has to do with the rights
and right behaviour of persons in relation to their government.

Cl, Sign for CHLORINE.

clack valve. [Engin.] An automatic VALVE,
sp. one in the form of a flat plate resting
on an opening, lifted by gas or liquid
going in one direction and dropping back
into its place with a sharp sound.

Clad'ocera, n.pl. [Zoo.] An ORDER of
CRUSTACEA gen. living in inland waters,
very small animals with a hard cover
over the body but not the head, swimming with sudden jumps.

'cladosi'phonic, a. [Bot.] (Of a SIPHONO-
STELE) having BRANCH GAPS but not
LEAF GAPS.

clair'voyance, n. [Psych.] Power of seeing
things not present to the senses, such as

75

persons or events at a great distance or in the past or future. **clair'voyant,** n., a. (Person) having c.

clan, n. [Mineral.] A number of different sorts of IGNEOUS ROCKS grouped together by reason of having the same general chemical make-up, but different in form and details, such as the addition or amount of certain substances, TEXTURE, and the conditions under which they are produced.

'clarify, v.t. Get (a liquid, etc.), make (an opinion, etc.) clear. **'clarifi'cation,** n. **'clarifier,** n. [Chem.] Apparatus for clarifying liquids or gases. **'clarificant,** n. [Chem.] Substance helping clarification.

Clark cell. [Phys.] A STANDARD electric CELL made up of a CATHODE of Hg coated with Hg_2SO_4 and an ANODE of Zn in a SOLUTION of $ZnSO_4$.

'clasper, n. [Zoo.] One or other of the two parts of any structure used by one sex for gripping the other in COPULATION.

class, n. [Biol.] Division of PHYLUM of plants or animals, made up of ORDERS (see pp. 560–4).

'classical, a. [Phys.] Naming or to do with the science of physics before the discovery of the RELATIVITY and QUANTUM theories.

'classify, v.t. Get (things, for example, ROCKS, plants, animals) grouped in a system of groups, gen. based on common or like properties, structure, etc.; put (any example) into its right place in such a system. **classifi'cation,** n. The act of classifying; any way of classifying or system of groups used in classifying, for example that used in Botany and Zoology, ranging from the PHYLUM or DIVISION as the most general, to the SPECIES as the most detailed, group. (See pp. 560–4).

'clastic, a. [Geol.] (Of ROCK) formed of broken bits of other rocks.

'clathrate 'compound. [Chem.] CRYSTAL in which the MOLECULES of one substance are physically fixed in the spaces between the molecules of a second substance but are not chemically united with them.

'Clausius-Mo'sotti law. [Phys.] The law of the relation between the DENSITY, ρ, and the DIELECTRIC CONSTANT, κ, of a dielectric, which says that $\dfrac{\kappa-1}{(\kappa+2)\rho}$ is an unchanging value.

claustro'phobia, n. [Med.] Unnormal fear of being in completely shut-in place.

'clavicle, n. [Zoo.] One or other of two VENTRAL bones of the PECTORAL GIRDLE in back-boned animals, in man joined at one end to the SCAPULA and at the other to the STERNUM.

claw, n. [Bot.] Narrow, stem-like lower part of a PETAL in certain plants. [Zoo.] Sharp, strong, curved nail on toe of bird,

cat, etc.; gripping-apparatus of some CRUSTACEA and ARACHNIDA; small, curved, sharp-pointed outgrowth on leg of insect.

clay, n. [Geol.] Earth material, chiefly made up of $Al_2O_3.2SiO_2.2H_2O$, forming a paste when wet but turning very hard under the operation of heat.

C 'layer. [Radio] A part of the ATMOSPHERE from about 35 to 70 km. up in which radio waves undergo REFLECTION and DISPERSION.

'clean-up, n. [Elec.] Further clearing of gas from a VACUUM TUBE as the effect of the ABSORPTION by the glass of some of that which has not been taken away by pumping.

'clearance, n. [Mach.] The free space between any two parts of a machine, sp. between two moving parts, or between a moving part and a fixed part.

'cleavage, n. [Mineral., Cryst.] Property of CRYSTALS and some ROCKS of readily undergoing division in one or more fixed directions parallel to faces of the crystal etc. [Zoo.] The process of CELL-division in a FERTILIZED OVUM by which an EMBRYO is formed. [Chem.] The division of a complex, sp. a PROTEIN, MOLECULE into simpler molecules. **c. 'nucleus.** The NUCLEUS of a FERTILIZED OVUM. **c. plane.** [Mineral. Cryst.] The plane on which a CRYSTAL or ROCK undergoes division.

'cleaving, n. [Phonet.] The sound-change by which a long VOWEL or CONSONANT sometimes becomes broken up into a complex of two shorter ones.

cleft, 1.n. A deep crack or cut, or a long narrow hollow or division, as [Astron.] on the face of the moon. 2.a. Having a c. or cc., sp. [Bot.] (of a leaf) with deep divisions going from the edge more than half-way to the middle. [Phonet.] Having undergone CLEAVING. **c. 'palate.** [Med.] A deep crack in the roof of the mouth from birth, causing trouble in talking.

'cleido-. [Zoo.] (Of) a CLAVICLE (and . . .).

'cleisto-. [Bot.] Shut.

'cleisto'carp, n. [Bot.] CLEISTOTHECIUM. **-ous,** a. (Of MUSCI) having CAPSULE without a separate cover, opening irregularly; (of FUNGI) having or forming shut ASCOCARPS.

cl(e)is'togamy, n. [Bot.] The producing of small two-sexed flowers which undergo self-FERTILIZATION without opening. **cleisto'gamic, cleis'togamous,** aa.

'cleistogene, n. [Bot.] CLEISTOGAMOUS flower, or plant producing such flowers.

cleisto'thecium, n. [Bot.] ASCOCARP in the form of a completely shut vessel, the wall of which becomes broken down to let out the SPORES.

click, n. [Phonet.] Any of group of sharp sounds in S. African languages, made by putting tongue against roof of mouth or teeth.

cli'macteric, n. [Med.] Time at which important physical change in person takes place, sp. when woman's power to give birth to young comes to an end.

'climate, n. [Meteor.] The general weather conditions of a place all the year round, taking into account its range of TEMPERATURES, AVERAGE RAINFALL, amount of water in the air, and so on. **cli'matic**, a. **climatic 'region** or **zone**. [Geog.] Any of the divisions of the earth based on c., the chief of which are the TROPICAL. SUBTROPICAL, TEMPERATE and POLAR. **clima-'tologist**, n. **clima'tology**, n. The science of cc., their causes, and their effects on the physical form of, and the living conditions for, animals and plants in different countries.

'climax, n. The highest stage or point, freq. the turning-point, in a process of development, for example in a disease. [Bot., Geog.] The last stage in the development of plant-growth in a place, when complete adjustment has been made to the weather conditions, the sort and quality of the earth, and the structure of the land, so that no further change is to be looked for. **c. associ'ation**. The plant-growth forming a c. in any given sort of place.

'climber, n. [Biol.] Plant able to make upright growth only by twisting round or gripping in some other way such supports as trees, sticks, walls; animal able to go up trees and so on, and having feet or other APPENDAGES formed for this purpose. **'climbing**, n., a. (The act of) going up trees, etc. as a c. does.

'clinic, n. [Med.] Place where medical learners are given teaching by watching the work of experts on ill persons; group giving teaching at c. **'-al**, a. Of, to do with, taking place in, a c.; to do with the fighting of disease by observation of and work on ill persons, as opp. medical work done in a LABORATORY etc. **clinical an'alysis**. Test of substances from the body of a living person for purpose of discovery of disease. **clinical ther'mometer**, THERMOMETER for getting body TEMPERATURE of person or animal. **cli'nician** n. Expert on clinical work.

cli'nometer, n. [Surveying, etc.] Handinstrument for measuring slope of mountain, gun, part of building, etc. **clino'metric**, a. To do with a c. or clinometry; to do with solids, sp. CRYSTALS, with AXES not at right angles. **cli'nometry**, n.

'clinostat, n. Apparatus for keeping plants in motion in such a way as to make less or take away the effect of light or GRAVITY. **clino'static**, a.

cli'tellum, n. [Zoo.] Thick part of skin on the body of certain worms having in it GLANDS producing a sticky substance used for covering the eggs.

'clitoris, n. [Zoo.] In female MAMMALS, small mass of TISSUE at front end of VULVA, representative of the PENIS in the male.

clo'aca, n. [Zoo.] Vessel into which INTESTINAL, GENITAL, and URINARY CANALS go in birds, fishes, and other animals which have only one opening for all these. [Med.] Hole through bone into shut hollow place.

'clockwise, a. and adv. (Moving round) in the same direction as the hands of a clock.

'clockwork, n. Machine working automatically by the acting on one another of wheels and springs and weights after being started, like a clock.

clone, n. [Biol.] All the animals (or plants) produced by a sex-produced animal (or plant) by process other than a sex-process.

'clonus, n. [Med.] A process of sudden and irregular CONTRACTION and expansion of muscles caused by nerve damage. **'clonic**, a. To do with c.; having an irregular, violent, CONTRACTING motion. **clonic spasm**, A short SPASM, sp. one forming part of a c., as opp. TONIC SPASM. **clo'nicity**, n.

closed, a. Shut, without a parting or opening; complete, so that there is no room for further development or addition, sp. [Bot.] of a VASCULAR BUNDLE having no CAMBIUM. **c. chain**. [Chem.] A group of ATOMS joined together in the form of a ring. **c. 'circuit**. [Elec.] A CIRCUIT in which there is CONDUCTING material all the way. [Phys.] *See* HYDRAULICS. **c. curve** [Maths.] A line so curved that it comes back to its starting-point, for example a circle.

close 'vowel. [Phonet.] A VOWEL made with some part of the tongue near the roof of the mouth.

clot, 1.n. A COAGULATED mass produced in or from a liquid, sp. blood. 2.v.t. and i. (Make) undergo clotting. **'clotted**, a. Having undergone clotting, being in the form of a c. or cc. **'clotting**, n. The COAGULATION of a liquid, sp. of blood at the opening of a wound, the natural process which keeps all the blood from being drained out of the body when wounded.

cloud, n. A mass of very small drops of water keeping at more or less the same distance over the earth, caused by CONDENSATION from warm air moving up to a colder level. **c. 'chamber**, n. [Phys.] Apparatus for observation of IONS in gas, formed of vessel full of dust-free air having in it water in the form of gas, which becomes liquid when

IONIZED by electric PARTICLES, so that the way taken by a particle is seen as a line of mist.

club, n. [Zoo.] Part of body increased in size at end, as insect's feeler.

'clubbing. n. [Med.] The becoming thick of the ends of the fingers which takes place, in CHRONIC disease of the LUNGS.

clubbed, a. Having undergone c.

'clubfoot, n. [Med.] TALIPES.

clutch, n. [Engin.] An apparatus in a machine etc. by which two working-parts, such as two SHAFTS or a shaft and a PULLEY, may be put into or out of connection with one another by the operation of a LEVER, as in an auto-mobile; the lever by which a c. is worked.

'clypeus, n. [Zoo.] A hard plate on the middle of the front of the head in insects, before the FRONS.

Cm, Sign for CURIUM.

c.n. = COORDINATION NUMBER.

cnida (cnidae), n. CNIDOBLAST.

Cni'daria, n.pl. [Zoo.] A SUB-PHYLUM of COELENTERATA armed with NEMATO-CYSTS and moving by the use of muscles, not CILIA, e.g. jelly-fish, CORALS, etc. **cni'darian,** n.

'cnidoblast, n. [Zoo.] A CELL housing or producing a NEMATOCYST, sp. in CNI-DARIA.

'cnidocil, n. [Zoo.] Small sense-part coming out from a CNIDOBLAST which when touched etc. makes it send out poison.

'cnidophore, n. [Zoo.] A part supporting CNIDOBLASTS.

Co, Sign for COBALT.

co-, With.

'coacer'vation, n. The coming together of the drops of an EMULSION, forming greater drops.

co'action, n. [Ecol.] The effect on one another of different sorts of plants, or of plants and animals, living in the same place.

'coaggre'gation, n. [Meteor.] Uniting of drops of mist or cloud into greater drops.

coagu'lation, n. [Chem.] The becoming stiff, jelly-like, or solid of all or part of a liquid as the effect of chemical change, as in the CLOTTING of the blood, the FLOCCULATION of COLLOIDAL SOLUTIONS, the becoming hard of PROTOPLASM and ALBUMEN when heated, etc. **co'agulate,** v.t. and i. Make undergo c. **co'agulum,** n. The solid part formed when a liquid coagulates.

coal, n. [Mineral.] A black natural solid present in great beds under the earth, formed from plant material of thousands of years back which has undergone DECOMPOSITION away from the air and been specially changed by the operation of water, heat, the weight of the earth over it, etc., made up chiefly of C and having the property of burning slowly,

producing much heat. **c. tar.** The thick, black, oil-like liquid produced by the DISTILLATION of c., made up of HYDRO-CARBON oils, PHENOLS, and other substances of value.

coa'lesce, v.i. Come together, become united, into one thing or substance; **coa'lescence,** n. **coa'lescent,** a.

coarse, a. (Of threads, grains, etc.) of some size, thick, (of a substance) formed of c. grains, threads, etc., (of cloth, etc.) loosely made, with holes of some size between its threads, etc. **c. grained.** Sp. [Geol.] (of ROCKS) having grains or CRYSTALS of a size to be seen separately by the eye without the help of an instru-ment.

coast, n. [Geog., Geol.] The part of any land edging the sea or other great body of water and acted on by it. **'-line,** n. The outline of a c. **'coastal,** a.

co'axial, a. (Of two things) having the same AXIS. **c. 'cable.** [Elec.] A cable formed of two CONDUCTORS, one of pipe-like form, the other going down the middle of it and separated from it by INSULATING MATERIAL.

'cobalt, n. Chemical ELEMENT, at. no. 27, at. wt. 59·94, sign Co, a silver-white metal somewhat like iron but harder.

'cobble, n. [Geol.] A weather-rounded stone of a size between a BOULDER and a PEBBLE in some groupings.

'coccus (cocci), n. [Med.] Any BACTERIUM having the form of a ball or an egg. [Bot.] A one-seeded division of a SCHIZOCARP, sp. when round.

'coccyx (coccyges), n. [Zoo.] In man, the lower end of the backbone; in other animals, the base of the tail. **coccy'geal,** a.

'cochlea, n. [Zoo.] The twisting pipe of the INNER EAR in higher animals, where sound-waves are changed into the NERVE IMPULSES effecting hearing. **'cochlear,** a.

cock, n. [Zoo.] A male bird.

co'coon, n. [Zoo.] Cover formed of silk or of other material united by silk, made by the LARVA of an insect for the PUPA; cover formed by some animals for their eggs.

code, n. Any system of SIGNS or SIGNALS representative of words, letters, etc., as used, for example, in sending telegrams.

co'dominant, 1.a. [Ecol.] Being one of two or more DOMINANT sorts in a plant COM-MUNITY. 2.n. A c. sort.

coef'ficient, n. [Phys., etc.] A fixed number or unchanging RATIO measuring some given effect or property of a thing or substance in given conditions, for unit amounts and so on, and used in working out values in connection with this—having much the same use as the word FACTOR and freq. forming another name for the same thing, as **c. of ab'sorption**

(=ABSORPTION FACTOR), **c. of re'flection** (=REFLECTION FACTOR), **c. of 'safety** (=SAFETY FACTOR). **c. of ex'pansion.** (Of a given substance) the increase in LENGTH per unit AREA, or in VOLUME per unit volume, caused by an increase in TEMPERATURE from 0°C to 1°C. **c. of mo'lecular de'pression.** Amount by which FREEZING POINT of a given liquid is made lower by the SOLUTION in 1 litre of it of 1 GRAM MOLECULE of a substance. **c. of rigidity.** RIGIDITY MODULUS.

Coe'lenterata, n.pl. [Zoo.] A PHYLUM of DIPLOBLASTIC METAZOA which have only one hollow inside the body wall, the ENTERON, having only one opening, the mouth—water animals with RADIAL or BIRADIAL SYMMETRY. **coel'enterate,** n., a. (Animal) of, to do with, the C.

coe'lenteron, n. [Zoo.] Hollow in body of COELENTERATA in which digestion takes place.

'c(o)eliac, a. [Zoo.] To do with the hollow of the ABDOMEN in back-boned animals. **c. 'artery, c. 'axis.** Short, thick blood-vessel coming out of AORTA. **c. 'plexus.** Group of nerves round coeliac axis.

'Coelomata, n.pl. [Zoo.] The group of TRIPLOBLASTIC METAZOA which have a COELOM at every stage in their development.

'coelom(e), n. [Zoo.] The hollow formed in and walled with the MESODERM in the bodies of most METAZOA higher than sponges and COELENTERATA, sometimes forming all the body-hollow, sometimes taking in only the sex and EXCRETORY apparatus. **'coelomate,** a. **coel'omic,** a.

coel'omoduct, n. [Zoo.] Pipe going from COELOM to outside.

'coelostat, n. [Astron.] An instrument made up of a plane looking-glass turning by CLOCKWORK on an AXIS parallel to that of the earth in a direction opposite to that in which the earth is turning, used to keep the same part of the sky REFLECTED into the field of view of a fixed TELESCOPE independently of the turning motion of the earth.

coe'nobium (coenobia), n. [Biol.] Mass of one-CELLED living things in bag of skin, acting as one and producing other cc.

'coenocyte, n. [Bot.] Plant-body having a number of NUCLEI formed by the division of one nucleus, but not separated into CELLS by cell-walls. **coeno'cytic,** a.

co'enzyme, n. [Biochem.] A substance which is present with, and necessary for the operation of, an ENZYME.

coercive force, coer'civity, n. [Elec.] The MAGNETIC force needed for the destruction of the RESIDUAL MAGNETISM of a substance.

cog, n. [Mach.] One tooth of a cogwheel or like toothed part. **'-wheel,** n. A wheel with a toothed edge designed for turning against a like wheel or toothed part so as to keep pushing it round or on, the cc. of the two being so placed that those of one come between those of the other.

'cognate, a.[Biol., Philol.] of the same family.

cog'nition, n. [Psych.] Process by which the mind gets knowledge, becomes conscious of things. **'cognitive.** a.

oo'herer, n. [Radio] Apparatus having metal powder between two small metal plates used in early work for the DETECTION of radio waves.

co'hesion, n. [Phys.] The force of attraction between the MOLECULES of a substance by which it is kept together. [Bot.] The uniting of like parts of a plant. **co'hesive,**a.

'cohort, n. [Biol.] Old name for a group of plants or animals without clear limits.

coil, n. Wire, pipe or cord forming one or more rings or turns, sp. [Elec.] a HELIX or SPIRAL of wire put round a solid middle part for the purpose of producing ELECTRO-MAGNETIC effects; [Engin.] A number of pipes, rods, or cc. in connection with one another forming a unit, as in steam-heating or water-heating apparatus.

co'incidence, n. The taking place of two events at the same time; the coming together of two or more points in space. **c. 'counting.** Way of getting the number and direction of RADIO-ACTIVE PARTICLES or rays going past a point by the use of not less than two GEIGER COUNTERS, recording an effect only when it is made on the two of them.

co'incident, a. Taking place at the same time; being at the same point in space. **coin'cide,** v.i. Be coincident.

co'ition, co'itus, nn. [Zoo.] COPULATION.

coke, n. [Chem.] The solid material, chiefly C, produced when coal is strongly heated with no air present.

'colchicine, n. [Chem., Biochem.] An ALKALOID got from the CORMS and seeds of the plant *Colchicum*, used medically for GOUT and noted for its effect on CELL-DIVISION in plants and animals, and for causing an increase in the CHROMOSOMES of young plants to twice the normal number, so producing plants of great size.

cold, n. [Med.] Common name for CORYZA.

cold-'blooded, a. [Zoo.] (Of animals) having the degree of body heat not fixed, but changing with that of the air or water round, as fish and snakes, opp. WARM-BLOODED.

'cold-working, n. [Metal.] The process of rolling, pulling, stamping, or in any way working metals into a desired form without making them soft by heating.

Cole'optera, n.pl. [Zoo.] An ORDER of ENDOPTERYGOTE insects with hard front wings covering back part of body and back wings, if present, MEMBRANOUS. **cole′opterous**, a.

coleo′rhiza, n. [Bot.] Thin skin covering root of young plant.

′colic, 1.n. [Med.] Sharp, sudden pain in INTESTINES. 2.a. Of the COLON.

′coli group, n. [Med.] A group of disease BACILLI, such as that causing TYPHOID, which are common in man's INTESTINE and in dirty water.

co′litis, n. [Med.] INFLAMMATION of the COLON.

′collagen, n. [Chem., Zoo.] PROTEIN substance producing GELATIN on boiling, and forming strong FIBRES present in CONNECTIVE TISSUE, bone, etc.

col′lapse, 1.v.i. (Of a structure) give way suddenly under some force or inner process and become broken, or without form or support; of an elastic vessel full of gas, undergo the loss of this so that the walls come together. [Med.] (Of a person) undergo a sudden loss of force, fighting power, become very feeble, sp. as the effect of a serious slowing of the blood-current caused by disease, nerve-shock, loss of blood, etc.; (of a LUNG) undergo a complete loss of air. 2.v.t. Make (an elastic vessel, or sp. a LUNG) c., as is done sometimes for medical purposes in lung disease. 3.n. A collapsing, a sudden falling down or in, giving way, loss of physical force, etc. **coll′apsed**, a. Sp., having had the gas or air sent out of it.

′collar, n. [Bot.] Join between root of plant and its stem; ring round middle of stem of BASIDIOMYCETES. [Zoo.] Any collar-like structure, as that round FLAGELLUM in MASTIGOPHORA.

col′lateral, a. [Biol.] Side by side, parallel, said of family lines having common ANCESTOR; said of blood-vessel joining with others near it so as to make a way for the blood when chief vessel is stopped up, or of CIRCULATION kept up in this way. **c. ′bundle**. VASCULAR BUNDLE in which the PHLOEM and XYLEM are side by side, with the xylem on the outer side.

coll′ect, v.t. and i. Get or come together into one place; (of vessels, etc.) take in, be a collecting place for. **coll′ecting**, a. Sp., being a place where something collects, as [Biol.] the **collecting ′tubules** where URINE collects in the KIDNEY, or [Elec.] the **collecting e′lectrode** on which material is put down in ELECTROLYSIS. **coll′ector**, n. Collecting part, sp. [Elec.] the part of an ELECTROSTATIC GENERATOR storing the ELECTRICITY produced. **coll′ective**, a. Formed of, to do with, a number of like things united or taken together. **collective fruit**. [Bot.] A fruit formed by the uniting of the OVARIES of a mass of small flowers.

coll′embola, n.pl. [Zoo.] An ORDER of small insects without wings, jumping by the use of two elastic outgrowths at the tail-end, which may be bent under the body and then suddenly let go, acting like a spring—gen. living under stones, leaves, etc.

col′lenchyma, n. [Bot.] Supporting material seen in young stems, etc., made up of long living CELLS with walls made stronger by bands of CELLULOSE. [Zoo.] The middle LAYER of a sponge.

′Colles's ′fracture. [Med.] A FRACTURE of the lower end of the RADIUS of the arm, in which the broken bone is pushed back out of place.

col′lide, v.i. Have a COLLISION (with).

′colligative ′property. [Chem.] A property of a SOLUTION which is dependent only on the CONCENTRATION, and not on the sort of MOLECULES, etc. forming the SOLUTE.

′collimate, v.t. [Phys.] Make (anything, sp. rays of light or AXIS of instrument) parallel. **′collimator**, n. OPTICAL apparatus which makes rays parallel. **colli′mation**, n.

col′lision, n. Violent meeting of bodies, sp. of ATOMS, MOLECULES, etc., generally with exchange of ENERGY.

col′lodion, n. [Chem.] A sticky solution of mixed NITROCELLULOSES in ALCOHOL and ETHER or in ACETONE, used medically for covering wounds and in camera work for coating FILMS etc. with SENSITIVE chemicals.

′colloid, n. [Chem.] A substance which normally undergoes DISPERSION in the colloidal state, forming colloidal solutions, for example, soap, GELATIN. **col′loidal**, a. Of, to do with, having the properties of a c.; being in a condition of colloidal solution. **colloidal so′lution**. A DISPERSION of one substance in another in which the dispersed substance is in the colloidal state, sp. such a dispersion of a solid in a liquid. **colloidal state**. The condition of a substance DISPERSED in another in the form not of separate MOLECULES but of groups of molecules (measuring between about 10^{-4} and 10^{-7} cm. across), only the greatest of which may be seen separately through a common MICROSCOPE but which make it impossible for a liquid colloidal solution to go through a SEMI-PERMEABLE MEMBRANE, and give it special properties different from those of a true solution, sp. that of forming a GEL.

′collotype, n. Printing-plate used in, or print made by, the c. process. **c. ′process**. A process of printing pictures from a plate of glass coated with hard GELATINE which has been made SENSITIVE to light, and on which the desired picture is printed from a camera NEGATIVE, the gelatine then going through a process which gives it the property of taking up printing ink in a way to make a very good copy of every degree of light and shade—used for pictures in which small detail is desired.

colo′boma, n. [Med.] A LESION in any part of the eye which is present from birth, a natural error in development.

′colon, n. [Zoo.] That part of the LARGE INTESTINE between the SMALL INTESTINE or the CAECUM, if any, and the RECTUM, in man going up the right side of the body (the *ascending c.*), turning and going across it (the *transverse c.*), coming down on the left side (the *descending c.*), and ending in the SIGMOID FLEXURE; the wider, back division of an insect's intestine. **co′lonic,** a.

′colony, n. [Zoo.] Group of animals of the same sort living together and having some degree of organization for work, forming a common store of food, building a common living-place, etc.; a COMPOUND ANIMAL. [Bot.] A group of plants which has come up naturally on land where it has not been before; a mass of BACTERIA which are the offspring of one, or of a small group, making growth on something solid or half-solid. **co′lonial,** a. Sp. [Zoo.] forming, living in, cc. **′colonize,** v.i. and t. Get formed into cc.; go into, take up, new land, sp. of plants.

colo′phonium, co′lophony, nn. [Chem.] ROSIN.

color′ation, n. Condition of being coloured or way a thing is coloured, sp. the colours and their grouping on an animal.

color′imeter, n. [Optics] Instrument for the measuring or comparison of CHROMATIC colours. [Chem.] Instrument for the comparison of colours in colorimetric analyses. **colori′metric,** a. **colorimetric an′alysis.** [Chem.] ANALYSIS of a SOLUTION by a comparison of the colour produced on the addition of a certain substance with that produced on its addition to a STANDARD solution. **color′imetry,** n. The measuring or comparison of colours as a science or a process.

co′lostomy, n. [Med.] An operation to make an opening in the COLON and through the body-wall to take out waste material when there is some reason why the normal use of the ANUS is not possible; such an opening.

co′lostrum, n. [Zoo.] The milk of a MAMMAL formed in the first days after the birth of the offspring. **co′lostr-ic, -ous,** aa.

co′lotomy, n. [Med.] The operation of making an opening in the COLON; loosely COLOSTOMY

′colour, n. [Psych., Optics] That part of the sense-experience of seeing which is different from form, and from light and shade, and which is dependent on the

WAVE-LENGTH, or the mixed wave-lengths, of the light acting on the eye (*see* CHROMATIC and ACHROMATIC); this effect looked on as a property of light dependent on its wave-length, ranging through a fixed scale of colours from red for the longest to VIOLET for the shortest wave-lengths. **c. base.** [Chem.] A BASE which is a DYE or has the property of forming dyes. **c. ′blindness.** [Psych.] Common name for DEFECTIVE COLOUR VISION. **′c. ′filter.** Coloured glass or like material stopping rays of light of certain cc. **c. phase.** [Zoo.] Any of the different systems of colouring seen in the coat of an animal or the feathers of a bird at different times of the year or different stages of its existence. **c. ′quality.** [Psych.] CHROMA. **c. ′solid.** [Optics, Psych.] Form in three DIMENSIONS, such as a PYRAMID, representative of three properties of c., one dimension for every property (for example HUE, VALUE, and CHROMA in the MUNSELL COLOUR SYSTEM), used for placing colours in relation to these three COÖRDINATES. **c. ′temperature.** [Phys.] Of a body, TEMPERATURE of a BLACK-BODY giving out light of same colour as body. **c. ′theory.** [Zoo., Psych.] Any theory as to the physical apparatus in the eye and brain by which cc. are seen (*see* TRICHROMATIC THEORY, LADD-FRANKLIN THEORY, HERING THEORY). **c. ′vision** [Zoo., Psych.] The power or process of seeing different cc. **′c.-blind.** Having DEFECTIVE COLOUR VISION.

co′lumbite, n. [Mineral.] A MINERAL formed of iron and Mn SALTS of NIOBIUM and TANTALUM, from which tantalum is got.

co′lombium, n. Another name for NIOBIUM.

colu′mella, n. [Bot.] A MASS of STERILE substance in the middle of the SPORANGIUM in MUSCI and some HEPATICAE; SEPTUM like an arched roof in the sporangium of some FUNGI. [Zoo.] Middle structure in framework of some CORALS; rod, made of bone and CARTILAGE, joining the TYMPANIC MEMBRANE and the inner ear of birds, REPTILIA, and AMPHIBIA (*c. auris*); middle structure in SHELLS of GASTROPODA; middle structure of the COCHLEA. **colu′mellar,** a.

′column, n. A tall, regular, upright, solid structure, formed of a mass of substance or of a number of things put one on top of the other, for example, a c. of gas or liquid in an upright pipe; numbers, words, etc., put under one another on paper, etc., and giving the suggestion of a c. **co′lumnar,** a. Sp. having a structure of cc. or upright rods. **co′lumnar ′crystals.** [Metal.] In a metal which has been put when liquid into a MOULD, long narrow CRYSTALS at right-angles to the

outside, formed after the CHILL CRY-
STALS as the second stage of becoming
solid. **columnar epi'thelium** [Zoo.] A
sort of EPITHELIUM made up of tall
narrow CELLS on a BASEMENT MEMBRANE
and gen. only one cell thick, present in
man on the inside of the INTESTINES.

co'lure, n. [Astron.] One of two circles
through the CELESTIAL POLES, the
equin'octial c., going through the EQUI-
'NOCTIAL points, and the **sol'stitial c.,** at
right angles to it.

co'lustrum, n. [Zoo.] COLOSTRUM.

'colza oil. A yellow oil got from the seeds
of a plant used as food for sheep, etc., the
oil itself being of value for lighting, as a
LUBRICANT, as a food, and in QUENCHING
steel.

'coma, n. [Astron.] The mist-like part
round a COMET's head. [Bot.] A massed
group of hairs, branches, etc., as the
brush of hairs on certain seeds or the
leaves at the end of the stem in MUSCI.
[Optics] Error in the IMAGE formed by a
LENS caused by RAYS not parallel to the
AXIS. [Med.] Condition in which a person
is completely unconscious and unable to
give a reaction to any STIMULUS. **'com-al,
-ate, -ose,** aa. [Bot.] Of, to do with,
having, a c. **'comatose,** a. [Med.] Of, like,
in a condition of, c..

comag'matic, a. [Geol.] Formed from the
same MAGMA.

comb, n. Soft, c-like outgrowth on head of
some birds; c.-rib; HONEYCOMB. **c.-rib,** n.
[Zoo.] CTENE.

combi'nation, n. Uniting, sp. that of
chemical substances to make COMPOUNDS.
c. note, c. tone. [Acous.] Note formed in
addition when two notes of almost equal
FREQUENCIES are sounded together.
com'bine, v.t. and i. (Make) undergo c.
com'bining, a., n. **combining weight.**
[Chem.] CHEMICAL EQUIVALENT.

com'bustion, n. Any chemical process in
which light and heat are produced,
commonly by the uniting of a substance
with O, as the burning of anything in
air. **c. 'chamber.** [Eng.] In a boiler
FURNACE, a space in which gases given
off by the fire become mixed with air
and themselves take fire; in an INTERNAL
COMBUSTION ENGINE, the space in the
CYLINDER where c. takes place. **c.
'furnace.** Apparatus used for heating a
pipe in which ANALYSIS of a substance is
done by burning it in a current of O.

'comet, n. [Astron.] Light-giving body of
small MASS but freq. very great size
moving through space under the attraction of the sun, and seen by us as a bright
mass (the *head*) with a body of mist
round it and gen. a long, mist-like tail
pointing away from the sun.

com'mensalism, n. [Biol.] Condition in

which animals or plants of different sorts
are living together, generally taking the
same food, without having much effect
on one another. **com'mensal,** a. Of, living
in a condition of, c.

'comminute, v.t. Get (anything) broken
into very small bits, or crushed to a
powder. **commi'nution,** n. **'comminuted
'fracture.** [Med.] Place at which bone is
broken into a number of small bits.

'commissure, n. [Biol.] Line down which
parts are joined together; [Zoo.] A JOINT;
a parcel of NERVE-FIBRES joining two
greater masses of nerves, as those joining
the right and left sides of the brain in
higher animals.

common 'logarithms. LOGARITHMS which
are POWERS of 10.

com'munity, n. [Bot.] Any group of different
sorts of plants living in the same place
and having in common the need for
certain weather etc. conditions, a more
general name than ASSOCIATION, not
being limited to fixed groups of regular
organization having well-marked chief
sorts and covering wide stretches of
country. [Zoo.] Any group of animals of
the same or different sorts living together
or in the same place.

'commutate, v.t. [Elec.] Get the direction
of (an electric current) changed to the
opposite. **commu'tation,** n. **commu'tator,**
n. Apparatus for changing connections,
automatically or by hand, in an apparatus
through which electric current is going,
for the purpose of the commutation or
distribution of the current. **commutator
bar, commutator 'segment.** Any of the
rods forming the c. of a DYNAMO or
motor.

com'panion cell. [Bot.] Any of a number of
small NUCLEATED CELLS by the side of
the cells of a SIEVE TUBE, seemingly
playing some part in sending food
through it.

com'parative, a. Of, to do with, based on,
using, comparison. **c. a'natomy.** Science of
the comparison of the structure of
plants and animals, sp. as giving light
on the process of their development.

com'parator, n. [Phys.] Instrument for the
comparison of measures of LENGTH, gen.
made up of a TELESCOPE or MICROSCOPE
moving up and down a scale. [Optics]
Instrument for making a comparison
between two lights or colours, more
limited in its range of colours than a
COLORIMETER.

'compass, n. MAGNETIC COMPASS; an instrument for making circles or parts of
circles on paper etc., formed of two
pointed legs so joined that one may be
kept fixed at one point while the other
(gen. having a pen or pencil point) is
turned round it at the desired distance

(gen. named **cc.** or **pair of cc.**).

com'patibility, n. (Of two things) the property of being in harmony with one another, able to be present or in existence together without one ruling out or overcoming the effect of the other. [Chem.] (Of two SOLUTIONS) the property of mixing together without causing PRECIPITATION or other reaction.

'compensate, 1.v.i. (Of a thing or effect) make up for the loss of some other thing, or have an effect balancing another (damaging or undesired) effect, or (of person) make a compensating effect come about. 2.v.t. [Mach.] Make some adjustment in (a machine or instrument) so as to overcome the effect of some irregular tendency or outside force, such as that of TEMPERATURE, FRICTION, a MAGNETIC FIELD, etc., by balancing it with an opposite force or effect. **'compensated,** a. (Of an instrument or machine) so designed that some tendency to error, loss, etc. is compensated for. **compensated** or **compen'sation 'pendulum.** [Phys.] A PENDULUM made up of two different materials such that the effect of any change in TEMPERATURE on one of them is balanced by its effect on the other, and the measure of the pendulum keeps the same at all temperatures. **'compensating,** a. Effecting compensation, sp. of a machine-part or apparatus. **compen'sation,** n. The act or process of compensating, or condition of being compensated; a compensating effect. [Biol.] Adjustment or tendency to adjustment to the loss of an ORGAN or its full working-power by increased working of another organ or of the undamaged parts of the same organ. [Psych.] The process of fixing one's desires, feelings, etc., strongly on something to make up for the loss etc. of some other thing, or the process of covering up some undesired quality or condition of body or mind by the development and putting forward of some other quality or power. **'compensator,** n. [Mach., Elec., etc.] Any apparatus, machine-part, etc. effecting compensation for some undesired effect. [Elec.] AUTO-TRANSFORMER. **com'pensatory,** a. Designed or used for, acting as, produced by the need for, compensation. **compensatory 'after-'image.** [Psych.] The COMPLEMENTARY AFTER-IMAGE experienced by the eye after looking fixedly till it is tired at some brightly coloured thing. **compensatory 'doubling.** [Phonet.] The DOUBLING of a CONSONANT in writing a word when a STRESSED long VOWEL-sound in front of it has become short. **compensatory 'lengthening.** [Phonet.] The making longer of the sound of a letter in a word after the dropping or VOCALI-

ZATION of the letter coming after it.

'complement, n. A thing COMPLEMENTARY to a given thing, sp. a complementary angle. [Biochem., Med.] A PROTEIN normally present in the blood which takes a necessary part in the operation of any ANTIBODY against an ANTIGEN, and without which the antibody has no power of acting. **c. fix'ation.** [Biochem., Med.] The taking up of the c. in the reaction between an ANTIBODY and an ANTIGEN so that it is no longer free to do its work if further antigens are put into the blood, a condition on which tests for antibodies and antigens are based (see WASSERMAN TEST).

comple'mental air. [Physiol.] Amount by which the air taken in by the deepest possible breath is greater than that taken in by a normal breath.

comple'mental male. [Zoo.] In certain water-animals, a small DEGENERATE form with male sex-parts living fixed to the body of the normal female or HERMAPHRODITE form.

comple'mentary, a. Being one of two things which together make a third or which go together to produce a certain effect. [Geom.] (Of an angle) being that angle which together with a given angle makes a right angle. [Optics] (Of a CHROMATIC colour) being that colour of light or paint etc. which when mixed with a given chromatic colour makes white if light is in question (as by the addition of yellow and blue light) or grey, if it is a question of paints (as red and green). [Geol.] Said of small masses of ROCK of different sorts present, freq. in the form of DYKES, in or with a greater mass of another sort from which they have been chemically produced. **c. 'after-'image.** [Psych.] An AFTER-IMAGE of a seen thing in colours c. to those of the thing itself.

com'plete meta'morphosis. [Zoo.] A METAMORPHOSIS in which there is a PUPA as well as a LARVA stage before the stage of full development.

com'plete re'action. [Chem.] A chemical reaction which is not a REVERSIBLE REACTION and so goes on until one or other of the substances taking part in it is used up.

'complex, n. [Psych.] A group of feelings, memories and desires which is fixed on something outside the self and has become an unhealthily controlling force in conscious and unconscious behaviour.

com'plexus, n. A complex system of parts, sp. [Zoo.] in higher animals, a deep structure of muscles making a connection between different parts of the backbone.

com'pliance, n. [Mech.] (Of a material or structure) the property of giving way to force up to a certain limit by becoming bent, not broken, or the measure of this property as given by the amount of change of form produced by a unit of force. com'pliant, a.

'complicated 'fracture. [Med.] Broken bone with the parts round it damaged.

'compole, n. INTERPOLE.

com'ponent, n. Any of the parts, substances, etc. making up a more complex thing or substance. [Mech.] Of a given force or VELOCITY in a given direction, any of the two or more forces or velocities in other directions of which it is made up, or into which it may be broken up. [Phys., Chem.] In a system of PHASES in EQUILIBRIUM, a necessary chemical c., that is, the cc. of such a system are the separate chemical substances necessarily forming part of it, for example, in an ice—water—WATER VAPOUR system there is only one c., H_2O. [Astron.] Any of the stars forming a DOUBLE or MULTIPLE STAR.

Com'positae, n.pl. [Bot.] A great group or FAMILY of flowering plants, having flower heads made up of tightly massed small flowers with a GAMOPETALOUS, LIGULATE, or TUBULAR COROLLA and a CALYX in the form of a PAPPUS, for example the CARDUCEAE.

'composite, 1.a. Made up of different parts or, sp., materials. [Bot.] Of, to do with, like, the COMPOSITAE. 2.n. A c. thing or flower.

compo'sition, n. The make-up of anything, sp. [Chem.] the different simpler substances of which a complex substance is formed and the PROPORTIONS in which they are united. c. 'formula. [Chem.] EMPIRICAL FORMULA. c. of a force. [Mech.] (The process of working out) the amount and direction of the force which is produced at a point by two other forces acting at that point in different directions.

'compost, n. Plant material which has undergone DECAY as the effect of BACTERIA, naturally or with the help of chemicals, used for putting on the earth for helping the growth of plants.

'compound, 1.a. Made up of, produced by the uniting of, different substances or separate parts or things, different or like. [Bot.] Of an INFLORESCENCE etc. in which the chief stem puts out branches in the order and form of the inflorescence in question, which themselves put out flowers in the same design, as a c. RACEME or UMBEL. 2.n. A c. thing, sp. a CHEMICAL COMPOUND. c. animal. [Zoo.] A number of small and simple animals of the same sort united into one mass and acting as one animal, the units, though to some degree complete in themselves, being dependent on one another and some of them generally having special forms for

special work, for example CORALS. c. 'engine. [Mach.] A steam-engine in which the steam undergoes expansion in stages. c. eye. [Zoo.] The sort of eye seen in insects, which is made up of a great number of very small and simple eyes, with division walls between, massed together on a round arched base and covered with a stiff TRANSPARENT outer skin, every unit being made up of an outer part by which light is REFRACTED and an inner part by which it is sensed. c. 'flower. [Bot.] Old name for a COMPOSITE flower having a flat middle made up of small pipe-like flowers with LIGULATE flowers raying round it like PETALS. c. 'fracture. [Med.] A FRACTURE in which broken bone is pushed out through the skin. c. fruit. [Bot.] PSEUDOCARP. c. leaf [Bot.] Leaf made up of separate leaf-like parts, the divisions between them going down to the MIDRIB (see picture p. 223). c. 'lever. [Mach.] System of two or more simple LEVERS. c. microscope. [Optics] The common microscope having two LENSES or lens-systems, one forming the EYE-PIECE and the other the OBJECTIVE. c. 'ovary. [Bot.] An OVARY formed from two or more CARPELS. c. 'pendulum. [Phys.] Any (PENDULUM formed of a) solid body or system of bodies free to go round on a fixed HORIZONTAL AXIS and kept in STABLE EQUILIBRIUM by the force of GRAVITY. c. prism. [Optics] A PRISM made of prisms of different glass, used, for example, to give DEVIATION without DISPERSION.

com'press, v.t. Get (something) by force into a smaller space, make smaller by PRESSURE. com'pressed, a. Having undergone compression. [Biol.] Flat from side to side as if having undergone compression, as the stems of some leaves, the bodies of some fish. compressi'bility, n. The property of being able to be compressed, or, sp. [Phys.] the degree to which a substance may be compressed, $=1 \div$ the BULK MODULUS. com'pression, n. Act, process, of compressing; condition of being compressed, or of looking as if compressed; amount by which a thing or substance is made smaller by compression. [Astron.] The degree to which a PLANET is flat at the POLES. com'pression-ig'nition-'engine. An INTERNAL COMBUSTION ENGINE in which the necessary heat for firing the oil is produced by compression of the air in the CYLINDER. com-'pression-al, -ive, aa. com'pressor, n. Pump or other machine for compressing a gas. [Zoo.] Any muscle which by its operation compresses some part.

'compress, n. [Med.] A dressing, for example, a folded cloth, put over a wound or other part so as to COMPRESS it.

'Compton effect. [Phys.] The effect by which the WAVE-LENGTH of X-RAYS or GAMMA RAYS is increased by COLLISION with electrons, seen when they are scattered on meeting a chemical ELEMENT of little weight. **Compton e'lectron.** RECOIL ELECTRON.

com'pute, v.t. and i. Get (a number or amount) worked out by arithmetic, etc.

com'puter, n. A machine designed to do the operations of Mathematics on numbers or MAGNITUDES, or to give the answers to questions of the sort which it is possible to get broken up into ARITHMETICAL or simple LOGICAL steps, very much more quickly than a man is able to do in the normal way. *See* ANALOGUE COMPUTER and DIGITAL COMPUTER.

co'nation, n. [Psych.] Conscious desire, tendency, or purpose to do something, conscious impulse to an act. **'conative,** a.

'concave, a. Hollow, curved in. **c. lens.** [Optics] LENS with its two opposite faces c., so that it is thinner in the middle than at the edges. **con'cavo-con'vex,** a. Having one face c. and the other curved out, sp., of LENS with the c. face curved to a greater degree than the other face. **con'cavity,** n. Condition of being c.

con'catenate(d), aa. Joined together forming a chain or SERIES. **concate'nation,** n. The condition of being, or the process of becoming, or the act of making something, c.

con'ceive, v.i. and t. [Med.] Become PREGNANT, undergo the start of the development of (offspring) in the WOMB.

concen'tration, n. The process of concentrating anything or the condition of being concentrated. [Chem.] Number of MOLECULES or IONS of a substance in a given space, or in a given VOLUME of another substance; process by which the c. of a substance is increased. **c. cell.** [Elec.] CELL having ELECTRODES of the same metal in separate SOLUTIONS of the same substance but with different degrees of c. **'concentrate,** 1.v.t. Get (rays, attention, forces, etc.) turned or bent to one point, get anything massed or united more tightly together. [Chem., etc.] Make anything more concentrated, for example, a SOLUTION by taking away some of the SOLVENT or an ORE by washing out some of the undesired material. 2.v.i. Become massed into a smaller space or bent to a common point. [Psych.] Get all one's mind fixed on one (or *on* a given) thing. 2.n. Substance, etc. which has undergone c., sp. [Metal.] an ORE from which as much undesired material as possible has been taken by physical operations and which is now ready for the separating of the metal by chemical processes. **'concentrated,** a. Having

undergone c., sp. [Chem.] of a SOLUTION, very strong.

con'centric, a. [Geom.] (Of circles, etc.) having the same middle point.

con'ception, n. [Med.] The act of CONCEIVING.

conch, n. [Zoo.] Any hard two-VALVED or, and sp., SPIRAL one-valved SHELL of a sea animal. **'conchate,** a. **'conchiform,** a.

'concha, n. [Zoo.] A CONCH-like hollow or structure in the body, sp. the hollow of the outer ear in higher animals.

con'chiferous, a. [Zoo.] Producing or having SHELLS.

con'chitic, a. [Geol.] (Of ROCKS) made up chiefly or to a great degree of SHELLS.

con'chiolin, n. [Zoo.] A horn-like material of which the outer coat of MOLLUSC SHELLS is formed.

conch(o)-. CONCH; CONCHA:— **con'chitis,** n. [Med.].

con'choid(al), a. Having an out- or in-curving, roughly 3-sided form, like one-half of a BIVALVE SHELL; (of a SURFACE) having hollows or outcurvings of this form, sp. [Mineral.]. **c. 'fracture.** The sort of FRACTURE in which the two broken edges or faces are roughly c. in form, one outcurving and one incurving, seen in hard, non-CRYSTALLINE substances.

con'chology, n. [Zoo.] The science of the SHELLS of animals, sp. MOLLUSCA.

con'crescence, n. [Biol.] The growth together of parts at one time separate, so as to become one structure. **con'crescent,** a.

'concrete, n. A building-material formed of a mass of small stones and sand kept together by CEMENT.

con'cretion, n. Any solid mass formed by the uniting of small bits or parts. [Med.] A hard mass of Ca SALTS or other material formed in some part of the body. [Geol.] Mass of a different sort of ROCK formed in a rock from a SOLUTION present in its spaces, as FLINT in chalk. **con'cretionary,** a.

con'cussion, n. Shaking, shock. [Med.] Loss of the normal power of working, without any seen wound, in some part of the body, sp. the brain, as the effect of a violent blow or fall. **con'cussed,** a. Sp. [Med.].

conden'sation, n. Act or process of condensing or condition of being condensed. [Chem.] A chemical reaction between two or more MOLECULES, of the same or different sorts, in which certain ATOMS are united into a more complex molecule with the loss of the rest in the form of some simple substance such as water or HCl. [Phys.-Chem.] The changing of a gas into its liquid form as the effect of a loss of heat or increase in PRESSURE. [Meteor.] The changing of WATER VAPOUR in the air into water drops through loss of heat, forming mist, cloud, rain, or drops on cold SURFACES. **c. 'polymer.** [Chem.] A POLYMER produced by c. **c. 'polymeri'zation.** [Chem.] C. **con'dense,** v.t. and i. Get (something into, or come to be in, a more solid, tightly massed, or CONCENTRATED form, taking up less space. [Chem., Phys.] Undergo or make (MOLECULES, a gas) undergo, c. **con'densed,** a. Sp. [Bot.] (Or a flower-group) having the flowers grouped in a solid mass and with no or very short stems. **con'denser,** n. [Elec.] Apparatus for storing ELECTRICITY made up of two or more parallel plates near together, freq. with oil, paper, wax, or some other DIELECTRIC between them, the storing-power being measured by the CAPACITANCE—now generally named *capacitator*. [Chem., Engin.] Any vessel or apparatus for condensing gas, for example, the gas produced in DISTILLATION or the used steam from a steam-engine. [Optics] a LENS or MIRROR used for CONCENTRATING light and sending it onto something, sp. a MICROSCOPE SLIDE, a motion-picture SCREEN, or the slide used with a PROJECTION LANTERN, **con'densing,** a. **condensing engine.** [Engin.] Steam or other VAPOR engine in which the outgoing vapour is condensed.

con'dition, v.t. [Psych.] Get a conditioned reflex produced in (an animal). **con'ditioned 'reflex.** A reaction caused by a STIMULUS A and later produced by a stimulus B which was present earlier together with A.

con'duct, v.t. Take from one place to another, or (of a pipe etc.) be a way through which a liquid or gas goes to a desired place. [Phys.] (Of substances) send on, let through (heat, electric current, etc.). [Zoo.] (Of nerves) send on (impulses, STIMULI). **'-ing,** a. **'-ion,** n. Sp. the motion of heat from one part of a substance to another by the heat ENERGY going from MOLECULE to molecule. **'conduc'tivity,** n. Quality or power of conducting something. [Elec.] The CONDUCTANCE of a CUBE of a given material having sides 1 unit long. **con'ductor,** n. A material which conducts something, sp. [Elec.] one offering very little RESISTANCE to an electric current; any of the parts of an electric system or machine through which current goes.

con'ductance, n. [Elec.] The property of a material which makes it possible for an electric current to go through it when there is a POTENTIAL DIFFERENCE between one part and another,

$$= \frac{1}{\text{RESISTANCE}}.$$

con'ductimeter, n. [Phys.] Apparatus for measuring electric CONDUCTIVITIES of substances, sp. liquids.

'condyle, n. [Zoo.] A rounded expansion at the end of a bone which goes into the hollow end of another bone, forming a JOINT with limited power of motion. **'condyl-ar, -oid,** aa.

'Condy's 'fluid. [Chem.] Trade name for a SOLUTION of $CaMnO_4$ and $NaMnO_4$, used as a DISINFECTANT.

cone, n. A solid with round base and pointed top. [Bot.] The sort of SPORE-producing structure seen sp. in CONIFERAE, made up of a somewhat c.-like group of SPOROPHYLLS ranged round a solid middle part. [Zoo.] One of the two sorts of RECEPTOR in the RETINA of the eye of higher animals, giving a reaction to bright light (*see* ROD). [Astronautics] The name sometimes given to the SATELLITE fired into outer space by a ROCKET or rockets. **c. of rays.** [Optics] Rays going out from or to a point from a LENS or round hole.

con'figuration, n. The form of anything, sp. [Geog.] the HORIZONTAL and VERTICAL form of a part of the earth; the design made by a group of units, the way they are ranged in space in relation to one another, sp. [Chem.] the space-structure of ATOMS in a MOLECULE. [Psych.] A GESTALT. **'configura'tional,** a.

'confluent, 1.a. Running together, meeting and uniting into one, said sp. of rivers etc., or [Med.] of PUSTULES so thickly massed as not to seem separate. 2.n. [Geog.] A river c. with another, greater one. **'confluence,** n. A running together to make one. [Geog.] The joining-point of c. rivers.

con'formable, a. [Geol.] (Of beds put down on top of one another by water, VOLCANOES, etc.) put down regularly one after the other with no space of time between in which earlier material has been taken away by EROSION, and so still complete and in unbroken order. **con'formity,** n. Of beds, the condition of being c.; the relation or the SURFACE between c. beds.

con'geal, v.t. and i. (Make) become changed from a liquid to a solid condition as the effect of cold or by COAGULATION.

con'generic, con'generous, aa. Produced in. the same way or from the same thing, having like properties, being of like sort, sp. [Biol.] of the same GENUS. **con'gener,** n. [Biol.] An animal or plant which is c. with another.

con'genital, a. [Zoo., Med.] Present from birth.

con'gested, a. [Med.] Of a part of the body having overmuch blood in it, as may generally be seen from its being red and SWOLLEN. [Bot.] Tightly massed. **con-**

'gestion, n. Sp. [Med.] the condition of being unhealthily c., freq. causing serious INFLAMMATION, etc.

con'glomerate, 1.a. Grouped or massed together. 2.n. [Geol.] ROCK made of round stones fixed in sand which has become solid.

'congruent, a. [Geom.] Of plane forms, the same in size and form so that if one was slipped over, or turned so as to be on top of, the other, their edges would be together all round. 'congruence, n.

'conical, a. Formed like a CONE.

'conic, a. [Geom.] To do with a CONE. c. 'section. Any curve got when a CONE is completely regular form is cut by a plane.

con'idiophore, n. [Bot.] A HYPHA producing CONIDIA.

con'idium (conidia), n. [Bot.] Sort of SPORE produced without a sex-process at the ends of special HYPHAE in a great number of FUNGI. co'nidial, a. conid-'iferous, a.

Con'iferae, Conifer'ales, nn.pl. [Bot.] CLASS or ORDER of GYMNOSPERMS producing CONES, and freq. themselves somewhat cone-like in form because the middle stem goes to the top, forming a point—chiefly great evergreen trees. 'conifer, n. Tree of the C. co'niferous, a. Of, to do with the C.; producing cones.

'coniine, n. [Chem., Med.] $C_8H_{17}N$, a liquid ALKALOID with a strange smell got from a plant, a strong poison causing death by stopping the operation of the MOTOR nerves and so keeping a person from breathing.

'coniometer, n. Apparatus for measuring amount of dust in air, specially in mines.

con'jugate, a. [Bot.] United, or grouped, in twos. c. 'double bonds. [Chem.] (In C compounds) two DOUBLE BONDS separated by a SINGLE BOND. c. 'foci, c. points. [Optics] Two points such that rays of light coming from any one of them come to a FOCUS at the other. conju'gation, n. [Bot., Zoo.] The uniting of the substance of two ISOGAMETES or of two one-CELLED animals or plants as the first stage in producing offspring, a common form of SYNGAMY in lower plants and animals. conjugation tube. [Bot.] Pipe-like outgrowth by which male sex-CELLS are transported to the female sex-cells.

con'junction, n. Act of joining or condition of being joined together; the taking place of two events at the same time. [Astron.] The condition in which two PLANETS, etc. have the same CELESTIAL LONGITUDE or RIGHT ASCENSION, or come together in the same part of the ZODIAC, named *superior c.* when the planet is on the other side of the sun from the earth and *inferior c.* when it is between the earth and the sun.

'conjunc'tiva, n. [Zoo.] The MUCOUS MEMBRANE covering the front of the eye and the inside of the eye-cover in higher animals. 'conjunc'tival, a. con'juncti-'vitis, n. [Med.] INFLAMMATION of the c.

con'junctive, a. Joining, acting as a connection between, other things, as [Bot.] c. paren'chyma. c. 'symbi'osis. [Biol.] SYMBIOSIS in which the two plants or animals are physically united, as in LICHENES.

'connate, a. [Bot.] United in growth, solidly united. 'c.-per'foliate. Of a leaf, joined at the base so as to go completely round the stem like a wide collar. con'nation, n.

con'nective, a. Forming a connection between other things or parts. c. 'tissue. [Zoo.] Sorts of TISSUE whose business is the support and connection of other tissues in the body of an animal, made up of a framework of non-living substance, such as COLLAGEN and ELASTIN, with FIBRES running through it and CELLS and blood-vessels here and there—for example, bone, CARTILAGE, and AREOLAR TISSUE.

consan'guinity, n. [Zoo.] The relation between animals having a common ANCESTOR. [Geol.] The relation between ROCKS which have come from the same or like material, as seen from certain common properties of structure, chemical make-up, etc. 'consan'guineous, a.

consciousness, n. [Psych.] The property of the mind by which it has sense-experiences in reaction to physical STIMULI acting on the normal instruments of sense, and by which thoughts, feelings, ideas, etc. become present to it so that it has knowledge of them; the part of the mind having this property, as opp. the UNCONSCIOUS or SUBCONSCIOUS; the physical condition in which this part of the mind is in operation, as opp. sleep, COMA, etc.; all the experiences of which a person is conscious at a given time; conscious experience or knowledge.

con'sensual, a. [Psych.] Said of an automatic act or motion which goes with a VOLUNTARY one, or of which, though without power of controlling it, a person is conscious.

'consequent, 1.a. Coming after, and gen. as the effect of, some other event. 2.n. [Maths.] The second number in a RATIO. c. river, etc. [Geog.] A river etc. draining a stretch of country in the direction of the natural slope of the land.

conser'vation, n. The act or process of conserving, as the c. of the woods in a country. c. of 'energy, c. of mo'mentum, etc. Laws of Physics and Chemistry recording the fact that in any separate system the amount of ENERGY (MOMENTUM, etc.) is unchanging, whatever changes take place inside the system. **c. of 'matter.** The law that material substance never undergoes destruction and no new substance is ever produced by chemical or physical change, that is, the amount of material substance in the UNIVERSE is unchanging. **con'serve,** v.t. Keep (anything) from destruction or unchanged in quality or amount.

con'servative, a. Having a tendency to CONSERVE, or effecting CONSERVATION. **c. 'system.** [Phys.] System of bodies acted on only by forces inside the system, so that the ENERGY of motion of the parts of the system, taken together, is unchanged.

con'sistometer, n. [Chem.] Instrument measuring the force acting in a thick liquid or paste against change of form.

con'sociation, n. [Bot.] A division of a plant ASSOCIATION made up chiefly of one of the DOMINANTS of the association.

con'solidate, v.t. and i. Get or become united into a solid, hard mass. **con'solidated,** a. **consoli'dation,** n. Sp. [Geol.] the process by which SEDIMENTARY ROCKS become dry, hard, and solidly massed, chiefly as the effect of PRESSURE, after they have been put down, gen. in a soft, wet or loose condition.

'consolute, n., a. [Chem.] (One of two liquids) able to be mixed in all amounts.

'consonance, n. [Phys.] Agreement in rhythm of two VIBRATIONS. **'consonant,** a.

'consonant, n. [Phonet.] Sound made with some part of the mouth or throat shut or almost shut, or letter representative of such a sound: in English, any letter but a, e, i, o, u, and sometimes y.

'constant, 1.a. Unchanging, the same at all times or all through a given time or group of operations. 2.n. [Maths., Phys.] A c. value, sp. one representative of some physical property or relation. **c. 'deviation 'spectroscope.** [Optics] A sort of SPECTROSCOPE in which only the PRISM (named **c. deviation prism**) is turned, the COLLIMATOR and the TELESCOPE being fixed.

'constantan, n. A metal made of 60% Cu and 40% Ni whose electric RESISTANCE is almost independent of its TEMPERATURE, used in electric apparatus, sp. for measuring resistance.

'constell'ation, n. [Astron.] Any of the groups of fixed stars which have been given names picturing the design they seem to make, as '*Pisces*' ('the Fish'), or the division of the sky where such a group is.

consti'pation, n. [Med.] Condition in which EVACUATION takes place less frequently than is healthy, and generally with trouble, as the effect of the waste material having become massed and hard. **'constipated,** a. Having c.

con'stituent, 1.n. Any of the parts or substances making up a more complex thing or substance, 2.a. Being a c., making up or helping to make up something.

consti'tution, n. The make-up of anything, that is:—the number, size, and position in relation to one another, of its parts, sp. [Chem.] of the ATOMS forming a MOLECULE; the substances present in a mixed or COMPOUND substance, and their relation of amount. [Med.] The general physical make-up of a person, his normal physical powers, as strong or feeble, etc. **'consti'tutional,** a. **constitutional 'formula.** [Chem.] A CHEMICAL FORMULA making clear the distribution of the ATOMS in a MOLECULE, though not the sort of VALENCY BONDS joining them, as CHHC.

con'strain, v.t. Keep (anything) limited to a fixed position, degree of motion, etc.

con'strict, v.t. and i. Make or become narrower, nearer together, sp. at one or more separate points as if circled by a tight band. **con'strictive,** a. **con'stricted,** a. [Biol.] Narrowed suddenly or at regular distances, sp. of pipe-like parts, stems, etc. **con'striction,** n. Sp. a constricted part, a narrower part.

con'structive me'tabolism. [Biol.] ANABOLISM.

'contact, n. Touch, act of touching or meeting or condition of being in touch. **c. elec'tricity.** [Elec.] The ELECTRICITY produced when two substances are put in c. **c. e.m.f.** [Elec.] The ELECTROMOTIVE FORCE produced when two metals are put in c. **c. goni'ometer.** A form of GONIOMETER used sp. for measuring the angle between CRYSTAL faces, having two moving arms against which the faces are placed. **c. lens** [Med.] A very thin PLASTIC LENS which is slipped over the eyeball to overcome trouble in seeing in place of using glasses. **c. meta'morphism.** [Geol.] Physical and chemical changes in ROCK caused by coming in c. with MAGMA. **c. 'paper.** Paper coated with $AgCl_2$ used in printing camera pictures straight from the FILM. **c. po'tential.** [Elec.] The POTENTIAL DIFFERENCE seen between two different metals when they are touching, one of them getting a POSITIVE CHARGE and the other a NEGATIVE. **c. 'process.** [Chem.] A process for making H_2SO_4 in which the gases SO_2 and O are sent over a CATALYST forming SO_3, of which a SOLUTION is then made in H_2O. **c. re'ceptor.** [Zoo.] A RECEPTOR which is put in operation by c., or near-c., with something, as in the senses of taste and smell. **c. 'series.** [Chem.] A list of metals every one of which is made POSITIVELY electric by c. with the one nearest to it in the list. **c. zone.** [Geol.] Band of ROCK which has undergone c. metamorphism round a mass of IGNEOUS rock. **con'tactor,** n. [Elec.] Apparatus making and unmaking electric cc.

con'tagion, n. [Med.] The giving of disease through touch. **con'tagious,** a. (Of disease) given by touch.

con'taminate, v.t. [Med.] Make contaminated. **con'taminated,** a. (Of food, water, air, etc.) having in it disease BACTERIA sp. as the effect of getting mixed with or touched by substances producing them. **con'tamination,** n. Sp. a contaminating substance.

con'tempor'aneous, a. In existence or starting or taking place at the same time. **'-ly,** adv. **'-ness, 'contemporan'eity,** nn.

'content, n. Whatever a vessel has in it (freq. cc.); the amount a vessel is able to take in; the substance of a field of science or of a writing etc., what is covered by it. [Chem.] The amount of a given substance present in a mixed one.

con'tiguous, a. Touching or very near, with nothing between. [Geom.] ADJACENT.

'continent, n. [Geog., Geol.] Any of the great unbroken land masses forming the chief divisions of the earth, that is, Europe, Asia, America (or North America and South America), Africa, and Australia. **conti'nental,** a. Of, to do with, a c. or cc.; (of CLIMATE or conditions) of the sort experienced in the inner parts of the cc., higher than the sea and far from it, in which the range of TEMPERATURE between night and middle-day and summer and winter is very great, the air is dry and the rainfall quite small, and rivers are not very common. **continental drift.** The slow motion of the cc. by which in WEGENER'S HYPOTHESIS they are all the time changing their positions. **continental shelf.** The sea-bed round the edge of a c. which takes the form of a shelf sloping down only a little, over which the water is generally not more than 2000 m. deep, and ending in a much sharper drop (named the **continental slope**) to the deep sea-bed.

con'tinuant, n. [Phonet.] CONSONANT going on for a short time, as *m, l, v, f, z* (but not *p, t, k*).

contin'uity, n. Condition or property of being an unbroken stretch or chain etc. in space or time, or of going on in time without a stop. **c. of germ plasm.** *See* GERM PLASM. **con'tinuous,** a. Having c., going on unbrokenly. **continuous phase** or **'medium.** [Chem.] DISPERSION MEDIUM. **continuous 'spectrum.** [Optics] A SPECTRUM formed by a complete

range of WAVE-LENGTHS, changing by degrees from one end to the other.

con'tinuum, a. Anything which is taken to have no parts or structure, being completely CONTINUOUS and the same all through, for example, space; anything which, though able to undergo change over a certain range, does so by continuous degrees and keeps a common property all through, as a *sense c.*

'contour, n. The outline of any form or body; **c. feather.** [Zoo.] PLUMA. **c. 'interval.** [Geog., etc.] The distance between a c. line and the one nearest to it, higher or lower. **c. line.** [Geog., etc.] Line made on a map joining points which are all at the same level measured from sea-level.

contra-. In the opposite direction or of the opposite tendency or effect to what is named, acting against it.

contra'ception, n. [Med.] The act of keeping COPULATION from effecting FERTILIZATION. **contra'ceptive,** n., a. (Substance) having the effect of c.

con'tract, v.t. and i. (Make) become smaller in one or all directions as the effect of the pulling together of its parts, the opposite process to expansion. **con'tractile,** a. Able to be contracted, having the power of contracting or causing contraction, sp. [Biol.]. [Zoo.] Of a part, able to be folded up and kept against the body or pulled into shorter form or under some covering, etc. **contractile 'tissue.** [Zoo.] Muscle. **contractile 'vacuole.** [Zoo.] In some PROTOZOA a hollow which after slowly becoming more and more full of liquid contracts suddenly, driving it all out of the body—a way of sending out liquid waste. **contrac'tility,** n. Sp. [Zoo.] the power or property of contraction of a muscle, CELL, or part. **con'traction,** n. **con'tracture,** n. [Med.] A condition in which some part is twisted or shorter than normal, for example as the effect of damage to the muscles. [Zoo.] A contraction of the muscles which goes on after the STIMULUS has been taken away.

'contrast, n. [Psych.] The effect produced by experiencing two markedly different STIMULI of the same sort together, or near enough together for them to be viewed in that way by the mind, by which the ways in which they are different are made specially marked and the degree to which they are different is made to seem greater than it is. **con'trast,** 1.v.t. Make a comparison between (opposite or markedly different things of the same sort). 2.v.i. Of things, etc. be markedly different, such as to make a c.

con'trol, 1.n. Anything used in LABORATORY work as a STANDARD by comparison with which other things are tested or measured, sp. [Biol., Med.] in testing for the effects of a medical etc. substance or process, the group of animals, plants or persons to which the substance is not given or which do not undergo the process, by comparison of the others with which its effects are made clear. 2.v.t. Put (a statement, test, law theory, etc.) to the test, make certain there is no error in it, by comparison with other knowledge, observations, tests, etc. **c. ex′periment.** A test used for controlling the facts pointed to by other tests, gen. by keeping the same conditions all but one and changing this till the part it takes in the process becomes clear.

con′tusion, n. [Med.] A place where the skin and the TISSUES under it have been damaged by a blow without the skin being broken, freq. coloured black and blue as the effect of blood coming out under the skin. **con′tuse,** v.t. Make a c. on. **con′tused,** a.

′conus, n. [Zoo.] Any structure having the form of a CONE. **c. arter′iosus.** Division of the heart between VENTRICLE and AORTA in fishes and AMPHIBIA; in higher animals, part of VENTRICLE in the form of a c., from which the ARTERY taking blood to the LUNGS comes. **c. medul′laris.** The narrowed end of the SPINAL CORD.

con′vection, n. [Phys.] Motion in a liquid or gas caused by different conditions of DENSITY in different parts, sp. the distribution of heat through a liquid or gas by the moving up of a heated part and the taking of its place by a colder part, causing **c. currents. con′vective,** a. **con′vector,** n. A heater designed for warming the air of a room chiefly as the effect of c. currents caused by the air coming in touch with its heated parts, and not by sending out RADIANT HEAT.

con′verge, 1.v.i. Of straight lines, rays, etc., come to a common point, or nearer and nearer together. [Biol.] Be convergent. 2.v.t. Make c. **con′vergence,** n. The process of converging or the condition of being convergent. [Biol.] Convergent evolution. [Zoo., Optics] The automatic turning of the two eyes so that their VISUAL AXES c. and they are looking at the same point. **con′vergent,** a. Sp. [Biol.] having properties, becoming more and more like, as the effect of convergent evolution. **con′vergent evo′lution.** [Biol.] The development of like properties by groups of animals or plants of different sorts in the process of EVOLUTION, gen. as the effect of adjustment to common living-conditions. **convergent lens.** [Optics] A LENS causing or increasing the convergence of light-rays going through it or making DIVERGENT rays less so. **con′verging,** a.

′converse, 1.a. Turned in the opposite direction, opposite in order or relation, acting in the opposite way. 2.n. A thing which is c. in relation to a given thing.

con′version, n. The act or process of CONVERTING or condition of being converted. **c. ′factor.** The number by which value of a physical amount as given in one system of units has to be changed to get its value as given in another system of units. **c. hys′teria.** [Med., Psych.] A form of HYSTERIA in which the trouble of mind gets an outlet in producing, by its operation on the nerves, the conditions of physical disease, such as the loss of hearing or of the use of the eyes, the mind at the same time becoming untroubled.

con′vert, v.t. Get (something) changed into some other thing, or from one condition, form, etc., into another, as c. water *into* steam, c. chemical ENERGY *into* electric energy. [Chem.] (Of a substance) get a different substance produced from it by a chemical process, as c. coal *into* COKE, iron *into* steel. **con′vert-er, -or,** n. Apparatus for converting anything, sp. [Elec.] one for converting ALTERNATING CURRENT into DIRECT current or any current from one FREQUENCY to another. [Metal.] Vessel in which PIG IRON is changed into steel by the BESSEMER PROCESS. **con′vertible,** a. **con′verting,** a.

′convex, a. Curved out, like the outside of a ball. **c. lens.** [Optics] A LENS with two opposite faces curved out, so that it is thicker at the middle than at the edges. **con′vexo-con′cave,** a. Having one face c. and the opposite face hollow, said sp. of a LENS with the c. face curved to a greater degree than the hollow one, **con′vexity,** n.

′convolute, a. [Bot.] Folded or rolled over so that one half is covered by the other. [Zoo.] Having one part twisted over another part; twisted. **′convo′luted,** a. C. or much twisted. **′convo′lution,** n. The condition of being convoluted; a twist, turn, or roll, sp. [Anat.] any of the twisting folds on the outside of the brain.

con′vulsion, n. [Med.] A violent general SPASM of the muscles, sometimes with loss of CONSCIOUSNESS, sp. one of a number of such spasms as seen in EPILEPSY or freq. in babies as the effect of different causes. **con′vulsive,** a. To do with, caused by, like, a c. **con′vulsant,** n., a. [Med.] (Substance) producing cc.

cool, v.t. and i. (Make) become cold after being heated, (make) undergo loss of heat. **′coolant,** n. A substance used for cooling a part of a machine or keeping it from getting over-heated, as the water in the JACKET of an INTERNAL COMBUSTION engine, or mixed oil and water sent over the cutting edge in a machine-cutter, etc. [Phys.] A liquid or gas transporting the heat produced by a NUCLEAR REACTOR from it to the apparatus putting it to use. **cooled,** a. **'cooling,** a.

'Coolidge tube. [Phys.] A sort of X-RAY TUBE in which the ELECTRONS are produced by a heated twist of W in the CATHODE, and the ANODE is a mass of W.

co'ördinate, 1.v.t. Put on an equal footing, make c.; get (the parts of a system, etc.) into right relation, adjustment, with one another. [Chem.] Get (a new ATOM or MOLECULE) fixed to the middle atom of the molecule of a substance, 2.v.i. (Of parts) be coördinated, be working in harmony with one another to a certain effect, sp. [Zoo., Psych.) of nerves, muscles, etc. 3.a. On an equal footing, at or to do with the same level in any ordered system or scale, for example in a system of grouping. 4.n. One or other of two or more c. things. [Geom.] One or other of two or more measures, numbers, etc., forming a system for fixing the position of a thing in space or its relation to other things of a group (*see* CARTESIAN COÖRDINATES, POLAR COÖRDINATES), c. **'linkage.** [Phys., Chem.] The uniting of two ATOMS by coördination valency. c. **bond.** [Phys., Chem.] Coördination valency. **co'ördinated,** a. Having undergone coördination [Chem.] (Of a salt) produced by coördination. **co'ördinating,** a. **'coördination,** n. **coördination number** [Chem.] The number of ATOMS or groups round the middle atom of a complex SALT. **coördination 'valency.** [Chem.] The VALENCY BOND between two ATOMS which have in common two ELECTRONS from one of the atoms.

'copal, n. Any of a group of natural, generally FOSSIL, RESINS.

Co'pepoda, n.pl. [Zoo.] A great SUB-CLASS of CRUSTACEA, water-animals most of which are of very small size and a great number of which are PARASITES, having forked swimming feet on the THORAX but no other legs, gen. without a hard outer cover, and forming an important part of the PLANKTON food of fish. **'copepod,** n., a. (Animal) of the C.

Co'pernican system. [Astron.] The general account of the sun's system first given by Copernicus and looked on as true today, by which the PLANETS go round the sun and the earth goes round every day on its AXIS.

co-'planar, a. [Maths.] Being or acting in the same plane.

'co-'polymer, n. [Phys.-Chem.] A great MOLECULE, or a substance formed of such molecules, produced, in the same way as a POLYMER, by the addition of smaller molecules, but of different sorts. **'copoly'meric,** a. **'co-'polymeri'zation,** n. The process of producing c.-pp., of

special value in the making of PLASTICS.

'copper, n. Chemical ELEMENT, at. no. 29, at. wt. 63·57, sign Cu, a red-brown metal very readily worked by hammering, rolling, pulling etc., not readily acted on by air, water etc., and one of the best transporters of heat and electric current.

'copperas, n. [Mineral., Chem.] Natural or chemically produced $FeSO_4.7H_2O$ (*ferrous sulphate*), light green CRYSTALS used in making ink and paints, as a MORDANT, and medically as a TONIC.

'coprecipi'tation, n. [Chem.] PRECIPITATION of two or more substances together.

copr(o)-. [Biol.] EXCREMENT, FAECES: **copro'phil-ic, -ous,** aa. [Bot.]

copro'daeum, n. [Zoo.] The inner division of the CLOACA, where the ANUS has its opening, in birds, snakes, and LACERTILIA.

'coprolite, n. [Geol.] The FOSSILIZED EXCREMENT of animals, used for putting on land to make it more fertile.

copro'phagous, a. [Zoo.] Taking the EXCREMENT of other animals as food, as some insects and birds, and [Med.] man in certain diseases of the mind. **copro'phagy,** n. The property or condition of being c.; the act of taking excrement as food.

copro'zoic, a. [Biol.] Living on or having its growth in EXCREMENT.

'copula (copulae), n. [Zoo.] A bridging or joining structure, sp. any of the CARTILAGES joining the GILL ARCHES in fish.

'copulate, v.i. [Zoo.] Of a male and female animal, come together in the act by which SPERMATOZOA from the male are put into the body of the female. **copu'lation,** n. **copu'lative, copu'latory,** aa.

'coracoid bone. [Zoo.] Bone going from the SCAPULA to, or in the direction of, the STERNUM, in snakes, birds, and MONOTREMES.

'coracoid 'process. [Zoo.] The pointed or hooked part united to the SCAPULA which in man and most MAMMALS is representative of the CORACOID BONE.

'coral, n. [Zoo.] Stone-like or horn-like white or coloured outer framework of certain ANTHOZOA and some HYDROZOA, of which islands and REEFS are formed in the Pacific and some sorts of which, sp. the red, are valued for ornament; c.-producing animal. **coral'iferous, coral-'igenous,** aa. Producing c. **'coralline,** 1.a. Formed of or like c. 2.n. Any c.-like animal, sp. a POLYZOAN forming delicate c.-like growths. **'coralloid,** a. Like c., sp. in having a branching-structure like some c.

cor'bicula, n. [Zoo.] Line of hairs on 4th joint of leg in insects, MYRIAPODA and some ARACHNIDA, sp. part of bee on which POLLEN is transported.

cor'bino ef'fect. [Elec.] Form of HALL EFFECT in which, when a current is sent from middle point to edge of a round metal plate in a MAGNETIC FIELD, a current goes round the outside edge.

cord, n. [Anat.] Cord-like structure, as SPINAL C., UMBILICAL C.

'cordate, a. [Bot.] (Of leaves) having the form of a heart (*see* picture, p. 221).

'cordite, n. An explosive producing little smoke, made of NITROGLYCERINE and NITROCELLULOSE and used in fire-arms.

core, n. The middle part of anything, sp. when harder than, or different in some other way from, the outer parts. [Chem.] In ALKALI METALS, the complete ATOM but for the outside ELECTRONS. [Elec.] Rod of iron, parcel of iron wires, etc., put through the middle of a current-transporting COIL to make an INDUCED MAGNETIC FIELD stronger, as in a TRANS-FORMER, etc. **cored 'carbon**. [Elec.] A CARBON rod with a c. of softer material formed of mixed SALTS, used in ARC-LAMPS. **'-less**, a. Without a c., sp. [Elec.].

cori'aceous, 'corious, aa. [Biol.] Leather-like, strong and not readily parted.

'corium, n. [Zoo.] DERMIS.

cork, n. [Bot.] The substance produced on the inside of the outer skin of the stems and roots of most wood-forming plants, made up of dead CELLS with thick SUBERIZED walls, forming an almost completely water-tight and air-tight covering, which in some trees becomes very thick and of use to man. **c. 'cambium**. PHELLOGEN.

corm, n. [Bot.] Short, thick, rounded expansion under the earth of the stem of a plant, like a bulb in form but solid, BUDDING and producing a new plant when the time for growth comes again.

corn, n. [Med.] An overgrowth of the horn substance of the skin at some point, sp. on a toe, forming a small hard place giving pain, caused by the rubbing or PRESSURE of shoes etc. at that point.

'cornea, n. [Zoo.] In back-boned animals, the TRANSPARENT coat covering the middle of the front of the eye under the CONJUNCTIVA and REFRACTING light to the CRYSTALLINE LENS. **'corne-al, -ous**, aa.

cor'niculate, a. [Biol.] CORNUTE.

'cornification, n. [Zoo.] The process of becoming horn or horn-like.

'cornu (cornua), n. [Zoo.] Horn-like outgrowth, as on certain bones. **cornual**, a.

'cornute(d), aa. [Biol.] Having horns or horn-like outgrowths; having the form of a horn.

co'rolla, n. [Bot.] The ring of flower-parts inside the CALYX, made up of PETALS. **c. tube**. Pipe formed by the lower part of the c. in some flowers. **'corol'laceous, 'corol-line**, aa. **'corollate, 'corol'liferous**, aa.

co'rona, n. [Astron.] System of coloured rings round sun or moon when viewed through very thin mist; the milk-white band round the sun seen only at times of TOTAL ECLIPSE. [Zoo.] The head or upper part of a structure, sp. when in the form of a circle of outgrowths or any ring-structure. [Bot.] In certain flowers, a ring-like or pipe-like outgrowth or circle of outgrowths coming from the upper side of the PETALS, and sometimes looking like an inner ring of petals. **'coronal**, a.

'coronal, a. [Zoo.] To do with the top of the head or FRONTALIS. **c. 'suture**. Join going across head between the FRONTAL and the PARIETAL bones. **c. plane**. The FRONTAL PLANE.

'coronary, a. [Zoo.] Forming a circle round, going round, a part; to do with the c. arteries. **c. 'arteries**. The blood-vessels taking blood to the heart muscle. **c. 'cushion, c. band, c. ring**. Names for the ring of TISSUE at the top edge of the HOOF of a horse, etc., which has to do with the producing of the horn coat.

'coronet, n. [Zoo.] The bulb-like part at the base of the ANTLER in CERVIDAE; in the horse, the part where the skin of the PASTERN is joined to the HOOF; a small circle of stiff hairs etc. on some part.

co'ronograph, n. [Astron.] Instrument for recording the sun's CORONA in full sunlight.

'corpora, n.pl. [Zoo.] The Latin word for 'bodies', used in naming certain groups of bodies forming part of an animal. **c. al'lata**. Two white, egg-like GLANDS in the head of some insects. **c. bi'gemina**. In lower back-boned animals, two round outgrowths on the DORSAL side of the MID-BRAIN where the nerves of the eye have their starting-point. **c. 'quadri-'gemina**. In MAMMALS, four round outgrowths in the same position as the c. bigemina, of which the front or higher two have to do with seeing and the other two with hearing.

'corpus (corpora), n. The Latin word for 'body', used in naming different special structures forming part of an animal's body, sp. in the brain. **c. call'osum**. Band of FIBRES by which the CEREBRAL HEMI-SPHERES are joined in back-boned animals. **c. 'luteum**. Small yellow body formed inside a GRAAFIAN FOLLICLE after the loss of the OVUM, by which PROGESTERONE is produced. **c. stri'atum**. The GANGLION forming the base of the wall of a CEREBRAL HEMISPHERE in back-boned animals.

'corpuscle, n. [Phys.] Any very small body taken, for the purpose of theory, as a unit of material substance or ENERGY, for example, an ATOM, ELECTRON, or PHOTON. [Bot.] Any very small CELL or body in a cell having a fixed form. [Zoo.] Any separate CELL in body TISSUE or in free motion in body liquid, sp. blood. **cor-'puscular,** a. **corpuscular theory (of light).** [Optics] The theory current at the time of Newton that light was made up of cc. of material substance moving at a very high rate, given up for the theory of light as ELECTROMAGNETIC WAVES, but now again supported by the idea of the PHOTON.

cor'rasion, n. [Geol.] Slow destruction of ROCKS by moving water and the material moving in it.

cor'rect, v.t. Put right, sp. make a change in (the reading given by an instrument or a measure got from a scale, etc.) so as to take into account some special condition or some shortcoming of the instrument, etc. **corr'ected,** a, Having undergone correction. **corr'ection,** n. Act of correcting; the amount by which a reading or measure has to be changed to give a true value.

'correlate, v.t. Make clear the degree to which one changing value is dependent on another, as in STATISTICS, etc.; make or see a connection between (one observation, fact, etc. and another); get (facts, etc.) so ordered as to make clear the connection between them. **'corre'lation,** n. **correlation coe'fficient.** The number giving the degree to which one group of facts is dependent on another.

corres'pond, v.i. Be like, parallel in form, structure, development, etc., *to*; be in agreement *with* or adjustment *to*, some other thing. **corres'pondence,** n. The relation or condition of corresponding. **corres'ponding,** a.

corres'ponding states. [Phys.] Conditions of two or more substances in which their PRESSURES, VOLUMES, and TEMPERATURES are in same relation to their CRITICAL pressures, volumes, and temperatures.

cor'rosion, n. Slow destruction by chemical effects, for example [Chem.] that of a metal by an acid or [Geol.] of ROCKS by water, air, etc. **cor'rosive,** a. **'corrosive 'poison.** One causing destruction of inside coat of stomach. **'corrosive 'sublimate.** HgCl (*mercuric chloride*), used as an ANTISEPTIC and in camera work.

'corrugate, v.t. Make corrugated. **'corrugated,** a. Lined or banded with narrow, sp. parallel, RIDGES or hollows, as **corrugated iron, corrugated paper. cor-ru'gation,** n. Sp. any RIDGE or hollow of a corrugated SURFACE. **'corrugator,** n. [Zoo.] A muscle effecting corrugation of the skin, for example, in lifting the EYEBROWS.

'cortex, n. [Biol.] The outer coat or part of a structure, specially if it is different from the inner part, sp.:—[Zoo.] The GREY MATTER forming the outer part of the brain in back-boned animals (*cerebral c.*);

[Bot.] the part of a stem or root under the EPIDERMIS, of which, in a tree, it takes the place, becoming the BARK, after forming cork. **'cortical,** a. **'corticate,** a.

'cortico'sterone, n. [Biochem.] Any of the HORMONES of the SUPRARENAL BODIES.

'cortin, n. [Biochem.] HORMONE produced by the outer part of the SUPRARENAL GLAND. [Med.] Substance made from the outer part of the SUPRARENAL GLAND and used medically, sp. against ADDISON'S DISEASE.

'cortisone, n. [Biochem., Med.] A substance present in the outer part of the SUPRARENAL GLAND, used medically in certain diseases, for example RHEUMATOID ARTHRITIS.

'Corti's 'organ. [Zoo.] That part of the COCHLEA resting on the BASILAR MEMBRANE, in which are the RECEPTORS of the sense of hearing.

co'rundum, n. [Mineral.] Natural Al_2O_3 (*aluminium oxide*), a very hard substance used as an ABRASIVE.

'corymb, n. [Bot.] A RACEMOSE flower-group in which the stems of the outer flowers are longer than those of the inside flowers, forming a flat-topped mass (*see* picture p. 199).

co'ryza, n. [Med.] An ACUTE attack of CATARRH of the nose and nearby hollows of the head, INFECTIOUS and probably caused by a VIRUS, marked by much mucous discharge from the nose, pain in the head, and freq. FEVER—commonly named 'a cold'.

co'secant, n. [Geom.] Of an angle, $1 \div$ its SINE (short form **cosec**).

co'seismal line. A line on map through all points at which the shock of an EARTHQUAKE is equally strong.

'cosine, n. [Geom.] (Of an angle) in a right-angled three-sided plane form ABC, of which B is the right angle, the c. of angle A (short form **cos** A) is $\dfrac{AB}{AC}$ and the c. of angle C is $\dfrac{BC}{AC}$.

'cosmic, a. *See* COSMOS.

cos'mology, n. [Astron.] The branch of Astronomy which has to do with the form, structure, size, and space-relations of all the great bodies in space of which we have knowledge; a complete picture of the COSMOS and its working. **'cosmo-'logical,** a.

cos'mogony, n. [Astron.] The science of the development of the stars, PLANETS, etc.; a theory as to how the great bodies in space came into existence and their present form.

'cosmo'nautics, n.pl. ASTRONAUTICS. **'cos-monaut,** n. ASTRONAUT.

'cosmos, n. [Phys.] All bodies in space

93

looked on as an ordered system ruled by physical laws. 'cosmic, a. To do with the c. cosmic rays. [Phys., Astron.] Different sorts of RADIATIONS of very high ENERGY and very short wave-length coming to earth from outer space, some of which have the power of going through substances as DENSE as lead even when deep in the earth. cosmic radi'ation. C. rays.

'cosmotron, n. [Phys.] A form of PROTON ACCELERATOR.

cosmo'zoic theory. Theory that living beings came to the earth from outer space.

'costa (cos'talia), n. [Biol.] A RIB or rib-like structure, sp. any of the chief NERVURES of an insect's wing or the VEINS of a leaf. 'costal, a. costal 'respir'ation. Breathing produced chiefly by the motion of the ribs and chest muscles. 'costate, a. [Bot.] having a c. or cc. [Zoo.] Having rib-like lines on it. costo-. Rib or c., costal (and . . .).

co'tangent, n. [Geom.] Of an angle, 1 ÷ its TANGENT (short form cot).

co'terminous, a. Having a common limit or the same limits in space or time. [Biol.] (Of groups of plants or animals) having a like distribution.

co'tidal line. Line on map through points at which it is high water at same time.

'cotton, n. [Bot.] A soft mass of hair-like white or brown FIBRES, made up chiefly of CELLULOSE, covering the seeds of certain plants, most important among which is the c. plant, produced by man for the purpose of making c. thread and c. material. c. wool. [Med.] Loose natural c., made white and put up in rolls, etc., used medically as an ABSORBENT, or for washing wounds, making thick, soft dressings, and so on. 'cottony, a. C.-like. [Bot.] Covered with thick soft hairs.

'Cotton-'Mouton effect. [Phys.] BIREFRINGENCE in some liquids when in a MAGNETIC FIELD.

'cotyla, n. [Zoo.] Cup-like hollow or part. 'cotyl-ar, -oid, aa. Cup-like; to do with the cotyloid cavity. 'cotyloid 'cavity, ACETABULUM.

coty'ledon, n. [Bot.] First simple leaf, or one or other of the first two or more such leaves, formed inside a seed and from which the plant gets food in the first stages of its development, gen. without CHLOROPHYLL at first, but sometimes coming up with the young plant and then becoming green and doing the work of a normal leaf. [Zoo.] A small space on a PLACENTA covered with VILLI. coty'ledon-ary, a. [Zoo.] (Of PLACENTA) having the VILLI in small separate groups. coty'le-donous, a. [Bot.].

'couloir, n. [Geol.] Deep cut, down which water sometimes comes, in side of mountain.

'coulomb, n. [Elec.] The PRACTICAL UNIT of amount of ELECTRICITY, equal to that transported by 1 AMPERE in 1 second. c. forces. [Phys.] The forces causing CHARGED bodies or FUNDAMENTAL PARTICLES of the same electric sign (+ or −) to go away from one another, and of different electric sign to go to one another. c. 'meter, Coulometer. cou'lo-meter, n. Instrument for measuring the amount of an electric current in cc. by the use of ELECTROLYSIS.

'Coulomb's law. [Elec.] The law that the force of attraction or its opposite between two CHARGED bodies is DIRECTLY PROPORTIONAL to the PRODUCT of their CHARGES and INVERSELY proportional to the SQUARE of the distance between them.

'coumarone, n. [Chem.] Substance, C_8H_6O, made up of a BENZENE and a FURAN ring with two C ATOMS in common, from which SYNTHETIC RESINS are produced.

count, n. Number of given units in a representative example of some substance, as blood c., number of the different sorts of CELLS present in blood.

count down. The space of time before an important test etc., such as the sending up of a space ROCKET, in which details are gone over, parts tested etc., for the last time.

'counter, n. [Mach.] Instrument recording number of turns of a wheel or other machine motions.

'counter-. Against, working in opposite direction, having opposite effect, as a c. ELECTROMOTIVE FORCE.

'counter-irri'tation, n. [Med.] The use of heat or substances having a violent and to some degree damaging effect on the skin to take blood from a part where there is INFLAMMATION and so make pain less. 'counter-'irritant, n. Substance, etc. effecting c.

'counterpoise, n. [Mach.] A weight balancing or acting against another weight. c. an'tenna. [Radio] A system of wires, etc. placed parallel to the AERIAL structure of an ANTENNA and near but not in connection with the earth, used in place of an earth connection.

'countershaft, n. [Mach.] In a BELT DRIVE, a SHAFT put between that of the engine or motor and that of the machines worked by it, so that by changing the size of the wheels on the c. different rates of motion may be given to different machines.

'counterstain, 1.n. [Biol.] A STAIN used for colouring differently those parts of something under observation which have not been coloured by an earlier stain. 2.v.t. Get coloured by a c.

'country rock. [Geol., Mining] The ROCK of different material, without value, in which a LODE etc. of ORE is bedded.

couple, 1.n. Two, said of like things sp. when joined or grouped together. [Mech.] Two equal forces acting at different points on a rod, wheel etc., in parallel but opposite directions, giving a twisting or turning effect. 2.v.t. Get (two things) joined or grouped together. **coupled,** a. Sp. united by a coupling. **'coupler,** n. Any of a number of parts for making connections between two things, sp. two electric CIRCUITS. **'coupling,** n. Act of joining or grouping two things together; part used for coupling, sp. railway carriages or moving machine-parts. [Elec.] The joining of two electric CIRCUITS so that ENERGY is taken from one to the other, named *direct coupling* when this is done by giving them a part in common (as in CAPACITANCE COUPLING), and *inductive coupling* when it is effected by MUTUAL INDUCTION (as in TRANSFORMER COUPLING). [Chem.] The uniting of two substances, sp. in forming dyes. [Biol.] LINKAGE.

'co'valency, 'co'valence, nn. [Chem.] Of two ATOMS, condition of being united by having two electrons in common, one from one atom and one from the other. **'co'valent,** a. **covalent bond.** The VALENCY BOND between two covalent ATOMS.

'cover glass, 'cover slip, [Biol.] Small, very thin glass plate used for covering delicate cuttings etc. fixed on a SLIDE.

'covert, n. [Zoo.] Any of the special small feathers covering the bases of the long feathers of a bird's tail and wings.

co'volume, n. [Phys.-Chem.] The VOLUME of the MOLECULES of a gas themselves without the space between them

cow, n. [Zoo.] The female of those animals of which the male is named a BULL, sp. that of the GENUS *Bos*.

'Cowper's glands. [Zoo.] Two GLANDS, one on the right side and one on the left, of the male URETHRA, into which they send their produce.

'cowpox, n. [Med.] VACCINIA.

'coxa, n. [Zoo.] The HIP or hip JOINT; that part of the leg of an insect which is nearest the body. **'coxal,** a.

cox'opodite, n. [Zoo.] The lowest JOINT of the leg of CRUSTACEA.

Cr, Sign for CHROMIUM.

'cracking, n. [Chem.] The process of getting the complex HYDROCARBONS making up PETROLEUM broken up by heat and PRESSURE into simpler ones of less weight, for example for the purpose of getting more VOLATILE oils for use in INTERNAL COMBUSTION engines. **crack,** v.t. and i. (Make) undergo c.

cramp, n. [Med.] A SPASM of the muscles of a part, marked by sharp pain; a c. producing a loss of the use of the muscles of a part for some time, caused by overwork-

ing them, as in certain sorts of work, and gen. given a special name, as *writer's c.* [Mach.] An apparatus for keeping wood etc. parts together while they are being joined.

'crampon, n. [Bot.] AERIAL root.

crane, n. [Eng.] A machine for lifting or lowering weights and at the same time moving them a certain distance, sometimes made up of a long moving arm worked by a PULLEY, sometimes of an overhead rail from which a gripping apparatus is hanging and on which it is moved from end to end.

'Crani'ata, n.pl. [Zoo.] VERTEBRATA.

'crani'ometry, n. [Anthrop., etc.] The science of measuring men's heads for the purpose of comparison between RACES, sexes, or stages of development.

'cranium (crania), n. [Zoo.] In back-boned animals, that part of the bone-structure of the head walling in the brain. **'cranial,** a. **'cranial 'index.** CEPHALIC INDEX. **cranial nerves.** In back-boned animals the nerves starting in the brain or upper part of the SPINAL CORD and coming out of the openings in the bone structure covering the brain, chiefly going to the different parts of the head and face, some being SENSORY, some MOTOR, and some mixed—in MAMMALS, birds, and REPTILES, 12 on the right side and 12 on the left, in fish and AMPHIBIANS only 10 to a side. **'craniate,** a.

crank, n. [Mech.] Bent part of SHAFT, or arm at right angles to shaft, by which a motion back and forward is changed into a motion round and round, or the opposite. **'-case,** n. A box-like metal structure covering the crankshaft and rods in some engines or pumps. **'-shaft,** n. Any SHAFT working or worked by a c., sp. the chief shaft of an engine etc. supporting a c. or cc. to which are joined the rod or rods making connection with the PISTON.

'crater, n. [Geol.] The hollow round the opening of a VOLCANO; the basin-like opening of a GEYSER. [Elec.] Cup-like hollow formed at end of POSITIVE CARBON in ARC LAMP.

cream of 'tartar. [Chem.] $KHC_4H_4O_6$ (*potassium hydrogen tartrate*), a white CRYSTALLINE substance with an acid taste got by taking other substances out of TARTAR, used in BAKING POWDER and medically as an APERIENT.

creatine, n. [Biochem., Chem.] A feebly BASIC CRYSTALLINE substance, $C_4H_9N_3O_2$, present in the muscles and blood of backboned animals.

cre'atinine, n. [Biochem.] A substance produced from creatine present in muscles and URINE.

creep, 1.v.i. [Bot.] Of a plant, go flat over

the face of the earth etc., putting out roots from time to time. [Zoo.] Go with body on or very near to the face of the earth, etc., as a worm or certain insects. 2.n. A very slow motion, expansion, etc., sp.:—[Eng.] A slow change in the size or form of a material, sp. metal, caused by heat, PRESSURE, or STRAIN going on for a long time, the material sometimes undergoing the opposite process when the pressure etc. is taken away, but sometimes never getting back its normal form. [Mining.] The forcing up by degrees of the floor of a mine. [Geol.] the slow motion of loose material into a new, gen. lower position, or of the sides of a FAULT. [Chem.] The forming or moving up of a PRECIPITATE on the sides of a vessel over the level of the liquid.

'creeper, n. [Bot.] A creeping plant.

'cremocarp, n. [Bot.] Fruit formed of two one-seeded divisions becoming separate from one another when ready.

'crenate, a. [Biol.] Having an edge formed in small regular curves, not very deeply cut in, said sp. of leaves. (See picture p. 223) cre'nation, n.

'creosote, n. [Chem.] Brown oil-like liquid got by DISTILLATION from TAR, formed chiefly of $CH_3.C_6.H_4.OH$ and used as a DISINFECTANT and for IMPREGNATING wood to keep it from being attacked by FUNGI.

'crepitation, n. A noise like a number of very small, sharp cracks such as is freq. made by burning wood. [Med.] CREPITUS. 'crepitate, v.i. Make, give out, a c. 'crepitus, n. [Med.] A small CREPITATION or rough, sharp, rubbing sound produced in the body, for example when the two edges of a broken bone are rubbed together, or in the chest in diseases of the LUNGS, etc.; the feeling of two rough things rubbing against one another, or of something cracking, experienced for example in a broken bone or a stiff JOINT when moved.

cre'puscular, a. To do with the TWILIGHT. [Zoo.] (Of animals) awake and going about their business in the TWILIGHT at the end or start of the day, as certain birds. c. rays. Raying lines of light, freq. coloured, seen coming from the sun when it is lower than the sky-line, as the effect of its light being broken up by clouds, mountains, etc.

'crescent, n. Form like that of the new moon (see MOON).

'cresol, n. [Chem.] Any of three ISOMERS of $CH_3.C_6H_6.OH$, oil-like liquids or PHENOL-like CRYSTALLINE substances without colour, got from TAR and used as DISIN-FECTANTS and in making EXPLOSIVES, PLASTICS, and DYES.

crest, n. [Zoo.] Outgrowth of feathers or skin on top of head or back of animal; long narrow outgrowth on some bones, sp. of leg; CRISTA.

cre'taceous, a. [Geol.] Of, like, having in it, chalk. C., a., n. (To do with) the last PERIOD of the MEZOZOIC or the SYSTEM of ROCKS then formed. (See p. 558).

'cretify, v.t. and i. Make into or become chalk, or full of Ca SALTS.

'cretin, n. [Med.] Person whose development of mind and body comes to a stop at an early stage as the effect of little or no working of the THYROID GLAND from birth. 'cretinous, a. 'cretinism, n.

cre'vasse, n. [Geol.] A deep, wide crack in a GLACIER or ice-field.

cri'bellum (cribella), n. [Zoo.] In certain ARACHNIDA, a special SPINNING apparatus in the form of a plate full of small holes in front of the SPINNERETS, by which a band made up of a number of threads is made. cri'bellar, a. cribellar glands. The GLANDS producing the silk which goes through the holes in the c.

'cribriform, a. [Biol.] Full of small holes to let substances or structures through. c. cell. [Bot.] A SIEVE CELL. c. plate. [Zoo.] Part of the ETHMOID bone, having holes for letting through the nerves from the nose.

crico-. CRICOID.

'cricoid, 1.a. [Zoo.] In the form of a ring. 2.n. A c. CARTILAGE in the LARYNX.

Cri'noidea, n.pl. [Zoo.] Class of ECHINO-DERMATA with flower-like body and feather-like branching arms, gen. fixed in one place on a stem. 'crinoid, n., a. (Animal) of the C.

'crisis (crises), n. [Med.] That stage in the process of a disease which is a turning-point for better or worse, that is, at which if a certain change takes place the danger is probably over, sp. the quick fall of TEMPERATURE marking the end of a FEVER; a sudden attack marked by violent pain in diseases such as LOCO-MOTOR ATAXIA.

'crispate, crisped, aa. [Bot.] Having, twisted into, short, sharp-edged folds or waves.

'crista (cristae), n. [Zoo.] Long, narrow outgrowth, RIDGE. c. a'custica. A c. in the AMPULLA of the ear in back-boned animals, where the nerve-threads come in. 'cristate, a. 'cristiform, a.

'critical, a. [Med.] Of, to do with, a CRISIS; (of a condition) in which there is danger of death. [Phys.] To do with a point in a process at which a sudden change may take place; of c. size; said of a CHAIN REACTION which is being kept up at an unchanging rate, that is, is self-supporting and no more, or of the NUCLEAR REACTOR in which such a reaction takes place. c. angle. [Optics] Of light going from one substance to another by which it is less bent, the greatest angle which it may make with the NORMAL to the face of the second substance at the point of meeting without undergoing complete REFLECTION. **c. ex′periment.** [Phys.] An EXPERIMENT in which FISSIONABLE material is increased by degrees in a NUCLEAR REACTOR till a c. condition is produced. **c. mass.** [Phys.] The mass of FISSIONABLE material in a c. REACTOR. **c. point.** The point on the c. temperature curve of a substance at which the PRESSURE and VOLUME have their c. values. **c. ′pressure.** The PRESSURE necessary to make a gas into a liquid at its c. temperature. **c. so′lution ′tempera-ture.** The temperature over which two liquids may be mixed in any amounts. **c. size.** [Phys.] (Of FISSILE material) the smallest amount necessary for keeping up a CHAIN REACTION. **c. state.** The condition of a gas at its c. point when it seems to be between a liquid and a gas. **c. ′temperature.** The TEMPERA-TURE over which it is not possible to make a given gas into a liquid; the temperature at which there is a loss of MAGNETIC properties; the temperature at which some important change takes place in a metal in the process of heating or the opposite. **c. ve′locity.** [Phys.] The VELOCITY at which the motion of a current of a given liquid or gas in given conditions is changed from smooth to TURBULENT. **c. ′volume.** [Phys.] The VOLUME of unit mass of a substance at its c. temperature and c. pressure.

Croco′dilia, n.pl. [Zoo.] LORICATA.

Cro-′Magnon man. [Anthrop.] One sort of early man, living somewhere about the middle of the PALAEOLITHIC, noted for the great size of the head.

′cromlech, n. [Archaeol.] A circle of MEGA-LITHS; a DOLMEN.

Crookes′ dark space. CATHODE DARK SPACE. **Crookes′ radio′meter.** [Optics] Apparatus made up of a system of plates polished on one side, black on the other in a glass bulb, turning round when acted on by light. **Crookes′ tube.** [Phys.] Early form of ELECTRON DISCHARGE TUBE.

crop, n. [Zoo.] INGLUVIES, sp. of bird. **cross,** 1.v.t. [Biol.] (Of man) get offspring produced from (two animals or plants of different sorts, sp. different VARIETIES of the same SPECIES). 2.n. Plant or animal which is the offspring of two plants or animals of different sorts. **c.-′breed,** v.t. and i. C. or (of animals and plants of different sorts) MATE with one another so that cc. are produced. **′c.-′bred,** a. (Of animals or plants) produced by c.-breeding. **c.-′fertilization,** n. [Biol.] The FERTILIZATION of female GAMETES from one plant or animal by male gametes from

another. **c.-polli′nation.** [Bot.] The trans-porting of POLLEN from one flower to the STIGMA of a different flower.

cross, crossed, aa. Placed, going, across. **cross hair** or **wire.** One or other of two or more delicate hair-like threads or wires placed across one another at right angles on, or in front of, the EYEPIECE of some OPTICAL instruments as a help in getting whatever is to be looked at in the very middle of the field of view, and in seeing the space relations of different details to one another. **′cross-′linking,** [Chem.] In POLYMERIZATION, the joining together of chains of MOLECULES by BONDS going across from the molecules of one chain to the molecules parallel to them in another. **′cross-′section,** n. A cut across something at right angles to its AXIS, sp. its long axis, or a thin bit cut from it in this direction.

′crossed lens. [Optics] Simple LENS so de-signed as to give the smallest possible SPHERICAL ABERRATION, formed of two out-curving faces one having some number of times, gen. six, the RADIUS of the other.

′crossing-′over, n. [Biol.] Exchange of parallel parts of two HOMOLOGOUS CHROMOSOMES in MEIOSIS.

Cross′opterygii, n.pl. [Zoo.] A SUB-CLASS, or in some systems an ORDER, of CHOAN-ICHTHYES of which only one or two SPECIES are still in existence, made up almost completely of inland-water fish, and having normal, pointed teeth (as opp. DIPNOI), CYCLOID SCALES, and PAIRED FINS, from some early repre-sentative of which land animals are said to have come.

croup, n. [Med.] An INFLAMMATION of the LARYNX or TRACHEA in young boys and girls, marked by a specially loud and rough-sounding cough and trouble in breathing, and sometimes by the forming of false MEMBRANES as in DIPHTHERIA, freq. caused by the diphtheria BACILLUS but sometimes by others.

crown, n. [Zoo.] Part of tooth used in biting, the part which is seen; part of animal's horn farthest from body; top of head; cup and arms of CRINOIDEA. **c. wheel.** [Mach.] Wheel having teeth pointing parallel to AXIS.

′crucible, n. [Chem., Metal.] Vessel in which material is burned or heated to a very high degree of heat.

Cru′ciferae, n.pl. [Bot.] A FAMILY of common plants having 4 units in every ring of flower-parts, with the 4 PETALS ranged round the middle point like 4 quarters of a circle, and the fruit a SILIQUE or SILICLE.

′cruciform, ′cruciate, aa. Having, or grouped in, the form of two lines cutting one another at right angles. sp. [Bot.].

crude, a. (Of substances) in the natural condition, unworked; not free from other, undesired, substances.

crumb 'structure. Of a substance, a structure of small sp. soft bits, not powder or hard separate grains, said sp. of earth, in which this structure is the best for the growth of plants. 'crumminess, n. C. structure. 'crumbly, a. Readily broken up into small bits, like bread.

'crural, a. [Zoo.] To do with the leg or CRUS; leg-like.

crus (crusa), n. [Zoo.] The lower part of the leg, in man that between the knee and the foot, in other animals, birds, and insects, the part having a like position.

crust, n. A hard outer coat or cover, sp. one which is readily broken up or through like the c. of bread, such as the c. formed on snow when it is cold enough, or one formed by the becoming hard of a PRECIPITATE or EXUDATION, for example [Med.] a c. of dried blood, PUS etc., over a wound or a diseased place on the skin. [Geol.] The LITHOSPHERE. crus'taceous, a. Sp. [Bot.] (of plants) forming a thin c.-like cover on stones, etc., as LICHENES.

Crus'tacea, n.pl. [Zoo.] A CLASS of ARTHRO-PODA, gen. living in water and breathing by GILLS, and having 4 feelers on the head (which is not marked off from the THORAX), legs etc. with two branches, and in some sorts a cover of CHITIN forming a hard SHELL. crus'tacean, n., a. (Animal) of the C. crus'taceous, a.

'cryo-. Cold.

'cryogen, n. Any FREEZING MIXTURE. cryo'genic, a. To do with very low TEMPERATURES or ways of getting them.

cryolite, n. [Mineral.] Natural Na_3AlF_6 (sodium aluminium fluoride), a white substance used in making Al and glass.

cry'ophorus, n. [Phys.] Apparatus made of two glass bulbs with no air inside joined by a glass pipe, one bulb having some water in it which becomes ice when the other bulb is made as cold as ice, used to give an example of the lowering of TEMPERATURE produced by EVAPORA-TION.

cryo'plankton, n. [Bot.] Very small plants, chiefly ALGAE, covering the snow and ice near the POLES and on the top of high mountains.

cryo'scopic, a. [Phys.] To do with point at which a liquid becomes solid. c. method, cry'oscopy, n. The discovery of the MOLECULAR WEIGHT of a substance by observation of the change produced by it in the FREEZING POINT of a SOLVENT.

'cryostat, n. Apparatus for keeping anything at the same degree of cold.

crypt, n. [Zoo.] A small hollow; a simple, pipe-like GLAND.

'cryptic color'ation. [Zoo.] The sort of colouring which makes an animal not readily seen in its natural conditions, and so safer from attack or better able to get near to animals it has designs on.

'crypto-. Secret, covered, not seeming to be what it is.

'cryptocarp, n. [Bot.] CYSTOCARP.

'crypto'crystalline, a. [Crystal., Mineral., etc.] Made up of CRYSTALS so small as not to be seen separately even under a MICROSCOPE.

'cryptogam, n. [Bot.] Plant without flowers and frequently without separate stems, leaves, or roots. crypto'gamic, cryp'to-gamous, aa.

Crypto'gamia, n.pl. [Bot.] In older systems of plant-grouping, a SUB-KINGDOM made up of all the plants not producing flowers or seeds.

'cryptomere, n. [Biol.] A quality which is not seen in an animal or plant but of which the GENE has been handed on to it, so that the quality may come to light again in its offspring. cryp'tomerism, n. The condition in which a quality does not come to light in an animal or plant though the GENE of which it is repre-sentative has been handed on to it.

'crypto'zoic, a. [Zoo.] Living in dark places, as in cracks, under stones, etc.

'crystal, n. Glass of specially good quality, noted for being beautifully clear and bright. [Mineral.] A clear, ice-like sort of QUARTZ. [Phys., Chem.] A unit of struc-ture in a solid substance in which the ATOMS are grouped in a fixed design giving it a SYMMETRICAL form limited by a number of plane faces, the angles between which are the same, whatever its size. c. an'alysis. The discovery of the ATOM structure of cc., chiefly by the use of X-RAYS. c. de'tector, c. 'rectifier. [Radio] A DEMODULATOR made of a delicate wire touching a c., gen. of GALENA or GER-MANIUM, or sometimes made of two touching cc. c. 'grating. A c. fixed in position for use as a DIFFRACTION GRATING, for example for X-RAYS. c. 'oscillator. [Radio] An OSCILLATOR in which one part of the CURRENT is a PIEZO-ELECTRIC CRYSTAL. c. set. A radio RECEIVER having a c. detector. c. 'structure. The design formed by the ATOMS of a c., which is the same for all cc. of a given substance or c. system. c. 'system. Any of the 6 (or sometimes 7, see RHOMBOHEDRAL) groups in which cc. are put based on the RATIOS between the measures of their three AXES and of the angles these make with one another (see p. 99). crystall'iferous, a. 'crystal-line, a. Clear and bright like c. glass. [Phys.-Chem.] Of, to do with, a c. or cc.; (of a solid substance) formed of cc.; having the inner structure of a

CLASSIFICATION OF CRYSTALS

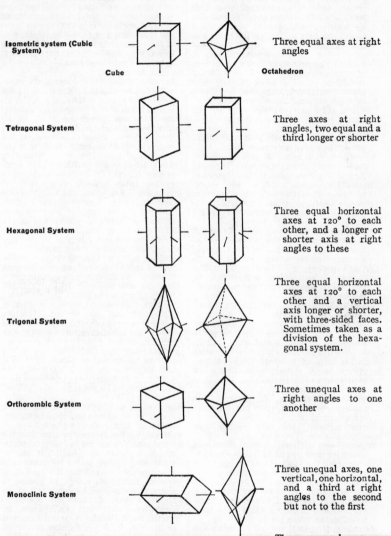

Isometric system (Cubic System)

Cube   Octahedron

Three equal axes at right angles

Tetragonal System

Three axes at right angles, two equal and a third longer or shorter

Hexagonal System

Three equal horizontal axes at 120° to each other, and a longer or shorter axis at right angles to these

Trigonal System

Three equal horizontal axes at 120° to each other and a vertical axis longer or shorter, with three-sided faces. Sometimes taken as a division of the hexagonal system.

Orthorombic System

Three unequal axes at right angles to one another

Monoclinic System

Three unequal axes, one vertical, one horizontal, and a third at right angles to the second but not to the first

Triclinic System   **Without Symmetry**

Three unequal axes no two of which are at right angles.

crystalline substance, but not necessarily formed into clearly marked and complete cc. **crystalline cone**. [Zoo.] The CONE-like part of an OMMATIDIUM by which incoming light is REFRACTED. **crystalline lens**. [Zoo.] The clear LENS-like structure by which incoming rays are FOCUSED so as to make a picture on the RETINA in the complex eye of back-boned and some other animals. **crystalli'zation**, n. [Chem.] The process of changing into cc. or crystalline form, sp. from a liquid condition, or of causing this to take place. **'crystallize**, v.t. and i. (Make) undergo crystallization. **'crystallized**, a. (Of a substance) in the form of cc., having undergone crystallization. **'crystall(o)-**.

'crystallin, n. [Biochem.] A GLOBULIN present in the CRYSTALLINE LENS.

'crystallite, n. [Chem.] A very small and incompletely formed CRYSTAL. [Mineral.] Any of the very small bodies present in glass-like IGNEOUS ROCKS and representative of the start of CRYSTALLIZATION.

'crystallo'blastic, a. [Geol.] Said of CRYSTALLINE ROCKS produced by METAMORPHISM, sp. of their TEXTURE.

crys'tallogram, n. [Phys.-Chem., Cryst.] A camera picture of the DIFFRACTION of X-RAYS sent through a CRYSTAL, giving the design of the crystal structure.

'crystall'ography, n. The science of the structure, properties, and forms of CRYSTALS. **'crystall'ographer**, n. **'crystallo'graphic**, a.

'crystalloid, 1.a. Like a CRYSTAL. 2.n. [Bot.] Any of certain very small c. grains of PROTEIN seen in some CELLS. [Phys.-Chem.] Any substance which normally DISSOLVES in the normal way, that is, which when put into a liquid is DISPERSED in the form of separate MOLECULES or groups small enough to go through a SEMI-PERMEABLE MEMBRANE, as opp. a COLLOID. **'crystall'oidal**, a.

'crystallolumi'nescence, n. [Chem.] The sending out of light when CRYSTALS are being formed from SOLUTION.

'crystic, a. [Geol.] To do with ice, or changes caused by ice.

'crystosphene, n. [Geol.] A great stretch of ice under the TUNDRA of North America, caused by the FREEZING of spring water before it gets to the top of the earth.

Cs, Sign for CAESIUM.

ctene, n. [Zoo.] A comb-like swimming instrument seen in CTENOPHORA, made up of a line of strong CILIA with their bases united into a band.

cten'idium (ctenidia), n. [Zoo.] A comb-like structure, sp. the breathing-apparatus in MOLLUSCA; line of hard, pointed structures on the head or body in some insects.

'ctenoid, a. [Biol.] Comb-like; having a c. edge, sp. [Zoo.] of fish-SCALES.

Cten'ophora, n.pl. [Zoo.] A SUB-PHYLUM of COELENTERATA swimming by CTENES, of which there are 8 lines running from end to end of the body, HERMAPHRODITE animals without ALTERNATION OF GENERATIONS and living independently, gen. of egg-like outline with marked BIRADIAL SYMMETRY and without CNIDOBLASTS, some sorts with TENTACLES.

Cu, Sign for copper.

cube, n. [Geom.] Solid having six equal square sides. [Arith.] (Of a number) the third POWER, as x^3 is the c. of x. **c. pho'tometer**. Form of PHOTOMETER for measuring AVERAGE power of light in all directions. **c. root**. [Arith.] (Of a number) the number of which it is the c., as x is the c. root of x^3. **'cubic**, a. To do with cc.; cubical; of measures, solid, measuring three DIMENSIONS. [Arith.] Of the third POWER. [Cryst.] Of, to do with, the cubic system. **cubic 'content**. (Of a substance) VOLUME, (of a vessel) CAPACITY. **cubic 'system**. [Cryst.] The ISOMETRIC SYSTEM. **'cubical**, a. Having the form of a c. **cubical epi'thelium**. [Zoo.] COLUMNAR EPITHELIUM in which the CELLS are short, more or less cubical.

'cuboid, a. Roughly CUBICAL in form.

'cucullate, a. [Biol.] Having the form of the sort of soft loose head-covering framing the face like an arch and coming down over the sides and back, sp. [Bot.] said of leaves of which the base edges are folded in and come together in the middle. [Zoo.] Having an arched structure forming a head-covering, sp. of insects in which the first division of the THORAX is pulled up and over the head.

cu'cullus (cuculli), n. [Bot.] Any CUCULLATE part of an animal or plant, sp. [Zoo.] any structure on the head giving the suggestion of a covering pulled over it.

culm, n. [Bot.] The JOINTED, gen. hollow, stem of a grass.

culmi'nation, n. [Astron.] The highest or lowest point of TRANSIT of a star, etc. across the MERIDIAN of a place.

'cultivate, v.t. Get (plants) produced for the use of man by planting and care; c. plants, sp. food plants on (land); get (earth, fields, etc.) broken up for the purpose of planting seed or helping the growth of plants. **'cultivated**, a. Sp. (of plants) of the sort cultivated by man and given specially good qualities by selection, CROSS-BREEDING, etc. **culti'vation**, n. **'cultivator**, n. [Mach.] A farm instrument or machine having a number of curved or round blades or teeth on a frame, which is pulled over the earth, gen. by a horse or motor, so as to get it broken into small bits—used after ploughing, or round plants in growth.

'**culture,** n. [Biol.] The growth in a c. medium for science purposes of BACTERIA, FUNGI, bits of living substance, etc.; a c. medium in which such growth is taking place. [Anthrop.] The system of ways, ideas, group-behaviour and so on produced by and representative of any society. **c. 'medium.** [Biol.] A substance having the right properties for the growth of BACTERIA etc. to take place in it.

'**cumulative,** a. (Of a force, property, etc.) becoming greater, stronger, by one addition after another, sp. having no or little effect at first but producing one in time as the effect of addition; (of an effect) produced in this way. **c. error.** An error which goes on becoming greater or more important in the process of working something out, sp. through being made again and again in a group of observations. **c. poison.** [Med.] Any poison which may be taken in small amounts for a long time with seemingly little or no bad effect, and then at one point has a sudden and serious one.

'**cumulo-'nimbus,** n. [Meteor.] Cloud in the form of tall mountain-like masses of which the base is thick and dark and sending down, or about to send down, rain or snow, the top thinner and in threads.

'**cumulus,** n. [Meteor.] Thick cloud generally on a flat base, with the upper part solid-looking and clearly outlined.

'**cuneal,** a. [Zoo.] CUNEATE.

'**cuneate,** a. [Biol.] Wide at one end and narrowing to a point at the other, sp. [Bot.] (of a leaf) having this form and fixed to the stem by the point.

'**cuneiform,** a. [Zoo.] CUNEATE.

'**cupel,** n. [Metal.] A flat vessel of POROUS material able to undergo great heat, used in cupellation. '**cupell'ation,** n. The freeing of gold, silver, etc. from other metals, sp. lead, by putting the mixed metal in a c. and sending onto it a strong current of highly heated air, causing OXIDATION of the undesired substances which are then ABSORBED by the vessel or taken off by the air current.

'**cupola,** n. A small DOME or dome-like structure, sp. [Geol.] an addition like a small dome on top of a MAJOR INTRUSION. [Metal.] A high, round FURNACE in which iron and other metals are made liquid. [Astron.] The DOME of an OR-SERVATORY.

'**cupric,** a. [Chem.] Having in it copper with a VALENCY of two.

cupro-. Copper (and . . .):—'-'**nickel,** n.

'**cuprous,** a. [Chem.] Having in it copper with a VALENCY of one.

cu'rare, cu'rari, n. [Chem., Med.] A strong poison got from plants of the GENUS *Strychnos*, made up of two ALKALOIDS, one of which puts a stop to the working of the heart, the other to that of the NERVE-ENDINGS by which the muscles of the arms, legs, etc. are moved, used medically to keep muscles from acting while the body is undergoing an operation.

cure, 1.v.t. Get (a natural material) ready for marketing or use by putting it through some chemical or other process, sp. one designed to keep DECOMPOSITION from taking place, as in the curing of skins to make leather. [Med.] Overcome (a disease or unhealthy or damaged condition), make (person) well again, by medical care. 2.n. A process or way of curing; a substance used for curing a material, for example leather. '**cured,** a. '**curing,** n. Sp. the process by which a THERMOSETTING substance becomes suddenly hard.

'**curie,** n. [Phys.] That amount of a RADIOACTIVE substance undergoing DECAY at the rate of 3.7×10^{10} DISINTEGRATIONS per second, used as a unit for measuring RADIOACTIVITY.

'**Curie 'balance.** [Phys.] Apparatus for measuring the force on a body in a MAGNETIC FIELD.

'**Curie point.** [Phys.] The TEMPERATURE for a given FERROMAGNETIC substance at which it becomes simply PARAMAGNETIC.

'**curium,** n. Chemical ELEMENT, at. no. 96, sign Cm., a TRANSURANIC element.

'**current,** n. A body of liquid or gas moving in a certain direction, or the motion of such a liquid or gas. [Elec.] The transport of ELECTRICITY through a body as the effect of the motion from end to end of it of loose ELECTRONS, in the same way as of a c. of liquid or gas MOLECULES. **c. 'bedding.** [Geol.] Irregular form of STRATA of SEDIMENTARY ROCK caused by the currents which put it down. **c. 'density.** [Elec.] The amount of electric current going through unit AREA of a CROSS-SECTION of a CONDUCTOR.

'**cursor,** n. A part of a measuring-instrument which has to be moved into position to get the measure, sp. the moving part of a SLIDE-RULE.

'**curtate 'distance.** [Astron.] Distance of a body from the sun or earth as measured in the plane of the ECLIPTIC.

'**curvature,** n. The process of curving or condition of being curved; measure of the amount by which a line or other thing is curved.

curve, n. A GRAPH, sp. one taking the form of a curved line representative of a changing value.

curvi'linear, a. Formed of or limited by curved lines.

cusp, n. [Biol.] A sharp-pointed PROJECTION, sp. on the cutting edge of a tooth. [Astron.] One or other of the points of the new moon (*see* MOON). [Math.] The meeting-point of two curves. **'cuspate, 'cuspid, 'cuspidal, 'cuspidate, aa. cuspidate leaf.** [Bot.] Leaf with rounded end coming out into small sharp point in the middle.

cu'taneous, a. [Zoo.] To do with the skin.

'cuticle, n. [Biol.] Thin outer skin of non-CELLULAR material covering an animal or plant; in higher animals, the EPIDERMIS; dead epidermis, as that round a finger- or toe-nail. **cu'ticular,** a. **cu'ticularization,** n. The forming of c., sp. [Bot.] CUTINIZATION.

'cut-in, -ose, nn. [Bot.] Wax-like substance made up of mixed fats, by the forming of which on or in the outer coat of CELL-WALLS the CUTICLE of a plant is produced. **'cutiniz'ation,** n. The development of c. in or on CELL-WALLS.

cutis, n. [Zoo.] The skin or sp. the DERMIS of a back-boned animal.

'cutting, n. [Bot.] Any bit cut off a plant, sp. off the stem or root, which if planted in the earth, etc. will put out roots and so may be used for producing a new plant.

'cuttlebone, n. [Zoo.] The SHELL of certain CEPHALOPODA which is bedded in the body like bone, used crushed for making polishing powder etc.

cwt. = HUNDREDWEIGHT.

'cyan, n. A blue-green colour, *see* SUBTRACTIVE PRIMARY.

'cyanate, n. [Chem.] Any SALT having in it the group –OCN.

'cyanide, n. [Chem.] Any SALT having in it the group –CN. **c. process.** [Metal.] Process for getting gold and silver by acting on their powdered ORES with a feeble SOLUTION of KCN or NaCN, by which these metals are DISSOLVED. **'cyaniding,** n. [Metal.] (The use of) the c. process.

'cyanin, n. [Biochem.] A colouring-substance with GLUCOSE in it present in certain flowers.

cyan(o)-. [Biol.] Dark blue or blue-green. [Chem.] CYANOGEN.

cy'anogen, n. [Chem.] C_2N_2, a poison gas without colour and with a bitter, nut-like smell, like in its chemical behaviour to the HALOGENS and forming CYANIDES.

Cyano'phyceae, n.pl. [Bot.] The group of ALGAE having a blue-green colour as the effect of PHYCOCYANIN present in the CELLS together with CHLOROPHYLL, very small and simple one-celled or thread-like plants, with no clear NUCLEUS and producing offspring only by division, living separately or massed into groups, of very wide distribution in sea and inland waters and wet places.

cy'anophyll, n. A blue-green colouring-material present in plants.

'cyan'osis, n. [Med.] Condition in which the skin becomes blue as the effect of not having enough O in the blood.

'cyber'netics, n. The science based on a comparison of the workings of the control system formed by the brain and nerves of man and the workings of present-day electric and other machines designed to do operations which were at one time looked on as needing a living brain—for example, COMPUTERS, PHOTO-ELECTRIC sorting machines etc.

'cybo'taxis, n. [Phys.-Chem.] The grouping of MOLECULES in a liquid in a design like that of CRYSTALLINE structure.

Cyca'dales, n.pl. [Bot.] An ORDER of GYMNOSPERMS, the lowest form of seed-plants still in existence, trees with tall unbranching stems topped by great feather-like leaves.

'cycle, n. A train of changes, motions, or events of any sort coming back to its starting-point, gen. one of a number of such cc. taking place again and again in a regular rhythm, sp. [Mach.] the different STROKES of the PISTON forming one complete operation in an INTERNAL COMBUSTION ENGINE. [Phys.] The change of some physical value from + through 0 to − and back again, sp. [Elec.] the change in an ALTERNATING CURRENT from its greatest value in one direction to its greatest value in the other and back again. **c. of e'rosion.** [Geol.] The stages in the development of a stretch of country under the operation of weather, rivers, etc. till it becomes more or less level and fixed in form. **'cyclic,** a. In the form of, to do with, a c., circle, or sometimes a SPIRAL. [Bot.] Having the flower-parts ranged in circles, opp. SPIRAL. **cyclic 'compound.** [Chem.] Substance in which some or all of the ATOMS make a ring, sp. a HYDROCARBON.

cycliz'ation, n. [Chem.] The forming of RING COMPOUNDS.

'cycl(o)-. Cyclic. [Chem.] Being a CYCLIC COMPOUND, as **'cyclobu'tane,** n., **'cyclohex'ane,** n., **'cyclopen'tane,** n., **'cyclopro'pane,** n. (*See* p. 392.)

'cycloid, a. [Zoo.] Curved in a regular way, said sp. of fish SCALE having a smooth, c., free edge.

cy'clometer, n. Instrument for recording the number of turns made by a wheel, and so freq., the distance covered by a wheeled thing.

'cyclone, n. [Meteor.] A great stretch of low ATMOSPHERIC PRESSURE over part of the earth, with the PRESSURE lowest at the middle and a system of winds all the time circling round this to the outer edge, south of the EQUATOR in the same direction as the hands of a clock, and north of the EQUATOR in the opposite direction; a wind-system seen sp. in the TROPICS, of the same structure as a c. but much more violent, gen. smaller in size, and moving at a great rate over the earth, causing much destruction. cy'clonic, a.

'cyclonite, n. HEXOGEN.

Cyclo'stomata, n.pl. [Zoo.] A CLASS of VERTEBRATES, snake-like water animals without SCALES, JAWS or legs, having a round mouth with which they SUCK the blood of fish, GILLS for breathing, and only one nose-opening. cyclo'stom-ate, -atous, aa. Of, to do with, the C.; having a round mouth. 'cyclostome, n. Animal of the C.

cyclo'thymia, n. [Med., Psych.] The process of going from a happy and EXCITED condition of mind to a DEPRESSED one and back again without reason, in a regular rhythm, as seen in MANIC-DEPRESSIVE INSANITY, or, less violently, in persons who are not diseased in mind but have a natural tendency to such unreasoning changes of feeling, which is probably a sign of a tendency to become so.

'cyclotron, n. [Phys.] Apparatus for giving a high rate of motion and great ENERGY to POSITIVE PARTICLES, for example, PROTONS, by driving them in a SPIRAL between two hollow, box-like ELECTRODES in the form of half-circles, placed in a MAGNETIC FIELD, used in NUCLEAR PHYSICS.

'cylinder, n. A solid or hollow body in the form of a c. [Geom.] The curved SURFACE, or solid or hollow form limited by this, made when one side of a RECTANGLE is turned in a complete circle round the opposite side as its axis, as seen, for example, in a round, straight, regular rod, of which the ends are circles at right angles to it. [Mach.] In a pump or engine the vessel of this form in which the PISTON is moved forward and back. cy'lindrical, a. cy'lindroid, a., n.

'cymbiform, a. [Bot.] Formed like a boat.

cyme, n. [Bot.] A flower-grouping in which the chief stem is ended by a flower, and other flowers are then produced at the ends of side-branches, freq. like a CORYMB in form, but different in the fact of opening in order from the middle to the outer ring (see picture, p. 199). 'cymoid, a. 'cymose, a. 'cymule, n. Small c.

cy'mometer, n. [Elec.] An early form of WAVE-METER.

cy'nopodous, a. [Zoo.] Having CLAWS which are unable to be pulled in or back, as a dog.

'cypsela, n. [Bot.] An ACHENE formed from an INFERIOR OVARY. (See picture p. 158).

cyst, n. [Med.] Bag-like part without an opening, full of liquid or half-liquid substance, such as LYMPH, produced by INFLAMMATION in any part of the body. [Biol.] Bag-like part or cover, sp. [Bot.] that covering a RESTING SPORE in some ALGAE, [Zoo.] that covering a PROTO-ZOÖN in a resting condition. 'cyst-ic, -ose, -ous, aa. To do with, forming, having, covered with, a c. 'cystoid, a.

'cystic, a. [Zoo.] To do with the GALL- or the URINARY BLADDER.

cysti'cercoid, n. [Zoo.] A TAPEWORM LARVA of the sort having only a small BLADDER freq. with a sort of tail (see BLADDER-WORM).

cysticer'cosis, n. [Med.] The condition of having CYSTICERCI in the body.

cysti'cercus (cysticerci), n. [Zoo.] A BLADDERWORM. cysti'cercoid, a.

'cystine, n. [Biochem.] An AMINO ACID in the form of a white CRYSTALLINE substance produced when PROTEINS are broken up, and present in horn, hair, and so on, a necessary part of the food of animals.

cyst(o)-. [Zoo., Med.] CYST; URINARY BLADDER: cys'titis, n., cys'totomy.

'cystocarp, n. [Bot.] Form of SPOROCARP produced in RHODOPHYCEAE after FERTILIZATION of the PROCARP.

'cystolith, n. [Bot.] Mass of $CaCO_3$ on a stem-like part on the walls of some plant-CELLS.

cys'toma, n. [Med.] TUMOUR formed of CYSTS.

'cytase, n. [Biochem.] Any ENZYME acting on CELLULOSE. [Med.] ALEXIN.

'cytaster, n. [Biol.] A further ASTER at a distance from the NUCLEUS.

-cyte, n. [Biol.] CELL.

cyt(o)-. [Biol.] CELL. cyto'genesis, n., cy'togenous, a., cy'tolysis, n., cyto'lytic, a.

'cytochrome, n. [Biol.] A material present in the CELLS of certain plants and most animals which is not readily damaged by heat and has an important part in the use by the cell of O from the air.

cy'togamy, n. [Biol.] The joining or uniting of CELLS.

cy'tology, n. The branch of Biology which has to do with the structure and behaviour of CELLS.

cyto'lysin, n. [Biol.] A substance causing CYTOLYSIS.

cy'tolysis, n. [Biol.] The destruction of CELLS. cyto'lytic, a.

'cytoplasm, n. [Biol.] The PROTOPLASM of a CELL other than the NUCLEUS. cyto'plasmic, a.

'cytostome, n. [Zoo.] The mouth of a one-CELLED animal.

cyto'taxis, n. [Biol.] Motion of CELLS to one

another, probably as effect of chemical attraction.

'cytotax'onomy, n. [Bot.] A system of grouping and naming plants, based on their CELL structure.

'cyto'toxin, n. [Med.] CELL-poison produced in the blood.

'cyto'zoic, a. [Zoo.] Living as a PARASITE inside a CELL, said of PROTOZOA.

'cytula, n. [Zoo.] A FERTILIZED ovum.

D, Sign for DEUTERIUM.

d, Sign for DEXTROROTATORY.

Δ, δ. See DELTA.

'dactyl, n. [Zoo.] A finger, toe, or like part. '-ar, '-ose, '-ous, aa. 'dactylo-.

'dactylo'zooid, n. [Zoo.] HYDROID, sometimes with but generally without a mouth, having special apparatus for gripping small animals, and whose business is getting food for the COLONY and keeping off attackers.

da'guerreotype, n. Early form of camera picture, taken on a silver or silver-coated plate acted on by I and Br and then undergoing DEVELOPMENT by Hg in the form of gas.

'Dalton's law. [Chem.] The LAW OF MULTIPLE PROPORTIONS. Dalton's law of 'partial 'pressures. [Phys., Chem.] Law that the PRESSURE of gases mixed in a vessel is given by the addition of the pressures which would be produced by every gas separately taking up the same amount of space and at the same TEMPERATURE. Dalton's theory. [Phys., Chem.] The ATOMIC THEORY.

dam, n. A structure of earth, stone etc. put up to keep back water, sp. one across the current of a river.

dam, n. [Zoo.] The mother of an animal, sp. a horse or a dog.

'dammar, n. [Chem.] A natural RESIN got from certain evergreen trees in Australia and the East Indies, used chiefly in making VARNISH for camera pictures.

'damping, n. [Mech., Elec.] The making or getting less by degrees of the AMPLITUDE of a VIBRATION or wave; the stopping or making less of the vibration of a part such as the pointer of an instrument. damp, v.t. and i. Make undergo, or undergo, d. 'damped, a. 'damper, n. [Mach., Elec.] Sp. a part put onto an engine or electric machine to damp undesired VIBRATIONS, or keep current from increasing as the effect of HUNTING. [Eng.] A sort of shutter put across the outlet-pipe from a FURNACE

or boiler by which the current of air may be controlled.

'dandruff, n. [Med.] SCURF formed on the skin where it is covered with hair, sp. the skin of the head, as the effect of SEBORRHEA.

'Daniell cell. [Elec.] An electric cell made up of a zinc ANODE in a SOLUTION of $ZnSO_4$ and a copper CATHODE in a solution of $CuSO_4$, the two solutions being separated by a wall with a great number of small holes in it.

'Darcy law. Law that the amount of liquid going through a POROUS body ∝ PRESSURE.

dark 'current. [Elec.] The current present in a PHOTOELECTRIC CELL when it is not giving out light.

dark ground, dark field. [Optics] The FIELD of a MICROSCOPE when the light does not come through the SLIDE but is let in from the side in such a way that TRANSPARENT or very small PARTICLES may be seen as bright points in a black field, used in the ULTRAMICROSCOPE.

dark l. [Phonet.] The English 'l' as sounded before a CONSONANT and at the end of words after a consonant, as in 'trouble'.

dark room. A room used for camera work with light-SENSITIVE material, from which all light having in it ACTINIC RAYS is kept.

dark slide. (The cover of) a flat box in which a camera PLATE is put into a camera, so that the plate may then be uncovered by slipping out the cover.

dark space. [Phys.] Space from which no light comes, in gas through which electric current is going.

dark star. [Astron.] Star giving out no light, or so little light that it is not seen.

'D'Arsonval galva'nometer. [Elec.] A GALVANOMETER in which the current goes through a number of turns of thin wire hanging in a MAGNETIC FIELD.

dart, n. [Zoo.] Any small, sharp-pointed part used for wounding, sp. a small, sharp-pointed rod of $CaCO_3$ formed in the d. sac. d. sac. In certain GASTROPODA, a pipe-like part housing and sending out the d., part of the female sex-apparatus.

Dar'winian vari'ations. [Biol.] The small ways in which the offspring of living things are different from their producers, on which DARWINISM is based.

'Darwinism, n. [Biol.] Darwin's theory of the development of living SPECIES by NATURAL SELECTION as the effect of DARWINIAN VARIATIONS, as opp. MUTATIONS.

dash, n. The sign '—' used in writing or print for marking off an addition to a statement, marking the place of words or letters which are not put in, and so on; see MORSE CODE.

da'symeter, n. [Phys.] A thin glass bulb at one time used in measuring the DENSITY of a gas.

date line. [Geog.] Line on the map of the earth fixed by international agreement as that on which every CALENDAR day is taken as starting, roughly the same as MERIDIAN 180° from Greenwich.

'datum (data), n. A fact, observation, experience, taken as material on which an argument, theory or test is based. **d. point** or **line** or **level.** [Surveying, etc.] A fixed point, line, or level in relation to which measures, positions, and so on are worked out.

'daughter, a. [Biol.] Of the first group of offspring, as **d. cell,** a CELL formed in the first division. **d. 'element.** [Phys., Chem.] The first ELEMENT formed from another by RADIOACTIVE DECAY.

'Davis appa'ratus. An apparatus designed for helping persons in a damaged SUBMARINE to get out and come up to the top of the water, formed of a structure going round the person from which he is able to get O for breathing and which at the same time gives him BUOYANCY.

'Davisson–'Germer ex'periment. The first observation of the DIFFRACTION of ELECTRONS on the face of a metal.

'Davy lamp. An oil-burning light used in mines before electric light came into use, the flames being kept from the gases in the mine by wire net.

day, n. *See* MEAN SOLAR DAY, SOLAR DAY.

'daylight 'factor. Daylight at any point inside a building etc. ÷ light under the open sky at the same time.

'daylight 'vision. [Psych.] PHOTOPIA.

D.C. = DIRECT CURRENT.

D.D.T. [Chem.] $(C_6H_4Cl)_2$: $CHCCl_3$, a white powder used for the destruction of insects.

de-. Un-, sign for the opposite act, process, or condition to that named:— **de'ioniza-tion,** n. **decon'taminate,** v.t.

'Deacon 'process. [Chem.] Process of making Cl by sending air and HCl gas over a heated substance with CuCl in it.

'deacti'vation, n. [Chem.] Destruction of power of acting of CATALYST or ADSORB-ENT; the going back of an ACTIVATED ATOM or MOLECULE to its normal con-dition. **de'activate,** v.t. **de'activated,** a.

dead, a. [Mach.] Not in motion, or not giving motion or power to any other part. [Elec.] Not in connection with a current-producing apparatus, with no current going through it and no CHARGE on it. **d. 'axle.** An AXLE which does not go round with the wheels supported by it, opp. LIVE AXLE.

dead-beat, a. [Phys.] Acting without OSCILLATION, said, for example, of an

instrument whose pointer goes almost straight to the position measuring some force and comes to rest with little or no further motion.

dead space. [Physiol.] The amount of space in the air pipes of the body from which the air does not get to the air-CELLS of the LUNGS in breathing.

deaer'ation, n. The process of getting air and other gases out of something, sp. [Engin.] the water used in a boiler. **de'aerate,** v.t. **de'aerator,** n.

deaf, a. [Med.] With no, or with much less than the normal, sense of hearing. **'-ness,** n.

deaf-mute, n. A person who has no power of hearing or talking. **deaf-'mutism,** n. Condition of being a d.-m.

'deami'nation, n. [Chem.] The taking away of the NH_2 group from AMINO ACIDS. **de'aminate,** v.t.

death cup. [Bot.] Cup-like part of the VOLVA which keeps its place at the base of the stem in some FUNGI, generally those which are poison, after the rest has been broken through.

death rate. Number of deaths among a given number of persons in a given time.

de'bility, n. [Med.] Feeble physical condi-tion, general loss of power by the body. **de'bilitate,** v.t. Make feeble. **debili'tation,** n. **de'bilitative, de'bilitant,** a.

de'bridement, n. [Med.] The cutting away from wounds of all damaged or diseased material. **de'bride,** v.t.

De 'Broglie equation. [Phys.] The EQUATION giving the WAVE-LENGTH of a De Broglie wave. **De Broglie wave.** Any of the waves said to be produced by the motion of any FUNDAMENTAL PARTICLE.

'dec(a)-. (Used in forming names of METRIC units) 10 times the unit named :—**'deca-gram,** n. **'decalitre,** n. **'decameter,** n., **'decare,** n.

'decade, n. A group of 10, sp. 10 years. **d. bridge.** Form of WHEATSTONE BRIDGE in which the OHMS of the RESISTORS are in the RATIO of 10, 100, 1000, etc. to 1.

'decagon, n. [Geom.] Plane form with 10 straight sides and 10 angles.

deca'lage, n. Angle between the upper and lower wings of an airplane.

de'calcify, v.t. [Chem.] Take away Ca salts from, sp. [Med.] from bone or other body substance. **de'calcifi'cation,** n. Sp. [Med.] the decalcifying of bone. **de'calcifier,** n. Substance causing decalcification. **de-'calcifying,** a., n.

deca'lescence, n. [Metal.] The sudden slowing of the rate of increase in the TEMPERATURE of a metal in process of heating at a certain point, caused by a change of structure using the heat as ENERGY at this point. **deca'lescent,** a.

de'camerous, a. [Bot.] With the different

parts in groups of 10, short form 10-*merous*.

de′cant, v.t. [Chem., etc.] Get clear liquid drained off from solid material put down by it. **decan′tation**, n.

′decaploid, n., a. [Genet.] (CELL, etc.) having 10 times the HAPLOID number of CHROMOSOMES.

Deca′poda, n.pl. [Zoo.] An ORDER of CRUSTACEA, made up chiefly of free-swimming sea animals, having 5 PAIRS of legs on the THORAX of which the first pair have generally undergone development into strong gripping-instruments, and a hard cover, forming a GILL CHAMBER at the sides, over the united head and thorax; an ORDER of DIBRANCHIA having 10 arms (of which two are longer than the others with expansions at the ends and able to be pulled in), SUCKERS on stems, and an uncovered body in which the SHELL is bedded. **′decapod**, n., a. (Animal) of the D.

de′capsu′lation, n. [Med.] The operation of taking away the covering of an ORGAN, sp. of a KIDNEY.

de′carbonize, v.t. Take away C from, for example, the blood, steel, an engine. **de′carboni′zation**, n.

de′carburize, v.t. DECARBONIZE.

de′cay, 1.n. [Phys.] The process by which RADIOACTIVE elements are broken up naturally, giving off PARTICLES or RAYS from their NUCLEI and at different stages becoming different substances. [Biochem.] The chemical process by which animal or plant substances are broken up after death. 2.v.i. Undergo d. **d. ′constant.** [Phys.] For any given RADIOACTIVE substance, a fixed number used in working out its rate of d. **d. ′period.** [Phys.] HALF LIFE.

deceler′ation, n. The slowing of the rate of a motion or process, opp. ACCELERATION. [Phys.] The rate of d. of a moving body, measured by unit of distance/unit of time/unit of time. **de′celerate**, v.t. and i. (Make) undergo d.

decem-. 10.

de′cemfid, a. Having, cut into, 10 divisions.

decem′partite, a. Having, cut into, 10 LOBES.

de′cephali′zation, n. [Zoo.] Loss, or getting smaller, of the parts of or to do with the head.

de′cere′bration, n. [Zoo.] The taking away, or stopping working, of the front part of the brain. **de′cerebrate**, 1.v.t. 2.a. Without, or having undergone loss of, the front brain. **de′cere′brize**, v.t.

deci-. $\frac{1}{10}$, as: **′decigram, decilitre, ′deci-′metre**, nn.

′deciare, n. METRIC measure of AREA, = 10m².

′decibel, n. 0·1 BEL, the common unit for measuring the level of sound, or of

electric power, in a sound-producing apparatus.

de′cidua, n. [Zoo.] In higher animals, the part of the inside skin of the UTERUS touching the PLACENTA, which is changed while the development of offspring is taking place and pushed out after it at birth. **de′cidual**, a. **de′ciduate**, a. Sp., of PLACENTA, formed in part from the d.

de′ciduous, a. [Biol.] Put off at certain times, as leaves, horns, etc. [Bot.] Having leaves put off every year before winter etc.

′decimal, 1.a. To do with the number 10 or with d. fractions; (of a measuring- or numbering-system) based on the number 10, in which all units are some POWER of 10 or some d. fraction of a fixed unit. 2.n. A d. fraction. **d. ′fraction.** A FRACTION of which the DENOMINATOR is 10 or some POWER of 10, put in writing not as $\frac{x}{10}$ and so on but as **·x. d. point.** The point used in writing as a sign that a number to the right of it is the NUMERATOR of a FRACTION whose DENOMINATOR is 10, 100, 1000 and so on, as ·456 = $\frac{456}{1000}$.

deci′normal, a. [Chem.] (Of a SOLUTION) 1/10 as strong as a NORMAL solution.

decli′nation, n. [Astron.] Of a star, its distance north or south of the CELESTIAL EQUATOR, given as an angle. [Phys.] MAGNETIC D. **d. ′circle.** [Astron.] (Of a star, etc.) HOUR CIRCLE; the scaled circle on an EQUATORIAL TELESCOPE for reading d. **decli′nometer**, n. Instrument for measuring d.

de′coction, n. [Med.] Liquid made by boiling in water a plant having medical properties, decocting. **de′coct**, v.t. Make (such liquid), or get medical substances from (plant) in this way. **de′coctive**, a.

de′colo(u)ration, n. DECOLOURIZATION. **de′colourate**, a. [Bot.] Without colour.

de′colo(u)rize, v.t. Take away colour from. **decolo(u)ri′zation**, n. **de′colo(u)rant**, n. Substance causing d.

′decom′pose, v.t. and i. Get or become broken up into parts or [Chem.] into simple substances. [Biochem.] (Make) DECAY. **′-d**, a. Sp. [Zoo.] Separate, not touching, said of certain feathers or parts of a feather. **′decompo′sition**, n.

de′composite, de′compound, aa. [Bot.] Made up of divisions which are themselves made up of divisions, as certain leaves.

′decom′pression, n. [Phys.] Act or process of taking away PRESSURE or making it less. [Med.] Any operation to take pressure from a part, sp. from a vessel.

′deconju′gation, n. [Biol.] In MEIOSIS, the separating of the CHROMOSOMES before the end of the PROPHASE.

'decorti'cation, n. [Biol., Med.] The taking away of an outer cover or coat, sp. the CEREBRAL CORTEX or the BARK of a tree. de'corticate, 1.v.t. 2.a. Decorticated; not having an outer coat.

'decrement, n. (Amount of) getting less.

de'crepitate, v.t. and i. [Phys.] Get (salt or other substance) heated to the point of decrepitation. decrepi'tation, n. The bursting or cracking of the CRYSTALS of certain substances, such as salt, when heated, making a cracking noise.

de'cumbent, a. [Bot.] Stretched flat on earth but with end turned up, as the stem of some plants.

de'current, a. [Bot.] (Of a leaf) with base running down stem, forming two wing-like parts.

de'cussate, a. [Biol.] (Of nerves) going across one another, in the form of an X: (of leaves or branches) being in twos at right angles to those over and under them. decus'sation, n. Sp., two groups of nerves going across one another.

de'duct, v.t. Take away from an amount, SUBTRACT. de'duction, n. Sp. amount deducted.

de'duction, n. Reasoning from general laws to facts, or from facts or laws taken as fixed to others which are necessarily true if the first ones are. de'duce, v.t. Get (a fact, law, etc.) by d.

dee, n. The D-like part of a CYCLOTRON, in which a SPIRAL of rays of ELECTRONS is all the time ACCELERATED.

'def(a)ecate, v.t. and i. Make (liquid, etc.) clear, clean, free from undesired material. [Zoo.] (Of an animal) send out waste from ANUS after digestion. def(a)e'ca-tion, n.

de'fect, n. Something wrong with a thing damaging to its properties or operation, or some DEFICIENCY in it. de'fective, a. Incomplete, having some d. [Psych.] Markedly under normal in some power, sp. in general brain power (see MENTAL DEFECTIVE). de'fective 'colour 'vision. [Psych.] See DICHROMAT, DEUTERANOM-ALY, PROTANOMALY, and TRITANOMALY.

de'fence 'mechanism or re'action. [Med.] Reaction by which a living body puts up a fight against something attacking it, such as disease. [Psychol.] Form of behaviour, belief, taken up by a person, gen. unconsciously, to keep from himself or others a knowledge of certain facts about himself, or certain beliefs or tendencies, which would be a cause of shame etc. to him.

de'ferred, a. DELAYED.

de'fibri'nation, n. [Med.] The taking away of FIBRIN, for example, from the blood by keeping it in motion.

de'ficient, a. Not having, or not having enough of, something necessary to make

it complete (d. in something); (of something necessary) not being present or enough. de'ficiency, n. The condition of being d. [Psych.] Sp. MENTAL DEFICIENCY. deficiency disease. [Med.] Any disease caused by certain VITAMINS not being present in food.

'definite, a. [Bot.] (Of a stem or flower-grouping) ending in a flower, sp. CYMOSE.

de'finitive, a. Limiting, being an end or putting an end to (further change, doubt, etc.). [Biol.] (Of a structure or part) complete, having full development.

'defla'gration, n. [Chem.] A sudden burning or bursting into flame as effect of chemical reaction.

de'flate, v.t. and i. Let gas or air out of an elastic vessel (for example, a hollow rubber ball) so that its walls are no longer kept stretched; undergo deflation. de'flation, n. Sp. [Geog.] driving away of dust or loose earth by the wind so that ROCKS are without cover against the weather.

de'flect, v.t. and i. Make or become turned out of its way, as a ray of light, or to one side, as the pointer of an instrument, or bent, as a structure or machine-part as the effect of weight. de'flection, n. Sp., the amount by which anything is de-flected; the motion of the pointer of a recording instrument. de'flectional, a. deflec'tometer, n. [Eng.] An instrument for measuring the amount by which a rod and so on is bent by a weight or force. de'flector, n., a. (Instrument) used for deflecting anything, sp. light. deflector plate. [Phys.] One or the other of two ELECTRODES in a CATHODE RAY TUBE producing between them an ELECTRO-STATIC FIELD by which the line of ELECTRONS is deflected as desired.

de'flocculate, v.t. and i. Get or become broken up from a FLOCCULANT condition. defloccu'lation, n.

'defluent 1.a. Moving down like a liquid. 2.n. Lower end of GLACIER.

de'foliate(d), a. [Bot.] Without its leaves, as a tree in the winter. defoli'ation, n.

de'form, v.t. [Phys.] Make change in the form of (a body) by the operation of a force. [Med.] Be the cause of deformation in. '-able, a. Able to have its form changed by a force. deforma'bility, n. defor'ma-tion, n. [Phys., Med.] Sp. condition of being deformed. '-ed, a. Sp. [Med.], of unnatural form, from birth or as the effect of disease or other damage. '-ity, n. [Med.] Condition of being deformed; deformed part.

de'gas, de'gasify, vv.t. [Phys., Chem.] Make free from gas. de'gasifi'cation, n. de-'gassing, n.

de'gaussing, n. [Elec.] Overcoming the MAGNETIC effect of a body by sending an electric current round it, sp. as done to ship for purpose of keeping it safe from magnetic MINES.

de′generate, 1.v.i. [Biol.] Go back in development from a higher and more complex organization or structure to a lower and simpler one. [Med.] (Of a TISSUE or part) d.; undergo loss of power, as effect of chemical change or the unnormal addition of some substance; (of a condition) become worse. 2.a. Having degenerated; (of a person) sp. much lower than the normal in the tendencies of mind and body. 3.n. D. person. **de′generacy,** n. **de′gene′ration,** n. **de′generative,** a.

deglu′tition, n. Act of taking food down throat.

de′grade, v.t. [Geol.] Get (ROCK, etc.) broken up, wasted away (said of effects of weather, etc.). [Chem.] Get (a complex substance) changed into a less complex substance. **degra′dation,** n. [Geol., Chem.] Act of degrading or condition of being degraded. [Med., Biol.] DEGENERATION. **degradation of ′energy.** [Phys.] Any process by which ENERGY becomes less AVAILABLE, sp. by being turned into heat. **degradation of radi′ation.** [Phys.] Process by which FREQUENCY of RADIATION becomes less.

de′grease, v.t. Take fat out of wool, silk, and so on.

de′gree, n. [Phys.] Unit of measure of TEMPERATURE, generally fixed by division into equal parts of the range between boiling-point of water and the temperature at which it becomes ice, sign °. [Geom.] Unit of measure of angles, equal to 1/90 of a right angle, sign °. **d(d). of freedom.** [Mech.] (Any of) the independent ways in which a body or system may undergo motion, for example, for a solid body of fixed form there are six, that is:—straight-line motion in any one of the three directions of space, as given by three lines at right angles, or a turning motion about any of these three lines. [Phys., Chem.] Of a MOLECULE, the number of independent motions by which it may have ENERGY, that is, line motion, ROTATION, and VIBRATION. [Phys., Chem.] Of a physical or chemical system, the number of the controlling conditions, TEMPERATURE, PRESSURE, CONCENTRATION, etc., which may be changed independently as desired. **d(d). of frost.** [Meteor.] The one or more dd. by which the air TEMPERATURE at any time and place is lower than that at which water becomes ice (32°F, 0°C).

de′hiscence, n. [Biol.] The opening of a part to let out what is inside it, sp. [Bot.] the bursting open of a seed-vessel when seeds are ready. **de′hisce,** v.t. and i. **de′hiscent,** a.

dehu′midifi′cation, n. The process of getting a gas free from water, sp. of drying air in mines, buildings, etc. **dehu′midify,** v.t.

de′hydrate, v.t. [Chem.] Take away water from (a MOLECULE or substance) by heating or chemical reaction. **dehy′dration,** n. Sp. [Med.] an over-great loss of water from the body substance or the condition of having undergone this.

de′hydrocortico′sterone, n. [Physiol.] One of the HORMONES of the SUPRARENAL bodies.

de′hydroge′nation, n. [Chem.] The act or process of taking H out of a substance.

de′jecta, n.pl. [Zoo.] Waste material sent out from body, sp. by DEFAECATION.

de′jection, n. [Zoo.] DEFAECATION; material sent out in d.

deka-. DECA-.

delami′nation, n. [Biol.] Development by the division of CELLS into LAYERS. **de′laminate,** v.i.

′delay, 1.v.t. Put off (an event or operation), make take place late or later, after a time, not straight away. 2.n. Amount of time by which something is delayed. 3.a. (Before names of instruments, etc.) designed to keep an effect from taking place for a certain time after the putting into operation of its cause. **de′layed,** a. Not taking place or coming about straight away, as a **delayed res′ponse** or **re′action** [Psych.], **delayed shock** [Med.]. **delayed-′action,** a. Designed not to do what it has to do for a fixed time, or till some other event comes about, as a **delayed-action bomb. delayed action.** [Elec.] Any d. instrument, system, or part.

de′lignifi′cation, n. The destruction of LIGNIN in trees by the operation of a FUNGUS. **de′lignified,** a.

del′inquent, n., a. [Psych.] (Person, sp. young person) having no or very little sense of right and wrong, though not feeble in mind, and frequently getting into trouble by acting against the law or the rules of normal society. **de′linquency,** n.

deli′quesce, v.i. [Chem.] Become wet and in time liquid by attraction of water from the air. [Bot.] Undergo branching into smaller and smaller divisions. **deli′-quescent,** a. **deli′quescence,** n.

de′lirium, n. (Med.) Loss for a time by ill or wounded person of power of controlling mind, marked by physical unrest, outbursts of unclear talk, taking one person or thing for another, seeing things which are not present, and so on. **de′lirious,** a. Sp. in a condition of d. **d. ′tremens.** Condition of violent d. with shaking of hands and tongue and strong reactions of fear to animals etc. which seem to be present, caused by serious ALCOHOLISM.

de′livery, n. [Med.] Birth of baby, the

sending or taking out of young from the UTERUS. [Engin.] The sending or taking out of material from a vessel or a machine such as a pump. **d. tube.** Pipe by which gas comes from vessel in which it is produced. **de′liver,** v.t. (Of medical man, etc.) oversee, give help in, d. of (baby).

′Dellinger ′fade-out. [Radio] A complete stopping of short-wave radio as the effect of the D-LAYER.

′delta, n. The Greek letter δ or Δ. [Geog.] Land at the mouth of a river, frequently in the form Δ with the river branching round it, formed of earth taken down by the current. **del′taic,** a.

delta metal. [Metal.] An ALLOY made up chiefly of copper and zinc with a little iron and other metals.

delta (or δ) **ray.** [Phys.] Any of the ELECTRONS given off by a substance as the effect of the going through it of an IONIZING PARTICLE, such as an ALPHA PARTICLE.

′deltoid, 1.a. [Biol.] Having the form of the Greek letter Δ, sp. [Bot.] of a leaf. 2.n. [Zoo.] Any structure of d. form, as the d. muscle, where the arm is joined to the neck.

de′lusion, n. [Med., Psych.] A fixed false belief to do with the self, as in a number of diseases of the mind. **d. of ′grandeur.** A d. that one is a very great and important person. **d. of perse′cution.** A d. that other persons are acting (gen. together) against one and that all unpleasant events or experiences are caused by their bad designs. **de′lusive,** a.

de′magnetize, v.t. [Phys.] Take away MAGNETIC properties of. **de′magneti′zation,** n.

de′mentia, n. [Med.] Disease of mind in which there is a more or less complete loss of reasoning power, memory, common sense, and generally of interest and the power of feeling. **d. ′pr(a)ecox.** Well-marked form of d. common in young persons.

de′mersal, a. [Zoo.] Present, living, on the sea-bed or in the water near it.

′demi-. Half; of smaller size or lower quality, less complete(ly).

de′modulate, v.t. [Radio] Get the AUDIOFREQUENCY part of incoming radio waves separated from the RADIOFREQUENCY part. **demodu′lation,** n. **de′modulator,** n. An apparatus, sp. a CRYSTAL or a THERMIONIC VALVE, used for effecting demodulation.

de′mography, n. Science of the number and distribution of persons and the rates of increase or other change, based on records of births, deaths, etc. **demo′graphic(al),** aa.

′demoid, a. [Geol.] Present in great numbers, said of FOSSIL.

de′moniac, n. [Med.] To do with DEMONOMANIA, (person) having demonomania.

de′mono′mania, n. [Med.] Disease of the mind in which a person has the belief that he is controlled by a bad, non-material being which has got into his body.

′demonstrate, v.t. Make a fact clear to the mind by reasoning or example; make clear to onlookers how something is done or used or takes place by doing or using it, or causing it to take place. **′demon′stration,** n. **′demonstrator,** n. Sp. in a medical or science school, a teacher or helper whose business is to do tests and operations in front of the watching learners.

de′mulcent, n., a. [Med.] (Substance, freq. an oil) making skin etc. soft, acting against, helping to take away pain and heat from, INFLAMMATION.

de′mulsifi′cation, n. [Chem.] Process of separating an EMULSION into its parts; process of changing into a form which does not readily undergo EMULSIFICATION. **de′mulsify,** v.t. **de′mulsibility,** n. Property of being able to undergo d.

de′nigrate, a. [Bot.] Made black, having become black.

de′nature, v.t. [Chem.] Get (alcohol or other substance) so changed in taste or other qualities that it is impossible to make use of it for food or drink. **de′naturant,** n. Substance used for denaturing. **denatu′ration,** n.

′dendrite, n. Any branching tree-like structure or marking in a stone or metal. [Zoo.] Branching outgrowth of nerve-CELL (*see* NERVE FIBRE). **den′dritic,** a.

′dendr(o)-. Tree. **den′drology,** n. **den′drologist,** n.

′dendron, n. DENDRITE of NERVE-CELL **′dendric,** a.

dene hole. [Archaeol.] Pipe-like hole made by early man down through the earth to chalk, and ending there in a room-like hollow, chiefly in Essex and Kent in England.

′dengue, n. [Med.] Disease common in very warm countries, transported by a flying insect and marked by FEVER and sharp pains in arms, legs, and head.

de′nitrate, de′nitrify, vv.t. [Chem.] Make free from N. **de′nitr(ifi′c)ation,** n. The freeing of N from substances in the earth by BACTERIA, making earth less fertile. **de′nitrifying ′bacteria.** BACTERIA causing denitration.

de′nominator, n. [Maths.] That part of a FRACTION which in writing is put under the line, as 10 in $\frac{1}{10}$.

dens, n. [Zoo.] Tooth, or tooth-like structure. **d. epi′strophei.** ODONTOID PROCESS.

dense, a. (Of a group or mass) having the units very near together, having a great number of units in a unit of space. [Phys.] Of great DENSITY. [Optics]

Having great REFRACTING power; of dark parts of a camera picture, very OPAQUE.

den'simeter, n. [Phys.-Chem.] Instrument for measuring DENSITY.

densi'tometer, n. Instrument for measuring how DENSE any part of camera-picture is.

'density, n. The property of being DENSE. [Phys.] The MASS or weight of unit VOLUME of a substance; amount of anything (electric CHARGE, MAGNETIC FIELD, electric current) in unit AREA or unit volume. **d. bottle.** [Phys.] SPECIFIC GRAVITY BOTTLE.

'dental, 1.a. [Zoo.] To do with teeth. [Phonet.] Made with point of tongue touching top teeth. 2.n. [Phonet.] A d. CONSONANT.

'dentale or **'dentary bone,** n. [Zoo.] A bone of the lower JAW in back-boned animals from which teeth generally come.

'dentate, a. [Biol.] Having a sharply toothed edge, sp. [Bot.] of a leaf; having tooth-like parts (*see* picture p. 223). **den'tation,** n. The condition of being d.; a tooth-like part or group of such parts, as on the edge of a leaf. **'dentate-.** [Bot.] **dentato-.**

dent(i)-. [Zoo.] Tooth, to do with teeth: **'dentiform,** a.

'denticle, n. [Zoo.] Any small tooth-like structure or point. **den'ticulate(d),** a. [Bot.] Having very small teeth on edge. **denticu'lation,** n. Sp. very small tooth-like part or group of such parts.

'dentine, n. [Zoo.] Material like bone but harder, forming chief part of teeth. **dentifi'cation,** n. Forming of d.

'dentiphone, n. [Med.] Apparatus for helping persons with bad hearing, which when placed against the teeth sends sound waves through them to the inner ear.

'dentist, n. [Med.] An expert in the care of the teeth. **'dentistry,** n. Science of caring for teeth.

den'tition, n. The forming and growth of teeth in the young; the system of teeth of an animal.

'denture, n. False teeth fixed onto a plate which may be taken out of the mouth.

denu'dation, n. [Geol.] The uncovering and getting broken up of ROCKS by chemical and physical forces, and the transporting of the loose material by water and wind, having as outcome the levelling of the land. **de'nuded,** a. Uncovered.

de'odorant, n. Anything which takes away smell, sp. a substance used for overcoming bad smells in a place, or for putting on the body to overcome body smells.

de'ossification, n. [Med.] The loss of bone substance, or the loss by bone of its natural properties. **de'ossify,** v.t. and i. (Make) undergo d. **de'ossified,** a.

de'oxidize, v.t. [Chem., Metal.] Take away O from. **deoxidi'zation,** n. **de'oxidizer,** n.

Any substance used for deoxidizing.

de'oxyribo'nucleic acid. *See* NUCLEIC ACID.

de'oxyribose, n. [Chem.] The SUGAR present in DEOXYRIBONUCLEIC ACID.

de'phosphorize, v.t. [Chem., Metal.] Take P away from, sp. a metal.

'depilate, v.t. [Med.] Take the hair off (some part of the body). **depi'lation,** n. **de'pilatory,** n., a. (Substance) effecting depilation.

dephlo'gisticated air. [Chem.] Name given by PRIESTLEY to O.

de'polarization, n. [Elec.] The process of overcoming the POLARIZATION caused in some electric CELLS by the coating of the ELECTRODES with certain freed substances. **de'polarize,** v.t. **de'polarizer,** n. Substance effecting d. by uniting with freed substances.

de'polymerize, v.t. and i. [Chem.] Get complex MOLECULES changed into the simpler molecules of the same sort from which they were formed.

de'posit, 1.n. Any solid substance (such as dust, metal, earth) put down by a liquid or gas on something, as the effect of any physical or chemical process. 2.v.t. and i. Put down or be put down as a d.; natural mass of coal, metal, or other material for mining, in the earth. **depo'sition,** n. **depo'sition po'tential.** VOLTAGE necessary for separating a solid from a liquid by electric current.

de'pressant, n., a. [Med.] (Substance) making living processes slower.

de'pressed, a. [Bot.] Flat or curved-in on top face; in a position flat on earth. [Zoo.] Having measure from top to foot smaller than that from side to side. [Med., Psych.] In a condition of DEPRESSION. **de'press,** v.t. Make lower, sp. in relation to parts round, get pushed down. [Med., Psych.] Make d.

de'pression, n. The act or process of DEPRESSING; a DEPRESSED part, a hollow. [Geol.] A part of the land which has become lower than the parts round it, or sp., lower than sea-level. [Meteor.] A distribution of air PRESSURE in which it is least at the middle point (*see* CYCLONE). [Med.] Condition of having physical force greatly lowered; the pushing out of place of some part in a down direction. [Psych.] Condition of being without the normal impulse to act, unhappy, and generally with lowered forces. **d. of the 'freezing-point.** [Phys.] The lowering of the FREEZING-POINT of a liquid when a solid is DISSOLVED in it, the amount of lowering generally being dependent, for any given liquid, only on the CONCENTRATION of the dissolved substance and not on what the substance is.

de'presso'motor nerve. [Zoo.] Any nerve making the working of muscles feebler.

de'pressor, n. [Zoo.] Muscle pulling down a part. [Med.] Apparatus for keeping down a part, such as the tongue, while medical operation is taking place; medical substance used for slowing the rate of METABOLISM.

depth, n. The degree to which anything is deep in measure or position, or thick in an up-and-down direction; distance into some solid thing, as the d. to which a ray goes into some substance; in a camera or other picture, the effect of distance in a straightforward direction from the eye. d. charge. A BOMB designed to go off at a given d. in the sea, etc.

de'ranged, a. [Med.] Unbalanced, off one's head. de'rangement, n. The process of becoming or condition of being d.

de'ribose, n. [Chem.] The SUGAR present in RIBONUCLEIC ACID.

de'rive, v.t. and i. Get or come from some other thing, sp. by development. deri'vation, n. Sp. [Philol.] the forming or development of a word from an older word in the same or a different language. de'rivative, n. a. (Anything) made by some addition to or change in another thing. [Chem.] Substance produced, in theory or fact, by putting a different ELEMENT or group in the place of one of those forming a COMPOUND. de'rived, a. Derivative. [Geol.] Not produced in the place where it is seen, having been moved there. derived unit. [Phys.] A unit which is not one of the FUNDAMENTAL UNITS but is derived from them, as a unit of VOLUME or VELOCITY.

'derma, n. [Zoo.] DERMIS. 'dermal, a. Of the skin, or, sp., of the d. derma'titis, n. [Med.] INFLAMMATION of the skin, a general name for a number of skin diseases.

Derm'aptera, n.pl. [Zoo.] An ORDER of EXOPTERYGOTE insects with soft back wings folding under stiff front wings.

'dermatogen, n. [Bot.] The outer skin covering the growth-point of a plant, and becoming the EPIDERMIS.

derma'tology, n. [Med.] The science of the skin and its diseases. derma'tologist, n.

'dermatome, n. [Med.] Instrument for cutting skin. [Zoo.] One of the skin divisions in the development of the EMBRYO. derma'tomic, a.

'dermatomy'cosis, n. [Med.] Any skin disease caused by a plant PARASITE.

'dermatophyte, n. [Med.] FUNGUS living in skin of man or animal. 'dermato'phytic, a. 'dermatophy'tosis, n. Any disease caused by d., sp. RINGWORM of foot.

derma'tosis, n. [Med.] Any disease of the skin, sp. of the DERMIS.

'dermis, n. [Zoo.] The under coat of the skin, in which are nerve-endings and blood-vessels (see DERMA).

dermo-. Skin.

'derm(at)oid, a. Skin-like.

dermo'skeleton, n. [Zoo.] EXOSKELETON.

des'cending, a. [Bot.] Hanging or having growth down. [Zoo.] Going in direction of tail or, in man, lower part of body, as blood-vessels, nerves, etc., d. 'colon. [Zoo.] See COLON.

des'criptive, a. Giving facts of observation only, without any account of theories, said of a branch of science.

de'sensitizer, n. Chemical substance making something less SENSITIVE, sp. one making a camera plate etc. less sensitive to light. de'sensitize, v.t. de'sensiti'zation, n.

'desert, n. [Geog.] Great stretch of infertile country with very little or no rainfall and so no or very poor plant growth. de'sertic, a. deser'ticolous, a. [Biol.] Living in dd.

'desiccate, v.t. [Geog., Biol., Chem.] Make very dry, get (chemical substance, food, etc.) free from water. 'desiccant, n. [Chem.] A substance with the property of taking in water, used for drying other things. desi'ccation, n. 'desiccator, n. A vessel, etc. in which things are dried. 'desiccatory, a.

de'silverize, v.t. [Chem.] Take silver away from.

'desmogen, n. MERISTEM.

de'sorption, n. [Phys.-Chem.] Taking an ADSORBED substance from the body by which it has been adsorbed.

de'soxycortico'sterone, n. [Physiol.] One of the HORMONES of the SUPRARENAL bodies.

'desquamate, v.i. [Med.] To come off in bits, as the skin in certain diseases. desqua'mation, n.

des'tructive distil'lation. [Chem.] DISTILLATION of liquids or gases from solid substances, for example, coal, which undergo destruction in the process.

des'tructor, n. Oven or other apparatus for burning waste material from a town etc.

de'sulphurize, v.t. [Chem.] Take S away from.

de'tect, v.t. Make the discovery, see some sign, of (some substance being present or some change taking place). [Radio] DEMODULATE. de'tecting, a., n. de'tection, n. de'tector. n. Sp.: [Radio] DEMODULATOR. [Elec.] A simple form of GALVANOMETER used for detecting an electric current without measuring it.

de'tergent, 1.n. [Chem.] Any substance used with water for cleaning dirty clothing etc., but in present-day use gen. limited to those which get the dust, fat, etc. out of the material by some process other than simply DISSOLVING them, for example, SURFACE-ACTIVE AGENTS. 2.a. Being a d.

de'terminate, a. [Bot.] CYMOSE. d. vari'ation. ORTHOGENESIS.

determi′nation, n. Measuring, getting clearly fixed, the value or amount of anything, or the place of something in a system. [Biol.] The process by which, in the development of a plant or animal, the future of every part is fixed at an early stage. **de′termine**, v.t. **de′termined**, a. **de′termining**, a., n.

de′terminism, n. The theory that all events in material existence take place by necessary law

′detonate, v.t. and i. (Make) EXPLODE very violently and suddenly. **deto′nation**, b. Sp. violent EXPLOSION; in an INTERNAL-COMBUSTION engine, the sudden taking fire of gas through over-heating, causing loss of power and a sharp sound. **′detonating**, a. **′detonator**, n. Substance or apparatus effecting detonation.

de′torsion, n. Untwisting, or twisting in opposite direction, sp. [Med.] making a twisted part of body normal again. [Zoo.] Twisting in opposite direction to that at start.

de′tox-icate, -ify, vv.t. [Med.] Take away poison or effect of poison from. **de′toxi-′cation**. n.

de′trition, n. [Geol.] Natural rubbing or washing away of stone by wind and water.

de′tritus, n. [Geol.] Loose material, broken stones, mixed with earth, sand, etc., produced by DETRITION.

detu′mescence, n. [Med.] The going down of a swelling.

′deuteran′omaly, n. [Optics, Psych.] A form of DEFECTIVE COLOUR VISION in which a person, though normal in being TRICHRO-MATIC, sees the green part of the SPEC-TRUM more feebly than a normal person.

′deuteran′opia, n. [Optics, Psych.] A form of DICHROMATISM in which a person is unable to see different CHROMATIC colours in the red-yellow-green part of the SPECTRUM but in which, as opp. PROTA-NOPIA, the LUMINOSITY of all parts of the spectrum is almost the same as for a normal person (earlier named '*green blindness*') **′deuteranope**, n. Person having d.

deu′terium, n. [Chem.] An ISOTOPE of H with at. wt. 20·0147, sign D, MASS NUMBER 2, having a NEUTRON as well as a PROTON in the NUCLEUS—commonly named *heavy hydrogen.*

′deuter(o)-. Second or SECONDARY.

deute′rogamy, n. [Bot.] Any process which takes the place of normal FERTILIZATION.

deutero′genic, a. [Geol.] (Of ROCK) formed of material from older rock.

′deut(er)on, n. [Chem.] NUCLEUS of D ATOM.

deut(o)-. Second, or SECONDARY.

de′velop, v.t. and i. (Make) undergo development. [Photog.] Put (a camera PLATE or FILM on which a picture has been taken) through the chemical process, gen. the changing of silver SALTS to silver metal, by which the effect which the light has had on it is made clear in the form of a picture, or get (picture) formed on a plate etc. in this way. **de′veloper**, n. Sp. [Photog.] Any chemical substance used for developing a camera picture.

de′velop′mental me′chanics. [Zoo.] Science of the chemical and physical processes causing development of the different parts of an animal before birth.

devi′ation, n. Change of direction of anything in motion, as light. **d. of the ′compass**. Regular error of ship's MAG-NETIC COMPASS caused by the magnetic effect of the iron in the structure of the ship.

de′vitrify, v.t. and i. [Geol.] Get changed from a glass-like into a CRYSTALLINE condition. **de′vitrifi′cation**, n.

de′vocalized, a. DEVOICED.

de′voiced, a. [Phonet.] Said of a VOICELESS sound put in the place of a VOICED sound in ASSIMILATION.

De′vonian, n. [Geol.] System of ROCKS forming part of the PALAEOZOIC group.

′Dewar flask or **′vessel**. Glass vessel with an outer and inner wall between which there is no gas so that heat is not able to get through, used for putting anything in which has to be kept unchanged by heat or cold, for example, liquid air.

dew, n. [Meteor.] The water which is put down onto solid things by the air in the night. **′d.-point**. The TEMPERATURE at which a given mass of wet air becomes SATURATED, so producing d.

′dextral, a. Of or to the right; right-handed.

′dextrin, n. [Chem.] Any of certain GUM-like substances formed when STARCH is broken down.

′dextr(o)-. To the right. [Chem.] DEXTRO-ROTATORY.

′dextro′gyrate, a. DEXTROROTATORY.

′dextroro′tatory, a. Turning in direction of hands of clock, sp. [Optics] of the turning of the plane of POLARIZED light by a substance. **′dextroro′tation**, n.

′dextrorse, a. [Biol.] Twisting from left to right from the point of view of a person looking at it, opp. SINISTRORSE.

′dextrose, n. [Chem.] DEXTROROTATORY GLUCOSE, the sugar present in fruit.

d-′glucose, n. DEXTROSE.

′di-. Two, twice.

Di. Sign for DIDYMIUM.

dia-. Through, between, across.

′diabase, n. [Geol.] ROCK, commonly named 'greenstone', made up of PLAGIOCLASE, MAGNETITE, AUGITE, and sometimes OLIVINE.

dia′betes, n. [Med.] Any of certain diseased conditions marked by an over-great output of URINE. **d. ′mellitus**. D. in which over-much sugar is present in the blood and URINE, caused by not enough INSULIN being produced by the PANCREAS, and marked by serious loss of weight and a great desire for food and drink. **d. in'sipidus.** A d. caused by there being something wrong with the working of the PITUITARY GLAND, in which there is a very great desire for liquids. **dia-'betic,** n., a. (Person) having, to do with, d.

'diabeto'genic 'hormone. [Med.] One of the HORMONES of the PITUITARY GLAND causing DIABETES.

dia'delphous, a. [Bot.] (Of STAMENS) in two groups formed by the joining of their stems; having d. stamens.

diag'nosis, n. [Med.] Act of making decision as to what is wrong with ill person, judging what disease is present; such decision. [Biol.] Full account of plant, animal, or group, making clear its special properties. **diag'nostic,** a. Sp. [Biol.], (of qualities) marking the ways in which a group is different from others.

di'agonal, n., a. [Geom.] Line joining two (opposite) points, sp. angles, of a plane form, for example a square.

'diagram, n .Design used to make something clear, picturing for example the relation of parts of a system, directions of motion, a comparison between values, the distribution of anything, and so on. **diagram-'matic(al).**

diaki'nesis, n. [Biol.] Last stage of PROPHASE in MEIOSIS.

'dial, n. Plate, generally round, of instrument, with scale on which reading is seen, as the face of a clock, or marked with letters, numbers etc. round edge for use in operation, as on telephone instrument.

'diallage, n. [Mineral.] A dark green or brown sort of PYROXENE having SCHILLERIZATION, seen in BASIC IGNEOUS ROCKS.

Di'alypetalae, n.pl. [Bot.] POLYPETALAE.

dialy'petalous, a. [Bot.] POLYPETALOUS.

dialy'phyllous, a. [Bot.] With separate leaves.

dialy'sepalous, a. POLYSEPALOUS.

di'alysis, n. [Chem.] The separating of a COLLOID from a substance in true SOLUTION by draining the solution through a MEMBRANE. **'dialyzer,** n. Apparatus used in d.

dialy'stely, n. [Bot.] Condition in which STELES in stem of plant are more or less separate. **dialy'stelic,** a.

diamag'netic, a. (Of substances) having MAGNETIC PERMEABILITY less than that of a VACUUM, that is, less than 1. **dia-'magnetism,** n. The properties seen in a d. substance as the effects of a MAGNETIC force.

di'ameter, n. [Geom.] (Measure of) straight line going from one side to another

through middle point of a form or body, sp. at its widest part. [Optics] Unit for giving how much the size of a thing is increased by MICROSCOPE or TELESCOPE, as "an increase of 10 dd." **dia'metric(al),** aa.

'diamond, n. [Mineral.] C present naturally in the earth in the form of CRYSTALS, gen. with 8 three-sided faces, the hardest natural substance, used in industry for cutting etc. and highly valued as a jewel stone because of its great BRILLIANCE.

di'androus, a. [Bot.] Having two free STAMENS.

'diaphone, n. [Phonet.] Group of different forms of the same sound as said in different parts of the country, or by same person talking in different conditions.

'diaphor'esis, n. [Med.] The producing of a great amount of PERSPIRATION for medical purposes. **'diaphoretic,** n., a. (Substance) causing, to do with, d.

'diaphragm, n. [Biol.] A thin plate or stretch of substance, such as skin or muscle, acting as a division, sp. muscle substance separating chest from ABDOMEN. [Optics] Plate with hole in it put in front of LENS and limiting the amount of light going through. [Acous.] A thin plate of metal or of stretched rubber etc. used for producing sound-waves by its VIBRATIONS, for example, in a telephone. [Elec.] A plate or other structure of material with small holes in it, natural or made, used for separating two SOLUTIONS in an electric CELL.

dia'pophysis (diapophyses), n. [Zoo.] TRANSVERSE PROCESS of higher back-boned animals.

di'aphysis, n. [Bot.] Unnormally long growth of the chief stem of a flower-group. [Zoo.] That part of a long bone between the two ends. **dia'physial,** a.

di'apsid, a. [Zoo.] (Of the SKULL of a REPTILE) having a division across the deep hollow at the side, forming two hollows, opp. SYNAPSID.

'diarch, a. [Bot.] Having two groups of XYLEM, as certain roots.

diar'rh(o)ea, n. [Med.] Condition in which FAECES are liquid and sent out over-frequently.

diar'throsis, n. [Zoo.] Form of joining of two bones which makes possible free motion of the parts joined, as in most JOINTS of man's body. **diar'throdial,** a.

dia'schisis, n. [Med.] A change in or stopping of the working of one part of the brain caused by disease of or damage to another part at some distance away, but having some connection with the first in its operation.

dia'schistic, a. [Geol.] To do with, being, different IGNEOUS ROCKS got from the same heated liquid mass. [Biol.] In

MEIOSIS, said of a TETRAD which undergoes division from end to end and again from side to side.

'diastase, n. [Chem.] ENZYME changing STARCH into sugar. dias'tatic, dias'tasic, aa.

'diastem(a), n. [Zoo.] Space in JAW without teeth, generally between two different sorts of teeth.

di'aster, n. [Biol.] Stage in CELL division at which CHROMOSOMES are grouped near ends of SPINDLE. di'astral, a.

di'astole, n. [Biol.] The expansion of any part, sp. the heart, in regular rhythm. di'astolic, a.

dia'thermancy, n. [Phys.] The property of letting through heat rays. dia'thermanous, a.

dia'thermy, n. [Med.] The heating of parts of the body by HIGH-FREQUENCY electric current. dia'thermize, v.t. Make undergo d. dia'thermic, a.

di'atom, n. [Zoo.] Small, one-CELLED ALGA with a cell-wall of Si formed like a box and its cover. diatom'aceous, a. To do with, like, formed chiefly of the cell-walls of, dd. d. earth, diato'maceous earth. [Mineral.] A white, powder-like earth substance made up chiefly of the covers of dd. and not readily acted on by heat or chemicals, used in making FIREPROOF and electric INSULATING materials. d. ooze, diatomaceous ooze. [Geol.] MUD formed chiefly of the covers of dd. present on deep sea-beds.

dia'tomic, a. [Chem.] Made up of two ATOMS; having two atoms or groups which may be changed for others; DIVALENT.

di'atomin, n. [Biochem.] The colouring material of DIATOMS.

di'atomite, n. [Mineral.] DIATOM EARTH.

'diatonic scale. [Acous.] The music scale in which the FREQUENCIES of the notes are in the relation 24, 27, 30, 32, 36, 40, 45, 48, a scale possible for the voice and for instruments like the violin, but not for instruments with fixed notes such as the piano.

di'atropism, n. [Bot.] Tendency of plants or their parts to put themselves at right angles to the line in which a STIMULUS is acting. dia'tropic, a.

di'axon, n. [Zoo.] Having two chief AXES.

di'azo, a. [Chem.] Naming N COMPOUNDS of the general make-up R.N:N.R.

di'basic, a. [Chem.] (Of acids) having two H ATOMS whose place may be taken by a metal.

Di'branchia, n.pl. [Zoo.] A SUB-CLASS of CEPHALOPODA in which the SHELL is bedded in the body, and which has 8 to 10 arms ending in hooks or SUCKERS, two CTENIDIA, two NEPHRIDIA, eyes with CRYSTALLINE LENSES, and an apparatus for sending out an ink-like liquid when attacked. di'branchiate, n., a. (Animal) of the D.; having two GILLS.

di'caryon, n. [Biol.] A group of two NUCLEI which have a connection and undergo division at the same time.

di'chasium, n. [Bot.] A CYME of which every branch has two opposite and roughly equal branches. di'chasial, a.

di'chogamous, a. [Bot.] Having male and female sex-parts coming to full growth at different times. di'chogamy, n.

di'chotomy, n. Division into two parts. [Biol.] Forking, as of a blood-vessel. [Bot.] System of branching in which end of branch is forked into two equal branches which are again forked in the same way. di'chotomous, a.

di'chroic, a. [Optics] (Of CRYSTALS) having different colours when looked through in different directions; (of liquids) having two very different colours dependent on how thick the vessel is or on CONCENTRATION.

di'chromat, n. [Psych.] Person having dichromatism. di'chromatism, n. A form of DEFECTIVE COLOUR VISION in which a person is able to MATCH any given colour with another formed by mixing two colours of light, as opp. a normal person (a 'trichromat') who for certain colours has to have three colours of light mixed.

'dichromate, n. [Chem.] A SALT having the group $-Cr_2O_7$.

dichro'matic, a. Having two colours. [Zoo.] Being of two sorts different in colour.

di'clinous, a. [Bot.] Having separate male and female flowers on the same plant. 'diclinism, n.

Dicoty'ledones, n.pl. [Bot.] The greater of the two groups (classes) of flowering plants (Angiospermae) with two COTYLEDONS in every seed. dicoty'ledon, n. One of the D. dicoty'ledonous, a.

'dictaphone, n. Instrument for recording what a person says on wax and giving it back as sound when desired.

'dictyo'stele, n. [Bot.] POLYSTELE. 'dictyo'stelic, a.

di'dymium, n. [Chem.] A metal made up of NEODYMIUM and PRASEODYMIUM, at one time taken to be an ELEMENT.

die, n. A metal stamp used for making designs, printing letters etc., on things; a hollow pipe or other form used in cutting or forming metal etc., sp. one with design cut on the inside, such as is used in making screws. '-casting, n. [Metal.] A process by which metal is given form by being put into MOULDS, freq. opening into two separate halves, which may be used again and again, as opp. those moulds made of sand which are broken up after use.

'dielectric, 1.n. [Elec.] A substance which does not CONDUCT electric current, that is, one in which an ELECTRIC FIELD has the effect of causing an ELECTRIC STRESS, producing a DISPLACEMENT of ELECTRONS but not a current of them running through it, sp. such a substance when used where an electric stress may be produced in it, e.g., between the plates of a CONDENSER. 2.a. Of, to do with, being, a d. **d. ab-'sorption.** The property of a d. effect of not coming to an end when the FIELD is no longer in operation but going on for some time after. **d. 'constant.** (Of a substance) the RATIO of the CAPACITANCE of a CONDENSER in which the substance is the d. to the capacitance of the same condenser with air or a VACUUM between the plates. **d. fa'tigue.** The loss of the properties of a d. substance after undergoing a certain STRESS again and again, though it may undergo the same stress a smaller number of times without damage. **d. loss.** Loss of ENERGY in a d. caused by an ALTERNATING electric field.

dien'cephalon, n. THALAMENCEPHALON.

'Diesel engine or **motor.** A COMPRESSION-IGNITION ENGINE using HEAVY oil.

'diet, n. The sort and amount of food and drink taken regularly by person or group. [Med.] Special food and drink to which person is limited for medical purposes. **die'tetic,** a. **die'tetics,** n.pl. Science of d.

'difference of po'tential. POTENTIAL DIFFERENCE.

difference tone. Note in music of FREQUENCY a − b produced by two notes of frequency a and b acting together.

difference 'threshold. [Psych.] See THRESHOLD.

differ'ential, 1.a. DIFFERENTIATING; different for different conditions, persons, etc.; to do with, being a sign of, the ways in which, or the amounts by which, given things are different. 2.n. [Mach.] A d. gear. See CALCULUS. **d. gear.** [Mach.] Apparatus causing an automobile's back wheels to go at different rates from one another when going round curves. **d. 'motion.** [Engin.] A motion in which the rate of motion of the part being put in operation is equal to the rate of one of two parts with which it is in connection less that of the other. **d. 'winding** [Elec.] A WINDING in an electric machine in which one part is producing a MAGNETO-MOTIVE force acting against that produced by the other part, so that the magneto-motive force effected is one of these less the other. **'-ly,** adv.

differ'entiate, 1.v.t. Make different, sp. of properties, in the sense of being that in which a thing is different; see or make clear how things are different. 2.v.i. Become different by development. **differ-enti'ation,** n. Sp. [Biol.] the development of different parts or substances from the same first-formed mass, as in an egg, or the becoming different of parts, in the process of EVOLUTION, to make them of use for special purposes. [Geol.] The process by which a HOMOGENEOUS MAGMA becomes separated, as it gets cold and solid, into different sorts of ROCK.

di'ffraction, n. [Optics] The process by which light waves are bent at the edge of a solid body so as to give light and dark bands. **d. 'grating.** Flat glass plate covered with a great number of parallel lines ruled very near together, by sending a narrow band of light through which d. SPECTRA are produced. **dif'fractive,** a. **dif'fract,** v.t.

di'ffuse, a. Not all together in one place, having more or less wide distribution, not having sharp limits. [Phys.] (Of light, sound) going in all directions over a certain range. [Bot.] Branching widely and freely (sp. of stem running over the earth). [Zoo.] (Of PLACENTA) having the VILLI here and there over almost all the CHORION, not grouped or limited to one part. **d.'series,** [Optics]. Any of certain groups of lines in the SPECTRA of ALKALIS and ALKALINE EARTH METALS, so named because the lines are not sharply marked.

di'ffusion, n. The sending or going out of something in all directions, sp. [Optics] of light as the effect of irregular REFRACTION through a TRANSLUCENT substance or of irregular REFLECTION (**diffuse reflection**) from a rough body. [Phys.] The natural process by which the equal distribution of a condition all through a substance takes place, for example, of TEMPERATURE through a body, of one gas through another, or of a solid through a SOLVENT, caused by the motion of the MOLECULES. **d. pump.** [Phys.] Pump used for increasing still further the VACUUM produced by a normal VACUUM PUMP. **diff'use,** v.t. and i. (Make) undergo d. **diff'used,** a. **diff'user,** n. **diff'using,** n., a. Sp. causing d. of light.

diga'matic, a. [Zoo.] Having GAMETES of two different sorts. **'digamy,** n. The condition of being d.

di'gest, v.t. and i. [Zoo.] Get (food) changed by digestion; (of food) undergo digestion. [Chem.] Make soft by heating, sp. in water or other liquid. **'-er,** n. [Chem.] Vessel in which substance is heated under PRESSURE, gen. with water or other liquid. **'-ant,** n., a. [Zoo., Med.] (Substance) helping digestion. **'-ible,** a. [Zoo., Med.] Which may be digested. **'-ive,** a. [Zoo. Med.] To do with or helping digestion.

di'gestion, n. [Biol.] Process by which food is broken down into simpler chemical substances in the bodies of animals, and in some plants, so that substances of value may be taken into the blood and the rest sent out as waste.

'digit, n. [Zoo.] Finger or toe or like part. [Maths.] Any of the numbers from 1 to 9. **'-al,** a. **'digital com'puter,** n. The sort of COMPUTER (*see* ANALOGUE) designed for work on DISCRETE material such as numbers, words etc., by ARITHMETICAL operations on numbers given to it in the form of a CODE using DIGITS – gen. the BINARY code, in which the two digits, 0 and 1, may be put together so as to be representative of any desired numbers. **digiti-, digito-.**

'digitiform, a. [Bot.] Formed like a finger.

'digitate, a. [Bot.] Having divisions like fingers, said of certain leaves.

'digitigrade, a. [Zoo.] Walking on the DIGITS, said of animals touching the earth only with their toes.

di'gression, n. Going away from a direction or line, sp. going of sun away from EQUATOR. **'-al, '-ary, di'gressive,** aa.

'digynous, a. [Bot.] Having two PISTILS.

di'hybrid, n. [Biol.] Offspring of two animals or plants which are different in two different CHARACTERS. **di'hybridism,** n.

di'latancy, n. [Phys.] (Of a substance made up of grains) the property of taking up more space when moved or changed in form because of an increase of space between the grains. **di'latant,** a.

di'la'tation, n. Expansion. **dila'tometer,** n. Instrument for measuring d.'of substance caused by change of TEMPERATURE.

di'late, v.t. and i. (Make) undergo expansion. **'-d,** a. Sp. wide and flat, said sp. of parts of insects having such an edge. **di'lation,** n. **di'lator,** n. Sp. [Zoo.] Any muscle effecting the expansion of an opening or part.

di'luent, n. [Chem.] Liquid used for DILUTING.

di'lute, 1.v.t. [Chem.] Make a SOLUTION less strong by the addition of more of the SOLVENT, or of water. 2.a. [Chem.] Diluted, having only a small amount of the SOLUTE in a given VOLUME. **di'lution,** n.

di'luvi'al, a. [Geol.] Caused or produced by great mass of water; to do with DRIFT.

di'luvium, n. [Geol.] DRIFT.

di'mension, n. Any one of the directions forming the framework of space—in the space of our common experience, three at right angles to one another, giving us the ideas of LENGTH, BREADTH, and THICKNESS; measure (of a space or a solid) in one direction. **dd.** Sp. [Phys.] the POWER(s) of the FUNDAMENTAL UNITS making up any physical measure, for example AREA, or LENGTH², is of two dd. of length. **di'mensional,** a. To do with d. or dd.; having the named number of dd., as *3-dimensional space.*

'dimer, n. [Chem.] A POLYMER made up of two MOLECULES. **di'meric,** a.

'dimon'oecious, a. [Bot.] Having every sort of flower from a sex point of view, male only, female only, unsexed, and male and female.

di'morphism, n. [Biol.] POLYMORPHISM in which there are two different forms of a plant or animal. [Bot.] Sp.the property of having two different sorts of leaves or flowers on the same plant. **di'morph-ic, -ous,** aa.

'dinergate, n. [Zoo.] A special worker ant with a head of great size and very strong mouth parts.

di'neric, a. [Phys.] Being or to do with the face between two separate bodies of liquid in one vessel, for example, oil and water.

'diode, n. [Phys.] A form of ELECTRON DISCHARGE TUBE having only two ELECTRODES.

di'oecious, a. [Zoo.] Having two sex-groups. [Bot.] Having male and female flowers on separate plants.

di'oestrum, n. [Zoo.] Time between one OESTRUS and another in which there is no sex feeling or process. **di'oestrous,** a.

di'opter, di'optre, nn. [Optics] Unit of power of a LENS, the power in dd. being equal to 1 ÷ the FOCAL LENGTH in metres. **di'optric(al),** aa.

diop'tometer, n. Instrument used for measuring the power of adjustment of the eye. **diop'tometry,** n.

di'optrics, n. [Optics] Old name for the branch of Optics having to do with the REFRACTION of light. **di'optric(al),** aa. To do with d. or with refraction; REFRACTIVE.

dio'rama, n. Picture with special lighting, part falling on and part going through it, to give natural effects.

'diorite, n. [Geol.] A sort of COARSE-GRAINED IGNEOUS ROCK (*see* p. 192).

dip, 1.n. Slope down. [Geol.] The amount of slope down of a STRATUM, measured by the greatest angle between it and the face of the earth. [Phys.] MAGNETIC D. 2.v.i. Be sloping down. **d. fault.** [Geol.] A FAULT whose direction is the same as that of the d. of the STRATA. **dip(ping) 'circle,** or **'compass,** or **'needle.** Instrument for measuring MAGNETIC D. **dip of the ho'rizon.** [Astron.] The angle between the true HORIZON and the one seen, measured at any point *O* by the angle between the line through *O* touching the earth and the HORIZONTAL plane through *O*.

di'petalous, a. [Bot.] Having two PETALS.

'diphase, a. [Elec.] DIPHASIC.

di'phasic, a. Having two PHASES, sp. [Zoo.] of TRYPANOSOMES, having a free stage of existence.

diph'theria, n. [Med.] A serious INFECTIOUS disease caused by a BACILLUS and marked by the forming of false MEMBRANES, produced by a coating of FIBROUS DIS-CHARGE, in the breathing-pipes, sp. the throat.

'diphthong, n. [Phonet.] Two VOWEL sounds put together and running into one, forming a complex unit sound, as the English long '*i*'.

'diphy'cercal, a. [Zoo.] (Of tail of certain fish, etc.) with backbone going straight to end, without turning up, and the FINS on the top and under side the same size; having such a tail. 'diphy'cercy, n.

diphy'letic, a. [Biol.] Produced by two different lines of ANCESTORS.

'diphyo'dont, a. [Zoo.] Having two growths of teeth, the first group coming out and a second taking their place.

dip'leidoscope, n. [Astron.] Instrument for fixing time of APPARENT NOON by the use of two REFLECTIONS of the sun.

dipl(o)-. Two, two times.

diplo'blastic, a. [Zoo.] Having only two separate GERM LAYERS in the EMBRYO, the ENDODERM and the EXODERM, a condition seen only in COELENTERATA.

diplo'cardiac, a. [Zoo.] Having a complete division of the heart, one side in connection with LUNGS, the other with the rest of the system, as in birds and higher animals.

diplo'coccus, n. Two round BACTERIA joined together. diplo'cocc-al, -ous, aa.

'diploid, a.1. Having two parts. [Biol.] Having twice the GERM-CELL number of CHROMOSOMES, as most body cells. 2.n. ISOMETRIC form of CRYSTAL having 24 like 4-sided faces in groups of two. dip'loidy, n.

'diplont, n. [Biol.] Plant or animal having the body-CELLS DIPLOID.

'diplophase, n. [Biol.] The stage in the LIFE-CYCLE of a living thing when the NUCLEI are DIPLOID.

dip'losis, n. [Biol.] Process of making the number of CHROMOSOMES twice as great by uniting two HAPLOID groups.

'diplosome, n. [Biol.] CENTROSOME having two like parts formed outside the skin of the NUCLEUS; one or the other of a group of two HETEROCHROMOSOMES.

'diplotene, a. Said of the stage in MEIOSIS at which TETRADS are formed.

diplo'zoic, a. [Zoo.] Of a form which may be cut by a middle line into equal and opposite sides.

'Dipnoi, Dip'neusti, nn.pl. [Zoo.] A SUB-CLASS or ORDER of CHOANICHTHYES of which only three sorts are still in existence, all living in TROPICAL inland waters, marked by having LUNGS as well as GILLS and teeth in the form of plates designed for CRUSHING. dip'noan, n., a. (Animal) of the D. 'dipnoid, a. Like the D., sp. in having LUNGS as well as GILLS.

di'pole, n. [Elec.] In a DIELECTRIC, a POSITIVE and a NEGATIVE CHARGE at a small distance from one another. [Chem., Phys.] An ATOM or group of atoms having two opposite MAGNETIC or electric POLES. d. 'moment. POLE STRENGTH × distance between the poles. di'polar, a. dipolar liquid. Liquid in which there are dd.

di'protodont, a. [Zoo.] Having the two top and lower front cutting teeth of great size and pointing out, the other cutting teeth being smaller or not present.

dip 'sector. [Astron., etc.] Instrument for measuring the DIP OF THE HORIZON.

dipso'mania, n. [Med.] Condition in which there is from time to time an unnatural and overpowering desire for drink, sp. alcohol. dipso'maniac, n. Person with d. dipsoma'niacal a.

'Diptera, n.pl. [Zoo.] Order of INSECTA having only two wings. 'dipteral, 'dipter-ous, aa. Having two wings or wing-like structures; to do with order D. 'diptero-.

di'rect, a. Straight, straightforward, having an unbroken connection with some other thing, not acting through or going by way of a third thing. d. 'coupling. [Elec.] See COUPLING. d. current. [Elec.] Electric current going in one direction only. d. de'velopment. [Zoo.] Development without any METAMORPHOSIS. d. dye. SUB-SUBSTANTIVE DYE. d. meta'morphosis [Zoo.] INCOMPLETE METAMORPHOSIS. d. pro'portion or 'ratio. [Maths.] The relation between two amounts, values, of which one is increased when the other is increased and becomes less when the other becomes less. d. ray or wave. [Radio] GROUND WAVE. d. 'vision. [Optics] The act of seeing when the IMAGE is formed by rays coming directly from the seen thing to the eye, not REFRACTED to it through a LENS or REFLECTED to it from a looking-glass and so on. d. 'vision prism. AMICI PRISM.

di'rectly, adv. In a d. way or in d. ratio.

di'rection 'finder. Apparatus giving direction from which radio waves are coming.

di'rectional, a. Of, to do with direction. [Radio] Designed for DETECTING the direction from which radio waves come, or for sending them out in one direction only.

'dirigible, 1.a. Able to be guided. 2.n. A d. AIRSHIP.

dis-. De-:—disa'cidify, v.t., disass'imila-tion, n.

di'saccharide, n. [Chem.] Substance formed by uniting two MONOSACCHARIDES with the loss of water.

disarticu'lation, n. [Med.] The separating of bones at a JOINT.

disassoci'ation, n. DISSOCIATION.

disc, n. A round, flat, plate-like structure. 'discoid(al), aa. Sp.:—[Bot.] said of button-like middle part of COROLLA of certain complex flower-heads, or of the small pipe-like flowers making up such a part; [Zoo.] (of PLACENTA) in which the VILLI are massed in a d.-like form on one part of the CHORION.

dis'charge, 1.v.t. and i. Send out (liquid, etc.). [Elec.] Send out an electric CHARGE. 2.n. The act of discharging; substance etc. discharged by something. [Elec.] The loss of electric CHARGE on the levelling out of a POTENTIAL DIFFERENCE between parts of a system; an electric current through a gas, gen. producing light. [Chem.] A chemical substance used for taking a DYE or MORDANT out of cloth. [Med.] Liquid coming away from a wound or a diseased part of the body. **d. tube.** [Elec.] General name for any bulb etc. in which an electric d. takes place in a VACUUM or in a gas at low PRESSURE. **dis'charged,** a. Having been sent out as a d.; having sent out what was in it, as a discharged gun. **dis'charger,** n.

disci'flor-ous, -al, aa. [Bot.] Having flowers in which the part of the stem supporting the flower-leaves is a great DISC.

'disc(o)-. DISC.

'Discome'dusae, n.pl. [Zoo.] An ORDER of SCYPHOZOA with a flat 'umbrella' and 8 or more TENTACULOCYSTS.

'discon'formity, n. [Geol.] UNCONFORMITY between level beds.

discon'tinuous, a. Not CONTINUOUS, broken, unjoined, having space(s) between or something dropped out at some point or points. **d. vari'ation.** [Biol.] A MUTATION coming quite suddenly, not as the outcome of small changes producing it by degrees; the process of changing by a d. variation. **dis'contin'uity,** n.

discopla'centa, n. [Zoo.] A DISCOIDAL PLACENTA.

dis'crete, a. Separate, not united, formed of d. parts, sp. [Bot.].

disin'fect, v.t. [Med.] Make free from disease BACTERIA. **disin'fection,** n. **disin'fectant,** n. Substance used for the destruction of disease BACTERIA outside the body, for example, in a room or in clothing, as opp. an ANTISEPTIC.

disin'fest, v.t. [Med.] Make (the body of a person) free from insects. **'disinfest'a-tion,** n.

dis'integrate, v.t. and i. Become separated into parts or small bits, sp. as effect of slow natural process; be cause of disintegration of. **dis'inte'gration,** n. Sp:— [Geol.] the disintegrating of ROCKS through chemical changes, weather, etc.; [Phys.] the disintegrating of the NUCLEUS of a RADIOACTIVE ELEMENT, naturally or by BOMBARDMENT. **disintegration 'constant.** [Phys.] DELAY CONSTANT.

dis'integrator, n. [Mining, etc.] Apparatus for getting massed substances broken up.

dis'junct, a. Not joined together, with parts clearly separate, sp. [Zoo.] with deep divisions between head, THORAX and ABDOMEN. **dis'junction,** n. The condition of being d., or of becoming separate, parted. **dis'junct'ive,** a. To do with, having a tendency to, disjunction. **dis'junctive symbi'osis,** n. [Biol.] Condition in which two living things, such as bees and flowering plants are of help to one another but have separate existences.

disk, n. DISC.

dislo'cation, n. The putting out of place of one part in relation to another, sp. [Med.] the separating of two bones at a JOINT. **'dislocate,** v.t. Make (sp. a bone or a JOINT) undergo d. **dislo'catory,** a.

dismu'tation, n. [Biochem.] The change of one substance into two by OXIDATION and REDUCTION going on at the same time.

di'spermous, a. [Bot.] Having two seeds.

di'spermy, n. [Zoo.] The going of two male GERM-CELLS into one egg.

dis'persal, n. The process of the separation and distribution of anything in all directions, sp. [Biol.] the process by which plants and animals get to new places and become of wider distribution.

dis'persion, n. DISPERSAL. [Phys.] The process by which anything is broken up into a great number of parts which undergo d., as a solid or liquid in a liquid or gas (see COLLOIDAL SOLUTION), or rays of light, ELECTRONS, ATOMS etc. into groups of different FREQUENCY, rate of motion, etc.; the condition of being dispersed; a system formed of one substance dispersed in another. **d. 'medium.** [Chem.] A substance in which a COLLOID is dispersed. **dis'perse,** 1.v.t. and i. (Make) undergo d. 2.a. Having undergone d. (said sp. of COLLOIDS). **di'spersed,** a. **disperse(d) phase.** [Phys.-Chem.] The COLLOID dispersed in a COLLOIDAL SOLUTION or GEL. **dis'persible,** a. **dis'personal, dis'persive,** aa. **dispersive power** or **dis-per'sivity.** [Optics] The measure of the degree to which rays of light are dispersed by a given PRISM or DIFFRACTION GRATING. **dis'persoid,** n. [Phys.-Chem.] COLLOID; dispersed substance.

dis'placement, n. (Amount of) change of place. [Chem.] Chemical change in which one substance takes the place of another in a COMPOUND. [Phys., Engin.] Amount of liquid or gas pushed out of place by a solid body put into it, or by one motion of a pump, etc. **d. 'current.** [Elec.] The effect produced on a DIELECTRIC in an ELECTRIC FIELD by a change in ELECTRIC STRESS, in which there is a d. of

ELECTRONS in which ENERGY is used up, but without the motion of electrons from one end of the substance to the other as in a normal current. **dis′place**, v.t. Put out of place; take the place of.

dis′ruption, n. Sudden bursting open or to bits; act of causing d. **dis′rupt**, v.t. and i. (Make) undergo d. **dis′ruptive**, a. **dis′-ruptive dis′charge**. [Elec.] Electric current suddenly forcing its way through INSULATING material and damaging it.

diss′ection, n. Act of cutting something, sp. plant or animal, into parts, for purpose of getting knowledge of its structure; a thing, sp. plant or animal, cut into parts. **diss′ect**. v.t. **diss′ected**. a Sp. [Bot., Geog.] having deep, well-marked divisions, hollows etc. cutting into it.

diss′eminate, v.t. and i. Give distribution to, undergo distribution in all directions, as the seeds of plants. **diss′eminated**, a. **diss′eminated scle′rosis**. [Med.] MULTIPLE SCLEROSIS. **diss′emination**, n.

diss′epiment, n. [Biol.] A division wall, sp. [Bot.] in a COMPOUND OVARY, or [Zoo.] in certain CORALS, a HORIZONTAL division between the upright divisions, to some degree shutting off the lower part of the cup.

dissimi′lation, n. [Phonet.] The changing of like sounds to unlike when there are two near one another in a word, in the growth of languages, as of the first *′r′* to the Latin ′peregrinum′ to the *′l′* of the English ′pilgrim′. [Biol.] CATABOLISM.

dissi′pation, n. DISPERSION, sp. to the point of no longer having any effect, of becoming wasted away. [Elec.] Loss of electric power. **d. of energy**.[Phys.] DEGRADATION OF ENERGY. **′dissipate**, v.t. and i. (Make) undergo d.

dissoci′ation, n. [Chem.] Process by which all or some of the MOLECULES of a substance are broken up into parts in certain conditions, and become united again when these conditions are no longer in operation—for example as the effect of heat or of ELECTROLYSIS, when the dissociated parts become IONS. **di′ssociate**, v.t. and i. (Make) undergo d. or become separate by d.

diss′olve, v.t. and i. [Chem.] Go, put, or take into SOLUTION. **disso′lution**, n.

′dissonance, n. [Phys.] Condition of two sounds or waves not being in rhythm. **′dissonant**, a.

dis′symmetry, n. Condition of not having complete SYMMETRY. [Cryst.] Sp. condition of being ENANTIOMORPHOUS. **dis-sym′metric(al)**, aa.

′distal, a. [Biol.] At the outer end, farthest from the point where it is fixed or from the middle of the body, as the d. end of a bone.

′distance re′ceptors. [Zoo.] Sense structures having a reaction to effects at a distance.

dis′temper, n. Common INFECTIOUS disease of young dogs, frequently causing death; like disease of cats and some other animals.

distil′lation, n. [Chem.] Process of sending off gas from liquids or solids by heating and then turning gas back to liquid by making cold, used for producing desired substances or taking away undesired ones, separating a mixed liquid into its parts, etc. **dis′til**, v.t. Make undergo d.; get by d. **dis′tillable**, **distill′atory**, aa. **′distillate**, n. Substance produced by d.

dis′tortion, n. Undergoing or causing to undergo a change of form from what is normal, desired or true. [Phys.] The change in form of electric or sound waves on their way from one point to another, caused by the apparatus sending them etc. [Psych.] The taking on of false forms by impulses and ideas sent up from the unconscious mind in sleep, as effect of a desire to keep them secret, not to be conscious of them. **dis′tort**, v.t.

dis′tributed ca′pacitance. [Elec.] The CAPACITANCE of an electric apparatus other than that of the CONDENSERS in it.

distri′bution, n. [Biol.] The range of places on the earth or in a given part of it where a sort of plant or animal has its existence.

distri′bution coef′ficient or **′constant** or **′ratio**. [Chem.] Relation between the amounts of a substance taken into SOLUTION by two liquids which are in the same vessel but unmixed.

distri′bution curve. A special sort of GRAPH making clear the distribution of such things as marks, amounts, properties, and so on among a group.

dis′tributor, n. That part or apparatus of a distribution system from which electric, gas, or liquid current is sent out to different points.

dis′turbance, n. Any unnormal stopping or changing of a regular process or motion, such as a wave motion, caused by something acting against it. **dis′turb**, v.t. Be cause of d. in.

diu′retic, n., a. [Med.] (Substance, etc.) causing increase in output of URINE.

di′urnal, a. [Astron., Meteor.] Taking place in, measuring, a day. [Bot.] Open by day, shut at night. [Zoo.] Awake by day.

di′valent, a. [Chem.] Having a VALENCY of 2.

di′vergent, a. (Of lines, rays, parts, etc.) going further and further away from one another after starting near together or at a common point, having more distance between them at the ends than at the bases. **di′verge**, v.i. Be d. **di′ver-gence**, **di′vergency**, nn. The condition of being d. **di′verging**, a. **d. lens**. [Optics] A LENS causing or increasing divergence of rays going through it, or making CON-VERGENT rays less so. **d. evo'lution.** [Biol.] EVOLUTION by which different groups become more and more different.

diver'ticulum, n. [Zoo.] Pipe or bag with shut end branching from hollow or vessel in body. [Med.] Such an expansion caused by the stretching of the wall of a vessel at a point where it is not strong. **diver'ticular**, a.

di'vide, v.t. and i. Get or be separated into parts or *from* something, make division(s) in. [Arith.] See what number of times a certain number goes into, has to be taken to get, a certain other number. **di'vided**, a. Sp. [Bot.] (Of a leaf etc.) with deep divisions cutting it into separate narrow parts. **'dividend.** [Arith.] Number (to be) divided by another. **di'visible**, a. Able to be divided. **di'vision**, n. Sp. [Arith.] dividing, the opposite process to MULTIPLICATION. **di'visor**, n. [Arith.] Number by which another number is (to be) divided.

di'viders, n. COMPASS used only for DIVIDING lines, measuring distances and so on, not for making circles.

di'viding 'engine. Machine for marking degrees or smaller divisions on scales.

'diving bell. A room-like structure, some-times of bell-like form, without a floor, which is let down into a river, harbour and so on with men inside it so that they may do work on the bed of the water, the inside being kept free from water by pumping COMPRESSED air into it.

division, n. [Bot.] Name used in some systems of plant-grouping for the third greatest group, between a SUB-KINGDOM and a CLASS, in place of PHYLUM (*see* p. 560).

di'visor, n. [Arith.] *See* DIVIDE.

D-'layer, n. [Radio] A stretch of the IONOSPHERE from 25 to 40 miles up, formed under the HEAVISIDE and APPLE-TON LAYERS as the effect of outbursts of H PARTICLES from the sun, and stopping short-wave radio, though being of a little help in sending on long waves.

D-lines, n.pl. The two chief lines in the SPECTRUM of Na.

DNA. DEOXYRIBONUCLEIC ACID.

'doctor so'lution. A SOLUTION of $Na_2Pb_6O_2$ in water, used for taking bad-smelling COMPOUNDS out of PETROLEUM.

doe, n. [Zoo.] Name given to the female of those animals of which the male is named a BUCK.

'doldrums, n.pl. [Geog., Meteor.] Part of the sea near the EQUATOR noted for having little or no wind for long spaces of time, and for its frequent violent rains, thunder, etc.

dolerite, n. [Geol.] A general name for BASIC IGNEOUS ROCKS of MEDIUM-GRAINED structure (*see* p. 192).

'dolicho-. Long, narrow.

'dolichoce'phal-ic, -ous, aa. [Anthrop., etc.] Long-headed, having CEPHALIC INDEX 77·6 or smaller. **'dolicho'cephaly**, n. Condition of being d.

'dolmen, n. [Archaeol.] Great flat stone supported by others so as to make a room-like structure, put up by early man, probably marking resting-place of dead chief.

'dolomite, n.[Mineral.] A white CRYSTALLINE natural substance made up of Ca and Mg CARBONATES.

dome, n. [Astron.] Great glass structure in the form of a hollow half-ball roofing and walling a room for the observation of the stars and so on, sp. for housing an EQUATORIAL TELESCOPE. [Geol.] A FOLD in ROCK in which the beds are sloping out in all directions from a middle point.

do'mesticate, v.t. Get (plants or animals) trained to growth or existence under man's control, as food-producers or for other purposes. **do'mestic**, a. (Of animals) kept by, living with, man. **do'mesti-cated**, a. **domesti'cation**, n.

'dominant, a. Chief, overtopping or con-trolling others. **d. 'character.** [Biol.] *See* MENDEL'S THEORY OF INHERITANCE. **d. gene.** [Biol.] GENE responsible for a d. character. **d. wave-length.** [Optics, Psych.] The WAVE-LENGTH of the light-STIMULUS from a part of the SPECTRUM which has to be mixed with an ACHRO-MATIC light-stimulus to MATCH a given colour. **'dominance**, n.

'donor, n. [Chem.] ACTOR. [Med.] One who lets blood or skin, etc. be taken from him for use in BLOOD TRANSFUSION or GRAFTING.

'Donovan's so'lution. [Med.] SOLUTION of AsI_3 and HgI_2, used for skin diseases.

'Doppler (or **Doppler's**) **'principle.** [Phys.] Rule that on going in the direction of the point from which sound or light waves are coming the FREQUENCY seems to get higher than the true frequency, and on going in the opposite direction it seems to get less, as seen by the change in the note or colour experienced, used in astronomy for measuring direction and rate of motion of stars by observation of their SPECTRA. **'Doppler shift.** [Radio, Astron.] The seeming change in the FREQUENCY of a wave as the effect of the D. p.

'dormant, a. Resting, not undergoing growth, as a plant in winter, or not acting for a time, as a HIBERNATING animal, a disease, or a VOLCANO. **'dormancy**, n.

'dorsad, adv. [Zoo.] To the back.

dorsal, a. [Zoo.] Of, at, or near the back of man, or the back-boned or upper side of an animal, or the back of a part. [Bot.] Of, at, or near, the side turned away from the middle line. **d. a′orta.** Zoo.] In back-boned animals, that great branching ARTERY under the back-bone through which blood is sent to all the body but, in fish, the GILLS. **d. ′nucleus.** [Zoo.] A part of the MEDULLA OBLONGATA. **d. root.** [Zoo.] That part of a NERVE ROOT made up of SENSORY FIBRES.

dor′salis, n. [Zoo.] Blood-vessel on the DORSAL face of an ORGAN.

dorsi-, dorso-. [Zoo.] Back of the body, etc.

dorsi′ventral, a. [Bot.] (Of a flat part) having well-marked DORSAL and VENTRAL faces, as most leaves. [Zoo.] Going from back to front. **d. ′symmetry.** BILATERAL SYMMETRY.

′dorsum, n. [Zoo.] The back of an animal; the upper side of a part such as the foot or tongue.

dose, n. [Med.] Amount of a medical substance to be taken at one time.

dot, n. A small point such as is made by a pencil on paper; see MORSE CODE.

′double, a. Twice as great; formed of two like things or parts. [Bot.] (Of a flower) having more than the normal number of PETALS, gen. as the effect of special CULTIVATION. **d. bond.** [Chem.] A connection between two ATOMS of such a sort that it is still possible to take in two atoms with a VALENCY of 1 for SATURATION. **d. decompo′sition.** [Chem.] A reaction between two MOLECULES in which there is an exchange of ATOMS, producing two new molecules. **d. person′ality.** DUAL PERSONALITY. **d. re′fraction.** BIREFRINGENCE. **d. salt.** [Chem.] A complex of two normal SALTS. **d. star.** [Astron.] Two stars very near together, sp. those forming a system as the effect of their attraction for one another and going round their common CENTRE OF MASS. **′d.-acting,** a. Acting in two directions or with two moving parts; doing two operations. **′d.-acting ′engine.** [Mach.] Any RECIPROCATING ENGINE in which the air, gas, oil and so on working the PISTON comes in first at one end and then at the other, pushing it forward and back, as in most steam-engines. **′doubly,** adv. **doubly ′concave.** BICONCAVE. **doubly ′convex.** BICONVEX.

′doublet, n. Two of the same sort together. [Optics] Two LENSES put together so as to make ABERRATION and DISPERSION less; two lines very near together in the SPECTRUM of a substance. [Elec.] System of two equal and opposite electric CHARGES near together.

douche, 1.n. [Med.] Current of liquid forced into some part of body; apparatus for giving d. 2.v.t. Give d. to (part).

down, n. [Biol.] Mass of delicate, soft feathers, on young birds, and under outer feathers of older birds; soft coat or outgrowth of short hairs on a part of plant or animal.

′downcast, 1.a. [Mining., Geol.] Going in a down direction. 2.n. [Mining] A SHAFT down which new air from outside goes into a mine. [Geol.] DOWNTHROW.

′downthrow, n. [Geol.] The side of a FAULT on which beds have been moved down, or the amount by which they have been moved down.

dra(ch)m, n. Unit of APOTHECARIES WEIGHT used for medical substances, equal to 0·888 gm.; unit of AVOIRDUPOIS WEIGHT equal to $\frac{1}{16}$ oz. or 1·772 gm. (See p. 565.)

draft, n. DRAUGHT.

drag, n. [Mech.] The force of the current of air or liquid acting on a body moving through it, such as an airplane, in the opposite direction to, that is, against, the body's motion.

draught, n. A current of air or gas, sp. one sent through a boiler, etc. fire.

dream, 1.n. [Psych.] A train of ideas, feelings, pictures of events in which one seems to be taking part, experienced by a person while sleeping, used in PSYCHOANALYSIS as a key to the SUBCONSCIOUS. 2.v.i. and t. Have a d. or dd. (that . . .).

′dreikanter, n. [Geol.] A small, sharp-angled, sp. three-edged stone, given this form by driving sand in very dry parts of the Earth.

′dressing, n. Any substance put onto something, for example, leather, cloth, the top of a road, to make it stiff, soft, smooth, or whatever is desired. [Med.] Any material put on a wound for medical purposes or to keep it clean and so on. **dress,** v.t. Put d. on.

drift, n. Motion as the effect of currents of air or water, as the sideways motion of an airplane caused by air currents, or the motion of a ship away from its direction caused by currents in the sea etc. [Geol.] Mass of earth, sand etc. taken away by water, ice, or wind from one place and put down in another—a general name for the looser covering substances on the face of the earth as opp. the solid ROCK etc. structure under these.

drill, 1.n. [Mach.] An instrument with a sharp-edged or pointed end, worked by turning round and round or stamping, for making holes in hard substances, for example metal or the earth or a tooth, or getting them broken up, for example stone; machine working a d.; a machine used by farmers for planting seed in regular lines. 2.v.t. and i. Make holes in, get broken up, with a d. **′drilling,** n. Sp. the operation of making deep holes into or under the earth in mining.

′dripstone, n. STALACTITE or STALAGMITE.

'**driving-shaft,** n. [Mach.] The SHAFT of an engine or MOTOR.

'**driving-wheel,** n. [Mach.] Any wheel by which motion is given to some other part, sp. the first of a train of wheels, which puts the rest in motion; one of the great wheels turned by the engine of a train and so on and by which the pulling force is produced.

drone, n. [Zoo.] The male bee, which does no work and is of value only for its part in producing offspring.

'**dropsy,** n. [Med.] Diseased condition in which there is great increase in the water-like liquid in the TISSUE spaces of some part of the body, sp. under the skin. '**dropsical,** a.

Dro'sophila, n. A common sort of fly, living in fruit, much used in work on HEREDITY.

dross, n. [Metal.] The waste material formed on top of metal when made liquid by heat.

drug, n. Any substance used for medical purposes; a NARCOTIC.

drum, n. Any hollow or solid CYLINDER of some size as used for a great number of different purposes, for example as a vessel for storing oil in, as a machine-part for mixing substances in or round which wire, chain, etc. is rolled, or as the turning structure round which marks are made by a pen etc. in certain sorts of recording-instrument, and so on. [Zoo.] The MIDDLE EAR or the TYMPANIC MEMBRANE.

'**drumlin,** n. [Geol.] Hill in the form of a half-egg made of BOULDER CLAY.

'**drunken,** a. (Of machines, etc.) at an angle, not level, not normal, having a shaking motion, as a screw of which the THREAD is not quite regular.

drupe, n. [Bot.] Fruit formed of one seed with a very hard cover (the 'stone') in the middle of a generally soft, but sometimes dry mass covered by an outer skin. **dru'paceous,** a. '**drupel,** '**-let,** nn. Any of the small dd. massed together to make up an AGGREGATE fruit. (*See* p. 158).

druse, n. [Geol.] Hole in ROCK lined with CRYSTALS.

dry 'battery. [Elec.] A BATTERY of DRY CELLS.

dry-bulb 'temperature. [Meteor.] TEMPERATURE given by normal THERMOMETER as against that given by one which has bulb covered with wet cloth (wet-bulb temperature, *see* PSYCHROMETER).

dry cell. [Elec.] Electric CELL in which the necessary liquid is mixed with powder, forming a jelly or paste.

dry ice or **dry snow.** Solid CO_2, used as a REFRIGERANT.

'**drying oil.** Oil changing readily into a hard elastic substance when open to the air.

dry pile. [Phys.] Early form of VOLTAIC PILE in which the material between the metal plates was paper, and no ELECTROLYTE was used other than the small amount of water present in the paper itself.

dry rot, n. Disease of wood caused by a FUNGUS, the wood becoming very dry and coming to bits.

'**dual,** a. Made up of two parts; having two purposes or operations. **d. person'ality.** [Psych.] The commonest form of MULTIPLE PERSONALITY, in which there is a division into two persons. '**-ism,** n. The property or condition of being d.; any theory based on the existence of two independent forces, sp. that looking on mind and material substance as two separate things. '**-ist,** n. Person supporting any theory of dualism. -'**istic,** a. To do with, being, a condition or theory of dualism. **dualistic system** or **theory.** [Chem.] The old theory put forward by Lavoisier that all chemical COMPOUNDS are made up of two parts (which themselves may be simple or complex) having opposite electric properties. **du'ality,** n. The condition of being d.

duct, n. Any pipe or like structure by which gas, liquid, etc. is transported. [Zoo.] Short, pipe-like structure through which gas, liquid, or other substance goes. [Bot.] Pipe or vessel formed by a line of CELLS end to end whose division walls have gone. '**-less,** a. [Biol.] Without a d. or outlet. **ductless gland.** [Zoo.] A GLAND without a d., sending what is produced by it straight in to the blood, for example, an ENDOCRINE GLAND, a LYMPH GLAND.

duc'tility, n. That property of metals which makes it possible for their form to be changed by pulling, rolling etc. when cold, while they become more and more RESISTANT to this process. '**ductile,** a. Having d., able to be rolled etc. into very thin plates or pulled out into thin wires, when cold

'**ductule,** n. [Zoo.] A small DUCT, or the thin, thread-like end of a larger duct.

'**ductus,** n. [Zoo.] DUCT.

dull e'mitter. [Radio] VALVE which does not give out light, having a CATHODE of substance which gives off ELECTRONS at a lower degree of heat than is necessary to make it bright.

'**Dulong and 'Petit law.** Law that the SPECIFIC HEAT × the ATOMIC WEIGHT of a solid ELEMENT is unchanging, and roughly equal to 6·4, true for most elements at middle TEMPERATURES.

du'losis, n. [Zoo.] The form of HELOTISM seen among certain ants, who make prisoner the young of other sorts and keep them as servants to do the work of the colony. **du'lotic,** a.

'**Dumas appa'ratus.** [Phys.] Heated bulb with long pipe ending under water, used for measuring VAPOUR DENSITY of the liquid of which a measured amount is dropped into bulb.

dune, n. [Geog.] Round mass, HILL, of sand formed by wind.

duo-. Two.

duo′denum, n. [Zoo.] In man and higher animals, the first, and the widest and shortest, part of the SMALL INTESTINE, going from the stomach to the JEJUNUM, and into which the BILE and the PANCREATIC DUCTS have their opening. **duo′denal,** a. **duo′deno-.**

′duplex, a. (Of machines) having two parts working at the same time or in the same way; working in two directions or doing two things at the same time. [Genet.] Having three times the HAPLOID number of CHROMOSOMES, with a given DOMINANT ALLELOMORPH present on two of them and its RECESSIVE allelomorph on the other.

′duplicate, 1.n. Copy, thing which is in every way the same as a given thing. 2.v.t. Make, get produced, or be, a d. of. 3.a. Being a d. of the thing named; formed of two like parts; produced in two′s. **′duplicated,** a. **dupli′cation,** n.

′dupli′cature, n. [Zoo.] A fold.

du′rain, n. [Mineral.] A part of coal which is not bright and has much ASH.

′dura ′mater. [Zoo.] Strong outer skin covering the brain and SPINAL CORD in back-boned animals.

Dur′alumin, n. [Metal.] Trade name for an ALLOY of Al with small amounts of Ca, Mg, and Mn, noted for its small weight and used for airplane parts and so on.

′duramen, n. [Bot.] The hard, dark, middle part of a tree stem.

Dutch metal. Mixed copper and zinc in thin leaves used to take the place of GOLD-LEAF in sign-writing and the gold-leaf ELECTROSCOPE.

dwarf, n., a. [Biol.] (Animal or plant) much less than the normal size. **d. male.** Small 3- or 4-CELLED plant formed in OEDOGONIACEAE and producing only male sex-cells. [Zoo.] A male animal which is very much smaller and gen. less complex than the female of its sort, freq. not free-living but having some sort of connection with the female. **d. star.** [Astron.] Small star of very great mass for its size and giving out little light. **′dwarfism,** n. [Biol.]

dwt. = PENNYWEIGHT.

Dy. Sign for DYSPROSIUM.

dy-. Two.

′dyad, n. [Biol.] Half of a TETRAD. [Chem.] An ATOM or group of atoms with VALENCY 2.

dye, [Chem.] 1.n. A chemical substance having the power of colouring silk, wool, cotton, etc. by becoming regularly and fixedly united to it all through. 2.v.t. and

i. Get (material) or (of material) become coloured by dyeing. **′dyeing,** n. The process or art of making materials undergo the operation of dd.

dyke, n. [Geol.] A wall-like body of IGNEOUS ROCK formed as the effect of having been pushed up into a crack in the material over it when in a heated and liquid condition. **d. swarm.** n. Great numbers of dd. of the same age together.

dy′namic(al), aa. To do with force or motion. **dy′namic meta′morphism.** [Geol.] Physical changes in ROCK caused chiefly by outside force.

dy′namics, n.pl. That branch of MECHANICS having to do with the operation of forces in producing or changing the motion of bodies.

′dynamite, n. An EXPLOSIVE used for getting ROCK broken up, made of NITRO-GLYCERINE and an ABSORBENT.

′dynamo, n. [Elec.] ELECTROMAGNETIC GENERATOR, sp. one producing DIRECT CURRENT, a name now generally limited to small machines.

dyna′mometer, n. [Elec.] Instrument for measuring power of muscles, or power needed for or produced by machines, or the rate at which WORK is done by a machine (gen. given in WATTS or HORSE-POWER). **dyna′mometry,** n.

dy′natron, n. [Phys.] A THERMIONIC VALVE with three of more ELECTRODES, so designed that the current to the ANODE becomes less as the anode POTENTIAL becomes greater, used as an OSCILLATOR.

dyne, n. [Phys.] C.G.s. unit of force, equal to that which, acting for one second on 1 gm. gives it an ACCELERATION of 1 cm. per sec. per sec.

dy′sarthria, n. [Med.] Condition of not talking rightly, caused by nerve trouble. **dy′sarthric,** a.

dysar′throsis, n. [Med.] Bad condition of a JOINT, limiting its power of motion.

′dysentery, n. [Med.] Sorts of disease of the great INTESTINE, marked by sharp pains and FAECES mixed with blood, caused by certain AMOEBAE and BACTERIA.

dys′function, n. [Med.] Condition of being out of order, not working in the right way.

dys′genic, a. [Zoo.] Acting against the producing of a good quality of offspring, causing DEGENERATION of a group. **dys′genics,** n.pl. Science of d. effects and changes. **dys′genesis,** n. Condition of being infertile, sp. of HYBRIDS.

′dysmenor′rh(o)ea, n. [Med.] Pain and trouble in MENSTRUATION. **′dysmenor-′rh(o)eal,** a.

dys′pepsia, n. [Med.] Bad or incomplete digestion, causing pain, troubled feeling, in stomach etc. **dys′peptic,** n., a. (Person) having bad digestion, to do with d.

dys'phoria, n. [Med.] The condition of not having a feeling of well-being, feeling unwell and unhappy.

dys'plastic, a. [Psych.] Having a body structure which is not in complete agreement with any of KRETSCHMER'S TYPES, or which is mixed, being like one type in some ways and like another in others.

'dyspnoea, n. [Med.] Trouble in breathing.

dys'prosium, n. Chemical ELEMENT, at. no. 66, at. wt. 162·46, sign Dy, one of the RARE EARTH METALS.

dys'tectic 'mixture. [Chem.] Complex of metals mixed in such amounts as to have highest possible MELTING-POINT for a substance formed of these metals.

dys'trophia, n. [Biol., Med.] Condition, caused by GLAND trouble, in which an animal, plant, or part is not taking in enough food material for growth. **dys'trophic,** a

'dystrophy, n. DYSTROPHIA. [Bot.] Condition in which insects get NECTAR from a flower by forcing their way through the cup, damaging it and giving no help in POLLINATION.

dy'suria, 'dysury, nn. [Med.] Trouble or pain in URINATING.

e, Sign for the charge on an ELECTRON, $=4·770 \times 10^{-10}$ e.s.u.

E, Sign for EINSTEINIUM.

E, Sign commonly used for ELECTROMOTIVE FORCE.

'eagre, n. [Geog.] BORE (of river, etc.)

ear, n. [Zoo.] Sense apparatus which gives a reaction to sound (see INNER EAR, MIDDLE EAR, and OUTER EAR); in MAMMALS, the PINNA; in some birds and MAMMALS, a pointed structure of hair or feathers near the opening to the ear; any ear-like structure. [Bot.] The flower or seed-SPIKE of a grain plant. **e. stone, e. sand.** See OTOLITH. **'-ache,** n. [Med.] Pain in the e. **'-drum,** n. TYMPANIC MEMBRANE. **'-phone,** n. A small electric instrument working like a telephone RECEIVER, designed to be put in or on the ear as the necessary part of a HEARING AID.

earth, n. [Astron.] The third of the PLANETS from the sun, at an AVERAGE distance of 92,000,000 miles, and the fifth in order of size, its mass being $\frac{1}{329,390}$ of the sun's mass—an OBLATE ball somewhat flat at the POLES, turning completely round on its AXIS in 24 hours, and at the same time moving completely round the sun in a year, in an ORBIT which is almost a circle. (*See* p. 331).

earth, 1.n. [Elec.] A connection to the e. 2.v.t. and i. Put into a connection with the e. **e. in'ductor.** Apparatus measuring E.'s MAGNETIC FIELD by current produced in a number of turns of wire which are turned suddenly round. **-ed,** a. Having a connection with the e.

'earthquake, n. Shaking motion of the outer part of the earth.

'ebonite, n. Hard black material made by heating rubber with S.

e'bracteate(d), a. [Bot.] Without BRACTS.

e'caudate, a. [Zoo.] Having no tail.

ec'bolic, n., a. [Med.] (Substance) causing strong CONTRACTION of the UTERUS, and used for helping DELIVERY of baby or producing ABORTION.

ec'centric, 1.a. Not CONCENTRIC; not at, or with AXIS not going through, middle point; (of ORBIT or moving body) not in form of circle, not moving in a circle. 2.n. Apparatus for turning motion in a circle into straight-line motion. **e. a'nomaly.** [Astron.] *See* ANOMALY. **eccen'tricity,** n.

ecchon'droma, n. [Med.] A TUMOUR formed of CARTILAGE in or on bone.

ecchy'mosis, n. [Med.] Black or blue mark on skin caused by blood coming out of vessels under it as effect of blow.

'eccrine gland. [Zoo.] SWEAT GLAND.

eccrin'nology, a. [Physiol.] Science of SECRETIONS and EXCRETIONS.

ec'demic, a. (Of disease) coming from outside a country, opp. ENDEMIC.

'ecdysis, n. [Zoo.] The putting off of a skin or other covering. **ec'dysial,** a.

'echard, n. Water in the earth unable to be used by plants.

'echelon, n. [Optics.] Apparatus for producing light SPECTRUM, made of equal glass plates put together like steps. **e. cell.** Glass vessel narrow at one end and wide at the other, used in measuring ABSORPTION of light by a liquid. **e. 'grating.** E.

'echinate(d), a. [Biol.] Covered with needle-like points, outgrowths.

e'chinochrome, n. [Zoo.] A red or brown RESPIRATORY PIGMENT present in ECHINODERMATA.

e'chinococc'osis, n. [Med.] A disease caused by ECHINOCOCCUS.

e'chino'coccus (echinococci), n. [Zoo.] The LARVA of a TAPEWORM, in the form of a great CYST with smaller cysts inside it, which undergoes its development in man, sheep, pigs, and cows, the tapeworm itself living at full growth in dogs and like animals.

E'chino'dermata, n.pl. [Zoo.] PHYLUM of RADIALLY SYMMETRICAL sea animals having the body walls made stronger with CALCAREOUS plates. **e'chinoderm,** n. One of the E.

E'chinoidea, n.pl. [Zoo.] CLASS of ECHINODERMATA, somewhat round in form, and covered with sharp CALCAREOUS points or needles.

e'chino'pluteus, n. [Zoo.] LARVA of ECHINOIDEA.

e'chinulate(d), aa. [Biol.] Having small, sharp points. echinu'lation, n.

e'chinus, n. [Zoo.] One of the ECHINOIDEA.

'echo, 1.n. [Acous.] Sound copying and coming later than another as the effect of REFLECTION of the sound waves from a distance. [Radio] Radio SIGNAL echoing another some time later, as the effect of the wave transporting it having gone round the earth in the opposite direction, by a longer way than the other. 2.v.i. and t. (Of sound, etc.) Be or make an e. of (an earlier one). e. 'sounder. Apparatus for measuring how deep water is by time taken for sound or ULTRASONIC wave to go from ship to sea-bed and back.

ec'lampsia, n. [Med.] Sudden attack of CONVULSIONS while giving birth.

e'clipse, n. [Astron.] The making dark of a body such as the moon by its moving into the shade of another, or the covering of a light-giving body, such as the sun, by a dark body, such as the moon, coming between it and the earth.

e'cliptic, n. [Astron.] The circle in which the CELESTIAL SPHERE is cut by the plane in which the sun seems to be moving when seen from the earth.

e'closion, n. [Zoo.] Act of coming out of the egg or PUPA.

e'cology, n. Branch of biology to do with relations between living beings and the natural conditions under which they are living. eco'logica(l), aa. e'cologist, n.

eco'nometer, n. Instrument recording amount of CO_2 in gases.

eco'nomics, n.pl. Science of ways by which material needs of man are taken care of, that is, of the conditions and laws of the producing, distribution and use of goods. e'conomist, n.

e'conomizer, n. [Engin.] In the operation of a machine or chemical plant, an apparatus for making some use of heat taken away by waste gases or water, sp. system of pipes in boiler for heating incoming water in this way.

ecta'denia, n.pl. [Zoo.] Sex-GLANDS in insects formed from ECTODERM.

ec'tamnion, n. [Zoo.] In EMBRYOS of higher VERTEBRATA, start of head fold.

ec'ta-sia, -sis, nn. [Med.] Expansion of a hollow ORGAN or vessel.

ec'tental line. [Zoo.] Meeting-line of ECTODERM and ENDODERM in EMBRYO.

ecto-. Outside, outer: ecto'cranial, a.

'ectoblast, n. [Zoo.] Outer CELL-LAYER of EMBRYO producing the ECTODERM.

ecto'bronch-us, -ium, nn. [Zoo.] Side branch of bird's breathing apparatus going to AIR-SAC.

ecto'condyle, n. [Zoo.] CONDYLE, sp. EPICONDYLE. ecto'condyl-ar, -oid, aa.

'ecto'cuneiform, n. [Zoo.] A bone between foot and leg.

'ectocyst, n. [Zoo.] Outer LAYER of a ZOOECIUM.

'ectoderm, n. [Zoo.] Outer CELL-LAYER forming the wall of a GASTRULA, or the TISSUES which undergo development from this. ecto'dermal, a.

ec'togenous, a.[Med.] Able to go through development away from the body of an animal, said of disease-producing BACTERIA.

ecto'lecithal, a. [Zoo.] (Of egg) having YOLK at side.

-ectomy. [Med.] Operation of cutting out what is named.

ecto'parasite, n. [Zoo.] PARASITE living on outside of animal. ectopara'sitic, a.

'ectophyte, n. [Bot.] PARASITE living on outside of plant. 'ecto'phytic, a.

ec'top-ia, -y, nn. [Med.] (Of part or ORGAN) condition of being out of place. ec'topic, a. ectopic 'pregnancy. [Med.] The development of the FERTILIZED OVUM somewhere other than the UTERUS.

'ectoplasm, n. [Biol.] The outer part of the PROTOPLASM of a CELL, gen. clear and jelly-like, and with less GRANULES than the liquid ENDOPLASM.[Bot.] ECTOPLAST.

'ectoplast, n. [Bot.] The outer PLASMA MEMBRANE of a CELL, touching the cell-wall.

'ectosarc, n. [Zoo.] The ECTOPLASM of one-CELLED animals and some OVA.

'ectospore, n. [Bot.] SPORE formed at end of thin stem in BASIDIOMYCETES. ecto-'sporous, a.

'ecto'zo-on, -an, nn. [Zoo.] ECTOPARASITE.

'eczema, n. [Med.] Common skin disease caused by IRRITANTS, ec'zematous, a.

e'daphic, a. To do with, controlled, by some property of the earth having an effect on the growth of plants.

'edaph'ology, n. The science of the properties of, and conditions in, earth which have an effect on plant growth.

'eddy, n. Round and round motion of liquid or gas. e. current. Electric current produced in mass of metal by changes in MAGNETIC FIELD. e.flow.[Phys.] Irregular motion of a current of liquid or gas marked by ee.

e'dema, n. OEDEMA.

Eden'tata, n.pl. [Zoo.] An ORDER of MAMMALS with no teeth or with teeth at a low stage of development.

e'dentate, e'dentul-ate, -ous, aa. [Biol.] Having no teeth or teeth-like parts.

edge 'runner. [Mech.] Apparatus for crushing stone etc. having stone or iron rollers moving round and round on their edges in a vessel.

'Edison effect. [Phys.] The effect, first noted by Edison, on which the THERMIONIC

VALVE is based, by which, if a heated wire and a cold metal plate are together in the same bulb an electric current goes from the first to the second.

e'duction, n. [Psych.] The name given by Spearman to the process by which the mind, given two qualities, facts, etc., sees the relation between them, or given one quality etc. and the relation joining it to another is able to say what that other is.

'eelworm, n. [Zoo.] Round NEMATODE worm which is a PARASITE in man and in animals kept by him.

ef'fective, a. Being that part of anything which in fact has an effect, as the e. **'heating 'surface** of a boiler, that part which is in touch with heated gas on one side and the water to be heated on the other, or e. **'horsepower**, that part of the horsepower of an engine which does the moving of a ship, automobile, etc., as opp. that which is used up in overcoming the FRICTION of the engine's parts and so on; VIRTUAL, as e. **value**, that is, ROOT-MEAN-SQUARE VALUE, or e. **'temperature (of a star)**, that is the TEMPERATURE which a given star would have, judging by the ENERGY it gives out, if it was a BLACK BODY giving out its energy in a completely regular way.

ef'fector, n. [Zoo.] Any structure in the body which does something in reaction to a NERVE IMPULSE, as a muscle or a GLAND.

'efferent, a. [Zoo.] Taking something from an inner to an outer part, sp. of nerves transporting NERVE IMPULSES from the brain and SPINAL CORD to the muscles.

effer'vesce, v.i. (Of liquid) send off gas produced in it with violent motion and sound, as of boiling; (of gas) go off in this way. **'-nce**, n. Condition of effervescing. **'-nt**. a.

ef'ficiency, n. Of an engine, process, etc., $\frac{\text{output}}{\text{input}} \times 100$.

efflo'rescence, n. [Bot.] Condition or time of flowering; flower or flower-group produced. [Chem.] Changing into or becoming covered with a powder-like substance as effect of loss of water to air. [Med.] ERUPTION. **efflo'resce**, v.i. **efflo'rescent**, a.

'effluent, n. Liquid coming out of drain and so on; smaller river branching from another.

ef'fluvium, n. Any unseen gas given off from a body, sp. one having a bad smell.

'efflux, n. The coming out of liquid, gas, rays, etc. from a body or vessel; liquid, gas or rays sent out.

ef'fuse, a. [Bot.] Thin and flat in growth and without clear-cut edge.

ef'fusion, n. [Phys.] The motion of a gas through openings which are great in comparison with the distance between its MOLECULES. [Med.] Loss of liquid from its

normal vessel through the walls into some shut space in body; liquid getting out in this way.

ef'fusive, a. [Geol.] To do with, or (of ROCK) formed from, lava forced out of the earth.

e'gest, v.t. Send out as waste substance from body. **e'gesta**, n.pl. The substances sent out from the body.

egg, n. [Biol.] OVUM. [Zoo.] Structure made up of the OVUM and materials needed for its development, sp. the body, gen. hard-covered, housing the ovum together with a mass of food-material, which is produced by birds and REPTILES and in which their young undergo development outside the body of the mother. **e. app'aratus**. [Bot.] The group formed of the e. cell and the two SYNERGIDAE at one end of the EMBRYO SAC in seed-plants. **e. case, e. 'capsule**. [Zoo.] A bag-like or other cover in which the ee. of an insect or other animal are put down. **e. cell.** The OVUM as opp. other parts of an e. **e. tooth.** [Zoo.] An outgrowth on the mouth by which the eggshell is broken by a young bird when it is ready to come out of the e. **'-shell**, n. [Zoo.] The hard outer cover of an e.

'ego, n. [Psych.] The self; that part of the self formed by the adjustment of the ID to experience; in Freud's system, the driving forces based on love of and fear for the self, as opp. those based on sex-impulses.

ei'detic, a. [Psych.] To do with, being, e. imagery. **e. 'imagery.** AFTER-IMAGES so strong and clear as to seem like something physically seen.

'Einstein-de 'Haas effect. [Phys.] The turning force produced in a free body by sudden MAGNETIZATION. **Einstein mass 'energy 'formula.** $Mc^2 = E$ where M is mass, E ENERGY and c the speed of light. **Einstein shift.** The fact that lines in the SPECTRUM of a substance in the sun are nearer the red end than in the spectrum of the same substance on earth, because of the sun's GRAVITATIONAL FIELD.

'einsteinium, n. Chemical ELEMENT, at. no. 99, at. wt. 254, sign Es produced by man by the BOMBARDMENT of PLUTONIUM with NEUTRONS, RADIOACTIVE.

Einstein's theory. [Phys.] See RELATIVITY.

'Einthoven galva'nometer. STRING GAL-VANOMETER.

ejacu'lation, b. [Biol.] The sending out suddenly and with force of liquid from part of body, sp. SEMEN, or of SPORES from spore-vessel of plant. **ejacu'latory**, a. **ejacu'latory duct.** [Zoo.] Narrow pipe forming outlet of VAS DEFERENS.

e'jecta, n. Substance forced out, as from a VOLCANO or the body of an animal.

e'jective, a. [Phonet.] (Of VOICELESS sounds) made with GLOTTIS shut.

e′labo′ration, n. [Biol.] The building up of complex substances forming part of plant or animal from simpler substances. **e′laborate**, v.t. **e′laboratory**, n. Part of plant or animal having purpose of e.

E′lasmo′branchii, n.pl. [Zoo.] In some systems, CHONDRICHTHYES, in others a division of Chondrichthyes taking in all but the HOLOCEPHALI. **e′lasmobranch**, n., a. (Animal) of the E.

elaso′nometer, n. [Phys.] instrument measuring elastic changes in a body by the changing effects the body has on light.

elas′ticity, n. [Phys.] The tendency of a body to come back to its first size or form after having been stretched, put under PRESSURE, or changed in form by force. **e′lastic**, a. Having e., to do with e;. having a marked degree of e., as rubber. **elastic fa′tigue.** [Phys.] The loss for a short time of the elastic properties of some materials, which after undergoing PRESSURE, stretching, or other loss of form, come back only slowly to their first form. **elastic ′fibres.** [Zoo.] YELLOW FIBRES. **elastic fibro′cartilage.** [Zoo.] FIBROCARTILAGE with elastic fibres. **elastic ′limit.** [Phys.] The greatest force which may be put on an elastic body, causing a change of size or form, without the destruction of the body's power to come back to its first form or size when the force is taken away. **elastic ′modulus.** MODULUS OF ELASTICITY.

e′lastica ex′terna. [Zoo.] Outer cover of NOTOCHORD.

e′lastica in′terna. [Zoo.] Inner cover of NOTOCHORD.

e′lastin, n. [Biochem.] Substance of which ELASTIC FIBRES are formed.

′elater, n. [Bot.] Any of certain long, narrow elastic CELLS helping the distribution of SPORES in HEPATICAE.

′E-′layer, n. [Radio]. The HEAVISIDE LAYER of the IONOSPHERE.

′elbow. n. [Anat.] JOINT in the arm between the HUMERUS and the ULNA.

E′lectra ′complex. [Psych.] In Freud's system, unconscious sex-love of a daughter for her father and hate for her mother, the parallel of the OEDIPUS COMPLEX (which see) in males.

elec′tricity, n. [Phys.] The form of ENERGY seen in operation when ELECTRONS are moving in a current or are taken from or given to ATOMS. **e′lectric**, a. Of, to do with, having, produced by, worked by, e. **electric cell.** See CELL [Elec.]. **electric charge.** See CHARGE [Elec.]. **electric conn′ective ′tissue.** [Zoo.] Jelly-like CONNECTIVE TISSUE in which the ELECTROPLAXES of certain sorts of electric organ are placed. **electric current.** [Phys.] The motion of e. through a CONDUCTOR. **electric di′scharge.** [Phys.] The motion of

e. through a gas produced by the IONIZATION of the gas, gen. giving out light. **electric field.** [Phys.] The space near a CHARGED BODY in which electric effects are produced on other bodies. **electric ′generator.** Any machine for changing MECHANICAL ENERGY into an electric current or electric CHARGE (see ELECTROMAGNETIC GENERATOR, ELECTROSTATIC GENERATOR). **electric in′duction.** See INDUCTION. **electric light.** Light produced by the heating effect of an electric current, as in a FILAMENT LAMP, or by an electric discharge, as in a GAS-DISCHARGE LAMP or ARC LAMP. **electric-light bulb.** The glass vessel of a FILAMENT LAMP, or, loosely, the filament lamp itself. **electric ′organ.** [Zoo.] Mass of muscle or other TISSUE, present chiefly in certain fishes, producing and storing electric power and giving an electric shock when touched. **electric ′oscill′ation.** [Phys.] An ALTERNATING CURRENT of very high FREQUENCY, used sp. in radio. **electric shock.** [Med.] Sudden pain and CONVULSION produced in the body of an animal by an electric current going through it, causing death if the current is great enough. **electric spark.** See SPARK. **electric storm.** [Meteor.] A condition of strong electric field inside a cloud such that a BRUSH DISCHARGE is experienced by an airplane going through it. **electric stress.** [Phys.] The force put on a body by an ELECTRIC FIELD, causing a current in a CONDUCTOR and an impulse to the DISPLACEMENT of ELECTRONS in a DIELECTRIC. **electric wave.** [Phys.] An ELECTROMAGNETIC WAVE moving through a CONDUCTOR. **electric wind.** [Phys.] A current of air, gas, or liquid produced by REPULSION from the sharp point of a body having an electric charge. **e′lectrical**, a. Electric. **e′lectrifi′cation**, n. Electrifying. **e′lectrify**, v.t. Give an electric charge to a body; put electric apparatus into machines, buildings, etc. so that they may be worked, lighted, and so on by e.

e′lectro-. To do with, caused by, or using, ELECTRICITY:—′-me′tallurgy, n. ′-thera-′peutics, n., ′-′tropism, n.

e′lectroa′nalysis, n. [Chem.] The measuring of the amounts of different metals present in a substance by ELECTROLYSIS.

e′lectrobi′oscopy, n. [Med.] BIOSCOPY by noting reaction of muscles to electric impulses.

e′lectrocapil′larity, n. [Phys.] The producing or taking place of CAPILLARY effects as effect of ELECTRIC CHARGE or current.

e′lectro′cardiogram, n. [Med.] Camera picture recording the change in electric POTENTIAL which takes place every time the heart-muscle CONTRACTS. **e′lectro-′cardiograph**, n. An instrument based on the STRING GALVANOMETER for making ee.

e′lectro′chemistry, n. Science of the chemical effects produced by electric power. **e′lectro′chemical,** a. **e′lectro′chemical e′quivalent.** The amount in GRAMMES of a substance made free by unit current going through an ELECTROLYTE for 1 second.

electrocoagulation, n. [Med.] COAGULATION of body TISSUES by use of HIGH-FREQUENCY electric current.

e′lectrode, n. [Elec.] The part, generally of metal or C, by which an electric current goes into or out of a liquid, gas, or VACUUM TUBE, etc. **e. po′tential.** The POTENTIAL DIFFERENCE between an e. and the liquid it is in. **′-less,** a. Not having an e. **electrodeless dis′charge.** [Elec.] A DISCHARGE produced in a gas in certain conditions without use of ELECTRODES. ′**e′lectrode′posit,** n. Coat of metal produced another by electrodeposition. ′**electrodepo′sition,** n. The coating of one metal with another by using them as ELECTRODES in a SOLUTION of a SALT of the covering metal.

e′lectrodi′alysis, n. [Phys.] The taking of an ELECTROLYTE from a COLLOIDAL SOLUTION by ELECTROLYSIS and DIALYSIS.

e′lectrody′namics, n.pl. Science of the motion of electric CHARGES and currents and of the effects of electric currents one on another. **e′lectrody′namic,** a. **electrodynamic instrument.** ELECTRODYNAMOMETER.

e′lectrodyna′mometer, n. Instrument for measuring electric current by force of attraction or the opposite between a current going through a fixed COIL and one going through a moving coil.

e′lectro-en′cephalography. [Psych.] The operation of recording the electric currents caused by brain processes.

e′lectro-hy′draulic ′forming. [Metal.] The process of working metals using the ENERGY of an electric DISCHARGE in liquid.

elec′trolysis, n. [Phys.] The motion of an electric current through a liquid or SOLUTION causing it to be broken up into ATOMS or atom-groups in the form of oppositely-CHARGED IONS, one sort moving to one ELECTRODE and the other to the other, where the material may be made free, put down as a coating on the electrode, or undergo some chemical reaction. ′**electrolyte,** n. SOLUTION, or substance in solution, in which e. takes place. **electro′lytic(al),** aa. **electrolytic cell.** A vessel in which e. takes place. **e′lectrolyze,** v.t. Make undergo e.

e′lectro′magnet, n. [Phys.] Mass of iron made MAGNETIC by sending an electric current through wire round it. **e′lectro′magnetism,** n. Science of MAGNETIC effects produced by electric currents, and

electric effects produced by magnetic fields. **e′lectromag′netic,** a. **electromagnetic ′generator.** An ELECTRIC GENERATOR producing electric current as the effect of electromagnetic induction, gen. by the turning of a system of CONDUCTORS in a MAGNETIC FIELD or the turning of a system of MAGNETS inside CONDUCTING COILS. **electromagnetic in′duction.** The producing of an ELECTROMOTIVE FORCE in a CIRCUIT as the effect of a change in MAGNETIC FLUX caused by a change in an electric current going through another circuit near to but not in connection with the first. **electromagnetic mass.** The addition to a body's mass caused by an ELECTRIC CHARGE. **electromagnetic radi′ation.** Any RADIATION made up of electromagnetic waves—a general name for HERTZIAN WAVES, GAMMA RAYS, X-RAYS, light, ULTRA-VIOLET, INFRA-RED, and radio waves. **electromagnetic wave.** A WAVE moving through space or a substance made up of an ELECTRIC FIELD at right angles to a MAGNETIC FIELD, the two fields moving at the same rate in a direction at right-angles to their plane.

elec′tromerism, n. [Chem.] Form of TAUTOMERISM caused by a change in the distribution of the ELECTRONS among the ATOMS of a MOLECULE or group. **elec′tromer,** n. Substance having e.

elec′trometer, n. [Elec.] Instrument measuring electric POTENTIAL DIFFERENCE by the force of attraction between CHARGED plates or needles.

electro′motive, a. To do with, producing, the motion of ELECTRICITY. **e. force.** Force causing the motion of ELECTRICITY, that is, producing an electric current round a CIRCUIT, sp. as produced by an ELECTRIC GENERATOR or BATTERY—measured in VOLTS. **e. ′series.** [Chem.] The metals ranged in the order of the amount of e. force in operation between the metal and a NORMAL SOLUTION of any of its SALTS in which it is placed.

e′lectron, n. [Phys.] A very small PARTICLE, $\frac{1}{1840}$ of the mass of the H ATOM, having the smallest possible NEGATIVE ELECTRIC CHARGE (e), of 4.8045×10^{-10} e.s.u., normally forming part of an atom but which may have a separate existence. **e. aff′inity.** The tendency of a substance to have an attraction for free ee., and, by the addition of them to itself, to make NEGATIVE IONS. **e. ′camera.** ICONOSCOPE. **e. di′ffraction.** DIFFRACTION effects got when ee. are sent through very thin plates of metal. **e. dis′charge.** An electric current produced when ee. go through space with nothing in it. **e. dis′charge tube.** VACUUM TUBE in which an e. discharge takes place. **e. gas.** A mass of ee., whose behaviour is in some ways like that of a gas. **e. lens.** A special distribution of an electric field for the purpose of making a BEAM of ee. take a desired direction, gen. so as to come to a FOCUS. **e. 'microscope.** [Phys.] A MICROSCOPE using in place of light a BEAM of ELECTRONS for transporting a picture of a thing to a SCREEN, as in TELEVISION—able, because of the very short WAVELENGTH of the rays, to make clear the structure of things so small (for example, MOLECULES) that it would be quite impossible to see them by the use of light. **e. 'multiplier.** A sort of PHOTOELECTRIC CELL in which SECONDARY EMISSION is used for increasing the current. **e. volt.** Unit of ENERGY used in NUCLEAR PHYSICS, equal to the loss of energy undergone by an e. whose POTENTIAL is lowered by 1 VOLT, or 1.602×10^{-12} ERGS. **elec'tronic**, a. **elec'tronics**, n.pl. The science of the behaviour of free ee.

electro'negative, a. Having a NEGATIVE ELECTRIC CHARGE; having a tendency to give negative IONS.

e'lectro-'optics, n. Science of relations between ELECTRICITY and light.

e'lectro-os'mosis, n. [Phys.-Chem.] The motion of a liquid through a MEMBRANE when placed in it between two ELECTRODES having a POTENTIAL DIFFERENCE.

e'lectropho'resis, n. ANAPHORESIS or CATAPHORESIS.

elec'trophorus, n. [Phys.] Instrument in the form of a flat plate of hard rubber or like substance on which, when CHARGED by rubbing, a metal plate is placed to become charged by INDUCTION.

e'lectro'plating, n. ELECTRODEPOSITION as used in industry. **e'lectroplate**, v.t.

e'lectroplax, n. [Zoo.] Any of the plates of which the ELECTRIC ORGAN of certain animals is made up.

e'lectro'positive, a. Having a POSITIVE (+) ELECTRIC CHARGE; having a tendency to give positive IONS.

e'lectro'puncture, n. [Med.] Operation of putting needles into part of body and sending electric current between them for purpose of ELECTROCOAGULATION.

e'lectrore'fining, n. Process of getting metals free from other substances by ELECTROLYSIS.

e'lectroscope, n. [Elec.] An apparatus for testing to see if a small electric CHARGE or POTENTIAL DIFFERENCE is present, based on the REPULSION between charged bodies.

e'lectrosol, n. [Phys.-Chem.] COLLOIDAL SOLUTION of a metal produced by sending electric SPARKS between bits of the metal under water.

electro'static, a. [Phys.] Of, to do with, those electric effects not dependent on the motion of ELECTRICITY, that is, with

electric CHARGES and POTENTIALS. **e. field.** ELECTRIC FIELD. **e. 'generator.** An ELECTRIC GENERATOR dependent for its working on e. processes producing CHARGES at high POTENTIALS. **e. in'duction.** The producing of a CHARGE in a body as the effect of an opposite charge in another body near it. **e. units.** The system of electric measuring units based on the force between two unit electric CHARGES at unit distance from one another. **electro'statics**, n.pl. The science of e. effects.

e'lectroste'nolysis, n. [Phys.-Chem.] The forming of a coat of metal on the walls of a very narrow pipe or in spaces of a MEMBRANE by ELECTROLYSIS.

e'lectro'striction, n. [Phys.] Change in form of a DIELECTRIC in an ELECTRIC FIELD.

e'lectro'synthesis, n. Building up of chemical substance by use of electric current.

e'lectro'taxis, n. [Biol.] TAXIS produced by electric current.

e'lectro'techn-ics, -ology, nn. The science of the uses of ELECTRICITY in industry.

e'lectro-thera'peutics, -therapy, nn. [Med.] The use of electric current or rays against disease. **electro'therapist**, n.

e'lectro'thermal, a. To do with producing heat by electric current.

e'lectro'tonus, n. [Med.] Condition of nerve when electric current is going through it. **e'lectro'tonic**, a. **elec'tro-tonize**, v.t.

elec'trotropism, n. [Biol.] TROPISM produced by electric current.

e'lectro'valency, n. [Phys.-Chem.] Of two ATOMS or groups of atoms, condition of being united by attraction based on the giving of one or more ELECTRONS from one to the other. **electro'valent**, a. **electrovalent bond.** [Chem.] VALENCY BOND produced by the changing of one or more ELECTRONS from one ATOM to another, the one getting the electron(s) becoming NEGATIVELY and the one undergoing the loss becoming POSITIVELY CHARGED.

e'lectrum, n. An ALLOY of gold and silver present naturally in the earth.

'element, n. [Chem.] Any of those substances which are not able to be broken up chemically into simpler substances, and of which all other snbstances are made. *See* pp. 550-2 and 554-5.

ele'mentary, a. To do with, being one of, the chemical ELEMENTS; simple, to do with the simplest, earliest stages, smallest units, and so on. **e. an'alysis.** [Chem.] The discovery of the amounts of the chief ELEMENTS (C, H, and N) present in ORGANIC substances. **e. electric charge.** [Phys.] The CHARGE on an ELECTRON, $= 4.774 \times 10^{-10}$ e.s.u.

'elephan'tiasis, n. [Med.] Disease in which

skin becomes very thick, and diseased part greatly increased in size, as effect of the stopping up of LYMPHATICS by a NEMATODE worm. ele'phantoid, -ous, aa.

ele'vation, n. HEIGHT; the process of becoming, or of making something, higher. [Astron.] The ANGULAR DISTANCE of a star over the HORIZON. e. of the 'boiling-point. [Chem.] An increase in the boiling-point of a liquid when any substance is DISSOLVED in it, the amount of the increase generally being dependent for any given liquid only on the CONCENTRATION of the SOLVENT and not on what it is.

'elevator, n. [Zoo.] LEVATOR.

'elide, v.t. [Phonet.] Not say, or say incompletely as part of the sound coming after, a letter in a word—as a VOWEL at the end of a word before a word starting with another, or an unsounded 'h', or the 'p' in 'cupboard'.

e'liminant, n., a. [Med.] (Substance) causing ELIMINATION.

elimi'nation, n. The taking away of (condition, substance from another, and so on). [Med.] Process of sending out waste etc. from body. e'liminate, v.t.

e'lision, n. [Phonet.] ELIDING.

e'littoral 'zone. The sea-bed more than 40 m. lower than sea-level.

el'lipse, n. [Geom.] Regular, plane, shut curve with two unequal AXES at right angles to one another, having 2 fixed points (the foci) on the longer of these, the sum of whose distances from any point on the e. is the same, for example the outline of the end of a round rod which has been cut at an angle other than 90°. ell'iptic(al), aa. (See picture p. 223 for the special use of elliptic in naming the form of a leaf.) elliptic polari'zation. [Optics, Radio] POLARIZATION of light or ELECTROMAGNETIC WAVES in which there are two planes of VIBRATION of unequal INTENSITY at right angles to one another, in electromagnetic waves these two being the MAGNETIC FIELD and the ELECTRIC FIELD. ell'iptically, adv. elliptically polarized. Having undergone elliptic polarization.

el'lipsoid, 1.n. [Geom.] A solid form produced by an ELLIPSE turning about one of its AXES. 2.a. In the form of an e. ellip-'soidal, a.

e'locular, a. [Biol.] Having only one CELL; (of space or hollow) without division.

elon'gation, n. Becoming longer; amount of e. [Astron.] Distance, measured by an angle from the earth, of a PLANET from the sun, i.e. the e. of a planet P is ESP where E is the earth and S the sun. 'elongate, v.t. and i. Make or become longer. 'elongated, a.

e'lute, v.t. Get a substance separated from an ADSORBENT. 'eluate, n. The liquid got

by the process of eluting. 'eluant, 'eluent, nn. Liquid used for eluting.

e'lutri'ation, n. Process of separating powder into different sizes based on their different rate of falling through a liquid. e'lutriate, v.t. e'lutriator, n. Apparatus for e.

'elytron (elytra), n. [Zoo.] Front wing of an insect when formed as a cover for back wing; any of the flat plates on the back of some worms. 'elytr-oid, -iform, aa.

eman'ation, n. [Phys., Chem.] Anything, such as a gas or rays, sent out from a substance; the RADIOACTIVE gases produced when Ra, Th, or Ac is broken up, that is, RADON and its ISOTOPES, sign Em. 'emanate, v.i. Come from, be sent out by, as light, smell, gas etc.

e'marginate, a. [Bot.] Having end (of leaf or PETAL) curved in a little in the middle. [Zoo.] (Of tail feathers of bird) forked but not deeply. [Cryst.] Having edges cut off. e'margination, n.

e'masculation, n. [Biol.] Taking away male sex-parts. 'emasculate, v.t. Make (animal) undergo e.

'embolism, n. [Med.] The stopping up of a blood-vessel by an EMBOLUS.

'embolus, n. [Med.] Small mass of half-solid blood in the blood-current transported from one part of system to another; any other undesired small body going round in the blood, such as an air BUBBLE.

embro'cation, n. [Med.] Process of rubbing part which is stiff or paining with medical liquid; liquid used for this purpose.

'embryo, n. [Zoo.] Living being in the first stages of development in the mother's body or before coming out of the egg. [Bot.] Plant in stage between the FERTILIZATION of the female CELL and the opening of the seed. e. cell. That one of two CELLS formed from first division of a FERTILIZED egg in certain plants, which later becomes the e. e. sac. In seed plants, the great, thin-walled CELL in the NUCELLUS inside which the FERTILIZATION of the OVUM and the development of the e. takes place. 'embry'onic, a. Sp., at the e. stage. embry'ogeny, n. The process by which an e. is formed. embry'ology, n.

'emerald, n. [Mineral.] A clear green form of BERYL, $3BeO.SiO_2Al_2O_3.3SiO_2$, one of the most beautiful and highly valued of jewel stones.

e'mergence, n. [Bot.] Outgrowth from or under outer skin of plant. [Astron.] EMERSION.

e'mersed, a. [Bot.] Coming up out of water, not flat on top of it, said of leaves of water plants.

e'mersion, n. [Astron.] The coming into view again of a body in sky after ECLIPSE or OCCULTATION.

'emery, n. [Mineral.] A very hard natural substance formed of Al_2O_3 mixed with

Fe₃O₄ or Fe₂O₃, used for rubbing and polishing metals, etc. **e. paper** or **cloth.** Paper or cloth coated with grains of e. for rubbing purposes.

'emesis, n. [Med.] The sending up of food from stomach through the mouth. **e'metic,** n., a. (Substance) causing e.

e.m.f. = ELECTROMOTIVE FORCE.

-emia, n., **emic,** a. -AEMIA, -AEMIC.

'eminence, n. [Zoo.] An outgrowth on a bone.

e'mit, v.t. Give out (something, for example, light, heat, sound, a liquid or gas). **e'mission,** n. The act of emitting. **emission 'spectrum.** [Phys.] The SPECTRUM of the light given out by a body. **e'missive,** a. Emitting. **emissive power.** [Phys.] The RADIANT ENERGY emitted per second from 1 cm.² of the outside of a body at a given TEMPERATURE. **emiss'ivity,** n. [Phys.] The emissive power of a body ÷ the emissive power of a BLACK BODY at the same TEMPERATURE; the RADIANT HEAT given out per second by 1 cm² of the outside of a body when its TEMPERATURE is higher than that of the space round it by 1°C.

'Emitron, n. Trade name for a form of ELECTRON CAMERA used in TELEVISION.

em'menagogue, n. [Med.] Substance causing or increasing MENSTRUATION.

em'menic, a. [Med.] To do with MENSTRUATION.

emme'tropia, n. [Med.] Normal condition of eye, in which parallel rays of light falling on the LENS come to a meeting point on the RETINA. **emme'tropic,** a.

e'mollient, n. [Med.] Substance put on part to make skin soft, take away INFLAMMATION.

e'motion, n. [Psych.] Any strong feeling, such as love, hate, fear, surprise, etc., experienced in the mind and marked by inner physical changes such as quicker breathing, working of GLANDS, etc., and a strong tendency to give outer signs of it by acting, moving, etc. **e'motional,** a. To do with, caused by or causing, e.; (of person) readily moved by e. **e'motionally,** adv. **e'motive,** a. To do with e.

emphy'sema, n. [Med.] Condition of air being present in CONNECTIVE TISSUE of body, sp. of LUNGS.

em'piric(al), aa. (Of knowledge, rules, processes, etc.) based on experience and observation only, not reasoned from theory, or not having undergone organization into a theory making a connection with other knowledge in the same field. **e. 'formula.** [Chem.] A CHEMICAL FORMULA giving only the RATIO of the number of ATOMS of different substances united in a MOLECULE, not the numbers themselves, as CH for BENZENE which by weight is C₆H₆.

em'piricism, n. Theory that all our knowledge is based only on experience. **em'piri'cist,** n.

empy'ema, n. [Med.] Mass of PUS in some part of body, generally LUNGS. **empy-'emic,** a.

e.m.u. = ELECTROMAGNETIC UNIT(S).

e'mulsion, n. [Chem.] A COLLOIDAL SOLUTION of a liquid in a liquid, freq. used for medical purposes. [Photog.] A substance acted on by light which is used for coating camera PLATES and FILMS. **e'mulsifier,** n. Apparatus for making ee. **e'mulsifi'cation,** n. **e'mulsify,** v.t. Make into an e. or emulsoid. **e'mulsive,** a., n. **e'mulsoid,** n. [Chem.] LYOPHILIC COLLOID.

en-. In, inside, inner.

e'namel, n. [Zoo.] Hard CALCAREOUS material forming the outer coat of a tooth, and present in the SCALES of certain fish. **e. cell.** Any of the special CELLS on the outside of the DENTINE in the teeth of higher animals from which the e. is produced.

e'nantio'blastic, a. [Bot.] (Of EMBRYO) coming into existence at the end of the seed opposite to the HILUM.

e'nantio'morph-ous, **-ic,** aa. [Crystal., Chem.] (Of two CRYSTALS or MOLECULES) having like structure but turned round, as a thing and its picture in a looking-glass. **e'nantiomorph,** n. CRYSTAL, etc. having this relation to another.

e'nanti'otropic, a. [Phys., Chem.] Changing into a different CRYSTAL form at a fixed TEMPERATURE. **e'nantio'tropy,** n.

enar'throsis, n. [Zoo.] BALL-AND-SOCKET-JOINT.

en'capsulate(d), a. [Biol.] Covered by a CAPSULE.

en'cephal'itis, n. [Med.] INFLAMMATION of the brain. **encephalitic,** a.

en'cephalocele, n. [Med.] A part of the brain substance pushed out through a crack in the SKULL.

en'cephalography, n. [Med.] The taking of X-ray pictures of the brain after air has been put into its spaces.

en'cephaloid 'cancer. [Med.] A CARCINOMA which is soft and which becomes greater in size very quickly.

en'cephalon, n. [Anat.] The brain. **ence-'phal-ic, -oid,** aa. **encephalo-.**

'enchyma, n. TISSUE.

'enclave, n. [Med.] Something shut up in an ORGAN or TISSUE but not uniting with it.

en'cysted, a. [Biol., Med.] Inside a CYST, with cyst formed over it. **en'cyst,** v.t. and i. make or become e. **en'cystment, encys-'tation,** nn.

'endarch, a. [Bot.] Having the first-formed wood-substance nearest middle, as in the stems of seed-plants, opp. EXARCH.

'end-bulb, n. [Zoo.] Bulb-like NERVE-ending in the skin of back-boned animals en'demic(al), aa. [Med.] (Of disease) regularly present in certain places or certain groups of persons and limited to them. [Biol.] Limited to a certain stretch of country.

en'dermic, a. [Med.] Acting through the skin, or by being put on the skin.

en'dite, n. [Zoo.] One of the structures on the inner side of leg of CRUSTACEA.

'end(o)- Inside, or inside of:—'enda'ortic, a. [Med.]

'endoblast, n. ENDOSPERM.

enco'cardium, n. [Anat.] ENDOTHELIUM on the inside of the hollows in the heart. endo'cardiac, -al, aa. endocar'ditis, n. INFLAMMATION of e.

'endocarp, n. [Bot.] Inner side of PERICARP.

endo'chondral, a. [Anat.] Present, taking place, inside CARTILAGE.

en'dochylous, a. [Bot.] Having water-cells in the inside TISSUE.

'endocrine, 1.a. [Zoo.] Said of GLANDS producing special chemicals or HORMONES when these are sent straight into the blood without going through a DUCT. 2.n. Substance formed by e. GLANDS. 'endocrin'ology, n. endo'crino'therapy, n. Use of e. substances against disease.

endo'cyclic, a. [Chem.] In or joined to a ring of ATOMS. [Zoo.] Said of CRINOIDEA having mouth in middle of screw-like part; said of ECHINOIDEA having two circles of plates round lower opening of body.

endo'derm-al, -ic, aa. [Biol.] To do with, produced from the ENDODERM or ENDODERMIS.

'endoderm, n. [Zoo.] The inner wall of a GASTRULA.

endo'dermis, n. [Bot.] A coat of CELLS one cell thick with no spaces between them and with thicker bands in certain parts of their walls, present on the inside of the CORTEX in almost all roots and some stems.

en'dogamy, n. [Anthrop.] System by which person may only be married to one of his or her group. [Biol.] The uniting of sex CELLS produced by the same plant or animal.

en'dogenous, a. [Biochem., Biol., Med., Psych.] Formed, taking place, inside a CELL, or part, or the body or the mind, not coming from outside; e. and used for the building up of the body; (of CELLS) formed in the walls of earlier cells. e. spore. [Bot.] SPORE formed inside a SPORANGIUM.

en'dogeny, n. [Biol., etc.] Growth from the inside; the forming of ENDOGENOUS CELLS.

'endolymph, n. [Zoo.] The liquid inside the LABYRINTH of the ear.

'endolym'phatic, a. [Zoo.] To do with LYMPHATICS, sp. with the LABYRINTH of the ear.

endo'metrium, n. [Zoo.] MUCOUS MEMBRANE forming the inside of the UTERUS.

'endome'tritis, n. INFLAMMATION of e.

'endomorph, n. CRYSTAL of a different sort shut inside another. endo'morphic, a.

endo'mysium, n. [Anat.] Delicate TISSUE between threads of muscle uniting them into groups.

endo'neurium, n. [Anat.] Delicate TISSUE between threads of a nerve, uniting them into groups.

endo'parasite, n. [Biol.] PARASITE living inside animal or plant.

en'dophyllous, a. [Bot.] Said of a PARASITE living inside a leaf.

'endophyte, n. [Bot.] Plant living inside another plant but not necessarily as PARASITE. endo'phytic, a.

'endoplasm, n. [Biol.] Middle part of the living substance of a CELL, gen. more liquid and having in it more grains, than the outer part. [Bot.] The substance of a CELL inside the PLASMA MEMBRANE.

endo'pleurite, n. [Zoo.] In CRUSTACEA, structure formed from EPIMERON; in insects, structure on THORAX going into body hollow.

en'dopodite, n. [Zoo.] Inner branch of a forked leg etc., in CRUSTACEA.

'Endoptery'gota, n.pl. [Zoo.] A SUB-CLASS of INSECTA in which the end-form is very different from the LARVA and the change from one to the other is sudden and complete, the wings having undergone their development inside the body. endop'terygote, n. Insect of the E. 'endoptery'gotic, a.

en'doral, al [Zoo.] Inside the mouth, said sp. of structures in the mouth-like hollow of certain PROTOZOA.

end-'organ, n. [Zoo.] Structure formed by branching outer ends of nerves, by which STIMULI are taken in or motion effected.

'endosarc, n. ENDOPLASM.

'endoscope, n. [Med.] Instrument for seeing inside some part of the body. endo'scopic, a. en'doscopy, n.

endo'skeleton, n. [Zoo.] The inside supporting framework of an animal.

endos'mosis, n. [Phys.] OSMOSIS from outside to inside a vessel or in the direction of the stronger SOLUTION.

'endosperm, n. [Bot.] Food-substance stored inside a seed.

'endospore, n. [Bot.] ENDOSPORIUM; in BACTERIA, a SPORE without sex.

endo'sporium, n. [Bot.] The inner coat of a SPORE wall.

en'dosteal, a. [Anat.] Of ENDOSTEUM or ENDOSTOSIS.

en'dosteum, n. [Anat.] The TISSUE on the inside walls of the hollows in certain bones.

en'dostoma, n. [Med.] TUMOUR in a bone.

endos'tosis, n. [Anat.] The forming of bone starting in CARTILAGE.

'endostyle, n. [Zoo.] Folds in wall of PHARYNX in TUNICATA or CEPHALOCHORDA.

endo'theca, n.pl. [Zoo.] Substance inside spaces of most CORALS; ENDOTHECIUM.

endo'thecium, n. [Bot.] Inner coat of an ANTHER CELL. **endo'thecial**, a.

endo'thelium, n. [Anat.] Very thin skin on inside of certain hollow parts of body, as heart, blood-vessels, etc. **endo-'thelioma**, n. [Med.] TUMOUR on e.

endo'thermic, a. [Chem.] Taking place, formed, by a process using up heat.

endo'thorax, n. [Zoo.] The framework of body walls in the middle body-division of CRUSTACEA.

endo'toxin, n. Poison in the substance of BACTERIA which becomes free only after their death.

endo'trophic, a. [Bot.] Getting food from inside, said sp. of FUNGI living inside the root of another plant.

'end-plate, n. [Zoo.] Plate-like END-ORGAN.

end 'product. [Chem.] The substance produced at the end of a number of reactions.

'end-sac, n. [Zoo.] Bag-like part of EXCRE-TORY system in certain CRUSTACEA.

en'dysis, n. [Zoo.] Development of new CUTICLE, sp. in ARTHROPODA.

en'ema, n. [Med.] Liquid forced into the body through the ANUS for medical purposes, sp. cleaning out waste.

e'nergid, n. [Biol.] The unit of structure of a CELL, that is a NUCLEUS together with the PROTOPLASM under its control.

'energy, n. [Phys.] Power of doing WORK, looked on as one of the two FUNDAMENTAL things in the make-up of the physical UNIVERSE (the other being MASS, with which, in the RELATIVITY THEORY, e. is INTERCONVERTIBLE), handed on by one body to another when the first does work on the second, and taking a number of forms which may be turned into one another, as MECHANICAL, electric, chemical, and RADIANT e. (*see* in addition KINETIC e., POTENTIAL e.)—measured in ERGS or FOOT-POUNDS. **e. 'level**. Any of the different conditions, marked by different degrees of e., and dependent on the position of its PLANETARY ELECTRONS, which it is possible for an ATOM to be in.

'engine, n. [Mach.] A machine for changing heat into MECHANICAL ENERGY, such as a steam engine.

en'glacial, a. [Geol.] Fixed in, or, of currents, going through, the body of a GLACIER.

en'gorgement, n. [Med.] (Of part) condition in which vessels are overfull of blood. **en'gorged**, a.

en'graft, v.t. GRAFT.

'engram, n. [Psych.] An unconscious memory.

en'graved, a. [Zoo.] Covered with unregular cuts.

en'hydrite, n. Any MINERAL having in it small spaces full of water. **en'hydrous**, a.

-ennial, a. Coming again, taking place, every ... years, as *biennial*, 'every two years'.

'ensiform, a. [Bot., Zoo.] Formed like a long narrow blade.

enstatite, n. [Mineral.] One of the PYROX-ENES, $MgSiO_3$.

en'telechy, [Biol.] In the theory of VITAL-ISM, the guiding force pictured as having existence in, and controlling the development of, living things.

ente'rectomy, n. [Med.] The operation of cutting out part of the INTESTINE.

en'teric, a. [Med.] To do with the INTESTINES. **e. fever**. TYPHOID FEVER.

ente'ritis, n. [Med.] INFLAMMATION of INTESTINES.

'enter(o)-, INTESTINE. **ente'ropathy**, n. **ente'rotomy**, n.

'entero'c(o)ele, n. [Zoo.] A COELOM formed by a number of hollow outgrowths from the ARCHENTERON.

en'terokinase, n. [Biochem.] KINASE by which in the later stages of digestion TRYPSIN is produced.

'enteron, n. [Zoo.] In lower animals, hollow inside body, in higher animals, ALIMEN-TARY CANAL. **'enteral, en'teric**, aa. **'enteroid**, a. **'entero'genous**, a. Produced inside the e.

'entero'sepsis, n. [Med.] Poisoning caused by taking up of substances by body from INTESTINE.

ente'rostomy, n. [Med.] The operation of making an opening into the INTESTINES from outside the body, for the purpose of draining them.

en'thalpy, n. [Phys.] Amount of heat in unit mass of a substance.

en'tire, a. [Bot.] (Of leaf) having a smooth, unbroken edge, without teeth or divisions (*see* picture p. 223).

'ento-, ENDO-.

ento'mology, n. Science of insects. **ento-mo'logic(al)**, aa. **ento'mologist**, n.

ento'mophilous, a. [Bot.] Made fertile by insects. **ento'mophilly**, n.

ento'plastron (entoplastra), n. [Zoo.] Middle bone-plate on front of CHELONIA.

'entrance-'pupil, n. [Optics] Of a system of LENSES, the IMAGE of the APERTURE STOP formed by all the lenses in front of it.

'entropy, n. [Phys.]. In a THERMODYNAMIC system the measure of the amount of heat ENERGY in it which it is not possible to make use of by changing it into MECHANICAL WORK, given as the RATIO of the amount of heat present to the TEMPERATURE.

e'nucle'ation, n. [Biol.] The taking out of the NUCLEUS from a CELL. **e'nucleate**, v.t.

enu'resis, n. [Med.] Uncontrolled URINA-TION.

'envelope, n. [Astron.] Mist round the

NUCLEUS of a COMET. [Biol.] Cover, covering vessel, covering leaves, and so on.

en'vironment, n. [Biol.] All the outside conditions and forces having an effect on the existence and development of a living thing.

'enzyme, n. [Chem.] Any of a number of complex substances present in living things and acting as CATALYSTS in chemical changes. enzy'matic, en'zymic, aa. enzy'mo(ly)sis, n. Chemical change produced by e. enzymo'lytic, a.

'Eocene, n. [Geol.] The second earliest SYSTEM of ROCKS in the TERTIARY group. (*See* p. 558.)

eo'lation, n. [Geog., etc.] Effect of wind on land.

'eolith, n. Rough stone instrument made by earliest man of STONE AGE. eo'lithic, a. Of the time when ee. were used (the **Eolithic Period**).

'eosin, n. A bright red DYE used sp. [Biol.] for colouring TISSUES.

eo'sinophil(e), n., a. [Physiol.] (CELL) readily coloured with EOSIN, sp. one form of LEUCOCYTE. eo'sino'philia, n. Great increase in ee. in blood.

Eo'zoic, a., n. [Geol.] PRE-CAMBRIAN.

eo'zoon, n. [Geol.] Banded structure present in certain LIMESTONES of Canada, at one time taken as representative of an early animal.

e'palpate, a. [Zoo.] Having no feelers.

ep'axial, a. [Zoo.] Over the middle line, sp. the backbone, and so, in back-boned animals, at the back.

epei'rogeny, n. [Geol.] Changes in earth by which the great land masses have been produced. ep(e)iro'genic, a.

e'pendyma, n. [Zoo.] In back-boned animals the CILIATED EPITHELIUM coating the inside of the hollows in which are brain and SPINAL CORD.

e'phemeris, n. [Astron.] Book giving positions of sun, moon, and important stars for every day in the year and other details of use to sailors and ASTRONOMERS.

E'phemer'optera, n.pl. An ORDER of EXOPTERYGOTA in which the insects at full development have great thin front wings and very small back ones, no mouths or other parts for taking in food or drink, and very short existences—sometimes measured in minutes, never longer than a day.

e'phippium (ephippia). [Anat.] PITUITARY FOSSA. [Zoo.] Thick outer skin of CARAPACE of certain CRUSTACEAE.

e'phyra (ephyrae), n. [Zoo.] The small, free-swimming LARVA of certain jellyfish.

epi-. Upon, over, on the outside of, in front of:—'-'cerebral, a. [Zoo.]

epi'basal, a. [Bot.] To do with top part of oöSPORE in process of development.

epi'benthos, n. [Biol.] Animals and plants living on sea-floor between low-water mark and 200-metre line.

'epiblast, n. [Zoo.] ECTOBLAST. [Bot.] Small body in front of PLUMULE in certain grasses.

epi'blema, n. [Bot.] Outside covering (not true skin) of roots and stems of water-plants.

e'piboly, n. Growth of one part of EMBRYO round another so as to get it shut in. epi'bolic, a.

epi'branchial, a., n. To do with (the second part from the top of the BRANCHIAL ARCH.)

epi'calyx, n. [Bot.] A false CALYX outside the true one.

epi'canthus, n. [Anat.] A fold of skin over, so as to be almost covering, the inner angle of the eye, as seen in most Mongols.

epi'cardium, n. [Zoo.] The part of the PERICARDIUM round the heart.

'epicarp, n. [Bot.] Outside covering of a fruit.

epi'central, a. Starting from the CENTRUM of a VERTEBRA.

'epi-centre, -'centrum, nn. Point on the earth over the FOCUS of an EARTHQUAKE.

epi'chordal, a. [Zoo.] On or over the NOTOCHORD.

epi'condyle, n. [Zoo.] CONDYLE, sp. the outer one of the HUMERUS or FEMUR. epi'condylar, a.

epi'cotyl, n. [Bot.] The part of the middle stem of a very young plant, between the COTYLEDONS and the first leaf.

'epicoty'ledonary, a. [Bot.] Placed over the COTYLEDONS.

epi'cranium, n. [Zoo.] Back wall of head of insects. [Anat.] The structures covering the CRANIUM.

epi'critic, a. [Zoo.] Said of the nerve systems of the skin responsible for the special sense effects of delicate touch and small degrees of heat or cold.

epi'demic, n., a. [Med.] (Outburst of disease) taken by one person from another, and so attacking a great number of persons at the same time. 'epidemi'ology, n.

epi'dermis, n. [Zoo.] The outside skin of an animal. [Bot.] Thin skin covering leaves and young stems of plants. epi'dermoid, a.

epi'diascope, n. A form of PROJECTION LANTERN by which pictures of solid things as well as of TRANSPARENT plates are sent onto a white wall, etc.

epi'didymis, n. [Zoo.] Thin, much twisted pipe through which the SPERMATOZOA are sent out in certain animals. epi'didymal, a. 'epididy'mitis, n.

epi'dural, a. [Zoo.] On the DURA MATER.

epi'focal, a. [Geol.] Over the FOCUS of an EARTHQUAKE.

epi'gamic, a. [Zoo.] Having attraction for opposite sex.

epi′gamous, a. [Zoo.] Said of that stage in POLYCHAETA in which sex-parts are in process of development.

epi′gastrium, n. [Zoo.] Lower side of the two back divisions of the THORAX of an insect. epi′gastric, a.

epi′geal, a. [Bot.] EPIGEOUS. [Zoo.] Living on the face of the earth, as certain insects.

′epigene, a. [Geol.] Not natural to the substance in which it is present, said of CRYSTALS; formed on the earth and not deep inside it, said of ROCKS.

epi′genesis, n. [Biol.] Theory that the development of a living thing is not the unfolding of parts present in the GERM from the start, but a process of the birth and organization of parts by degrees.

e′pigenous, a. [Bot.] Having its growth on top face of a leaf or other part.

epi′geous, a. [Bot.] Having its growth on or over the earth; having COTYLEDONS outside the earth.

epi′glottis, n. [Anat.] Thin leaf of CARTILAGE at back of tongue, covering GLOTTIS while food is going down throat. epi-′glottal, a.

e′pignathous, a. [Zoo.] Having top half of mouth or BEAK longer than lower half.

e′pigynous, a. [Bot.] Coming from the top of a RECEPTACLE by which the OVARY is completely covered—said of the other parts of a flower; (of a flower) having an e. CALYX, COROLLA, and STAMENS. e′pigyny, n. (See picture p. 151).

epi′hyal, a.n. [Zoo.] (To do with) top part of back of HYOID ARCH, in some back-boned animals a separate bone.

′epi′lation, a. [Med.] Process of taking hair off part of body by destruction of roots, gen. by electric process. epi′latory, n., a. (Substance) effecting e.

′epilepsy, n. [Med.] Chronic brain disease in which person is given to falling suddenly and becoming unconscious, sometimes with CONVULSIONS. epi′leptic, a., n. epi′leptoid, a. Lke e

′epimer (epimerides), n. [Chem.] One or other of two substances different only in the positions of H and OH on the last C ATOM of chain. ′epimeri′sation, n. Process by which an e. is formed. e′pimerism, n.

′epimere, n. [Zoo.] In the EMBRYOS of back-boned animals, the DORSAL part of the MESOTHELIUM.

epi′meron, n. [Zoo.] Back plate of PLEURON in insect. epi′meral, a.

epi′morpha, n.pl. [Zoo.] LARVAE which have full number of divisions on coming out of egg.

epi′nasty, n. [Bot.] Condition of part of plant, as leaf, in which growth of top side is quicker than that of under side, causing curved form.

epi′nephros, n. [Zoo.] SUPRARENAL BODY.

epi′neural, a. [Zoo.] Being on a NEURAL ARCH.

epi′neurium, n. [Zoo.] The outside covering of a nerve, by which the nerve FIBRES are united and the nerve joined to the parts round it.

epi′otic, a., n. [Zoo.] (Said of, to do with) top outer bone of INNER EAR in back-boned animals.

epi′parasite, n. ECTOPARASITE.

′epipha′ryngeal, a. [Zoo.] On, at back of, PHARYNX.

epi′pharynx, n. [Zoo.] Forward out-growth on roof of mouth in certain insects; cover of roof of mouth stretching over lip and forming sharp point, as in DIPTERA.

′epiphe′nomenon (epiphenomena), n. Event which is present with another but is not necessarily caused by it and has no effect on it. [Med.] A seeming effect of a disease which is not present at all times and has no necessary connection with the disease. ′epiphe′nomenal, a. ′epiphe-′nomenalism, n. Theory that the mind and events in it are only ee. of physical processes in the brain. ′epiphe′nomenalist, n.

′epiphragm, n. [Zoo.] Cover made by a number of GASTROPODA for shutting opening of SHELL at resting times.

epi′physis, n. [Zoo.] End of long bone which is formed separately and not joined to rest till later in development. e. ′cerebrae. PINEAL GLAND. epi′phys-eal, -ial, aa. epi′phy′sitis, n.

′epiphyte, n. [Bot.] Plant fixed to another plant, such as a tree, but not dependent on it for food, getting the water needed by it from the air—seen sp. clothing the branches of the woods in warm places. [Med.] Plant PARASITE on body. epi′phytic, a.

epi′plankton, n. [Biol.] Very small water plants and animals living anywhere less than 200 metres down.

e′pipodite, n. [Zoo.] Outgrowth on lower part of front legs of some CRUSTACEA.

epi′pterygoid, n., a. [Zoo.] (Bone or CAR-TILAGE) over or on the PTERYGOID in some REPTILES.

epi′pubic, a. [Zoo.] To do with, supported by, the PUBIS; to do with the EPIPUBIS.

epi′pubis, n. [Zoo.] Bit of CARTILAGE or bone in front of PUBIS in some REPTILIA and AMPHIBIA.

epi′rhizous, a. [Bot.] Having growth on a root.

epi′sepalous, a. [Bot.] (Of STAMENS) on, joined to, SEPALS.

epi′spastic, 1.a. [Med.] Causing BLISTER(s). 2.a. An e. substance etc.

′epispo′rangium, n. INDUSIUM.

epi′static, a. [Genet.] Said of a quality DOMINANT to another of which it is not an ALLELOMORPH.

epis′taxis, n. [Med.] Loss of blood from the nose.

e′piste′mology, n. Theory of the way in which man's knowledge of things outside himself comes about, its bases and limits.

epi′sternum, n. INTERCLAVICLE.

e′pistome, n. [Zoo.] The part between the ANTENNA and mouth in CRUSTACEA; a small part overhanging mouth of POLYZOA and having in it part of the body hollow; the part of an insect head at back of LABRUM; part of ROSTRUM of certain DIPTERA.

e′pistrophe, n. [Bot.] Position of CHLOROPLASTS when in feeble light.

epi′thalamus, n. [Zoo.] Part of the top or back side of the THALAMENCEPHALON.

epi′theca, n. [Zoo.] Outer covering round lower part of SPORE-vessel in CORALS.

′epitheli′oma, n. [Med.] MALIGNANT growth formed of EPITHELIAL CELLS.

epi′thelium, n. [Zoo.] Sort of TISSUE with very little substance between CELLS, and based on a thin MEMBRANE which is present as a covering on the outside and inside of the body, the inside of blood-vessels and so on, and massed solidly in GLANDS. **epi′thel-ial, -(i)oid,** aa.

epi′trochlea, n. [Anat.] Inner CONDYLE at lower end of HUMERUS.

′epitym′panic, a. [Anat.] Over the ear-DRUM.

eip′zoön, n. [Zoo.] An animal living as a PARASITE or COMMENSAL on the body of another animal.

epizo′otic, a., n. (Said of) disease which is EPIDEMIC among animals.

′epoch, n. [Geol.] A division of a PERIOD, the stretch of time in which a SERIES of ROCKS was formed. (*See* p. 558.)

′epsomite, n. [Mineral.] $MgSO_4.7H_2O$, a white CRYSTALLINE substance, present naturally in the earth, sp. in MINERAL SPRINGS.

′Epsom salts. [Mineral., Med.] EPSOMITE, sp. as used medically as an APERIENT.

′equal-′tempered scale, ′equi-′tempered scale. [Acous.] TEMPERED SCALE.

e′quation, n. Statement giving an equal relation between two amounts (*see* CHEMICAL E.). **e. of state.** [Chem.] Relation given in the form of an e. between PRESSURE, VOLUME and TEMPERATURE for a substance. **e. of time.** [Astron.] Amount by which the RIGHT ASCENSION of the MEAN SUN is different from the right ascension of the true sun, and so the amount by which APPARENT time is different from MEAN TIME.

e′quator, n. Line, measure, round the middle or the widest part of a regular, curved, solid form, for example a ball or an egg. [Geog.] The GREAT CIRCLE round the earth half-way between the North and South POLES (the *terrestrial e.*). [Astron.] The CELESTIAL E. **equa′torial,** 1.a. 2.n. Equatorial telescope. **equatorial ′forest.** [Geog.] TROPICAL RAIN FOREST. **equa-**

torial ′furrow. [Biol.] Hollow line round e. of OVUM undergoing CLEAVAGE. **equatorial plate.** [Biol.] A group of CHROMOSOMES placed at the e. of the SPINDLE in MITOSIS.

equatorial ′telescope. [Astron.] TELESCOPE able to be turned in two directions at right angles, and having scales for reading these directions, used to keep a star in view for any time without adjustment.

equ(i)-. Equal(ly):—′-′**distant,** a.

′equi-′axed. Measuring about the same in all directions. **equi-axed ′crystals.** [Metal.] The POLYHEDRAL CRYSTALS formed in the middle part of a mass of metal put when liquid into a MOULD, as the last stage in the process of becoming solid.

′equi′axial, a. Having equal AXES.

equi′cellular, a. Made up of equal CELLS.

equi′librium (equilibria), n. A condition of balance, sp.:—[Mech.] E. between opposite forces, as seen in a body at rest or moving at an unchanging rate (*see* STABLE E., UNSTABLE E., and NEUTRAL E.). [Phys., Chem.] The condition in a REVERSIBLE REACTION or process when the two opposite processes are going on at the same rate so that there is no further change in the amounts of the two substances or PHASES.

′equimo′lecular, a. [Chem.] Having an equal number of MOLECULES; made up of substances in amounts representative of their MOLECULAR WEIGHTS.

′equimo′mental, a. [Mech.] Having equal MOMENTS OF INERTIA.

′equine, a. To do with, like, a horse.

′equinox, n. [Astron.] One or other of the two equinoctial points; one or other of the two times (about March 21, named the **vernal e.**, and September 23, named the **autumnal e.**) when the middle point of the sun goes across the EQUATOR through one of the ee., and day and night are equally long. **equi′noctial,** a. **equinoctial co′lure.** [Astron.] GREAT CIRCLE going through the ee. **equi′noctial points.** The two opposite points where the CELESTIAL EQUATOR is cut by the ECLIPTIC, that is, the FIRST POINT OF ARIES and the FIRST POINT OF LIBRA.

′equipar′tition of energy. [Phys.] The equal division of the KINETIC ENERGY of a MOLECULE, etc., sp. the molecule of a gas, among its DEGREES OF FREEDOM.

equi′potent, a. TOTIPOTENT.

′equipo′tential, a. [Phys.] Having the same POTENTIAL.

′Equi′setales, n.pl. [Bot.] An ORDER of PTERIDOPHYTA in which the leaves are small in comparison with the stem and the SPORANGIA are at the top of the stem.

′equitant, a. [Bot.] Said of plant or leaves when the base of every leaf is folded round and covering part of the leaf over it.

e′quivalence, n. The condition of being

equal. **e. principle.** [Phys.] The statement forming part of the general theory of RELATIVITY that GRAVITATION and ACCELERATION have the same effects from the point of view of a body acted on by them.

e′quivalent, n., a. (Thing) equal in value, size, effect, etc. (*to* another). **e. weight.** [Chem.] CHEMICAL E. **e. conduc′tivity.** [Phys.-Chem.] SPECIFIC CONDUCTIVITY ÷ the number of GRAM-EQUIVALENTS in 1 c.c.

Er, Sign for ERBIUM.

′era, n. [Geol.] Any of the three chief time-divisions in the history of the earth, as the PALAEOZOIC E.

′erbium, n. Chemical ELEMENT, at. no. 68, at. wt. 167·2, sign Er, one of the RARE EARTH METALS.

erect, 1.a. Upright. [Bot.] Not flat on the earth, said of stems. 2.v.t. Get lifted into an e. position.

e′rection, n. [Zoo.] Act of lifting a part, making it upright; (of a part) the condition of undergoing e.; (of a part or substance) the condition of being made hard by the forcing in of blood. **e′rectile,** a. Able to undergo e., said sp. of a special sort of sponge-like TISSUE in different parts of the body.

′erema′causis, n. [Chem.] Very slow OXIDATION or COMBUSTION as in the RUSTING of iron or the DECAY of wood.

e′rector, n. [Zoo.] Muscle by which an ORGAN or part may be lifted or made upright. [Optics] Group of LENSES in instrument making things seem upright.

′eremo′phyte, n. [Bot.] Plant living in great stretches of very dry land.

e′repsin, n. [Biochem.] Substance in small INTESTINE by which the digestion of PROTEINS is completed.

′erethism, n. [Med.] Unnormal IRRITABILITY of a body substance or part.

erg, n. C.G.S. unit of work or ENERGY equal to a force of 1 DYNE acting through 1 cm.

er′gastic, a. [Biol.] Any unliving substance present in CELLS, such as fat.

′ergmeter, er′gometer, nn. [Phys.] Instrument for measuring ENERGY.

′ergograph, n. Instrument measuring work done by a group of muscles.

er′gosterol, n. [Biochem.] A STEROL giving VITAMIN D under operation of sunlight.

′ergot, n. [Bot.] Disease of grain caused by a FUNGUS, or the dark growths produced by this disease; diseased seed with dried bodies of this fungus, which has certain medical properties. [Zoo.] Small outgrowth in the hair on back of horse's foot; small place without hair on horse's leg, taking the place of the part without hair in middle of hand or foot in other animals.

′ergotism, n. Diseased condition in man and animals got from taking grain having e. **ergo′toxine, ergo′metrine.** nn. [Chem.]

Alkaloids got from e. and used for producing ABORTION, helping in childbirth, and stopping loss of blood from blood vessels.

eri′ometer, n. [Optics] Instrument measuring size of very small things by DIFFRACTION.

eri′ophyllous, a. [Bot.] Having leaves with a covering like wool or cotton.

′Erlenmeyer flask. Glass vessel having round flat base and straight sides sloping up to narrow neck.

e′rose, a. [Bot.] Having edge unregular as if ERODED.

e′rosion, n. Slow destruction of substance by chemical or physical effects, as by rubbing, acid burning into SURFACE, etc., sp. [Geol.] the general process of the e. of the surface of the earth by weather, water and so on. **e′rode,** v.t. Make undergo e. **e′rodent,** a., n.

e′rotic, a. [Psych.] To do with, strongly moved by, sex desire. **e′roticism,** n. **eroto′genic,** a. Producing sex desire. **eroto′mania,** n. Diseased condition of mind marked by over-strong sex desire.

′eruc′tation, n. [Med.] A sudden burst of gas from the stomach through the mouth.

e′rumpent, a. [Bot.] Bursting out, as seeds from covering.

e′ruption, n. [Geol.] Outburst of VOLCANO or GEYSER. [Med.] Outburst of mass of small red places on skin, as in certain diseases. **e′rupt,** v.i. **e′ruptive,** a. Sp. [Geol.] produced by e.

ery′sipelas, n. [Med.] A disease attacking the LYMPHATICS of the skin, caused by a STREPTOCOCCUS and marked by FEVER and a very red and stretched condition of the diseased places, sp. on face, neck.

ery′thema, n. [Med.] Condition in which skin is very bright red, caused by expansion of small blood-vessels, an effect of disease or sun's rays, as in sunburn. **e. ′permio.** A red SWELLING on hands or feet causing pain, the effect of cold. **ery′themal, ery′thematous,** aa.

e′rythrin, n. [Chem.] Substance formed in certain LICHENS which, though itself without colour, has property of colouring things red.

e′rythrism, n., a. [Zoo.] (Condition of) having overmuch red colouring-material in feathers or hair. **ery′thrismal, ery-′thristic, ery′thritic,** aa. To do with erythrism.

e′rythro-, Red.

e′rythroblast, n. [Zoo.] CELL which undergoes development into ERYTHROCYTE, normally present chiefly in substance inside bones, not free in blood, but seen there in diseases.

e′rythrocyte, n. [Zoo.] Any of the red CELLS, having in them HAEMOGLOBIN, in the blood of back-boned animals, smooth, flat, round or egg-like cells without the property of independent motion, the chief transporters of O from the LUNGS to other parts of the body, formed in bone-MARROW. **e'rythrocy'tolysis,** n. [Med.] Process of destruction of ee. **e'rythrocy'tometer,** n. [Med.] Instrument for getting number of ee. in blood. **e'rythrocy'tosis,** n. [Med.] Condition in which number of ee. in blood is greater than normal.

e'rythro'dermia, n. [Med.] Red condition of skin.

e'rythro'genic, a. [Physiol.] Producing a sense of red. [Zoo.] Producing ERYTHRO-CYTES.

e'rythrome'lalgia, n. [Med.] Nerve disease in feet or hands marked by red colour of skin and burning pain.

e'rythrophore, n. [Zoo.] Red-blue colour-CELL present in certain fish.

e'rythrophyll, n. [Bot.] Red substance colouring leaves of trees in the fall.

Es, Sign sometimes used for EINSTEINIUM.

es'cape, n. [Bot.] Garden plant living in fields or woods in competition with plants of natural development.

es'capement, n. The connection between the train of wheels and the BALANCE WHEEL or PENDULUM of a clock, by which motion is given from one to the other.

escape velocity. VELOCITY OF ESCAPE.

es'carpment, n. [Geog., Geol.] A high, sharply sloping or almost upright face of ROCK on a mountain-side or in some other inland position.

'eschar, n. [Med.] Dry mass of burned skin separating from body.

Es'clangon ef'fect. [Optics] Change in direction of ray of light caused by motion of MIRROR.

e'septate, a. Having no SEPTUM.

'eserine, n. [Chem.] PHYSOSTIGMENE.

'esker, n. [Geol.] A long, twisting line of GRAVEL, or of separate gravel masses, put down at the front of a GLACIER which has gone back by the waters coming from it or which at one time were running under it.

e'sophagus, n. OESOPHAGUS.

eso'teric, a. [Biol.] Produced inside body.

'essence, n. The most important, necessary, qualities of a thing, that which makes it what it is. [Chem.] Substance got from another by taking away water and so on, and so having its special properties in stronger form, sp. one got from plant or fruit keeping its smell or taste. **es'sential, a. es'sential me'tabolite.** [Physiol.] Any substance which is necessary for the METABOLISM of any living thing, sp. a substance produced by one META-BOLIC process and necessary for another such process in the same being. **es'sential oil.** [Chem.] Any of a group of VOLATILE

oils present in plants, gen. in the flower, and giving them their special smell— one of the three chief groups of oils, made up chiefly of HYDROCARBANS (see OIL).

'ester, n. [Chem.] Substance formed by the reaction of an ALCOHOL with an ACID in which the H of the acid is exchanged for a HYDROCARBON group. **'esterifi'cation,** n. **'esterify,** v.t. and i. Get or be changed into an e.

es'tipulate, a. Having no STIPULES.

'estr-one, -in, n. OESTR-ONE, -IN.

'estuary, n. [Geog.] The mouth of a river into which the sea comes, mixing with its waters. **'estuarine,** a. [Geol., Biol.] To do with, living in, an e.

e.s.u. = ELECTROSTATIC UNIT(s).

'etalon, n. Form of INTERFEROMETER with fixed parallel plates.

etch, v.t. Make a design on (some substance such as metal, stone, glass) by using a chemical, for example an acid, with the power of biting into it. [Metal.] Make the highly polished face of (a mixed metal) undergo the operation of a chemical having an unequal effect on the different metals of which it is made up and so making clear its structure. **'etching 'figure.** Marks seen on the face of a metal which has been etched. **'etching,** n. Sp. a print made from an etched plate.

'ethane, n. [Chem.] A gas, CH_3CH_3, without colour or smell, not SOLUBLE in water, and burning with a light-coloured flame—present in small amounts in coal gas.

'ethanol, n. [Chem.] ETHYL ALCOHOL.

'ether, n. [Chem.] Any of a group of sub-stances in which two HYDROCARBON groups are joined by an ATOM of O, sp. $C_2H_5.O.C_2H_5$, a liquid without colour and with a special sweet smell used medically as an ANAESTHETIC. **'-ism,** n. [Med.] Condition caused by taking over-much e. **e'thereal, a. ethereal oil.** ESSEN-TIAL OIL.

'ether, n. [Phys.] Substance pictured in older physical theory as being present in all space and making possible the motion of light waves and electric and MAGNETIC forces from one place to another. **e. drift.** The motion of the e. in relation to the earth or other body.

'ethmoid, 1.a. [Zoo.] To do with the hollow of the nose, sp. with the bones forming its walls, etc. 2.n. An e. bone. **eth'moidal,** a. **'ethmoi'ditis,** n. INFLAMMATION of e. or e. bones. **e. notch.** 4-sided space separating the two eye-hollows. **ethmo-.** (Of) an e. and (. . .): **'-'palatine,** a.

ethmo'turbinal, n., a. [Anat.] (One of two bones or CARTILAGES) supporting side parts of nose.

ethmo'vomerine, a. [Anat.] To do with ETHMOID and VOMER, **e. 'cartilage.** Plate of CARTILAGE in early EMBRYO which later becomes ETHMOID.

'ethnic(al), aa. To do with science of the different sorts of man, their distribution, physical qualities, behaviour, and way of living.

'ethno'botany, n. The science of plants, their properties, development, distribution, uses etc., in relation to the history of man.

eth'nography, n. The part of ETHNOLOGY which gives accounts of different groups without attempting to go deeper.

eth'nology, n. ETHNICAL science generally. ethno-.

eth'ology, n. The science of animal behaviour. etho'logical, a.

'ethyl, a., n. [Chem.] (Having) the group C_2H_5. e. 'alcohol. C_2H_5OH, an uncoloured liquid with a wine-like smell and a burning taste—the alcohol present in strong drink, made by the FERMENTATION of SUGARS. e. mer'captan. See MERCAPTAN. 'ethyl'amine, n. Any of the three substances formed by putting C_2H_5 in place of one, two, or three H ATOMS in AMMONIA (NH_3), a liquid or gas which goes into SOLUTION in water. (See p. 556.) ethy'lation, n. The addition to a substance of an e. group.

'ethylene, n. [Chem.] C_2H_4, a gas of the OLEFINE group with a sweet smell, present in common gas. e. 'glycol. A thick liquid without colour, $(CH_2OH)_2$, used as an ANTI-FREEZE.

'etio'lation, n. [Bot.] Condition of a plant which is feeble and without normal green colour through not getting enough light. 'etiolate, v.t. and i. (Make) undergo e. 'etiolated, a.

eti'ology, n. AETIOLOGY.

eu-. Well, good.

Eu. Sign for EUROPIUM.

Euca'rida, n.pl. [Zoo.] A SUB-CLASS of CRUSTACEA having the eyes on moving stems and the THORAX covered by and united with a hard outer case.

eu'cephalous, a. [Zoo.] Having the head complete in development, said of certain insect LARVAE.

eu'chlorine, n. [Chem.] A gas formed of Cl and ClO_2 mixed.

eu'cyclic, a. [Bot.] (Of flowers) made up of WHORLS every one, or every other one, of which has the same number of parts.

eudi'ometer, n. Instrument for measuring amounts of different gases in a mixed gas by firing them in turn, in a vessel marked with a scale, by sending electric SPARK through.

eu'gamic, a. [Biol.] Said of, to do with, the time of full development, between the young stage and the old.

e'ugenic, a. To do with, or having power of, producing good offspring. eu'genics,

n.pl. Science of the ways of producing offspring of better quality, sp. in man.

Eu'glena, n. [Zoo.] A sort of very small, green, FRESH-WATER PROTOZOAN looking like a leaf, swimming with the help of one long, thin FLAGELLUM and in addition by a special twisting, worm-like motion of its body, effected by CONTRACTION and expansion of its outer cover. eu'glenoid, a. euglenoid movement or motion. The sort of twisting motion for which the E. is noted.

eugra'nitic, a. [Geol.] To do with, like, normal GRANITE. e. 'structure. (Of IGNEOUS ROCKS) in which the bits of different materials are of the same size.

eu'hedral, a. [Crystal.] Having well-formed CRYSTAL faces.

eupe'lagic de'posit. [Geol.] Substance put down in wide, deep stretches of water (3,000 to 4,500 m. deep).

eu'peptic, a. [Med.] Having a good digestion.

eu'phoria, n. [Med.] A feeling of well-being, not necessarily a sign of a healthy condition.

'euphoto'metric, a. (Of leaves) turned to get greatest possible amount of light from sun.

eu'ropium, n. Chemical ELEMENT, at. no. 63, at. wt. 152·0, sign Eu, one of the RARE EARTH METALS.

eury'bathic, a. [Biol.] Able to live in water at a great range of levels.

eury'hyaline, a. [Biol.] Needing salt water for existence but having power of adjustment to very different degrees of salt.

eury'therm-ous, -ic, aa. [Biol.] With power of living in a wide range of degrees of heat.

eus'tachian, a. [Zoo.] To do with Eustachian tube. E. tube. Pipe going from middle ear to throat. E. valve. Fold of skin separating openings of forward and back blood-vessels in heart of FOETUS, but not working after birth.

eus'tatic, a. [Geol.] To do with, said of, wide flat stretch of country.

'eustele, n. [Bot.] Condition in which VASCULAR substance in stem takes the form of a group of long threads with joining substance between.

eus'tomatous, a. [Zoo.] With a clearly formed mouth, said of CILIOPHORA.

eu'taxite, n. [Geol.] IGNEOUS ROCK of banded structure.

eu'tectic, a., n. (Of, to do with, being) a e. mixture. e. 'mixture. Two or more substances, sp. metals, mixed while liquid in such amounts as to become solid at the same TEMPERATURE, forming a mixed solid with a sharply-marked MELTING-POINT which is lower than that of any substance made by mixing them in different amounts.

eu'tectoid, a. [Metal.] With properties like a EUTECTIC, but produced from material in solid condition, sp. of steel having C in it.

eutha′nasia, n. [Med.] Putting to death medically without pain, sp. as way, supported by some persons, of putting an end to those in the grip of cruel diseases from which they will never get better.

eu′thenics, n.pl. Science of making man's living conditions better for purpose of getting better offspring.

Eu′theria, n.pl. [Zoo.] A SUB-CLASS of MAMMALIA made up of most living mammals (but not taking in MAR-SUPIALS) in which the young come to a high stage of development in the body of the mother, united to it by a complex PLACENTA through which food substances are given to the EMBRYO.

′eutomous, a. [Mineral.] Readily broken in certain directions.

′eutrophy, n. [Med.] Condition in which body makes full and healthy use of food. **eutrophic,** a.

′euxenite, n. [Mineral.] An uncommon, gen. non-CRYSTALLINE, dark brown MINERAL, having in it Y, Er, Ce, and most importantly, U.

E.V., ev, eV, = ELECTRON VOLT.

evacu′ation, n. [Phys.] Getting gas out of a vessel, producing a VACUUM. [Med.] The clearing out of any part of the body or the sending out of the substance inside it, sp. the e. of waste from the INTESTINE. **e′vacuate,** v.t.

eva′nescent, a. [Bot.] Not living long, as flowers.

evagi′nation, n. [Anat., Med.] Turning inside out. **e′vaginate,** v.t. and i.

evapo′ration, n. Process by which a liquid or solid goes off as vapour, with or without boiling. **e′vaporate,** v.t. and i. Make (a liquid or solid) undergo e.; undergo e. **e′vaporator,** n. Apparatus for getting liquid away from solid by e.

e′vection, n. [Astron.] Change in regular motion of moon caused by attraction of sun.

even, a. Flat, smooth, regular, level; (of a number) into which 2 will go with nothing over.

e′vert, v.t. [Bot., Med.] Get turned out, or inside out. **e′version,** n. **e′verted,** a. Sp. [Bot.] Turned sharply out.

′Evipan, n. [Med.] Trade name for HEXO-BARBITONE.

e′viscerate, v.t. [Med.] Take out the parts or the material inside a part of the body, sp. take out the VISCERA or the eye from its hollow. **evisce′ration,** n.

′evolute, a. [Bot.] Turned out, unfolded.

evo′lution, n. [Biol.] Development by degrees of more complex forms (of plants, animals, or parts) from more simple ones; process by which groups of living things, or living things generally, have come to

be what they are. **e′volutionism,** n. Belief in the process of e. as responsible for present forms of living things. **e′volve,** v.i.

e′xacer′bation, n. [Med.] The getting or making worse, more violent, of a disease.

ex′act, a. (Of measure, statement, etc.) right in every detail, complete and completely true, without error; (of instruments and so on) able to give e. knowledge. **′-ly,** adv.

exal′buminous, a. [Bot.] Having no ENDO-SPERM or PERISPERM.

exal′tation, n. [Phys.-Chem.] Unnormally high REFRACTIVITY of a COMPOUND caused by the MOLECULE being formed with a CONJUGATED DOUBLE BOND.

′exarch, a. [Bot.] Having the first-formed wood-substance nearest to the outside skin, so that the nearer the middle the younger it is, as in all roots, opp. ENDARCH.

exar′ticulate, 1.a. [Zoo.] Not having JOINTS. 2.v.t. [Med.] Put (bone) out of place at JOINT; get arm or leg cut off at joint. **′exarticulation,** n.

′exasperate, a. [Bot.] Having rough skin with hard, stiff points.

ex′centric, a. [Bot.] Produced on, or pointing to, one side; ECCENTRIC.

ex′change, n. [Phys.] The making equal of the TEMPERATURE among bodies near together by RADIATION from one to another and back; the acting on one another with equal effect of ELECTRONS, PROTONS etc. in the same or different ATOMS. **e. ′energy.** ENERGY in the NUCLEUS of an ATOM caused by e. between NUCLEONS. **e. forces.** Forces acting between NUCLEONS by which ENERGY is all the time being exchanged inside the NUCLEUS, keeping it together. **e. re′action.** Process by which one ELECTRON, PROTON, etc. is taken into a NUCLEUS and another sent out.

ex′cipient, n. [Med.] Substance without chemical effect on body, mixed with chemical substances to give them desired form for medical purposes.

exci′tation, n. [Phys.] The producing of a MAGNETIC FIELD in an electric machine or the force effecting this; the changing of an ATOM from its normal ENERGY LEVEL to a higher one by the moving of one or more of its PLANETARY ELECTRONS to ORBITS further from the NUCLEUS, as the effect of heating, RADIATION, electron BOMBARDMENT, etc. [Biol.] The causing of a reaction or the putting in motion or giving of an impulse to any process. **exci′tatory,** a. **excitatory cell.** Nerve CELL of AUTONOMIC NERVOUS SYSTEM to do with motion. **ex′citable,** a. Able to undergo e. **excitable ′tissue.** TISSUE which gives a reaction to a STIMULUS. **ex′cite,** v.t. Make undergo e. **ex′cited,** a. Having

undergone e., sp. [Phys.] of an ATOM.
ex'citing. a. Causing e. **ex'citement,** n.
Sp. [Biol., Psych.] a condition in which
there is a greater than normal reaction
of an ORGANISM to STIMULI. **ex'cito-.**
Exciting.

ex'clusion principle. [Phys.] The law that no
two ELECTRONS in the same ATOM may
have the same ORBIT.

ex'conjugant, n. [Biol.] One-CELLED animal
which has become separate again after
CONJUGATION with another.

excori'ation, n. [Med.] Loss of part of top
skin by cutting, rubbing, etc. **ex'coriate,**
v.t. Make undergo e.

ex'corti'cation, n. The taking away of the
outer covering of a tree. **ex'corticate,** v.t.

'excrement, n. The more or less solid waste
sent out from the ANUS of an animal,
sp. when viewed simply as material, not
from the point of view of medical science
or zoölogy.

ex'creta, n.pl. [Biol.] Waste substances
sent out by animal, plant, or any special
part. **ex'crete,** v.t. Send out e. **ex'cretion,**
n. **ex'cret-ive, -ory,** aa.

ex'current, a. [Bot.] (Of tree) having long,
unforked chief stem; (of middle VEIN of
leaf) going out past point. [Zoo.] Having
an outgoing current of liquid.

ex'cursion, n. [Mech.] Motion out from a
middle position and back.

excys'tation, n. [Zoo.] The process of coming
out from a bag-like covering, as seen in
certain PROTOZOA. **ex'cyst,** v.i.

'exendo'spermous, a. Having no ENDO-
SPERM.

ex'foli'ation, n. [Biol., Geol., Med.] The
coming off of skin, stone, etc. in flat thin
bits. **ex'foliate,** v.i.

exha'lation, n. The giving out of breath or
gas; breath or gas given out. **ex'halant,
exha'latory,** aa. **ex'hale,** v.t. and i.

ex'haust, 1.v.t. Take gas etc. out of, get
(gas, etc.) drained away, completely.
2.n. The current of steam or gas sent out
from an engine; the pipe through which
it goes. **e. 'manifold.** See MANIFOLD.

exhi'bitionism, n. [Med., Psych.] Disease of
mind in which person takes off clothing
in public.

exin'dusiate, a. [Bot.] Having SPORE-vessel
uncovered.

'exine, n. [Bot.] The outer cover of the wall
of a HOLLOW grain or SPORE.

exis'tential. Taken as having existence; to
do with existence.

'exit-'pupil, n. [Optics] Of a system of
LENSES, the IMAGE of the APERTURE STOP
formed by all the LENSES coming after it.

'exocarp, n. [Bot.] Outer coat of seed-
vessel cover.

exoc'cipital bone. [Zoo.] In back-boned
animals, one or other of two bones
opposite one another in the lower back

part of the head, gen. united at full
growth.

exo'chorion, n. [Zoo.] The outer of the two
coats of skin round egg in insects.

'exoderm, n. [Bot.] EXODERMIS. [Zoo.] In
sponges, outer part nearest to skin.

exo'dermis, n. [Bot.] The outer part of the
substance of roots, which undergoes
development into a skin.

ex'ogamy, n. [Biol.] Uniting of SEX-CELLS
produced by different plants or animals.
[Anthrop.] System by which person may
be married only to someone outside his
or her group.

e'xogenous, a. [Biol., Biochem., Geol.,
Psych.] Coming from outside or as
reaction to outside causes; undergoing
growth by addition to outside; having
growth on outside of something. [Anat.]
Having growth from bone parts.

exo'morphic, a. [Geol.] Caused from outside,
said of changes produced in ROCKS by
liquid rock being forced into them.

exo'pathic, a. [Med.] Having an outside
cause.

'exope'ridium, n. [Bot.] The outer PERIDIUM.

e'xophagy, n. [Anthrop.] The using as food
of persons outside the group or family.

exoph'thalmia, n. [Med.] The pushing
forward of the eyeballs. **exophthalmic,** a.
exoph'thalmic 'goitre. Disease of THYROID
GLAND, one of the signs of which is e.

'exoplasm, n. ECTOPLASM.

ex'opodite, n. [Zoo.] Outer branch of leg of
CRUSTACEA.

'Exoptery'gota, n.pl. [Zoo.] A SUB-CLASS of
INSECTA in which the young form, gen. a
NYMPH, becomes changed into the end-
form by degrees without any sudden and
marked change, the wings starting from
folds on the outside of the body. **exop-
'terygote,** n. Insect of the E. **'exoptery-
'gotic, a.**

exo'skeleton, n. [Zoo.] Hard supporting
structure outside body as in ARTHRO-
PODA, opp. ENDOSKELETON.

'exos'mos-is, -e, nn. [Phys.-Chem.] OSMOSIS
out from a vessel or in the direction of
the less strong SOLUTION.

'exospore, n. [Bot.] EXOSPORIUM; CONIDIUM.

'exo'sporium, n. [Bot.] Outer coat of seed-
vessel wall.

ex'ostosis, n. [Med.] An outgrowth of bone
from a bone.

exo'thermic, a. [Chem.] Taking place with
the producing of heat.

ex'otrop-ism, -y, nn. [Biol.] The condition
or process of curving away from the
middle line. **exo'tropic,** a.

ex'pand, v.t. and i. [Make] undergo expansion. **expansive,** a.

ex'panding 'universe 'theory. [Astron.]
The theory, based on the observation
that light from GALAXIES outside ours is
moved in the direction of the red end of

the SPECTRUM, that these galaxies are moving away from us, so that the UNIVERSE is all the time undergoing expansion.

ex'pansion, n. [Phys.] Increase in size of body in one or more directions caused generally by PRESSURE becoming less or heat becoming greater.

ex'pectorant, n. [Med.] Medical substance helping person with cough to expectorate. **ex'pectorate,** v.t. and i. Send out (MUCOUS) from the throat by coughing etc.

ex'periment, n., v.i. Operation or system of operations done for the purpose of observation of the behaviour of something in certain conditions, so as to get new knowledge or make test of theory, and designed in such a way as to give an answer to some question. **experi'mental,** a. **ex'perimen'tation,** n.

'expiration, n. [Zoo., Med.] The act of sending breath out, breathing out. **ex'pire,** v.t. and i. **ex'piratory,** a.

explan'tation, n. [Zoo.] The process of taking TISSUE away from a living animal and keeping it in a tissue CULTURE.

ex'plore, v.t. [Med.] Go into wound, or some part of body, with fingers or instruments, looking and feeling and recording, for purpose of getting a complete knowledge of its condition. **ex'ploring,** a. **exploring coil.** [Phys.] COIL used for measuring how strong a MAGNETIC FIELD is by the current produced in the coil. **explo'ration,** n. **ex'ploratory,** a.

ex'plosion, n. [Chem., etc.] Sudden and violent burst caused by development of gas in shut-in space, **e. engine.** [Mach.] Engine working by e. of air mixed with gas or oil. **ex'plosive,** n., a. (Substance) suddenly changed by heating or force into gas and so used for causing ee. **ex'plode,** v.t. and i. (Make) undergo e.

ex'ponent, n. [Math.] The number, etc. put at the right top side of another giving the POWER to which it is to be taken, as 2 in x^2, **expo'nential,** a. **expo'nentially,** adv.

ex'posure, n. Act. of putting anything in the way of, uncovering it *to*, the operation of something, or condition of being open to the operation of something, as camera plate to light, etc. **e. 'meter.** Instrument measuring time of e. needed for taking camera picture in the light present. **ex'pose,** v.t. Put in the way of, let be acted on by something. **ex'posed,** a. Sp. said of a camera plate, etc. which has been used.

ex'pression, n. [Phys.] Process of forcing liquid out of solid mass by crushing. **ex'press,** v.t.

'exsangui'nation, n. [Med.] The taking of blood from the body.

ex'serted, a. [Biol.] Stretching out, coming farther than the edge of the part round, as STAMENS over the cup of a flower.

ex'sertile, a. [Biol.] Able to be pushed out.

ex'stipulate, a. [Biol.] Having no STIPULES.

'exstrophy, n. [Med.] The turning inside out of a hollow ORGAN, sp. the BLADDER.

exsuf'flation, n. [Med.] Forced blowing out of breath.

ex'tend, 1.v.t. Get stretched or unfolded; give greater range to. [Zoo.] Put (leg, arm, or other such part) out straight, in an unbent position. 2.v.i. Take up space in a given direction (as 'e. *from* one given point *to* another').

ex'tensile, -ible, aa. Able to be stretched or pushed out.

exten'simeter, exten'someter, nn. Instrument used in testing metals for measuring small changes in form caused by force, heat, etc.

ex'tension, n. The act of EXTENDING; increase in size or range. [Phys.] The property of taking up space.

ex'tensor, n. [Zoo.] Muscle used for stretching or EXTENDING arm, leg, or other part of body.

ex'terior, 1.a. EXTERNAL. 2.n. The outside of anything.

ex'ternal, a. To do with, coming from, things or conditions outside a thing; on the outer side of a thing. [Zoo.] Nearer the outside of the body, or further from middle line or plane of a part. **e. di'gestion.** [Zoo.] The process seen in some lower animals of sending a liquid out of the body onto the food, causing part digestion of it before it is taken in. **e. fertili'zation.** [Zoo.] The uniting of male and female GERM CELLS outside the bodies of the animals producing them, as in most water animals. **e. respi'ration.** *See* RESPIRATION. **e. se'cretion.** [Zoo.] A SECRETION sent out of the body or into some hollow part having a connection with the outside. **e. work.** [Mech.] The work done by a machine or engine against outside force. **'-ly,** adv.

'extero'ceptor, n. [Zoo.] Sense apparatus or nerve-ending acted on by effects coming from outside the body, as in touch, smell, hearing, etc. **'extero'ceptive,** a. To do with ee. or the sort of effects to which they give reactions.

ex'tinct, a. (Of sorts of animals and plants) no longer in existence, having no representatives at the present time; (of VOLCANOES) no longer having any tendency to ERUPT.

ex'tinction, n. [Phys.] The cutting off of a ray of POLARIZED LIGHT by an ANALYZER or other apparatus. **e. 'coefficient.** [Optics] Of a substance, a number giving the loss by ABSORPTION and SCATTERING of light going through it.

'extine, n. EXINE.

'extr(a)-. Outside of: 'extra-axi'llary, a. [Bot.] 'extra-'nuclear, a. [Biol.] 'extra-'ocular, a. [Zoo.]

extra'branchial, a. [Zoo.] Outside the BRANCHIAL ARCHES.

extra'cellular di'gestion. [Bot.] Digestion of material by ENZYMES sent out by CELL and acting outside it.

'extracolu'mella, n. [Zoo.] The outer division of the part of the ear forming the connection between the inner ear and the TYMPANUM in birds and some other back-boned animals.

ex'tract, v.t. Get (something) out of something, sp. [Chem.] get a substance out of a mixed substance by the use of a SOLVENT acting only on the substance desired. ex'traction, n.

'extract, n. [Chem.] A substance EXTRACTED from another.

'extra-embry'onic, a. [Zoo.] In eggs of birds, etc., placed in, to do with, the part outside the true EMBRYO.

extra'floral, a. [Bot.] Placed outside the flower.

'extraga'lactic, a. [Astron.] Outside the GALAXY.

'extrame'ridian, n. [Astron.] An observation of body in sky when it is near the MERIDIAN.

extra'ordinary ray. [Optics] That one of the two rays into which light is broken up by BIREFRINGENCE which does not undergo normal REFRACTION.

extra'planetary, a. [Astron.] Outside the space in which the motion of the PLANETS takes place.

'extra'polation, n. The working out of possible values of a number outside the range of values of it given by observation. 'extrapolate, v.t.

extra'sensory, a. [Psych.] To do with sense-experiences not produced by normal STIMULATION of the sense-apparatus, as in TELEPATHY, or with the sensing of things by NERVE-ENDINGS other than those forming part of the special sense-ORGANS, as in the theory that some parts of the skin of the back, etc. have a RUDIMENTARY power of seeing.

extra'stelar, a. [Bot.] Outside the STELE.

extra'vaginal, a. [Bot.] Forcing a way through a covering, as most grasses. [Anat.] Outside the VAGINA.

ex'travasate, v.i. and t. [Med.] (Of blood, LYMPH, etc.) get out of normal vessels and into the TISSUES round them; let or make blood etc. e. [Geol.] Come bursting out in liquid form from hole in earth as lava, boiling springs, etc. extrava'sation, n.

'extraven'tricular, a. [Zoo.] Placed outside VENTRICLE of heart or brain.

extra'version, n. extravert, n. EXTROVERSION, EXTROVERT.

ex'tremity, n. [Zoo.] Leg or arm or like structure, or the end part of such a structure.

ex'trinsic, a. Not in or forming part of a thing, coming from outside it, opp. INTRINSIC. e. 'muscle. [Zoo.] A muscle working a part such as an arm, leg, etc., but going only to the point where the part is joined to the body, not down the part itself.

ex'trorse, a. [Biol.] Turned out away from a middle line.

extro'version, n. [Med.] Condition of being turned inside out. [Psych.] Condition of being an EXTROVERT.

'extrovert, n. [Psych.] Person whose interest is chiefly taken up by things and events outside himself.

ex'trude, v.t. and i. (Make) be forced, pushed, out through something. ex'trusive, a. Extruding, sp. [Geol.] (of ROCKS) having been forced up out of the earth in liquid condition and become hard outside it. ex'trusion, n. Sp. [Metal.] the process of forming rods, pipes, etc. by forcing metal or rubber through holes or pipes, at one time possible only with heated metals, but now used with cold metals, sp. steel (cold e.).

exu'dation, n. Process by which liquid gets or is sent out of a body through very small holes, or cracks. e'xude, v.t. and i. ex'udat-ive, -ory, aa. 'exudate, n. Substance exuded, sp. [Med.] from blood-vessels into parts round as effect of disease or damage.

exum'brella, a. [Zoo.] Arched top side of a MEDUSA. exum'brellar, ex'umbrel, aa.

ewe, n. Female of sheep and like animals.

eye, n. [Zoo.] Sense ORGAN which gives a reaction to light, the RECEPTOR by which seeing is effected. [Biol.] Any mark or part giving the suggestion of an e., sp. the middle part of a flower. e. 'speculum. [Med.] Instrument for keeping the eyelids open in an e. operation. '-ball, n. [Zoo.] The ball-like seeing part of the e. in back-boned animals. '-brow, n. [Zoo.] An arch over an e., or the line of hair on this arch, as in man. 'e.-cup. [Zoo.] OPTIC CUP. [Med.] A small glass or cup of e.-like form used for washing the ee. 'e.-ground. That part of the inner hollow of the eyeball which may be seen through the PUPIL with an OPHTHALMOSCOPE. '-lash, n. Any of the hairs on the edge of the eyelid. '-lid, n. [Zoo.] Moving structure of skin by which the eyeball may be covered, of which most back-boned animals have two, an upper and a lower. '-piece, n. [Optics] In an OPTICAL INSTRUMENT, the LENS or lens-system through which the user sees the IMAGE formed by the OBJECTIVE. **'-spot,** n. A small place giving reaction to light in some lower animals and plants; mark on head of EMBRYO where development of e. takes place. **'-tooth,** n. CANINE TOOTH.

F, Sign for FLUORINE.

F. = FAHRENHEIT.

F₁, F₂, etc., Sign for 1st, 2nd, etc. FILIAL GENERATION.

fa'bella, n. [Zoo.] Small bit of CARTILAGE, frequently changing to bone in animals, and sometimes in man, in the muscle in the angle of the knee.

'fabric, n. [Geol.] Look, design, produced by CRYSTAL grains in stone.

'face-centred, a. [Crystal.] Having the ATOMS so placed that they may be pictured as being at every angle, and in the middle of every face, of a structure of CUBES.

'facet, n. A small flat SURFACE, as at end of a bone, sp. one of a number of such ff., as in a CRYSTAL, the complex eye of an insect, etc.

'facial angle. [Craniom.] The angle made at the meeting-point between the AXIS of the face and the axis of the head.

-facient, n. Making, causing.

'facies, n. [Biol.] The general form or look of anything, as a group of like animals or plants; a division of a BIOTOPE. [Geol.] The properties of a group of ROCKS—the sort of MINERALS, marks, structure, TEXTURE, colour, FOSSILS, which it has—taken all together.

fa'cilitation, n. [Physiol.] The readier transport of a reaction through a nerve chain because of an earlier reaction, sp. to a different STIMULUS, having taken the same line; degree of this effect.

facio-. Face.

'factor, n. Anything having a part in producing some effect. [Biol.] GENE. [Biochem.] VITAMIN. [Med.] Any food or chemical in food which is necessary or important for a healthy condition. [Arith.] (Of a given number) any number which goes into it with nothing over. [Phys., etc.] A fixed number or RATIO measuring some physical property of a substance or system for a unit amount, etc., in given conditions, and used as a MULTIPLIER in working out measures dependent on this (see COEFFICIENT). **f. of 'safety.** [Mech., Engin.] The greatest load which may be put on a structure or CONDUCTOR without getting it broken ÷ the load which is looked on as safe to put on it when in use.

'facula (faculae). n. [Astron.] Bright mark on face of sun.

'facul'tative, a. Not necessary, which may or may not take place. [Biol.] Having power of existence as thing named but not necessarily limited to this way of living, as a *f. aerobe,* a *f. parasite.*

fade, v.t. and i. Make or become, less clear, as motion picture, or, more feeble, as radio-wave.

'f(a)eces, n.pl. [Zoo., Med.] Solid waste from ALIMENTARY CANAL of animals. **'f(a)ecal, 'f(a)eculent,** aa.

fago'pyrism, n. Disease of animals caused by the effect of the sun's rays after taking certain sorts of grain.

'fahlerz, n. [Mineral.] A grey ORE of copper.

'Fahrenheit scale. Scale for measuring TEMPERATURE, on which the boiling-point of water is at 212° and the ice-point at 32°.

'failure, n. A stopping, falling short of what is designed. **fail,** v.i. (Of an attempt or a person making one) not do what is designed, come short. [Med.] (Of senses, powers etc., or of a person) DETERIORATE.

'fairing, n. [Engin.] Part, specially of airplane, designed to give a smooth outline to part meeting air-current, etc.

'Fajans and 'Soddy laws. [Phys.] The laws that, in the DISINTEGRATION of a RADIOACTIVE substance, (a) the sending out of an ALPHA PARTICLE makes the ATOMIC NUMBER of the substance less by 2, and (b) the sending out of a BETA PARTICLE makes its atomic number greater by 1.

'falciform, 'falcate, aa. [Biol.] Flat and curved into form somewhat like a question-mark. **'falciform 'ligament.** Fold of PERITONEUM joining DIAPHRAGM and LIVER in higher animals.

'falcula, n. [Zoo.] Curved and sharp-pointed CLAW. **'-r,** To do with a F. or FALX. **'-te,** a. Curved and sharp at point.

'falling 'sickness. [Med.] EPILEPSY in its worst form.

Fall'opian tube. [Zoo.] One or other of the two pipes by which the eggs go from the OVARY to the UTERUS in female MAMMALS.

'fall-out, n. The RADIOACTIVE substances falling from the sky after the EXPLOSION of an ATOMIC or H BOMB.

false 'amnion. *See* CHORION.

false di'ssepiment. [Bot.] SPURIOUS DISSEPIMENT.

false fruit, PSEUDOCARP.

false ribs. [Zoo.] In higher back-boned animals, the lower or end RIBS which are not joined to the STERNUM.

false vocal cords. [Zoo.] *See* VOCAL CORDS.

falx, n. [Anat.] Any FALCIFORM structure, sp. a fold of the DURA MATER of the brain.

'family, n. [Biol.] Division of ORDER of animals or plants, made up of GENERA.

fan, n. Anything opening out from a point roughly in the form of a △, for example the tail-feathers of a bird. [Geol.] F.-formed coat of material put down by a river, sp. where it comes out of a narrow opening between mountains, etc.

fang, n. [Zoo.] A long, pointed tooth, sp. poison tooth of snake; the root of a tooth, or one of its long, pointed divisions.

'**fantasy,** n. [Psych.] The process of forming mind-pictures unlike things or events in our experience, or which are representative of something greatly desired but not true to facts and with no chance of becoming so; a mind-picture of this sort.

'**farad,** n. [Elec.] Unit of ELECTROSTATIC CAPACITANCE, that capacitance needing 1 COULOMB of ELECTRICITY to make its POTENTIAL greater by 1 volt, $=9 \times 10^{11}$ ELECTROSTATIC UNITS.

fa'radic, a. [Elec.] Of, to do with, INDUCED electric currents. **f. current.** Electric current got from an INDUCTION COIL, used for medical purposes. **faradi'zation,** n. '**faradize,** v.t. [Med.] Give impulse to nerve or muscle by use of f. current. '**faradism,** n. [Med.] The medical use of f. currents.

'**faraday,** n. [Chem., Elec.] Unit of electric current, that amount which in ELECTROLYSIS makes free in 1 sec. 1 GRAM-ATOM having a VALENCY of 1, $= 96,500$ COULOMBS.

'**Faraday 'cylinder** or **col'lector.** Vessel taking an ELECTRIC CHARGE completely away from a charged body put into it. **Faraday dark space.** The dark space in a GAS DISCHARGE TUBE between the NEGATIVE GLOW and the POSITIVE COLUMN. **Faraday disk.** Round flat plate of metal turning on a metal rod in a MAGNETIC FIELD, as the effect of sending current from middle to edge. **Faraday effect.** The turning of the PLANE OF POLARIZATION of light by a body in a MAGNETIC FIELD. **Faraday's laws of 'elec-'trolysis:** 1. The amount of a substance freed in ELECTROLYSIS is PROPORTIONAL to the amount of current used. 2. The amounts of different substances freed by the same amount of current are in the RATIO of their CHEMICAL EQUIVALENTS.

fa'rina, n. Powdered grain, meal, or like substance; STARCH, sp. from potatoes. **fari'naceous,** a.

'**farinose,** a. [Biol.] Covered with white grains or powder, or with white very short hairs giving a powder-like effect.

'**fascia** (fasciae), n. [Anat.] (Band of) specially strong TISSUE covering, supporting, joining or uniting inner parts of body, sp. any of the bands keeping parts of muscles together. '**fascial,** a. **f. 'lata.** Deep f. in top part of leg. **fascio-.**

'**fasciated,** a. [Bot.] FASCICULATE; having FASCIATION. [Zoo.] With bands of colour.

fasci'ation, n. [Bot.] Diseased condition of

plants in which stems are wide and flat, caused by growth together of a number of them side by side.

'**fascicle,** n. Small parcel or group of threads, rods, stems, leaves, etc. very near together. **fa'scicular, fa'sciculate,** aa. **fa'sci-culus,** n. F., sp. of nerve threads, as in SPINAL CORD.

fa'sciola, a. [Zoo.] Narrow band of colour.

'**fasciole,** n. [Zoo.] In certain ECHINOIDEA, band of small hairs for sending water round parts of body.

fast, a. (Of colour) not changed by acid, light, air, or washing.

fast 'neutron. [Phys.] A NEUTRON having ENERGY of 1 MEV or more.

fat, n. [Chem.] Natural substance which may be broken up into GLYCEROL and LONG-CHAIN CARBOXYLIC ACIDS, and which (as opp. oil) is solid at normal TEMPERATURES, for example, butter. [Physiol.] ADIPOSE TISSUE. **f. 'body.** [Zoo.] Mass of fat in an animal, forming store of food. '**-ty,** a. **fatty acid.** Acid made up of a long chain of C ATOMS joined to one CARBOXYLIC group. **fatty de'generation.** [Med.] DEGENERATION of CELL substance, in which drops of f. may be seen, caused by poisons, not having enough O, etc. **fatty oil.** [Chem.] FIXED OIL.

'**fathom,** n. Unit of distance used sp. in measuring how deep the sea or other body of water is, 1·829 m. or 6 feet.

fa'tigue, n. [Med., Zoo.] Condition of being over-tired, sp. of nerves, muscles, CELLS, etc. which, as effect of over-much STIMULATION have for a time no further power of reaction. [Phys.] Loss or slowing up of elastic power of a substance caused by over-use or by over-much force being put on it.

'**fauces,** n.pl. [Zoo.] The opening from the mouth to the PHARYNX; the mouth of a SPIRAL SHELL. [Bot.] The throat of a COROLLA of which the PETALS are united. '**faucial,** a.

fault, n. [Geol.] Crack in the ROCK structure of the earth, the beds on the opposite sides of which have been moved out of line with one another as the effect of a lift or a slip. **f. plane.** The plane on which the motion of the beds has taken place. (*See* NORMAL F., REVERSED F., DIP F., and STRIKE F.) '**faulting,** n. The producing of ff.

'**fauna,** n. [Zoo.] Animals generally, sp. the different sorts living in a certain stretch of country or at a certain time in the earth's development. '**faunal,** a.

fa'veolate, 'faviform, 'favose, aa. [Biol.] Made up of small CELLS like those in bees wax. **fa'veolus,** n. Small hollow or CELL.

'**favus,** n. [Med.] Skin disease, sp. on top of head, caused by a FUNGUS. **fa'vose,** a.

Fe, Sign for iron.

feather, n. [Zoo.] Any of the outgrowths forming the body-cover of birds. **feather-veined,** a. [Bot.] (Of leaf) with nerves branching from middle nerve to edge at an angle of less than 90°.

'febrile, a. [Med.] To do with FEVER. **'febricant, febri'facient,** nn. aa. (Substance) producing FEVER. **feb'riferous,** a. **feb-'rific,** a. **'febrifuge,** n. Substance acting against FEVER. **febri'fugal,** a. **febri-.**

'fecal, 'feces. See FAECAL, FAECES.

'Fechner's law. [Psych.] Law that a sense experience, as of light or sound, gets stronger to the degree that the LOGARITHM of the STIMULUS gets greater.

'fecund, a. Fertile. **'fecundate,** v.t. FER-TILIZE, sp. [Biol.] **fecun'dation,** n. **fe'cundity,** n.

feeble-'minded, a. [Psych.] MENTALLY DEFICIENT, sp. MORONIC. **feeble'-mindedness,** n.

feed, 1.n. (Apparatus producing) motion of material into machine or of cutting instrument into material; (amount of) material sent into apparatus. 2.v.t. Send f. into. **f. back.** Radio valve apparatus in which PLATE CURRENT of valve is used to make stronger the incoming current in the GRID. **f. pump.** [Engin.] Pump sending water into boiler, **f. 'water.** Water sent into boiler. **'feeder,** n. Sp. part, such as pipe or wire, by which water, steam, gas, electric current, etc., are taken into engine or other apparatus.

'feeler, n. [Zoo.] Thread-like part of animal, such as those on head of insects, used as ORGAN of touch.

'feeling tone. [Psych.] A sense of pleasure or the opposite experienced together with, or forming part of, a sense-experience.

'Fehling's so'lution. [Chem.] SOLUTION used in testing for sugars, made by mixing equal parts of a solution of 34·639 grams $CuSO_4$ in 500 cc. water and a solution of 173 grams KNa $C_4H_4O_6$ + 30 grams $NaOH$ in 500 cc. water.

'fel(d)spar, n. [Geol.] Any of a group of MINERALS made up of Al_2O_3 and SiO_2, united with Na_2O or K_2O or CaO or BaO.

felon, n. [Med.] PARONYCHIA.

'felsite, n. [Geol.] A sort of FINE-GRAINED IGNEOUS ROCK (see p. 192).

'female screw. [Mach.] INTERNAL SCREW THREAD.

'femur, n. [Zoo.] The long bone in the higher part of leg in man; the like bone in back leg of other animals; (in insects) COXA. **'femoral,** a. To do with f. or higher part of leg; to do with two plates of horn on front of CHELONIA.

fe'nestra (fenestrae), n. [Zoo.] An opening in a bone, or between two or more bones; any of the clear, window-like spaces on

wings of certain insects, **f. o'valis.** The higher of the two openings in the wall between the MIDDLE and the INNER EAR. **f. ro'tunda.** The lower of the two openings in the wall between the middle and the inner ear. **'fenestrate(d),** aa. [Zoo.] (Of insect wings) having ff. [Bot.] Having a great number of small holes or openings; having network marking.

'feral, a. [Biol.] In natural condition, not under man's care.

'fergusonite, n. [Mineral.] An uncommon dark brown MINERAL having in it a small amount of URANIUM.

'Fermat('s) 'principle or law. [Optics] Law that a light-wave going from one point to another regularly takes the quickest way.

fermen'tation, n. [Biochem.] Process by which a complex substance, such as sugar, is broken down into simpler substance, such as alcohol, by a CATALYST produced by a living thing (YEAST, etc.). **fer'ment-ative, -able, -ive,** aa. **fer'ment,** v.t. and i. (Make) undergo f. **'ferment,** n. CATALYST, or its producer, causing f.

'fermium, n. Chemical ELEMENT, at no. 100 at. wt. 153, sign Fm, a RADIOACTIVE metal.

fern, n. [Bot.] Any plant of the FILICALES.

-ferous. Having in or on it, producing, giving out.

ferri-. (Of) iron, sp. FERRIC, (and . . .): **'-'cyanide,** n., **ferr-iferous,** a.

'ferric, a. [Chem.] (Of complex substances) having in it iron with a VALENCY of 3.

'ferro-, (Of) iron, sp. FERROUS, (and . . .): **'-'cyanide,** n.

ferro'concrete, n. REINFORCED CONCRETE.

ferromag'netic, a. [Phys.] (Of substances) having a MAGNETIC PERMEABILITY much greater than 1 and so very readily MAG-NETIZED, as iron is.

'ferroso'ferric 'oxide. [Chem.] Fe_3O_4, a black, MAGNETIC substance, present naturally in the earth as MAGNETITE.

'ferrotype, n. [Photog.] A positive picture made on a thin iron plate using COL-LODION as a coating; the process of making ff., little used today.

'ferrous, a. (Of substances) having in it iron with a VALENCY of 2; of, to do with iron. **ferri-, ferro-.**

fer'ruginous, a. Having iron in it; red or red-brown in colour, as Fe_2O_3.

fertile, a. [Biol.] (Of female GERM-CELL, seed or egg) having power of development into fruit or offspring as effect of having undergone fertilization; (of plants or animals) having power of producing offspring, seeds, or SPORES. **'fertilize,** v.t. (Of male GERM-CELL) put female germ-cell into a f. condition by uniting with it; make fertilization come about, sp. [Bot.] by taking POLLEN from ANTHER to STIGMA; make earth f.; put fertilizer on the earth for this purpose. **fertili′zation,** n. Sp. the uniting of a male GERM-CELL with a female germ-cell. **′fertilizer,** n. Any natural or chemically-produced substance put on the earth to make it f. [Bot.] Anything effecting POLLINATION, as an insect.

fer′tility, n. (Of land) the condition of being fertile, of producing much plant growth. [Biol.] The property or power of producing offspring.

′fetal, ′fetus. See FOETAL, FOETUS.

′fetlock, n. [Zoo.] Soft cushion-like part on back side of leg of horse and like animals at lowest JOINT; outgrowth of hair on f.; part of the leg where f. is.

′fever, n. [Med.] Diseased condition in which degree of body heat is higher than normal and rate of heart increased; name given to certain diseases in which this condition is marked. **′-ish,** a. With, having, giving signs of, f.

′fibre, n. A thread or thread-like body. [Bot.] Long, narrow thick-walled CELL, pointed at ends and frequently with no substance inside. [Zoo.] Any of the long CELLS forming muscle; AXIS CYLINDER; see NERVE-FIBRE. **′fibril,** n. [Biol.] Very thin, delicate f. such as those making up a MUSCLE F. **fi′brillae,** n.pl. Thread-like branches of roots; thread-like parts of some very small animals. **′fibrillate(d),** a. [Biol.] Having, made up of, threads or ff. **fibril′lation,** n. [Med.] Disease of heart in which the motions of different groups of muscle ff. are not in rhythm with one another. **′fibrillose,** a. [Bot.] Having fibrils. **′fibro′cartilage,** n. CARTILAGE, or cartilage substance, chiefly made up of ff. **′fibroid,** 1.a. 2.n. [Med.] Fibroid tumour. **′fibroid ′tumour.** [Med.] Fibrous growth in the UTERUS which is not MALIGNANT. **fi′broma,** n. Fibroid tumour. **fi′brosis,** n. Disease marked by development of fibrous TISSUE in some part of body. **fibro′sitis,** n. INFLAMMATION of ′fibrous TISSUE. **′fibrous,** a. ′fibro-.

′fibrin, n. [Biochem.] PROTEIN formed in COAGULATING blood and seen in the form of network of FIBRES.

fi′brinogen, n. [Biochem.] PROTEIN in blood by which FIBRIN is produced and blood caused to COAGULATE.

′fibroblast, ′fibrocyte, nn. [Zoo.] A sort of flat CELL of irregular, branching form, present in CONNECTIVE TISSUE, whose business seems to be the producing of the COLLAGEN from which the WHITE FIBRES are formed. **′fibro′blastic,** a.

fibro′vascular ′bundle. [Bot.] A VASCULAR BUNDLE with a band of SCLERENCHYMA, generally on the outside.

′fibula (fibulae), n. [Zoo.] The outer of the two long bones going from the knee to the foot in the leg of man or the back leg of other animals.

fibu′lare, n. [Zoo.] One of the outer bones at back of foot, in line with the FIBULA—in higher animals the CALCANEUM.

′fictile, a. (To do with, formed of, substance) which may be given form when soft and then made hard, said sp. of pots or potter's material.

-fid, a. [Biol.] Having the number or sorts of LOBES or like divisions named.

fi′ducial, a. [Phys.] (Of line or point) taken as fixed starting-point in relation to which other things are judged, etc.

field, n. Range of observation or operation, sp. [Optics] the space which may be seen through an instrument such as a TELESCOPE or MICROSCOPE, the part of the view framed by its opening.

field coil. [Elec.] The wire on an ELECTRO-MAGNET.

field ′magnet. [Elec.] The ELECTROMAGNET producing the FIELD OF FORCE in an electric MOTOR, DYNAMO, etc.

field of force. [Phys.] The space through which a force of some sort (GRAVITATIONAL, electric, MAGNETIC) has its effect.

field stop. [Optics] Plate with a hole in it, limiting amount of light let into an instrument.

field ′winding. [Elec.] The COIL round a FIELD MAGNET through which current is sent or in which it is produced.

′figure, n. Picture in book or paper, helping to make clear the account given in writing; sign for a number, as ′2′.

′figure of ′merit. Number giving relation between reading of instrument and force acting (generally electric current).

′filament, n. [Biol.] Thread-like thing or part, sp. thin stem of STAMEN, a line of CELLS end to end, or the stem of one of the small, soft, under feathers of a bird. [Astron.] Long narrow flame coming out of sun. [Elec.] The heated wire in an electric bulb or VALVE. **f. lamp.** [Elec.] A lighting-apparatus made up of a shut glass vessel, gen. bulb-like in form, having inside it, in a VACUUM or an INERT GAS. a delicate f. of high electric RESISTANCE, which is heated to the point of giving out light by sending an electric current through it. **fila′mentous,** a. Thread-like.

′filar, a. To do with, in the form of, marked by, using, thin threads or lines, sp. of a MICROSCOPE etc. having threads stretched across field of view.

fi′laria (filariae), n. [Zoo.] Any of a group of thread-like NEMATODE worms PARASITIC in the blood etc. of higher animals and responsible for a number of diseased conditions. **fil′arial,** a. [Med.] Caused by ff. **fila′riasis,** n. Filarial disease, sp. ELEPHANTIASIS.

fi′lator, n. [Zoo.] Part of silk-worm controlling the size and form of its thread.

file, 1.n. A blade or rod of very hard steel, sometimes pointed, sometimes with parallel sides, of which the face is cut into small teeth or thin RIDGES, used as a hand instrument for rubbing down, smoothing, or cutting through metal, etc. 2.v.t. Make use of a f. on. **'filing,** n. Sp. bit rubbed off a metal etc. with a f., gen. pl. in the sense of a powder-like mass, as *iron ff.*

'filial gener'ation. [Biol.] A GENERATION of offspring produced by CROSS-BREEDING, those coming from the first two plants or animals CROSSED forming the *first f.g.*, and those produced from the first 'f.g. forming the *second f.g.*, and so on.

Fili'cales, n.pl. |[Bot.] ORDER of PTERIDO-PHYTA in which the leaves are great in comparison with the stem and the SPORANGIA are on the under side of the leaves.

fili'cauline, a. [Bot.] Having a thread-like stem.

fi'liciform, a. [Bot.] Formed like FILICALES.

'filiform, a. [Biol.] Thread-like. **f. pa'pillae.** PAPILLAE on tongue with thread-like ends.

'filler, n. Substance, such as wood powder, mixed with a material for increasing its weight or making it stronger, harder, or more readily worked.

'fillet, n. [Anat.] A band, sp. any of certain bands of white substance in brain.

film, n. [Biol., Chem., etc.] A very thin skin or stretch of substance, sp. on outside of something and having properties different from those of the rest of the substance. [Photog.] Thin material made of some form of CELLULOSE coated with a substance giving a reaction to light, such as silver salts, on which camera-pictures are taken.

'filoplume, n. [Zoo.] Delicate hair-like feather having almost no side branches.

filo'podia, n. [Zoo.] Thread-like PSEUDO-PODIA.

'filose, a. [Zoo.] Thread-like.

'filter, 1.n. Instrument or substance keeping back some part of something which is sent through it, such as solid material in liquid or gas, or certain waves or currents in a complex. 2.v.t. Put through a f., make free from certain parts in this way; take out (certain parts) by use of f. **f. press.** [Chem.] Apparatus having a number of iron plates with cloth between, kept together by screws, through which a liquid to be filtered is forced by a pump. **'filt(e)rable,** a. **filt(e)rable bac'terium** or **'virus.** [Med., etc.] A filter-passer. **'filter-'passer,** n. [Med., etc.] A BACTER-IUM or VIRUS so small that it is unable to be seen through a common MICROSCOPE and goes through any f. used for keeping back other bacteria. **'f.-'passing 'virus** or

bac'terium, F.-passer. **fil'trate,** n. Filtered liquid. **fil'tration,** n.

'fimbria, n. [Zoo.] An edging of short, delicate threads or hairs, sp. round the opening of the OVIDUCT in higher animals. **'fimbriate(d),** aa.

fin, n. [Zoo.] Thin, flat wing-like part fixed to body of fish and other water animals and used for swimming and balancing. [Mech.] F.-like part of machine, sp. a fixed upright part on an airplane helping to keep its motion smooth. **'f.-ray.** Any of the rods of horn-like substance support-ing ff. of fish.

'finalism, fi'nality, nn. (Belief in) TELE-OLOGY.

fine, a. (Of grains, threads, etc.) very small, thin, delicate, (of a substance) made up of f. grains, threads, etc. or (of a net, skin, etc.) having very small holes, PORES and so on, opp. COARSE. **f.-'grained,** a. [Geol.] (Of ROCK) made up of grains so small as not to be seen without the help of an instrument. **'-ly,** adv. **'fineness,** n. The condition of being, or the degree to which anything is, f. [Metal.] The degree to which gold or silver ALLOYS, as used in the jewel trade, etc., are made up of gold or silver.

fine 'structure. [Phys.] The property of an ATOMIC SPECTRUM of having in it certain seeming lines which on further ANALYSIS are seen to be groups of two, three, or more lines very near together. [Cryst.] The structure of ATOMS in a CRYSTAL as made clear by X-RAYS.

'Finsen lamp, Finsen light. [Med.] Electric light strong in ULTRA-VIOLET rays for use in skin diseases.

'fiord, n. [Geol.] Long, narrow, twisting inlet of the sea between mountain slopes.

'fire-ball. [Astron.] Great METEOR, like ball of f.; very uncommon form of LIGHTNING seen as very bright balls moving across sky.

'fire-blende. Mineral, $3Ag_2S.Sb_2S_3$.

'fire-clay, n. [Geol., Metal., etc.] CLAY with much Al_2O_3 and SiO_2 in it, becoming soft only at very high TEMPERATURES and so used as a REFRACTORY.

'fire-damp. CH_4 air mixed, in coal-mine.

'fire-proof, a. Not readily taking fire.

firn, n. [Geol.] The hard snow, like massed ice-grains, which is ever present on tops of high mountains. **f. 'region.** The space in which the growth of a GLACIER takes place.

First Point of 'Aries. [Astron.] The point of ARIES farthest west, being that one of the EQUINOCTIAL POINTS where the sun goes across the CELESTIAL EQUATOR from south to north, and the starting-point from which RIGHT ASCENSION and CELESTIAL LONGITUDE are measured.

First Point of 'Libra. [Astron.] The point of

LIBRA farthest west, being that EQUI-NOCTIAL POINT where the sun goes across the CELESTIAL EQUATOR from north to south.

first 'quarter (of the moon). [Astron.] *See* MOON.

'Fischer-'Tropsch 'process. A process for making HYDROCARBON oils from coal, LIGNITE or NATURAL GAS, first used in Germany as the effect of the need for producing oil from German materials.

'fish-glue, n. ISINGLASS.

'fissile, a. Readily cracked open or separated on certain lines, as wood. [Phys.] Able to undergo FISSION.

'fissi'lingual, a. [Zoo.] Having a forked tongue.

'fission, n. Act of getting or becoming broken, or undergoing division, into parts; [Phys.] sp. f. of the NUCLEUS of an ATOM into two parts, of more or less equal mass, as the effect of BOMBARD-MENT by NEUTRONS, much ENERGY and more NEUTRONS being given off in the process so that it may give birth to a CHAIN REACTION if conditions are right [Biol.] REPRODUCTION by a process of division into two or more parts. **f.' cap-ture.** [Phys.] The taking in by the parts of a NUCLEUS of URANIUM 235 etc., of NEU-TRONS which have been fired at it causing **f. f. 'product.** [Phys.] One or other of the two NUCLEI formed by f. **'fissionable,** a.

fiss'iparous, a. [Biol.] Increasing, producing new units, by FISSION.

'fiss'ipedal, a. [Zoo.] Having toes separate from one another, not joined by skin.

fissi'rostral, a. [Zoo.] Having a BEAK with a very deep division between the upper and the lower parts, so that it may be opened very wide.

'fissure, n. [Geol., Anat.] Long, narrow, deep cut, opening, or division. **F. of 'Sylvius.** [Anat.] F. separating TEMPORAL LOBE from FRONTAL and PARIETAL LOBES of the brain.

'fistula, n. [Med.] Unnormal and diseased opening or pipe formed between one hollow in the body and another, or between part of body and the outside. **'fistul-ous, '-ular,** aa.

fit, n. [Med.] Sudden, violent attack of a disease having an effect on the brain, such as EPILEPSY, freq. causing person to become unconscious.

Fitz'gerald-'Lorentz con'traction. [Phys.] Change in measure which quickly moving bodies are taken to undergo in the direc-tion of their motion, every unit of their measure in this direction becoming

$$\sqrt{1 - \frac{u^2}{c^2}},$$ where u is rate of motion of the body and c that of light.

fix, 1. v.t. Make fixed in a certain condition, unchanging, sp.:—[Chem.] Get away

from a used camera plate etc. those silver SALTS which have not been acted on by light, so that it will undergo no further change; make (a liquid) non-VOLATILE by uniting it with some other substance; get (a gas) united with some other substance. [Biol.] Make (certain qualities, etc. of a sort of plants or animals) fixed, regularly produced, by special BREEDING. 2.n. The position of a ship, airplane etc., on a map given by lines cutting one another at a point—got in any way but so named sp. when the position is fixed by radio. **fix'ation,** n. Sp. [Psych.] condi-tion caused by the fixing of love or desire on something at early stage of development, stopping the natural development of these feelings and their normal direction when older. [Biol.] The use of chemicals on a dead plant or animal to keep it looking as it was when it was living. [Zoo.] The operation of certain muscles so as to keep the body in balance. **fixation 'muscles.** Muscles keeping body in balance. **fixation of 'nitrogen.** [Chem.] Process of uniting N from the air with other sub-stances so that it may be of use. [Bot.] Forming of substances with N in them by BACTERIA in the earth from the N of the air. **fixed,** a. **fixed air.** [Chem.] Early name for CO_2. **fixed oil.** [Chem.] Any of the oils present in animals and plants (gen. in their seeds) which are not VOLA-TILE—one of the three chief divisions into which oils are grouped. **fixed star.** [Astron.] Any star whose position in relation to other such stars seems to our observation to be unchanging.

fjord, n. FIORD.

fla'gellispore, n. FLAGELLULA.

fla'gellum (flagella), n. [Biol.] Long, thread-like part coming from CELL, sp. [Zoo.] sort of very long CILIUM with whipping motion. **Flagell'ata,** n.pl. [Zoo.] MASTI-GOPHORA. **'flagellate,** 1.a. Having f(f). 2.n. Animal of the MASTIGOPHORA. **fla'gelliform,** a. **flage'llula** (flagellulae), n. [Zoo.] ZOOSPORE with ff.

'flag-stone, n. [Geol.] A sort of SANDSTONE which readily undergoes division at its BEDDING PLANES.

flame-cell, n. [Zoo.] SOLENOCYTE.

'flammable, a. Able to take fire, readily taking fire.

flange, n. [Mach.] Collar-like part coming out round edge of something such as a pipe or wheel, for joining it to some other thing, keeping it in position on rail, etc.

flap, n. Narrow band on edge of airplane wing, which may be moved so as to have effect on motion of plane.

flapped, a. [Phonet.] (Of sounds) made with one quick blow of the point of the tongue against the roof of the mouth; TRILLED.

flash, 1.n. Sudden short burst of light. 2.v.t. Give out a f. **f. 'boiler.** [Eng.] A boiler in the form of a long COILED steel pipe kept heated to a high degree into which water is let in small amounts which are straight away turned into steam. **f. 'spectrum.** [Astron.] The sun's SPECTRUM as seen for the very short time at the start and end of a TOTAL ECLIPSE, when the light from the middle body of the sun is completely cut off, at which point the dark FRAUNHOFER LINES are suddenly changed into bright lines. **'f.-over.** [Elec.] The undesired forming of an ARC between two parts of an electric apparatus, or between one part and the earth. **'f.-point.** [Chem.] the lowest TEMPERATURE at which a liquid, sp. an oil, gives off enough of its gas to make a short f. when touched by a small flame, but not enough to take fire.

flask, n. Vessel with narrow neck, for use in chemical operations.

'flat-'foot, n. [Med.] A condition of the foot in which the long arch is so flat that all the underside of the foot is touching the earth. **flat-'footed, a.**

'flatulence, n. [Med.] Condition of having over-much gas or air in the stomach or INTESTINES. **'flatulent, a.**

'flatus, n. [Med.] Gas or air formed in stomach or INTESTINES.

'flatworm, n. [Zoo.] Worm of ORDER PLATY-HELMINTHES.

fla'vescent, a. [Bot.] Having yellow or yellow-green places on green of leaves, etc.

'F-'layer, n. [Radio] APPLETON LAYER.

fleam, n. [Med., Vet.] Sharp-pointed, two-edged, narrow instrument, sp. used for opening blood-vessels of animals.

'flection, n. See FLEXION.

flesh, n. [Zoo.] The soft substance of the body, formed chiefly of muscle, between skin and bones. [Bot.] The soft substance of a fruit or root.

flex, 1.v.t. and i. Make, become bent, sp. arm or leg at JOINT. 2.n. [Elec.] Flexible cord. **'-ible,** a. Readily bent, folded, twisted, etc. **'flexible cord.** [Elec.] Cord for transporting electric current made up of a great number of very thin wires inside an INSULATING cover so as to be completely flexible. **'-ion,** n. Act of flexing; condition of being flexed. **'-or,** n. Muscle by which part of the body, such as arm or leg, is bent.

'flexure, n. Condition of being or becoming bent or curved. [Astron.] Error in instrument produced by its being bent by its weight. **'flexural, a. flexural 'moment** or **torque.** [Mech.] BENDING MOMENT.

'flexuous, a. [Bot.] (Of a stem) turning first one way and then the other, gen. at the NODES.

'flexuose, a. Wave-like.

flint, n. [Geol.] A common very hard stone formed chiefly of SiO₂, of a grey or almost black colour, generally in form of irregular stones with very sharp edges. **f. glass.** Very bright clear glass made from best quality SiO₂, at one time got by crushing ff., and generally having lead in it.

flip coil. [Elec.] COIL which may be turned suddenly through 180°, used for measuring MAGNETIC FIELD.

'flipper, n. [Zoo.] In certain sea animals, arm or leg of broad, flat form, with no toes, used for swimming.

float, 1.v.t. and i. Make f.; be supported by, moving on top of, water or other liquid, or in a gas. 2.n. Floating body used for marking the position of something, or the level of the liquid, or keeping a body of greater weight up in liquid, and so on. **'floating 'cartilage** ('kidney, etc.) [Med.] CARTILAGE (KIDNEY, or other part of body) normally fixed in place, which has come more or less loose. **'floating ribs.** [Zoo.] RIBS not joined at end to STERNUM. **'floating-card 'compass.** See MARINER'S COMPASS.

'floccose, a. [Bot.] Having covering or growth of soft wool-like hairs which are readily rubbed off.

'flocculate, v.t. [Chem.] Come together in small, frequently cloud-like, masses, said of a powder or COLLOID in a liquid. **floccu'lation,** n.

'flocculent, a. Having, producing FLOCCI, in form of flocci, sp. [Chem.]. **'flocculence,** n.

'flocculus (flocculi), n. [Zoo.] Group of wool-like hairs. [Anat.] One or other of two small parts of lower side of CEREBELLUM. [Astron.] Cloud-like mass of Ca, H or other substances in gas round sun. **'floccular, a.** Sp. [Anat.].

'floccus (flocci), n. Soft wool- or cloud-like mass, sp. [Chem.] one formed in liquid by FLOCCULATION.[Zoo.] First soft covering of feathers in young birds; group of hairs like bit of wool at end of tail of animals. [Bot.] Little wool-like mass of hairs.

flock, n. Soft waste substance produced in the process of making wool cloth.

flood, n. [Geol., Geog.] The overrunning of what is normally dry land by water, as the effect of long or very violent rain, snow coming down from the mountains into rivers, the sea becoming unnormally high, and so on. **f. tide.** The TIDE when it is coming in, between LOW TIDE and HIGH TIDE. **f.-light (pro'jector).** A lighting apparatus with a REFLECTOR of special form designed to send a very wide BEAM of light from a distance onto a SURFACE of great size, such as the face of a building, and giving an equal distribution of strong light all over it. **f.-plain.** [Geol., Geog.] Stretch of

FLOWER STRUCTURE

(Vertical Section)

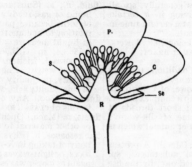

PERIGYNOUS

P   **PETAL**
S   **STAMEN**
Se   **SEPAL**
C   **CARPEL**
R   **RECEPTACLE**

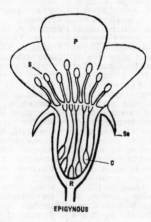

EPIGYNOUS

flat land edging a river which is flooded whenever the river becomes over-full, and so by degrees becomes higher as the effect of material put down by the f. water.

'**flora,** n. [Bot.] Flowers generally, sp. all the different sorts living in a certain stretch of country or at a certain time in the earth's development.

'**floral,** a. To do with, being like, flowers. '**f. leaf.** A SEPAL, PETAL or BRACT.

flo'rentium, n. ILLINIUM.

flo'rescence, n. [Bot.] Condition, time, of being in flower, flowering.

'**floret,** n. [Bot.] Small flower of a group, sp. any of those making up a complex flower.

floss, n. [Biol.] Mass of short threads of natural silk on outside of silk-worm's COCOON; part of plant or animal which is like f.

flo'tation, n. FLOATING. [Metal.] A process of separating mixed substances, sp. MINERALS from crushed ORE, by the use of a liquid in which one of them FLOATS, or may be made to float by some process, and the rest do not.

flow, 1. n. Motion in some direction like that of a river, the motion of any current. [Phys.] The sort of motion seen in a liquid or gas, in which the parts are moving freely and so the form is not fixed; liquid-like change of form in solid under great force. [Geol.] A mass of solid substance which has flowed into its present position while liquid, as lava. [Med.] MENSTRUA-TION. **2.** v.i. Go with such motion; (of solid) undergo such change. **f. lines.** [Metal.] Lines seen on the face of a metal, sp. iron or steel, when it is stretched etc. to the point at which it is no longer elastic, and marking the planes on which it has given way. **f. 'structure.** [Phys.] The structure of a solid after flowing '-**ing.** a., n. '-**meter,** n. Instrument for measuring the rate of f. of a liquid gas.

'**flower,** n. [Bot.] The sort of REPRODUCTIVE structure special to ANGIOSPERMS, made up of a short supporting part (the *receptacle*) at the end of a stem, with, in its most complete form, four groups of parts ranged on it, that is, one or more CARPELS in the middle, ringed by STAMENS, which are ringed by PETALS, which in turn are ringed by SEPALS; the reproductive structure in other seed-plants, which is without petals and sepals. '-**less,** a. (*See* picture p. 151.)

fluctu'ation, n. Wave-like motion or change this way and that between limits. [Med.] Wave-like motion of a liquid in a body hollow, which may be noted by touching part. [Phys.] Change of a completely chance sort, without regular rhythm, but between certain limits. [Biol.] A small change from the normal,

sp. as caused in plant by living conditions. '**fluctuate,** v.i. Undergo f.

flue, n. Pipe taking current of air, gas, smoke, etc., sp. from or to a fire, or round or through water in steam boiler.

'**fluid,** n., a. (Substance) in condition of liquid or gas, readily undergoing change of form because parts are not fixed in relation to one another. **f. drachm.** Unit of liquid measure = 3·697 cc. in U.S.A., 3·55 cc. in G.B., used for medical purposes. **f. 'friction.** VISCOSITY. **f. ounce.** Unit of weight of liquids = 8 f. drachms. **flu'idity,** n. Quality of being f.; measure of this quality = 1 ÷ VISCOSITY.

fluke, n. [Zoo.] Any of a number of flat worms of CLASS TREMATODA.

flume, n. [Mach.] Open drain taking water or other material to or from machine.

fluo'rescence, n. [Phys.] The property of a body of taking in X-RAYS, ULTRA-VIOLET RAYS, or light-waves and giving them out again as longer waves, that is, of changing them into seen light or light of a different colour from that taken in; this process; rays given out by a fluorescent body. **fluo'resce,** v.i. Have the property of f., or be in the process of f. **fluor'escent,** a. **fluorescent screen.** A plate of glass or other substance coated with a fluorescent SALT which gives off light when acted on by CATHODE RAYS, X-RAYS, etc., sp. this part of a CATHODE-RAY TUBE.

'**fluoride,** n. [Chem.] Substance formed by uniting one ELEMENT with F. '**fluorid-'ation,** n. Sp. the addition of ff. to the drinking-water of towns etc. for the pur-pose of stopping tooth DECAY in young persons.

'**fluorine,** n. Chemical ELEMENT, at. no. 9, at. wt. 19, sign F, a green-yellow gas.

'**fluorite,** n. [Mineral] FLUORSPAR.

'**fluoro'carbon,** n. [Chem.] Any of the im-portant group of substances formed of F and C, having some properties like those of the HYDROCARBONS, not readily broken up by chemical processes or heat.

'**fluorogen,** n. [Phys., Chem.] Substance causing or increasing FLUORESCENCE of another when mixed with it.

'**fluorophore,** n. [Phys., Chem.] Group of ATOMS giving a MOLECULE the power of FLUORESCENCE.

'**fluoroscope,** n. [Phys., Med.] Instrument for observation or use of FLUORESCENCE, sp. plate of glass etc. with coat of FLUORESCENT substance, used medically for observation of processes inside body.

'**fluorspar,** n. [Mineral.] CaF$_2$ (*calcium fluoride*) of which certain sorts are very FLUORESCENT in ULTRA-VIOLET light.

'**fluvial, 'fluviatile,** aa. [Geol.] Of, to do with, present in or about, produced by, rivers. [Biol.] Living in rivers.

'**fluvio-.** River. '**fluvioma'rine,** a. [Geol.]

Formed by a river and the sea, as beds of material put down at river-mouth. [Zoo.] With power of living sometimes in river sometimes in sea. **'fluvio'glacial,** a. Formed by water from ice or GLACIER. **'fluvioter'restrial,** a. [Biol.] Living in rivers and on land near them.

flux, n. [Phys.] Rate of FLOW of liquid or gas or rate of transport of light or other ENERGY through an AREA. [Chem.] Any substance put with a solid, sp. a metal, to make it more readily become liquid when heated; substance put on parts of metal being SOLDERED together to get them clean and free from OXIDE. [Med.] An unnormal FLOW of liquid from some part of the body; the liquid sent out. **f. 'density.** [Phys.] The amount of any f. going through unit AREA, sp.:—[Elec.] MAGNETIC FLUX DENSITY; the amount of ELECTRICITY going through 1 cm^2 of a DIELECTRIC at right angles to the direction of motion. (*See* in addition LUMINOUS FLUX DENSITY.)

flux'meter, n. [Phys.] Instrument for measuring MAGNETIC FIELD.

fly (flies), n. Apparatus formed of two or more thin plates going round on rod turned by machine for purpose of slowing down its motion. **'flywheel,** n. Wheel of great weight put on the SHAFT of an engine or machine to make its motion more regular.

'flying boat. [Aero.] A SEAPLANE of which the FUSELAGE is designed to give support on the water.

foam, n. A thick mass, generally white, of BUBBLES, such as is formed on the top of a liquid by violent motion, as on the sea, or by FERMENTATION, as on beer, or in and round the mouth of an animal after violent running etc., or in a FIT.

'focal, a. To do with a FOCUS. **f. 'distance, f. length.** [Optics] Distance of FOCUS of a LENS or MIRROR from its middle point or its second PRINCIPAL POINT. **f. plane.** [Optics] A plane parallel to a LENS or MIRROR and going through its FOCUS. **f. plane 'shutter.** (Of camera) flat cloth moving in f. plane, with hole letting light through to plate. **f. spot.** The small circle from which X-rays go out in an X-ray bulb.

fo'cimeter, fo'cometer, nn. An instrument for measuring FOCAL LENGTH.

'focus (foci), n. Meeting-point of lines, rays, etc. [Optics] (Of a LENS, MIRROR, etc.) sp. the point on the AXIS at which rays parallel to it are made to come together after REFRACTION or REFLECTION by it (the *real f.*), or from which they are made to seem to come (*virtual f.*), named the *principal f.*; point at which thing has to be placed to get a clear view or picture of it through LENS; adjustment of lens of

eye or instrument to get clear view of thing. [Med.] Point in body which is seat of disease sp. INFECTION (**septic f.**). [Math.] *See* ELLIPSE. 2.v.t. and i. Make (rays) come to a f.; (of rays) come to f.; make adjustment of (eye or instrument) so as to get clear picture of something; **'focalize,** v.t. Focus. [Med.] Get (disease) limited to certain part of the body. **'focused,** a. (Of eye or instrument) in the right adjustment to the distance etc. of what is being looked at; (of camera picture) taken with camera rightly focused. **'focusing,** n., a. **focusing screen.** Glass plate in a camera on which a thing may be seen and got into f. before a picture of it is taken.

'f(o)etid, a. Having a bad smell.

'f(o)etus, n. [Zoo.] The young of an animal in the later stages of development inside mother or egg, from the time when the development of ORGANS is starting to the time of birth. **'foetal,** a. **foe'tation,** n. PREGNANCY.

fog, 1.n. [Meteor.] Thick cloud of water drops, smoke or dust, or all these mixed, over the face of the earth, sp. one making it impossible to see as much as or more than 1000 m., as opp. MIST. 2.v.t. Make a mist-like effect on the face of a body, sp. of light acting on a camera-plate.

foil, n. Leaf or paper-thin stretch of metal.

fold, n. [Geol.] A bent condition of STRATA caused by motions of the outer earth. **'-ed,** a. (Of STRATA) bent. **'-ing,** n. The process of causing ff. or becoming folded.

foli'aceous, a. [Bot.] Of, like, a leaf; having leaves.

'foliage, n. A mass of f. leaves; the f. leaves of a plant taken together. **f. leaf.** The part of a plant, gen. green, normally named a LEAF (which *see*), as opp. other leaf-like parts having special names such as BRACTS, COTYLEDONS.

'foliate, 1.a. [Bot.] Having leaves. 2.v.t. Make or become like a leaf. **'foliated,** a. Made up of thin, flat, plates, sp. [Geol., Metal., etc.]. **foli'ation,** n. Sp. [Geol.] a structure of MINERALS in thin, flat, parallel plates, like the leaves of a book, the outcome of great PRESSURE. [Bot.] VERNATION. **'-foliate,** a. [Bot.] Having the named number or sort of leaves.

fo'licolous, a. [Zoo.] Living on leaves.

'folio'branchiate, a. [Zoo.] Having leaf-like GILLS.

'foliole, b. [Biol.] Small leaf or flat, leaf-like part. **'foliolate, folio'liferous,** aa.

'foliolose, a. [Bot.] Made up of very small flat outgrowths.

'foliose, a. [Bot.] Said of a THALLUS which is flat and leaf-like.

'folium (folia), n. Any small, thin, flat plate,

sp. [Geol.] A thin leaf of stone. [Zoo.] Any of such parts in the CEREBELLUM.

'follicle, n. [Bot.] Dry, one-celled fruit. [Zoo.] GRAAFIAN F.; any small and simple GLAND or narrow-mouthed hollow, such as that out of which the growth of a hair takes place; LYMPH NODE. foll'icu-'litis, n. [Med.] foll'icul-ar, -ose, aa.

foll'iculin, n. [Biochem.] OESTRONE.

fonta'nel(le), n. [Zoo.] Space where bones of head of very young animal do not come together.

fon'ticulus, n. [Med.] Wound kept open for medical reasons. [Anat.] Hollow at base of neck in front.

food 'vacuole. [Zoo.] Hollow in PROTOZOA in which digestion of food takes place.

foot, n. [Zoo.] In higher animals, insects, etc. the end part of a walking-leg, the part coming in touch with the earth etc.; in other animals any f.-like or leg-like part used for walking or swimming; in MOLLUSCS a mass of muscle in the middle of the underside of the body by which the animal gets about or gets itself fixed to a support.'-stalk, n. [Biol.] PETIOLE or PEDICEL.

foot, n. Unit of distance = 30·48 cm. f.-'candle. [Optics] A unit of ILLUMINA-TION = that produced on a SURFACE which is at all points at a distance of 1 f. from a light of 1 CANDLEPOWER. 'f.-'lambert. [Optics] A unit of LUMINANCE = that of a completely DIFFUSING SURFACE measuring 1 f.² giving out or REFLECTING 1 LUMEN. 'f.-'pound, n. English unit of work = 1·356 × 107 ERGS. f.-'poundal, n. Unit of work = 431·402 ERGS. f.-'pound-second, a. (Of measuring systems) based on the f., pound, and second. f.-'second, n. Unit of VELOCITY = one f. in one second. 'f.-'ton, n. Unit of work = 2240 f.-pounds.

'foot-and-mouth dis'ease. Common VIRUS disease of cows and like animals, marked by an outburst of VESICLES on MUCOUS MEMBRANE, sp. in the mouth and between the divisions of the HOOF.

fo'ramen (foramens or foramina), n. [Zoo.] Small opening, sp. in bone or other hard structure. [Bot.] Small opening in coat of OVULE through which POLLEN gets to it. f. 'magnum. Hole in bone structure of back of head through which SPINAL CORD goes. fo'ramin-ate, -iferous, -ose, -ous, aa. fo'raminule, n. fora'minul-ate, -ose, -ous, aa.

Fo'rami'nifera, n.pl. [Zoo.] A group of PROTOZOA, chiefly sea animals of very small size, having hard outer cover, generally formed of CaCO₃, with a great number of holes for sending out PSEUDO-PODIA. foramin'iferal, a.

for'bidden, a. [Phys.] Taking place, pro-duced, very unfrequently or never, said of certain ATOMIC effects.

force, a. [Mech.] The cause of the starting or stopping of motion in bodies or of any change in their motion; any acting example of f., measured in DYNES or POUNDALS. f. 'polygon, Straight-sided form of which the sides, taken in order, are representative of the value and direc-tion of a system of forces in balance. f. pump. [Mach.] Pump having a PISTON-head without a VALVE, and other valves so placed that the liquid is not lifted to its outlet by the piston, but forced out into another pipe at the side, where it is sent up and out by increasing PRESSURE.

forced vi'bration or 'oscillation. [Phys.] VIBRATION of any sort produced in a body by an outside force acting again and again.

'forceps, n.pl. Scissors-like instrument of different forms and sizes for gripping or pulling things; part of animal formed like f. 'forcipate, a. [Biol.] F.-like, deeply forked. for'cipiform, a. Said sp. of PEDI-CELLARIAE with ends of jaws going across one another. for'cipulate, a. Said sp. of PEDICELLARIAE with jaws longer than they are wide.

fore-, At the front; before.

'forebrain, n. [Zoo.] The front division of the brain in the EMBRYO of a back-boned animal, or the part of the full brain undergoing development from it, taking in the CEREBRUM, OLFACTORY LOBES, etc.

'forecast, v.t., n. [Meteor.] (Make) statement as to what weather will be for a certain time in a certain place, based on weather map of conditions at the time.

'foregut, n. [Zoo.] Front part of ALIMEN-TARY CANAL in lower animals or in EMBRYO of back-boned animals.

fo'rensic 'medicine. Medical science used for the purposes of the law, for helping police, etc.

'forest, n. [Geog.] A great stretch of land thickly covered with trees.

forge, 1.v.t. Give form to (metal) by heating and then hammering, by hand or machine. 2.n. Place, sp. the fire, where forging is done.

-form, a. In the form of, like in form to (gen. -iform).

form'aldehyde, n. [Chem.] The simplest ALDEHYDE, H.CHO, used as a DISIN-FECTANT and in making PLASTICS.

formalin, n. [Chem.] A 40% SOLUTION of FORMALDEHYDE in water.

'formant, n. [Acous.] A special sort of wave-form produced by the voice and by certain instruments, and giving the sounds or notes made by them a special quality, as the group of sound-waves special to any one VOWEL sound.

for'mation, n. Act of forming; form or structure of anything; that which has been formed. [Geol.] Group of STRATA on top of one another, forming a unit from some point of view. [Bot.] ASSOCIATION.

'formative, a. (To do with) giving form, forming. [Biol.] Said of living material having power of, or being in the stage of, growth and development. f. 'centre. [Biol.] A NUCLEUS. f. disc. [Zoo.] GERMINAL DISC. f. ma'terial. [Biol.] PROTOPLASM, sp. mass of CELLS on top of YOLK of egg. f. 'region [Bot.] The growth-point of a stem or root.

form 'factor. ROOT-MEAN-SQUARE value ÷ AVERAGE value, taken over half a CYCLE, of anything such as an ALTERNATING CURRENT.

'formic acid. [Chem.] A FUMING liquid without colour, having a biting smell and the effect of burning, making holes in, whatever comes in touch with it, present in certain plants and in ants, HCOOH.

formi'cation, n. [Med.] A feeling in the skin as if ants were walking over it.

'formula (formulae), n. Directions for making some substance or putting through some process, sp. a list of what has to be mixed to make some medical substance. [Chem.] See CHEMICAL FORMULA. f. weight. GRAM-MOLECULE.

'fornix, n. [Anat.] An arch or fold; mass of white threads under CORPUS CALLOSUM of brain.

'fossa (fossae). [Zoo.] A hollow in part of body, as the hollows in bones of head over eyes, or the hollows of the nose. fos'sette, n. [Zoo.] Small hollow, such as that round base of feeler in some insects, or that in which the elastic substance joining two halves of a SHELL is rooted. [Med.] Small deep ULCER on eye.

'fossil, n. [Geol.] Any body or structure, such as a bone, SHELL, or the print of these or any other thing, bedded in the earth from very early times and having kept its form, generally by being changed into stone or stone-like substance, which is a part or a sign of a plant or animal of the far past. f. 'fuels. Coal, LIGNITE and NATURAL GAS, all used for burning. f. 'resin. RESIN-like substances got from certain trees and made hard in the earth. fossil'iferous, a. 'fossilize, v.t. Get changed into f.

fos'sorial, a. [Zoo.] Able to make holes in the earth, as a f. animal, a f. part.

'fossula, 'fossulet, nn. [Zoo.] Small, not deep, hollow, sp. in brain or in certain CORALS. 'fossulate, a.

'Foucault 'current. [Elec.] Current produced in metal when moved in MAGNETIC FIELD. Foucault 'pendulum. [Phys.] PENDULUM in form of metal ball of great weight, hanging from very long thin wire, used for making clear the turning of the earth by the change in the plane of motion of the pendulum as time goes on.

'founding, n. Art of CASTING metal. 'foundry, n. Building where f. is done.

four-stroke 'cycle. [Engin.] In an INTERNAL COMBUSTION ENGINE, one complete operation when it is made up of four motions of the PISTON, of which, by the first air and gas are pulled into the CYLINDER, by the second they are forced into a small space and fired, by the third they are made to undergo expansion and do their work, and by the fourth the waste gases are sent out.

fourth di'mension. [Phys., Math.] Time in the RELATIVITY THEORY.

'fovea, n. [Zoo.] A small hollow, sp. that in the middle part of the RETINA where seeing is clearest. '-al, a. '-ate, a. fo'veiform, a. fo'veola, n. Very small hollow. 'foveo'late(d), a.

'Fowler's so'lution. [Chem.] $KOH + As_2O_3$ in water, used for medical purposes.

f.p.s. = FOOT-POUND-SECOND.

Fr, Sign for FRANCIUM.

'fraction, n. A part, sp. a small part, of an amount. [Arith.] Number less than 1, that is, which is one or more of a certain number of equal parts of 1, put in the form $\frac{x}{y}$, where y is the complete number of parts and x the number of them to be taken, as $\frac{2}{3}$ = 'two-thirds', or two parts out of three. (See DECIMAL FRACTION). [Chem.] Any of the parts separated out of a complex substance, such as an oil, by FRACTIONATION. 'fractional, a. To do with, being, in the form of, a f. [Chem.] To do with, for the purpose of, effecting, produced by, FRACTIONATION. 'fractional distill'ation. FRACTIONATION by DISTILLATION, used for separating liquids with different boiling-points. 'fractional sterili'zation. [Med.] STERILIZATION by heating again and again, giving time between for SPORES to undergo development into VEGETATIVE CELLS which more readily undergo destruction.

'fraction'ation, n. [Chem.] Separating out the different substances in a complex substance one by one by using again and again a process such as DISTILLATION, CRYSTALLIZATION, PRECIPITATION. 'fractionate, v.t. 'fractionating 'column. Long upright pipe with a number of divisions generally small metal rings or plates with holes, put between boiler and CONDENSER, and used for FRACTIONAL DISTILLATION, the low-boiling and high-boiling parts of the liquid separating inside the pipe.

'fracto-, Broken, sp. of clouds: 'fracto'cumulus.

'fracture, 1.n. Act of getting or becoming broken, condition of being broken;

[Med.] F. of bone or CARTILAGE. [Mineral., Metal.] The look, structure of the SURFACE formed by the f., of a solid (sp. metal or stone) as against that formed by natural division. 2.v.t. and i. (Make) undergo f.

'fraenu(lu)m, n. FRENU(LU)M.

'fragment, n. A broken bit of something. [Bot.] Sp. a bit off a CHROMOSOME. [Geol.] ROCK made up of bits of broken material. 'fragmentary, frag'mental, aa. fragmen'tation, n. Separating into ff. or parts, Sp. [Biol.] simple division of NUCLEUS into two.

fram'b(o)esia, n. [Med.] YAWS.

frame, n. Unit picture in a motion-picture FILM; in TELEVISION, the picture formed by one complete SCANNING of the thing to be pictured.

frame of 'reference. [Phys.] A system of fixed points, lines, or planes in relation to which the position or motion of anything is given or measured, or physical laws are made clear, as CARTESIAN COÖRDINATES.

fra'ternal twins. [Zoo.] See TWIN.

'Fraunhofer line. [Optics, etc.] Any of the dark lines in the SPECTRUM of the sun, representative of a chemical ELEMENT which has a bright line in its spectrum in the same position, caused by ABSORPTION of certain waves by the gases round the sun.

free, a. [Chem.] Not united with another substance, said sp. of ELEMENTS present naturally in this condition.

free associ'ation. [Psych.] The producing of words automatically, in reaction to words said by a questioner, without taking time for conscious thought or selection, a process by which unconscious connections may be made to come to light, used in PSYCHO-ANALYSIS.

free ball'oon. A BALLOON let go freely through the air, without any connection with the earth or any apparatus in itself for causing, guiding, or controlling its motion.

free-'central placen'tation. [Bot.] Condition of flower in which PLACENTA is not fixed to wall of OVARY.

free 'energy. [Phys.] That part of the ENERGY of a system which is able to be turned into work.

free path. [Phys.] Distance through which an ATOM, MOLECULE, etc., in gas goes without touching another.

free 'valence. [Chem.] A VALENCE not united with another.

freeze, v.t. and i. [Phys.] Get or become changed from liquid to solid condition through loss of heat. 'freezing point. TEMPERATURE at which a given liquid freezes. [Meteor.] The freezing-point of water. freezing 'mixture. Two substances, such as ice and salt mixed, which together

have property of producing great cold and are used for freezing other substances, etc.

'freeze-'drying, n. [Chem.] The process of taking water away from a substance by lowering the PRESSURE of the air on it so that the water quickly EVAPORATES causing FREEZING of the rest, a process used for COLLOIDAL substances whose properties would be damaged by heating.

'frenum ('frena), n. [Zoo.] A structure or fold of skin or MEMBRANE supporting, keeping in place, or limiting the motion of a part, such as that under the tongue. 'frenate, a.

'frenulum ('frenula), n. [Zoo.] FRENUM; in some LEPIDOPTERA a stiff hair or group of hairs on front edge of back wing, which becomes locked with a part on back edge of front wing to keep them together in flight.

fre'netic, a. [Med.] To do with, or in a condition of, violent DELIRIUM or MANIA.

'frequency, n. Number of times anything takes place in unit time, sp. [Phys.] in a wave motion, the number of waves or VIBRATIONS in a second, [Elec.] the f. of the ALTERNATIONS of a current. f. 'changer or con'verter. Machine used for changing f. of an A.C. CIRCUIT. [Radio] A system of VALVES used in a SUPER-HETERODYNE RECEIVER for changing the high FREQUENCY of the currents produced by incoming radio waves to a lower one. f. 'standard. A STANDARD of time in which a second is measured by an unchanging wave-FREQUENCY in place of by the turning of the earth on its AXIS, though it is kept almost equal to the AVERAGE value of the MEAN SOLAR second for the past 200 years. See ATOMIC.

fresh, a. [Geog.] (Of water) not salt. '-water, a. [Geog.] Formed of f., not salt, water. [Biol.] Living in f., not salt, water.

Fres'nel('s) mirrors. [Optics] Two plane MIRRORS touching one another at an angle of not quite 180° used for producing INTERFERENCE effects. Fresnel('s) rhomb. A glass RHOMB so cut as to give ELLIPTICALLY POLARIZED light.

'Freudian, a. [Psych.] To do with the system of Sigmund Freud, his theory of the unconscious mind and of the part played by sex impulses in man's behaviour, and of the use of PSYCHOANALYSIS in disease.

'fricative, a., n. [Phonet.] (Of) sound made when breath is sent out throuth the mouth with the tongue near to the roof or the upper teeth, e.g. 'f', 'v', 's', etc.

'friction, n. [Mech.] Force acting against the rubbing of one thing on another; force needed to get motion started. [Med.] Rubbing of body for medical purpose; sound produced by the rubbing together of two INFLAMED parts inside body, as sign of certain diseases. **f. gear.** [Eng.] Any GEAR in which one wheel puts another in motion by the f. of their two touching SURFACES, in place of by the MESHING of teeth. **f. wheel.** A wheel of a f. gear; any of a group of small, freely-turning wheels supporting the part of a turning SHAFT in a BEARING for the purpose of overcoming f. between them. **'frictional,** a. **frictional clutch** or **'coupling.** Apparatus in which the engine driving a machine is acting by f. **frictional ma'chine.** Machine producing electric charge bv r.

'frigid, a. (Of CLIMATE) very cold. [Psych.] Having no or unnormally little sexdesire, or not experiencing the normal sense and feeling reactions in the act of COPULATION, said sp. of women. **F. Zone.** One or other of the two coldest divisions of the earth, the *North F. Zone* between the ARCTIC CIRCLE and the NORTH POLE and the *South F. Zone* between the ANTARCTIC CIRCLE and the SOUTH POLE. **frig'idity,** n. Sp. [Psych.].

'fringe, n. [Biol.] Edge formed of hairs or hair-like growths. [Optics] Any of the range of dark and light bands formed by INTERFERENCE of light. [Photog.] Unclear outline seen in coloured motion picture, caused by the outlines of separate pictures used in colour process not being quite on top of one another. [Psych.] Unclear feelings and ideas grouped in the mind round some clear idea. 2.v.t. Be on the edge of (something), sp. being in the form of, or giving the suggestion of, a f. **'fringed,** a. **'fringing,** a. **fringing reef.** [Geog.] Shelf-like structure of CORAL edging the land, gen. under the sea.

'Fröhlich's 'syndrome. [Med.] Unnormal condition in which person becomes very fat and undergoes loss of sex power and of certain marks of sex, caused by disease of PITUITARY GLAND.

frond, n. [Bot.] Leaf of a plant of the FILICALES; THALLUS.

frons, n. [Zoo.] Part of face over the eyes; hard plate in same place on head of insect.

front, 1. [Phonet.] That part of the tongue between middle and point, touching hard part of roof of mouth when shut. 2.v.t. [Phonet.] Make (sound) with tongue a little more forward than it generally is in making that sound, as the *k*-sound in *key* in comparison with that in *cold.*

front, n. [Meteor.] The line between masses of air at different degrees of heat.

'frontal, a. Of, to do with, at, the front. [Zoo.] Sp. to do with, near, the FRONS. 2.n. F. bone. **f. bone.** [Zoo.] One or the other of two bones between the eyehollows in back-boned animals. **f. lobe.**

[Zoo.] The most forward of the 4 chief divisions of a CEREBRAL HEMISPHERE.

'fronto-. To do with the FRONS or a FRONTAL bone: **'-cere-bellar,** a. **'-eth'moidal,** a. **'-'nasal,** a. **'-sphe-noidal,** a.

fronto'cylpeus, n. [Zoo.] Plate on head of insects formed by the uniting of the FRONS and the CLYPEUS.

'frontopa'rietal, a. [Zoo.] To do with FRONTAL and PARIETAL bones.

frost, n. [Meteor.] A TEMPERATURE of the air as low as or lower than FREEZING-POINT; the coating of small ice CRYSTALS formed of FROZEN DEW or water drops from the air which is produced on the face of the earth, etc. when there is a f.

froth, n. FOAM, sp. somewhat thin foam in which the separate BUBBLES are clearly seen.

fruc'tiferous, a. [Bot.] Producing fruit.

fructifi'cation, n. [Bot.] The forming of bodies having in them seeds or SPORES, sp. as the outcome of FERTILIZATION; any body having in it seeds or spores. **'fructify,** v.t. and i.

'fructose, n. [Chem.] Fruit-sugar, $C_6H_{12}O_6$, one of the HEXOSES.

fruit, n. [Bot.] Any FRUCTIFICATION, sp. that formed from the OVARY of an ANGIOSPERM after FERTILIZATION, gen. having other structures formed from other parts of the flower united with it. (*See* p. 158.)

'frustule, n. [Bot.] Shell of DIATOM, formed of two parts one going over the other like cover of a box.

'frutex, n. [Bot.] SHRUB. **frut'escent, 'fruticose,** aa. Like a f. **fru'ticulose,** a. Like a small f.

f.s. = FOOT-SECOND.

'f-state, 'f-level. [Phys.] The condition of an ATOM in which the AZIMUTHAL QUANTUM NUMBER is 3.

f-e'lectron, n. [Phys.] ELECTRON with AZIMUTHAL QUANTUM NUMBER 3.

ft. = foot, feet (measuring units). **ft.lb.** = FOOT-POUND.

fu'civorous, a. [Zoo.] Using sea plants for food.

'fucoid, 1.n. [Bot.] Plant of the common group of brown sea ALGAE (*Phaophyceae*) seen covering ROCKS on the sands etc. when the sea goes out. 2.a. Of or like a f. [Geol.] Having in it FOSSIL ff. or markings of this form.

fuco'xanthin, n. [Biochem., Bot.] The redbrown colouring-substance present with CHLOROPHYLL in PHAEOPHYCEAE.

'fuel, n. Substance which may be burned to give heat or power.

fu'gacious, a. Living only a short time, said of flower.

'fugitive, a. Not fixed, coming and going, or not in existence for long, said sp. of DYES which do not keep their colour. [Bot.] Of plants, seen only here and there,

FRUIT FORMS (not to scale)

ACHENES

FOLLICLES

LEGUMES

CAPSULE

CARYOPSIS

CARCERULUS

REGMA

NUT (Vertical Section

BERRY

DRUPE (Vertical Section)

MULTIPLE DRUPE

HESPERIDIUM (Vertical Section

SAMARA

CYPSELA

PLUME

WINGED ACHENES

HOOKED CALYX   HOOKED STYLE

HOOKED FRUIT

AGGREGATE FRUIT   POME (Vertical Section)

PSEUDOCARPS

in danger, as a group, of going out of existence.

fugue, n. [Med.] A condition in which a person does things, sometimes going on for days, of which he has no memory later, in an attempt to get away from himself and some unconscious trouble of mind, seen in HYSTERIA, etc.

'fulcrum, n. [Mech.] The point of support of a lever. [Biol.] Supporting part such as TENDRIL; any of certain hard, f.-like parts in some insects, fishes, or sea-animals, for example ROTIFERA. **'fulcrate,** a. [Biol.] Having f.

'fulgurite, n. [Geol.] Glass-like mass, freq. pipe-like, produced by LIGHTNING in loose sand, etc.

full, a. [Astron.] (Of the moon) *see* MOON.

'fuller's earth. [Geol.] A non-PLASTIC form of CLAY, white or light brown in colour and like soft earth in structure, used at one time for taking fats out of wool cloth and now as a FILTER for oils and fats.

full 'radiator. [Phys.] BLACK-BODY RADIATOR.

'fumarole, n. [Geol.] Small hole in earth near VOLCANO from which smoke and gas comes.

fuma'torium, fu'matory, nn. Room or box in which clothing, etc. is put for fumigation.

fume, 1.n. Smoke or gas, sp. one with a strong effect on the nose and eyes, given off by chemicals or chemical reaction. 2.v.i. Give off ff. 3.a. [Chem.] (Of an ACID) giving off a gas which, uniting with the WATER VAPOUR, in the air, gives an effect of smoking. **f. 'chamber** or **'cupboard.** Cupboard in which chemical work producing ff. is done. **'fuming 'nitric 'acid.** 86% HNO₃. **'fuming sul'phuric 'acid.** $H_2S_4O + SO_3$.

'fumigate, v.t. [Med.] DISINFECT room, clothing, etc., by use of FUMES causing destruction of disease bodies. **fumi'gation,** n. **'fumigant,** n. Substance used for fumigating.

'function, n. [Biol.] Part played normally by any structure in plant or animal. **'functional,** a. [Biol.] To do with a f. or ff., sp. with the working of something as opp. its structure; (of a part), working normally. **functional dis'ease.** [Med.] A disease in which some f. or ff. are out of order but no damage to body or change of structure seems to be present.

'fundament, n. [Anat.] ANUS. [Biol.] ANLAGE.

funda'mental, 1.a. Of, to do with, forming, the first or lowest part on which structure is based or reasoning is dependent. [Phys.] Sp. to do with a fundamental. 2.n. F. component. **f. component.** [Phys.] The longest WAVE, that is, the wave of lowest FREQUENCY or greatest WAVE-LENGTH, in

a mixed wave, as a sound-wave. **f. gas e'quation.** The EQUATION $pv = RT$, where $p =$ PRESSURE, $v =$ VOLUME, $R =$ GAS CONSTANT and $T =$ ABSOLUTE TEMPERATURE. **f. 'interval.** [Phys.] Number of degrees between the two fixed points on the scale of a THERMOMETER. **f. 'particle.** [Phys.] A unit of material substance (a NEUTRON, PROTON, ELECTRON, POSITRON, MESON, NEUTRINO) or of ENERGY (a PHOTON), which it is impossible to get broken up into smaller units—the simplest form of material substance which has the power of free existence. **f. plate** or **zone.** [Anat.] Back-side part of MEDULLARY TUBE. **f. point.** TRIPLE POINT. **f. 'primary.** PHYSIOLOGICAL PRIMARY. **f. tone.** [Acous.] In a complex TONE seen as made up of separate WAVES of different FREQUENCIES, the one with the lowest frequency. **f. units.** The units of LENGTH, mass and time upon which a system of units of measuring is based.

'fundiform, a. [Anat.] Formed like a cord turned back across itself, somewhat like the letter '*t*'.

'fundus, n. [Anat.] The lowest part or base, or part opposite the opening, of the inside of a hollow ORGAN, sp. EYE-GROUND.

'Fungi, n.pl. [Bot.] A PHYLUM of the THALLOPHYTA in which no CHLOROPHYLL is present and which are SAPROPHYTIC or PARASITIC on other plants or on animals. **'fungal,** a. **'fungicide,** n. Substance causing the death of F. **fung'ivorous,** a. Using F. as food. **'fungoid,** a. **'fungous,** a. **'fungus,** 1.n. Plant of the F. 2.a. Of, to do with, or sp. caused by, F.

'funicle, fu'niculus, nn. [Bot.] The stem of an OVULE. [Zoo.] Cord or band, sp. 1. UMBILICAL CORD, 2. any of certain bands of white substance in nerves or brain, 3. any of the cord-like structures joining the digestion organs to body wall in some animals. **fu'niculate,** a.

fu'nicular, a. Using, made up of, worked by, a cord. [Biol.] To do with a FUNICLE. **f. 'polygon.** [Mech.] Form taken by a cord supported at its two ends from which a number of weights are hanging. **f. 'railway.** A railway going up a short, sharp slope, as a mountain side, in which the train or carriage is pulled up by an unending chain running under it or overhead.

fu'nicular 'souffle. [Med.] Blowing sound sometimes noted in AUSCULTATION, in rhythm with heart of FOETUS.

'funnel, n. Vessel with wide round mouth and sloping sides narrowing into pipe at lower end for putting liquids into bottle, etc. [Zoo.] SIPHON of CEPHALOPODA. **'funnelform,** a.

fur, n. [Zoo.] Very thick, soft coat of hair on skins of certain animals; the thick under-coat of soft, short hair in animals having an outer coat of stiffer hair. [Med.] Coat of substance on tongue produced by bad digestion or disease. **furred,** a.

'furan(e), 'furfuran, nn. [Chem.] C_4H_4O, a readily burning liquid with a special smell and no colour got from wood-TAR. (*See* p. 392.)

'furca (furcae), n. [Zoo.] Any forked struc-ture, as, in certain insects, a forked APODEME in the middle of the body, and in CRUSTACEA one or other of two forked outgrowths at the end of the body. **'furcal, fur'cate,** aa. Branched, forked. **fur'cation,** n. Forking. **'furcula** (fur-culae), **'furculum** (furcula), nn. F., sp. part of the throat in an EMBRYO, or the forked structure formed by the CLAVICLES in a bird.

'furfur, (furfures) n. [Med.] SCURF. [Biol.] very small SCALE(s), freq. of a sort which is readily rubbed off, as thin bit(s) of dry skin. **fur'fur'aceous,** a.

furlong, n. British unit of distance = ⅛ mile or 201·17 m. (*See* p. 565.)

'furnace, n. Apparatus inside which great heat is produced by fire or electric system, used for heating building or boilers, or in the process of working metals, etc.

fur'uncle, n. [Med.] BOIL. **fur'unculous,** a. **fur'unculoid,** a. **fur'unculosis,** n. The condition of having ff.

'fuscin, n. [Biochem] Brown colouring material in outer skin of RETINA

fuse, fuze, 1.n. Apparatus by which CHARGE of EXPLOSIVE is fired. [Elec.] A wire or bit of metal of low MELTING-POINT put into an electric CIRCUIT so that if current becomes over-strong this will fuse, so parting and causing the current to be broken, putting a stop to the danger of damage. 2v.t. and i. Get (solid, sp. metal) into liquid form by heating, sp. for purpose of uniting; become fused or become united as effect of fusing. **'fusible,** a. **'fusi'bility,** n. **'fusion,** n. Fusing. [Biol.] Process of becoming or condition of being united into one by growth together. [Phys.] The uniting of two ATOMIC NUCLEI of small mass to make a nucleus of greater mass, an amount of ENERGY being given off in the process which is equal to the BINDING ENERGIES of the two first nuclei put together less the binding energy of the new nucleus. **fusion 'nucleus.** [Zoo.] Middle NUCLEUS of EMBRYO SAC, formed by fusion of free NUCLEI from the two ends.

'fuselage, n. Body of airplane to which the wings and tail are fixed.

'fusel oil, n. [Chem.] Mixed AMYL ALCOHOLS, got in process of making ETHYL ALCOHOL by FERMENTATION.

'fusible 'alloy. [Metal.] Mixed metal becom-ing liquid at quite a low TEMPERATURE.

'fusiform, a. [Biol.] Formed like a round stick coming to a long point at the two ends.

g = GRAM.

g, Sign for GRAVITATIONAL ACCELERATION.

Ga, Sign for GALLIUM.

'gabbro, n. [Geol.] A sort of COARSE-GRAINED IGNEOUS ROCK, made up chiefly of PLAGIOCLASE, sometimes with OLIVINE (*see* p. 192). **g. clan.** The CLAN of which g. is representative.

gado'linium, n. Chemical ELEMENT, at. no. 64, at. wt. 157·31, sign Gd, one of the RARE EARTH METALS.

gage, n. GAUGE.

ga'lactic, a. [Astron.] To do with the MILKY WAY.

ga'lacto-. Milk.

ga'lactopoi'etic, n., a. [Med.] (Substance) increasing amount of milk produced by a woman after the birth of a baby.

ga'lactor'rh(o)ea, n. [Med.] Condition in which overmuch milk is produced by a woman.

'galactose, n. [Chem.] One of the HEXOSES forming part of milk sugar.

galac'turia, n. [Med.] Condition in which person's URINE is milk-like.

'galaxy, n. [Astron.] MILKY WAY; any other such stretch of bright dust, gases and stars in the sun's system, or all the sun's system itself.

'galea, n. [Bot.] Any part of CALYX or COROLLA formed like old Roman military head-dress. [Zoo.] Outer part of MAXILLA of certain insects. **'galeate,** a.

ga'lena, n. [Mineral.] Natural PbS (*lead sulphide*), an important ORE of lead.

Ga'litzin 'pendulum. [Geol.] A form of SEISMOGRAPH.

gall, n. [Bot.] Sort of diseased growth or SWELLING on plant caused by different PARASITES, plant and animal.

gall, n. [Zoo.] BILE. **g.-'bladder.** [Zoo.] Bag-like part in which BILE is stored. **'gallstone.** [Med.] Small hard mass formed in g.-bladder, made up of CHOLESTEROL and other things.

'gallic acid. [Chem.] $C_6H_2(OH)_3COOH$, an acid present in NUTGALLS, tea, and a great number of other plants, used in making DYES and medically as an ASTRINGENT.

'gallium, n. Chemical ELEMENT, at. no. 31, at. wt. 69·72, sign Ga, a grey metal.

'gallon, n. Unit of liquid measure = 4 QUARTS or 4·55 1. (G.B.) or 3·79 1. (U.S.A.).

'Galton's law. [Biol.] Law that offspring gets half its qualities from father and mother ($\frac{1}{4}$ from the one, $\frac{1}{4}$ from the other), $\frac{1}{4}$ from their fathers and mothers, $\frac{1}{4}$ from theirs, and so on. 'Galton's 'whistle. Whistle giving very high note, used for testing limits of hearing.

gal'vanic, a. [Elec.] Word used at one time for naming moving, as opp. STATIC, ELECTRICITY. g. cell (or 'battery). PRIMARY CELL (or BATTERY).

'galvanism, n. [Phys.] Old name for the science of electric currents.

'galvanize, v.t. Put a coat of zinc on iron. [Med.] Send electric current through parts of body. 'galvani'zation, n.

'galvano-. To do with, produced by, electric current, ELECTRO-: -'taxis; -'tropism, nn.

'galvano'cautery, n. [Med.] CAUTERY by wire heated by electric current; instrument for this purpose.

'galva'nometer, n. [Elec.] An instrument for measuring small electric currents, dependent on the MAGNETIC effect produced by an electric current.

'galvano'scope, n. [Elec.] Instrument used for seeing if an electric current is present.

game'tangium (gametangia), n. [Bot.] Structure in which GERM-CELLS are formed.

'gamete, n. [Biol.] A GERM-CELL. 'gamet-al, -ic, aa. ga'metid, n. [Zoo.] CELL given off by SPORONT and later becoming a g. ga'metoblast, n. Simple living substance before development into gg. or other CELLS. ga'metocyst, n. [Zoo.] In PROTO-ZOA, bag-like covering inside which the uniting of gg. takes place. ga'meto-cyte, -'gonium, nn. CELL producing gg. 'gameto'genesis, game'togeny, nn. The forming of gg. 'gameto'genic, a. Caused by changes in CHROMOSOMES of gg. ga'metophore, n. [Bot.] Special part of gametophyte on which GAMETANGIA are. ga'metophyll, n. Special leaf having sex-parts. ga'metophyte, n. G.-producing plant or stage in plants having ALTERNA-TION OF GENERATIONS. gameto-.

'gamic, a. [Biol.] To do with sex; produced or producing as the effect of FERTILIZA-TION. -gamic, -gamous, aa. Having -gamy. -gamy, n. The property or process of uniting for the purpose of producing offspring.

'gamma, n. The Greek letter γ. g. 'iron (γ 'iron). Iron in form normally taken by it when heated over highest CRITICAL POINT (almost 900°), in which condition it is not MAGNETIC. g. ray. [Phys.] Ray like X-ray but shorter, sent out by RADIOACTIVE substance and having specially strong powers of going through substances.

'gamo-. Uniting (of parts named, or as sex process), united:— -gamo'petalous, a. gamo'sepalous, a.

gamo'genesis, n. [Biol.] The producing of offspring by the uniting of male with female GERM-CELLS. gamoge'netic, a.

Gamo'petalae, n.pl. [Bot.] SYMPETALAE.

'gangliar, a. [Zoo.] To do with, like, having a GANGLION, or made up of ganglia.

'gangliocyte, n. [Zoo.] GANGLION CELL outside CENTRAL NERVOUS SYSTEM.

'ganglion ('ganglia), n. [Zoo.] Mass of nerve substance from which nerve threads go out; NERVE CENTRE. gangli-'onic, a. 'gangli(on)ate(d), aa. 'gangli-form, 'ganglioid, aa. 'ganglio-.

'ganglio'neural, a. [Zoo.] Having a nerve system made up of GANGLIA joined by nerve threads.

'ganglio'plexus, n. [Zoo.] A GANGLION of a loose, net-like structure.

'gangrene, n. [Med.] The death and DECAY of a part of the body while the rest goes on living, caused by the cutting off of the blood going to the part. 'gangrenous, a.

'gangue, n. Stone or earth of no value from which metal or MINERAL is taken.

'gannister, n. [Geol.] Stone present in coal-mines, made up of CLAY and SiO_2, used for lining FURNACES, etc.

'ganoid, a. [Zoo.] (Of fish SCALES) four-sided and formed of a thin inner coat of bone with an outer coat of GANOIN; (of fish) having g. scales.

Gan'oidei, n.pl. A SUB-CLASS of fish made up of those having GANOID SCALES, most of which have now gone out of existence.

'ganoin, n. Very hard, bright substance forming outer cover of SCALES of certain fish.

gape, n. [Zoo.] Measure from top to base of the mouth of an animal, fish, or bird when fully open.

gas, n. [Phys.] A substance in which the connection between the MOLECULES is so loose that not only has it, like a liquid, no fixed form, but any amount of it, however small, takes up all of any limited space into which it is put; g. produced from coal, oil, etc. and used for lighting, heating, and so on. [Med.] Any g. used as an ANAESTHETIC, such as LAUGHING GAS. g. black. CARBON formed on cold metal put in a g. flame. g. cell. [Elec.] PRIMARY CELL in which at least one of the substances taking part is a g. g. coal. Coal used for making g. by DISTILLATION. g. 'constant. The fixed value R in the gas law = 8·315 × 10⁷ ERGS/GRAM-MOLECULE, or 1·988 CALORIES/gram-molecule. 'g.-cooled re-'actor. [Phys.] A NUCLEAR REACTOR in which the heat for making electric power is taken from the reactor by a gas, for example CO_2. **g. dis′charge lamp.** [Elec.] A g. discharge tube specially designed to make use of the POSITIVE COLUMN as an electric light, for example, a NEON LIGHT. **g. discharge tube.** [Elec.] Any DISCHARGE TUBE having in it a gas, gen. at low PRESSURE, through which the current goes, most commonly one having a heated CATHODE, a GRID, and an ANODE, and using Hg, A, or Ne gas, the special property of such a discharge tube being the producing of light at certain parts of it (*see* CATHODE GLOW, NEGATIVE GLOW, and POSITIVE COLUMN). **g. ′engine.** An IN-TERNAL COMBUSTION ENGINE using g. **g.-filled lamp.** [Elec.] An electric-light bulb using a FILAMENT but having an INERT GAS in it in place of a VACUUM. **g. ′gangrene.** [Med.] GANGRENE caused by poison gg. used in war. **g. gland.** [Zoo.] A structure in the wall of the air-BLADDER in certain fishes which is able to send gas into the bladder. **g. law.** General law that $PV = RT$ where P is PRESSURE, V VOLUME, T ABSOLUTE TEMPERATURE and R the gas constant. **g. ′mantle.** CYLIND-RICAL structure formed of a network of special chemical material ($ThO_2 + CeO_2$) which gives off very bright white light when heated, put over burning g. for increasing its lighting power. **g. mask.** [Chem.] An apparatus put over the face for breathing through when there is danger of poison g. in the air, as in war, and having in it some substance by re-action with which the g. is taken out of the air. **g. tar.** Thick black liquid pro-duced in making g. for burning. **g. thread.** Special screw-THREAD used in g. pipes. **g. ′turbine.** TURBINE in which hot gg. do the work. **′-iform,** a. **-o′genic,** a. **′-ify,** v.t. Make (a liquid or solid) into a g. **′-ifiable,** a. **′-ifi′cation,** n.

′gaseous, a. To do with, in the form of, having the properties of, a gas **g. dis-′charges.** Old name for g. electronics. **g. elec′tronics.** In PLASMA PHYSICS (the science of), the transporting of electric effects through gases.

′gaslight ′paper. Old name for CONTACT PAPER given to it because its reaction was so slow that it might be used openly in gaslight.

′gasolene, ′gasoline, nn. American name for PETROL.

ga′someter, n. Great iron vessel in which gas is stored in gas or other works.

Gas′serian ′ganglion. [Zoo.] In back-boned animals, great GANGLION on root of sense-nerve branching to eye and mouth.

gas′trectomy, n. [Med.] Operation of cutting out part of stomach.

′gastric, a. [Zoo., Med.] To do with the stomach, or with digestion. **g. ′fluid** or **juice.** Liquid produced by GLANDS in stomach (the **g. glands**), and responsible for part of the process of digestion. **′gastral,** a.

′gastrin, n. [Biochem.] HORMONE causing GASTRIC FLUID to be produced.

gas′tritis, n. [Med.] INFLAMMATION of the stomach, sp. of the MUCOUS MEMBRANE.

′gastro-, ′gastero-. Of, to do with, stomach: **gas′trology,** n., **′gastrointes′tinal,** a.

′gastroc′nemius, n. [Zoo.] The great muscle at back of lower part of leg in back-boned animals.

′gastrocoel(e), n. [Zoo.] The ARCHENTERON of a GASTRULA.

Gas′tropoda, n.pl. [Zoo.] A CLASS of MOLLUSCA having good development of the head, the underside of the body forming a wide, flat 'foot' by which the animal gets about, and the SHELL, if any, being without divisions and freq. of twisted form. **′gastropod,** a., n. To do with, one of, the G.

′gastropore, n. [Zoo.] Opening in the struc-ture formed by HYDROID CORALS where food is taken in by GASTROZOOID.

gas′trotomy, n. [Med.] Operation of cutting stomach.

gastro′zooid, n. [Zoo.] ZOOID having mouth and digestion system.

′gastrula, n. [Zoo.] EMBRYO at stage normally coming after the BLASTULA, taking the form of a cup or open-mouthed bag with an outside and an inside wall. **gastru′lation,** n. Process of forming g.

gate ′circuit. Radio apparatus in which one impulse makes its effect only after the effect of another and independent impulse.

ga(u)ge, n. Sorts of instrument used for measuring or testing such things as PRESSURE, rainfall, level of water in boiler, size or form of machine-part, the DIAMETER of wire, etc.

gauss, n. The C.G.S. unit of MAGNETIC FLUX DENSITY, $= 1$ MAXWELL per cm².

Gay Lus′sac's law. CHARLES'S LAW.

Gd., Sign for GADOLINIUM.

Ge., Sign for GERMANIUM.

ge′anticline, n. [Geol.] ANTICLINE of greatest size, produced by mountain-building motions of the earth at a point where there was a great SYNCLINE.

gear, n. [Mach.] Any system of moving parts designed for handing on motion sp. of toothed wheels (**g. wheels**), for example between the engine and the AXLE of an automobile; in an automobile, etc., any of the different connections, gen. three, of different-sized g. wheels turning the axle, which may be made with the g. wheel turned by the engine, by which the rate of turning of the axle may be made slower or quicker so as to give greater or less power; the condition of an automobile when one g. wheel is in the position for moving another. **g. box.** The part of an automobile housing the g. wheels. **'-shift,** n. The apparatus in an automobile by which it is put in or out of g. or by which changes of g., that is, from one g.-connection to another, are made.

'Geiger 'counter, 'Geiger-Müller 'counter. [Phys.] Apparatus formed of a highly CHARGED metal wire going through a metal pipe full of low PRESSURE air or other gas such as ARGON and ALCOHOL so that any electric PARTICLE going into the pipe IONIZES the gas, causing a current from the wire to the pipe by which a light or sound is produced, used for seeing if RADIOACTIVE substances or COSMIC RAYS are present and for getting the number of RADIATIONS in a second, etc.

'Geissler tube. [Elec.] A glass tube with almost all the air taken out of it so that when an electric current goes through it it gives a bright light broken up by dark spaces.

gel, 1.n. [Chem.] The seemingly solid, gen. jelly-like substance formed from a liquid COLLOIDAL SOLUTION when it is not kept heated or in motion. 2.v.i. Become a g. **gel'ation,** n.

gela'tin(e), n. [Chem.] Jelly-like animal PROTEIN, formed by boiling bones and like parts, used for food, in camera work, for making GLUE and so on. **ge'latinate,** v.t. and i. Get, become, changed into g. or jelly-like substance. **ge'latinize,** v.t. and i. Gelatinate; in camera work, get (paper, etc.) coated with g. **ge'latinous,** a.

ge'lignite, n. An EXPLOSIVE made up of NITROGLYCERIN, NITROCELLULOSE, KNO₃ and wood PULP.

'geminate, 1.a. In twos, having two like parts together. 2.v.i. Become g. **gemi'nation,** n.

'Gemini, n. [Astron.] The third SIGN of the ZODIAC.

'gemma (gemmae), n. [Biol.] BUD-like part put out by and separating from plant or animal, and undergoing development into offspring, without sex-process. **gem'mation,** n. The producing of offspring by gg. **gem'maceous,** a. **'gemmate,** a. **gem'miferous, 'gem'miparous,** aa. **'gemmiform,** a.

'gemmule, n. [Biol.] A small GEMMA, sp. in certain sponges, one formed under hard conditions and giving birth to a new COLONY when conditions become better.

'gena (genae), n. [Zoo.] Side part of head or face, sp. feathered side under mouth of bird, side part of head-covering of TRILOBITA, side plate on head of insect. **'genal,** a.

'gene, n. [Biol.] Any one of the parts of a SEX-CELL CHROMOSOME by which the different qualities are handed on to the offspring, every g. being responsible for handing on one quality, by itself or by uniting with another g.

'genera, n.pl. See GENUS.

general, a. [Med.] (Of disease, etc.) having effect on all the body, not limited to a part, as a g. anaesthetic.

'general par'alysis (of the in'sane). A form of INSANITY caused by slow destruction of the brain as effect of SYPHILIS, marked by increasing loss of powers of body and mind and ending in complete insanity, PARALYSIS and death.

'generalize, v.t. and i. [Med.] Make or become general. **'generalized,** a. Sp. [Biol.] (of a structure) uniting in itself properties of two or more different groups.

'generate, v.t. Make come into being, be producer of, sp. electric current, gas, heat, etc. by chemical process, or (of plant or animal) offspring. **gene'ration,** n. Sp. [Biol.] one stage or level in a family tree; all those in a family who are of the same generation; all plants or animals of a certain sort having their birth and living about the same time; time between the birth of one generation and the birth of another, in man taken to be 33 years. **'generative,** a. [Biol.]To do with generation, **'generator,** n. Machine or apparatus producing steam, gas, electric current, etc. **'generator gas.** Gas formed by blowing air through heated coal.

ge'neric, a. See GENUS.

'genesis, n. The starting-point of the process by which anything comes about or comes into being, or the process itself, sp. [Biol.], as the g. of a SPECIES or a plant or animal part. **-genesis,** n. Process of development, act of producing or condition of being produced, sp. by EVOLUTION. **ge'netic, ge'netical,** aa. To do with the g. of anything. [Biol.] To do with, produced by a GENE or genes; to do with genetics. **-ge'netic,** a. To do with -genesis; producing, forming; produced, by, from, in, etc. **ge'netics,** n. [Biol.] The science of GENES and their operation, that is, of the handing on of properties to offspring.

ge'netic 'spiral. [Bot.] Corkscrew line made by joining the points where leaves are joined to stem, from lowest to highest.

'genetype, n. GENOTYPE.

'genial, a., n. [Zoo.] To do with the chin.

'-genic, Producing; produced by, in, etc.

ge'niculate, a. Bent sharply at an angle.

'genital, a. [Zoo.] To do with sex, or with the producing of offspring. **g. ridge.** Outgrowth of WOLFFIAN BODIES from which the OVARIES in back-boned animals have their development. **geni'talia,** n. pl. The GONADS and their apparatus. **'genitals,** n. pl. The sex parts of an animal, sp. the outer parts.

'genit(o)-. [Zoo.] GENITAL or GENITALS.

genito'urinary, a. Of, to do with, the GENITAL and the URINARY systems.

'genome, n. [Biol.] A HAPLOID CHROMOSOME SET and its GENES.

'genoplast, n. GENOTYPE.

'genotype, n. [Biol.] A group of animals or plants, a sort, having in common those qualities which, are an outcome of HEREDITY.

'genus (genera), n. Division of FAMILY of plants or animals, made up of SPECIES. **ge'neric,** a.

-geny, n. The process or science of the birth or producing or development of what is named, or the condition of being produced from or by it.

'geo-. Earth.

geo-centric(al), aa. [Astron.] To do with, measured from, the middle point of the earth. **geo'centric 'latitude.** LATITUDE measured by the angle between the plane of the earth's EQUATOR and a line from the place to the middle point of the earth.

geo'chrony, n. System of time-divisions used in geology.

geo'cyclic, a. To do with the turning round of the earth; going round the earth.

'geode, n. [Geol.] Stone with a hollow in the middle which is coated with CRYSTALS. **ge'odic, geo'diferous,** aa.

ge'odesy, n. Science of measuring the earth or great distances and AREAS on it. **geo'desic, geo'detic,** 1.aa. To do with g. 2.nn. G. line. **geodesic (geodetic) line.** Shortest line between any two points on the face of a curved solid. **geodetic(al),** aa.

'geody'namic, a. To do with forces inside the earth.

ge'ogeny, ge'ogony, nn. Science or theory of the forming of the earth.

ge'ography, n. Science of the face of the earth, covering the distribution of land, sea, rivers, mountains, etc., of plants and animals, and of its countries, towns, railways, natural materials, weather conditions, and so on. **ge'ographer,** n. Expert in g. **geo'graphic(al),** aa. **geographical poles.** The points on the earth looked on as giving the true north and south directions for geographical purposes.

ge'ology, n. Science of the earth's structure, its history, the materials of which it is formed, the forces and effects working on it, and the animals and plants of past times of which parts or signs are to be seen in it. **geo'logical,** a. **geological time.** The way in which the physical history of the earth is grouped into divisions in the science of g., the system of spaces of time used as a framework for the earth's history. **ge'ologist,** n.

'geomag'netic, a. To do with the earth's MAGNETIC properties.

ge'ometry, n. [Math.] That branch of mathematics having to do with the properties, relations, and measuring of space and its forms, that is, with lines, angles, planes and solid forms. **geo-'metric(al),** aa. **geometrical mean.** [Arith.] Of two numbers, the SQUARE ROOT of their PRODUCT. **geometrical 'optics.** That branch of OPTICS which has to do with the behaviour of light rays looked on as straight lines, that is, with the g. of REFLECTION and REFRACTION. **geometrical pro'gression.** A group of numbers of which every one is the same number of times greater or smaller than the one before it, as 2, 4, 8, 16 . . . or 16, 8, 4, 2.

'geomor'phology, n. That part of Geography which has to do with the form of the earth's face, the distribution of land and water, etc. **geo'morphic,** a.

geo'physics, n. Science of the physical properties of the earth, its motions and forces and their effects. **geo'physical,** a.

'geophyte, n. [Bot.]. Any plant having its growth in earth.

'geosphere, n. The solid part of the earth, as opp. the water on and the air round it.

geo'static, a. [Engin.] To do with the force of the earth or like substance on a structure on or in it.

geo'statics, n.pl. Science of balanced forces acting on RIGID bodies.

geo'strophic, n. [Meteor.] Of forces, dependent on the turning of the earth.

geo'syncline, n. [Geol.] A great SYNCLINE.

geo'tax-is, -y, nn. [Biol.] TAXIS in reaction to the earth's attraction. **geo'tactic,** a.

'geotec'tonic, a. To do with the form and structure of ROCK masses.

geo'therm-al, -ic, aa. To do with the heat of the inside of the earth.

geo'tonus, n. [Bot.] Normal placing of an ORGAN in relation to earth.

ge'otropism, n. [Biol.] TROPISM in reaction to earth's attraction, sp. unequal growth of two sides of a part of a plant, curving it in the direction of the attraction.

ge'ranium oil. An oil got by DISTILLATION of the green parts of plants of the genus *Pelargonium*, sweet-smelling and used in such industries as soap-making.

geri'atrics, n. GERONTOLOGY.

germ, n. [Med.] Name used loosely for any disease-producing BACTERIUM. [Biol.] Small mass of living substance having power of development into a living thing, starting-point of an EMBRYO, seed or bud. **g. cell.** Any CELL whose purpose is the producing of a new plant or animal, sp. the male or female sex-cell. **g. 'layer.** Any of the LAYERS of CELLS formed early in the development of an EMBRYO. **g. 'nucleus.** [Biol.] NUCLEUS of a sex-CELL. [Bot.] Nucleus formed by male and female cells uniting. **g. plasm.** Substance in g.

cells by which qualities are said to be handed down to offspring. **g. pore.** [Bot.] Small opening or thin place in SPORE cover for g. tube, or in POLLEN grain for like part. **g. ′theory.** BIOGENESIS. **g. tube.** Short pipe-like outgrowth pushed out by SPORE in process of GERMINATION.

ger′manium, n. Chemical ELEMENT, at. no. 32, at. wt. 72·60, sign Ge, an uncommon grey-white metal, a SEMI-CONDUCTOR, used in TRANSISTORS.

′German measles. RUBELLA.

′germicide, n. [Med.] Substance causing death of disease GERMS.

′germinal, a. [Biol.] To do with a GERM, to do with the start of growth. **g. bands.** [Zoo.] Two lines of CELLS formed in early development of ANNELIDA. **g. disc.** Plate-like part of egg-YOLK where division first takes place. **g. epi′thelium.** TISSUE covering framework of OVARY and TESTIS. **g. ′layer.** [Anat.] LAYER of CELLS from which new cells are all the time being formed, sp. the lowest layer of the skin. **g. se′lection.** Fight for existence among sex-CELLS as effect of which only the strongest go on living. **g. spot.** Round body present in g. vesicle. **g. vesicle.** The NUCLEUS of an OVUM before the POLAR BODIES are formed.

′germinate, v.i. (Of a seed, etc.) Get started on process of development. **germi′nation,** n. **′germinative,** a. **′germinating,** a., n.

ger′ontic, a. [Biol.] To do with the process of getting old, with the last stage of existence when the powers and structure of a living thing are undergoing damaging changes.

geron′tology, n. [Med.] The science of the changes taking place in old persons and of the diseases special to this stage of existence.

-gerous, a. Producing.

ge′stalt (gestalten), h. [Psychol.] An organization or system of parts forming a unit with new and special properties, not simply those given by addition of the different parts. **g. psy′chology.** System of psychology based on ′the g. as the unit of living processes, sp. of PERCEPTION.

ges′tation, n. [Zoo.] The process of development of offspring in the body of the mother in certain animals.

′getter, n. Heated metal or other substance put inside electric light or other VACUUM bulb for purpose of gettering. **′gettering,** n. The process of taking up last small amount of gas from a bulb, etc. after pumping.

′geyser, n. [Geol.] Spring sending out bursts of boiling water and steam from time to time, caused by water under the earth meeting heated ROCK.

′giant, n., a. [Biol.] (An animal, plant, or part which is) of a size much greater than

normal for its sort. [Astron.] *See* RED GIANT.

′giant cell. [Zoo.] Any of a number of great CELLS present in the red substance inside bone, in parts of the brain, and in other places.

′giant ′fibre, n. [Zoo.] Any of the long nerve-threads, much greater than normal, present in the nerve on the under side of some lower animals.

′gibbous, a. [Astron.] Said of moon when its form is between a half-circle and a full circle.

gi′gantism, n. [Med.] Diseased condition marked by development to a size much greater than normal because of the overgrowth of the long bones of the arms and legs, caused by the overworking of the PITUITARY GLAND. [Bot.] Unnormal increase in size.

′Gilbert, n. [Elec.] C.G.S. unit of MAGNETO-

MOTIVE FORCE $= \dfrac{10}{4\pi}$ AMPERE-TURNS.

gill, n. Liquid measure $= \frac{1}{4}$ PINT or 0.142 l. (G.B.) or 0.118 l. (U.S.A.). (*See* p. 565.)

gill, n. [Zoo.] Structure for breathing under water, gen. one of two opposite outgrowths formed of thin plates or branches of MEMBRANE through which the O mixed with the water gets into the blood. [Bot.] Any of the upright plates forming the under side of the top part of BASIDIO-MYCETES. **g. arch.** Arch or curved rod of bone or CARTILAGE supporting one division of g. of fish or water animal. **g. ′basket.** Framework of gg. and g. slits, the g. arches. **g. book.** BOOK GILL. **g. cleft.** G. slit. **g. cover.** The fold of stiff skin forming outer cover of g. in most fish. **g. plume.** Sort of g. present in MOLLUSCA, which is like a feather or a comb with teeth on opposite sides. **g. pouch.** Any of bag-like g. slits of CYCLOSTOMATA. **g. rake(r).** In some fish, any of the needle-like outgrowths of bone on the g. arches keeping bits of food from getting into gg. **g. ′remnants.** Signs of gg. present in PHARYNX of back-boned animals. **g. rods.** Any of the rods supporting PHARYNX in CEPHALOCHORDA, **g. slit.** In fish, etc. any of system of openings going from PHARYNX to outside, on walls of which gg. are placed, and through which water taken in by mouth is sent over them; in EMBRYOS of some air-breathing animals, small hollows in like position; outer opening of g. in fish.

′gimbals, n.pl. Structure of two rings, one inside the other, turning on pins at right angles to one another, so that a body fixed inside has the power of turning freely in any direction, used for supporting things such as the COMPASS on ship, to keep them level whatever the motion of the ship.

gin′giva (gingivae), n. [Anat.] The soft

material covering the bone in which a tooth is rooted. **gin'gival**, a. **gingi'vitis**, n. [Med.] INFLAMMATION of the gg. **gingivo-**.

'**ginglymus**, n. [Zoo.] JOINT with motion in one plane only. '**ginglymoid**, a.

Ginkgo'ales, n.pl. [Bot.] An ORDER of GYMNOSPERMAE of which the only representative now in existence is a tree of East China.

'**girder**, n. Long strong rod, board, or more complex structure, bridging a space and supporting something over it, such as a floor, a bridge, etc.

'**girdle**, n. [Biol.] Ring-like or curved, band-like structure going round something, sp. [Zoo.] incomplete ring of bone open in front, supporting the legs or the arms. **g. sen'sation**. [Med.] Feeling of having something tight round the middle of the body, sometimes present in disease of the back-bone.

'**gizzard**, n. [Zoo.] The second stomach of birds, having very thick walls with strong muscles and a hard inner coating, in which food is crushed; stomach or part doing same work in insects and some other animals.

Gl, Sign for GLUCINUM.

'**glabrous**, '**glabrate**, aa. [Biol.] Smooth, sp. without hairs.

'**glacial**, a. To do with ice or with great cold. **G. Age, G. Period**, or **G. 'Epoch**. [Geol.] Any of a number of times in history of the earth when a great part of it was covered with ice, chiefly in the PLEISTOCENE PERIOD. (*See* p. 558.) **glaci'ation**, n. [Geol.] Process of becoming covered with ice.

'**glacier**, n. [Geol.] Field or body of ice formed from snow on high mountains and moving very slowly down mountain side or river-bed, with new ice all the time forming at the back of it.

glance, n. [Mineral.] Name given to some ORES having S in them and a bright look, sp. natural CuS.

'**glancing 'angle**. [Phys.] Very small angle between a ray and the body it is meeting.

gland, n. [Zoo.] Any of number of parts in an animal body whose purpose is the taking of certain substances from the blood and the producing from them of others to be used in, or sent out of, the body. [Bot.] Part having same purpose as animal g., such as a hair; any small outgrowth. '**-ular**, **a. g. cell**. [Biol.] Separate CELL acting as g.; cell of g.

glans. n. [Anat.] Sponge-like body forming end of PENIS and CLITORIS. [Bot.] Not having a cover or cup.

glass, n. A hard substance without CRYSTAL form made by heating together one or more OXIDES of Si, B or P with certain BASIC oxides and making them cold

quickly so as to keep crystals from forming. [Geol.] Solid substance formed by heated liquid made cold without there being time for crystals to be formed in it. **g. wool**. Mass of very thin threads of g. '**glassy**, a.

'**Glauber's salt**. [Mineral., Med.] Na_2SO_4. $10H_2O$ (*hydrated sodium sulphate*) a white CRYSTALLINE substance formed in SALT LAKES, etc., and used medically as an APERIENT.

'**glauconite**, n. [Mineral.] Natural SILICATE of Fe and K with H_2O, a green substance formed under the sea and freq. mixed with sea sand.

glau'coma, n. [Med.] A diseased condition of the eye in which the EYEBALL becomes hard as the effect of unnormal PRESSURE of liquid inside it, causing loss of power of seeing.

'**glaucous**, a. Blue-green or green-blue. [Bot.] Covered with grey-green delicate wax-like grains, as some fruit.

glaze, n., v.t. Very thin, glass-like covering or SURFACE given to brick or pot; material forming g. **glazed**, a.

'**glenoid** a., n. [Zoo.] (Having form of, to do with) a smooth hollow in a bone, sp. one into which another bone goes.

'**glia**, n. [Anat.] NEUROGLIA.

'**gliadin**, n. [Biochem.] A PROTEIN present in the seeds of certain grain-plants. **-s**. Group of which g. is one.

glide, n. [Phonet.] Unclear sound produced between two different named sounds, in going from one to the other without stopping.

glide- or **gliding-plane**. The common plane of the two AXES of a TWIN CRYSTAL; SLIP PLANE.

'**glider**, n. AIRCRAFT having planes like an airplane but no engine. '**gliding**, n. The use and control of gg.

gli'oma, n. [Med.] TUMOUR of the GLIA.

'**Glisson's 'capsule**. Structure of CONNECTIVE TISSUE covering and making divisions of LIVER.

globe, n. Anything in the form of a solid or hollow ball, sp. [Geog.] one with a map on it, representative of the Earth. '**glob-ate, -oid, -ose**, aa.

'**Globiger'ina**, n.pl. [Zoo.] An important GENUS of FORAMINIFERA. **g. ooze**. Soft sticky mass covering floor of deep sea, made up of CALCAREOUS SHELLS of very small sea animals, sp. G.

'**globin**, n. [Biochem.] PROTEIN part of HAEMOGLOBIN.

'**globule**, n. Small ball of substance, sp. liquid. '**globul-ar, -ose**, aa.

globu'limiter, n. Instrument for measuring number of red CELLS in blood.

'**globulins**, n.pl. [Biochem.] Certain PROTEINS of a number of body substances, not SOLUBLE in water, but soluble in salt and water, for example, that present in the blood as a part of HAEMOGLOBIN .

glo′chidium, n. [Bot.] Any of the hairs with hooked ends on SPORE masses of certain PTERIDOPHYTA. [Zoo.] LARVA of LAMEL-LIBRANCHIA. **glo′chidiate,** a.

′gloea, n. [Zoo.] Sticky substance covering some PROTOZOA.

glome′ration, n. Act of forming, getting together, into a ball, **′glomerate,** a. Formed into a ball.

glo′merular, a. [Biol.] To do with a GLOMERULUS or GLOMERULE.

glo′merulate, a. [Biol.] Grouped in GLO-MERULES or GLOMERULI.

′glomerule, n. [Bot.] Flowers in form of ball-like mass; ball-like mass of SPORES. **glo′meru′liferous,** a.

glo′merulus (glomeruli), n. [Zoo.] Mass of small blood vessels. sp. in KIDNEY.

′glossa (glossae), n. [Zoo.] Tongue-like part of lower lip of insect; tongue-like structure. **′glossate,** a.

′glossal, a. To do with the tongue.

′gloss(o)-. (Of) the tongue and (. . .):— **′-pharyngeal,** a.

′glossoid, a. Tongue-like.

′glottis, n. [Zoo.] In higher back-boned animals, the opening in the throat from the PHARYNX to the TRACHEA. **′glottal,** a. Sp. [Phonet.] made in the g. **glottal stop.** [Phonet.] The complete shutting of the g. under breath PRESSURE, sounding like a little cough.

glow dis′charge. [Elec.] Electric DISCHARGE through a gas taking the form of a soft light without sound or motion, such as is produced when the VOLTAGE is as low as possible. **glow lamp.** Light-apparatus in which light is produced without a flame; GAS DISCHARGE LAMP.

glu′cinum, n. [Chem.] A less frequently used name for BERYLLIUM.

gluco′samine, n. Substance, $C_6H_{13}O_5N$, got when CHITIN and like substances are broken up.

′glucose, n. [Biochem.] One of the HEXOSES got in fruit and from digestion of STARCH.

′glucoside, n. [Biochem.] Any of a great number of complex natural substances giving GLUCOSE when broken up.

glue, n. Substance got from bones, RESINS, GELATIN, etc., sticky when mixed with water, used for getting substances fixed together.

glume, ′gluma, nn. [Bot.] Small dry leaf at base of flower in grasses. **glu′maceous,** a. Thin, brown and paper-like, like a g. **glu′miferous, glu′miflorous,** aa. Having flowers with gg.

glu′teal, a. [Zoo.] To do with the BUTTOCKS.

′glutelins, n. [Biochem.] A group of PRO-TEINS in grain.

′gluten, n. A sticky PROTEIN substance present sp. in grain-plants.

glu′teus, n. In back-boned land animals, name given to any of certain muscles at back of top of leg. **glu′teal,** a.

′glutinous, a. Sticky, sp. [Bot.] covered with a sticky substance.

glu′tition, n. Act of getting food down throat.

′glyceride, n. [Chem.] Any of the ESTERS of GLYCERINE, chiefly FATS.

′glycerine, ′glycerol, nn. [Chem.] A sweet sticky alcohol without colour or smell, $CH_2OH.CHOH.CH_2OH$, produced from natural fats.

′glyceryl, n. [Chem.] The group CH_2CHCH_2 of which GLYCERINE is the HYDROXIDE.

′glycogen, n. [Biochem.] A STARCH-like substance, $C_6H_{10}O_5$, stored sp. in LIVER of animals, giving GLUCOSE when broken down. **glyco′genesis,** n. The making of g. from sugar in the body.

′glycol, n. [Chem.] ETHYLENE GLYCOL; any of a group of thick sweet liquids or CRYSTALLINE solids having the same general make-up as ethylene glycol and the behaviour of ALCOHOLS.

gly′colysis, n. [Biochem.] Process by which GLYCOGEN is broken up when acted on by water.

gly′coneo′genesis, n. [Physiol.] Change of a body substance which is not a sugar into GLYCOGEN.

glyco′suria, n. [Med.] Condition in which sugar is present in URINE. **glyco′suric,** a.

gm. = GRAM(s).

′gnathic, a. [Zoo.] To do with JAW. **′gnatho-.**

′gnathite, n. [Zoo.] Any of the mouth-parts of ARTHROPODA.

′gnathobase, n. [Zoo.] An in-turning growth on the inner side of the part of a GNATHITE nearest mouth, for crushing up food. **gnatho′basic,** a.

′gnathopod(ite), n. [Zoo.] Leg-like part near mouth of ARTHROPODA, sp. CRUSTACEA, used for taking in food.

Gnatho′stomata, Gnatho′stomi, nn.pl. [Zoo.] The branch, sometimes looked on as a SUB-PHYLUM, of back-boned animals with moving JAWS.

gnatho′stomatous, a. [Zoo.] Having JAWS.

gneiss, n. [Geol.] A METAMORPHIC ROCK with light GRANULITIC bands (QUARTZ and FELDSPAR) between dark FOLIATED bands (MICA and sometimes HORNBLENDE). **′gneissose, ′gneissic,** aa. Sp. like g. in having a structure of GRANULITIC bands of one substance between FOLIATED bands of another.

′goblet cell. [Anat.] CELL of columnar EPITHELIUM, as in stomach, stretched at its free end by MUCIN produced by it.

′goitre, n. [Med.] Diseased growth of THYROID GLAND.

gold, n. Chemical ELEMENT, at. no. 79, at. wt. 192·2, sign Au, a somewhat soft yellow metal of great weight, very readily worked and not attacked by air, water, or most acids, highly valued for ornament. **g. leaf.** Gold hammered into a thin, paper-like form. **'g.-leaf e'lectroscope.** [Elec.] An ELECTROSCOPE made up of a glass vessel having in it two bits of g. leaf fixed to a metal rod going through the top of the vessel, any CHARGE on the rod having the effect of causing a motion of the leaves away from one another.

'Golgi appa'ratus. [Biol.] Structure in CYTOPLASM of CELL, commonly a network but sometimes in the form of separate grains named **Golgi 'bodies,** which has to do with the building up of food in the cell.

'gonad, n. [Zoo.] GLAND producing sex-cells, male, female, or male and female. **go'nad-(i)al, -ic,** aa.

'gonado'trop(h)ic, a. [Med.] Said of substances having an effect on GONADS. **g. 'hormones.** [Zoo.] HORMONES of the PITUITARY GLAND causing increased sex development.

' gonaduct, n. [Zoo.] The pipe or opening from a GONAD.

gona'pophysis (gonapophyses), n. [Zoo.] Any of the outer sex-ORGANS of an insect, or in the female such a sex-part used for putting eggs down, or as a STING.

goni'dangium, n. [Bot.] A SPORANGIUM producing GONIDIA.

go'nidiophore, n. [Bot.] The part supporting a GONIDANGIUM.

go'nidiophyll, n. [Bot.] Leaf with GONIDIA on it.

go'nidium (gon'idia), n. [Bot.] SPORE without sex produced by GAMETOPHYTE. **go'nidial,** a. **go'nidial layer.** ALGAL LAYER. **goni'diferous,** a. **go'nidioid,** a.

go'nomic 'layer. ALGAL LAYER.

goni'ometer, n. Instrument for measuring angles sp. between the faces of CRYSTALS or [Craniom.] the planes of the head. **goni'ometry,** n.

gono-. [Zoo., Med.] Sex, to do with producing offspring.

gono'coccus, n. [Med.] The BACTERIUM by which the disease of GONORRHOEA is caused.

'gonocoel, n. [Zoo.] The body-hollow, or that part of it, in which are the GONADS.

'gonoduct, n. [Zoo.] Pipe going from GONAD to outside of body.

'gonophore, n. [Zoo.] Special offspring-producing unit of a HYDROID COLONY. [Bot.] Stem having SPORES on it.

'gonopore, n. [Zoo.] Opening in sex-part through which sex-substance is sent out.

gonor'rh(o)ea, n. [Med.] CONTAGIOUS disease of sex-parts caused by GONOCOCCUS and attacking sp. URETHRA and VAGINA.

gono'theca, n. [Zoo.] Expansion of PERISARC round part producing GONOPHORES.

gono'zovid, n. [Zoo.] Sex-ZOOID of TUNICATA; GONOPHORE.

Gooch 'crucible or **filter.** [Chem.] Small cup, with holes in base covered with thin threads of ASBESTOS, used as FILTER in chemical ANALYSIS.

goose flesh, goose skin. [Med.] The condition of the skin when the soft part round the base of every hair on it comes up in a little point, lifting the hair, caused by cold, fear, etc.

'goslarite, n. [Mineral.] Natural WHITE VITRIOL ($ZnSO_4.7H_2O$), an uncommon substance formed by the OXIDATION of ZINC BLENDE.

gout, n. [Med.] Disease in which, as effect of overmuch URIC ACID in the blood, grains of SODIUM URATE ($Na_2C_5H_4O_3N_4$) are formed in JOINTS, sp. that of great toe, causing much pain.

'governor, n. Part fixed to steam engine or other machine for automatically controlling its rate of turning.

g.p.i. = GENERAL PARALYSIS OF THE INSANE.

'Graafian follicle [Zoo.]. Any of the bag-like vessels having the OVA in them inside the OVARY of higher animals, formed of an outer skin covering a thicker wall of CELLS, with, in man, a thin liquid inside.

'gracilis, n. [Anat.] Muscle on inside of top part of leg.

gra'dation, n. [Geog.] A general levelling of earth over a wide stretch by weather, rivers, etc. [Phonet.] Change in a VOWEL-sound dependent on the degree of force with which it is said, or the effect of another vowel near it.

'gradient, n. The rate of change of anything over a distance, as HEIGHT, TEMPERATURE, ELECTRIC FIELD, for example, the g. of a slope is the distance in which it goes up (or down) one unit.

grad(i)'ometer, n. Instrument for measuring GRADIENT of slope.

'graduate, v.t. and i. Make division of into regularly increasing steps or stages, or into equal measures, degrees; get marked with scale; make, become, smaller or greater by degrees, come by degrees to a point. **'graduated,** a. **gradu'ation,** n. Sp. all or any one of the marks on a graduated vessel or instrument.

graft, 1.v.t. [Bot.] Get (bit of living plant) fixed into cut in branch, stem, or root of another, so that they are united in growth. [Med.] Get (bit of living substance) for example, skin or bone, from another part or animal, united to part of body where there has been a loss. 2.n. Part of plant grafted to another; plant formed by grafting. [Med.] Bit of living substance grafted onto wound, etc. **g. 'hybrid.** Plant formed by grafting in which the two parts do not keep their separate qualities but a new form is produced.

'**Graham('s) law.** [Phys.] Law that the rate at which different gases come out of a small hole is in INVERSE PROPORTION to the DENSITY of the gas.

grain, n. Unit of TROY and APOTHECARIES' WEIGHT, = 0·0648 GRAM. (*See* p. 565.)

grain, n. The size and grouping of the grains or PARTICLES of any substance, such as stone, skin, etc., which gives it its special properties to touch and view; the direction of FIBRES in wood or of STRATA in stone, or their grouping, sp. as forming a design seen when they are cut across. **g. size.** [Geol.] The size of the gg. in a sort of ROCK. **grain-size** 'classifi'cation. [Geol.] A grouping of ROCKS based on their g. size, as FINE-GRAINED, MEDIUM-GRAINED and COARSE-GRAINED.

grain, n. [Bot.] Small dry fruit with one seed, the coat of which is united to the fruit wall, produced by food grasses; such plants or their fruits or seeds.

gram(me), n. Unit of weight, at one time taken as being equal to the mass of 1 c.c. of water at 4°C. but now as $\frac{1}{1000}$ of the mass of a certain metal CYLINDER kept at Sèvres, France. **g. atom.** The amount of an ELEMENT whose mass in grams is equal to its ATOMIC weight. **g. e'quivalent.** The amount of an ELEMENT whose weight in gg. is equal to its CHEMICAL EQUIVALENT. **g.** 'molecule. The MOLECULAR WEIGHT in gg. of a substance. **g.-'calorie,** n. *See* CALORIE.

'**grammar,** n. [Philol.] The structure and rules of a language, that is, the way in which its words are put together in framing statements etc., its word-forms or other ways of making clear the relations between words as used in talk or writing, and its system of letters or other signs representative of sounds; the science of gg. **gramm'atical,** a.

gramme ring. [Elec.] An iron ring completely covered with turns of wire, used as an ARMATURE in some electric machines.

'**gramophone,** n. [Acous.] An instrument for recording sound on, and producing recorded sound again from, a plate or roll of hard material (a **g. record**) turning round under a needle in connection with a DIAPHRAGM, the needle cutting marks in the plate representative of the VIBRATIONS of the diaphragm when acted on by sound-waves from outside; or producing the same sound-waves in the diaphragm when itself put in vibration by going over the marks on the plate—an early, MECHANICALLY worked form of the present-day RECORD-PLAYER.

Gram's method. Process of colouring BACTERIA with Gram's solution, after which they are put in ALCOHOL and washed with water. **Gram-'negative.** Not coloured by Gram's solution.

Gram-'positive. Coloured by Gram's solution. **Gram's so'lution.** SOLUTION of I and KI in water.

grand mal. [Med.] EPILEPSY in its worst form.

gran'iferous, a. [Bot.] Producing grain.

'**granite,** b. [Geol.] A very hard, COARSE-GRAINED, IGNEOUS ROCK made up of at least three minerals, QUARTZ, FELDSPAR, and MICA. **g.-porphyry,** n. A ROCK of the same make-up as g. but MEDIUM-GRAINED and of PORPHYRITIC TEXTURE. **g. clan.** The CLAN of which g. is representative, taking in MEDIUM-GRAINED and FINE-GRAINED sorts. (*See* p. 192.)

'**granular,** a. Made up of grains or GRANULES. [Med.] Having GRANULATIONS. [Bot.] Sp. covered with very small points or outgrowths.

'**granulate,** v.t. and i. (Make) get into form of grains, GRANULES or small masses. [Med.] Undergo granulation. '**granulate(d),** a. GRANULAR. **granu'lation,** n. Sp.:—[Med.] (Process of forming) small, grain-like outgrowths. [Chem.] Sp. process of granulating metal, etc. by dropping it into water when in a heated liquid condition. [Astron.] GRANULE or granules. **granulation 'tissue.** [Med.] New TISSUE formed over place where there has been loss through wound, etc.

'**granule,** n. Very small grain or bit of anything. [Astron.] Any of the separate bright clouds of gas forming part of the sun's outer face and giving a suggestion, as seen from the earth, of small grains or leaves. **g. cell.** [Zoo.] CELL in CONNECTIVE TISSUE having in it gg. which may be deeply coloured by ANILINE DYES.

'**granulocyte,** n. [Zoo.] POLYMORPHO-NUCLEAR LEUCOCYTE.

granu'loma, n. [Med.] Diseased growth formed chiefly of GRANULATION TISSUE. '**-tous,** a.

-graph. Account in writing or other record; recording instrument.

graph, n. A DIAGRAM making clear the relation between two or more changing conditions, forces, for example a curve on squared paper giving price of something at different points of time. '**graphic(al),** aa. **graphic 'formula.** [Chem.] A CHEMICAL FORMULA in which the position of every ATOM in a MOLECULE in relation to the others is given, with lines between representative of the VALENCY BONDS joining them, as H–O–H for water, or

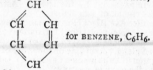

for BENZENE, C_6H_6.

'**graphics,** n.pl. Science of working out

questions of engineering and building-structure by geometry.

'graphite, n. [Mineral.] Natural C in form of black, 6-faced CRYSTALS, soft enough to make marks on paper. **gra'phitic,** a. **'graphitize,** v.t. Get changed into g.

grapho'mania, n. [Med.] Disease of mind in which person has desire to be writing all the time.

-'graphy. Process of recording, sp. by instrument.

'graptolite, n. [Geol.] A FOSSIL of any of certain small and simple animals, generally taken to be COELENTERATES, which went out of existence in the SILURIAN PERIOD, and whose fossils are present in the ROCKS of that and earlier times.

'graticule, n. [Optics] Glass, etc. plate marked into squares by thin lines, put into TELESCOPE or other instrument as help in getting position and size of things in the field of view. **'graticu'lation,** n. Marking on g. or like marking used for like purposes.

'grating, n. A structure of rods, stiff wires, etc. parallel to one another or forming a network, used for a number of purposes, such as covering a hole or the opening to a pipe etc., to keep things from getting into it. [Optics] DIFFRACTION GRATING.

'gravel, n. [Geol.] Loose material made up of small stones transported and rounded by water, gen. mixed with sand.

'gravid, n. [Zoo., Med.] Of a female animal, in the condition of having young or eggs in the body.

gravi'metric(al), aa. [Chem.] To do with measuring by weight; measured by weight. **g. a'nalysis.** ANALYSIS in which the different substances making up a complex one are measured by weight. g. **'density.** [Phys.] Weight of unit measure of any substance made up of grains. **gra'vimetry,** n. Process of measuring by weight.

gravi'tation, n. [Phys.] The attraction of all material bodies for one another. **'-al,** a. **gravi'tational 'constant.** The attraction of 1 gram for 1 gram at a distance of 1 cm $= 6.6579 \times 10^{-8}$ c.g.s. units.

'gravity, n. The attraction of the earth for bodies on it. **g. cell.** An electric CELL in which one liquid is resting on another of greater weight.

great 'calorie. LARGE CALORIE (*see* CALORIE).

great circle. [Geom.] The circle formed where a plane through the middle of a SPHERE is cut by the sphere. [Astron.] *See* CIRCLE OF THE SPHERE.

Great Ice Age. [Geol.] PLEISTOCENE PERIOD.

green 'Algae, n.pl. [Bot.] CHLOROPHYCEAE.

'green-'blindness. [Psych.] DEUTERANOPIA.

green gland. [Zoo.] One or the other of two green GLANDS in some CRUSTACEA, said to do the work of a KIDNEY.

green mud. [Geol.] A soft thick coating on the deep-sea bed formed chiefly of SHELLS of FORAMINIFERA mixed with GLAUCONITE, which gives it a green colour.

'green-stick 'fracture. [Med.] Damage to a bone by which it is not broken through, but to some degree broken and to some degree bent, common in very young persons whose bones are still not completely stiff.

'greenstone, n. [Geol.] Name given loosely to any of different sorts of dark green ROCK, such as DIABASE.

green 'vitriol. *See* VITRIOL.

'Greenwich mean time. [Astron.] MEAN SOLAR TIME measured at the MERIDIAN of Greenwich.

gre'garious, a. [Biol.] Living or having growth together in groups.

Gre'gorian 'calendar. The CALENDAR in general use today, put out by Pope Gregory XIII in 1582—the JULIAN CALENDAR with a small adjustment to make the VERNAL EQUINOX come on March 21 every year.

grenz ray. The longest X-ray, used medically in certain skin diseases.

grey, a., n. [Optics] (Of) any colour of the range of ACHROMATIC colours between black and white, different from one another only in their degree of LIGHTNESS.

grey 'matter. [Anat.] Material formed of nerve CELLS and FIBRES without MYELIN covering, sp. in the brain and SPINAL CORD, the substance of the brain NUCLEI, *see* WHITE MATTER.

'greywacke, n. [Geol.] Sort of SANDSTONE, gen. dark grey, made up of more or less round bits of SiO_2 and other dark-coloured stone formed into a hard mass.

grid, n. A structure of lines, wires, rods, pipes, etc., parallel to one another or forming network. [Elec.] In a THERMIONIC VALVE, an ELECTRODE, gen. in the form of a wire g., put between two other electrodes—in a TRIODE, between the ANODE and the CATHODE—for controlling the current between them. **g. leak.** [Elec.] A very high RESISTANCE joining g. to earth.

'Grignard re'action. [Chem.] Reaction in which GRIGNARD REAGENTS are used to make ETHERS, ALCOHOLS, KETONES, etc. **Grignard re'agent.** [Chem.] Substance made by the addition of Mg to dry ETHER with an ALKYL BROMIDE in it.

Grimm's law. [Philol.] A statement of the regular changes undergone by the STOPPED CONSONANTS of the early INDO-EUROPEAN languages in their development into German and its sister languages, as *g* into *k*.

grind, v.t. and i. Get (a substance) crushed to bits or powder by rubbing it on or between something very hard, as between two stones; give a desired form, sp. a sharp point or edge, to (something) by grinding away some of its substance. **'grinder,** n. **'grinding,** a., n. **grinding teeth.** [Zoo.] MOLAR TEETH. **ground,** a. Powdered or made sharp by grinding.

grit, n. [Geol.] Loose material like sand, but of which the grains, unlike those of sand, are sharp-pointed; gritstone. **'-stone.** A stone of COARSE and irregular grains formed of massed g.

groin, n. [Anat.] GROOVE, line of join, between the lower front part of body and the top of leg, or the part round it.

groove, n. A line cut more or less deeply into anything, a long narrow line-like hollow. **grooved,** a. Having a g. or gg.

ground, 1.n. The face of the earth, the earth under our feet; the base or support of anything, that on which it is resting; the chief part of a mixed or complex substance. 2.a. Of or near the g.; being the g. of something. **g. frost.** [Meteor.] In Britain a TEMPERATURE on the g. of two or more degrees lower than FREEZING-POINT, at which there is danger to plants in growth. **g. ice.** [Geog.] Ice sometimes formed on the base and sides of the bed of a river or other body of water before the rest becomes solid. **g. speed.** The rate at which an airplane goes in relation to a point on the g., that is, taking into account the effect of air currents causing it to go over a greater or less measure of g. than its rate of motion would take it over with no current acting with or against it. **g. state.** [Phys.] Condition of an ATOM at which ENERGY LEVEL is lowest. **g. 'substance.** [Biol.] Substance in spaces between CELLS, or between network of PROTOPLASM inside cell, **g. water.** [Geol.] Water inside the earth anywhere between the top and the deeper parts through which it is unable to make its way down. **g. wave.** [Radio] That part of a radio WAVE which goes straight over the g. from the sending station to RECEIVERS without being REFLECTED from the IONOSPHERE. **'groundmass,** n. [Geol.] The small-grained or glass-like chief substance of certain IGNEOUS ROCKS in which greater CRYSTALS of other substances are bedded.

group, n. [Geol.] STAGE.

Grove cell. Electric CELL made up of Pt in HNO$_3$ and Zn in H$_2$SO$_4$.

grow, 1.v.i. Undergo growth. 2.v.t. CULTIVATE (plants). **'growing point, growth point,** [Bot.] The point in a plant body at which growth by CELL DIVISION is taking place. **growth,** n. [Biol.] The natural process by which a living thing or any part of it becomes greater in size, effected by CELL DIVISION and the use of food; addition made to a plant or animal body by further g., or structure or mass which has grown out of it at some point, sp. [Med.] a CARCINOMA or SARCOMA. [Bot.] Plants which have grown or are growing in a place. **growth (pro'moting) substances** [Bot.] AUXINS.

grub, n. [Zoo.] Any soft, thick, worm-like LARVA.

'guanidin(e), n. [Chem.] Substance, NH:C(NH$_2$)$_2$, produced from GUANIN when acted on by O.

'guanin(e), n. [Chem.] Substance, C$_5$H$_5$N$_5$O, present in waste material from animals, in parts of their bodies, and in certain plants.

'guano, n. [Chem.] Substance formed chiefly of the waste sent out by seabirds, got from islands etc. of Central America and Africa, and widely used for making land fertile.

guard, n. [Mach.] Structure or apparatus put near or round a thing, or forming part of a machine, etc., to keep it, or persons using it, from damage. **g. cell.** [Bot.] One or other of two small CELLS at edge of STOMA, controlling its opening. **'g.-ring.** [Elec.] Ring of metal put round but not touching a CHARGED body such as a plate of a CONDENSER, to get an equal distribution of POTENTIAL or make an ELECTRIC FIELD take a desired form.

guber'naculum, n. [Zoo.] In the EMBRYO of higher animals, the cord by which the TESTIS is joined to the SCROTUM; narrow band joining tooth to GUM; back FLAGELLUM of CILIOPHORA, used for guiding motion.

'guided 'weapon. Any military PROJECTILE, such as a ROCKET BOMB, whose motion to a desired point is guided and controlled by some structure inside it or some apparatus at a distance, gen. ELECTRONIC.

'guiding 'centre. [Phys.] The middle point of the ORBIT of a CHARGED PARTICLE which is moving round in a MAGNETIC FIELD.

'Guldberg and 'Waage's law. LAW OF MASS ACTION.

'gullet, n. [Zoo.] Pipe through which food goes from mouth to stomach, the inside of the throat; pipe between CELL-mouth and ENDOPLASM of CILIOPHORA.

gum, n. [Zoo.] GINGIVA. [Chem., Bot.] Any of a group of COLLOIDAL substances, sticky when wet but hard when dry, sent out by plants. **g.-'resin.** Mixed g. and RESIN from a plant. **gumm'iferous,** a.

'gummite, n. [Mineral.] A yellow or red-brown non-CRYSTALLINE material substance from which U is got.

'guncotton, Substance produced by acting on CELLULOSE with HNO$_3$ and H$_2$SO$_4$, readily burning and EXPLOSIVE.

'**gunmetal.** A mixed metal made of 90% copper and 10% tin.

'**gunpowder,** n. An EXPLOSIVE made of C, S and KNO$_3$ mixed, much used for getting coal in mines broken up.

gus'**tatory,** a. [Zoo.] To do with sense of taste.

gut, n. Animal INTESTINE; cord formed of gg. used for medical and other purposes.

'**gutta-'percha,** n. Rubber-like substance formed by LATEX from certain trees, used sp. as electric INSULATOR.

'**guttural,** n., a. [Phonet.] VELAR.

'**gutturo-.** Throat.

'**gymno-.** [Biol.] Uncovered.

gymno'carpous, a. [Bot.] Having uncovered fruit.

gym'nogenous, a. [Zoo.] Of bird, coming out of the egg without any growth of feathers, with skin completely uncovered.

gym'nogynous, a. [Bot.] Having uncovered OVARY.

'**Gymnophi'ona,** n.pl. APODA.

Gymno'spermae, n.pl. [Bot.] One of the two great CLASSES of seed-plants with uncovered seeds, in which the seeds are ranged on the flat side of a SCALE LEAF, these leaves being massed together in the form of a CONE. '**gymnosperm,** n. Plant of the G.

'**gymnospore,** n. [Bot.] A SPORE without covering.

gy'**naec-ium, -eum,** n. GYNOECIUM.

'**gyn(a)eco-.** Of, to do with, women, **gyn(a)e-'cology,** n. [Med.] Science of body-processes and diseases of women. **gyn(a)e-'cologist,** n.

gy'**nandrism,** n. [Biol.] HERMAPHRODITISM.

gy'**nandromorph,** n. [Zoo.] Unnormal animal, in part like male, in part like female. **gy'nandro'morphism,** n.

gy'**nandrous,** a. [Bot.] Having STAMENS and STYLE(s) united into one thick stem.

gy'**nantherous,** a. [Bot.] Having STAMENS changed into CARPELS.

gyni'**atrics,** n.pl. Medical care of women.

gy'**n(o)ecium,** n. [Bot.] The complete female apparatus of a flower, the CARPEL or group of carpels.

gyno'**genesis,** n. [Zoo.] Development of egg in which only female CHROMOSOMES take part.

'**gynophore,** n. [Bot.] A small stem supporting the GYNOECIUM.

'**gypsophyte,** n. [Bot.] Plant living best in earth with CaO in it.

'**gypsum,** n. [Mineral.] Natural CaSO$_4$. 2H$_2$O, a CRYSTALLINE or MASSIVE substance without colour, used for making PLASTER OF PARIS (see ALABASTER, SELENITE).

gy'**ration,** n. [Phys.] Act of turning round on an AXIS or circling a middle point with twisting motion forward; one such turn. '**-al, gy'ratory,** aa.

'**gyro-.** Turning or twisting round.

gyro 'compass. COMPASS having in it an electrically turned GYROSCOPE, so that it is kept ever parallel to the earth's AXIS.

'**gyrody'namics,** n.pl. Science of motion of turning bodies, sp. the effects of PRECESSION.

gy'**roidal,** a. [Cryst.] Having planes in the form of a SPIRAL so that they are sloping right or left in relation to the middle line.

'**gyromag'netic,** a. [Phys.] To do with the MAGNETIC properties of turning electric CHARGES, sp. of ELECTRONS moving inside ATOMS. **g. effect.** The twist given to an iron or other rod when made MAGNETIC.

gy'**rometer,** n. INSTRUMENT measuring rate of turning round.

'**gyroplane,** n. Airplane balanced and supported by quickly turning HORIZONTAL or somewhat sloping planes.

'**gyroscope,** n. Small wheel of great weight turning round quickly in a frame moving freely about one or two AXES at right angles to that of the wheel and to one another, so that any force with a tendency to make a change in the direction of the axis of the wheel is overcome by a turning motion, used in an apparatus for flying an airplane automatically, as a STABILIZER in ships, etc. **gyro'scopic,** a.

'**gyrose,** a. Having waving lines.

'**gyrostat,** n. GYROSCOPE. **gyro'static,** a.

'**gyrus,** n. [Anat.] Any of the RIDGES in the CONVOLUTIONS of the brain. **gyral,** a.

H, Sign for HYDROGEN.

h, Sign for PLANCK'S CONSTANT.

'**Haber's 'process.** [Chem.] A process for making NH$_3$ from N and H with help of a CATALYST.

'**habit,** n. [Biol.] Form of growth, behaviour, etc., normal to a plant or animal. [Pysch.] A certain act done regularly, so forming a tendency to it. '**h.-forming,** a. [Med.] (Of a medical substance or DRUG) causing person who takes it to become dependent on its effects, unable to do without it. **h. spasm.** [Med.] A quick automatic CONTRACTION of certain muscles taking place from time to time, for which there is no physical cause. **ha'bitual,** a. Done, etc., regularly, as a h.

'**habitat,** n. [Biol.] Natural living place of plant or animal.

ha'bitu'ation, n. The process of getting used to anything. [Biol.] Of a CELL, adjustment to effects of the same STIMULUS coming over and over.

'habitus, n. [Biol.] HABIT.

hade, 1.n. [Geol.] The angle of slope which the slope of a FAULT makes with the VERTICAL. 2.v.i. Be sloping from the VERTICAL.

'Haeckel's law. RECAPITULATION THEORY.

h(a)em-, h(a)ema-, h(a)emat-, h(a)emato-, h(a)emo-. Blood: 'h(a)em(at)o'genesis, nn. h(a)ematologist, n., h(a)em(at)oid, aa.

haem, n. [Biochem.] A red substance forming part of HAEMATIN, responsible for the red colour of blood and other body liquids, present in YEAST and BACTERIA as well as in most animal CELLS.

'h(a)em(at)al, aa. [Zoo.] To do with blood or blood-vessels; to do with, being on, same side of backbone as the heart and chief blood-vessels. 'h(a)emal arch. Structure of bone(s) or CARTILAGE arching from backbone in direction of the under side, or, in man, the front, of the body. 'h(a)emal ca'nal. Space framed by backbone and h. arch in tails of fish, snakes, etc., through which go blood-vessels. 'haemal spine. Point, outgrowth, where two sides of h. arch are united under h. canal.

h(a)emangi'oma, n. [Med.] Diseased growth made up of blood-vessels.

'h(a)ema(ta)poi'esis, nn. [Zoo.] The forming of blood. 'h(a)ema(ta)poi'etic, aa.

'h(a)ema'pophysis, n. [Zoo.] The front or lower division of a HAEMAL ARCH; one or other of two opposite plate-like outgrowths forming the HAEMAL ARCH in certain animals.

h(a)e'mat(in)ic, a. [Med.] To do with, acting on, the blood, sp. increasing ERYTHROCYTES.

h(a)ema't-imeter, -ometer, nn. [Med.] Instrument for measuring number of ERYTHROCYTES in blood.

'h(a)ematin, n. [Chem.] Almost black substance, having iron in it, formed when OXYHAEMOGLOBIN is broken up.

'haematite, n. [Mineral.] Natural Fe_2O_3 (*iron oxide*), present in the earth in the form of metal-like CRYSTALS or as earth-like substances, red or red-brown in colour—used for producing iron and as a PIGMENT.

h(a)e'matocele, n. [Med.] A space full of blood which is not a blood-vessel.

h(a)e'matochrome, n. Red colouring-substance of certain ALGAE.

h(a)e'matocyst, n. [Med.] CYST full of blood.

h(a)ema'togenous, a. Formed in the blood.

h(a)ema'tolysis, n. HAEMOLYSIS.

h(a)ema'tophagous, a. [Zoo.] Living on blood.

h(a)e'mato'porphyrin, n. [Chem.] Iron-free brown powder formed when HAEMATIN is broken up.

h(a)ema'tosis, n. [Zoo.] The forming of blood; the operation of the air acting on the blood in the LUNGS.

'h(a)emato'zoön, n. [Zoo.] Any PARASITE living in blood.

h(a)ema'turia, n. [Med.] Diseased condition in which blood is present in URINE.

'h(a)emic, a. [Zoo.] To do with the blood. h. 'murmur. [Med.] Low sound over the heart and greater blood-vessels in diseases.

'h(a)emin, n. [Biochem.] Substance got by reaction of blood with HYDROCHLORIC ACID.

h(a)emo'chromogen, n. [Biochem.] Colour-producing part of HAEMOGLOBIN; HAEMATIN.

'h(a)emocoele, n. [Zoo.] A hollow in the body formed by expansion of parts of the system of blood-vessels and taking the place of a true COELOM, as in ARTHROPODA.

'h(a)emo'cyanin, n. [Zoo.] Any of a number of blue substances with copper in them, by which O is taken up in blood of certain ARTHROPODA and MOLLUSCA.

'h(a)emocyte, n. An ERYTHROCYTE. 'h(a)emocy'tometer, n. Glass plate ruled in squares used for measuring number of ERYTHROCYTES in blood.

'h(a)emoe'rythrin, n. [Biochem.] Red substance taking up O in blood of worms and like animals.

h(a)emo'flagellate, n. [Zoo.] PROTOZOAN with FLAGELLAE, living in blood and causing serious diseases.

h(a)emo'fucsin, n. [Biochem., Med.] A yellow-brown colouring substance present in the healthy body in a small amount which is greatly increased in certain diseases.

h(a)emo'globin, n. [Zoo., Biochem.] Red substance present in blood of all back-boned animals and some others, and uniting with O in the breathing apparatus. 'haemoglobi'nometer, n. Instrument for measuring amount of h. in blood. 'haemoglobi'nuria, n. Diseased condition in which there is h. in URINE.

'h(a)emogluti'nation, n. [Med.] The massing together of ERYTHROCYTES.

'h(a)emolymph, n. [Zoo.] Liquid in HAEMOCOELE of some lower animals, looked on as doing work of blood and LYMPH in higher animals.

h(a)e'molysis, n. [Med.] Destruction of red blood-CELLS. h(a)emo'lytic, a. h(a)e'molysin, n. Any of a group of substances formed in blood as reaction to BACTERIA and having the property of causing h., sp. of the blood of another animal. h(a)e'molyzate, n. Substance produced by h.

'h(a)emophage, n. [Zoo., Med.] A LEUCOCYTE with the power of taking in ERYTHROCYTES. h(a)e'mophagy, h(a)emo-'phagia, nn. [Med.] (Condition caused by) the destruction of ERYTHROCYTES by hh.

h(a)emo'philia, n. [Med.] Condition present from birth and generally HEREDITARY in which loss of blood from wound is not able to be stopped because COAGULATION does not take place, seen only in males, but handed on by females. **h(a)emo-'philic**, a. **h(a)emo'philiac**, n. Person having h.

'h(a)emoplas'modium, n. [Zoo., Med.] One-CELLED PARASITE living in blood.

'h(a)emorrhage, n. [Med.] Loss of blood from damaged blood-vessel(s). **h(a)emor-'rhagic**, a.

'h(a)emorrhoid, n. [Med.] Expansion of a blood-vessel in or near ANUS, causing pain and sometimes loss of blood. **h(a)emor'rhoidal**, a. To do with ANUS or with hh.

h(a)emo-'stasis, -'stasia, nn. [Med.] The stopping of the current of blood in the body; the stopping of a HAEMORRHAGE. **h(a)emo'static**, n., a. [Med.] (Substance) producing h.

h(a)emo'toxin, n. [Med.] Poison in blood causing destruction of blood CORPUSCLES. **h(a)emotoxic**, a.

haemo'zoin, n. [Med.] Black grains formed after digestion of HAEMOGLOBIN by PARASITES causing MALARIA.

'hafnium, n. Chemical ELEMENT, at. no. 72, at. wt. 178·6, sign Hf, a metal.

hair, n. [Zoo.] Long, delicate, thread-like structure formed of KERATINIZED CELLS produced by cell-division from the EPI-DERMIS of MAMMALS: loosely, any h.-like outgrowth from the skin in other animals. [Bot.] A thread-like outgrowth from an EPIDERMAL CELL. **h. 'follicle**. Narrow, deep, cup-like hollow going down through the EPIDERMIS into the DERMIS, in which a h. is rooted.

'hair-spring. Spring controlling VIBRATION of BALANCE WHEEL of watch or clock.

ha'lation, n. Mist effect on camera plate sp. round edges of very bright parts of picture, caused by REFLECTION from back.

half-beam width. [Phys.] The distance between those points in a radio or other WAVE, normally at the middle of the wave, at which the degree of ENERGY is equal to half the greatest value.

half-de'cay 'period. HALF LIFE.

half-in'ferior, a. [Bot.] Having the end of the stem supporting the flower in the form of a cup, to the inside of which the base and the sides of the OVARY are united for some distance up.

'half-life ('period). [Phys.] The time taken by any amount of a RADIOACTIVE substance to undergo the DECAY of half its ATOMS.

half-sur'vival dose. [Med.] That amount of a substance causing the death of half a group of animals being tested for their reaction to it.

half-'tone process. [Printing] Way of print-ing pictures in which delicate shading is effected by grouping masses of small points.

half-'value 'period. HALF LIFE.

half-wave plate. A plate of CRYSTAL so cut as to make the ORDINARY and EXTRA-ORDINARY RAYS of light sent through it different in PHASE by 180°.

half-wave rectifi'cation. [Elec.] The changing of an ALTERNATING into a DIRECT CURRENT by stopping every other half-CYCLE, that is, by stopping all the impulses going in one of the two directions.

ha'lide, n. [Chem.] Substance formed by uniting one ELEMENT or RADICAL with F, Cl, Br, or I.

hali'tosis, n. [Med.] Condition of having bad-smelling breath.

Hall ef'fect. [Elec.] The change of direction of electric current in metal produced by a MAGNETIC FIELD.

ha'lluci'nation, n. [Psych.] Experience of sense effects seeming to have outside cause, but caused in fact by nerve or brain trouble. **ha'lluci'natory**, a. Caused by, to do with, producing, being, a h. **hallucino'genic** a. Producing hh. **ha'llu-cinosis**, n. [Med.] Mind-disease marked by hh.

'hallux, n. [Zoo.] In man the great toe, in higher animals, like division of back foot.

'Hallwach's ef'fect. PHOTOELECTRIC EFFECT.

'halo, n. A ring of light or shade round something, sp. [Meteor.] any of the rings of light round the sun or moon caused by ice in the air, or [Crystal.] any of the rings of dark colour round points in a CRYSTAL.

'halogen, n. [Chem.] Any of the ELEMENTS F, Cl, Br, and I, which make HALIDES by simple uniting with a metal, for example NaCl. **haloge'nation**, n. Process of getting a substance united with a h.

'haloid, n. HALIDE

ha'lophilous, a. [Bot.] Living, or having power of living, in salt water. **'halophile**, n. H. plant.

'halophyte, n. [Bot.] Plant living in earth having much salt in it, for example by the sea.

halo'plankton, n. [Biol.] The animals and plants living at or near top of the sea.

'halter (halteres), n. [Zoo.] One or other of two small thread-like structures taking place of back wings in some two-winged insects, probably used for balancing and maybe sensing.

ham, n. [Zoo.] Part at back of knee or JOINT between top and lower part of leg; upper back part of leg nearest body; HOCK.

ha'matum, n. [Zoo.] One of the bones between the hand and the arm or the like parts in other animals.

'hammer scale or **slag**. A sort of skin chiefly Fe_2O_3 and Fe_3O_4, produced on iron when heated for working with hammer etc.

'hammer-toe, n. [Med.] A toe not joined to foot in normal way but bent up; condition of foot having h.

'haplodont, a. [Zoo.] Having MOLAR teeth with simple tops, without points on them.

'haploid, a. [Biol.] (Of GERM-CELLS after development) having the h. number of CHROMOSOMES; (of the number of chromosomes) equal to half the number present in other than germ-cells.

haplo'phase, n. [Biol.] The stage of CELL development at which the CHROMOSOMES of the sex-cells become h.

hapt(o)-. Touching, uniting.

'haptoph-or, ore, hap'tophorous, aa. [Med.] Having power of uniting.

'haptotropism, n. [Bot.] A form of STEREO-TROPISM in which there is one-sided growth of a plant-part causing it to curve, seen in the twisting of a stem or TENDRIL round its support.

hard, a. [Phys.] (Of X-RAYS) having a short WAVE-LENGTH; (of a VACUUM) as complete as possible; (of a VACUUM TUBE) having a h. vacuum. [Chem.] (Of water) having in it SALTS of Ca, Fe, or Mg, so that when soap is used with it a hard SCUM is formed in place of a LATHER. [Phonet.] VOICELESS; of the letters c and g, said as STOPPED CONSONANTS, as in the words 'cup' and 'go'. h. soap. Solid soap, made by the reaction of NaOH with fats. '-ness, n. The property of being h., or the degree to which a thing is h., in any sense. hardness scale. [Mineral.] A scale of ten MINERALS used for making comparisons of how hard a mineral is by testing it against them.

hard 'palate. [Anat.] Hard part in middle of roof of mouth.

hare lip. [Med.] Division, present from birth, in top lip.

har'monic, 1.n. [Phys., Acous.] (In a complex WAVE when broken up into a number of simple waves) any wave having a FREQUENCY which is a complete MULTIPLE of the frequency of the FUNDA-MENTAL COMPONENT, that with twice its frequency being the *second h.*, etc. 2.a. To do with hh. h. 'analyser. [Phys.] An apparatus by which a complex WAVE is broken up into its COMPONENT waves. h. mean. [Math.] The RECIPROCAL of the ARITHMETIC MEAN of the reciprocals of two numbers, for example, $\frac{1}{8}$ is the h. mean of $\frac{1}{6}$ and $\frac{1}{10}$. h. pro'gression. [Math.] A PROGRESSION of numbers whose RECIPROCALS are in ARITHMETIC PRO-GRESSION. h. 'motion. SIMPLE H. MOTION.

har'monograph, n. [Phys.] An instrument for making LISSAJOUS FIGURES.

'Harvey 'process. Process for making the face of steel hard by heating it in certain

gases from which it will take up C.

'hastate, a. [Bot.] (Of leaf) having two out-turned parts at base (*see* picture p. 223).

haulm, n. [Bot.] The JOINTED stem of a grass.

haus'tellum, n. [Zoo.] Long thin TUBE-like mouth-part of certain insects, used for getting blood out of an animal or liquid out of a flower. 'haustellate, a.

haus'torium, n. [Bot.] Outgrowth of stem, root etc., of PARASITE plants, through which food is got. haus'torial, a.

Ha'versian ca'nals, n.pl. [Zoo.] Small pipes in bones through which go blood-vessels and nerves.

hay 'fever. [Med.] Condition marked by attacks of sneezing and watering of eyes and nose, as in a bad cold, caused by the effect on the MEMBRANES of these parts and of the throat etc. of breathing in the POLLEN of plants.

haze, n. [Meteor.] Very thin, dry cloud, or mist of dust or smoke, on the face of the earth, limiting the range of view to 2000 m. or less, but not less than 1000 m.

H-bomb, n. HYDROGEN BOMB.

He, Sign for HELIUM.

head, n. [Bot.] CAPITULUM.

head, n. [Hydraulics] The ENERGY per unit weight given to a body of liquid or gas as the effect of its HEIGHT, its VELOCITY, and its PRESSURE.

head 'kidney. [Zoo.] In back-boned animals PRONEPHROS; in LARVAE of certain other animals, a NEPHRIDIUM near the head end.

head-phone. (One of) two telephone or radio RECEIVERS put over the ears, which are joined and kept in place by a metal band resting on the head.

'hea'ring aid. An instrument for helping those whose hearing is very poor, put on or in the ear and making louder the sound coming to it, gen. made up of a MICROPHONE, an AMPLIFIER and a RECEIVER.

heart, n. [Zoo.] A hollow ORGAN with walls of muscle which CONTRACT in a regular rhythm, so acting as a pump to keep the blood going round through the blood-vessels. 'h.-block, n. [Med.] A condition in which the AURICLE and the VENTRICLE of the heart have different rhythms as the effect of damage to the special TISSUE taking the CONTRACTION impulse from the first to the second.

'heartburn, n. [Med.] A burning feeling in the throat and chest caused by acid coming up from the stomach into the OESOPHAGUS.

'heartwood, n. [Bot.] The hard wood forming the inner part of a tree or branch.

heat, n. [Phys.] A form of ENERGY which bodies have as the effect of the motions of their MOLECULES, any change in the amount of which is seen from their becoming warmer or colder. **h. ca'pacity.** [Phys.] The amount of h. needed for increasing the TEMPERATURE of a body through 1°C = the mass of the body × its SPECIFIC H. **h. 'engine.** Any machine in which work is done by change of h. into MECHANICAL ENERGY. **h. light'ning.** [Meteor.] Sudden bright wave of electric light covering a great stretch of the sky, seen near the HORIZON after a very warm day. **h. of for'mation.** [Chem.] The amount of h. produced in the uniting of two or more substances to make one GRAM MOLECULE of a complex substance. **h. of so'lution.** [Chem.] The amount of h. taken in or given out when a substance goes into SOLUTION. **h. spot.** [Zoo.] Point on skin at which there is a nerve-ending acted on by h. **h. 'treatment.** [Metal.] Any heating operation(s) done to a solid metal to give it a desired form or quality, sp. the processes of NORMALIZING and TEMPERING steel. **'heating curves.** [Metal.] Curves representative of the relation of TEMPERATURE and time in a metal heating in unchanging conditions, to the changes, such as MELTING, which the metal undergoes. **heating 'element.** The heating resistor and its frame in an electric heater. **heating re'sistor.** Wire or other material used as a RESISTANCE through which an electric current is sent for the purpose of producing h.

'heatstroke, n. [Med.] A condition of PROSTRATION or COMA, sometimes with CONVULSIONS, caused by great heat.

heave, n. [Geol.] The amount by which a STRATUM has been moved back or forward in a FAULT.

'Heaviside (or **'Kennelly-Heaviside) layer.** The most regular of the LAYERS of the IONOSPHERE, about 110 km. up from the earth, very important for radio, other name the E-layer.

'heavy, a. [Phys., Chem.] Having great weight, of high SPECIFIC GRAVITY. **h. 'chemical.** Sp. chemical substance made on a great scale, e.g. H_2SO_4, NaOH. **h. hydrogen.** DEUTERIUM. **h. 'minerals.** [Mineral.], MINERALS with a SPECIFIC GRAVITY greater than 2.9. **h. oils.** Oils got by DISTILLATION from COAL TAR. **h. spar.** BARYTES. **'h. 'water.** [Chem.] Water made of O and DEUTERIUM, having same chemical properties as normal water but different physical ones, such as weight and boiling point, used in some forms of NUCLEAR REACTOR. **h.-oil 'engine.** An INTERNAL COMBUSTION ENGINE burning h. oil, in which the firing is done not by an electric SPARK but by high COMPRESSION of air mixed with the oil.

'Hebri'dean gneiss. LEWISIAN GNEISS.

hebe'phrenia, n. [Med.] A form of SCHIZO-PHRENIA marked by violent outbursts of EXCITEMENT coming in turn with times of unhappy feeling, bitter crying etc., gen. attacking younger persons than other forms.

hect(o)-. 100, 100 times: **'hectolitre,** n. (*See* p. 566.)

'hedmic, a. [Psych.] Having to do with the experiencing of pleasure and pain. **'-s,** n.pl. H. psychology.

heel, n. [Zoo.] The back part of the foot in man; like part, or part parallel in its development, in other back-boned animals.

'heeling 'error. Error in ship's COMPASS caused by ship sloping over to one side.

'Hefner 'candle. [Optics] Old unit of INTENSITY of light = 0·90 INTERNATIONAL CANDLE.

'Hefner number. [Chem.] The PERCENTAGE in a fat or oil of FATTY ACIDS not SOLUBLE in water.

'Heidelberg man. [Anthrop.] The sort of very early man of which ideas are based on a JAW-BONE which came to light near Heidelberg in 1907.

height, n. Measure of a thing from base to top, how high it is.

he'liac(al), aa. [Astron.] To do with, near, the sun. **h. rising (setting).** The coming up (going down) of a star at same time as sun.

helic-al, -ine, -oid, *See* HELIX.

He'licidae, n.pl. [Zoo.] A FAMILY of land GASTROPODA with HELICAL SHELLS, freq. coming to a point, very common in gardens, living under stones, etc.

'helicopter, n. Airplane supported in flight by reaction of air to a system of planes turning on an upright AXIS, having, unlike machines with HORIZONTAL planes, the power of going straight up from or down to the landing-place.

helio-. Sun.

'helio'centric(al), aa. [Astron.] To do with middle point of sun; having, viewed in relation to, the sun as middle point. **'helio'centricism,** n.

'heliochrome, n. Camera-picture in natural colours.

'heliograph, n. Instrument for sending news from one place to another by REFLECTION of sun's rays from a looking-glass, etc.

'helio'gravure, n. PHOTOGRAVURE.

heli'ometer, n. [Astron.] Instrument for measuring small ANGULAR DISTANCES in the sky.

'helio'phobia, a. [Med.] Fear of sunlight. **'helio'phobic,** a. Sp. [Bot.] Shade-loving.

'helioscope, n. [Astron.] Instrument for looking at sun without damaging eyes, using coloured glass or some other way of shutting out part of its rays.

'heliostat, n. [Astron.[Instrument formed of a looking-glass moved by clockwork so as to give a REFLECTION of the sun to one unchanging point all through the day.

'helio'taxis, n. [Biol.] TAXIS in reaction to sun's rays.

'helio'therapy, n. [Med.] Letting sun's rays come to uncovered body as way of attacking disease.

heli'otropism, n. [Biol.] TROPISM in reaction to sun's rays.

'helium, n. Chemical ELEMENT, at. no. 2, at. wt. 4·002, sign He, an INERT GAS without colour or smell, of less weight than any gas but H and so used in airships and BALLOONS.

'helix, n. A corkscrew-like line, thread, wire, or structure of any sort. [Anat.] The curved-in edge of the outer ear. 'helicine, a. Sp. [Anat.] to do with the h. of the ear. 'helical, a. 'helicoid, a. Sp. [Biol.] 'helicoid cyme. [Bot.] A CYME having helicoid dichotomy, with the branches all on the same side of the stem but not in the same plane. ''helicoid di'chotomy. [Bot.] A form of forking of a stem in which only one branch of the fork comes to full development, and that regularly on the same side of the stem.

'Helmholtz 'resonator. [Acous.] A hollow vessel used for the ANALYSIS of complex sounds.

'helminth, n. [Zoo.] Worm, sp. [Med.] a worm PARASITE in the INTESTINES. Hel'minthes, n.pl. Name at one time given to a great group of such worms now covered by different names. helmin-'thiasis, n. [Med.] A disease in which hh. are present in the body. hel'minthic, n., a. [Med.] (A substance) acting against hh. helmin'thology, n. The science of worm PARASITES. hel'minthoid, a.

'helophyte, n. [Bot.] Any plant living in BOGS.

'helotism, n. [Biol.] System of living together of two sorts of animals or plants in which one gets food for the other.

hem(a)-, hemo-. HAEMA-.

'hemera, n. [Geol.] A division of an AGE, the time in which a ZONE of ROCKS was formed; the time in which a sort of plant or animal is at the highest stage of its EVOLUTION.

hemi-. Half, in part:— -'circular, -crystalline, aa. '-cycle, n.; sp. [Biol., Med.] to do with one half of the body; -anas'thesia, -anal'gesia, -a'taxy, -'atropy, nn., -'cho-'rea, -pa'ralysis, nn..

'hemi'basidium, n. [Bot.] Short, thread-like body supporting sex-CELLS in USITILA-GINALES.

'hemic, a. HAEMIC.

hemi'cellulose, n. [Chem.] Any of a number of substances which are somewhat like CELLULOSE in properties and make-up, but less complex and more readily broken down into simple sugars.

'Hemi'chorda, n.pl. [Zoo.] A SUB-PHYLUM of CHORDATA with very poor development of the NOTOCHORD. 'hemi'chordate, a. Having a NOTOCHORD of poor development.

hemi'cyclic, a. [Bot.] Having some flower leaves in a circle, others in a corkscrew curve.

hemicy'lindrical, a. Formed like a CYLINDER cut in half from end to end.

hemi'hedral, a. [Cryst.] In a form having half the full number of faces normal to the substance. hemi'hedrism, n. hemi-'hedron, n. H. CRYSTAL.

hemi'hydrate, n. [Chem.] HYDRATE in which two MOLECULES of a substance are united with one molecule of water.

'hemime'tabolism, hemi'metamor'phosis, nn. [Zoo.] METAMORPHOSIS in which there is no PUPA stage but the LARVA is not like the end-form, sp. in having parts designed for living in water. 'Hemime-'tabola, n.pl. Insects having h. 'hemi-meta'bolic, 'hemime'tabolous, aa.

hemi'morphic, n. [Cryst.] Of a CRYSTAL, having two ends different in form from one another. hemi'morphism, n.

'hemin, n. HAEMIN.

hemi'parasite, n. [Biol.] PARASITE plant getting part of its food from the air; PARASITE which has power of living as a SAPROPHITE if necessary. 'hemipara-'sitic, a.

hemi'plegia, n. [Med.] Loss of power of motion on one side of body as the effect of damage in the brain or SPINAL CORD.

Hem'iptera, n.pl. [Zoo.] A great ORDER of EXOPTERYGOTA with sharp-pointed, SUCKING mouth-parts, with which they get through the skin of animals or plants and take in blood or plant-liquids, and gen. having four wings of which the forward two are harder than the back two, most of them living on the outside of plants or animals.

'hemisphere, n. Half of a ball-like body, sp. earth or sky, on one or the other side of a middle plane. [Zoo.] See CEREBRAL. hemi'spheric(al), aa.

'hemitrope, n. TWIN CRYSTAL. hemi'tropic, a. he'mitropism, n.

he'mitropous. [Bot.] AMPHITROPOUS. [Zoo.] Getting food from a number of different flowers, said of insects such as bees.

hemo-. H(A)EMO-.

'Henle's 'layer. [Zoo.] Outer part of the covering round root of a hair. 'Henle's loop. That part of any of the small pipes of a KIDNEY which, after going into the middle, makes a turn to come out again.

'henry, n. [Elec.] Unit of INDUCTANCE, being that of a system in which 1 VOLT is produced by current changing at rate of 1 AMPERE in 1 second, $= 10^9$ c.g.s. units.

'Henry's law. [Phys., Chem.] Law that the weight of gas taken up by a liquid is dependent on the PRESSURE of the gas.

'Hensen's line. [Zoo.] Clear line running across the darker part of a muscle FIBRE.

he'patic, a. [Zoo.] To do with the LIVER. [Bot.] Of, like, to do with, the HEPATICAE.

h. portal. Blood-vessel taking blood from INTESTINES to the LIVER.

He'paticae, n.pl. [Bot.] CLASS of BRYO-PHYTA in which there is no development of the GAMETOPHYTE into stem and leaves.

hepa'titis, n.[Med.] INFLAMMATION of LIVER.

hepat(o)-, LIVER; hepa'tectomy n., hepa-'tology, n., hepa'toma, n.

'hepato'pancreas, n. [Zoo.] Any of certain digestion GLANDS of some lower animals, as CRUSTACEA, which seem to do work of LIVER and PANCREAS in higher animals.

hept(a)-. 7.

'heptad, a. [Chem.] Having a VALENCY of 7.

hepta'hydrate, n. [Chem.] Substance in which one MOLECULE is united with 7 molecules of water.

hep'tamerous, a. [Bot.] Having parts in sevens.

hepta'tomic, a. [Chem.] Having 7 ATOMS.

hepta'valent, a. [Chem.] Having a VALENCY of 7.

herb, n. [Bot.] Seed plant having no wood in stem; any such plant used for medical purposes or in cooking. her'baceous a. 'herbage, n. Thick growth of hh. sp. grass. her'barium, n. Group of dried plants got together and kept for purpose of Botany.

her'bivorous, a. [Zoo.] Using plants for food.

he'redity, n. [Biol.] The handing on to offspring of qualities of family; the hereditary qualities of an animal or plant. h. factor. GENE. he'reditable, 'heritable, aa. Able to be handed on to offspring. he'reditary, a. To do with h.; having been, or able to be, handed on.

'Hering (colour) theory. [Psych.] Theory about how colours are seen based on the idea that there are 3 PAIRS of opposite-acting processes in the eye, the white-black, the yellow-blue, and the red-green.

her'maphrodite, n., a. [Biol.] (Living being) having male and female SEX-ORGANS. her-maphro'ditic, a. her'maphro'ditism, n.

her'metic, a. Airtight.

'hernia, n. [Med.] The pushing of a part of the body through the wall normally keeping it in, sp. of a part of the INTESTINE through the inner wall of the ABDOMEN.

'herpes, n. [Med.] Disease in which hard VESICLES are formed on skin on line of nerve, specially common round the middle of the body. h. 'simplex or labialis. Forming of VESICLES round mouth in person with a cold. her'petic, a. 'herpet-ism, n.

herpe'tology, n. [Zoo.] Science of REPTILIA.

'herring-bone structure. Line, structure, of

V-forms as in back-bone of fish.

hertz, n. [Phys.] Unit of FREQUENCY = 1 CYCLE/sec.

'Hertzian, a. [Elec.] To do with, being, radio waves, that is, ELECTROMAGNETIC waves ranging in length from 1 cm. to 2000 m. h. 'radiator. Early apparatus for giving out very short radio waves.

Herzberg stain. $KI + I + ZnCl_2$ in water, which has the property of colouring linen threads red, paper blue, and wood yellow.

'hesper'idium (hesperidia), n. [Bot.] A SYNCARPOUS fruit with somewhat thick skin, as an orange. (See p. 158.)

Hess's law. [Chem.] Law that the amount of heat produced or taken in by a chemical reaction which takes place in stages is the ALGEBRAIC SUM of the amount produced or taken in at every stage.

'heter(o)-. Other, different, made up of different sorts.

'heter'androus, a. [Bot.] Having STAMENS of different sizes or forms.

'hetera'tomic, a. [Chem.] Made up of different sorts of ATOMS.

'heterau'xesis, n. [Bot.] Unequal growth, as when one side of a part undergoes quicker growth than the other, so causing turning, etc.

hete'raxial, a. [Zoo.] Having 3 unequal AXES at right-angles to one another.

'heteroag'glutination, n. [Zoo.] The massing together of SPERMATOZOA as effect of substance produced by the OVUM of a different species; massing of ERYTHRO-CYTES when blood from different BLOOD-GROUPS is mixed. 'heteroag'glutinin, n. Any of certain substances necessary for h.

'heterobares, n. [Chem.] ATOMS having different ATOMIC WEIGHTS.

'hetero'blastic, a. [Biol.] Having develop-ment from CELLS of another sort. [Bot.] Having INDIRECT DEVELOPMENT.

'hetero'carpous, a. [Bot.] Producing fruit of two different sorts.

'hetero'cellular, a. [Biol.] Made up of more than one sort of CELL.

'hetero'cephalous, a. [Bot.] Producing male and female flowers in separate HEADS.

'hetero'cercal, a. [Zoo.] (Of tail FIN of certain fish) having top division of greater size than lower one, with back-bone running into it and turning up somewhat; having h. tail fin.

'heterochla'mydeous, a. [Bot.] Having CALYX and COROLLA different in colour etc., as most flowers.

'heterochro'm(at)ic, aa. Complex in colour.

'hetero'chromosome, n. [Biol.] Special CHROMOSOME having some part in con-trolling sex of offspring, such as an X-CHROMOSOME.

'hetero'chronic, a. [Biol.] Not normal in order of development of different ORGANS or parts. [Zoo.] (Of TISSUES doing like

work) having different CHRONAXY. ′hetero′chron-ism, -y, nn.
′hetero′clin-e, -ous, a. HETEROCEPHALOUS.
′hetero′coelous, a. [Zoo.] Said of back-bone units with one end curved out and the other curved in.
′hetero′cyclic, a. [Chem.] (Of ORGANIC COMPOUNDS) having a ring structure formed of ATOMS of more than one sort. (See p. 392.)
′heterodont, 1.a. [Zoo.] (Of teeth) having different forms for different purposes; having h. teeth. 2.n. H. animal.
′heterodyne effect. [Radio] The effect produced by making a new FREQUENCY by mixing two different WAVES together, the new frequency being equal to that of one wave less that of the other. hetero-dyne re′ception. The use in radio of the h. e. for changing the FREQUENCY of incoming currents to a lower frequency (see SUPERHETERODYNE). heterodyne whistle. A high whistle produced in a radio receiver by the h. e. when two SIGNALS of almost the same FREQUENCY are taken in together.
hete′roecious, a. [Biol.] (Of PARASITE) going through the different stages of its existence in HOSTS of different sorts. het′ero-ecism, n.
′hetero′gamete, n. [Biol.] Sex-CELL which is different in size or form from that uniting with it. ′heteroga′metic, a. To do with h.; producing offspring by the uniting of hh.
heteroga′metic sex. [Biol.] That sex having in their NUCLEI one X-CHROMOSOME and one Y-CHROMOSOME together, or one X-chromosome by itself, producing equal numbers of different GERM-CELLS, one sort with, and one sort without, an X-chromosome, gen. the male sex.
hete′rogamy, n. [Zoo.] ALTERNATION OF GENERATIONS, sp. PARTHENOGENETIC and DIOECIOUS. [Bot.] Condition of having male, female, male-and-female, and unsexed flowers, or any two of these, in same group of flowers. [Biol.] Condition of producing offspring by the uniting of HETEROGAMETES. hete′rogamous, a. Having, to do with, h.
′hetero′geneous, a. Of different sorts or qualities; made up of different parts. ′heteroge′neity, n. (Of a substance, etc.) not the same all through, having different properties in different parts. [Phys.-Chem.] Of a system, made up of more than one PHASE.
′hetero′gen-esis, -y, nn. ALTERNATION of GENERATIONS. ′heterogen(et)ic, a.
hete′rogony, n. [Bot.] The producing, by plants of the same sort, of complete flowers of two or more sorts, in one of which the female sex-parts and in the other the male sex-parts are the longer,

so as to make certain of CROSS-FERTILIZATION. [Zoo.] ALTERNATION OF GENERATIONS sp. of DIOECIOUS and HERMAPHRODITE. hete′rogonous, a. hetero′gonous di′morphism. [Bot.] H. in which the flowers are of two sorts. heterogonous tri′morphism. [Bot.] H. in which flowers are of three sorts.
hete′rogynous, a. [Zoo.] Having females of more than one sort, as bees.
′heteroion, n. [Chem.] Complex, sp. COLLOID, ION formed by the ADSORPTION by a MOLECULE of a simple ion.
′hetero′lalia, n. [Med.] Condition in which person says words other than those purposed.
′hetero′lecithal, a. [Zoo.] (Of eggs) having unequal distribution of YOLK.
hete′rologous, a. [Biol.] (Of parts of different sorts of plants or animals, or of different parts of same one) unlike one another, not produced in the same way; [Med.] (of SERUM) coming from a different animal; (of parts, TISSUES) not normal in structure, hete′rology, n.
hete′rolysis, n. [Biochem.] Destruction (sp. of blood-CELLS) by substance (sp. blood) from another body.
heter′omerous, a. (Of chemical substances or CRYSTALS) not formed of same materials. [Bot.] (Of flower) not having same number of PARTS in all its circles; having THALLUS with LAYER of ALGAL CELLS between other layers.
′heterometa′bolic, a. [Zoo.] Having INCOMPLETE METAMORPHOSIS. ′heteromet′abol-ism, n.
′Heterome′tabola, n.pl. EXOPTERYGOTA.
′hetero′morph-ic, -ous, aa. Different from normal form; having a number of different forms. [Biol.] Unlike in form or size, said sp. of CHROMOSOMES; POLYMORPHIC. [Bot.] Having more than one sort of flower on the same plant. hetero′-morphism, n. hetero′morphous rocks. [Geol.] ROCKS chemically very like one another but formed of different MINERALS.
hetero′morphosis, n. [Zoo.] The new growth of a lost part in a form different from the first form; the producing of an unnormal structure.
′hetero′petalous, a. [Bot.] Having unlike PETALS.
′hetero′phasia, n. [Med.] Condition in which person makes wrong use of words.
′hetero′phyllous, a. [Bot.] (Of plant) having leaves of different forms on different parts, or on same stem. ′hetero′phylly, n.
′heterophyte, n. [Bot.] Plant dependent on other plants or animals, living or dead, for food.
′hetero′plasia, n. [Biol.] Development of TISSUE from tissue of different sort. [Med.] Forming of TISSUE which is not normal, or of normal tissue in wrong

place. 'heteroplasm, n. TISSUE so formed.
'heteroplastic, a. 'hetero'plasty, n. [Biol.]
HETEROPLASIA. [Med.] GRAFTING of a
part or substance taken from one person
onto another.

'heteroploid, a. [Biol.] Having one CHROMO-
SOME more than the normal number.

'hetero'polar, a. Having different POLES. h.
bond. [Chem.] ELECTROVALENT BOND.
'heteropo'larity, n.

'hetero'sexual, a. [Med.] Having sex-desire,
as is normal, for person of opposite sex.
[Biol.] Of, to do with, different sexes.

'hetero'sporous, a. [Bot.] Having SPORES of
more than one sort. hete'rospory, n.

'hetero'static, a. [Elec.] Of, to do with, the
measuring of one electric force by comparison with another.

'hetero-'styled, -'stylous, aa. [Bot.] Having
STYLES of two or more different sizes or
forms; HETEROGONOUS. 'hetero'styl-y,
-ism, nn.

'hetero'thallic, a. [Bot.] (Of FUNGI) having,
producing, two different forms of
MYCELIUM acting as opposite sexes.
'hetero'thallism, n.

heter'otomy, n. [Bot.] Condition of having
the parts of the VERTICELS of the flower
unequal or unlike.

hete'rotopy, 'hetero'topia, nn. [Biol.] Condition of being different in position, out
of place, sp. [Med.] the growth of a part
in an unnatural position. 'heterotopic, a.
'heterotopic pain. REFERRED PAIN. 'het-
eroto'picity, n.

hete'rotrichous, a. [Zoo.] Having two or
more sorts of CILIA.

'hetero'trophic, a. [Biol.] Unable to make
food from simple substances and so
dependent for it on other living things,
said of animals and PARASITIC plants.
hete'rotrophy, n.

'hetero'tropic, a. AELOTROPIC. h. 'chromosome [Biol.] SEX-CHROMOSOME.

hete'rotropous, a. AMPHITROPOUS.

'hetero'typic division, n. [Biol.] MEIOSIS as
opp. other forms of CELL-division, sp. the
first stage in meiosis.

'hetero'zygosis, n. [Biol.] The condition of
being a HETEROZYGOTE; the producing of
a heterozygote.

'hetero'zygote, n. [Biol.] Animal or plant
having at least two opposite ALLELO-
MORPHIC GENES, so that the same quality
is not necessarily handed on to all its
offspring. hetero'zygous, a. Being a h.

'Heusler 'alloy, n. Any of a number of
metals made up of Cu, Mn, and Al, having
MAGNETIC properties, which are not
present in the simple metals of which it is
formed.

hex(a)-. 6. [Chem.] Formed with 6 ATOMS
of a given ELEMENT in the MOLECULE,
as 'hexa'chloride.

hex'actinal, a. [Zoo.] With 6 rays.

'hexad, n. A group of 6. [Chem.] ATOM or
group of atoms having 6 free VALENCIES.
h. 'axis. [Cryst.] AXIS round which 6 like
faces are equally spaced.

'hexagon, n. [Geom.] A plane form with 6
straight sides and 6 angles. hex'agonal,
a. hex'agonal 'system. [Cryst.] A CRYSTAL
system with three equal AXES in the
same plane cutting one another at an
angle of 60° and one unequal axis at
right-angles to these (see p. 99).

hexa'hydrate, n. [Chem.] HYDRATE with
6 MOLECULES of water to one molecule of
the substance.

hexa'hydric, a. [Chem.] Having in it 6 OH
groups.

hexa'hydro-. [Chem.] Having in it 6 ATOMS
of H.

he'xamerous, a. [Bot.] Formed of 6 parts;
having parts in groups of 6. [Zoo.]
Having 6, or some number times 6, parts
or rays going out from a middle point.

hexa'methylene, n. [Chem.] C_6H_{12}, a RING
COMPOUND in the form of a gas having
no colour and a somewhat sweet smell.
'h.-'tetramine, n. $(CH_2)_6N_4$, a white
CRYSTALLINE substance, strongly ANTI-
SEPTIC and used medically.

'hexamine, n. [Chem.] HEXAMETHYLENE-
TETRAMINE.

'hexane, n. [Chem.] Any of four substances
C_6H_{14}, all liquids without colour, present in PETROLEUM, sp. n-h. (See p. 557).

'hexapod, n., a. [Zoo.] Animal having 6 feet.

'hexarch, a. [Bot.] Having 6 VASCULAR
STRANDS.

'hexatetra'hedron, n. [Cryst.] A 24-faced
form of the TETRAHEDRAL SYSTEM.

hexa'valent, a. [Chem.] Having a VALENCY
of 6.

hexi'cology, n. BIONOMICS.

hexo-.

'hexo'barbitone, n. [Med.] One of the
BARBITURATES used as an ANAESTHETIC
by putting it into the blood by INJECTION.

hexocta'hedron, n. CRYSTAL with 48 equal
3-sided faces.

'hexogen, n. A violent EXPLOSIVE made
from HEXAMETHYLENE-TETRAMINE.

'hexose, n. [Chem.] Any of a group of CARBO-
HYDRATES with 6 C ATOMS, some natural,
sp. in fruit.

'hexyl, n. [Chem.] The group $-C_6H_{13}$.
'hexyl-. [See p. 557.]

Hf, Sign for HAFNIUM.

H.F. = HIGH FREQUENCY.

Hg, Sign for MERCURY.

hi'atus, n. An opening or space, sp. in a
chain or line of things; in talking, a short
stop necessary to keep separate two
VOWELS coming together.

hiber'naculum, n. [Zoo.] Winter covering
of an animal; in certain POLYZOA, a BUD
of which development is stopped at start
of winter and started again in spring.

hiber′nation, n. [Biol.] The process of living through winter in a resting condition. **′hibernate,** v.i. Undergo h. **′hibernating glands.** GLAND-like stores of fat substance present under skin of some higher animals for use as food while hibernating.

′hiccup, ′hiccough, nn. [Med.] Sharp-sounding intake of breath caused by a sudden uncontrolled pulling together of the DIAPHRAGM and shutting of the GLOTTIS.

hi′drosis, n. [Zoo.] The giving off of water through the skin. [Med.] Condition in which there is overmuch h. **hi′drotic,** n., a. [Med.] (Substance) causing h.

′hierarchy, n. Scale of orders or degrees, system of groups going from the most general to the most special, as in biology, etc.

high, a. [Geog.] (Of the TIDE) having come to its highest level, its farthest point on the land. **h. tide.** The highest level of the TIDE, or the condition or time when the tide is h.

high ex′plosive. EXPLOSIVE of great power.

high ′frequency. [Elec.] FREQUENCY of ALTERNATING CURRENT greater than about 10 k.c.p.s., sp. any of those frequencies used in radio.

high-pass, a. [Radio] Letting through high FREQUENCIES only.

high-′pressure physics. The science of the behaviour of materials under high PRESSURES and at high TEMPERATURES, by which it may be possible, without chemical reactions, to get the structure of some substances so changed that they are turned into others, sometimes copying certain natural substances, sometimes completely new—very important in present-day physics and engineering.

high-speed steel. [Metal.] A very hard steel having in it W, Cr. and small amounts of other substances, which, because it does not become less hard even when heated to a low red heat, is used for blades in metal-cutting machines working very quickly.

high ′tension. [Elec. HIGH VOLTAGE.

high ′voltage. [Elec.] Generally a VOLTAGE of 650 or more.

high water. [Geog.] The condition of a body of water which has come to its highest level, or the time when it is there—in relation to the sea, HIGH TIDE.

hill, n. [Geog.] A mass of land higher than the parts round it, having a clearly marked outline narrowing as it goes up like a mountain, but lower and gen. with less sharp slopes and a more rounded top.

′hilum, n. [Bot.] Mark on seed where it was fixed to the plant; NUCLEUS of STARCH grain. [Zoo.] HILUS. **hi′liferous,** a.

′hilus, n. [Zoo.] A small hollow on the face of an ORGAN, marking point where a blood-vessel or other pipe-like part goes in or out.

′hind-brain, n.[Zoo.] In back-boned animals, the back brain-VESICLE of the EMBRYO or the part of the brain into which it undergoes development, taking in the CEREBELLUM and the MEDULLA OBLONGATA.

′hind-gut, n. [Zoo.] Pipe-like part of YOLK-SAC going into tail-fold of EMBRYO of man; back end of ALIMENTARY CANAL.

hinge, n. Part joining two parts so that they have the power of turning or folding in relation to one another. **h. joint.** [Zoo.] A JOINT making possible motion in one plane only. **h. ′ligament,** [Zoo.] Elastic structure joining the two parts of a BIVALVE SHELL. **h. line.** [Zoo.] The part on the edge of a BIVALVE SHELL where h. is. **h. tooth.** Outgrowth on one half of BIVALVE SHELL going into hollow in other half where the two are hinged. **hinged,** a. JOINED by h.

hip, n. [Anat.] The part of the side of man's body where leg and body are joined. **h. bone.** In man and higher animals the great bone at side of body into which the long bone at the top of the leg is fixed. **h. joint.** JOINT between leg and body.

hippo′campus, n. [Zoo.] A line of white nerve substance running from the OLFACTORY LOBE to the back end of the side VENTRICLE of brain in man and higher animals. **hippo′campal,** a.

hip′puria, n. [Med.] Diseased condition in which overmuch ACID is present in URINE.

hip′puric acid. [Chem.] Acid, $C_6H_5CO.NH.CH_2CO_2H$, present in URINE, sp. of animals living on grass, etc.

′hirsute, a. [Biol.] Covered with hairs, sp. stiff, rough hairs, or with hair-like feathers.

′hirudin, n. [Med.] Substance from head of HIRUDINEA used for keeping blood in liquid condition.

Hi′rudinea, n.pl.[Zoo.] CLASS of ANNELIDA, HERMAPHRODITE ringed worms living on blood of other animals, having a SUCKER at front and back, and generally no SETAE or PARAPODIA.

′histamine, n. [Med.] AMINE having effect of making body processes slower and blood PRESSURE lower. **hista′minic,** a.

′histidine, n. [Biochem.] An AMINO ACID produced from PROTEIN.

histo-. TISSUE:— **′-′chemistry, ′-′genesis,** his′togeny, nn. -′genic, ′-′ge′netic, aa.′

′histocyte, n. [Zoo.] A TISSUE-CELL, as opp. a sex-cell.

′histogen, n. [Bot.] PRIMARY TISSUE of which part has undergone development into PERMANENT TISSUE.

his′tology, n. [Biol.] The science of the structure of TISSUES and parts of living things as seen by the MICROSCOPE. **histo′logic(al),** aa. **his′tologist,** n.

his'tolysis, n. [Biol.] Process by which TISSUE is broken up, destruction of tissues; process by which in certain insects most of inside of liquid in PUPA stage.

'histone, n. [Biochem.] Any of a group of strongly BASIC animal PROTEINS, present for example in ERYTHROCYTES.

hive, n. Vessel, etc. housing bees; the bees living together in one h., as one society.

hives, n. [Med.] Common name for URTICARIA, sp. as caused by food.

Ho, Sign for HOLMIUM.

hoar frost. [Meteor.] Ice CRYSTALS formed on things, specially on cold clear nights, when the DEW POINT is lower than FREEZING POINT.

hock, n. [Zoo.] Middle JOINT of back leg of horse and like animals, or part round this.

ho'dometer, n. Instrument for measuring curved lines on maps.

ho'lard, n. [Bot.] All the water in the earth viewed in relation to plants.

'holdfast, n. [Bot.] Any part of a plant, other than a root, for gripping it to a support.

'holism, n. Theory that a complete living being is more than the addition of its parts, and that it is ORGANISMS and not their parts which are the important things in EVOLUTION.

'holmium, n. Chemical ELEMENT, at. no. 67, at. wt. 164·94, sign Ho, one of the RARE EARTH METALS.

holo-. Complete.

holo'blastic, a. [Zoo.] Undergoing complete division, said of eggs.

Holo'cephali, n.pl. [Zoo.] A SUB-CLASS or ORDER of CHONDRICHTHYES, most sorts of which have now gone out of existence, having great, flat crushing teeth and only 4 GILL-SLITS, which have a gill-cover over them, and living chiefly on MOLLUSCS.

'holo'crystalline, a. [Geol.] Completely CRYSTALLINE in structure, having no glass.

holo'gamete, n. [Zoo.] In PROTOZOA, a GERM-CELL which is the same size as other cells, not formed by special division.

ho'logamous, a. [Biol.] Having GERM-CELLS which are like other cells in size and form.

ho'logamy, n. The condition of having h. GERM-CELLS; the uniting of h. germ-cells.

holo'gastrula, n. [Zoo.] GASTRULA formed from HOLOBLASTIC egg.

ho'lognathous, a. [Zoo.] Having JAW formed as one part.

holo'hedral, a. [Cryst.] Having highest number of faces possible in a certain CRYSTAL SYSTEM, being a complete example of that system. holo'hedron, n.

'holometa'bolic, a. [Zoo.] (Of insects) undergoing COMPLETE METAMORPHOSIS. 'holome'tabolism, n.

holo'morphic, a. [Cryst.] Having two like ends.

holo'morphosis, n. [Biol.] The complete new growth of a part which has undergone destruction.

holo'phytic, a. [Biol.] Able to make food from simple substances, and getting it only in that way, as a green plant does.

holo'styly, n. [Zoo.] Condition in certain fish of having mouth-bones which are united with head-bones in place of being joined to them and supported by the HYOID ARCH. holo'stylic, a.

'holosym'metric(al), a. HOLOHEDRAL. holo'-symmetry, n.

'Holothur'oidea, n.pl. [Zoo.] A CLASS of ECHINODERMATA having a long, soft round body without arms, and only small bits of hard substance bedded in the mass, in place of the hard outer plates of others in this group. holo'thurian, n., a. (Animal) of the H.

ho'lotrichous, a. [Zoo.] Having CILIA of equal size completely covering body.

'holotype, n. [Biol.] The one plant or animal taken as the TYPE on which the discovery of a new SPECIES is based.

holo'zoic, a. [Biol.] Using plants and/or animals as food, as most animals do, not able to make up food from simple substances.

Holz machine. [Elec.] An early form of ELECTROSTATIC GENERATOR having one fixed and one moving plate and needing to be CHARGED at the start.

'homeo-, homoeo-. Like, same.

'homeo'stasis, n. [Physiol.] The tendency for normal body conditions to keep unchanged.

'homeo'typic, a. [Genet.] Said of the second division in MEIOSIS, in which the CHROMOSOMES are cut in two from end to end.

homo-. Having common properties, etc., the same, like, opp. HETERO-.

homo'blastic, a. [Zoo.] Having straightforward development, without undergoing METAMORPHOSIS; coming from CELLS of same sort.

homo'carpous, a. [Bot.] Producing only one sort of fruit.

homo'centric(al), aa. Going through a common point, said of a group of rays.

homo'cercal, a. [Zoo.] (Of tail FIN of fish) having the two parts of same size and form, with backbone ending near point of division; having h. tail fin, as most higher fishes. 'homocercy, n.

'homochro'm(at)ic, a. Having same colour all over.

homo'cyclic, a. [Chem.] (Of ORGANIC COMPOUNDS) having a RING structure made up of ATOMS of one sort only, sp. CARBOCYCLIC.

homo'dermic, a. [Biol.] Having undergone development from same GERM LAYER.

'**homodont,** a. [Zoo.] (Of teeth) all the same in form; having h. teeth.

ho'modromous, a. [Botl] Having GENETIC SPIRAL with same direction in stem and branches.

'**hom(o)eo-'morphic, -'morphous,** aa. [Cyst.] Like one another in form, said of CRYSTALS of unlike chemical substances. [Med.] Having structure like that of parts round it, as a diseased growth. '**hom(o)eomorph,** n. [Cryst.] A h. substance. '**hom(o)eo'morph-ism, -y,** nn.

hom(o)e'opathy, n. [Med.] The use against disease of substances producing effects on body like those of the disease itself, in very small amounts. '**hom(o)eopath, hom(o)e'opathist,** nn.

'**hom(o)eo'polar,** a. HOMOPOLAR.

'**hom(o)eotype,** n. [Biol.] Plant or animal which, after comparison, is taken as being in every way like a certain TYPE.

'**homoga'metic,** a. [Genet.] Having GAMETES of one sort only. **h. sex.** That sex which has only X-CHROMOSOMES, producing only GERM-CELLS with X-chromosomes, gen. the female sex.

ho'mogamy, n. [Bot.] The condition of having all the flowers in a flower-group the same in sex and form; condition of having the STAMENS and the PISTIL come to full growth at the same time. [Zoo.] INBREEDING. **ho'mogamous,** a.

homo'geneous, a. Of the same sort; (of a substance) having the same properties or material all through. [Phys.-Chem.] (Of a system) made up of only one PHASE. [Biol.] HOMOGENOUS. **homoge'neity,** n.

homo'genesis, n. [Biol.] System of REPRODUCTION in which every GENERATION is like the one before it.

ho'mogenize, v.t. Put (milk, etc.) through process by which fat is broken up, for purposes of making it better for digestion. **ho'mogenization,** n. **ho'moge'nizer,** n. Machine for homogenizing milk, etc.

ho'mogenous, a. [Biol.] (Of animals, plants, or parts) like in structure because of having common ANCESTOR or having undergone development from like part. **ho'mogeny,** n.

ho'mogony, n. [Bot.] Condition of having only one sort of flower with no change in size of STAMENS and PISTIL. (See HETEROGONY). **ho'mogonous, 'homogone,** aa.

homohedral, a. [Cryst.] Having equal faces.

ho'moio'thermal, a. [Zoo.] WARM-BLOODED.

homo'lecithal, a. [Zoo.] (Of certain eggs) having YOLK small in amount and more or less equal in distribution.

ho'mologous, a. Having like position, value, structure, etc. [Med.] Having same structure as normal TISSUE, said of diseased growth. [Biol.] Like in structure and coming from common ANCESTOR or having undergone development from

EMBRYONIC parts having a like structure or a like position in relation to other parts. [Chem.] Being one of a group of COMPOUNDS of like structure, but formed one from the other by addition of same group, sp. CH_2, as: CH_4, C_2H_6, C_3H_8, etc. **h. 'chromosomes.** [Biol.] Two CHROMOSOMES, one from the male and the other from the female, which have the same space-grouping of GENES, with the same sorts of gene at the same fixed points, and which come together in the early stages of MEIOSIS. **h. field.** [Elec.] FIELD OF FORCE in which lines of force in one plane all go through one point. **h. temperatures.** [Phys.] ABSOLUTE TEMPERATURES which are in the same RATIO as the MELTING-POINTS of substances. '**homologue,** n. Anything h. in relation to some other thing. **ho'mology,** n. The condition of being h.

homo'morphic, a. [Biol.] Like in size and structure, said of a group of two CHROMOSOMES.

homo'morphism, n. [Biol.] Condition of being like in form or look but having different inner structure, said sp. of animals or plants of different groups. [Bot.] Condition of having flowers of one sort only. [Zoo.] Condition of having LARVA like ADULT, and no stage between. **homo'morphous,** a.

'**homonym,** n. [Biol.] Name given to group of plants or animals which is same as that given earlier to another group, and so is wrongly used. **ho'monymous,** a.

homo'petalous, a. [Bot.] Having like PETALS.

ho'mophony, n. [Psychol.] Agreement of NERVE IMPULSE with that caused earlier by same STIMULUS, as experienced in being conscious of having seen etc. a thing before.

homo'phylic, a. [Biol.] Being like because of having a common ANCESTOR.

'**homophyllous,** a. [Bot.] Having leaves all of one sort.

homo'plasma, n. [Zoo.] PLASMA from another animal of same SPECIES as that from which TISSUE is taken, used for tissue CULTURE.

homo'plas-sis, -sy, -(t)y, n. [Biol.] Like form or structure in different plants or animals or parts which is the outcome of development on like lines and not from common ANCESTOR. **homo'plas-tic, -mic,** aa.

homo'polar, a. [Biol.] Having POLES of AXIS like one another. [Phys.] Having one POLE round the other, said of a MAGNET or DYNAMO. [Chem.] (Of MOLECULE) having an equal distribution of CHARGE. **h. 'dynamo.** DYNAMO producing DIRECT CURRENT without COMMUTATOR.

ho'mopterous, a. [Zoo.] (Of insects) having like front and back wings.

homo′sexual, a. [Med.] Having sex desire for persons of same sex. **′homosexu-′ality,** n.

homo′sporous, a. [Bot.] Producing only one sort of SPORE.

′homostyled, a. [Bot.] Having equal STYLES; HOMOGONOUS.

homo′tax-is, -ia, -y, nn. [Geol.] Condition of beds in different places having a like order of parts and like FOSSILS, without necessarily having been formed at quite the same time. **homo′taxial,** a.

homo′thallic, a. [Bot.] (Of FUNGI) having MYCELIUM with property of producing two different sorts of CELLS acting as opposite sexes. **homo′thallism,** n.

homo′thermous, a. [Zoo.] WARM-BLOODED.

homo′tropic, a. Having like CRYSTAL structure.

homo′zygosis, n. [Biol.] Condition in which plant or animal has only one or the other of any two ALLELOMORPHIC GENES, so that the same quality is handed on to all offspring. **homo′zygote,** n. Such animal or plant. **homo′zygous,** a.

honey, n. Sweet sticky substance formed by certain insects, sp. bees, from the NECTAR of flowers. **′-comb,** n. Structure of 6-sided CELLS in which h. is stored by bees. **′-dew,** n. MANNA.

hood, n. Structure of umbrella-like or roof-like design, put at some distance over top of something, such as smoke-outlet, for such purposes as keeping out rain, sending current of air, etc. in desired direction. [Zoo.] Any structure or marking on head which gives a suggestion of a head-dress, sp. outstretched folds of skin at two sides of neck of certain snakes.

hoof (hoofs or hooves), n. [Zoo.] Curved covering of horn forming base of foot of animal of the UNGULATA. **hoofed,** a.

Hooke(′s) law, n. [Mech.] Law that the stretching of an elastic substance ∝ the force pulling it.

′hookworm, n. [Zoo.] Any of a number of PARASITIC NEMATODE worms, so named because of the hooks round the mouth.

hooves, n.pl. See HOOF.

horde′olum, n. [Med.] STYE.

ho′rizon, n. Circle limiting distance a person is able to see over the sea or flat land, the seeming line between earth and sky (**ap′parent, ′local,** or **′visible h.**). [Astron.] Plane TANGENT to the earth at the point of observation (**sensible h.**); plane parallel to the sensible h. through the middle point of the earth, and the GREAT CIRCLE formed by this cutting the CELESTIAL SPHERE (**rational** or **celestial h.**). **hori′zontal,** a. Parallel to the HORIZON, or to the earth, at right-angles to an upright. [Bot.] In a plane at right-angles to the chief AXIS, as leaves.

′hormone, n. [Physiol.] Any of the sub-stances produced by the ENDOCRINE GLANDS, which are taken by the blood to different parts of the body and have a special effect on their working.

horn, n. [Zoo.] Hard pointed out-growth, which may be straight, curved, or branching, on the head of certain animals, such as the cow—sometimes formed of a middle part of bone with a thick covering of KERATIN, sometimes all of bone (*see* ANTLER). [Biochem.] The substance KERATIN, of which the hard outer part of hh. other than ANTLERS is made. [Biol.] Any h.-like part or outgrowth, as a group of feathers on head of certain birds or parts of flowers. [Anat.] Any of a number of structures giving suggestion of hh., such as those seen in SPINAL CORD when cut through. **′horny,** a.

horn′blende, n. [Geol.] An important ROCK-forming MINERAL made chiefly of SILIC-ATES of Mg, Ca, Fe, black in colour.

′hornfels, n. [Geol.] Very hard sort of ROCK, formed by operation of great heat, weight, etc. on SEDIMENTARY rock having in it Si.

ho′rology, n. Science of measuring time or making time-measuring instruments.

′horripi′lation, n. [Med.] The lifting up of the hairs on the skin as the effect of cold, fear, etc. (*see* GOOSE-FLESH).

′horse-power, n. [Mach.] Unit of rate of doing work, = 33,000 FOOT-POUNDS per minute or 745·8 WATTS (Britain), 746 watts (U.S.A.), and 736 watts (Europe).

′horse-shoe ′magnet. MAGNET bent in the form of a horseshoe so that the two ends are near one another.

′horsetail, n. Any plant of the EQUISETALES.

host, n. [Biol.] Plant or animal having PARASITE living on it.

hot ′atom. [Phys.] An ATOM with special power of chemical reaction as the effect of having a RADIOACTIVE NUCLEUS.

hot bulb (**′surface, pot, tube,** or **spot**) **ig′nition.** [Eng.] System of firing DIESEL engines by pumping oil against or into heated part joined to CYLINDER.

hot ′galvanizing. Coating iron with zinc by putting it in the liquid metal.

hot spring. [Geol., Geog.] THERMAL SPRING.

hot well. [Eng.] Vessel or pipes into which heated water from CONDENSER of steam engine is pumped, to be taken back from there to boiler.

hot-wire, a. [Elec. Engin.] (Of instruments) dependent for its operation on the expansion or change in RESISTANCE of a wire or band when an electric current is sent through it.

hour angle. [Astron.] (Of the sun or a star) the angle between some fixed MERIDIAN OF LONGITUDE and the plane going through the body in question and the middle of the earth.

hour circle. [Astron.] Any CIRCLE OF THE SPHERE going through the CELESTIAL POLES, sp. one going through a given star, etc., or one of the 12 by which the CELESTIAL EQUATOR is cut into 12 equal parts of one hour; the circle in an EQUATORIAL TELESCOPE marked off into hours and divisions of hours for reading RIGHT ASCENSION.

'housing, n. Framework or other support for machine parts.

'hovercraft, n. A structure for transport, moving over but very near to the face of the earth supporting itself on a cushion of air.

H.P. = HORSE-POWER.

H.T. = HIGH TENSION.

hue, n. [Psych.] That quality of colours, independent of their LIGHTNESS, by which they are seen as red, blue, green, etc., as opp. grey, black or white. (*See* MUNSELL SYSTEM.)

'human, a. Of, to do with, man. **h. 'being.** Person. **'humanize,** v.t. [Med.] Get turned into form like that produced by man's body or able to be used by it, as humanized milk, a humanized VACCINE.

'humerus, n. [Zoo.] The bone of the top part of the arm in man, or the front leg in higher animals. **'humeral,** a.

'humic acid. [Chem.] Any of group of complex acids present in earth, produced by chemical changes in dead plants.

hu'midity, n. Condition, sp. of air, of having water in it. [Meteor.] Measure of amount of water in the form of gas in a unit measure of air (**absolute h.**) or of the RATIO of this to the amount needed for complete SATURATION. **'humid,** a. **hu'midify,** v.t.

'humo(u)r, n. [Zoo.] Any of the normal liquids in the body of an animal, sp. in eye. **'humoral,** a.

'humus, n. [Bot.] The dark brown or black earth material formed by the DECOMPOSITION of dead plant and animal substances to the point where there is no longer any sign of what they were, and forming the most fertile part of earth.

'hundredweight, n. British measure of weight = 100 (U.S.) or 112 (G.B.) pounds. (*See* p. 565.)

'hunting, n. [Elec.] A regular increase and the opposite in the rate of turning of SYNCHRONOUS electric machines, having a like effect on the current between them, which sometimes takes place when they are used in PARALLEL.

'hurricane, n. [Meteor.] Wind moving at rate of over 75 miles an hour, the strongest wind on the common scale of wind force.

husk, n. [Bot.] Stiff dry outer covering of certain seeds or fruits. [Zoo.] Coughing disease of sheep or cows caused by NEMATODE worms in breathing-pipes.

'Huyg(h)ens' 'eyepiece. [Optics] EYEPIECE of instrument, sp. MICROSCOPE, formed of two PLANO-CONVEX LENSES, their plane sides turned to eye, and one at a certain distance in front of the other. **Huyg(h)ens' (wave-front) 'principle.** [Phys.] Theory that every point of a WAVE-FRONT is sending out waves, the effect of which is the complete wave.

'hyaline, a. [Zoo.] Clear; without FIBRES or GRANULES.

'hyalo-. Glass, glass-like, HYALINE.

'hyaloid, a. HYALINE. **h. 'membrane.** [Zoo.] Delicate skin covering VITREOUS HUMOUR of eye.

'hyalo-'mucoid, n. [Biochem.] A MUCOID present in VITREOUS HUMOUR of eye.

hy'alophane, n. [Mineral.] A sort of FELDSPAR, $K_2BaAl_2(SiO_3)_4$.

'hyalopi'litic, a. [Geol.] In the form of a mass of very small, needle-like CRYSTALS with glass between.

'hyaloplasm, n. [Biol.] The clear liquid part of PROTOPLASM.

hya'lopterous, a. [Zoo.] Having wings which let light through.

'hybrid, n., a. [Biol.] (Offspring) produced by male of one SPECIES uniting with female of another. **'hybridism, hy'bridity,** nn. **'hybridize,** v.t. CROSS-BREED. **'hybridi'zation,** n. **'hybrid'izable,** a.

'hydathode, n. [Bot.] Small hole, hair, etc. by which water is given out from skin of plant.

'hydatid, n. [Med.] Small, bag-like structure full of water-like liquid, in any part of body, sp. formed by LARVA of CESTODA. **'hyda'tidiform, hy'datiform,** aa. **'hyda'tidinous,** a. **hydatigenous,** a.

hy'dracid, n. [Chem.] Acid having in it no O.

hy'dr(a)emia, n. [Med.] Condition in which there is over-much water in blood. **hy'dr(a)emic,** a.

'hydranth, n. [Zoo.] Food-getting unit of HYDROID COLONY.

'hydrate, n. [Chem.] COMPOUND having water as such chemically united with it, sp. a SALT having in it WATER OF CRYSTALLIZATION. **'hydrated,** a. Being a h., having water chemically united with it, having undergone hydration. **hy'dration,** n. [Chem., Geol.] The process of becoming, or causing to become, chemically united with water.

hy'draulic, a. [Mach.] To do with, worked by, water or other liquid. **h. ram.** Automatic apparatus by which the motion of great amount of water at low PRESSURE is used for pumping a small amount to high pressure. **hy'draulics,** n.pl. Branch of engineering to do with the motion of liquids, having two chief divisions, **open 'channel hydraulics,** having to do with the motion of rivers, TIDAL effects in harbours, and so on, and closed 'circuit hydraulics, to do with the use of liquids in driving machines, with pumps, and with the transporting of material by the force of water etc.

'hydride, n. [Chem.] Substance formed by uniting one ELEMENT with H.

'hydr(o)-. To do with water: hydroki'netics, n.pl., hydromech'anics, n.pl.

'hydroba'rometer, n. Instrument for measuring how deep water is by its PRESSURE.

hydro'bromic acid. [Chem.] An acid formed by dissolving HBr (*hydrogen bromide*) in water, used as a CATALYST.

hydro'carbon, n. [Chem.] Any of a great number of complex substances formed of C and H, present in living substance.

hydro'caulis, n. [Zoo.] Pipe-like, branching, common stem, joining the units of a HYDROID COLONY.

hydro'cephal-us, -y, nn. [Med.] Diseased condition in which there is a great increase in the amount of CEREBROSPINAL FLUID in the brain hollows, causing their expansion and a stretching of the substance of their walls. hydro'cephaloid, a. hydro'cephalous, a.

hydro'chloric acid. [Chem.] Acid formed by DISSOLVING HCl (*hydrogen chloride*), in water.

hydro'clastic, n., a. [Geol.] ROCK made up of broken bits of stone put down by water.

hydrocoel(e), n. [Zoo.] Sponge-like system of water-pipes in ECHINODERMATA, or the part of the EMBRYO from which this comes.

'hydrocy'anic acid. [Chem.] Acid formed by DISSOLVING HCN (*hydrogen cyanide*) in water, having wide uses in industry.

'hydrocyst, n. [Med.] CYST having water in it. [Zoo.] DACTYLOZOOID.

h'ydrody'namic(al), aa. To do with the behaviour of liquids in motion. 'hydrody'namics, n.pl. Science of the behaviour of liquids in motion, their ways of moving, their ENERGY, their PRESSURE, based on Mathematics and most important in ship-designing.

'hydroe'lectric, a. To do with producing electric current from water power.

'hydro'fluoric acid. [Chem.] Acid formed by DISSOLVING HF (*hydrogen fluoride*) in water, a very VOLATILE burning liquid, a strong poison, used in making F and FUELS for automobiles etc.

'hydrofoil, n. [Mach.] A plane structure, flat or curved, such as a blade or wing, designed for producing motion of machine of which it is part, by the effect on it of the force of water round it.

'hydrogen, n. Chemical ELEMENT, at. no. 1, at. wt. 1·0078, sign H, the element having the least weight, a gas without colour

having some of the properties of a metal and some of a non-metal and uniting with O to make water. h. bomb. A BOMB in which ENERGY is produced by the uniting of NUCLEI of ATOMS of little weight, such as h. atoms, into atoms of greater weight. h. 'bromide. HBr., a gas without colour and with an IRRITATING effect on eyes and nose etc. h. 'chloride. HCl, a sharp-smelling, non-burning gas without colour, gen. kept in SOLUTION in water and named *hydrochloric acid*, of great use in chemistry and industry. h. 'cyanide HCN, a very VOLATILE poison gas with a strong special smell. h. 'fluoride. HF, a gas without colour and with a strong special smell. h. 'ion. The POSITIVE ION of acids, being an H atom of which the ELECTRON has gone over to the NEGATIVE ion of the acid, sign H+. h. 'ion concen'tration. See *p*H-VALUE. h. per'oxide. H_2O_2, a thick, sticky liquid, gen. marketed in the form of a SOLUTION in water, used as a BLEACH, and medically as a DISINFECTANT. h. 'sulphide. H_2S, a poison gas without colour having the very unpleasing smell of bad eggs, produced naturally when dead animal and plant material with S in it is broken up, and made by acting on metal SULPHIDES with a SOLUTION of HCl or H_2SO_4, used as a chemical REAGENT.

'hydrogen'ation, n. [Chem.] The process of causing a substance to undergo reaction with, or become united with, H, sp. used in the making of MINERAL OIL from coal, and in changing liquid plant and animal oils into solid fats.

'hydroge'ology, n. That part of the science of Geology which has to do with the effects of water on the Earth's structure.

hy'drography, n. Science of measuring and mapping natural waters (rivers, sea, harbours, etc.) and the bed of the sea. hydro'graphic(al), aa. hy'drographer, n.

'hydroid, 1.a. [Zoo.] Of, to do with, like, the HYDROZOA, sp. the unsexed stage. 2.n. Animal of the HYDROZOA, sp. a h. person. h. 'person. A unit of a COLONY of HYDROZOA in the unsexed stage.

hy'drology, n. The science of water, its properties and distribution, sp. of water under the earth, as against HYDRO-GRAPHY.

hy'drolysis, n. [Chem.] Chemical process in which a substance is broken up by reaction with water, frequently caused by there being present a small amount of some other substance, for example, an acid. hydro'lytic, a. 'hydrolyze, v.t. and i. 'hydrolyte, n. Substance undergoing h.

hydro'mania, n. [Med.] Strong desire for water, caused by disease.

'hydrom(e), n. [Bot.] Plant TISSUE or structure by which water is transported.

'hydrometa'morphism, n. [Geol.] Change in ROCKS produced by water.

hy'drometer, n. Instrument for measuring DENSITY of liquid, formed of a hollow metal or glass body with a long stem, weighted so as to keep upright in the liquid and freq. marked with a scale, the degree to which the instrument goes down in the liquid giving the density. hydro'metric(al), aa. hy'drometry, n.

hy'drophanous, a. [Mineral.] Letting light through when put in water.

hydro'phil-e, -ic, aa. [Chem.] Having strong attraction for water, taking up water, keeping water, said sp. of a COLLOID which readily goes into SOLUTION in water.

hydro'phobia, n. [Med.] RABIES, sp. so named when taken by man. hydro-'phobic, a.

'hydrophobe, n. [Chem.] Substance not made wet by water.

hydro'phobic colloid. [Chem.] COLLOID which does not readily go into SOLUTION in water.

'hydrophone, n. Instrument for hearing sounds through water.

hydro'phyllium (hydrophyllia), n. [Zoo.] In some SIPHONOPHORA, any of certain leaf-like parts, possibly special developments of MEDUSOIDS, hanging down over the COLONY to keep it from damage by rubbing etc.

'hydrophyte, n. [Bot.] Plant living on or in or completely under water or in very wet earth. hydro'phytic, a.

hy'dropic(al), a. DROPSICAL.

'hydroplane, n. MOTOR-BOAT of very flat, plane-like form supporting it almost on top of the water, and making it possible for it to go at a very great rate; a wing-like structure on a SUBMARINE used for STABILIZING it as it goes down.

'hydropneu'matic, a. To do with, worked by, water and air or other gas.

hydro'polyp, n. [Zoo.] A HYDROZOA POLYP.

hydro'ponic, a. [Bot.] To do with growth of plants in water with addition of certain salts, in place of earth.

hydro'rhiza, n. [Bot.] Any of the root-like outgrowths of the common stem by which some COLONIES of HYDROZOA are fixed to other bodies.

'hydroscope, n. Apparatus by which bed of deep sea may be seen.

'hydrosol, n. [Chem.] A COLLOIDAL SOLUTION in water.

'hydrosphere, n. All the water in the air round the earth; all the water on the earth.

'hydrostat, n. [Mach.] Apparatus for keeping water in a boiler or other apparatus at a certain level automatically.

hydro'static, a. To do with hydrostatics; based on the physical properties of liquids at rest. h. b'alance. Scales for getting the DENSITY of a body by measuring its weight when put into water. h. ex'trusion, [Metal.] A system of giving metals form by EXTRUSION in which the extrusion PRESSURE is TRANSMITTED by a liquid. h. trans'mission. [Engin.] System of TRANSMITTING ENERGY from an engine or MOTOR to the part to be moved by using the PRESSURE of a liquid, so making it possible to do without gears. hydro'statics, n.pl. Science of liquids at rest.

'hydrosul'phuric 'acid. [Chem.] A SOLUTION of H$_2$S (hydrogen sulphide) in water, forming a feeble ACID.

hydro'taxis, n. [Biol.] TAXIS in reaction to water.

hydro'theca, n. [Zoo.] Cup-formed part round a HYDRANTH.

'hydro'thera'peutics, hydro'therapy, nn. [Med.] Use of baths and water-drinking against disease, sp. water of MINERAL springs, etc.

hydro'thermal, a. [Geol.] To do with heated water in the earth, sp. its effects on ROCKS.

hy'drotropism, n. [Biol.] TROPISM in reaction to water. hydro'tropic, a.

'hydrous, a. [Chem.] Chemically united with water, having water in it.

hy'droxide, n. [Chem.] Any substance formed by the reaction of a BASIC OXIDE with water and having in it the group —OH.

hy'droxyl, n. [Chem.] The group —OH. h. 'ion. The NEGATIVE ION which gives to ALKALINE SOLUTIONS their special properties.

'Hydro'zoa, n.pl. [Zoo.] CLASS of COELENTERATA having as a rule a well-marked ALTERNATION OF GENERATIONS, the unsexed stage being a POLYP, frequently COLONIAL, which gives birth to the sexed stage, a MEDUSA, by BUDDING. 'hydro' 'zoan, a., n. [Animal] of, like, the H.

hy'drula, n. [Zoo.] The simplest sort of POLYP.

'hyetograph, n. [Meteor.] CHART giving normal rainfall for a year; instrument recording rainfall. 'hyeto'graphic, a. hye'tography, n. Science of the distribution of rainfall over the earth.

hye'tology, n. [Meteor.] Science of rain, snow, etc.

'hygiene, n. The science of keeping healthy in so far as that is dependent on keeping persons, places, and things clean, breathing in the right way, giving the muscles enough to do, and so on. hy'gienic, a.

hy'gro-, Wet.

hy'grology, n. Science of the behaviour of the water in the air.

hy'grometer, n. [Phys.] Instrument for measuring amount of water in the air. hy'grometry, n.

hy'grophanous, a. Letting light through only when wet.

hy'grophilous, a. [Biol.] Living in inland water or wet places.

'hygrophobe, n. [Bot.] Plant getting on best in dry places.

'hygrophyte, n. [Bot.] Plant living in places where earth is wetter than normal.

'hygroscope, n. Instrument recording changes in amount of water in air.

hygro'scopic, a. Readily taking up, acted on, by water, sp. [Bot.] (of motions or changes of form) caused by loss or intake of water. **hygrosco'picity,** n.

'hylophyte, n. [Bot.] Plant living in woods, where earth is somewhat wet.

'hymen, n. [Zoo.] Fold of MUCOUS MEMBRANE by which opening into VAGINA is in part shut. **'hymenal,** a.

hy'menium, n. [Bot.] The stretch of CELLS on which SPORES are formed in higher FUNGI. **hy'menial, hymen'i-ferous.** aa.

Hymen'optora, n.pl. [Zoo.] An ORDER of ENDOPTERYGOTE insects which, when winged, have four wings, of which the front ones are frequently hooked to the back ones in flight, for example ants and bees.

hyme'nopterous, a. [Zoo.] Having thin skin-like wings, said of insects, sp. HYMENOPTERA.

hy(o)-. [Zoo.] To do with HYOID BONE or HYOID ARCH: **hyo'branchial, hyo'glossal,** aa.

'hyoid arch. [Zoo.] The second PAIR of VISCERAL ARCHES in lower back-boned animals and the EMBRYOS of higher, between the MANDIBULAR ARCH and the first BRANCHIAL ARCH.

'hyoid bone, n. [Zoo.] Bone structure at base of tongue in back-boned animals.

'hyoman'dibular, 1.a. [Zoo.] To do with the HYOID ARCH and the mouth-bone, sp. of fish. 2.n. A CARTILAGE or bone forming the top part of the HYOID ARCH.

'hyoscine, n. [Chem.] SCOPOLAMINE.

hyo'stylic, a. [Zoo.] Having bones of mouth joined to head bone by HYOMANDIBULAR, as most fishes. **hyo'styly,** n.

'hypa'byssal, a. [Geol.] (Of ROCK) formed nearer the top of the earth than PLUTONIC rocks, and so having a structure between that of those and that of VOLCANIC rocks. **h. in'trusion.** MINOR INTRUSION.

'hyp(a)es'thesia, n. [Med.] Incomplete power of feeling. **hyp(a)es'thesic,** a.

'hypapo'physis, n. [Zoo.] Forward outgrowth from, or forward part of, a unit of the backbone, as in some birds and fishes; the HAEMAL SPINE.

hypar'terial, a. [Zoo.] Placed under an ARTERY.

hy'paxial, a. [Zoo.] Under the backbone.

hyper-. Over, very great, greater than normal, SUPER: **'hypera'cidity,** n. [Med.]

hype'raemia, n. [Med.] Condition of having overmuch blood in a part of the body. **hype'raemic,** a.

'hyper(a)es'thesia, n. [Med.] Condition in which senses are unhealthily delicate, giving reaction to very small STIMULI of every sort.

'hyperam'nesia, n. [Med.] Condition of mind in which person has no memory of anything but events which took place a very long time before.

hy'perbola, n. [Geom.] The curve outlining a plane cut down through a round-based CONE to the base from any point lower than the top and making a greater angle with it than the side does. **hyper'bolic,** a.

hyper'chromic, a. [Chem.] Said of a group of ATOMS causing an increase in the colouring-power of a substance.

'hypercon'duction, etc. See SUPERCONDUCTION, etc.

hyper'fine, a. [Phys.] With FINE STRUCTURE.

hyper'focal distance. The distance in front of a camera LENS at or past which everything is in good FOCUS.

hyper'function, n. [Med.] Condition in which part of body is overworking.

'hypermeta'morphosis, n. [Zoo.] A METAMORPHOSIS in which there are two or more clearly different LARVAL stages. **'hypermeta'morphic,** a.

'hyperme'tropia, n. [Med.] Condition of seeing things at a distance better than things near, caused by rays coming together at back of RETINA, common in old persons. **'hyperme'tropic,** a.

hype'ropia, n. HYPERMETROPIA.

'hyper'parasite, n. [Biol.] PARASITE living on another PARASITE. **'hyper'parasitism,** n.

'hyperpi'esi-a, -s, n. [Med.] Condition in which blood-PRESSURE is over-high.

'hyperpi'tuitarism, n. [Med.] Condition in which output of PITUITARY GLAND is greater than normal.

hyper'plasia, n. [Med., Biol.] Unnormal increase in number of CELLS in some part, or general over-growth of body substance.

hyper'pn(o)ea, n. [Med.] Uncommonly quick breathing.

'hyperpy'remia, n. [Med.] Condition in which a greater than normal amount of heat- and ENERGY-producing material is present in the blood.

hyper'sensitive, a. Acted on by anything (as chemical, light, etc.) to an uncommon degree, sp. [Med.].

'hyper'thyroidism, n. [Med.] Disease caused by over-working of THYROID GLAND.

'hyper'tonic, a. [Chem.] Said of a SOLUTION whose OSMOTIC PRESSURE is higher than that of the solution with which a comparison is being made, sp. higher than that of SERUM.

hy'pertrophy, n., v.i. [Med., Biol.] Unnormal

increase in size of CELL or part, such as may be caused by over-use. **hyper-'trophic(al)**, a., **hy'pertrophied**, a.

'**hypha** ('hyphae), n. [Bot.] Any of the thread-like parts of the MYCELIUM of a FUNGUS. '**hyphal**, a.

hy'pidiomorphic, a. [Geol.] (Of ROCK) formed in part of CRYSTALS, in part of grains.

'**hypno-**. Sleep.

hyp'nology, n. Science of sleep, sp. HYP-NOTIC. **hypno'logic(al)**, aa. **hyp'nologist**, n.

hyp'nosis, n. [Med., Psych.] Sleep-like condition produced by suggestion, in early stage of which person is under control of hypnotist, acting on any suggestion made by him, but in later stages of which he may become deeply unconscious. **hypno-'therapy**, n. Use of hypnotism against disease. **hyp'notic**, 1.a. Producing sleep; to do with h. 2.n. Sleep-producing substance; person readily hypnotized. '**hyp-notism**, n. The producing of the condition of h. '**hypnotist**, n. Person able to hypnotize others. '**hypnotize**, v.t. Put into condition of h.

'**hypo**, n. Substance used for FIXING camera-pictures, $Na_2S_2O_35H_2O$ (*sodium thiosulphate*).

'**hypo-**. [Chem.] Having less than the normal number of ATOMS or groups. [Biol.] Under, lower in position or number. [Med.] Much less strong, lower in quality, effect, than normal.

'**hypo'basal**, a. [Bot.] Said of the part of the EMBRYO at back of the BASAL WALL.

'**hypoblast**, n. [Zoo.] Inside coat of BLASTO-DERM; inside CELLS of EMBRYO. **hypo-'blastic**, a.

hypo'branchial, 1.a. [Zoo.] Under the GILLS; to do with the h. 2.n. Lowest division of BRANCHIAL ARCH.

hypo'centrum, n. [Zoo.] CARTILAGE under NOTOCHORD.

hypo'chlorite, n. [Chem.] A SALT having the ACID group ClO.

hypo'chondria, '**hypochon'driasis**, nn. [Med.] Unnormal fear and tendency to false belief that one is ill, with great attention to one's physical feelings as possible signs of disease. **hypo'chondriac**, a., n.

hypo'chondriac 'region. [Zoo.] The parts of the ABDOMEN on the two sides under the RIBS. **hypo'chondrium**, n. H. r.

hypo'chordal, a. [Zoo.] Under the NOTO-CHORD.

hypo'cotyl, n. [Bot.] The part of the stem under COTYLEDONS of EMBRYO plant. **hypo'cotylous**, '**hypocoty'ledonary**, aa.

hypo'derma, n. [Bot.] TISSUE under outside skin of plants. **hypo'dermal**, a.

hypo'chromia, n. [Med.] Condition of not having the normal amount of colouring-material in skin, hair, and eyes.

hypo'dermic, 1.a. [Zoo.] To do with parts

under skin. 2.n. [Med.] Substance put into body by h. injections. **h. in'jection**. The putting of medical substance into body through skin; substance put in at one time. **h. needle**. The needle of a h. syringe. **h. 'syringe**. SYRINGE with a hollow needle for giving h. injections.

hypo'dermis, n. [Zoo.] LAYER under the hard outside skin of some lower animals.

hypo'function, n. [Med.] Condition in which part of body is not doing its full work.

hypo'gastrium, n. [Anat.] Lower middle part of ABDOMEN. **hypo'gastric**, a.

hypo'ge-al, -ous, aa. [Biol.] Having growth, living, or placed, under the earth. [Bot.] (Of plant) starting development with COTYLEDONS under the earth.

'**hypogene**, a. [Geol.] Formed, taking place, deep under the earth.

hypo'genesis, n. [Biol.] Development without ALTERNATION OF GENERATIONS.

hy'pogenous, a. [Bot.] Having its growth on the under side of anything, sp. leaves.

hypo'glossal, n., a. [Zoo.] (Nerve) going from brain to base of tongue and controlling its motion, in higher back-boned animals.

hypo'glottis, n. [Zoo.] Part of the under 'lip' in COLEOPTERA; the under part of the tongue in back-boned animals.

hypogly'c(a)emia, n. [Med.] Condition in which amount of sugar in the blood is less than normal. '**hypogly'c(a)emic**, a.

hypo'gnathous, a. [Zoo.] Having lower JAW longer than top jaw.

hypo'gonadism, n. [Med.] Condition in which not enough SEX-HORMONES are produced.

hy'pogynous, a. [Bot.] (Of a flower) having the PISTIL on the top of a bulb-like RECEPTACLE, with the STAMENS, PETALS, and SEPALS at lower levels round the pistil and free from it; (of other flower-parts) having this position in relation to the pistil. **hy'pogyny**, n.

hypo'hyaline, a. [Geol.] Glass-like in part.

hypo'nasty, n. [Bot.] Growth of flat structure, as leaf, more quickly on under side than on top, causing up-curved form.

hypo'petalous, a. [Bot.] Having HYPO-GYNOUS PETALS.

'**hypopha'ryngeal**, a. [Zoo.] Under the PHARYNX.

hypo'pharynx, n. [Zoo.] Fold or tongue-like structure on floor of mouth of a number of insects, sp. ORTHOPTERA.

hypo'phyllous, a. [Bot.] Joined to or making its growth from under side of leaf.

hy'pophysis, n. [Zoo.] The PITUITARY GLAND (**h. 'cerebri**). [Bot.] In seed plants, CELL or cells producing point of root. **hypo-'physial**, a.

hypo'piesis, n. [Med.] Blood-PRESSURE much less than normal.

'hypopi'tuitarism, n. [Med.] Underworking of PITUITARY GLAND, generally causing person to become very fat and stopping sex-development.

hypo'plasia, n. [Med.] Uncomplete development.

hypo'podium, n. [Bot.] Base of leaf, with its stem, if any.

hy'postasis, n. [Med.] SEDIMENT; HYPER-AEMIA in a part of the body which is hanging down, caused by the blood-current not being strong enough to keep the blood moving out of the lower part of it. [Biol.] The controlling or overcoming of one GENE by another which is not its ALLELOMORPH. hypo'static(al), aa. Sp. [Med.] caused by tendency of liquid, as blood, to get down to lowest level and become massed there. [Biol.] (Of GENE) able to, with tendency to, undergo h.

hypo'stomatous, n. [Zoo.] Having mouth on underside of head, as certain fish.

hy'potenuse, n. [Geom.] Of a right-angled TRIANGLE, the side opposite the right angle.

hy'pothesis, n. Theory put forward to give reasons for connection between certain facts, or as a suggestion to be tested, on which further work may be based. hypo-'thetical, a. Taken to be true for working purposes, or put forward as suggestion.

hypo'thyroidism, n. [Med.] Condition in which output of THYROID GLAND is under normal.

hypo'tonic, a. [Chem.] Said of a SOLUTION whose OSMOTIC PRESSURE is lower than that of the solution with which a comparison is being made, sp. lower than that of SERUM.

'hypsodont, a. [Zoo.] (Of teeth) having high CROWNS and short roots; (of animal) having h. teeth.

'hypsochrome, n. [Chem.] Group of ATOMS which put into a substance have effect of moving its ABSORPTION SPECTRUM nearer to blue.

hyp'sography, n. [Geog.] The measuring and mapping of the distance of places up from sea-level.

hyp'someter, n. Instrument used for measuring how high a place is over sea-level (sp. by taking boiling-point of water), or for testing THERMOMETERS. hypso'metric, a. hyp'sometry, n.

'Hyra'coidea, n.pl. [Zoo.] An ORDER of small UNGULATE MAMMALS living in Africa and parts of Asia, having short legs and ears and almost no tail—the present-day representatives of a very old line of development.

hyster'esis, n. [Phys.] A LAG in the change of effect when the forces acting on a body are changed, as in the STRAIN on an elastic body when the force on it becomes less, or in the MAGNETIZATION of a sub-stance when the magnetizing force is made greater or less—for example, an automobile TYRE of high h. rubber is slower to go back to its normal form after braking than one of other rubber. h. loss. The work done in changing the force acting on a body from a certain value, through 0, to an equal and opposite value and back again, sp. of a MAGNETIC FIELD acting on a FERRO-MAGNETIC material. hyster'etic, a.

hys'teria, a. [Med.] Diseased condition of mind, caused by unconscious COMPLEXES and marked by loss of self-control, and freq. loss of memory, together with a number of serious physical effects, such as loss of power of seeing, hearing, etc. hys'teric(al), aa. hys'teric, n. Person having h.

'hystero-. UTERUS; HYSTERIA.

'hystero'genic, a. [Biol.] Of late development or growth. [Med.] Producing HYSTERIA.

hyste'ropathy, n. [Med.] Any disease of the UTERUS.

I, Sign for IODINE.

i-, Sign for ISO-.

I.A. = INTERNATIONAL ANGSTROM.

-'iasis, n. Process or condition, sp. [Med.] diseased condition.

-'iatry, -i'atrics, nn. Medical science or processes to do with diseases of what is named.

-ic, a. [Chem.] Ending put on to Latin names of ELEMENTS as a sign that in COMPOUNDS so named the element has its higher or highest VALENCY, as *ferric oxide*, Fe_2O_3. *See* -OUS.

I.C. = INTERNAL COMBUSTION.

I.C.B.M. = INTERCONTINENTAL BALLISTIC MISSILE.

ice, n. Water made solid by cold. I. Age. [Geol.] Any of the stretches of time in the earth's history when a much greater part of it than at present was covered with i. i. cap, i. sheet. [Geog.] Great flat stretch of i. and snow covering the land near the North or South POLE. i. point. The TEMPERATURE of i. and water in EQUI-LIBRIUM at a pressure of 760 mm. , = 0°C. '-berg, n. Great mass of i., broken off GLACIER, etc., on the sea with about $\frac{9}{10}$ of it under the water. -'blink, n. [Meteor.] A white look in the sky over an unseen i.-field, caused by light sent back from it.

'Iceland spar. [Mineral.] Natural $CaCO_3$ (*calcium carbonate*) noted for its strong BIREFRINGENCE, used in NICOL PRISM for the producing and observation of POLARIZED light.

'ichnite, 'ichnolite, nn. [Geol.] A FOSSIL footprint.

'ichnograph, n. Design to scale of one level of a building. ichno'graphic, a.

'ichthyic, a. To do with or like fish. 'ichthy(o)-.

'ichthyolite, n. [Geol.] A FOSSIL fish.

ichthy'ology, n. Science of fishes. 'ichthyo-'logic(al), aa. ichthy'ologist, n.

ichthy'ophagous, a. [Zoo.] Living on fish as food. ichthy'ophagy, n. ichthy'ophagi, n.pl. I. persons or animals.

'ichthyopte'rygium (ichthyopterygia), n. [Zoo.] One or the other FIN of two opposite one another, such as take the place in fish of the front or back legs of a land animal.

I.C.I. = INTERNATIONAL COMMISSION ON ILLUMINATION.

i'conoscope, n. Apparatus for changing a light picture into electric currents to be changed again into radio waves for TELEVISION.

icos(a)-, icosi-. 20.

'icosa'hedron, n. Solid having 20 faces, all with 3 equal sides. 'icosa'hedral, a.

ico'sandrous, a. [Bot.] Having 20 or more STAMENS.

'icterus, n. [Med.] JAUNDICE. ic'teric(al), aa.

'ictus, n. [Med.] A sudden attack of disease, sp. a STROKE.

id, n. [Psychol.] In Freud's theories, the deepest, completely unreasoning impulses and tendencies of man, see EGO and LIBIDO.

-ide, n. [Chem.] Formed of the ELEMENT named united with one other.

i'deal, a. Having properties, behaviour, or structure completely in agreement with theory (sp. as opp. substances, machines, etc. having material existence, which are gen. only almost, or roughly, in agreement with it). i. gas. [Phys., Chem.] A gas for which BOYLE'S LAW and CHARLES'S LAW would be completely true. i. gas constant. The CONSTANT R in the EQUATION $PV = RT$, which gives the fixed relation between PRESSURE (P), VOLUME (V), and ABSOLUTE TEMPERATURE (T) for an i. gas (see GAS CONSTANT).

i'dealism, n. Theory that our knowledge is limited to knowledge of ideas or events in the mind; theory that material things have no existence independent of mind, that everything is, in fact, mind in some form.

i'dentical, a. The same in the sense of not other; the same in the sense of completely like in every way. i. twins. See TWINS.

i'dentity, n. Fact, condition, of being i. [Psych.] The condition of being a person clearly marked off from others, one, and more or less the same, all through existence

'ideogr-am, -aph, nn. [Philol.] Simple picture representative of an idea, not of a sound, the earliest form of writing. ideo'graphic(al), aa. ide'ography, n.

ide'ology, n. System of ideas, sp. in relation to the organization of society. 'ideo-'logical, a.

'idio-. Special, separate. [Biol., Med.] Self-produced.

idio'chromatin, n. [Biol.] That part of CHROMATIN controlling the REPRODUCTION of the CELL.

'idiochro'midium (idiochromidia), n. [Biol.] Any bit of CHROMATIN outside the NUCLEUS which has the power of REPRODUCTION.

'idiocy, n. [Med.] Lowest degree of MENTAL DEFICIENCY, in which person is so much under normal in development of mind as to be unable to take care of himself or to make use of language normally, gen. caused by incomplete or unnormal development of brain. 'idiot, n. Person marked by i. idi'otic, a.

idi'ometer, n. [Astron.] Instrument for measuring the PERSONAL EQUATION in observation.

'idio'morph-ic, -ous, aa. [Geol.] Having the form normal to their substance, said of CRYSTALS in ROCK which have been free to undergo regular development.

'idioplasm, n. [Biol.] CHROMATIN looked on as the part of a CELL having to do with the qualities of a plant or animal and their handing on to offspring, as opp. TROPHOPLASM.

'idiosome, n. [Zoo.] A CELL markedly different from those round it in form, size, or substance.

'idio'syncracy, n. Some uncommon property special to a person or thing, sp. [Med.] that of giving a reaction which is not normal to certain foods, medical substances, etc. 'idiosyn'cratic, a.

I.F. = INTERMEDIATE FREQUENCY.

'igneous, a. To do with, like, produced by, fire. [Geol.] Produced by the operation of great heat inside the earth. i. rock. A ROCK formed of substance from inside the earth which has been forced up into the outer part while liquid with heat and has become solid on getting cold—one of the three chief groups of rocks (see SEDIMENTARY, METAMORPHIC, and p. 192).

ig'nite, v.t. and i. (Make) take fire. ig'nition, n. Sp., the process of, or apparatus for, igniting the mixed gases in an INTERNAL COMBUSTION ENGINE. ig'nition point. The degree to which a substance has to be heated before it takes fire.

I.H.P. = INDICATED HORSE-POWER.

Il, Sign for the old name ILLINUM.

'ileac, a. [Zoo.] Of, to do with, the ILEUM.

'ile(o)-. (Of the) ILEUM (and . . .): ile'ectomy, n., ile'itis, n,

TABLE OF IGNEOUS ROCKS

Texture	Acid	Intermediate		Basic
		Orthoclase	Plagioclase	
Vitreous or fine-grained	obsidian, rhyolite	trachyte, phonolite	andesite	basalt, tachylite
Medium-grained	microgranite, granite-porphyry, felsite	microsyenite, syenite-porphyry	microdiorite, porphyrite	dolerite
Coarse-grained	granite	syenite	diorite	gabbro

'ileo'c(a)ecum, n. [Zoo.] The ILEUM and the CAECUM taken together. 'ileo'c(a)ecal, a. 'ileo'c(a)ecal valve. VALVE formed by two folds of MUCUOS MEMBRANE at opening of ILEUM.

ileo'colic, a. [Zoo.] To do with the ILEUM and the COLON. i. 'artery. ARTERY taking blood to end of ILEUM and start of COLON.

'ileum, n. [Zoo.] The last, smaller, and thinner-walled division of the SMALL INTESTINE, opening into the LARGE INTESTINE.

'iliac, a. [Zoo.] Of, to do with, near, the ILIUM. i. 'artery. One or other of the two great ARTERIES at the right and left of the lower ABDOMEN near the backbone. i. crest. Thick, curved upper edge of the ILIUM. i. fossa. Somewhat hollowed inner side of the ILIUM. i. 'index. [Anthrop.] Relation between the distance between the i. spines and that between the top of the i. crest and the lower edge of the ACETABULUM. i. spine. Any of four sharp outgrowths on the i. crest, two at one end and two at the other.

i'liacus, n. [Zoo.] Muscle by which top part of leg or lower part of body is bent forward.

'ilium, n. [Zoo.] In back-boned animals, the back, top bone of the three bones forming the right or left half of the PELVIS. 'ilio-.

'ill-conditioned, a. [Astron.] Said of a TRIANGLE having very unequal angles, so that in using it as a base for working out positions, etc., a small error of observation may give quite a wrong picture.

il'linium, n. [Chem.] Name first given to PROMETHIUM.

il'luminant, n. Anything, for example gas, used for giving light.

il'luminate, v.t. Send light onto or about. il'luminating, a. Sp., used for producing light. il'lumination, n. Sp., the amount of light falling on a unit of any SURFACE, measured by the LUX or the FOOT-CANDLE. il'luminative, illumi'national, aa.

i'llusion, n. [Psych.] (The producing of) a false idea of something seen, etc. caused by an error in INTERPRETING what is sensed, as when something seems to be nearer than it is or to be moving when it is not, or a false memory placing a past experience at the wrong time or putting into it something which was not in fact part of it. i'llusory, a. Produced by or being an i.

'ilmenite, n. [Mineral.] Natural FeTiO$_3$ (ferrous titanite), a black, MASSIVE substance important as an ORE of Ti.

im-. Not, see IN-.

'image, n. Picture of, or solid form copying, something. [Optics.] Picture of a thing produced by the REFRACTION or REFLECTION of light-rays from every point of the side of it facing a LENS or looking-glass etc., in such a way as to make them come, or seem to come, together again at points with the same distribution in space, for example the i. of a seen thing formed on the RETINA of the eye, or the i. formed on a camera plate or in a looking-glass (see REAL IMAGE, VIRTUAL IMAGE). [Psych.] Idea representative of a sense-experience produced in the mind when the sense-experience itself is not present. i. space. [Optics] In an OPTICAL SYSTEM, space in which every point is an i. of a point in the same position in the OBJECT SPACE. 'imagery, n. [Psych.] Mind ii, taken as a group.

i'magi'nation, n. [Psych.] Process or power of forming IMAGES in the mind, or of forming new ideas or mind-pictures out of the material given by past experiences, by putting it together in new ways, i'maginative, a. To do with, produced by i.; marked by, or having great power of, i. **imagi'national,** a. To do with the i. **i'maginary,** a. (Of a mind-picture or idea) having no agreement with fact. **i'magine,** v.t. Get the idea of (a sense or other experience) produced in the mind when the STIMULUS is not present or make a mind-picture of (something new) by the use of i.

i'mago, n. [Zoo.] An insect in the last stage of its development, having sex-powers and generally wings. [Psych.] Complex feeling based on unconscious memory of father and mother and on person's reactions to them when very young. **i. disk** or **bud.** [Zoo.] Group of CELLS in early stages of some insects, from which wings, legs, and other parts of i. are formed. **i'maginal,** a.

im'balance, n. [Med.] Incomplete balance, sp. of the eye muscles or the working of the ENDOCRINE GLANDS.

imbe'cility, n. [Med.] Degree of MENTAL DEFICIENCY less than that of IDIOCY, in which person has some power of using language and is able to keep out of common dangers, but is generally unable to make a living. **'imbecile,** n. Person in condition of i.

imbi'bition, n. [Chem.] The taking in of a liquid by a solid substance, sp. a GEL. **i. 'process.** In camera work, sp. coloured motion-pictures, any process in which a DYE IMAGE taken up by a GEL is printed onto another material. **im'bibe,** v.t. and i.

'imbricate(d), a. [Biol.] (Of leaves, SCALES, etc.) in regular order with one covering part of another.

'imid(e), n. [Chem.] Any ORGANIC substance formed of the group —CO.NH.CO.—, produced, from an ACID ANHYDRIDE.

'imitate, v.t. [Biol.] MIMIC. **imi'tation,** n. Sp., [Psych.] Act of copying behaviour of others, consciously or as unconscious reaction to the observation of it. **'imitative,** a.

im'maculate, a. [Biol.] Having no coloured marks.

imma'ture, a. Not at the stage of full development.

im'merse, v.t. Put completely into a liquid or gas. **im'mersion,** n. Sp., [Astron.] The going from view of a body in the sky as the effect of becoming covered by another or moving into its shade. **immersion lens** or **ob'jective.** [Optics] LENS designed to be used with a drop of liquid, such as oil or water, between the front of it and a covering glass, used for increasing the light in a high-powered MICROSCOPE.

im'miscible, a. [Chem.] (Of liquids) not able to be mixed. **immisci'bility,** n.

im'mobilize, v.t. Put a stop to the motion of something, take away its power of

motion, sp. [Med.] keep damaged part of body in fixed position by dressing, etc.

im'munity, n. [Med.] Condition or power of keeping free from a certain disease, sp. of overcoming disease bodies such as BACTERIA before development of disease takes place. **imm'une,** a. Having i. **immune body.** [Biochem.] Any of a group of substances produced in blood or CELLS, naturally or by medical immunization, which take part in overcoming disease bodies. **'immunize,** v.t. Make immune, sp. by medical process of INOCULATION, etc. **'immuni'zation,** n.

'immuno-. IMMUNE, or to do with IMMUNITY: **'immuno'chemistry,** n., **'immuno'therapy,** n.

'immun'ology, n. The branch of medical science having to do with the causes and producing of IMMUNITY. **'immun'ologist** n.

'impact, n. The shock of two bodies coming together with some force, or the blow given by one to the other. **i. fluo'rescence.** [Phys.] Rays produced in one substance by blows from EXCITED ATOMS of another. **i. pa'rameter.** Distance of line of motion of a body (sp. ELECTRON) from middle of body (sp. NUCLEUS) acting on it.

im'pacted, a. Very tightly or deeply fixed, as [Med.] a tooth which has no room to come completely through, or the edges of a broken bone which have been forced into one another. **im'paction,** n. Condition of being i.

im'pedance, n. [Elec.] Seeming RESISTANCE of an ALTERNATING electric current, given by $\sqrt{R^2 + X^2}$, where R = resistance in OHMS and X = REACTANCE. **i. coil.** REACTOR. **i. drop** (or **rise**). [Elec. Engin.] A drop (or increase) in the VOLTAGE at the TERMINALS of a CIRCUIT caused by the i. **i. 'factor.** The RATIO of the i. of a CIRCUIT to its RESISTANCE.

im'pediment, n. [Med.] (Of SPEECH) anything wrong with person's way of talking, forming words, caused by something wrong with the structure of the mouth or of other parts controlling the voice.

im'peller, n. [Mach.] A turning part with blades, used for producing a current of liquid or gas in certain forms of pump.

im'perfect, a. Not complete in form or development, not having the complete number of parts. **i. 'flower.** [Bot.] Flower without STAMENS or without CARPELS, or having one or the other in an i. form and not in operation. **i. fungus.** FUNGUS having only an i. stage. **i. stage.** (Of FUNGUS) CONIDIAL stage.

im'perforate, a. [Zoo.] Having no hole or opening. [Med.] Having an opening shut or stopped up.

im'permeable, im'pervious, aa. (Of substance) not letting something through, as *i. to* liquid or gas.

impe'tigo, n. [Med.] A skin disease, chiefly of face and hands, marked by PUSTULES and caused by BACTERIA.

'impetus, n. [Mech.] Force of a quickly moving body, used loosely for KINETIC ENERGY or MOMENTUM; force putting body in motion, sp. suddenly, push, impulse.

im'pinge, v.i. Come against, sp. with force, for example, sound waves *i. on* the ear; be touching. **'-ment,** n. **im'pingent,** a.

implan'tation, n. [Med.] The putting of a substance into the body under the skin, or into some diseased growth, by use of instrument; GRAFTING.

im'plosion, n. [Phonet.] The COMPRESSION of air between the shut GLOTTIS and shut mouth and nose, sp. the forming of the sounds *p, t, k,* in this way. **im'plode,** v.t. Say (a given letter etc.) with i. **im'plosive,** n., a. (Sound) said with i.

im'ponderable, n., a. (Substance) having very little weight.

'impotent, a. [Med.] (Sp. of a male) unable to COPULATE because of some DEFECT of structure or nerve-processes. **'impotence,** n.

im'pound, v.t. Make store of (natural water) by building structures shutting it in.

im'pregnate, v.t. Get (a substance) mixed all through with grains, etc. of another, for example, *i.* rubber *with* S, *i.* wood *with* oil. [Biol.] Put male GERM-CELLS into the ovary of (female); POLLINATE. **impregnated 'carbon.** C impregnated with some other substance, for use in ARC-LAMPS to make a flame arc. **'impregnation,** n. that with which a substance is impregnated. [Geol.] A distribution of small grains of ORE through ROCK.

im'pression, n. A print of anything made by forcing it into a soft substance, sp. for the purpose of making a copy of its form, as [Med.] an i. of teeth made by biting into a mass of wax, etc. **im'press,** v.t. Make an i. of (something) or make an i. in (something). **im'pressed,** a. Sp. [Bot.] of a SURFACE, having hollow marks like ii. on it.

'impulse, n. [Phys.] Force acting for a short time only, sp. measure of such a force given by the PRODUCT of its AVERAGE value and the time through which it is acting. [Physiol.] A change started at one point of a train of nerves, muscles, etc. and moving through it to an outcome in some reaction of the body (*see* NERVE IMPULSE.) [Psych.] A strong and sudden tendency to do something which is not the outcome of conscious decision and not an automatic reaction to a STIMULUS but has something of the quality of the

second. [Elec. Radio] An electric or radio effect going on for only a short time, sp. one putting something into operation. **i. radi'ation.** [Phys.] Any rays given out by a body as the effect of blows given to it by quickly-moving ELECTRONS etc., for example X-RAYS. **im'pulsion,** n. [Phys.] Short push given by body in motion to another body; act of giving impulsion to. [Psych.] An i. over which person has no control. **im'pulsive,** a. [Phys.] Putting in motion by impulsion. [Psych.] Given to acting on i.; (of an act) done on i.

im'pure, a. Not PURE. **im'purity,** n. The condition of being i.; a small amount of any different, sp. undesired, substance, sound, FREQUENCY, RADIATION, effect, and so on, present in or mixed with a greater amount of some other substance, sound, etc.

in-. Not (becomes **il-** before '1', **ir-** before 'r', and **im-** before 'm'. 'p', and 'b'):— **'-har'monic,** a.; in(to):— **'-land,** a.

In, Sign for INDIUM.

in. = INCH.

in'active, a. Not ACTIVE. [Phys., Chem.] Having no power of chemical reaction; having an ASYMMETRIC C ATOM but not OPTICAL ACTIVITY. **in'activate,** v.t. Make i., sp. [Chem.] a CATALYST, or [Immunology] a SERUM. **inacti'vation,** n.

in'adequate, a. Not ADEQUATE. [Psych.] (Of a STIMULUS) not the normal sort for a given sense but producing the same effect, for example electric current acting on the nerve of the eye to give a sense-experience of seen light.

ina'nition, n. [Med.] Feeble condition of body caused by not taking in enough food, or by being unable to make full use, by digestion, of what is taken in.

inar'ticulate, a. [Biol.] (Of worms, plant stems, etc.) not SEGMENTED; without JOINTS, sp., of certain sea-animals, having a SHELL in two parts without a HINGE.

'inborn, a. [Psych., Med.] (Of a quality or tendency) present in a person from birth.

'inbreeding, n. [Zoo.] The producing of offspring from brothers and sisters or other near relations. **'in'bred,** a. (Of offspring) produced by i.; (of a family, etc.) having undergone or been used for i.

inca'liculate, a. [Bot.] Without a CALYCLE.

incan'descent, a. Heated to the point of giving out light. **i. lamp.** Lighting apparatus in which light is produced by heating some substance to incandescence, as in the common electric bulb where wire is heated by current. **i. 'mantle.** GAS MANTLE. **incan'descence,** n.

in'casement **'theory.** PREFORMATION THEORY.

in'cendiary, a. Causing fire, causing other things to take fire. **i. bomb.** A BOMB designed for i. purposes, having in it materials which take fire when the bomb goes off.

inch, n. British unit of distance = 2·5400 cm., sign ˝.

'incidence, n. The falling of a moving thing, such as a ray of light, on a SURFACE (*i. on*); range of distribution or effect. **'incident,** a. (Of ray, etc.) touching, meeting, falling (*on* a SURFACE).

in'cinerate, v.t. Get something completely burned. **incine'ration,** n. **in'cinerator,** n. Apparatus for incineration.

in'cised, a. [Biol.] Having deep, sharp, and gen. not quite regular cuts round the edge, said sp. of leaf (*see* picture p. 223).

in'cision, n. [Med.] Act of cutting into body; a cut made by a medical instrument. **in'cisive,** a. Cutting, or formed for cutting.

in'cisor, n. [Zoo.] A tooth with a cutting edge, sp. any of the front teeth in man and like animals. **in'cisiform,** a.

'incline, n. A slope, sp. a sloping way from one level of a mine to another, up which coal etc. is taken on rails. **in'clined,** a. Sloping, at an angle other than a right angle to something. **in'clined plane.** A plane SURFACE making less than a right angle with the HORIZONTAL.

'incli'nation, n. Angle of meeting of two lines, planes, rays, etc.; angle of slope from a VERTICAL or a HORIZONTAL plane; MAGNETIC DIP. **i. of an 'orbit.** [Astron.] The angle between the plane of the ECLIPTIC and the plane in which a PLANET etc. is moving.

'inclinometer, n. A SURVEYING instrument for measuring small slopes; an instrument used in an air-plane for giving the angle with the HORIZONTAL, from end to end or side to side, at which it is flying.

in'cluded, a. [Bot.] Said of STAMENS and PISTILS not coming out farther than mouth of COROLLA.

in'clusion, n. A bit or mass of different material inside some substance, as grains of non-metal in a metal. [Geol.] An amount, gen. very small, of any other substance, solid, liquid, or gas, inside a solid ROCK, sp. older rock in the middle of a mass of later development. [Biol.] Any separate body formed inside a CELL, such as the cell-NUCLEUS itself, or a grain of material, for example STARCH, produced by the cell. **i. 'body.** [Med.] Small body or grain of different substance in CELL, sp. one of those produced in cells attacked by a VIRUS. **in'clude,** v.t. Take or have in.

incom'bustible, a. Not able to be burned.

incom'patible, a. [Med.] Unable to be put or used together, because of undesired chemical reaction, or the undoing by one of the effect of the other, said of medical substances, blood of different sorts which may not safely be mixed in a living person or animal, etc. **incom'pati'bility,** n.

in'competent, a. [Geol.] (Of STRATA) not strong enough for supporting, without damage or change, the weight of material over them. [Med.] Not able to do the work needed, said sp. of diseased VALVES of the heart which let blood through in the wrong direction. **in'competence,** n.

incom'plete flower. [Bot.] A flower without CALYX and COROLLA or one of these.

incom'plete meta'morphosis. [Zoo.] Insect development in which the young when they come out of the egg are not greatly different from the insects by which they were produced, and take their complete form by degrees without going through a PUPA stage.

incom'pressible, a. Not COMPRESSIBLE. **incom'pressi'bility,** n.

in'congruent, a. [Zoo.] (Of parts of two bones coming together at a JOINT) not so formed that one comes naturally into adjustment with the other.

in'continence, n. [Med.] Condition in which person has no control over URINATION or DEFECATION. **in'continent,** a.

incoördi'nation, n. [Med.] The working of the different groups of muscles needed for some act independently of one another through loss of the power of controlling them, so that the right effect is not produced.

in'cretion, n. [Zoo.] INTERNAL SECRETION. **in'cretory,** a.

incrus'tation, n. A coat of solid substance, sp. as formed on something by chemical reaction, for example on metals by reaction with air, etc.

incu'bation, n. [Biol.] The process of the development of young from eggs; a mother bird's act of i. by keeping eggs warm under her body; any process of keeping eggs, BACTERIA etc. warm for the purpose of causing development; time of development between INFECTION and the first signs of the disease caused by it. **'incubate,** v.t. Make undergo i. **'incubator,** n. Apparatus used for i. of eggs etc. **in'cubatory,** a.

'incubous, a. [Bot.] Having the top edge of every leaf covering the base of the leaf in front of it further up the stem.

'incud(o)-. To do with the INCUS.

in'cumbent, a. [Bot.] Resting on or touching, sp. of COTYLEDONS so folded that the HYPOCOTYL is against the back of one of them. [Zoo.] Bent back so as to be resting on or touching something, said of hairs, etc.; resting flat on the earth, said of bird's back toe.

in'current, a. [Zoo.] Having an ingoing

current, said of holes through which sponges take in water, and like parts of other animals.

in'curvate(d), in'curved, aa. [Biol.] Bent in. incur'vation, n.

'incus, n. Something like an ANVIL in form, sp. [Zoo.] the middle one of the three AUDITORY OSSICLES in higher animals. 'incudal, a.

inde'ciduate, a. [Zoo.] Having an i. placenta, as the lower MAMMALS. i. pla'centa. A PLACENTA of which the part formed by the wall of the UTERUS does not come away at birth, the VILLI making the connection simply coming out of the wall.

in'definite, a. [Bot.] The number of which is great and not fixed; (of stem or flower-grouping) not ending in a flower, as a RACEME.

inde'hiscent, a. [Bot.] (Of FRUIT) not opening naturally when seeds are ready. inde'hiscence, n.

inde'terminate, a. Not fixed, not clear, sp. of which the limits are i. [Bot.] INDEFINITE, sp. RACEMOSE; having the parts of the PERIANTH separate and not folded over one another before opening. [Phonet.] (Of VOWEL on which no weight is put) of unclear or unfixed sound. i. growth. [Bot.] The growth of an i. stem, to which there is no fixed limit. inde'terminacy, inde'terminateness, indetermi'nation, nn. inde'terminacy principle, UNCERTAINTY PRINCIPLE.

'index ('indices or indexes), n. The finger nearest the thumb (freq. i. finger); the pointer of an instrument; a list making clear where the things named in it are to be looked for, as a list of names etc. with page-numbers at the back of a book; a RATIO or other number used as a measure of some property, for example the CEPHALIC INDEX. [Math. etc.] A letter, number, or other sign put to the left or right, over or under, another letter, number etc. to make clear its position in a system, or some operation in mathematics to be done to it, and so on—for example, an EXPONENT. i. of re'fraction. [Optics] A measure of the power of REFRACTION of a MEDIUM, being the RATIO of the rate of a light-wave in a VACUUM to its rate in the medium in question (see SNELL'S LAW). i. plane. [Geol.] Any plane, such as the top of a bed, on which the working out of a structure of beds is based.

'Indian ink. 'India ink, Ink in solid form made from LAMPBLACK and used, mixed with water, for art work, giving a very black effect and keeping its colour unchanged by time.

'indiarubber, n. The substance rubber, or a bit of it used for rubbing out writing etc.

'indican, n. [Biochem.] An AROMATIC substance present in small amount in URINE.

'indicate, v.t. Be pointing to, make clear, be a sign of. 'indicator, n. A pointer; any instrument or apparatus pointing out on a scale etc., or recording, anything, for example, the rate of something moving, the force of steam in an engine, etc. [Chem.] Substance which on being put into a liquid indicates by its colour if the liquid is acid or if it is ALKALINE, and so may be used for testing, or for indicating when a chemical reaction is complete. 'indicator 'diagram. [Engin.] Picture giving changes in the VOLUME and PRESSURE of gas, steam etc., in relation to the position of the PISTON, through one complete operation of a steam, gas, etc. engine.

'indicated horse-power. [Engin.] The power of an engine as worked out from the size of its parts, etc., see BRAKE HORSE-POWER.

in'digenous, a. [Biol., Geol.] Formed in, natural to, the place in question, not having been taken there from some other place.

'indigo, n. A blue colouring-material, $C_{16}H_{10}N_2O_2$, got from a number of plants.

indi'rect, a. Not DIRECT. i. de'velopment. [Zoo.] Development by METAMORPHOSIS. i. ray or wave. [Radio] SKY WAVE.

'indium, n. Chemical ELEMENT, at. no. 49, at. wt. 114·76, sign In, a soft, white metal.

indi'vidual, 1.n. [Biol.] A complete and separate living thing, or a unit of a group. 2.a. To do with ii. as opp. a group; separate, being an i.; one only, taken as a thing. i. psy'chology. Adler's system of psychology, based on the desire for power as the driving force of man's being and the feeling of not being equal to others as the chief cause of NEUROSIS. '-ism, n. Form of SYMBIOSIS in which the animals or plants living together make up a structure so united as to seem like one i., for example, in LICHENES.

'individua'tion, n. [Biol.] Development of units dependent on one another, as in a COLONY.

'Indo-Euro'pean, a. [Philol.] Name given to the great family of languages made up of most of those of Europe together with those of North India and other places in Asia.

'indole, n. [Chem.] The substance C_8H_7N, made up of a BENZENE and a PYRROLE RING with 2 C ATOMS in common, forming part of INDIGO and present in coal TAR and FAECES.

'indolent, a. [Med.] Causing little or no pain.

in'duce, v.t. Get (an effect) produced in some INDIRECT way, for example by a force acting at a distance or [Psych.] by CONTRAST or example. [Elec.] Get

(MAGNETISM or ELECTRICITY) produced in anything by INDUCTION. in′duced, a. **induced ′current.** [Elec.] Current in a CIRCUIT produced as the effect of an induced E.M.F. **in′duced drag.** [Aero.] That amount of the DRAG of an airplane part necessarily caused by its LIFT. **induced re′action.** [Chem.] A reaction whose rate is increased as the effect of a different and quicker reaction taking place at the same time in the same system and using one or more of the same substances.

in′ductance, n. [Elec.] That property of an electric CIRCUIT dependent on the way in which CONDUCTORS are placed (for example, in the form of a COIL), and measured in HENRIES, because of which any change in the current going through it takes a time to come into full effect by reason of INDUCED ELECTROMOTIVE FORCE in the opposite direction; (see MUTUAL I., SELF-I.); i. coil. **i. coil.** A COIL used as a REACTOR.

in′duction, n. Reasoning from like examples to general laws. [Phys.] Process by which a body put in an ELECTRIC (or MAGNETIC) FIELD becomes electric (or magnetic), or an electric current is produced in a moving wire in a fixed magnetic field or a fixed wire in a changing magnetic field (see ELECTROSTATIC I., ELECTROMAGNETIC I., MUTUAL I., SELF-I.). [Elec.] The DISPLACEMENT of ELECTRONS, or the amount of this displacement per unit AREA, in a DIELECTRIC in an ELECTRIC FIELD. [Biol.] The effect of one EMBRYONIC TISSUE in causing or helping the DIFFERENTIATION of another tissue near to it. [Chem.] The process seen in an INDUCED REACTION. **i. coil.** [Elec.] Apparatus having two COILS, one with a much greater number of turns than the other, producing by i. a current of high VOLTAGE in the greater as effect of a regularly broken current through the smaller. **i. ′furnace,** n. [Metal.] Apparatus for heating metals to a liquid condition by electric currents produced in them by i.

in′ductive, a. To do with, having, caused by, INDUCTANCE or INDUCTION. **inductivity,** n. [Phys.] I. power.

induc′tometer, n. [Elec.] An instrument for measuring INDUCTION.

in′ductor, n. [Elec.] A part of an electric apparatus causing or acted on by INDUCTION; REACTOR. [Chem.] That substance which by its quick reaction with one of the substances in an INDUCED REACTION makes their reaction with one another take place more quickly.

indu′mentum, n. [Zoo.] The hair or feathers covering an animal. [Bot.] A thick cover of hairs.

in′duplicate, a. [Bot.] Having the edges

bent or rolled in, said of flower-parts or leaves in the BUD. **in′duplicative,** a. Having i. parts.

′indurate, v.t. Make hard, sp. [Med.] of a TISSUE. [Geol.] Get liquid or loose ROCK formed into a hard, solid, mass. **′indurated,** a. **indu′ration,** n. Sp. [Geol.] the indurating of ROCK as the effect of heat, PRESSURE and chemical change.

in′dusium, n. [Bot.] In FILICALES, sorts of outgrowth on leaf forming cover for mass of SPORE-vessels; ANNULUS in certain FUNGI. [Zoo.] Any skin-like part acting as a cover, sp. bag in which EMBRYO has its development; cover of certain insect LARVA. **i. ′griseum.** [Zoo.] A thin skin of grey material over the CORPUS CALLOSUM. **in′dusial,** a. **in′dusial ′limestone.** [Mineral.] A LIMESTONE present in inland waters, made up chiefly of outer covers of certain worms.

in′dustrial, a. To do with, of sort used in, industry. **i. dis′ease.** A disease common among persons in any special industry, caused by their work. **i. ′poison.** Substance which is a danger to workers making or using it.

in′duviae, n.pl. [Bot.] Leaves not separating from stem when dead; SCALE-LEAVES. **in′duviate,** a.

ine′lastic, a. Not elastic. **i. coll′ision.** [Phys.] A violent coming together of two bodies in which some of the KINETIC ENERGY is changed into some form of POTENTIAL ENERGY.

ine′quality, n. [Astron.] Any change in the rate or direction of motion of a PLANET.

i′nerm(ous), aa. [Bot.] Unarmed, having no sharp points.

i′nert, a. [Chem.] Having little or no power of chemical reaction. **i. gases.** The gases He, A, Kr, Ne, X, and Rn, which do not give any chemical reaction—other names for which are *rare gases* and *noble gases.*

i′nertia, n. [Phys.] That property of material substance by which a body keeps its condition of rest, or of motion at an unchanging rate in the same direction, if it is not acted on by an outside force; measure of this property as given by the force needed to overcome it (that is, to put a body in motion or to make a given change in its rate or direction). [Med.] Condition of not acting, loss of power of acting. **i′nertial, a**

′infantile, a. [Med.] To do with, like, a baby or very young person. [Geol.] (Of a stretch of country) in an early stage of development. **i. pa′ralysis.** Disease chiefly seen in the young, caused by a VIRUS attacking the nerve-CELLS in the grey substance of the SPINAL CORD and marked by PARALYSIS and wasting of the muscles. **in′fantilism,** n. [Med.] Condition of incomplete development of mind and body in which person keeps i. ways and reactions not normal for his years.

in'farct, n. [Med.] A part from which the blood has been sharply cut off by something stopping up the blood-current and which is in process of undergoing NECROSIS.

in'fect, v.t. [Med.] (Of living MICRO-ORGANISM) be the cause of a diseased condition in a body by attacking it; give disease to by handing on disease-causing organisms; give (instrument, food, etc.) power of infecting through having disease organisms. **'-ion,** n. The act or process of infecting; disease caused by a living MICRO-ORGANISM; micro-organism causing disease. **'-ious,** a. Causing infection; (of disease) of sort caused by infection and very readily given by one person to another, *see* CONTAGIOUS.

'inference, n. An opinion come to by IN-DUCTION or DEDUCTION. **in'fer,** v.t.

in'ferior, a. [Biol., Geol., Astron.] Placed low down or lower than some other, sp. like, part. [Bot.] Said of CARPELS of a flower when they are inside the RECEP-TACLE, with all the other flower parts over them, or of the OVARY formed of such carpels when it is united to the wall of the receptacle; on the side of flower nearest to BRACT; opposite or farthest from AXIS. **i. con'junction.** [Astron.] *See* CONJUNCTION.

in'feriority 'complex. [Psych.] A strong unconscious sense of not being the equal of others, deeply rooted in unconscious reactions to past experience, and having strong and complex effects on feelings and behaviour.

'infer(o)-. Lower, under (and . . .); **-an'terior,** a., **-'lateral,** a., **-pos'terior,** a.

'infes'tation, n. The process of infesting or the condition of being infested. **in'fest,** v.t. (Of insects, PARASITES etc.) get all over, be covering (plants, animals). **in'fested,** a. Covered with (insects, parasites etc.)

in'filtrate, 1.v.t. Get into a substance, or through a skin or wall, by slipping into spaces between its parts, sp. [Med.] of substances making their way by degrees into body CELLS. 2.n. Any substance infiltrating another, sp. [Med.] one whose infiltration is the cause of an unnormal condition in cells. **infil'tration,** n. Sp. [Med.] an i.; the distribution by degrees of an INFEC-TION through a part of the body. **infil'trative,** a.

'infinite, a. So great in number or amount as to be outside the range of measuring, unlimited. 2.n. That which is i., sp. space or time without end. [Math.] An i. QUANTITY. **i. 'series.** [Math.] A SERIES without end, for example, one of FRAC-TIONS of fractions, the SUM of which

never becomes equal to 1, as $\frac{1}{2}+\frac{1}{4}+\frac{1}{8}$, etc. **in'finity,** n. The quality of being i. [Math.] A number greater than any which may be named, or a distance greater than any which may be measured, sign ∞. [Optics] Point at such a distance that rays of light coming from it may be looked on as parallel.

in'flame, v.t. and i. [Med.] Make or become inflamed. **in'flamed,** a. In a condition of inflammation. **inflamm'ation,** n. Condition of a part of the body, caused by reaction to wound or INFECTION, in which the blood-vessels become over-full of blood, and LYMPH and blood-CELLS get out into the TISSUES, of which the signs are a red and heated SWELLING and pain. **in'flammatory,** a. Marked by, or causing, i.

in'flammable, a. FLAMMABLE—at one time commonly used but now going out of use and giving place to 'flammable'.

in'flate, v.t. Get any elastic vessel full of air, gas, or liquid, so that its walls are stretched tight; put air or gas into airship. **'-d.** Sp. [Bot.] hollow, thin-walled and inflated, as a stem or seed-vessel; open and stretched out, as a PERIANTH. **in'flation,** n.

in'flection, n. [Philol.] The change of form which words undergo to make clear their relations to others in a statement, the number and sex of the things of which they are representative, the time of an act, etc.; any ending put onto a word or root as a sign of i.; a change in the TONE or PITCH of the voice in talking. **in'flectional,** a. **in'flectional language.** [Philol.] a language making use of ii., as opp. an AGGLUTINATIVE or ISOLATING LANGUAGE.

in'flexed, a. [Biol.] Bent or curved sharply in or down, as the PETALS of a flower.

inflo'rescence, n. [Bot.] The grouping and order of development of the flowers on a stem; the flowers grouped on a stem taken together; that part of a plant by which flowers or, in BRYOPHYTA, sexed parts, are produced. (*See* p. 199.)

'influence machine. [Elec. Engin.] ELEC-TROSTATIC GENERATOR.

influ'enza, n. [Med.] An INFECTIOUS, sometimes EPIDEMIC disease, caused by a VIRUS, of which outbursts are common in winter, attacking the higher part of the breathing apparatus, marked by FEVER and great loss of power in muscles. **'-l,** a.

'infra-. Under, lower than, in position or scale: **-ax'illary,** a., **-'costal,** a., **-'renal,** a. **-umbilical,** a.

infra'clavicle, n. [Zoo.] A bone in the SHOULDER GIRDLE of certain fishes, working like the CLAVICLE in higher animals.

'infradyne, n. [Radio] A form of SUPER-HETERODYNE RECEIVER in which the

Sorts of Inflorescence

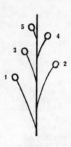

RACEME

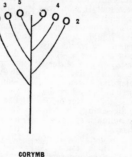

CORYMB

SPIKE

CAPITULUM

CYME

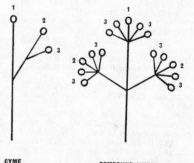

COMPOUND UMBEL

INTERMEDIATE FREQUENCY is higher than the incoming frequency.

infra′median, a. In, to do with, a part of the sea-bed between 50 and 100 metres from the top of the water.

′inframo′lecular, a. [Phys.] Smaller in size than a MOLECULE.

infra′orbital, a. [Zoo.] Under the ORBIT of the eye, said sp. of a CANAL in the MAXILLARY bone, its opening on the outside of the bone (**i. fo′ramen**), and the blood-vessels and nerves going through it.

′infra′protein, n. [Chem.] Substance produced by HYDROLYSIS of a PROTEIN.

′infra-′red, a. [Phys.] To do with, said of, the unseen heat rays coming after the red end of the SPECTRUM of light rays, having waves longer than light rays but not longer than about 0·03 cm.

′infra′sonic, a. [Phys.] To do with, said of, sound-waves longer than the longest in man's range of hearing.

′infraspi′natus, n. [Anat.] Muscle going from the SCAPULA to the HUMERUS.

infruc′tescence, n. [Bot.] An INFLORESCENCE coming after the development of the flowers into fruit.

infun′dibulin, n. [Biochem.] Substance sent out from the back division of the PITUITARY GLAND.

infun′dibulum, n. [Anat., Zoo.] ORGAN or part formed like a FUNNEL, having hollow stem opening out to wide mouth, sp. part of the PITUITARY GLAND. **infun′dibular,** a. **infun′dibulate,** a. **′infundib′uliform,** a.

in′fuse, v.t. Put (a substance) in water or other liquid to get from it substances having medical, etc. properties. **in′fusion,** n. Process of infusing; the liquid produced by infusion. [Med.] The process of putting a SOLUTION, sp. of salt and water, into a blood-vessel. **in′fusible,** a.

Infu′soria, n.pl. CILIOPHORA. **infusorial,** a. **infus′orial earth.** DIATOMACEOUS EARTH.

Ingenhausz's experiment. [Phys.] Way of making clear the rate at which heat is transported by different metals, by coating rods of these metals with wax and putting their ends into heated water to see how quickly the wax on the different rods becomes liquid.

in′gestion, n. [Zoo.] The act of taking anything into the body for use as food. **in′gest,** v.t. **in′gesta,** n.pl. Material ingested. **in′gestible,** a. **in′gestive,** a.

in′gluvies, n. [Zoo.] Bag-like expansion of throat of bird into which food is first taken and where it is made softer before undergoing further digestion; like structure in some other animals, sp. insects and worms. **in′gluvial,** a.

′ingot, n. [Metal.] Mass of metal CAST into some simple form in which it may be stored or transported before undergoing further working. **i. iron.** Iron having in it less than 0·1% C, very readily rolled or hammered. **i. ′structure.** The general structure of CRYSTALS in an i., which is formed normally of CHILL CRYSTALS, COLUMNAR CRYSTALS, and EQUI-AXED CRYSTALS.

′ingress, n. Act of coming in. [Astron.] The coming of the moon into the shade of the earth at certain times.

′inguen, n. [Zoo.] GROIN. **′inguinal,** a. **in′guinal ′ligament.** POUPART'S LIGAMENT.

in′hale, v.i. and t. Take in breath; take in (substance) with breath, up nose, etc., sp. into LUNGS. **in′halant,** 1.a. [Zoo.] Used for breathing. 2.n. [Med.] Substance inhaled for medical purposes. **inha′lation,** n. Sp., one act of taking in breath. [Med.] Inhalant. **′-r,** n. Apparatus for inhaling medical substance; apparatus for putting over mouth and nose to keep dust, gases, very cold air, etc., from being inhaled.

in′herit, v.t. [Biol.] Get (qualities) from ANCESTORS. **′-ance,** n. The process of inheriting; those qualities inherited by a plant or animal. **′-ed,** a.

inhi′bition, n. [Zoo.] A stopping or slowing down of any normal process or reaction of the body. [Psych.] The stopping or keeping back of certain impulses, behaviour, mind-processes, by others; anything in the mind getting in the way of free and normal behaviour; the condition of having ii. **in′hibit,** v.t. **in′hibited,** a. Sp., [Psych.] having ii. **in′hibitive,** a. **in′hibitor,** n. Anything causing i. of body processes. [Chem.] Any substance stopping or slowing down a chemical reaction. **in′hibitory,** a. **in′hibitory nerve.** [Zoo.] Nerve which when STIMULATED inhibits the operation of a muscle or GLAND.

′inhomo′geneous, a. Not of like substance or quality in all parts. **′inhomoge′neity,** n.

i′nitial, 1.a. To do with, present at, the start or earliest stage. 2.n. MERISTEMATIC CELL.

i′nitiator, n. [Chem.] The substance or MOLECULE starting a CHAIN REACTION.

in′ject, v.t. Get (liquid or gas) forced into something, sp. [Med.] under person's skin or into some opening of the body for some medical purpose, such as taking away pain, keeping off disease, etc. **′-ion,** n. Act of injecting; the liquid or gas injected, sp. into the body. [Geol.] The injection of MOLTEN material between, or into cracks in, ROCKS. [Astronautics] The firing of a SATELLITE from its last ROCKET STAGE into ORBIT. [Engin.] The process of blowing a rain of oil-drops into the CYLINDER of a COMPRESSION-IGNITION engine with a pump. **′-or,** n. Apparatus for forcing water into steam-boiler by first sending in a strong current of steam to make a way.

ink sac, n. [Zoo.] In some CEPHALOPODA, a GLAND which sends out a dark brown colouring-material when the animal is attacked.

′inlier, n. [Geol.] An OUTCROP of older ROCK framed in later-formed rock.

in′nate, a. [Zoo.] Present from birth, INHERITED. [Bot.] Fixed to its support by one end only, said of ANTHER; ENDOGENOUS.

′inner, a. [Chem.] INTRAMOLECULAR. **i. ear.** [Zoo.] That part of the ear of back-boned animals which is inside, or, in MAMMALS, furthest inside, the head, made up of a complex system of MEMBRANOUS pipes and hollows (the *membranous labyrinth*) housed in a like system of bone-spaces (the *bony labyrinth*) and full of liquid, with a middle hollow having OTOLITHS in it, and two divisions, the UTRICLE, opening into the SEMI-CIRCULAR CANALS, and the SACCULE, opening into the COCHLEA, where hearing is effected. **i. speech.** [Psych.] The use of words or word-pictures in thought.

inner′vation, n. [Zoo.] Distribution of nerves in any part.

′innocent, a. [Med.] BENIGN.

in′nominate ′artery. [Zoo.] In MAMMALS, the great blood-vessel branching right from the AORTA over the heart and undergoing division into the CAROTID ARTERY and the SUBCLAVIAN ARTERY. **in′nominate bone.** [Zoo.] Great bone forming one side of PELVIS. **in′nominate vein.** [Zoo.] One or other of two VEINS on lower sides of neck.

in′nomi′natum, n. INNOMINATE BONE.

i′noculate, v.t. Put SPORES, BACTERIA, etc. into (living plant or animal or any other substance in which they may undergo development) for science purposes.

[Med.] I. (person or animal) with disease-causing bacteria, etc., for purpose of getting ANTIBODIES produced by the body which will keep it safe from future attacks of the same disease. i'noculable, a. inocu'lation, n. Sp., [Bot.] the INFECTION of a plant by a PARASITE. [Chem.] The putting of a small CRYSTAL into a liquid to get the process of forming crystals started. inocu'lative, a. i'noculator, n.

in'operable, a. [Med.] Which is not possible to put right by an operation.

inor'ganic, a. Not formed of or to do with living substance or living beings; to do with i. chemistry; without organization, or not forming a natural and necessary part of a system or structure, sp. [Biol.] not having, not to do with, ORGANS. i. 'chemistry. The chemistry of all substances but those formed from C and produced by, or of like structure to those produced by, living things.

ino'tropic, a. [Physiol., Med.] Having an effect on the elastic property of muscles.

in 'parallel. [Elec.] *See* PARALLEL.

'in-phase, a. [Elec.] Being of the same PHASE.

'input, n. [Mach.] Power or ENERGY put into a machine, electric BATTERY, etc.

'inquiline, n. [Zoo.] An animal living in the house of another animal, or living on the food got together by another animal for its offspring and itself.

in'sanity, n. [Med.] Disease or condition of the mind, gen. as effect of physical disease or damage, in which person is not responsible for his behaviour and quite unable to have normal relations with others. in'sane, a. In a condition of i.

in'scribed, a. [Zoo.] Having deep lines or marks like letters.

'insect, n. [Zoo.] Animal of the INSECTA. in'sectile, a. Like, to do with, ii.; made up of ii. insec'tivorous, a. Using ii. as food. insec'tology, n. Science of ii., sp. in connection with farming, food-producing, etc. 'insec'tar-y, -ium, nn. Place in which living ii. are kept. in'secticide, n. Any substance used for causing death of ii.

In'secta, n.pl. [Zoo.] CLASS of small ARTHROPODA living on land, having 6 legs, a body with three divisions (head, THORAX, and ABDOMEN), TRACHEA for breathing, and gen. wings.

Insec'tivora, n.pl. ORDER of MAMMALS with poor development of teeth, living on insects. in'sectivore, n. One of the I.

'insemi'nation, n. [Zoo.] The IMPREGNATION of a female animal, the process by which male GERM-CELLS come to and become united with female germ-cells. in'seminate, v.t.

in 'series. [Elec.] *See* SERIES.

in'serted, a. [Bot., Zoo., Anat.] (Of a part) rooted in, fixed by natural growth to, another part.

in'sertion, n. [Biol.] Way in which, or place where, an ORGAN or part is fixed. [Anat.] The part of a muscle by which it is fixed to the part of the body moved by it.

inses'sorial, a. [Zoo.] (Of bird's foot) formed for gripping branch of tree etc., as support when resting.

in'sistent, a. [Zoo.] (Of back toe of bird) so placed that only the end is touching the earth when foot is resting on it.

inso'lation, n. [Med.] SUNSTROKE; medical use of sun baths, etc. [Meteor.] The RADIATION falling on the earth from the sun.

in'soluble, a. [Chem.] Not SOLUBLE or, loosely, soluble only to a very limited degree. in'solu'bility, n.

in'somnia, n. [Med.] Loss of power of sleeping.

inspi'ration, n. The act or process of breathing in, taking air or water into breathing-apparatus. in'spire, v.t. in'spiratory, a.

inspis'sation, n. [Chem.] The becoming thick of a liquid through loss of water to the air. in'spissate, v.t. and i. Make undergo, or undergo, i.

insta'bility, n. The condition of being UNSTABLE.

in'staminate, a. [Bot.] Having no STAMENS.

instan'taneous, a. Done, taking place, in so short a time, or so quickly after another event, that no time seems to have been taken or to have come between.

'instar, n. [Zoo.] The form taken by an insect in any of the stages of its development between the times of putting off the skin.

'instep, n. The arched middle part of man's foot.

'instinct, n. [Zoo.] The tendencies to behaviour which are handed down by ANCESTORS and common to all animals of a certain sort, sp. a special impulse to go through certain complex operations for a seemingly designed outcome, without any earlier experience of them or conscious purpose (for example, the building of special living-places, the storing of food for the winter). [Psych.] Any of the chief driving forces in man by which his fight for existence as an animal is kept up, as sex-desire, fear, the impulse to competition. in'stinctive, a.

insuf'ficiency, n. [Med.] (Of a part) condition of being unable to do its work fully, as effect of disease.

insuf'flation, n. [Med.] The process of blowing air, gas, powder, etc., into a hollow place in the body. in'sufflate, v.t. insuf'flator, n. Instrument.

'insula, n. [Zoo.] A small LOBE at the base of the SYLVIAN FISSURE of the brain.

'insular, a. [Med.] Of, to do with, an ISLAND; (of disease, etc.) present in separate places in body.

'**insulate,** v.t. [Phys.] Keep (electric current, heat, sound waves, etc.) from coming where not desired by using some non-transporting material; get (wire transporting electric current, etc.) covered with insulating material; get (room, etc.) cut off from noise or other undesired effects by use of insulating material. '**insulated,** a. '**insulating,** a., n. **insu'lation,** n. Sp. material used for the purpose of insulating. '**insulator,** n. An insulating structure or substance, sp. [Elec.] a substance with a high electric RESISTANCE

'**insulin,** n. [Med.] A HORMONE produced by the PANCREAS which makes possible the digestion of sugar, used to overcome effects of the disease DIABETES.

'**intake,** n. [Mach., Engin.] INPUT; the opening, pipe etc., by which something is taken in, as air into a mine or the mixed gas into an INTERNAL COMBUSTION ENGINE (freq. **i. pipe** etc.). **i. manifold.** *See* MANIFOLD.

'**integer,** n. [Arith.] Number made up of one or more complete units, number into which 1 will go with nothing over, opp. FRACTION.

'**integral,** a. Being a necessary part of something without which it would be incomplete. [Arith.] To do with INTEGERS. **i. 'calculus.** *See* CALCULUS.

'**integrate,** v.t. Get (parts, etc.) united so as to make a complete thing or system, or get (a part) united with others, for example [Psych.] sense DATA to give the idea, knowledge, of a thing outside the self. '**integrated,** a. (Of an organization of working parts) all working together, in harmony, sp. [Psych.] well-balanced. **inte'gration,** n. **integrative,** a.

'**integrating,** a. [Phys.] (Of instruments) making the addition of whatever is being measured, so as to give a complete reading, for example of electric current used from time to time. **i. cube** or **sphere.** [Optics] A CUBE or SPHERE inside which a light source is placed so that the light from it in all directions is REFLECTED through a small opening, used with a PHOTOMETER for measuring the INTENSITY of the source in all directions.

in'tegument, n. [Zoo.] Any covering of an animal or part, as the skin. [Bot.] The outer part of an OVULE; seed-coat.

'**intellect,** n. [Psych.] The higher powers or processes of the mind which have to do with knowledge, the power of reasoning, seeing or making the discovery of the relations between ideas, and so on. **intell'ectual,** a. Having, to do with, marked by a high degree of, i.

in'telligence, n. [Psych.] The power of making quick and good reactions, adjustments, physical or of the mind, to new experiences, of making ready use of

earlier experience and knowledge when faced with new facts or conditions. **i. 'quotient.** [Psych.] The RATIO of a person's MENTAL AGE, as fixed by i. tests, to his AGE in years, given as a PERCENT-AGE and used for rating his i. in relation to that of others. **i. test.** [Psych.] Special sort of test, first used by Binet, for measuring how intelligent a person is, independently of schooling or special training. **in'telligent,** a. Having i.

in'tense, a. (Of a force, effect, etc.) of high degree, very strong. **in'tensify,** v.t. Make (force, effect) stronger. **in'tensification,** n. **in'tensive,** a. Designed to get a very strong effect, sp. to make desired outcome come about in a shorter time. **in'tensity,** n. Degree, amount, of a force, quality or other effect; the quality of being INTENSE. [Phys.] The intensity of a physical effect per unit of the space, mass, CHARGE and so on through or on which it is acting (*see* MAGNETIC INTENSITY, LUMINOUS INTENSITY). [Acous.] The power of a sound WAVE, which is in DIRECT PROPORTION to its size, measured in ERGS per second per cm^2 at right-angles to the direction of the wave.

'**inter-.** Between, among: **-a'tomic,** a., **-'cellular,** a. [Biol.], **-e'lectrode,** a., **-mo'lecular,** a., **-space,** n., '**-vertebral,** a.

inter'acinous, a. [Anat.] Among or between the ACINI of a GLAND.

inter'action, n. The acting of two or more things on one another. **'-ism,** n. Theory that the mind and the body are separate things between which there is i. **inter' active,** a. Acting on one another.

'**interambu'lacrum,** n. [Zoo.] In ECHINODERMATA, the part between two AMBULACRA.

'**interar'ticular,** a. [Zoo.] Between JOINTS.

inter'brachial, a. [Zoo.] Between arms or rays.

inter'bedded, a. [Geol.] Being between two STRATA; being in a stratum parallel to other beds of different material.

inter'branchial, a. [Zoo.] Between the GILLS.

inter'breeding, n. [Biol.] The producing of offspring from two different sorts of plant or animal. **inter'breed,** v.i. and t. (Of two different sorts) have offspring by one another; get (animals, plants) to interbreed. **inter'bred,** a. Produced by i.; caused to interbreed.

in'tercalary, a. Put in or coming between other things, sp. (of day or month) put into the calendar to get it into agreement with physical facts, as February 29; (of year) having an i. day, etc. [Bot.] Placed at some point in a line of things or on a part of line-like form, such as a stem. **i. day.** [Med.] Day in the process of a disease on which it gives no signs. **i. growth.** [Bot.] Growth taking place at some point other than growth-point.

in'terca'lation, n. The putting in of something between other things. [Geol.] STRATUM between other strata. **in'tercalate,** v.t. **in'tercalative,** a.

inter'centrum, n. [Zoo.] CENTRUM-like unit coming between true centra in VERTEBRAE of certain animals.

inter'cept, v.t. Get (something moving, for example, a ray) stopped or turned on its way by coming between it and the point to which it is going. **'-ion,** n. **'-or,** n.

intercept, n. Part of a line or space between two points or lines. [Cryst.] The distance on a CRYSTAL AXIS between the meeting-point of all the axes and a face of the crystal.

inter'change, 1.v.t. and i. Get place of (one thing) exchanged with that of another; be ALTERNATE. 2.n. Act, process, condition of interchanging, sp. [Biol.] the exchange of parts between two CHROMOSOMES.

inter'clavicle, n. [Zoo.] In back-boned animals, a bone between the CLAVICLES in chest.

'intercon'nect, v.i. (Of machine-parts, etc.) be all in connection with one another, sp. so that motion of all is caused by the motion of any one. **'-ing,** a. **'-ion,** n.

'interconti'nental ball'istic 'missile. A military PROJECTILE which is GUIDED for part of its journey and then comes to earth at the desired point by falling freely—designed for use from one CONTINENT to another in war.

inter'costal, a. [Zoo.] Between the RIBS. [Bot.] Between the nerves of a leaf.

inter'coxal, a. [Zoo.] (Of insects) between the bases of the legs.

'inter'crystalline, a. [Metal.] (Of cracks in metals) going between the CRYSTALS, not through them as normally, opp. TRANS-CRYSTALLINE.

inter'crystalli'zation, n. [Cryst.] The forming of CRYSTALS of two different substances in one mass. **inter'crystallize,** v.i.

inter'current di'sease. [Med.] A further disease attacking a person while in the grip of another, and having an effect on the first disease.

inter'digital cysts. CYSTS which come between the toes of dogs, the cause of which is uncertain.

'interface, n. The common SURFACE between two spaces or bodies, sp. [Chem.] the surface separating two PHASES. **inter'facial.** a. **inter'facial 'angle.** The angle between two plane SURFACES. **inter'facial 'tension.** The SURFACE TENSION at the i. between two unmixing liquids.

'interfas'cicular, a. [Bot.] Between VASCULAR BUNDLES. **i. 'cambium.** Thread of CAMBIUM between two VASCULAR BUNDLES, the forming of which is the first stage in the increasing of the size

round of a stem or root when it has become as long as it is going to be.

inter'ference, n. Any effect, sp. undesired, of one thing or process on another, so as to keep it from taking place normally. [Radio] The mixing of sounds from a different WAVEBAND with those from the one desired. [Phys.] The effect produced by running together or SUPER-POSITION of two trains of waves of equal or almost equal WAVE-LENGTH. [Philol.] Effect on a sound, word, or word-group of one coming near it, by which its sound, form, or position is changed. **i. band** or **fringe.** [Optics] Any of the parallel dark bands formed on the meeting of two trains of light-waves as the effect of the coming together at certain points of the opposite parts of two waves, so that one group of VIBRATIONS is balanced by the other and no light is produced. **inter'fere,** v.i. Get in the way, be causing i. (*with* something).

interfer'ometer, n. [Optics.] Instrument for the comparison and measuring of WAVE-LENGTHS of light-rays by the producing and observation of INTERFERENCE FRINGES. [Acous.] An instrument for measuring the VELOCITY and ABSORPTION of sound or ULTRA-SONIC waves by separating the highest points in a wave-design—used sp. in RADIO-ASTRONOMY.

inter'fertile, a. [Biol.] Able to INTERBREED. **'interfer'tility,** n.

'interfluve, n. [Geol.] RIDGE between two parallel river hollows.

'interfoli'aceous, a. [Bot.] Between leaves placed opposite one another or in a ring.

inter'frontal, n. [Zoo.] A bone between the FRONTAL and the NASAL bones in some AMPHIBIA.

'intergangli'onic, a. [Zoo.]. Coming between and uniting nerve GANGLIA.

inter'glacial, a. [Geol.] Between two GLACIAL PERIODS.

'intergrowth, n. [Bot.] Growth by INTUS-SUSCEPTION.

inter'hyal, n. [Zoo.] In some fish, a small rod-like bone between the HYOMANDIBULAR and the rest of the HYOID.

in'terior, a. Inside. **i. 'planet.** [Astron.] PLANET whose way is inside the way of the earth round the sun.

'interki'nesis, n. [Biol.] Resting-stage between two MITOTIC divisions of a CELL.

'interlami'nation, n. [Geol.] Condition of being formed of, or process of forming, LAMINAE between laminae of a different substance. **inter'laminate,** v.t. and i. Get or be in form of LAMINAE between laminae.

inter'leave, v.t. [Geol.] INTERLAMINATE.

inter'lobar, a. [Med.] Between two LOBES, sp. of LUNGS.

inter'lobate, a. [Geol.] Between two PRO-
JECTIONS of a GLACIER.

inter'lock, 1.v.i. and t. (Of two things) be
fixed together by having parts of the
two slipping into parts of one another; (of
machines or parts of a system) have connection of such sort that the operation of
one is dependent on that of another or
others; make i. 2.n. Bit of electric or
other apparatus used for causing inter-
locking.

inter'mediate, 1.a. Placed or taking place
between other things or processes; of
degree, form, quality, etc., between two
others or somewhere in the middle of a
scale. 2.n. [Chem.] A COMPOUND formed
as a step in the process of forming some
other substance. **i. e'lectrode.** BIPOLAR
ELECTRODE. **i. host.** [Zoo.] The plant or
animal on which a HETEROECIOUS PARA-
SITE goes through the early or the i. stages
of its development. **i. 'frequency.** [Radio]
In a SUPERHETERODYNE RECEIVER, the
fixed FREQUENCY to which all incoming
waves are changed and at which they
are then AMPLIFIED, which is i. between
the frequency of sound waves and that
of radio waves. **i. 'igneous rock.** [Geol.]
An IGNEOUS ROCK having more SiO_2 than
a BASIC ROCK and less than an ACID ROCK,
that is, between 55% and 66%. **i. waves.**
[Phys.] ELECTROMAGNETIC WAVES between 50 and 200 m. long, that is,
between the short-wave and the long-
wave bands.

inter'medium, n. [Zoo.] A small bone or
CARTILAGE between RADIALE and ULNARE,
and between TIBIALE and FIBULARE.

inter'mittent, a. Stopping for a time and
then starting again, broken, with regular
or irregular stops between acting. **i. fever.**
[Med.] MALARIA. **inter'mittency,** n. Condition of being i.

'intern, n. A medical man living and working
in a hospital, sp. on first completing his
training, to get experience.

in'ternal, a. Of, to do with, placed in,
taking place in the inside of anything;
produced, caused by, thing in itself,
not as effect of outside forces. **i. combustion 'engine.** Engine in which power
is produced by the burning of a gas,
liquid, or solid SUSPENSION in air inside
a shut space (the CYLINDER) having in it
a PISTON which is worked by the expansion of the heated gas. **i. 'energy.** [Phys.]
All the ENERGY inside a system at any
time. **i. im'pedance.** [Phys.] The IMPE-
DANCE offered to ALTERNATING current
by the ANODE and the CATHODE of a
THERMIONIC TUBE. **i. medicine.** That
branch of medical science having to do
with diseases of the inside of the body.
i. po'tential. The electric POTENTIAL
of the free ELECTRONS in a metal. **i.**

'pressure. The PRESSURE in a liquid produced by the attraction of its MOLECULES
to one another, and acting against the
tendency to expansion caused by heat.
i. re'flection. [Optics] REFLECTION of light
inside a body from its inner faces. **i.
re'sistance.** [Elec.] The electric RESIST-
ANCE of an apparatus producing an
electric current. **i. respir'ation.** [Zoo.] *See*
RESPIRATION. **i. se'cretion.** [Zoo.] A
GLAND-produced substance which is sent
into the blood or the CEREBROSPINAL
FLUID to be transported to certain other
parts of the body on which it is designed
to have some special effect. **i. se'cretion
gland.** ENDOCRINE GLAND. **i. screw
thread.** [Mach.] A screw thread cut on
the inside of a hollow pipe. **i. work.** Work
done by a system in overcoming the
forces acting inside it or between its parts.

inter'nasal, a. [Zoo.] Between openings of
nose.

inter'national, a. Used before names of a
number of PRACTICAL measuring units
fixed by international agreement which
have now been given up for the new
ABSOLUTE units almost equal to them.
i. 'ampere. The current which when sent
through a SOLUTION of silver NITRATE in
water will put down silver at the rate of
·001118 gm. per sec. **i. Ångstrom.** Unit for
measuring the WAVE-LENGTH of light,
almost equal to the ÅNGSTROM and
fixed by giving the CADMIUM RED LINE
at 15°C and 760 mm. PRESSURE a
WAVE-LENGTH of 6438·4696 I.Å. **i.
candle.** Unit of light-power used before
the CANDELA and almost equal to it.
i. ohm. The RESISTANCE offered at 0°C
to an unchanging electric current by a
COLUMN of Hg 106·3 cm. long, the same
size from end to end, and 14.4521 gm. in
weight. **i. units.** The system of electric
measuring units based on the i. ampere
and the i. ohm, for example the **i. volt.**

'internode, n. [Phys.] Small NODE between
two greater ones. [Biol.] Part between
two nodes, as on nerve or plant stem.

inter'nodia, n.pl. PHALANGES.

inter'nuncial, a. [Zoo.] Transporting effects
from one part of body to another, as
nerves.

'intero'ceptor, n. [Zoo.] A RECEPTOR for
STIMULI acting inside the body, sometimes limited to all but those having to
do with motion and balance, or sometimes limited still further to those in the
inner wall of the ALIMENTARY CANAL and
of the breathing-apparatus, which give
reactions to substances coming into those
parts from outside.

inter'ocular, n. [Zoo.] Between the eyes.

inter'osculate, v.t. [Biol.] Have qualities in
common, said of two different sorts of

plants or animals. **inter'osculant,** a. **'interoscu'lation,** n.

inter'osseus (inter'ossei), 1.n. [Zoo.] Any of certain small muscles joining bones at base of fingers or toes to bones of hand or foot. 2.a. Placed between bones, said of muscles, nerves, etc.

'interpa'rietal, a. [Zoo.] Between the PARIETAL bones. **i. bone.** A three-sided bone in head of some back-boned animals between the PARIETAL and the OCCIPITAL bones.

'inter'penetrate, v.t. Have parts going into (one another), be so joined; of a substance etc., get into every part of (something). **interpene'tration,** n. **interpenetration twins.** [Cryst.] TWIN CRYSTALS united by growth through one another, interpenetrating one another.

'interphase, n. INTERKINESIS.

in'terpolate, v.t. Put (something) between other things or parts. **in'terpolated,** a. **interpo'lation,** n.

'interpole, n. [Elec.] Small POLE placed between the normal poles of a DYNAMO or MOTOR.

in'terpret, v.t. See or make clear the sense of (words, statements, signs, etc.) or what are judged to be the causes, relations, or tendencies of (facts or events looked on as signs). **interpre'tation,** n. Sp. the sense or idea put forward as interpreting something.

inter'radius, n. [Zoo.] In certain COELENTERATA a smaller RADIUS between two chief radii.

inter'ramal, a. [Zoo.] Between the branches of anything, sp. of the lower JAW.

inter'renal, a. [Zoo.] Between the KIDNEYS. **i. 'body.** GLAND between the KIDNEYS of certain fish, looked on as a parallel of the SUPRARENAL GLAND in higher animals.

inter'rupted, a. Having stops, not going on unbrokenly. [Bot.] Said of parts which are not equally spaced on stem, etc.

inter'rupter, n. [Elec.] An automatic apparatus by which electric current is broken and started again, freq. regularly.

inter'sect, v.t. and i. Make division of by going across or through; (of two lines, etc.) go across one another. **'-ion,** n. Sp., point where one thing intersects another, point or line common to lines or planes cutting one another.

'intersex, n. [Biol.] Plant or animal with qualities between those of the normal male and female of the sort. **inter'sexual,** a.

'interspe'cific, a. [Biol.] Said of a CROSS between two different SPECIES, sp. in CYTOLOGY.

'intersperse, v.t. Place here and there between or among other things; get (things) mixed *with* others by interspersing the others among them. **'-d,** a. Sp., [Bot.] said of MARGINAL RAY CELLS interspersed among other cells. **'inter'spersion,** n.

inter'spinal, n., a. [Zoo.] (Bone or part) between NEURAL or HEMAL SPINES, sp. forming base of FIN-ray in certain fish.

inter'stellar, a. [Astron.] Between the stars.

'interste'rile, a. [Biol.] (Of two animals or plants) unable to INTERBREED. **'inter'sterility,** n.

in'terstice, n. Narrow space between things very near together, or between the parts of a substance etc., a crack. **inter'stitial,** a. Of, in the ii. of anything. **inter'stitial cells.** Sp., CELLS of TESTIS and OVARY other than sex-cells.

'inter'stratifi'cation, n. [Geol.] Condition of being formed of, process of forming, STRATA between strata of different substance. **'inter'stratify,** v.t. and i. Get, be, in form of STRATA between strata.

inter'tidal, a. Sp. [Zoo.] Living in the space which is covered when the sea comes in and uncovered when it goes out.

inter'trappean, a. [Geol. Placed between masses of BASALT LAVA formed at different times.

'interval, n. A space between two things or a time between two events, sp. of a number of like things or events coming one after another; distance in degree between things ranged on a scale, as [Acous.] between the PITCH of two notes, sp. between a note and the one coming after it in a music scale.

'interva'rietal, a. Said of offspring produced by male of one VARIETY of a SPECIES and female of another.

'intervo'calic, a. [Phonet.] Coming between two VOWELS, as the 'd' in 'idea'.

in'testine, n. **in'testines,** n.pl. [Zoo.] The pipe-like part of the ALIMENTARY CANAL, in some animals taking in all of it, but in most going from the stomach to the outlet. **in'testinal,** a.

int'extine, n. [Bot.] Inner coat of the EXTINE when this has two.

'intima, n. [Zoo.] Inside coat of any part, for example a blood-vessel.

'intine, n. [Bot.] The inner skin of a POLLEN grain, opp. EXINE.

in'tolerance, n. [Med.] Uncommonly strong reaction of the body against any substance or effect.

inton'ation, n. [Phonet.] The changing PITCH of the voice in talking, (in languages other than TONE LANGUAGES) the way it goes up and down to give a special sense or feeling to what is said.

in'toxicate, v.t. [Med.] Get (person) into condition in which there is loss of self-control, freq. violent, or INERTIA, ending in unnatural sleep, said of alcohol, NARCOTICS, etc. **in'toxicant,** n. Intoxicating substance. **in'toxicating,** a. **in'toxication,** n.

intra-. Inside: **i.** -**'atomic,** a., -**mo'lecular,** a.,

-'muscular, a., -'nuclear, a., -'ocular, a.

intra'cellular, a. [Biol.] Inside a CELL.

'intra'fusal, a. [Zoo.] Inside a MUSCLE SPINDLE, as *i fibers.*

'intrame'dullary, a. [Zoo.] In the substance of the SPINAL CORD or of the stem-like part of the brain joined to it.

'intramo'lecular respi'ration. [Biol.] The producing by a plant or animal normally breathing air but unable to get it, of the needed CO_2 and other substances by reactions inside itself.

intra'stelar, a. [Bot.] Inside a stem or root.

'intratell'uric, a. [Geol.] Being, taking place, formed, very deep in the earth.

'intra'thecal, a. [Zoo.] Inside the covering or outer wall of a part. [Med.] (Of INJECTION) one put under the covering of the SPINAL CORD.

'intrava'sation, n. [Med.] The getting into blood-vessels of materials from their walls or from outside.

intra'venous, a. Inside a VEIN. [Med.] (Of INJECTION) put into a vein.

intra'vesical, a. [Zoo.] Inside the BLADDER.

'intra-'vitam, 'intravital, aa. [Biol., Med.] Done to a substance or thing while it is still living. intravital stain, etc. VITAL STAIN etc.

in'trinsic, a. INTERNAL. [Zoo.] (Of muscles) completely inside a part of the body, not going from it to another part, opp. EXTRINSIC. i. 'energy. [Phys.] INTERNAL ENERGY. [Chem.] (Of a COMPOUND) the amount of heat in CALORIES taken in or given out in forming it.

intro-. Into, in the direction of, the inside.

'introfier, n. [Chem.] Substance with property of, to some degree, changing a COLLOIDAL to a MOLECULAR SOLUTION, so that its addition to certain liquids gives them greater wetting power. intro-'faction, n. The change produced in a liquid by the use of an i.; the addition of an i. to a liquid for the purpose of getting it to go more readily and completely through all parts of a solid.

intro'jection, n. [Psych.] The mind-process by which outside things, other persons or their ideas and qualities, and so on, are made to seem a part of the self, so that person's feelings are moved by any attack on them, etc.

intro'mission, n. [Zoo., Med.] The putting of one part into another, sp. of the male sex-part into the female.

intro'mittent, a. [Zoo.] Formed for INTROMISSION, said of sex-part of male animal.

in'trorse, a. [Biol.] Bent or turned in, said sp. of an ANTHER opening in the direction of the middle of the flower.

intro'spection, n. [Psych.] The act of looking into one's mind, the observation by oneself of one's feelings, thoughts, private reactions to sense and other ex-

perience. intro'spect, v.t. intro'spective, a.

'introsus'ception, n. INTUSSUSCEPTION.

'introvert, 1.n. [Zoo.] A structure or part of the body which may be rolled in, or pulled inside another part forming a pipe-like cover for it. [Psych.] Person given to introversion. 2.v.t. Get (an i.) pulled in. 3.a. [Psych.] Marked by, to do with, introversion. intro'version, n. Act of introverting. [Psych.] The direction of one's interest chiefly to one's thoughts and feelings, taking more pleasure in what goes on in one's mind than in society or what goes on round one. intro'versive, a. '-ed, a. Sp., [Psych.] Turned in on oneself, marked by introversion.

in'trude, v.t. and i. (Make) come into something, or in between other things, by force or against what is natural or desired. in'trusion, n. Sp., [Geol.] The forcing of MAGMA into or between solid ROCKS; the body of rock formed by the intruded magma when cold. in'trusive, a Sp., [Geol.] (of ROCKS) formed by intrusion. intrusive 'r'. [Phonet.] An *r*-sound wrongly put in between two VOWELS in talking, as 'India-r-Office'.

intu'ition, n. [Psych.] Knowledge coming straight into the mind, without any conscious process of learning or reasoning. 'intuit, v.t. Have intuitive knowledge of. '-al, in'tuitive, aa.

intu'mescence, n. [Med.] A SWELLING; the process of swelling. [Bot.] An unnormal round swelling coming on leaves or other plant parts as effect of something working wrongly. [Chem.] The increasing in size of CRYSTALS on heating. intu'mescent, a.

'intussus'ception, n. [Med.] The slipping down of one part of the INTESTINE into the part nearest to it. [Biol.] The forming of new material in between parts of earlier-formed substance, the common process of growth of living things. 'intus-sus'ceptive, a. 'intussus'ceptum, n. [Med.] The part of the INTESTINE covered by another as the effect of i.

'inulase, n. [Biochem.] An ENZYME acting on INULIN and freq. present with it.

'inulin, n. [Biochem.] A form of STARCH present in the roots and under-earth stems of certain plants. '-ase, a. INULASE.

'inundate, v.t. (Of river, etc.) come over (land), get (land) covered with water. inun'dation, n. Sp., event of inundating.

in'vagi'nation, n. [Biol.] The process of slipping a part into a covering part or the condition of being covered in this way, [Zoo.] INTROVERSION, [Med.] INTUSSUSCEPTION; the pushing or folding in of one part of a hollow structure, sp. [Zoo.] the forming of the GASTRULA by i. of the BLASTULA. in'vaginate, 1.v.t. and i. (Make) undergo i. 2.a. Invaginated or marked by i.

'invar, n. A mixed metal, formed of about 36% Ni, 63% Fe, and very small amounts of other ELEMENTS, undergoing very little expansion when heated, used for measuring and other instruments for which this property is important.

in'variant, a. [Chem.] Having no DEGREES OF FREEDOM.

in'verse, a. Opposite in order, position, relation, or effect to the normal or whatever is in question. i. pro'portion or 'ratio. The relation between two numbers or amounts one of which gets greater as the other gets less. i. square law. [Phys.] The law that physical effects acting through a distance become less at the same rate as the SQUARE of the distance from their starting-point becomes greater, for example, the effect of GRAVITY on a body at a distance of 1 m. will be 4 times that on a body at a distance of 2 m.

in'version, n. Process of inverting or condition of being inverted. [Geol.] The folding back of STRATA so that their order seems to be inverted. [Med.] Sex-desire for persons of the same sex. [Psych.] The changing of a feeling, etc., to its opposite, as freq. in sleep-experiences. [Chem.] The changing of a DEXTROROTATORY substance, sp. sugar, into a LAEVO-ROTATORY one, gen. by HYDROLYSIS. i. 'temperature. [Phys.] The TEMPERATURE for a given gas at which, on undergoing expansion after going through very small holes from a greater PRESSURE to a less, it undergoes no change in temperature, and over which the JOULE-THOMSON EFFECT is no longer seen and the gas gets warmer on expansion, in place of, as at lower temperatures, colder.

in'vert, v.t. Make INVERSE, get places of (things) exchanged, get turned upside down, etc. 'invert sugar. What is produced by the inversion of SUCROSE. in-'verted, a. Sp., [Phonet.] (Of end of tongue) turned up and back; (of sounds) said with inverted tongue.

in'vertase, n. [Biochem.] ENZYME formed in a number of plants and animal IN-TESTINES causing INVERSION of SUCROSE; any enzyme getting DISACCHARIDES broken up into MONOSACCHARIDES.

in'vertebrate, n. [Zoo.] Animal having no backbone.

in'vest, v.t. [Biol.] Be the covering of. in'vesting, a. investing bones. MEMBRANE BONES. in'vestment, n. [Biol.] Outer covering of plant, animal, or part.

in'vestigate, v.t. Go fully into recorded facts, make observations, tests, etc., for the purpose of getting the answer to questions about (events, behaviour, properties of a substance, etc.). investi-'gation, n.

in 'vitro, adv. [Biol.] (Of the processes or reactions of living substance) taking place, under observation, in a glass, etc., as opp. in 'vivo, taking place, seen, in the living thing.

'involucre, n. [Biol.] A covering structure sp. a ring of leaves round the base of a flower-group by which it is covered in the early stage of development, or, in BRYOPHYTA, cup-like covering round sex-parts. [Med.] Cover of new bone, formed round part of bone in which NECROSIS has taken place. invo'lucr-al, -ate, -iform, aa. in'volucel, n. [Bot.] Small i. round smaller flower-group of a COMPOUND flower-group. in'volucel-'late, a.

in'voluntary, a. [Zoo.] (Of processes and reactions) not under conscious control, as the motion of the heart. i. muscle. UN-STRIATED MUSCLE, by which most of the i. processes of the body are effected.

'involute(d), aa. [Bot.] Turned or rolled in at the edges. [Zoo.] (Of SHELLS) having WHORLS very near together, tightly twisted.

invo'lution, n. [Biol.] Development back to simpler form, sp. of PROTOZOA which have had no chance of right development but may become normal again in better conditions. [Med.] Change of part back to normal size, as UTERUS after birth. invo'luted, a. Having undergone i., sp. [Med.]

Io, Sign for IONIUM.

'iodate, n. [Chem.] SALT having the group $-IO_3$.

'iodide, n. [Chem.] Substance formed by uniting one ELEMENT with I.

'iodine, n. Chemical ELEMENT, at. no. 53, at. wt. 126·92, sign I, a non-metal, formed normally in thin flat CRYSTALS, almost black in colour but giving off a VIOLET gas, used medically as an ANTI-SEPTIC. i. 'value or 'number. In ANALYSIS of oils, fats, etc., the number of mgm. of I taken up by 1 gm. of the substance. i'odic, a. To do with, having in it, I, sp. I with a VALENCY of 5. i'odic acid. HIO_3, produced by the reaction of I with NITRIC ACID. 'iodism, n. [Med.] Diseased condition produced by the use of I and its COMPOUNDS. 'iodo'phil-ic, -ous, aa. Colouring darkly when put in i. SOLU-TION, i'od(o)-.

i'odoform, n. [Chem.] CHI_3, a yellow, CRYS-TALLINE substance having an important medical use as an ANTISEPTIC for wounds, etc.

'ion, n. [Phys., Chem.] ATOM or group of atoms having an electric CHARGE, produced by the loss or addition to an uncharged atom or group, of one or more ELECTRONS. i. ex'change. A two-way exchange of IONS of like CHARGE going on between those present in an INSOLUBLE solid and those in a SOLUTION, which takes place naturally or may be effected for different purposes, for example, by sending a solution through certain RESINS, ZEOLITE etc., as in WATER-SOFTENING and other important processes in industry. **i. pair.** Two ii. made at the same time by an IONIZING RADIATION. **i′onic,** a. Sp. used of the structure of certain CRYSTALS formed of POSITIVE and NEGATIVE ii. fixed together by attraction. **i′onic mi′gration.** The motion of ii. in a liquid under electric force. **i′onic mo′bility.** The rate of motion of an i. produced by an electric force of 1 volt/cm. **′-o′genic,** a.

′ionize, v.t. [Phys., Chem.] Get ATOMS or MOLECULES in a substance changed into IONS. **′ioni′zation.** **′ioni′zation ′chamber.** Vessel in which ionization takes place, having two ELECTRODES between which a current is produced. **′ioni′zation ′current.** The electric current produced in an ionized gas when acted on by an ELECTRIC FIELD. **′ioni′zation gauge.** Apparatus measuring PRESSURE of gas by IONIZATION. **′ionizing** (or **′ionization**) **po′tential.** The ENERGY necessary for ionizing a given ATOM or MOLECULE, measured in ELECTRON-VOLTS. **ionizing radi′ation.** A RADIATION causing ionization of a gas, as opp. the radiation of NEUTRONS, which are not ionizing.

i′onium, n. [Chem.] A RADIOACTIVE ISOTOPE of THORIUM, sign Io.

i′onosphere, n. [Radio, etc.] The part of the ATMOSPHERE, starting at an AVERAGE distance of about 30 miles from the earth, where the air is IONIZED by ULTRA-VIOLET RAYS and other effects from the sun, and REFLECTION of radio waves takes place—made up of a number of different bands marked by special properties, the outermost being from about 150 to 200 miles away, for example, the APPLETON LAYER and the D LAYER.

ion′otrophy, n. [Phys., Chem.] The forming of TAUTOMERIC IONS.

i′ontopho′resis, n. [Phys., Chem.] CATA-PHORESIS. [Med.] The putting of IONS, for example of Ca, into the body by using an electric current.

Ir, Sign for IRIDIUM.

iri′descent, a. Having colours like a BUBBLE of soap and water, changing with the point of view or the direction of the light, caused by the INTERFERENCE of light sent back from two sides of a very thin SURFACE or from a great number of surfaces near together, as in feathers of some birds. **iri′descence,** n.

i′ridium, n. Chemical ELEMENT, at. no. 77, at. wt. 193·1, sign Ir, a very hard steel-

grey metal with a high MELTING-POINT, having a number of important uses in industry, for example, in watch-making and pen making.

′iridi′zation, n. [Med.] The IRIDESCENT ring round a light seen by person having GLAUCOMA.

′irid(o)-. Of, to do with the IRIS of the eye: **iri′dectomy,** n. [Med.]

′iridocyte, n. [Zoo.] Any of certain CELLS present in the skin of fish and some other animals and having in them grains of GUANINE causing IRIDESCENT colouring.

′iris, n. [Zoo.] The cover in front of the LENS of the eye, letting light in only through the small opening in the middle, which it has the power of making greater or smaller in adjustment to the amount of light.

i′ritis, n. [Med.] INFLAMMATION of the i.

′iron, n. Chemical ELEMENT, at. no. 26, at. wt. 55·85, sign Fe, a grey metal which is readily MAGNETIZED. **I. Age.** [Anthrop.] Stage in the history of man when i. came into use. **i. bac′teria.** Any of a number of BACTERIA with the property of acting on i. COMPOUNDS. **i. ′family.** [Chem.] The 3 metals, Fe, Co, and Ni. **i. lung.** [Med.] A box-like structure in which a person is put when the muscles of the LUNGS are not working, having an apparatus by which the air-PRESSURE inside is regularly increased and made less in the rhythm of normal breathing, so that the lungs are forced to take in and give out air automatically. **i. mould.** Brown mark on cloth, caused by i. RUST or ink.

ir′radi′ation, n. [Phys., Med.] The sending of RADIATIONS of any sort onto anything, sp. of X-RAYS, RADIUM rays, etc., for medical purposes. [Optics] Effect produced in a light-coloured IMAGE of a thing seen or PHOTOGRAPHED against a dark SURFACE, by which the light seems to go over the edge, making the outline of the image greater than that of the thing. **ir′radiate,** v.t.

ir′rational, a. [Psych.] (Of person, behaviour, statement, etc.) against, not in agreement with, reason, not based on reasoning. **irration′ality,** n.

irre′ducible, a. Which it is not possible to get into simpler form or condition, or [Med.] (of a condition caused by a part being out of place) to put right.

ir′regular, a. Not regular. [Biol.] Not balanced in structure. [Bot.] Not in a regular line or circle; sp. of flowers, MONOSYMMETRICAL. **i. ′nebulae.** [Astron.] NEBULAE having no well-marked or special form. **irregu′larity,** n. Sp. a part which is i.

irre′solvable, a. Of which it is not possible to see the details clearly through MICRO-SCOPE or TELESCOPE.

irre′versible, a. [Phys., Chem., etc.] (Of

machine, current, etc.) working only in one direction, not able to be turned back; (of process) which it is not possible to undo, or do the other way round, starting with the end condition and working back to the start; which may not be changed back from a SOL to a GEL and the other way round.

irri'gation, n. The natural watering of land by rivers; the distribution of water over land which is, or at times becomes, over-dry, by systems of man-made water-ways or other structures or processes for transporting water, for farming pur-poses. [Med.] Washing out a wound in the body by a current of water or medical liquid. **'irrigate,** v.t. Give water to (land, fields, etc.), sp. by man-made i. systems. **irri'gational,** a.

irrita'bility, n. [Biol.] The property of living beings, structures, or substance, of giving a reaction when acted on from outside. [Med.] The condition (of any part) of giving over-ready and over-strong reac-tions, being readily acted on in a way causing pain etc. **'irritable,** a. Having i.; being in a condition of i. **'irritant,** n., a. (Anything) irritating sp. [Med.] irritating substance. **irritant poison.** A poison which has its effect by causing destruction of the inner coats of the stomach. **'irritate,** v.t. [Biol.] Be cause of marked reaction in, sp. make (muscle) CONTRACT. [Med.] Make irritable. **irri'tation,** n. **irri'tative,** a.

isa'coustic, a. Equally strong in sound.

isa'delphous, a. [Bot.] Having division of STAMENS into two equal groups.

i'sandrous, a. [Bot.] Having the STAMENS like the PETALS and equal to them in number.

i'santhous, a. [Bot.] Having the flowers regular.

is'ch(a)emia, n. [Med.] The condition of not having enough blood in a part of the body.

'ischio-. ISCHIUM: **-'rectal,** a.

'ischio'pubis, n. [Zoo.] A united ISCHIUM and PUBIS.

'ischium, n. [Zoo.] Right or left lower back bone of the PELVIS, in man one or other of the two bones on which the body is resting when seated. **ischi-'adic, '-al, -'atic,** aa.

isen'tropic, a. [Phys.] Having, or repre-sentative of, equal ENTROPY.

'isinglass, n. [Chem.] A GELATIN made from AIR-BLADDERS of fish.

'island, n. [Anat.] Any group of CELLS different from those round them in structure, size, or other properties. **i. of 'Riel.** [Zoo.] A small LOBE of the brain placed deep down in the SYLVIAN FISSURE in man and higher animals.

'island 'universe. [Astron.] The name given to a SPIRAL NEBULA, based on the opinion that every such nebula is an independent system of stars like our GALAXY.

'islet, n. [Anat.] ISLAND, sp. small. **ii. of 'Langerhans.** Small irregular masses of clear CELLS in the PANCREAS of back-boned animals by which INSULIN is produced.

-ism, n. [Med.] Ending used as a sign of a diseased unnormal condition caused by over-much of the thing, or by over-acting of the part, named, as *alcoholism, thyroidism.*

'iso-. Same, like, equal. [Chem.] Sign of an ISOMER.

'isoag'glutinin, n. [Zoo.] An AGGLUTININ acting on CELLS of animals of the same SPECIES as that producing it.

'isoaggluti'nation, n. [Zoo.] The AGGLUTINA-TION of blood-CELLS as effect of an ISO-AGGLUTININ; the agglutination of male sex-cells as effect of some substance pro-duced by the female sex-cells of the same SPECIES.

'isobar, n. [Chem.] A curve making clear the relation between amounts measured at the same PRESSURE. [Meteor.] Line on map joining places at which the pressure of the ATMOSPHERE is the same at a given time.

'isobar(e), n. [Phys. Chem.] An ATOM of one ELEMENT having the same at. wt. as the atom of another element but different chemical properties.

iso'baric, a. [Chem., Meteor.] To do with an ISOBAR or (any system of) equal PRES-SURES. [Phys.-Chem.] Being, to do with, ISOBAR(E)S.

'isobase, n. [Geol.] Line on map through points where land was forced down to an equal degree in ICE AGE as effect of the weight of the ice.

'isobath(ic), a. Equally deep all over.

iso'bathytherm, n. [Geog.] Line on map joining points at which the TEMPERATURE of the earth is the same at the same distance under the SURFACE.

iso'carpous, a. [Bot.] Having the CARPELS and the divisions of the PERIANTH equal in number.

iso'cercal, a. [Zoo.] (Of the tail FIN of a fish) with backbone straight and making division of it into two equal parts; (of fish) having i. fin.

'isocheim, n. [Geog.] Line on map joining places having same AVERAGE winter TEMPERATURE. **iso'cheim-al, -ic,** aa.

'isochor(e), n. [Chem.] A curve giving the relation between the TEMPERATURE and PRESSURE of a gas when its VOLUME is unchanged. **iso'choric,** a.

'isochro'matic, a. [Optics] Having the same colour, said of INTERFERENCE lines. [Photog.] (Of an EMULSION) acted on to same degree by all colours.

i'sochron-al, -ous, aa. [Phys.] Taking place

at same time or in equal times, or again and again with equal time between. i′sochronism, n.

iso′clin-al, -ic, aa. [Geol., etc.] Being equal in degree of slope; i. line. i. fold. [Geol.] A FOLD which has been pushed over so that the two parts are sloping in the same direction. i. line. A line on a map joining the places at which the MAGNETIC DIP is the same.

′isocline, n. [Geol.] FOLD of which the two sides have the same degree of slope.

′iso′coria, n. [Anat.] Condition of having the PUPILS of the two eyes equal in size.

iso′crymal, n., a. [Geog.] (Line on map) joining points having the same TEMPERATURE at a given time of year. ′isocryme, n. I. line.

iso′cyclic, a. [Chem.] Having same number of ATOMS in a RING as another substance; HOMOCYCLIC.

′isodia′batic, a. [Phys.] To do with equal amounts of heat.

′isodia′metric(al), aa. Equal in DIAMETER. [Bot.] (Of CELLS, etc.) of equal size; as long as it is wide.

′isodi′morphism, n. [Chem.] ISOMORPHISM between the two forms of DIMORPHOUS substances. ′isodi′morph-ic, -ous, aa.

′isodis′perse, a. [Chem.] Able to be DIS-PERSED in liquids′having the same pH-VALUE.

isodis′persion, n. [Chem.] A SOL in which the DISPERSE PHASE is made up of bits of equal size.

′isodont, a. [Zoo.] Having all teeth like one another in size and form.

′isody′namic(al), aa. Having, to do with, equal force. i. e′quivalent. [Med.] That amount of a fat having the same heat-producing value as a certain amount of a CARBOHYDRATE. i. lines. [Geog.] Lines joining points on a map at which the MAGNETIC force is the same.

′isoe′lectric, a. Having same electric POTENTIAL. i. point. [Chem.] In a COL-LOIDAL DISPERSION, the pH-VALUE at which the opposite CHARGES of the PARTICLES are balanced and the charge on the disperson =0, so that ELECTRO-PHORESIS does not take place if a current is sent through—the point at which, if not stopped by some other property, the particles become massed into greater particles.

′isoelec′tronic, a. [Phys., Chem.] (Of ATOMS) having the same number of ELECTRONS round the NUCLEUS.

′isoe′nergic, a. [Phys., Chem.] Taking place without change of INTERNAL ENERGY.

isoen′thalpic, a. [Phys.] Having equal ENTHALPY.

′isoga′mete, n. [Biol.] One or the other of two uniting GAMETES which are like one another in size and form.

i′sogam-ic, -ous, aa. [Biol.] The producing of offspring by the uniting of ISO-GAMETES; condition of being i. i′sogamy, n. The uniting of ISOGAMETES; the condi-tion of being i.

iso′genesis, n. [Biol.] Condition of having like starting-point or development. ′isoge′netic, a.

iso′genic, a. [Bot.] Producing offspring only by APOGAMY.

i′sogenous, a. [Biol.] Having the same ORIGIN. ′isogen, n. I. structure.

iso′geotherm, n. Line or curved plane through points under the earth having the same AVERAGE TEMPERATURE.

i′sogonal, iso′gonic, aa. Having, to do with, equal angles. isogonic line. Line on map through places where the MAGNETIC DECLINATION is the same.

iso′goniostat, n. [Phys.] Apparatus for keeping a train of PRISMS automatically in the position of least DEVIATION.

′isograph, n. Instrument having two short straight edges joined at one end by a round part on which they may be turned, with scale round it giving the angle between them in any position.

iso′hal(s)ine, n. [Geog.] Line on map through places where the sea is equally salt.

′isohel, n. [Meteor.] Line on map through places having equal hours of sunlight.

iso′hydric, a. [Chem.] Having the same number of certain IONS, sp. H ions, as the same amount of another liquid, so that the two may be mixed without changing their power of electric CONDUCTION.

iso′hyetal, 1.a. [Meteor.] Having, to do with, equal rainfall. 2.n. Isohyet, iso′hyet, n. Line on map through i. places.

′isoke′raunic, n., a. [Meteor.] (Line on map joining places) having equally strong and/or frequent THUNDERSTORMS, or having them at the same time.

′isolate, v.t. Get or keep separate, away from other things, sp., [Phys.] INSULATE. [Med.] Keep (person with INFECTIOUS disease) away from other persons; get disease-causing BACTERIUM separate, pointed out. [Chem.] Get (substance) separate from all other substances. iso′lation, n. ′isolable, a. Which may be isolated. ′isolating, a. isolating language. [Philol.] A language in which words do not take different endings, their relations to one another being given by their order or by other separate words, so that every word is an independent and unchanging unit. iso′lation, n. ′isolative, a.

iso′lecithal, a. [Zoo.] (Of eggs) having an equal distribution of the YOLK through other substance.

i′sologous, a. [Chem.] Of two complex substances, having the same structure in the MOLECULE with ATOMS of the same VALENCIES but of different ELE-

MENTS. **i.** **'series.** [Chem.] A SERIES of chemical COMPOUNDS i. to those of another series. **'isolog(ue),** n. Any substance i. to another.

iso'lysin, n. HAEMOLYSIN. **i'solysis,** n. HAEMOLYSIS.

'isomag'netic, n., a. (Line on map joining places) having equal MAGNETIC force.

'isomere, n. [Zoo.] A HOMOLOGOUS part.

iso'meric, a. [Phys., Chem.] (Of compounds) made up of the same number of the same ATOMS and having the same MOLECULAR weight, as another substance, but different in properties because of different molecular structure; having NUCLEAR ISOMERISM. [Optics] (Of colours) which seem to be the same in a certain light but not the same in other lights, because caused by REFLECTION of different parts of the SPECTRUM. **'isomer,** n. Substance having an i. relation to another or others. **i'somerism,** n. The relation between isomers; the condition of being i. **i'somerize,** v.t. and i. Get or become changed into an i. form. **i'someriz'ation,** n.

i'someride, n. Any of a group of substances like but not the same in structure.

i'somero'morphism, n. [Cryst.] ISOMORPHISM between ISOMERIC substances.

i'somerous, a. Having the same number of parts, markings, etc. sp.:— [Bot.] (Of flower or circles of flower-parts) having the same number of parts in all circles. [Zoo.] (Of teeth of certain animals) having the same number of RIDGES.

i'somery, n. ISOMERISM.

iso'metric, n. [Phys.] Having the same VOLUME, or to do with anything whose volume is kept unchanged. [Cryst.] Of, to do with, the i. system. **i. con'traction.** [Zoo.] The sort of CONTRACTION undergone by a muscle pulling against a very strong force so that it is unable to make itself shorter. **i. line.** [Phys.] Line representative of the relation between two other changing physical properties of a body whose VOLUME is kept unchanged, such as TEMPERATURE and ENTROPY or temperature and PRESSURE (*see* ISOCHORE). **i. system.** [Cryst.] The group formed of CRYSTALS having 3 equal AXES at right-angles to one another.

iso'morph-ic, -ous, aa. Having like form. [Chem.] (Sp. of substances of like chemical structure) having CRYSTALS of the same form. [Biol.] (Of animals or plants) like in form though different in SPECIES or RACE. **'isomorph,** n. I. substance; i. animal, plant or group. **iso'morphism,** n.

isone'phelic, n., a. [Meteor.] (Line on map joining places) having equal amount of cloud. **'isoneph,** n. I.

'isophane, n. [Biol.] Line joining all places in a given stretch of country at which

something dependent on weather conditions, such as the flowering of a certain plant, takes place at the same time.

iso'phyllous, a. [Bot.] Having the leaves on the same plant or stem like in form.

'isopi'estic, 1.a. ISOBARIC. 2.n. ISOBAR.

'isopla'natic, a. [Astron.] Free from COMA.

'isoplere, n. [Phys.] An ISOMETRIC LINE.

I'sopoda, n.pl. [Zoo.] An ORDER of CRUSTACEA made up of gen. quite small land, sea, and inland-water animals without a hard cover, having body commonly flat and made up of 6 or more divisions with ISOPODOUS legs used for walking, and eyes with fixed or no stems.

i'sopodous, a. [Zoo.] Having all legs of like form, size, and direction.

I'soptera, n.pl. [Zoo.] An ORDER of soft-bodied, light-coloured, biting insects living in great societies in common living places hollowed out in the earth or formed of wood and earth, having 5 different CASTES, of which only the sexed forms are winged.

iso'pycnic, 1.a. [Phys.] Of equal DENSITY; going through points at which the density is equal. 2.n. An i. line.

'iso'quinoline, n. [Chem.] C_9H_7N, a CRYSTALLINE or liquid substance present in coal TAR.

i'sosceles 'triangle. [Geom.] A TRIANGLE having two of its sides equal.

'isoscope, n. Apparatus for testing the eye's power of turning.

iso'seismal, a. Undergoing, to do with, equally strong force of EARTHQUAKE. **i. line.** Line joining points on earth where EARTHQUAKE shock is equally strong. **iso'seismic,** a., n. I. (line).

isos'motic, a. [Phys.] Having, to do with, equal OSMOTIC PRESSURE.

'isospores, n. [Biol.] SPORES equal in size and taken to be PARTHENOGENETIC. **iso'sporous,** a. Sp., producing ii.

i'sostasy, n. [Geol.] Condition of balance of forces taken as present in the outer earth, by which all equal units of SURFACE have under them equal MASSES of substance stretching down to the middle part of the earth. **iso'static,** a. Undergoing equal PRESSURE from all sides; to do with i.

iso'stemonous, a. [Bot.] Having STAMENS equal in number to the PERIANTH divisions. **iso'stemony,** n.

'isostere, n. [Chem.] Any one of two or more MOLECULES having a like structure of ELECTRONS and so being like one another in certain physical properties. [Meteor]. Line on map joining places where DENSITY of the ATMOSPHERE is equal. **iso'steric,** a. **i'sosterism,** n.

i'sotely, n. HOMOPLASTY.

'isothere, n. [Meteor.] Line on map through places having the same AVERAGE summer TEMPERATURE.

'**isotherm**, n. [Meteor.] Line on map through places having the same TEMPERATURE at a given time. **iso'therm-al, -ic,** aa. [Phys., Meteor.] Having, to do with, representative of, equal TEMPERATURES. **iso'thermal line.** [Phys.] Line representative of changes of PRESSURE and VOLUME in conditions of unchanging TEMPERATURE. [Meteor.] Isotherm.

iso'thermobath, n. [Geog.] Line through points of equal TEMPERATURE in VERTICAL plane in sea.

iso'tonic, a. [Chem., Biochem., etc.] Having equal OSMOTIC PRESSURE, said sp. of SOLUTIONS i. with liquids in the body, for example a solution having in it the right amount of salt to keep red blood-CELLS unchanged in form and substance.

'**isotope,** n. [Chem.] One or two or more ELEMENTS having the same at. no. and the same chemical behaviour, but different in at. wt. and in properties, such as RADIO-ACTIVITY, dependent on the weight of, or the number of NEUTRONS in, the NUCLEUS. **i'sotopy, 'isotopism,** nn. **iso'topic,** a. **iso'topic 'number.** The number by which the number of NEUTRONS in an ATOM is greater than the number of PROTONS. **isotopic weight.** The at. wt. of an i., based on the at. wt. of the commonest i. of O as 16—all isotopic weights being very near to INTEGERS. (*See* MASS NUMBER.)

iso'trop-ic, -ous, aa. [Phys.] Having same properties in all directions. **i'sotropy,** n.

'**isotype,** n. [Biol.] Animal, plant, or group common to two or more countries or stretches of country. **iso'typic-(al),** aa.

'**isthmus,** n. [Geog.] A narrow neck of land joining greater masses. [Zoo.] A narrow part joining two greater parts, for example that between the middle and the back part of the brain in back-boned animals. '**isthmiate,** a.

-itis. [Med.] Diseased condition, sp. INFLAMMATION: **cyst'itis,** n. **-itic,** a.

'**ivory,** n. The hard white material of which teeth are chiefly made up, sp. that special sort of it forming the TUSKS of PROBOSCIDEA. **i. black.** A form of C produced from ANIMAL CHARCOAL.

I.W. = ISOTOPIC WEIGHT.

-ize, v.t. [Chem.] Get mixed or united with: **phosphorize, carbonize.**

J, Sign for: JOULE'S EQUIVALENT; JOULE.

'**jacket,** n. [Eng.] A coat or cover over a vessel such as boiler, pipe, etc., to keep heat from being wasted and so on, sp. one forming an outer wall with steam, water, air or other gas in the space between it and the vessel.

'**Jacobson's 'cartilage** or '**turbinal.** [Zoo.] Narrow structure of CARTILAGE between the VOMER and the middle division of the nose in some back-boned animals. '**Jacobson's 'organ.** In some back-boned animals, small hollow structure supported by J. cartilage and having to do with the sense of smell.

jacti'tation, n. [Med.] The unresting turning and moving about of a person who is very ill, for example in DELIRIUM.

jade, n. [Mineral.] Name given to JADEITE, NEPHRITE, and some like green or white stones having the property of taking a high polish and used as jewel stones, sp. in China etc.

'**jadeite,** n. [Mineral.] Natural $NaAlO_2$. $2SiO_2$, a smooth, solid, OPAQUE substance of a beautiful green colour, or with green markings, valued as a jewel stone and for ornaments, chiefly from Burma.

jam, v.t. [Radio] Make hearing of (certain radio station) unclear or impossible by sending out waves of like WAVELENGTH from another station. '**-ming,** n.

'**jasper,** n. [Mineral.] A natural OPAQUE form of SiO_2, mixed with other substances, and coloured by them green, brown, yellow, black or, very commonly, red.

'**jaundice,** n. [Med.] Condition, common to certain diseases, in which BILE is present in the blood and TISSUES, and the skin and eyes and URINE become deep yellow, for example, in HEPATITIS.

'**Java man.** [Zoo.] PITHECANTHROPUS.

ja'vel(le) water. [Chem.] KOCl or NaOCl in water, used as a DISINFECTANT, for taking colour out of cloth, etc., and in camera work. '**javelli'zation,** n. Addition of HYPOCHLORITES to water.

jaw, n. [Zoo.] The hard framework of the mouth of an animal, or the part of the head or face supported by this, sp., in back-boned animals, one or other of the two structures (the *upper j.* and the *lower j.* in which the teeth are rooted; any structure formed or working like a j., sp. one or the other of two parts of a machine for gripping, crushing, or cutting anything between them. **j. foot.** MAXILLI-PED(E). '**-bone,** n. The bone of the upper or lower j. in back-boned animals.

je'junum, n. [Zoo.] In MAMMALS, the middle division of the SMALL INTESTINE, between the DUODENUM and the ILEUM, wider across and thicker-walled than the rest, and with more and greater-sized VILLI. **je'junal,** a. **je'juno-.** **je'juno-**

co'lostomy, n. [Med.] Operation for making an opening between j. and COLON. **je'junoile'ostomy,** n. [Med.] Operation for making an opening between j. and ILEUM. **je'junojeju'nostomy,** n. [Med.] Operation for forming a connection between two turns of the j. so that the part in between is not needed.

'Jellet-'Cornu prism. [Optics] A NICOL PRISM of special structure.

'jelly of 'Wharton. [Zoo.] Sticky jelly-like material covering the blood-vessels of the UMBILICAL CORD.

'Jenner's stain, n. [Zoo., etc.] Substance used for colouring NUCLEI of blood-CELLS for science purposes.

jerk, n. [Med.] A sudden, automatic motion of muscles, sp. in reaction to a cause outside the body, as a blow on a nerve.

jet, n. [Mineral.] A very hard, deep black, natural substance, which may be given a high polish, formed in the same way as coal but of no value for burning, used for dress ornaments, buttons, etc.

jet, n. [Phys.] Current of gas or liquid coming with force from an outlet; short metal part on end of pipe etc., with a narrow opening or a number of small openings for letting out liquid or gas in a j. or SPRAY. **j. 'engine.** Engine, sp. of airplane, causing j. propulsion. **j. pro'pulsion.** The forcing of a boat, airplane etc. in one direction by a j. of liquid or gas sent out in the opposite direction, most importantly, in airplanes, by pumping or pulling air in at the front into a pipe, where it is mixed with oil and fired, sending out a j. of heated gas at the back, driving the plane forward. **j. pump.** [Mach.] Pump in which a j. of water, steam, or gas is used to give an impulse to the liquid or gas being pumped. **j.-pro'pelled.** a. Moved by j. propulsion.

jet-stream, n. [Meteor.] A narrow current of wind blowing regularly with great force between 10,000 and 40,000 ft. up, in certain parts of the earth, for example over the Atlantic.

Jo'hansson gauge (blocks). [Mach.] A number of equal and parallel plates of special metal, which gripped together become united, so that by building them up to the number needed they may be used for taking measures up to 6 in. with an error of less than 0·00001 in.

jig, n. [Mach.] An apparatus, such as a box-like metal structure, for keeping material in position and guiding the instrument which is cutting, forming, making holes in it and so on.

joint, n. Place at which, structure by which, two things or parts are joined, sp. [Zoo.] part or structure where two bones or parts of an animal's body are so joined that they have the power of motion in relation to one another; part between two jj. [Geol.] A very narrow crack running through ROCK where the material has been parted by some force, such as that produced by CONTRACTION, but not moved out of line, forming a plane on which the rock readily undergoes division. **'ed,** a. **'-ing,** n. The forming of a j. or jj.; a system of jj. [Geol.] A condition or structure marked by jj.

'Jolly 'balance. [Phys.] Very delicate SPRING BALANCE used sp. for measuring the DENSITY of a solid by getting its weight in air and in water.

Jolly's appa'ratus. [Chem.] Apparatus for the VOLUMETRIC ANALYSIS of air.

joule, n. Unit of ENERGY or work = 10^7 ERGS or 0·738 FOOT-POUNDS (the **absolute j.**) or 1.00018 times this (the **international j.**). **J.** or **'joulean effect.** Heating or loss of power caused by an electric current meeting RESISTANCE. **J.'s e'quivalent.** MECHANICAL EQUIVALENT OF HEAT. **J.'s law.** 1. Law that the heat produced by an electric current I going through RESISTANCE R for a time t is measured by I^2Rt. 2. Law that the TEMPERATURE of a gas is unchanged when it undergoes expansion without doing work against outside forces or getting heat from outside. **'J.-'Thomson effect.** The very small loss in TEMPERATURE of a gas undergoing sudden expansion by going through a very small hole from a space of greater PRESSURE to one of less, the non-agreement with J.'s law being accounted for by the work needed to overcome the attraction of the MOLECULES for one another. **'joulean,** a. Of, to do with, the changing into heat of some other form of ENERGY.

'journal, n. [Eng.] That part of a SHAFT, etc. turning in a BEARING.

'jugal bone. [Zoo.] In back-boned animals, a bone in the side of the face under the eye.

'jugular, 1.a. [Zoo.] To do with the throat or neck. 2.n. J. vein. **j. vein.** The chief VEIN taking blood from the head in back-boned animals.

'jugulum, n. [Zoo.] The lower part of the throat of a bird, where it goes into the chest; JUGUM.

'jugum, n. [Zoo.] In some insects, a finger-like structure on back edge of front wing by which it and the back wing are kept together when in flight.

juice, n. [Biol.] The liquid part of plant CELLS or structures or of animal bodies or substances.

'Julian 'calendar. The CALENDAR put into force by Julius Caesar in 45 B.C., based on a year of 365·25 days, of which the present-day calendar is an outgrowth (see GREGORIAN CALENDAR).

'jungle, n. [Geog.] (Stretch of) waste land in countries having great heat and rainfall, covered with very thick and high plant-growth and gen. harbouring great numbers of animals and insects, sp. a TROPICAL RAIN FOREST.

'Jupiter, n. [Astron.] The greatest of the PLANETS in the sun's system, the fifth in order from the sun, taking 11·86 years to go round it, and having a mass about 318 times that of the earth and 9 'moons'. (*See* p. 331.)

Ju'rassic, a. [Geol.] Said of the PERIOD or SYSTEM coming in the middle of the MESOZOIC (*see* p. 558) ranging from about 170 to 140 million years back, in which the first birds came into existence.

just into'nation. [Acous.] The ranging of notes as in the DIATONIC SCALE.

just scale. [Acous.] DIATONIC SCALE.

juve'nescence, n. Becoming young. juve-'nescent, a.

'juvenile, a. [Geol.] Coming out of the earth for the first time, said of water or gas from deep down in the earth. [Bot.] Of, to do with, a young plant when this is markedly different from the plant at full growth.

juxta-. Near, by the side of.

'juxtapose, v.t. Put side by side. 'juxtaposed, a. juxtapo'sition, n. juxtaposed or juxtaposition twins. [Cryst.] A TWIN CRYSTAL in which the two united crystals are simply side by side, not with parts going through one another, opp. INTERPENETRATION TWINS.

K. [Chem.] Sign for POTASSIUM. [Phys.] Sign for the KELVIN TEMPERATURE SCALE.

k, [Phys.] Sign for BOLTZMAN CONSTANT.

'kainite, n. [Mineral] A natural substance, $MgSO_4.KCl.3H_2O$, used as a FERTILIZER and for producing SALTS of K and Mg.

'Kainozoic, a. CAINOZOIC.

'kala-a'zar, n. [Med.] Disease common in India and China caused by one of the PROTOZOA, marked by an increase in the size of the LIVER and the SPLEEN, a lowering of the amount of HAEMOGLOBIN in the blood, wasting and FEVER, and frequently causing death.

'kalium, n. [Chem.] Another name for POTASSIUM.

kame, n. [Geol.] An irregular network of long masses of GRAVEL, broken by hollows

and holes, seen in a TERMINAL MORAINE, the effect of the dropping of gravel by currents running through the cracks formed in the terminal ice when MELTING.

'kanka(r), n. [Geol.] Small irregular mass of LIMESTONE bedded in soft or loose material put down by a river, etc.

'kaolin, n. [Geol.] A sort of white CLAY, made almost completely of $Al_2Si_2O_2$ $(OH)_4$, of great value in CERAMICS and used medically for heated dressings. 'kaolini'zation, n. The forming of k. as an effect of the natural destruction of MINERALS having aluminium in them. '-ize, v.t.

'Karlsbad twin. [Crystal.] TWIN CRYSTAL of $KAlSi_3O_8$ in which the TWINNING AXIS is the upright axis.

karst land. [Geol.] Very broken up LIMESTONE country, with deep holes (karst holes) and great irregular masses of ROCK.

'karyo-. [Biol.] NUCLEUS (of a CELL).

kary'ogamy, n. [Biol.] The uniting of two NUCLEI.

'karyoki'nesis, n. MITOSIS.

'karyolymph, n. [Biol.] The water-like liquid inside a CELL NUCLEUS.

kary'olysis, n. NUCLEOLYSIS.

'karyosome, n. [Biol.] Mass of CHROMATIN in a resting NUCLEUS; CHROMOSOME; nucleus of a CELL; NUCLEOLUS of sort seen in some lower plants, from which the chromosomes get material while MITOSIS is going on.

kata-. Down, away, *see* CATA.

kata'batic, a. [Meteor.] (Of winds) caused by the moving down of cold air, such as the night winds coming down mountain sides or those coming down the ice-slopes of Greenland and so on, opp. ANABATIC.

kat'abolism, n. [Biol.] The process made up of all those chemical changes in living things by which complex substances are broken down, separating out waste and freeing ENERGY for use in other processes. kata'bolic, a.

kata'genesis, n. [Biol.] The process of going back to a simpler and earlier form, against the normal direction of EVOLUTION.

'kata'kinetic, a. [Biol.] (Of process) freeing ENERGY.

kataki'netomeres, n.pl. [Phys., Chem.] ATOMS or MOLECULES poor in ENERGY, having no tendency to change.

kata'klastic, a. CATACLASTIC.

'kataphase, n. [Biol.] The stages of MITOSIS from the forming of the CHROMOSOMES to the division of the CELL.

'katapho'resis, n. CATAPHORESIS.

'kataplexy, n. [Zoo.] Condition copying death into which some animals put themselves as a reaction to danger.

'katastate, n. [Biochem.] Any substance formed by KATABOLISM.

'kata-ther'mometer, n. [Med.] A sort of

THERMOMETER having a great vessel full of ALCOHOL with a scale giving the loss of heat per cm² of the SURFACE of this vessel, used in measuring the effect of the air in taking heat from a person's body.

'Kater's 'pendulum. [Phys.] PENDULUM of complex design for seeing how long a simple pendulum has to be to make one complete SWING per second.

katha'rometer, n. [Chem.] Apparatus for measuring changes in the make-up of a mixed gas by changes in its CONDUCTIVITY of heat.

'kathode, n. CATHODE.

ka'thodic, a. [Bot.] (Of part of leaf) turned away from the direction of the GENETIC SPIRAL.

'kation, n. CATION.

KC, or Kc, or kc = KILOCYCLE(s).

KC.P.S., or Kcps, or kcps = KILOCYCLES per second.

keel, n. [Zoo.] CARINA or chest-bone of birds having power of flight. [Bot.] CARINA.

'keeper, n. [Elec., Engin.] Soft iron or steel rod kept on POLES of a MAGNET when not in use, so keeping the MAGNETISM from being used up.

K e'lectron. [Phys.] One or other of the two ELECTRONS in the K SHELL. K e. 'capture. The taking into the NUCLEUS of an ATOM of one of its K ee.

kelp, n. [Bot.] A general name for the greater sorts of SEAWEED.

'Kelvin 'balance. [Elec.] An instrument for measuring current, in which the force between two wires transporting it is balanced by the force of the earth's attraction on a weight moving a rod (other name *ampere balance*). Kelvin 'temperature scale. ABSOLUTE SCALE OF TEMPERATURE.

Ken'nelly-'Heaviside 'layer. HEAVISIDE LAYER.

'Kepler's laws. [Astron.] The laws that: 1. every PLANET is moving in an ELLIPSE with the sun at one FOCUS; 2. the line from the sun to a planet goes over equal AREAS in equal times; 3. the SQUARE of the time taken by a planet to go round the sun is in DIRECT PROPORTION to the CUBE of its AVERAGE distance from the sun.

kera'phyllous, a. [Zoo.] Said of that part of the HOOF in UNGULATA which comes between the outer cover of horn and the inner living substance.

'keratin, n. [Zoo., Biochem.] The PROTEIN substance forming the outer coat of the skin in back-boned animals and such substances and structures as horn, hair, nails, feathers, and wool. ke'ratinized, a. Having undergone keratinization. ke-'ratinization, n. The process by which

skin-CELLS are changed into k. ke'ratinous, a.

'kerat(o)-. [Zoo., Med.] 1. Horn, horn-like substance:— kera'togenous, a. 2. COR-NEA:— kera'titis, n., kera'totomy, n.

'keratoid, a. Horn-like.

kerauno-. Thunder and/or LIGHTNING.

ke'raunograph, n. [Meteor.] Instrument for recording THUNDERSTORMS at a distance. kerauno'graphic, a.

ke'raunophone, n. [Meteor.] Radio instrument for the observation by hearing of LIGHTNING at a distance.

'kernel, n. [Bot.] One seed of a grain plant; seed without its covers, sp. the seed inside the stone of a fruit. [Phys.] The part of an ATOM inside the VALENCE SHELL.

'kerosene, n. [Chem.] That part of PETROLEUM whose boiling-point is between 150° and 250° C., a thin oil used for lighting and heating and in some engines.

Kerr effect. [Optics] The turning round of the plane of POLARIZED LIGHT when it goes through certain clear substances across which an electric POTENTIAL DIFFERENCE is acting.

keto-. [Chem.] In which a KETONE is present.

keto'genesis, n. [Med.] The producing of KETONES in the body, sp. by the LIVER, from FATTY ACIDS. keto'genic, a. To do with or effecting k.

ke'tolysis, n. Process by which KETONES are broken up. keto'lytic, a.

'ketone, n. [Chem.] Any of a group of substances in which two HYDROCARBON groups are joined to the group –CO–. ke'tonic, a.

ke'tosis, n. [Med.] Condition in which over-much ACETONE or other KETONE substance is produced in the body, caused by incomplete OXIDATION of fats.

'kettle, n. [Geol.] Round hole formed in the ROCK of a river bed by the circling motion of stones etc. effected by the current at this place; deep straight-sided hollow without SURFACE draining, sp. in a MORAINE (freq. kettle hole).

keV = KILO-ELECTRON-VOLT.

Ke'weenawan, a., n. [Geol.] (Of) the youngest SERIES of the PROTEROZOIC in North America.

key, n. In a writing-machine, any of the lettered and so on parts pushed down by the finger to make the print of the letter on paper; in TELEGRAPHY, a metal part worked by hand for quickly opening and shutting the CIRCUIT so as to send SIGNALS.

'kidney, n. [Zoo.] In back-boned animals, one or other of two like complex GLANDS in the back by which certain waste substances are taken out of the blood and formed into URINE, to be sent on to the

BLADDER and from there out of the body.

'kieselguhr, n. [Geol.] DIATOMACEOUS EARTH.

killed 'spirits (of salts). A SOLUTION of $ZnCl_2$ (*zinc chloride*) made by putting Zn in HCl (*hydrochloric acid*), used in SOLDERING and so on.

killed steel. [Metal.] Steel which has been completely freed of O before CASTING by the addition of Mn, Si, or Al.

kiln, n. Oven for drying or firing pots, bricks, stone, etc.

'kilo-, 1,000, used in names of measures in the METRIC SYSTEM etc.:—'kilogram(me), n., 'kilometer, n., 'kilovolt, n.

'kilo-e'lectron-volt, n. 1000 ELECTRON-VOLTS.

'kilocalorie, n. KILOGRAM CALORIE.

'kilocycle, n. [Phys.] 1,000 CYCLES, one k. per second being used as a unit of FREQUENCY for ALTERNATING CURRENT, radio WAVES, sound and ULTRASONIC waves, and so on.

'kilogram 'calorie. *See* CALORIE.

'kiloton, n. [Phys.] A unit of EXPLOSIVE force, = that of 1000 TONS of T. N. T.

'kilowatt, n. Unit of electric power = 1,000 WATTS or about 1.34 HORSE-POWER. k.-hour, n. [Elec.] Unit of ENERGY = amount produced by one k. acting for one hour.

kinaes'thes-is, -ia, nn. [Zoo.] The sense whose ORGANS are in the muscles, TENDONS, etc., by which the motions of the body are experienced. kinaes'thetic, a. 'kinaesthesi'ometer, n.

ki'nase, n. [Biochem.] Any substance changing a ZYMOGEN etc. into an ENZYME.

kin(e)-. Motion, moving.

kine'matic, a. [Phys.] To do with motion. kin'ematics, n.pl. That part of MECHANICS which has to do only with the motions of bodies without taking into account the forces producing them. '-al, a.

kinesi-. Motion.

kine'simeter, kinesi'ometer, nn. [Physiol.] Instrument for measuring motions of the body.

ki'nesis, n. Motion. [Biol.] Sp. the moving of an animal from one place to another in reaction to a STIMULUS, but in a direction not controlled by the stimulus.

kine'sodic, a. [Zoo.] Transporting nerve and muscle impulses whose outcome is some motion.

kines'thesis, n. KINAESTHESIS.

ki'netic, a. [Phys.] To do with, caused by, motion. k. 'body. [Biol.] A very small body present at the place where a CHROMOSOME is joined to the SPINDLE. k. 'energy. [Phys.] The ENERGY which a moving body has because of its motion, dependent on its MASS and the rate at which it is moving. k. equi'librium.

[Phys.-Chem.] Condition of balance between PHASES, as when the number of MOLECULES of gas given off by a liquid in a shut vessel and the number taken back by it are equal. k. 'pressure. [Phys.] The PRESSURE of a group of PARTICLES in a PLASMA etc. which is effected by their k. energy. k. theory of gases. [Phys.] The theory that the MOLECULES of a gas are like rubber balls in quick motion in straight lines, all the time running into and being turned back by one another, and that this is the cause of the PRESSURE of the gas on the walls of a vessel and the cause of the heat inside the gas. ki'netics, n.pl. That branch of DYNAMICS which has to do with the changes of motion produced by forces. kinet(o)-.

ki'netoblast, n. [Zoo.] In some water LARVAE, an outer cover having CILIA used for transport.

ki'neto'nucleus, n. [Zoo.] Small, NUCLEUS-like body in TRYPANOSOMA having a connection with the FLAGELLUM and the VIBRATILE MEMBRANE.

'kingdom, n. *See* ANIMAL KINGDOM, VEGETABLE KINGDOM, MINERAL KINGDOM.

Kipp's appa'ratus. [Chem.] Apparatus for producing at need in the LABORATORY, any gas formed by the reaction of a liquid and a solid without special heating, sp. H_2S, by simply opening a VALVE which at the same time puts the gas-producing substances in touch with one another in the vessel and lets out the gas produced by their reaction.

'Kirchoff's law. [Optics] The law that at any given TEMPERATURE the relation of the EMISSIVE POWER of a substance to its ABSORPTION COEFFICIENT is the same for all substances.

'Kirchoff's laws. [Elec.] The two laws of the electric CIRCUIT:— 1. That in any network of electric waves, the ALGEBRAIC SUM of the currents meeting at any point = 0; 2. That the ALGEBRAIC SUM of the POTENTIAL DIFFERENCES in a circuit = the algebraic sum of the ELECTROMOTIVE FORCES in it.

kish, n. [Metal.] Solid GRAPHITE separating from and coming to the top of liquid iron.

kite, n. [Meteor.] Apparatus of paper or cloth stretched over thin framework of wood, sent up into the air on the end of a long cord for the purpose of taking up instruments to get weather recordings high over the earth, etc.

'Kjeldahl 'process or method. Process for measuring the amount of N in a substance by first heating it in a long-necked glass vessel with a round base (a **Kjidahl flask**) with H_2SO_4, so as to get $(NH_4)_2SO_4$, and from that producing NH_3.

klei'stogamous, a. CLEISTOGAMOUS.

klepto'mania, n. [Med.] Disease of mind

causing person to take the property of others without their knowledge. **klepto-'maniac,** n. Person having k.

'klystron, n. [Radio] A form of THERMIONIC VALVE for producing or making stronger OSCILLATING CURRENT of very high FREQUENCY.

knee, n. [Zoo.] The middle JOINT of the leg in man; in four-legged animals, the parallel joint of the back leg, the joint parallel to man's WRIST in the front leg; the joint between foot and leg in birds. **k.-jerk.** [Med.] The automatic kicking out of the foot which is the normal reaction to a sharp little blow at the base of the k. of a person seated with the k. in question supported by his other leg— used as a test for certain nerve diseases, by which the reaction is stopped or made over-violent.

knock, 1.n. Sharp noise made in an INTERNAL COMBUSTION ENGINE by DETONATION. 2.v.i. Make k.

knot, n. [Bot.] A very hard place in wood, formed from the base of a branch round which new coats of wood have been made hard by PRESSURE; a small grain of CHROMATIN at a meeting-point of threads in the network of a NUCLEUS.

knot, n. Unit measuring the rate of a ship's motion, =1 NAUTICAL MILE per hour.

Koch ba'cillus, TUBERCULOSIS BACILLUS.

Kopp's law. [Phys.] Law that the SPECIFIC HEAT of a solid ELEMENT is the same when united in a solid COMPOUND as it is when free.

Kr, Sign for KRYPTON.

Krause's 'membrane. [Zoo.] In STRIATED muscle, a MEMBRANE going across the middle of every light band, seen in the form of a dark line of division.

'Kretschmer's types. [Med.] The three sorts, based on the relation between body structure and the tendency to certain diseases of the mind, into which persons were grouped by Kretschmer (ASTHENIC, ATHLETIC, and PYKNIC).

'kryptol, n. A substance formed of GRA-PHITE, CARBORUNDUM and CLAY mixed, used as a RESISTOR in electric FURNACES.

'krypton, n. Chemical ELEMENT, at. no. 36, at. wt. 83·7, sign Kr, a gas giving no chemical reaction, of which a very small amount is present in the air.

'K-'series. [Phys.] A SERIES of lines in an X-RAY SPECTRUM caused by the sudden moving of ELECTRONS into the K-SHELL of an ATOM.

'K-'shell, n. [Phys.] The inmost SHELL of an ATOM, having no more than 2 ELECTRONS.

Kundt's tube. [Acous.] Glass pipe in which STATIONARY WAVES are produced, their effect being seen by the behaviour of a powder placed in the pipe.

'kupfer-'nickel, n. [Mineral.] Natural NiAs (*nickel arsenide*), gen. having in it a little iron, Co, and S, one of the chief ORES of Ni.

'Kupffer cells. [Zoo.] Great PHAGOCYTIC CELLS on the walls of the LIVER in some back-boned animals.

kv=KILOVOLT.

'kymograph, n. An instrument formed of a turning CYLINDER covered with smoked paper round which a curved line going up and down with changes of PRESSURE is made by an automatically moving pencil, used, for example for recording the motions of breathing or of the heart.

ky'phosis, n. [Med.] A condition of the back-bone in which it is curved markedly out in the upper part of the back and forward again at the neck.

l.=LITRE.

***l*-.** Sign for LAEVO-ROTATORY.

λ, Sign for WAVE-LENGTH.

La, Sign for LANTHANUM.

la'bellum (la'bella), in. [Bot.] The middle PETAL of a flower of the ORCHIDACAE. [Zoo.] A small lip-like part under the LABRUM of certain insects; spoon-like part at the front of the GLOSSA in bees; one or other of the two flat expansions at the end of the LABIUM in some DIPTERA. **'labelloid,** a. **'labellate,** a.

'labia, n.pl. *See* LABIUM. **l. 'cerebi.** [Zoo.] The edges of the CEREBRAL HEMISPHERES covering part of the CORPUS CALLOSUM.

'labial, a. To do with the lips. [Phonet.] Said of sounds made with the lips, as *b*, *p*, *m*. **labial palp,** [Zoo.] Any of 4 leaf-like structures near the mouth in certain MOLLUSCS; thin JOINTED feeler on lower lip in insects. **'labial teeth.** The 6 top and 6 lower front teeth in man or like teeth in other higher animals. **'labiate,** a. [Bot.] Having lip-like parts sp. of pipe-like COROLLA of which one part is longer than the other, forming a lipped opening. [Zoo.] Like a lip in structure, thick at edges.

'labiati'florous, a. [Bot.] Having a LABIATE COROLLA.

labi'dophorous, a. [Zoo.] Having a FORCEPS-like mouth-structure for gripping things.

'labile, a. [Chem., Phys.] Readily under-going change in structure. [Med.] Said of an ELECTRODE designed to be moved from place to place on the skin, or of the current acting on the body through such an electrode, opp. STABILE.

'labio-. Lip (and . . .).

'labio'dental, a. [Phonet.] (Of a sound) made with the lower lip and the top teeth, as *f*.

'labium (labia), n. [Biol.] A lip-like part, sp. the lower lip of a LABIATE COROLLA or the PROBOSCIS forming the lower lip of an insect (*see* LABIA).

la'boratory, n. A place in which science work using materials and apparatus for, for example, the testing of theories, the producing and observation of effects or new substances, goes on.

'labour, n. [Med.] The last stage in the process of producing offspring, the act of giving birth.

'labradorite, n. [Geol.] A sort of FELDSPAR chiefly coming from Labrador, commonly marked by a beautiful blue, green and grey IRIDESCENCE.

'labrum (labra), n. [Zoo.] Lip-like part, sp the plate-like top lip of insects and some other ARTHROPODA, or the lip-like edge of a SHELL. **'labral,** a.

'labyrinth, n. [Zoo.] Any net-work of pipes or twisting pipe-like structure, sp. that of the inner ear in back-boned animals, or the outer part of a KIDNEY. **laby'rinthine,** a. **labyrinthine sense.** [Psych.] The STATIC SENSE in back-boned animals, the instrument of which is the l. of the ear.

laby'rinthodont, a. [Zoo.] Having the substance of the teeth in complex folds.

lac, n. Sticky substance given out by an insect PARASITE on certain trees, sp. of the rubber family, used for making SHELLAC, etc.

'laccase, n. [Biochem.] An ENZYME present in BACTERIA and some FUNGI.

'laccate, a. [Bot.] Having a bright, smooth look, as if covered with VARNISH.

'laccolith, n. [Geol.] Mass of IGNEOUS ROCK pushing up the STRATA over it, lifting them into a rounded, arch-like form.

'lacerate, 1.v.t. [Med.] Get (FLESH) irregularly cut, broken, crushed. 2.a. [Biol.] (Of a part) having edge or point with deep and irregular cuts. **'lacerated,** a. **lace'ration,** n. Sp.,[Med.] irregular wound, mass of cuts, caused by crushing, etc.

'Lacer'tilia, n.pl. [Zoo.] A division of REPTILIA very like snakes, but with a shorter body and a long tail narrowing to a point, moving EYELIDS, and, in some groups, four legs.

'lac(h)rymal, a. [Zoo.] To do with, near, the l. gland. **l. duct.** Small pipe going, in higher animals, from the inner angle of the eye to the inside of the nose, and draining off the liquid produced by the l. gland. **l. gland.** GLAND at the outer angle of the eye of higher animals producing a clear salt liquid by which the eye is

normally washed, and which when produced in great amount takes the form of TEARS. **l. pa'pilla.** The small rounded part in the angle of the eye, on the face of which is the very small opening into the l. duct.

'lachry'mator, n. A TEAR GAS.

'lac(h)ryma'tory, a., n. LACHRYMAL; (substance) causing TEARS, as a gas.

'lac(h)rymose, a. [Bot.] Having parts formed like TEARS.

'lacinate, a. LACERATE.

la'cinia (la'ciniae), n. [Bot.] Any of a number of narrow tongue-like parts edging anything, for example a flower or leaf. [Zoo.] Narrow outgrowth inside insect's mouth or on head of certain fishes. **lacini'ation,** n. L.; condition of having ll. or being LACERATE. **la'cinula,** n. Small l.; turned-in point of PETAL in some plants. **la'cinul-ate, -ose,** aa.

la'ciniose, a. [Biol.] LACERATE.

lacri-. *See* LACHRY-.

'lacquer, n. [Chem.] A SOLUTION of a substance such as a GUM in a VOLATILE liquid, used for giving a clear, hard coat to wood, metal, paintwork, etc.

lactal'bumin, n. [Chem.] Any of the ALBUMINS present in milk.

'lactate, n. [Chem.] A SALT or ESTER of LACTIC ACID.

lac'tation, n. [Zoo.] The producing of milk by the MAMMARY GLANDS. **'lactate,** v.i. (Of GLAND or animal) give out milk, get milk produced.

lac'teal, 1.a. [Zoo.] LACTEOUS; transporting CHYLE. 2.n. Any of the l. vessels of the SMALL INTESTINE.

lac'teous, a. Of, to do with, producing, like, milk.

'lactic, a. [Zoo., Chem.] To do with milk. **l. acid.** A complex ACID formed of C, H, and O, of which a common form is produced when milk goes bad. **l. fermen'tation.** [Chem.] The producing of l. acid from ORGANIC substances such as LACTOSE by the operation of BACTERIA.

'lactifi'cation, n. The changing of a substance by LACTIC FERMENTATION. **'lactify,** v.t. Make undergo l.

'lacti-, lacto-. Milk: **lac'tometer,** n., **lacto-'protein,** n.

lac'tiferous, a. [Zoo.] Milk-producing. [Bot.] Producing, having in it, LATEX.

'lactobuty'rometer, n. Instrument measuring amount of butter-fat in milk.

'lactoden'simeter, n. Instrument measuring DENSITY of milk.

lacto'flavin, n. [Biochem.] RIBOFLAVIN.

'lacto'genic, a. [Zoo., Med.] To do with, or increasing, LACTATION. **l. 'hormone.** [Zoo.] A HORMONE produced by the ANTERIOR PITUITARY and playing an important part in starting or helping LACTATION, sp. PROLACTIN. **l. 'period.** The time after giving birth for which an animal goes on producing milk for its young.

'lactoscope, n. Instrument for measuring the amount of fat in milk.

'lactose, n. [Chem.] A sugar, $C_{12}H_{22}O_{11}$ + H_2O, present in milk and giving GLUCOSE and GALACTOSE when broken up (sometimes named *milk sugar*).

lacto'toxin, n. [Biochem.] A poison present in milk or cheese.

la'cuna, n. [Biol.] Space between CELLS [Zoo.] Any of the spaces in the TISSUES of a lower animal which do the work of. vessels in transporting the body liquids; any very small hollow, sp. of those in bone having in them bone-CELLS. [Bot.] Any of the small hollows in the THALLUS of a LICHEN. **la'cunar(y),** aa. **la'cunose,** a. Full of, covered with, small hollows.

la'custrine, a. [Biol., Geol.] To do with, formed in, living in or near, inland stretches of water.

Ladd-'Franklin 'theory. A theory of the process by which colours are seen, of which the chief ideas are that in the normal eye of man red, green and blue are seen as the effect of the freeing by light of certain substances in the RETINA, yellow by the uniting of the red- and green-producing substances, and white by the uniting of the yellow and blue, and that in early stages of EVOLUTION only white was seen, then later blue and yellow, after that yellow being broken up into red and green.

'laeo'tropic, lae'otropous, aa. [Zoo.] Turned, twisted, to the left. **lae'otropism,** n.

'l(a)evo-. At, to, the left. [Chem.] LAEVO-ROTATORY.

'l(a)evo'gy-rate, -re, -rous, aa. LAEVO-ROTATORY.

'l(a)evoro'tation, n. [Optics, Phys., Chem.] The turning of the plane of POLARIZATION of light to the left. **'l(a)evoro'tatory,** a. Sp. (of a substance, CRYSTAL, etc.) causing the l. of light going through it.

'l(a)evulose, n. FRUCTOSE. **'l(a)evulo'suria,** n. [Med.] Condition in which l. is present in URINE.

lag, 1.n. [Phys.] Time needed for an effect to come about after its cause 'has been put in operation, for example, for the elastic property of a material to undo the effects of a force no longer working on it. [Geol.] A FAULT in which the material on one side has been pushed down and under that on the other. 2.v.i. (Of a process or effect) be later, slower in coming about, than (some other in connection with it), or than it normally is. **'-ging,** a.

lag, v.t. Get (boiler, pipes, etc.) covered with material for keeping heat in or out. **'-ging,** n. Sp., material used for lagging.

la'gena, n. [Zoo.] A pocket of the inner ear in back-boned animals which in the

higher forms becomes the end part of the COCHLEA.

la'goon, n. [Geog.] Part of the sea cut off from it by some natural structure, sp. a wall of CORAL, so as to make a not very deep basin. **-al,** a.

la'gopodous, a. [Zoo.] Having hair or feathers on the feet.

lake, n. [Geog.] A stretch of inland water of some, freq. great, size, sometimes drained by a river, sometimes with no outlet and then gen. salt.

lake, n. [Chem.] The sort of INSOLUBLE colouring-substance produced by the reaction between a DYE and a MORDANT in dying, or made for use as a picture paint by a like reaction uniting a DYE with a metal.

-lalia, n. [Med.] Condition of trouble in talking.

'lalo-, [Med.] To do with talking: **-neu'rosis,** n., **-'phobia,** n.

'Lamarckism, n. [Biol.] Theory of Lamarck that EVOLUTION is the effect of changes in the structure of plants or animals in adjustment to their living conditions, and of the handing on of such developments to their offspring. **la'marckian,** a.

'lambda, n. The Greek letter λ. [Anat.] The meeting-point of the SAGITTAL and the lambdoid suture. **'lamb'doid,** a. **lam'bdoid 'suture.** The join between the OCCIPITAL and PARIETAL bones of the head, in form like the Greek λ.

'lambert, n. [Optics] Unit of BRIGHTNESS, being that of a SURFACE giving out or sending back 1 LUMEN/cm^2, or 0·318 CANDELAS/cm^2.

Lambert's law. COSINE EMISSION LAW.

la'mella (la'mellae), n. [Biol.] Thin plate or leaf-like structure, sp. [Bot.] a GILL of an AGARIC, [Zoo.] any of the ll. forming the gill of LAMELLI'BRANCHIA. **la'mellar(y), 'lamellate(d), 'lamellose,** aa. **'lamell'if-erous,** a. **la'melliform,** a.

La'melli'branchia(ta), n.pl. [Zoo.] CLASS of somewhat flat MOLLUSCA having BI-LATERAL SYMMETRY, a SHELL formed of two opposite parts opening like a book, and plate-like GILLS. **la'mellibranch,** n. Animal of the L. **'lamellibranchiate,** a. Sp. having GILLS formed of thin plates, like the L.

'lamina (laminae), b.[Phys., Biol., Mineral.] Thin, flat plate or leaf-like structure. [Geol.] A thin STRATUM or one of the ll. forming a stratum. [[Bot.] The flat blade of a leaf. **'laminable,** a. Able to be formed into ll. **'laminal, 'laminar,** aa. **'laminate,** 1.a. 1.v.t. [Mineral., Metal.] Get formed or cut into a thin plate or thin plates. **lami'nation,** n. Sp. [Geol.] the forming of very thin STRATA, as in SHALE; structure made up of ll. **'laminar flow.** [Phys.] STREAMLINE FLOW.

'lamini'plantar, a. [Zoo.] (Of birds) having sides of lower leg covered with plates of horn meeting at back in a smooth join.

'lampblack, n. [Chem.] The black substance produced when materials having much C in them are burned in little air so that their flame is mixed with smoke, used in making paints, ink, etc.

'lamprophyre, n. [Geol.] Any of a group of IGNEOUS ROCKS, gen. seen in the form of DYKES, having in them great amounts of coloured SILICATES and little or no FELDSPAR

'lanate, a. [Biol.] Covered with wool or wool-like hairs.

lance, v.t. [Med.] Make a small opening in (diseased part, blood-vessel, etc.) by cutting.

'lanceolate, a. [Bot.] (Of leaf) widest in middle, narrowing to a point at end and sometimes at base (*see* picture p. 223).

'lancet, n. Small medical knife, commonly sharp-pointed and two-edged, used for LANCING.

'lanciform, a. [Biol.] Narrow and pointed.

'lancinating, a. [Med.] (Of pain) sharp, jumping, going through the body like a knife.

land breeze. [Meteor.] A wind blowing from land to sea, sp. the more or less regular motion of air from a little way inland at the start of every day in warm, clear weather, caused by the air having undergone more loss of heat in the night over the land than over the sea—naturally dependent on the sort of country, and less well-marked than the SEA BREEZE.

land 'hemisphere. [Geog.] That half of the earth which has in it much the greater part of the earth's land, most of which is north of the EQUATOR with its middle point roughly at London.

land ice. [Geog.] Ice formed inland from FRESH water, as on rivers, etc.

'landslip, n. [Geol.] The sudden slipping of masses of earth, stone, etc. from a higher to a lower level, as down a mountain or into the sea.

'Langerhans' 'islets. [Zoo.] In back-boned animals, the irregular masses of small CELLS among the pipes of the PANCREAS by which INSULIN is produced.

'Langmuir probe. [Phys.] A small metal CONDUCTOR put into a PLASMA for getting the measure of the plasma current.

Langmuir's theory. [Phys.] The theory that the ELECTRONS outside the NUCLEUS of an ATOM are ranged in SHELLS, one outside the other, having a relation to the periods of the PERIODIC TABLE.

'laniary, a. [Zoo.] (Of teeth) CANINE.

la'ni-ferous, -gerous, aa. [Zoo.] Having, producing, wool.

'lanolin, n. [Chem., Med.] The fat of wool, a yellow wax-like mass used in making OINTMENTS, etc.

'lantern, n. A light-giving apparatus for outdoor use having the light covered by glass etc. in a framework of metal, sp. one designed to be taken from place to place by hand. [Optics] PROJECTION LANTERN. [Zoo.] ARISTOTLE'S L.

'lanthanide series, [Chem.] The group of RARE EARTH METALS from LANTHANUM to LUTECIUM with the addition of YTTRIUM.

lan'thanides, n.pl. RARE EARTH METALS.

'lanthanum, n. Chemical ELEMENT, at. no. 57, at. wt. 138·92, sign La, one of the RARE EARTH METALS.

la'nugin-ose, -ous, a. [Biol.] Covered with wool.

la'nugo, n. [Zoo.] Soft wool-like hair covering the FOETUS of man and other higher animals.

'laparo-. ABDOMEN: **lapa'rotomy,** n. [Med.]

lapi'diculous, a. [Zoo.] Living under stones.

la'pillus (la'pilli), n. [Geol.] Any of the small round bits of stone or glass-like substance sent out by a VOLCANO.

'lapis 'lazuli. [Mineral.] A complex natural SILICATE with S in it noted for its beautiful deep blue colour, not TRANSPARENT but taking a high polish and used as a jewel stone.

lap'paceous, a. [Bot.] Covered with small sharp points.

'lappet, n. [Zoo.] Part hanging down loosely, as from throat of certain birds.

large 'calorie. Old name for 1,000 CALORIES.

large in'testine. [Zoo.] The second, or lower, and greater of the two chief divisions of the INTESTINE in man and some other animals, taking in the COLON together with the RECTUM.

'Larmor 'orbit. [Phys.] The motion in a circle of a CHARGED PARTICLE in an unchanging MAGNETIC FIELD.

'larva (larvae), n. [Zoo.] An insect in the stage, or the first of the stages, between coming out of the egg and undergoing development into the IMAGO, in which it is without wings, gen. worm-like, and freq. very different in structure from its form at full growth; first self-supporting form of any animal whose early structure is markedly different from that which it has when its development is complete. **'larval,** a. **lar'varium,** n. Structure in which ll. are living. **'larviform,** a. **lar'viparous,** a. Producing offspring in the form of ll. **lar'virorous** a. Living on ll. **'larvule,** n. Young l.

laryng(o)-. LARYNX: **laryn'gitis,** n. [Med.], **laryn'gology,** n. [Med.] **laryn'gotomy,** n. [Med.].

la'ryngal, a. [Phonet.] (Of sounds) made the LARYNX.

la'ryngeal, a. [Zoo., Med.] To do with the LARYNX

laryn'gismus, n. [Med.] Condition in which there is a sudden shutting of the LARYNX from time to time. **l. 'stridulus.** L. causing a stopping of the breath, with a loud, rough intake when the attack is over.

laryn'gophony, n. [Med.] The sound of the voice as given by a STETHOSCOPE placed on the LARYNX.

la'ryngoscope, n. [Med.] Instrument for looking into the LARYNX, formed of a looking-glass on the end of a long rod for putting down the throat.

'larynx (larynxes or larynges), z. [Zoo.] The top part of the inside of the throat, opening into the mouth and nose—in all higher animals but birds, the voice-producing part, having in it the VOCAL CORDS.

'laser, n. [Phys.] An OPTICAL MASER, being a form of ELECTRO-MAGNETIC OSCIL-LATOR producing light-waves which may be massed into a very narrow band of WAVE-LENGTHS and sent in a fixed direction, giving light as much as a million times brighter and a million times PURER than that produced in any normal way.

'latebra, n. [Zoo.] Bulb-like mass of white YOLK stretching from the middle of the yellow yolk of a bird's egg to the CICA-TRICLE.

'latent, a. Giving no sign of itself, resting, not acting, not openly present but ready to undergo development when conditions are right. **l. heat of 'fusion.** [Phys.] The amount of heat needed to make 1 gm. of a given solid into a liquid. **l. heat of 'vaporization.** [Phys.] The amount of heat needed to make 1 gm. of a given liquid into a gas. **l. 'image.** The unseen changes made by light on a camera PLATE or FILM which become the seen picture produced by DEVELOPMENT. **l. 'period.** [Med.] The time in which a disease is present without giving signs of itself. [Physiol.] The time between the acting of a STIMU-LUS and the outer reaction, such as a motion, produced by it. **'latency,** n.

'laterad, adv. [Anat.] To the side; sideways.

'lateral, 1.a. Of, at, to, from, on, the side, sp. as opp. middle, base, or end; from side to side. 2.n. [Phonet.] Sound of *l* made with point of tongue against top teeth, so that the breath comes out at side(s) of tongue. **l. 'fissure.** [Zoo.] FISSURE OF SYLVIUS. **l. in'version.** [Optics] The INVERSION seen in the picture of a thing in a plane looking-glass, in which the left side of the thing is on the right side of the picture and the right on the left. **l. line** [Zoo.] Line down right and left of the body of a fish and other back-boned water-animals marking the position of a line of sense-CELLS (the **l. line 'organ**) which give a

reaction to changes in the PRESSURE or motion of the water. **l. mor'aine.** [Geol.] One or other of the two MORAINES regularly formed down the two sides of a GLACIER. **l. plane.** Sp. [Bot.] upright plane going through leaf, flower, etc. at right angles to the AXIS plane. **l. plate.** [Zoo.] In EMBRYOS of certain higher animals, the side part of the MESODERM. **l. 'ventricle.** [Zoo.] The inside hollow of one or the other of the CEREBRAL HEMISPHERES.

'lateri-, 'latero-.

'laterigrade, a. [Zoo.] Walking sideways.

'laterite, n. [Geol.] A sort of red earth produced by the weathering of certain ROCKS, formed chiefly of $Al(OH)_3$ and Fe_2O_5 and having very little SiO_2.

'latero'cranium, n. [Zoo.] Side part of insect's head.

'latex, n. [Bot., Chem.] Milk-like liquid, gen. white but sometimes yellow, made up of mixed fats, wax, and other substances and produced in special CELLS of some plants and trees, sp. rubber as got from the rubber-tree in this form.

lathe, n. [Mach.] A machine for cutting material such as wood and metal into desired, sp. rod-like, forms, or for making holes through it, cutting screws, polishing and so on, in which the cutting-part is kept fixed and the material turned round and round against it.

'lather, 1.n. The mass of very small BUBBLES produced when soap is rubbed between the hands in water or mixed with it by shaking and so on. 2.v.i. (Of soap and so on) get l. formed.

lati'ciferous, a. [Bot.] Producing or storing LATEX.

lati'rostal, a. [Zoo.] Having a wide BEAK.

la'tissimus 'dorsi, n. [Anat.] Wide flat muscle in back by which the arm is pulled back and down.

'latitude, n. [Geog., etc.] Position of a point on the earth given by the angle between the plane of the EQUATOR and the plane through the point and some other fixed point (gen. the middle of the earth), commonly measured north or south of the equator (*in. l.* 45° N., etc.), *see* PARALLEL. [Astron.] CELESTIAL LATI-TUDE. **lati'tudinal,** a.

lati'tudinal 'furrow. [Zoo.] In an OVUM undergoing division, a line of division over and parallel to the EQUATORIAL FURROW.

'lattice, n. Structure of lines, rails, etc. going across one another and forming a design of regular four-sided spaces, network. [Cryst.] The l. formed by lines joining the positions of the ATOMS in a CRYSTAL, picturing the regular structure which gives it its special properties.

'laudanum, n. [Chem., Med.] A TINCTURE

of OPIUM in alcohol used medically as a SEDATIVE.

'Laue 'pattern, 'Laue 'diagram. [Phys.] A design of black points on a camera-plate produced when a narrow parcel of X-RAYS is sent through a CRYSTAL to the camera, and representative of its distribution into separate rays as the effect of REFRACTION.

'laughing gas. [Chem.] N_2O (*nitrous oxide*) a gas with no colour and a somewhat sweet taste, used as a GENERAL ANAESTHETIC for small medical operations, sp. taking teeth out—so named because its first effect is to give a person an impulse to outbursts of laughing.

Lau'rentian, n. [Geol.] Naming or to do with the oldest group of GRANITIC ROCKS in Canada.

'Laurer-'Stieda ca'nal. [Zoo.] Pipe going from the meeting-point of the OVIDUCT and the VITELLINE DUCT in TREMATODA.

lauri'noxylon, n. [Geol.] FOSSIL wood.

'lava, n. [Geol.] The liquid ROCK-material sent out by a VOLCANO, or the solid rock which it later becomes. l. flow. Any ROCK formed from l., that is, formed of l. which has gone hard outside the earth, gen. very small-grained or glass-like. 'laval, a.

law of 'constant pro'portions. [Chem.] Law that any given COMPOUND is at all times made up of the same ELEMENTS in the same amounts in relation to one another.

law of e'quivalent pro'portions. [Chem.] The law that any ELEMENT may be united with another only in the RATIO of their CHEMICAL EQUIVALENTS.

law of mass 'action. [Chem.] The law that the rate at which a chemical reaction goes on between two or more substances is PROPORTIONAL to the CONCENTRATION of the substances.

law of 'multiple pro'portions. [Chem.] Law that when two ELEMENTS may be united into different COMPOUNDS, for the same amount of one element in all, the amounts of the other are such that the greater amounts are simple MULTIPLES of the smallest.

laws of re'flection. [Optics] When a ray of light is REFLECTED from a SURFACE:—1. The ANGLE OF INCIDENCE is equal to the ANGLE OF REFLECTION. 2. The INCIDENT ray, the reflected ray, and the NORMAL to the surface at the point of incidence are all in the same plane.

laws of re'fraction. [Optics] When a ray of light is REFRACTED on going from one MEDIUM to another:—1. The INCIDENT ray, the refracted ray, and the NORMAL to the SURFACE of the second medium at the point of incidence are all in the same plane. 2. The RATIO of the SINE of the ANGLE of INCIDENCE to that of the ANGLE OF REFLECTION is unchanging for the two media.

laws of 'thermody'namics. *See* THERMODYNAMICS.

lax, a. [Bot.] (Of flower-groups) loose. [Phonet.] (Of VOWELS) said with tongue and muscles somewhat loose, as in 'bit' 'put'.

'laxative, n. [Med.] APERIENT.

laxi-. Loose.

'layer, n. Flat stretch of material, thin in relation to its size, covering something or forming one unit in a structure of such ll., one on top of the other, as the two ll. of man's skin, the ll. of which certain ROCKS are formed.

lb., Sign for POUND (unit of weight).

'leaching, n. [Chem.] Process of washing out some part of a mixed solid by draining water or some chemical liquid through it. [Geol., Bot.] The washing away of MINERAL SALTS from the earth by water draining through it. leach, v.t. Make (a solid) undergo 1.; get (a substance) washed *out* of a solid by l.

lead, n. Chemical ELEMENT, at. no. 82, at. wt. 207·21, sign Pb, a blue-grey metal of great weight. l. 'chamber. Vessel with walls coated with l., used in making H_2SO_4 by the operation of NO_2 on SO_4 in the l-'chamber 'process. l. line. SOUNDING LINE. l-burning. The process of joining two bits of l. together by heating the edges with flame until they become liquid. l. soap. *See* SOAP.

lead, 1.n. [Engin.] In steam engines, the amount by which the inlet or outlet VALVE is open at the end of the STROKE; in INTERNAL COMBUSTION ENGINES, the distance of the PISTON from the end of the COMPRESSION STROKE when IGNITION takes place. [Elec.] An electric wire, cord, etc.; the angle between the line joining the BRUSHES of a DYNAMO and the line joining the ALTERNATING POLES; (of a process or effect) the condition of leading, or the amount by which it leads, another, sp. of current in relation to E.M.F. or the other way round. 2.v.i. and t. (Of process or effect) be earlier, quicker in coming about than (some other in connection with which it takes place). 'l.-in, n. [Radio] That part of an ANTENNA wire joining the indoor apparatus to the outdoor antennae system.

'leader, n. [Bot.] The highest part of a chief AXIS of a tree. [Meteor.] The first part of a FLASH of LIGHTNING.

leaf, n. [Bot.] An outgrowth from the stem of a plant, gen. with flat blade on a short stem, and green in colour, which is specially designed for the work of PHOTO-SYNTHESIS and TRANSPIRATION (foliage l.); any plant-part of like form and development but different purpose,

LEAF FORMS (not to scale)

COMPOUND

(ODD) PINNATE   BI-PINNATE   PALMATE—TRIFOLIATE   PALMATE—QUINQUEFOLIATE

SIMPLE

LYRATE   LINEAR   ELLIPTIC—DENATE   PALMATISECT   OBLONG—SINUATE

OBLANCEOLATE—DENTATE   CORDATE—SERRATE   OBOVATE—CRENATE   LANCEOLATE—ENTIRE   SPATULATE

ORBICULATE   PANDURIFORM   PELTATE   ACUMINATE—INCISED

LOBED   PINNATISECT   MULTICOSTATE   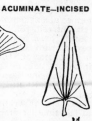   HASTATE

as a SEPAL, a PETAL, a SPOROPHYLL, etc.
l. gap. An opening in the structure of a
STELE where a l. trace goes out. **l. mosaic.**
See MOSAIC. **l. mould.** HUMUS produced
chiefly from dead leaves. **l. trace.** The
VASCULAR material branching out from
a STELE to the base of a l.

'leaflet, n. [Bot.] Any of the divisions of a
COMPOUND LEAF; a small leaf. [Zoo.] Any
leaf-like part, sp., in man, any of the
3 divisions of the DIAPHRAGM.

leak, 1.n. Hole or other way by which
liquid, gas, or electric current gets away
from a vessel or system in small amounts.
2.v.i. Get away through l(l). **'leakage,** n.
Leaking; amount of anything getting
away by leaking; part of MAGNETIC FIELD
not in position to be of use, as that round
a DYNAMO outside the ARMATURE.
'leaky, a. Having a l. or ll.

lean, a. Poor in quality or amount, sp.: of
potter's CLAY, not fully PLASTIC; of coal,
producing little gas when heated; of
ORE, having in it little MINERAL of value.

leap year. *See* YEAR.

least 'action. *See* PRINCIPLE OF L.A.

Le'blanc 'process. [Chem.] Old process for
making SODA ASH (Na_2CO_3) by heating
Na_2So_4, $CaCO_3$, and C together.

Le Cha'telier 'principle. [Phys.] The law
that if a SYSTEM of PHASES in EQUILI-
BRIUM is acted on by an outside force,
the system will have a tendency to undo
the effect of the force by changes in
itself.

'lecher wires. [Radio] Apparatus in form of
two parallel wires near together, used as
RESONATOR for short electric waves.

-'lecithal, a. [Zoo.] (Of egg) having a YOLK
of the sort named.

'lecithin, n. [Biochem.] Any of certain
complex substances, formed chiefly of
FATTY ACIDS and P, present in animals
and plants, sp. in brain and nerve substance, in the YOLK of eggs, and in
LEUCOCYTES.

'lecithoblast, n. [Zoo.] In eggs undergoing
division only in part, the BLASTOMERES
with YOLK in them, as opp. the BLASTO-
DERM. **'lecithocoel,** n. The BLASTOCOEL
of an egg which undergoes complete
division. **'lecithophore,** n. Skin on inside
of an egg-YOLK.

'lecitho'protein. [Biochem.] Any substance
formed of a LECITHIN and a PROTEIN.

Le'clanché cell. [Elec.] Current-producing
electric CELL having a CATHODE of C
covered with MnO_2 and an ANODE of Zn
in a SOLUTION of NH_4Cl, commonly made
into a DRY CELL by the addition of something changing the solution into a paste.

Le'duc ef'fect. RIGHI-LEDUC EFFECT.

leech, n. [Zoo.] Any worm of the HIRU-
DINEA, sp. the sort much used medically
at one time for draining blood from ill

person. [Med.] An apparatus formed of a
cutting part and a pipe, used for the
same purpose as a l.

lees, n.pl. The solid substance put down by
a liquid, sp. wine, in its vessel.

left-'handed, a. Going round, or having a
structure twisting, in the opposite
direction to the hands of a clock, as a *l.-h.
screw*, one screwing in in this direction.

left heart. [Anat.] The left AURICLE and
VENTRICLE of the heart.

'legume, n. [Bot.] A DRY fruit formed of
one CARPEL, gen. having two parts and
opening at the two joins when ready,
with a line of seeds on the inside of the
back join; plant producing ll. **le'gumin-
ous,** a. (*See* p. 158.)

le'gumin, n. [Biochem.] A GLOBULIN present
in the seeds of LEGUMINOUS plants.

'leio-. Smooth: **'-sporous,** a. [Bot.]

leio'trichous, a. [Anthrop.] Straight-haired.

'lemma, n. [Bot.] In the SPIKELET of a grass
that one of the two GLUMES at the base of
a flower from which the flower comes.

'Lemur'oidea, n.pl. [Zoo.] A SUB-ORDER of
PRIMATES made up of animals very like
the smaller monkeys but with pointed
faces, great eyes, a wool-like covering,
and tails without gripping-power. **'lemur,**
n. Animal of the L.

'Lenard rays. [Phys.] The rays going through
the window of a Lenard tube. **Lenard
tube.** A VACUUM TUBE having a very thin
window of Al opposite the CATHODE
through which the cathode rays get out
into the air.

length, n. The measure of a thing from one
end to the other, gen. at its longest part;
the measure of any distance or line
between two points.

len'itic, a. [Biol.] Living in quiet inland
waters.

'lenitive, n., a. [Med.] (Substance) making
pain less sharp, keeping off IRRITATION.

Le'noir cycle. [Engin.] The TWO-STROKE
CYCLE, without COMPRESSION, at first
used in the INTERNAL COMBUSTION
ENGINE.

lens, n. [Optics, etc.] Bit of glass or other
TRANSPARENT substance having two
opposite, gen. round, faces, at least one
of which is curved in or out, so that light-
rays going through the glass are bent, and
parallel rays may be made to come to, or
to seem to come from, a point, so forming
an IMAGE (*simple l.*); two or more simple
ll. used in connection with one another
in a camera, TELESCOPE or other instrument for forming images or helping the
eye; apparatus producing like effect on
CATHODE-rays and sound-rays; thing
formed like the sort of l. having its two
faces curved out. [Zoo.] Structure in eye
doing the work of a l. and forming on the
RETINA an IMAGE of what is before it.

'lenticel, n. [Bot.] Any of the small air inlets formed of cork CELLS in the hard outer parts of the stems of plants such as trees.

'lenticle, n. [Geol.] A LENS-formed mass of some substance present in a mass of some other substance.

lenti'conus, n. [Med.] Unnormal outcurving of the LENS of the eye into the form of a CONE.

len'ticular, a. Formed like a LENS with its two faces curved out; to do with l. nucleus. l. 'nucleus. [Anat.] The greater and outer NUCLEUS of the CORPUS STRIATUM. l. 'process. [Zoo.] The end of the INCUS of the ear by which it is joined to the STAPES.

len'ticulate, a. [Bot.] Meeting in a sharp edge; having LENTICELS.

'lentiform, a. LENTICULAR.

len'tigerous, a. [Zoo.] (Of eye) having a CRYSTALLINE LENS.

'lentil, n. [Geol.] STRATUM of limited size and thinner at edges than in the middle, coming between strata of different material.

Lenz's law. [Elec.] Law that the direction of a current produced by ELECTROMAGNETIC INDUCTION is such that the change in MAGNETIC FLUX caused by it is opposite in direction to the change in flux causing it.

'Leo, n. [Astron.] The 5th SIGN OF THE ZODIAC.

'leper, n. [Med.] Person having LEPROSY.

'lepidophyte, n. [Geol.] A FOSSIL plant of the group FILICALES.

Lepi'doptera, n.pl. [Zoo.] An ORDER of ENDOPTERYGOTE insects having 4 almost equal wings of great size and freq. beautiful colouring, covered with very small SCALES, and a pipe-like mouthpart. lepi'dopterous, a.

'lepidote, a. [Biol.] Covered with very small SCALES or scale-like hairs.

'lepido'trichia, n.pl. [Zoo.] The bone-like, branching, JOINTED FIN-RAYS of fish with a framework of hard bone.

lepo'spondylous, a. [Zoo.] Having VERTEBRAE with a CONSTRICTION in the middle.

'lepra, n. LEPROSY. 'lepric, a.

'leprose, n. [Bot., Zoo.] Covered with small loose bits of skin.

'leprosy, n. [Med.] A serious CHRONIC disease, INFECTIOUS but not EPIDEMIC, seen chiefly in warm countries, caused by a BACILLUS and marked by the forming of NODULES on the skin and inside the mouth and throat, the falling out of hair and nails, the destruction of the bones of the hands and feet, and a loss of the power of feeling. 'leprous, a.

-'lepsy, [Med.] Sudden and violent attack.

'lepto-. Narrow, small, feeble, thin. 'lepto-ce'phalia, n. [Med.] Condition in which head is very narrow. 'lepto-ce'phalic, -'cephaloid, -'cephalous, aa.

'lepto-'cephalus, n. [Zoo.] The LARVA of ANGUILLIDAE, a flat, thin, transparent animal with a very narrow head.

lepto'cerc-al, -ous, aa. [Zoo.] (Of tail of fish or PROTOZOA), narrowing to a long, thin point; having a l. tail.

lepto'dactylous, a. [Zoo.] Having thin fingers or toes.

lepto'derm-ous, -ic, -atous, aa. [Zoo.] Having a thin skin.

'Leptome'dusae, n.pl. [Zoo.] An ORDER of HYDROZOA having HYDROTHECAE and GONOTHECAE. 'leptome'dusa (leptome-dusae), n. A MEDUSA of the sort produced by the L.

lep'tometer, n. Instrument measuring the viscosity of oil by the number of drops falling through an opening of a certain size in a certain time.

lepto'nema, n. LEPTOTENE STAGE.

'leptophloem, n. [Bot.] PHLOEM at an early stage of development.

'leptosome, a. [Of person) tall and thin.

'leptospo'rangiate, a. [Bot.] (Of FILICALES) having every SPORANGIUM formed from one CELL.

'leptotene stage. [Biol.] Early stage in MEIOSIS at which the CHROMATIN is in the form of thin threads.

lepto'xylem, n. [Bot.] Wood TISSUE at an early stage of development.

'lesion, n. [Med.] Any wound, or any part marked by a diseased change of structure, in a TISSUE of the body.

'lethal, a. Causing death. l. 'factor. [Med.] GENE making it impossible for offspring to be produced living, or with power of going on living. le'thality, n. [Med.] Sp., the RATIO of the number of deaths caused by a disease to the number of persons having it.

'lethargy, n. [Med.] Unnatural condition in which person has tendency to go on sleeping, and, when awake, takes no interest in anything and seems unable to make any attempt at moving or acting.

'leucine, n. [Biochem.] A white, solid AMINO ACID produced when PROTEINS are broken up.

leuci'nuria, n. [Med.] Condition in which LEUCINE is present in a person's URINE.

'leucite, n. [Geol.] A natural SILICATE of K and Al present sp. in LAVAS.

leuco-. White.

'leuco base or 'leuco 'compound. [Chem.] Any of a group of substances without colour formed by taking O from DYES, and, able to be changed back into dyes again by uniting with O.

'leucoblast, n. [Zoo.] A LEUCOCYTE at an early stage of development.

leu'cocidin, leu'kocidin, n. [Med.] Any substance causing destruction of LEUCOCYTES.

leuco'cratic, a. [Geol.] (Of IGNEOUS ROCK)

light-coloured as the effect of having in it much FELDSPAR and little iron, etc.

leuco'cyan, n. [Bot.] A blue-green colouring-substance present in PHAOPHYCEAE and DIATOMS.

'leucocyte, n. [Zoo.] A sort of white or un-coloured CELL present in the blood and LYMPH of a great number of animals, and having the power of AMOEBOID motion. **'leucocy'th(a)emia,** n. LEUKAEMIA. **'leucocyto'genesis,** n. **'leucocytoge'netic,** a. **'leucocy'tolysis,** n. Destruction of ll. **'leucocyto'penia,** n. [Med.] Condition of having smaller number of ll. than normal. **'leucocyto'penic** a. **'leucocy'tosis,** n. An increase in the number of ll. in the blood seen in certain diseases, and to a small degree in certain healthy conditions, for example, when food is undergoing diges-tion after a meal. **'leucocy'turia,** n. [Med.] Condition in which there are ll. in person's URINE.

'leuco'penia, n. [Med.] A condition in which the number of LEUCOCYTES in the blood becomes less. **'leucopenic,** a.

'leucophore, n. [Biol.] CELL with yellow colouring-substance; IRIDOCYTE.

leuco'plakia, n. [Med.] The forming of a hard, smooth, white SURFACE on an INFLAMED part, gen. a sign of SYPHILIS when it takes place inside the mouth.

'leucoplast(id), n. [Bot.] PLASTID without colour, round which STARCH grains are formed, in the inner parts of plant sub-stance to which light does not get.

leucopoi'esis, n. [Zoo.] The forming of LEUCOCYTES. **'leucopoietic,** a.

leucor'rh(o)ea, n. [Med.] A thick white or yellow liquid coming from the VAGINA as effect of CONGESTION of the MUCOUS MEMBRANE, freq. at the start of the first time of MENSTRUATION.

leu'costasis, n. [Med.] The stopping of the CIRCULATION as effect of the massing together of LEUCOCYTES.

leu'cotomy, n. [Med.] The operation of cutting into the front LOBE of the brain and through NERVE FIBRES as a way of helping certain mind troubles. **'leuco-tome,** n. A narrow blade turning in a CANNULA which is used in l.

leuco'toxic, a. [Med.] (Of substance) causing destruction of LEUCOCYTES.

leu'k(a)emia, n. [Med.] Diseased condition in which LEUCOCYTES are over-produced, causing a great increase in the size of the SPLEEN and gen. death; LYMPHO-CYTHAEMIA.

'leuko-. LEUCO-.

le'vator, n. [Zoo.] Any muscle for lifting a part of body.

'leveé, n. Earthwork put up to keep river in its bed; a low wall of earth formed down flat sides of some rivers by natural processes.

'level, n. Any of a number of instruments dependent on a l. tube, used by builders, SURVEYORS, etc. for testing if a thing is HORIZONTAL, measuring distances be-tween levels, and so on. [Med.] Amount of a given substance present at any time in the blood or other body liquid. [Phys.] See ENERGY L. **l. tube.** Shut glass pipe not quite full of alcohol, so that there is room for a small, readily-seen BUBBLE of air which goes to the middle of the pipe when this is truly HORIZONTAL. **'levelling,** n. In SURVEYING, the operation of taking measures, etc., by the use of a l.

'lever, n. [Mech.] Rod or other RIGID body supported at and turning on a point in it named the *fulcrum*, so that a force acting on it at a distance from the fulcrum has the effect of producing a greater force at a point nearer to the fulcrum, used for lifting weights and so on.

levi'gation, n. [Chem.] Process of getting a substance into the form of a smooth dust, sp. by powdering it in water and then taking out the grains of greater size which are the first to come to the base of the vessel. **'levigate,** v.t.

levi'tate, v.t. and i. (Make) go up, against the pull of the earth's attraction, as if having no weight, as the body seems to do in sleep-experiences. **'levi'tation,** n.

levo-. LAEVO-.

Le'wisian gneiss. [Geol.] The oldest ROCK in Britain, seen in north-west Scotland and its islands, formed in the earlier part of the PRE-CAMBRIAN and of CRYSTALLINE structure.

'lewisite, n. [Chem.] An oil-like liquid used as a, 'poison gas' in war, causing serious BLISTERING and sometimes death.

'Lewis's 'theory. [Phys.] The theory that it is possible for ATOMS to become united by having one or more ELECTRONS in common.

lexi'cology, n. Science of the senses of words and their development from earlier words. **'lexico'logical,** a. **lexi'cologist,** n.

'Leyden jar. [Elec.] CONDENSER formed of a covered glass vessel coated with metal inside and out almost to the top, with a rod touching the inner coat and going through the cover, so that, by putting it in connection with an electric machine, the inner coat becomes CHARGED with POSITIVE or NEGATIVE ELECTRICITY and the outer coat with its opposite.

'Leydig's duct. [Zoo.] WOLFIAN DUCT. **'Leydig's 'organs.** Small structures in the feelers of some ARTHROPODA which probably have to do with the sense of smell.

Li, Sign for LITHIUM.

li'ana, n. [Bot.] Any plant which goes up trees or other supports, sp. one of the hard-stemmed sort, making great growth, common in TROPICAL countries.

'Lias or Li'assic 'System. [Geol.] A SYSTEM of ROCKS in Britain forming the oldest division of European JURASSIC.

li'bido, n. [Psych.] The driving-force at the root of the behaviour of men and women —in Freud's system, the sex-impulse, in the systems of other writers the general impulse to go on living. **li'bidinal,** a.

'Libra, n. [Astron.] The 7th SIGN OF THE ZODIAC.

li'bration, n. [Astron.] True or seeming motion forward and back like that of the pointer of an instrument before coming to rest. **l. of the moon.** Any of three effects (**l. in longitude, l. in latitude,** and **diurnal l.**) in which parts of the moon near its edge are seen and not seen in turn as if it underwent a slow l.

lice, n.pl. See LOUSE.

'Lichenes, n.pl. [Bot.] A great group of plants, made up of a FUNGUS and an ALGA so united as to seem one plant. **'lichen,** n. Any sort or plant of the L. **'lichen-ic, -oid,** aa. **'lichenism,** n. The SYMBIOSIS between FUNGI and ALGAE producing L. **liche'nology,** n.

lid, n. [Bot.] OPERCULUM. **l. cell.** [Bot.] A CELL forming the top or cover of some part, sp. one of those shutting the neck of an ARCHEGONIUM till the development of the egg-cell is complete.

'Lieberkuhn's crypts, n.pl. [Zoo.] Pipe-like GLANDS present in the inner coat of the SMALL INTESTINE in back-boned animals.

lien, n. [Zoo.] SPLEEN. **'lienal,** a. **lien(o)-.**)

'Liesegang rings. [Phys.-Chem.] Bands of a PRECIPITATE with clear spaces between them, freq. formed in PRECIPITATION from a GEL. **'Liesegang phe'nomenon.** The forming of L. rings.

'life-'cycle, n. [Biol.] The different stages through which a plant or animal goes from the start of its development to the producing of a form like that from which it came, or, where there is no ALTER-NATION OF GENERATIONS, to its death.

life 'history. [Biol.] The history of the changes through which a unit plant or animal goes from birth to death, some-times the same thing as a LIFE CYCLE, sometimes covering only part of it.

lift, n. In AERODYNAMICS, that force sup-porting an airplane in flight.

'lift-pump, n. [Mach.] The commonest sort of pump for lifting a liquid, gen. water, acting by taking away the air from the pump pipe and so causing the liquid to be forced up and out of it by the air round the pipe pushing on the liquid.

'ligament, n. [Zoo.] Strong band or cord of TISSUE joining bones or keeping ORGANS in place. **liga'mentous,** a.

'ligature, n. [Med.] A bit of thread or like

substance used for knotting tightly round anything, sp. round blood-vessels to keep the blood in while an operation is being done, etc. **'ligate,** v.t. Put a l. on. **li'gation,** n.

light, a. Of little weight. **l. 'alloy.** Any mixed metal of which Al or Mg is the chief part. **l. 'metals.** Metals of less DENSITY than 4, for example Li, Be, Na, Mg, Al, K, Ca, etc. **l. oils.** [Chem.] The oils produced from TAR whose boiling-points are between 100°C and 210°C. **'-ness,** n.

light, n. [Phys.] The form of RADIANT ENERGY whose effect on the eye is the cause of seeing, moving at a rate of 186,326 MILES per second, and whose WAVE-LENGTHS are between ·0000385 mm. and ·0000765 mm.; like rays com-ing outside these limits which have not this special effect on the eye but are in other ways like l.-rays. **l.-'negative,** a. Having less electric CONDUCTIVITY when acted on by l. **l.-'positive,** a. Having more electric CONDUCTIVITY when acted on by l. **l. 'quantum.** PHOTON. **l. 'ratio.** [Astron.] The number $2 \cdot 512$, which is the RATIO from step to step in the scale of star MAGNITUDES. **'l.-year.** [Astron.] The distance covered by light in one year = 63,290 ASTRONOMICAL UNITS, or about 6 million million MILES, used in measuring great distances in space. **'-ness,** n. The degree to which a body sends back the light falling on it as experienced by the eye, that is, LUMIN-ANCE FACTOR as judged by sense; of a colour, its place on the scale between black and white, how near to or far from white it is in comparison with other shades of the same colour.

'lightning, n. [Meteor.] Sudden line or flame of light across the sky caused by an electric DISCHARGE from a thunder cloud. **l. con'ductor, l. rod.** Pointed rod of metal on the top of a building from which a CONDUCTOR goes down to a metal plate in the earth, for the purpose of NEUTRALIZING a l. DISCHARGE or guiding it quickly to earth so that there is less chance of the building being fired by it.

'ligneous, a. [Bot.] Of or like wood.

lig'nescent, a. [Bot.] In the process of forming, changing into, wood.

ligni-, lign(o)-. Wood: **lig'niferous,** a. [Bot.], **lig'niverous,** a. [Zoo.]

ligni'fication, n. [Bot.] Process by which the CELL-walls of plants are made thick by the addition of LIGNIN, so forming wood substance. **'lignify,** v.t. and i. (Make) undergo l. **'lignified,** a.

'lignin, n. [Bot.] Complex substance the addition of which to their walls by cer-tain CELLS of plants makes wood, of which, with CELLULOSE, it is the chief part.

'lignite, n. [Geol.] Dark-brown coal-like

substance formed of FOSSIL wood at an incomplete stage of its development into coal.

ligno'cellulose, n. [Chem.] Any of a number ot substances formed of LIGNIN and CELLULOSE present in wood and other plant FIBRES.

'lignose, n. [Chem.] A form of CELLULOSE.

'ligroin, n. [Chem.] Part of natural PETROLEUM boiling between 90°C and 120°C.

'ligula, n. [Biol.] A band-like or tongue-like structure. [Anat.] A band of white substance in the wall of the 4th VENTRICLE of the brain. [Zoo.] In insects, structure between the LABIAL PALPS.

ligulate, a. [Biol.] Formed like a band, long, flat and narrow. [Bot.] (Of flowers) having l. PETALS or (of plant) l. flowers.

'liguli-. LIGULATE: **-'florous,** a. [Bot.]

limb, n. [Zoo.] Arm, leg or wing. [Geol.] One or other of the two sides of an ANTICLINE or SYNCLINE. [Astron.] Edge of body in the sky, sp. the sun or moon. [Bot.] Blade of leaf; the wide end-part of a PETAL whose base is stem-like or of a flower with petals united into a pipe opening out into a wide-edged mouth.

'limbate, lim'biferous, aa. [Biol.] Having a LIMBUS.

'limbic lobe. [Anat.] A LOBE of the brain going almost completely round the CORPUS CALLOSUM.

'limbous, a. [Zoo.] (Of SUTURE) with one edge going over the other a little.

'limbus, n. [Biol.] Edge of part when different in colour or structure from the rest, an edging band.

lime, n. [Chem.] CALCIUM OXIDE (CaO), a white CAUSTIC substance produced by heating some natural form of CALCIUM CARBONATE (CaCO₃) such as limestone, used in building, farming, the making of chemicals, etc. **'-light,** n. Light used in old days for lighting stage, produced by turning a flame of burning H and O onto a body of l. **'-stone,** n. [Geol.] SEDIMENTARY ROCK formed chiefly of CaCO₃, sometimes with MgCO₃, from which l. is got by heating. **'-water,** n. [Chem., Med.] CALCIUM HYDROXIDE (Ca(OH)₂) in water, used medically for an acid condition of the stomach, and in chemistry and the making of chemicals.

'limen, n. [Psych., Physiol.] THRESHOLD. **'liminal,** a.

li'micolous, a. [Zoo.] Living in wet sticky earth.

'limits of audi'bility. [Acous.] The limits of the range of FREQUENCIES of sound-waves having an effect on the sense of hearing, for man roughly from 20 to 20,000 per second.

li'mivorous, a. [Zoo.] Taking in wet, sticky earth as food.

lim'netic, a. [Biol.] To do with living in,

FRESH inland waters or wet places.

'limnobi'otic, lim'nophilous, aa. [Zoo.] Living in FRESH inland waters.

limno'plankton, n. [Biol.] FRESH-WATER PLANKTON.

'limonite, n. [Mineral.] An important ORE of iron, Fe₂O₃.H₂O, produced by natural processes from FeCO₃ and Fe₃O₄, and taking a number of forms, gen. dark brown or yellow in colour.

'linchpin, n. [Mach.] Pin put through end of rod on which wheel is fixed to keep it from slipping off.

line, n. [Phys.] LINE OF FORCE as a unit measuring MAGNETIC FLUX, = MAXWELL.

'linea, a. [Biol.] Line-like structure or mark.

'linear, a. Of, to do with, formed of, a line or lines; forming, placed in, a straight line; of, to do with, LENGTH. [Biol.] Band-like or thread-like in form, longer than it is wide and with edges almost completely parallel, said sp. of leaf (*see* picture p. 223). **l. ac'celerator.** [Phys.] Apparatus for increasing the rate of motion of IONS to high ENERGIES, formed of a line of ELECTRODES with very small spaces between, the 1st, 3rd, 5th etc. being in connection with one another and forming one group, and the 2nd, 4th, 6th etc. forming another group, with a high-FREQUENCY POTENTIAL between. **l. measure.** System of units for measuring lines, that is, distance, or size in one DIMENSION. **l. 'oscillator.** [Phys.] System of two parts in connection (for example two balls joined by a rubber cord) VIBRATING in the direction of the line joining them.

line of force, or **flux,** or **in'duction,** etc. [Phys.] A line representative of the direction of an electric or MAGNETIC force etc. in an electric or magnetic FIELD, all the lines together giving a picture of the distribution of the force etc., and so spaced that the number going through 1 cm² at right angles to them is a measure of the amount of the force etc. at any place.

'lineolate, a. [Biol.] Marked with thin lines.

line 'organ. [Zoo.] *See* LATERAL LINE.

'liner, n. A separate thin metal cover slipped inside a hollow machine-part to keep it from damage by rubbing, heat, etc.

lines of 'longitude. MERIDIANS OF LONGITUDE.

line 'spectrum. [Phys.] A SPECTRUM in which only certain WAVELENGTHS are present, so that it takes the form of a number of clear-cut lines with spaces between.

line test. [Med.] A test for the forming of bone based on the operation of light on a bone which has been acted on by SILVER NITRATE (AgNO₃), used in the disease of RICKETS.

'lingua, n. [Zoo.] Tongue or tongue-like

structure, sp. of insect; the floor of the mouth in ACARINA. **'lingual,** 1.a. To do with l.; tongue-like; to do with RADULA of MOLLUSCS. [Phonet.] (Of sound) made with the tongue. 2.n. L. sound.

lin'guistics, n. The science of language.

'lingula, n. [Zoo.] Part formed like a small tongue. **'lingulate,** a. Sp. [Bot.] Somewhat thicker and wider than LIGULATE.

linguo-. [Zoo.] Tongue. [Phonet.] LINGUAL (and . . .):— **'linguodental,** n., a.

'liniment, n. [Med.] Liquid for rubbing into the skin, for helping stiff JOINTS, overworked or damaged muscles, etc.

'linin, n. [Biol.] The FIBROUS substance forming the network of a CELL NUCLEUS, not coloured by STAINS.

'link, 1.n. One ring of a chain; a machine-part, such as a rod, making a connection between other, sp. moving, parts. [Chem.] BOND. 2.v.t. Get (loosely) joined, (as) by l. **'-age,** n. Sp.: [Eng.] A system of ll. [Chem.] BOND. [Biol.] The tendency of certain GENES or qualities to be handed down to offspring together. [Elec.] Number of lines of MAGNETIC force going through a COIL × the number of turns of wire. **linkage group.** [Biol.] A group of GENES having linkage. **linked,** a. Joined as by a l. [Biol.] Having linkage.

Lin'naean, a. [Biol.] To do with the system of CLASSIFICATION of plants and animals started by Linnaeus and gen. used till the present system came in, or with the way of naming by GENUS and SPECIES which was his invention and is still used.

li'noxyn, n. [Chem.] An elastic solid formed when LINSEED OIL becomes united with O.

'linseed oil. An oil got from the seeds of the linen plant, having in it more I than any other fat has, with the property of forming elastic coats when dry, used sp. in making paint but having other purposes.

lint, n. [Med.] Cotton or linen rubbed up on one side so as to be thick and soft, used for dressings.

lip, n. [Zoo.] One or other of the two soft folds round the opening of the mouth in man and other animals. [Biol.] Any l.-like structure, sp. [Bot.] LABELLUM. **lipped,** a. Having l(l).; LABIATE. **l. cell.** [Bot.] A CELL at the point where the opening of a SPORANGIUM takes place.

li'p(a)emia, n. [Med.] Condition in which overmuch fat is present in the blood.

'lipase, n. [Biochem.] Any of a group of ENZYMES effecting the digestion of FATS by getting them broken up into ALCOHOLS and ACIDS.

'lipid(e), n. [Biochem.] Any of the group of complex substances present in plants and animals having the properties of a FAT, that is, the fats themselves and other substances having in them FATTY ACIDS not SOLUBLE in water.

'lipin(e), n. [Biochem.] Any of the more complex LIPIDES.

lip(o)-. [Zoo., Chem.] Fat: **li'pogenous,** a. [Zoo.] **'-'protein,** n. [Chem.]

'lipochrome, n. [Biochem.] A general name for yellow to orange-red colouring-substances present in animals or their produce, for example in butter fat.

lipo'clastic, a. [Biochem.] (Of ENZYMES) having the power of getting FATS broken up into the FATTY ACIDS and GLYCERIN.

lipo'gastry, n. [Zoo.] Loss for a time of the hollow acting as a stomach, as in some sponges.

'lipoid, 1.a. [Chem.] FAT-like (substance), sp. fat-like and having in it N; LIPIN. **li'poid-al, -ic,** aa.

lipoi'd(a)emia, n. [Med.] Condition in which LIPOIDS are present in the blood, sp. in great amount.

li'polysis, n. [Biochem.] Process of getting FAT broken up. **lipo'lytic,** a.

li'poma, n. [Med.] An unnormal growth formed of fat.

li'pomerism, n. [Zoo.] In a METAMERIC animal, condition in which the metameric structure is not kept up, caused by overgrowth or some change in the position of the divisions.

li'postomy, n. [Zoo.] Loss for a time of the mouth-opening, as in sponges.

'Lipowitz' 'alloy. [Metal.] An ALLOY of Bi (50%), Pb (27%), Sn (13%) and Cd 10%) which is FUSIBLE.

li'poxenous, a. [Biol.] Of a PARASITE, going from the HOST before completing its development. **li'poxeny,** n.

li'puria, n. [Med.] Condition in which fat is present in the URINE.

li'quation, n. [Metal.] Process of separating one metal from another by heating the mixed metal to a point at which only one of them becomes liquid. **'liquate,** v.t.

'liquefy, v.t. and i. Get or become changed (from a gas or solid) to a, liquid. **lique-'faction,** n. **lique'factive,** a. **'liquified,** a. **'liquefier,** n. Apparatus for liquefying a gas etc. **lique'fiable,** a. **li'quescent,** a. With a tendency to become, or in the process of becoming, liquid.

'liquid, n., a. [Phys.] (Substance) in a condition between that of a solid and that of a gas, that is, whose MOLECULES are moving freely among themselves but without any tendency to become separated, so that the form is not fixed though the amount of space taken up by a given weight is almost unchanging. **l. air.** Air made l. by undergoing first great COMPRESSION and then great loss of heat by expansion till it gets to a TEMPERATURE lower than the boiling-point of its chief gases, used in REFRIGERATION. **l. 'crystal.** [Chem.] A l. having certain properties of CRYSTALS, such as BIREFRINGENCE. **l. 'measure.** System of units for measuring ll.

'liquido'genic, liqui'dogenous, aa. Liquid-forming.

'liquidus (curve), n. [Phys.-Chem.] A GRAPH giving the relation between changes in the PROPORTIONS of the metals forming a given mixed metal and changes in the TEMPERATURES at which its MELTING is completed.

liquo'crystalline, a. [Chem.] Being, to do with, a LIQUID CRYSTAL.

'liquor, n. [Med.] A SOLUTION of a medical substance in water. **l. 'amnii.** [Zoo.] AMNIOTIC FLUID. **l. 'scarpae.** Liquid inside LABYRINTH of ear. **l. co'tunni.** Liquid between LABYRINTHS of ear.

'Lissajou's 'figure. [Phys.] Curve representative of the motion of a point moved by two SIMPLE HARMONIC MOTIONS acting at right-angles to one another, for example, that of the end of a PENDULUM hanging from another pendulum moving at right-angles to it.

'literature, n. The writings on any given question, sp. the printed records of a SCIENTIFIC society, etc.

'lithanode, n. [Elec., Eng.] PbO$_2$ as used in ACCUMULATOR plates.

li'tharge, n. [Chem.] A red-yellow CRYSTALLINE substance, PbO (*lead monoxide*), used in the making of glass, paint, rubber and in other industries.

'lithia, n. [Chem.] LITHIUM MONOXIDE (Li$_2$O), a white CRYSTALLINE substance, formed by heating Li in air.

li'thiasis, n. [Med.] The forming of CALCULI as effect of overmuch URIC ACID in the blood.

'lithite, n. [Zoo.] A stone-like mass forming part of the ORGANS of hearing or balance, such as a LITHOCYST, in some animals.

'lithium, n. Chemical ELEMENT, at. no. 3, at. wt. 6·940, sign Li, the metal of least weight.

'litho-. Stone. [Med.] CALCULUS.

'lithocyst, n. [Zoo.] Small bag-like part with an inner coat of sense-CELLS and one or more freely-moving LITHITES inside, having to do with the sense of balance and possibly hearing in some lower animals.

li'thodomous, a. [Zoo.] Living in ROCKS.

litho'genesis, n. [Med.] The forming of calculi.

li'thogenous, a. [Zoo.] Rock-building, as certain CORALS.

li'thography, n. Process of printing from a stone or metal plate which is wetted where uncut and then inked with an ink having oil in it so that no coat is formed on the wet parts. **'lithograph,** n. A print produced by l. **litho'graphic,** a.

li'thoidal, a. Like a stone, having structure of stone.

li'thology, n. [Geol.] Science of ROCK structure.

li'thophagous, a. [Zoo.] Taking small stones into stomach for purpose of crushing food, as birds; LITHOTOMOUS.

li'thophilous, a. [Biol.] Having growth or living-place on or in stones.

'lithophyll, n. [Geol.] A FOSSIL leaf.

'lithophysa (lithophysae), n. [Geol.] A round hollow, freq. with a number of walls one inside the other, formed by gas in some LAVAS. **litho'physal,** a.

'lithophyte, n. [Bot.] Plant living on or among stones.

'lithopone, n. A white paint formed of roughly $\frac{2}{3}$ BARIUM SULPHATE (BaSO$_4$) and $\frac{1}{3}$ ZINC SULPHIDE (ZnS).

'lithosphere, n. [Geol.] The part of the earth which has become solid, that is, the outer part as opp. the liquid and gas in the middle.

li'thotomous, a. [Zoo.] BORING into stone, as some MOLLUSCS.

lith'otomy, n. [Med.] The operation of cutting into the URINARY BLADDER to take out a CALCULUS. **'litho'tomic,** a.

'lithous, a. [Med.] Like, made of same material as, a CALCULUS.

li'thuria, n. [Med.] Condition in which there is overmuch URIC ACID in the URINE.

'litmus, n. [Chem.] A colouring substance got from certain LICHENES which has the property of turning red when wet with an acid and blue when wet with an ALKALI. **l. paper.** Paper coated with l. used in making chemical tests.

'litre, 'liter, nn. Unit of VOLUME in the METRIC SYSTEM, being that of 1000 gm. of water at 4°C=1000·027 cc.

'litter, n. [Zoo.] All the young produced by an animal such as a dog or a pig at one birth.

'litter, n. [Bot.] The sticks, leaves and so on, on the floor of a wood before they have been fully changed into HUMUS.

'Little's dis'ease. [Med.] SPASTIC PARALYSIS of the lower half of the body caused by certain nerve-CELLS in the brain not working from birth.

'lit(t)oral, a., n. To do with, or [Biol.] living on, the edge of the sea or other great body of water. **l. de'posits.** [Geol.] The sort of material put down at and under the edge of the sea, ranging from sand to small stones made round and smooth by the work of waves and currents. **l. zone.** [Biol.] That part of the edge of the sea between high- and low-water mark or a little further out, as the living-place of certain sorts of animals and plants.

'Littrés glands, n.pl. [Zoo.] Small MUCOUS GLANDS in the URETHRA of male higher animals.

live, a. (Of a BOMB, mine and so on) CHARGED, able to go off, not used up. [Elec.] (Of a

CIRCUIT, wire and so on) through which an electric current is going, or at a higher POTENTIAL than the earth. **l. 'axle.** [Mach.] A turning AXLE supporting fixed wheels as opp. a fixed axle supporting turning wheels. **l. steam.** [Eng.] Steam coming straight from the boiler producing it, as opp. steam given off after doing work and so on, and which has undergone some expansion in the process.

'liver, n. [Zoo.] In back-boned animals, the complex GLANDULAR structure, branching from the first part of the INTESTINE, by which BILE is produced, GLYCOGEN made and stored, and other important changes in the substances transported by the blood effected; in some lower animals, a GLAND of simpler structure but like purpose, sp. the HEPATOPANCREAS of CRUSTACEA. **l.-'pancreas,** n. HEPATO-PANCREAS.

'liver of 'sulphur. [Chem.] A LIVER-coloured substance formed by heating K_2CO_3 (*potassium carbonate*) with S, used in gardening etc. for the destruction of insects and disease-causing FUNGI.

'livid, a. Of the colour of lead, or of the skin when the blood-vessels under it have been broken by a blow.

'lixivi'ation, n. [Metal.] The process of washing a substance, sp. a metal, out of another with a SOLVENT. **li'xiviate,** v.t.

load, n. The weight supported by a structure. [Mach.] The force to be overcome by a machine. [Elec.] The power going through or taken from an electric CIRCUIT or machine under given conditions. **'-ed,** a. Supporting a weight, weighted. [Med.] Having overmuch of a certain substance, for example, of the LIVER, over-full of BILE. [Elec., Radio] Having undergone loading. **'-ing,** n. [Elec.] The addition of loading coils. **loading coil.** [Elec.] A COIL put into a CIRCUIT as a way of increasing its IN-DUCTION.

loam, n. Paste of CLAY and sand from which bricks are made. [Geol.] A sort of readily broken, very fertile earth, made up chiefly of clay and sand, with some ORGANIC material. **'-y,** a. [Geol.]

lobe, n. [Biol.] A clearly-marked or almost separated division of a part, sp. with curved outline, as [Anat.] the ll. of the brain or of a LUNG, or [Bot.] one of the divisions of a leaf formed by a deep curve or cut in the edge; a flat, somewhat round outgrowth, as the loosely hanging skin over the sides of the toes of certain birds. **'lobar,** a. Sp. [Med.] To do with the l(l). of a LUNG. **'lobate,** a. **lo'bation,** n. Condition of having, process of forming, ll.; a l. or system of ll. **lobed,** a. Sp. [Bot.] of leaf (*see* picture p. 223).

lobo'podium (lobopodia), n. [Zoo.] A wide,

thick PSEUDOPOD as in some PROTOZOA.

lo'bose, a. [Zoo.] (Of PSEUDOPODS) short, thick and irregular in form, and having ENDOPLASM inside.

lo'botomy, n. [Med.] LEUCOTOMY.

'lobule, n. [Biol.] A small LOBE or a division of a lobe, sp. any of the small masses of TISSUE of which certain structures, such as the LIVER, are made up. **'lobular, 'lobulate,** aa. **'lobulation,** n. Condition of having, process of forming ll.; a l.

'local, a. Taking place at, to do with conditions at, a certain place, not general. [Med.] (Of condition or disease) limited to a certain part or parts of the body. **l. 'action.** [Elec.] The producing of currents between different parts of the same electric apparatus or of the same metal plate of an electric CELL. **l. anaes'thetic.** [Med.] Substance producing ANAES-THESIA of part of the body only. **l. group of 'galaxies.** [Astron.] ISLAND UNIVERSE. **l. time.** [Astron.] The time at a place as measured by the position of the sun in relation to the MERIDIAN at that place, as opp. STANDARD TIME. **'-ize,** v.t. Make discovery of where something is, get its position clear; keep disease etc. limited to a certain place. **locali'zation,** n. Sp. [Psych.], the connection of a sense-experience such as pain, with a certain part of the body as its seat, or of a sense-experience coming from an outside STIMULUS with a certain position in space, or of an experienced event with a certain position in time. **locali'zation of 'function.** [Zoo.] The development of different parts of the brain for special purposes, such as smell, hearing, and the other senses.

lo'cellus (lo'celli), n. [Bot.] A small space cut off by a division in the OVARY of a plant. **lo'cellate,** a.

lock, n. [Eng.] An apparatus for lifting or lowering ships from one level of a river or made water-way to another, being a walled structure in the water which may be opened at one end to let water in from the higher level, or at the other end to let water out to the lower level, till the level of the water in the basin is the same, and a ship which has come in on one side may be let out on the other.

'lockjaw, n. [Med.] TETANUS or TRISMUS.

'locomotion, n. The act or power of motion from place to place. **loco'motive,** 1.a. To do with, effecting, l. 2.n. Steam or other engine used for pulling trains. **loco'motor,** a. To do with l. **loco'motor a'taxia** or **a'taxy.** [Med.] Disease of the nerve system caused by damage to the SPINAL CORD as the outcome of SYPHILIS, having serious effects on all the organization of the body, one of the most marked of which is loss of the power of controlled motion, sp. in walking.

'loculi'cidal, a. [Bot.] (Of a CAPSULE) opening down the middle of the CARPELS of which it is formed.

'loculus ('loculi), **'locule,** nn. [Biol.] A walled-off division of a hollow part or structure, sp.:—[Bot.] one of the divisions of a COMPOUND OVARY or of a SPORE or an ANTHER; [Zoo.] one of the divisions in COELENTERATA or in the SHELL of FORAMINIFERA. **'locular, 'loculate,** aa. **-locular,** a. Having the named number of ll., as *'bilocular.*

'locus, n. Position or place, sp.:— [Biol.] the position of a GENE in a CHROMOSOME; [Psych.] the place in or on the body where a STIMULUS is LOCALIZED. [Math.] Curve or line formed of points fixed by some law or statement of relation, the line representative of a point moving in agreement with given rules.

lode, n. [Mining] A great body of ORE walled in by the sides of a wide, deep crack in the earth's structure. **'-stone,** n. [Mineral.] A natural form of Fe_3O_4 having MAGNETIC properties.

'lodicule, n. [Bot.] One of the two, or sometimes three, small, thin, skin-like leaves at the base of the STAMENS of the flower in a grass.

'loess, n. [Geol.] Earth substance formed chiefly of CLAY and sand put down by wind, covering great stretches of certain parts of the earth, sp. Asia.

log, n. Apparatus for measuring the distance covered by a ship with a view to judging its rate of motion through the water, of which the oldest and still common form is made up of a bit of wood let go into the water on the end of a measured line running freely out from the back of the ship, but generally today a **patent l.,** formed of a ROTATING part in the water, the turns of which are recorded automatically; record of journey or flight kept by chief of ship or airplane, or of the time taken by any other operation, for example that of a boiler or engine.

log = LOGARITHM.

'logarithm, n. [Math.] Of a number, N, the POWER of 10 (or some other fixed number) to which it is equal, that is, x in $10^x = N$, given in TABLES and used for the MULTIPLICATION and division of long numbers by the simple addition or SUBTRACTION of their ll. and the discovery of the desired PRODUCT or QUOTIENT by then using a table of ANTILOGARITHMS. **loga'rithmic(al),** aa. **loga'rithmic scale.** A system of measuring in which an increase of one unit is representative of an increase to ten times the QUANTITY being measured.

'logation, n. [Acous., Psych.] NONSENSE SYLLABLE.

'logic, n. Science of reasoning. **'-al,** a. **lo'gician,** n. Expert on l.

loin, n. [Zoo.] That part of the body of a man or four-legged animal forming the lower part of the back to the right or left of the backbone.

'loma, n. [Zoo.] Thin flat structure of skin-like material forming edge or cover of opening.

'lomastome, a. [Zoo.] Having edge or lip turned back, as some SHELLS.

'loment, lo'mentum, nn. [Bot.] LEGUME narrowing more and more between the seeds as it gets older, and in the end cracking across into one-seeded parts. **lomen'taceous,** a.

longe'ron, n. Back-bone-like part of the body of an airplane going from front to back, gen. across a number of supports.

longi-. Long.

'longicorn, a. [Zoo.] Having long feelers, sp. of COLEOPTERA.

longi'pennate, a. [Zoo.] Long-feathered or long-winged.

'longirostral, a. [Zoo.] Having a long BEAK.

lon'gissimus 'capitis. [Anat.] Long muscle joining the bones at the back of the ear to those at the back of the neck, and keeping the head upright.

lon'gissimus 'cervicis. [Anat.] Long thin muscle at back of neck.

lon'gissimus 'dorsi, n. [Anat.] The very long, strong muscle running from the neck down the middle of the back and keeping the body upright.

'longitude, n. [Geog.] Position of a place on the earth given by the angle between two planes going through the North and South POLES, one of which is fixed and the other goes through the place, gen. measured east or west from a fixed plane through Greenwich, England (*in l. 45°E.,* etc.). [Astron.] CELESTIAL LONGITUDE. *See* MERIDIAN.

longi'tudinal, a. To do with LENGTH; going in the direction of the length of a body or [Biol.] the chief AXIS of an animal, plant or part. **l. wave.** [Phys.] A WAVE in which the VIBRATION of the PARTICLES is parallel to the WAVE PATH, as in a sound wave.

long sight, long-'sightedness, n. [Med.] HYPERMETROPIA. **long-'sighted,** a.

'longus 'colli. [Anat.] A long flat muscle at the right and left sides of the back of the neck, used for getting it bent forward.

long wave, n. Radio wave having a WAVE-LENGTH of more than 1,000 m.

loom, n. Apparatus by which cloth is made by taking threads over and under one another.

loop, n. A shut or almost shut curve formed by a cord, wire, etc., sp. by turning back and then forward across itself; the part of a body in VIBRATION, such as a stretched wire, between two NODES; a complete electric CIRCUIT.

loop of 'Henle, n. [Zoo.] That part of a URINOIFEROUS pipe going from outer part of KIDNEY into the middle and back again.

loose, a. [Med.] (Of BOWELS) RELAXED.

loph, n. [Zoo.] Small outgrowth between the points of a tooth, frequently joining them into a line-like PROJECTION.

lopho-, lophi(o). [Zoo.] Marked PROJECTION, outgrowth, sp. on top of something.

'lophocercal, a. [Zoo.] Having the tail FIN without rays, forming a band-like structure round end of back-bone.

lopho'branchiate, a. [Zoo.] Having GILLS with groups of long outgrowths, or with LOBES.

'lophodont, a. [Zoo.] Having back teeth with line-like PROJECTIONS from side to side across the crushing faces.

'lophophore, n. [Zoo.] In POLYZOA and BRACHIOPODA, an outgrowth round the outside of the mouth supporting the feelers.

lo'phosteon, n. [Zoo.] The base of the KEEL of a bird.

lo'photrichous, a. [Biol.] Having FLAGELLA in a group at one end or point.

'lorate, a. [Biol.] Formed like a band.

lor'dosis, n. [Med.] A more than normal curving forward of the lower part of the backbone; any curving of bones which is not normal. **lor'dotic,** a.

lore, n. [Zoo.] Space between the mouth and the eyes in birds. **'loral,** a.

Lo'rentz-Einstein transfor'mation. Rule giving the relation between the position in space and time of a physical event as viewed in two systems, one of which is in straight-line motion in relation to the other.

Lo'rentz-Fitz'gerald con'traction. [Phys.] The amount by which, in the RELATIVITY theory, the size of bodies becomes less in the direction of their motion.

lo'rica, n. [Zoo.] A stiff or hard outer covering (used sp. of ROTIFERA and INFUSORIA). **'loricate(d),** aa. **lori'cation,** n. Condition of being loricate, process of forming a l.; a loricate covering. **lori'cation 'moment.** The stage at which a complete l. is formed all at one time.

Lori'cata, n.pl. [Zoo.] An ORDER of REPTILIA of which the animals now in existence are AMPHIBIANS of great size, having 4 legs used for swimming and walking, long, narrow heads with great mouths opening very widely, long sharp teeth, and a very thick skin covered with plates of horn and bone.

'lorum, n. [Zoo.] Any band-like structure, sp. that supporting the base of the LABIUM in insects.

'Loschmidt 'number. AVOGADRO NUMBER.

'lotic, a. [Biol.] Living in rivers or other moving water.

'lotion, n. [Med.] Any liquid with medical properties for putting on the skin.

'loudness, n. [Acous.] Power of a sound as judged by the ear, measured in PHONS or DECIBELS

loud'speaker, n. [Acous., etc.] Apparatus for turning electric or radio waves into sound waves producing sounds loud enough for hearing at some distance.

louse (lice), n. [Zoo.] Any insect of a sort living on the bodies of animals or plants and SUCKING their blood or other liquid.

'Lovibond tin'tometer. [Chem. etc.] Form of COLORIMETER in which a colour is matched with light going through special coloured glasses. **'Lovibond-'Schofield tin-'tometer.** Form of L.t. made for working on the C.I.E. system.

'Lower, a. [Geol.] (Before names of divisions of time or ROCK SYSTEMS, etc.) earlier, the earlier part of, as the **L. Carboniferous** (see p. 559).

low-'pass filter. [Elec.] A FILTER letting through only currents having FREQUENCIES lower than a certain limit.

low 'tension. [Elec., Eng.] Low VOLTAGE.

low tide. [Geog.] The time or condition when the sea or TIDE is at its lowest level, when it has gone as far from the land as it is going.

low 'water. [Geog.] Of any body of water, the time when it is at its lowest level—in connection with the sea, LOW TIDE.

'loxodont, a. [Zoo.] Having LOPHODONT back teeth with hollows between the RIDGES.

L-shell, n. [Phys.] The SHELL of an ATOM outside the K-shell, having at most 8 ELECTRONS.

L.T. = LOW TENSION.

Lu, Sign for LUTECIUM.

lubri'cant, n. [Mach.] Substance, such as oil, used for putting between moving parts which are touching to keep them moving smoothly over one another without rubbing or becoming fixed together; any other thing, such as air, used for the same purpose, see AIR BEARINGS. **'lubricate,** v.t. Put l. on. **lubri'cation,** n.

'lucid, a. [Astron.] Able to be seen without an instrument, said of stars, etc. brighter than the 6th MAGNITUDE.

'lucida, n. [Astron.] The brightest star of a group.

lu'ciferase, n. [Biochem.] The ENZYME effecting the uniting of LUCIFERIN with O.

lu'ciferin, n. [Biochem.] Substance present in light-giving animals such as fireflies, by the uniting of which with O light is produced with almost no heat.

lu'cifu-gous, -gal, aa. [Biol.] Turning away from, keeping out of, light.

'lucule, n. [Astron.] GRANULE.

'Lüder's lines. FLOW LINES.

lum'bago, n. [Med.] RHEUMATIC condition in which muscles in the lower part of the back are stiff and give pain when used.

'lumbar, a. [Zoo.] To do with the LOINS. l. 'puncture. [Med.] Operation of putting a hollow needle into the l. part of the backbone and taking out some of the CEREBROSPINAL FLUID. 'lumb(o)-.

'lumbricalis (lumbricales), n. [Anat.] Any of the 4 small muscles on the front of the hand and the under side of the foot, which go to the four fingers or the four smaller toes.

lumbri'cosis, n. [Med.] Condition of having NEMATODE worms in the INTESTINES.

'lumen, n. [Optics] Unit of LUMINOUS FLUX such that a flux of one l. per unit SOLID ANGLE gives a LUMINOUS INTENSITY of one CANDELA.

'lumen, n. [Zoo.] The hollow inside a pipe-like part. [Bot.] Space inside CELL walls, sp. when there is no longer any substance in it.

'lumeter, n. [Optics] Form of light-measuring instrument.

lumi'nescence, n. [Phys., Chem., Zoo., etc.] The giving out of light as the effect of any cause other than burning or heating, seen, for example, in chemical reactions, in light-producing animals, in RADIO-ACTIVITY and so on, sp. FLUORESCENCE and PHOSPHORESCENCE. lumi'nesce, v.i. lumi'nescent, a.

lumi'niferous, a. Producing, transporting, light.

'lumophore, lu'minophore, nn. [Chem.] Any substance which gives off light at a normal indoor TEMPERATURE; any group of ATOMS causing or increasing the LUMINESCENCE of a substance.

'luminous, a. (To do with) giving out light. l. flux. [Optics] The amount of light given out by a body or the rate at which it is given out. l. in'tensity. L. flux in one direction, measured in CANDELAS. lumi-'nosity, n. The property or condition of giving out light; LUMINANCE as experienced by the eye. [Astron.] The amount of light given out by a star, its ABSOLUTE MAGNITUDE. lumi'nosity 'factor. VISUAL SENSITIVITY.

'lunacy, n. [Med.] INSANITY. 'lunatic, n. Person in a condition of l.

'lunar, a. To do with the moon. l. bone or lu'nare. One of the bones between the hand and the arm. l. month. [Astron.] SYNODIC MONTH.

'lunar probe. [Astronautics]. A SPACE VEHICLE sent from earth to get knowledge of conditions on and round the moon.

'lunate, lu'nated, aa. Formed like a new moon or a half-moon.

lu'nation, n. SYNODIC MONTH.

lung, n. [Zoo.] Apparatus for breathing air, gen. one of two, in the chest of air-breathing, back-boned animals, where the O of the breathed-in air is taken in, and waste CO_2 given out, by the blood, through the thin walls of the network of blood-vessels round the air-pockets forming a necessary part of the structure; any air-breathing apparatus in other animals. l. book. The breathing apparatus of some ARACHNIDA, made up of parts like the pages of a book.

luni-. Moon:— '-form, a., '-solar, a. 'luni-'solar pre'cession. [Astron.] PRECESSION OF THE EQUINOXES.

'lunik, n. [Astronautics]. Name given to the Russian SPACE VEHICLES sent up to get to the moon.

'lunistice, n. [Astron.] One or other of the two points in the motion of the moon round the earth at which it is farthest north or south. luni'stitial, a.

luni'tidal, a. To do with TIDES caused by the moon. l. 'interval. The space of time between the TRANSIT of the moon at a place and the first HIGH TIDE after this.

'lunoid, a. LUNATE.

'lunula, -e, nn. [Zoo.] LUNATE part or mark, as the white half-moon at the base of a finger-nail, 'lunular, 'lunu-late(d), aa. 'lunulet, n.

'lupulin, n. [Bot., Med.] (Bitter substance got from) the sticky yellow powder on the flowers of the plant which gives beer its bitter taste (Humulus lupulus), used medically as a SEDATIVE.

'lupus, n. [Med.] Any of different sorts of skin disease, most of them caused by the TUBERCULOSIS BACILLUS, in which red TUBERCLES are formed, the after-effects of which are deep marks in the skin.

'lura, n. [Anat.] The opening of the INFUN-DIBULUM of the brain.

'luster, 'lustre, nn. The property of being LUSTROUS. [Geol.] The look given to the face of a MINERAL by the degree and way in which light is turned back by it, making some minerals metal-like, others glass-like, others silk-like and so on. 'lustrous, a. REFLECTING light to such a degree as to be bright.

lute, n. Any substance for pushing into or coating joins, cracks etc., to make them air-tight or water-tight.

lu'teal, a. [Zoo.] Of, to do with, or like, the CORPUS LUTEUM.

lu'tecium, lu'tetium, n. Chemical ELEMENT, at. no. 71, at. wt. 174·99, sign Lu, one of the RARE EARTH METALS.

'lutein, n. [Biochem.] A yellow colouring-substance present in the leaves, flowers, and other parts of plants and in egg-YOLK, one of the two ISOMERS of which XANTHO-PHYLL is made up.

'luteinization, n. [Zoo.] The process in

MAMMALS by which egg-producing CELLS become part of the CORPORA LUTEA after sending out their eggs. **luteinizing 'hormone.** A HORMONE produced by the PITUITARY GLAND and helping l. in females and the producing of ANDROGENS in males.

'luteo-. [Bot., Chem.] Yellow (and . . .).

'luteo'henic, a. LUTEINIZING.

lu'teolous, a. [Biol.] Somewhat yellow.

lux, n. [Light] International unit of ILLUMINATION of a SURFACE = 1 LUMEN/m².

Lyco'podiales, n.pl. [Bot.] ORDER of PTERIDOPHYTA with leaves small in comparison with stem, and SPORANGIA on upper side of certain special leaves.

lyco'podium, n. [Bot., Chem., Med.] A yellow readily-burning powder of very little weight formed of the SPORES of a number of sorts of LYCOPODIALES, used in making fireworks, [Med.] for putting on skin wounds, and [Phys.] for marking the motion of waves (freq. **l. powder).**

'Lydian stone or **'lydite,** n. [Mineral.] TOUCHSTONE.

lye, n. [Chem.] Any strong SOLUTION of ALKALI, sp. of NaOH or KOH, used for cleaning.

'Lyman bands. [Phys.] Group of bands in the H SPECTRUM between 1450Å and 1650Å. **'Lyman con'tinuum.** A CONTINUOUS SPECTRUM in ULTRA-VIOLET as far as 300Å.

lymph, n. [Zoo.] In back-boned animals, a liquid made up chiefly of blood without its ERYTHROCYTES which has been sent out through the walls of the very small blood-vessels into spaces in the TISSUES, and from there drained into the smallest lymphatics, by which it is got together and sent back into the blood again, with the addition of lymphocytes, through the lymphatics and the THORACIC DUCT. **l. gland, l. node.** Any of the small masses of lymphoid tissue present at certain points in the chief lymphatics of MAMMALS and birds, which take out BACTERIA and other strange bodies from the l. going through them by the operation of MACROPHAGES. **l. heart.** An expansion of a lymphatic at the opening into a VEIN which has the power of CONTRACTING and driving the l. forward, present in some back-boned animals but not in birds or MAMMALS. **lym'phatic,** n. Vessel transporting or to do with l. **lymphatic system.** System of very thin-walled pipes (the lymphatics or **l. vessels)** through which the l. moves by a CONTRACTION of the pipes effected by muscles in their walls or in near-by parts. **lymphoblast,** n. CELL from which a lymphocyte is formed. **'lymphocyte,** n. Any of the somewhat small LEUCOCYTES, having a great, round, simple NUCLEUS and the property

of moving like an AMOEBA, being produced all the time by lymphoid tissue and transported into the blood by the l. **'lymphoid,** a. **'lymphoid tissue.** The substance producing lymphocytes, present in l. glands and other parts of the body and formed of a network of RETICULIN FIBRES with lymphocytes and lymphoblasts in the spaces, together with MACROPHAGES.

lymph(o)-. LYMPH: **lym'phogenous,** a. **lymphology,** n.

lym'phaemia, n.[Med.]LYMPHOCYTHAEMIA.

lym'phangial, a. [Zoo.] Of, to do with, the LYMPH vessels.

'lymphocele, n. [Med.] A SWELLING having more than a normal amount of LYMPH in it.

'lymphocy'th(a)emia, n. [Med.] A form of LEUKAEMIA marked by the overgrowth of the LYMPH GLANDS and an unnormal increase of LYMPHOCYTES in the blood.

'lymphocy'tosis, n. [Med.] LYMPHAEMIA. **'lymphocy'totic,** a.

lym'phuria, n. [Med.] Condition in which LYMPH is present in URINE.

'lyocy'tosis, n. [Zoo.] Destruction of TISSUE by ENZYMES produced outside it, as in change of form of insects.

ly'olysis, n. [Chem.] SOLVOLYSIS.

'lyophil, n., a. [Chem.] (COLLOID) readily going into SOLUTION, and going back into it, after COAGULATION, on the addition of more of the SOLVENT. **lyo'philic,** a. **lyo'philic drying.** FREEZE-DRYING.

'lyophobe, n., a. [Chem.] (COLLOID) readily coming out of SOLUTION, and not going back into it after COAGULATION on the addition of more of the SOLVENT.

lyo'tropic series. [Chem.] A group of SALTS ranged in the order of their SALTING-OUT power on HYDROPHILIC SOLS.

'lyrate, a. [Biol.] In form somewhat like a letter 'U' with sides curved in and out again near the top; sp. [Bot.] (of a leaf) with sides curved sharply out and deeply in again more than once, forming PAIRS of small opposite LOBES, and then curved out into one wide end-lobe of much greater size than the others (see picture p. 223).

lysi'genic, ly'sigenous, ly'sogenous, aa. [Bot.] Said of a space formed as the effect of CELLS in the middle of a mass being broken down.

'lysin, n. [Biochem.] Any of a group of ANTIBODIES causing the destruction of BACTERIA, blood-CELLS, etc., by making them liquid.

'lysis, n. [Med.] The going away by degrees of an ACUTE disease after the turning-point. [Biochem.] The destruction of CELLS, etc. by a LYSIN.

-lysis, [Chem., Biochem.] The process of getting a substance broken up chemically or into SOLUTION, or its destruction by a LYSIN.

lyso'genesis, n. [Biochem.] The producing of LYSINS or of their effects. **lyso'genic,** a.

'Lysol, n. [Chem.] Trade name for a SOLUTION of CRESOL in SOFT SOAP, used as a DISIN-FECTANT.

'lytta, n. [Zoo.] Rod of CARTILAGE forming part of tongue of some animals living on meat, for example the dog.

m. = MILE; METRE.

m-, Sign for MESO- or META- [Chem.].

M. = MOLAR [Chem.].

M, Sign for MOLECULAR WEIGHT.

M, Sign for a metal or an ELECTRO-POSITIVE RADICAL.

μ, Sign for:- MICRO- (before names of measuring units); MICRON; MAGNETIC PERMEABILITY; REFRACTIVE INDEX.

mμ, Sign for MILLIMICRON.

μμ, Sign for MICRO-MICRO- and MICRO-MICRON.

Ma, Sign for MASURIUM.

'macerate, v.t. Make soft, so as to be readily separated, by wetting or placing in water or other liquid. **mace'ration,** b. Sp., this process as taking place in the digestion of food, or as used in Zoology as a help in cutting up an animal, or to get soft parts away from bones, etc.

ma'chine, n. A structure in which a force acting at one point, or a motion given to one part, is the cause of a force acting at another point or the motion of another part, which may be used for doing work, sp. one made up of a number of parts in a complex relation to one another. **m. tool.** An instrument worked by a MOTOR for cutting or forming something. **ma'chinery,** n. Mm. in general or mm. working as a group.

'mach'meter, n. [Aero.] An airplane PILOT'S instrument for measuring the MACH NUMBER of his flight.

Mach 'number. [Phys.] The RATIO of the rate of motion of a body such as an airplane to the rate of motion of sound in air at the same place.

'mackerel sky. [Meteor.] Sky covered with small round masses of cloud in regular lines, like the markings on the back of some fish.

'macle, n. [Mineral.] A TWIN CRYSTAL, sp. of a DIAMOND; dark mark in a MINERAL. **'macled,** a. Having mm.

ma'crandrous, a. [Bot.] Having male plants of great size.

'macr(o)-. Great, greater than normal, the greater of two, etc.:— **'-'axis,** n. [Cryst.],

'-co'nidium, n.; MACROSCOPIC:— **'-'plankton,** n.

'macroa'nalysis, n. [Chem.] ANALYSIS not using substances in very small amounts needing very small-scale apparatus, opp. MICROANALYSIS.

'macroce'phal-ic, -ous, aa. [Med.] Having a head greater than normal. [Bot.] Having thick COTYLEDONS. **macro'cephaly, macroce'phalia,** nn. [Med.].

macro'chemistry, n. That part of chemistry which has to do with the make-up and properties of substances as far as these are open to observation without MICRO-ANALYSIS. **macro'chemical,** a.

'macrocosm, n. The UNIVERSE, sp. as opp. MICROCOSM.

macro'crystalline, a. [Mineral.] Made up of CRYSTALS great enough to be seen without the help of a MICROSCOPE.

'macrocyte, n. [Med.] A red blood-CELL of great size produced in certain ANAEMIAS. **'macrocy'tha(e)mia,** n. Condition in which mm. are present in the blood. **'macrocy'tosis,** n. The forming of mm.

macrodi'agonal, a., n. [Cryst.] (To do with) the longest AXIS of a CRYSTAL having 3 unequal axes.

'macro'gamete, n. [Biol.] The greater of two uniting GAMETES, looked on as the female.

'macroga'metacyte, n. [Biol.] CELL by which a MACROGAMETE is produced, sp. in PROTOZOA.

mac'rogamy, n. [Zoo.] In PROTOZOA, the uniting as GAMETES of two units which have come to full growth.

'macromere, n. [Zoo.] In an OVUM undergoing division, one of the great CELLS formed in the lower half.

'macrome'ritic, a. [Geol.] (Of ROCK) made up of grains of a size great enough to be seen without the help of an instrument.

macro'molecule, n. [Chem.] A great MOLECULE, sp. a complex of simpler molecules as in a POLYMER.

macro'nucleus, n. [Biol.] The greater of the two NUCLEI present in the CELLS of most CILIOPHORA, which is not REPRODUCTIVE.

'macrophage, macro'phagocyte, nn. Great PHAGOCYTE of a sort common in the bodies of back-boned animals, moving by PSEUDOPODIA and causing the destruction of BACTERIA, etc.

ma'crophagous, a. [Zoo.] (Of an animal) living on food of a size not small in comparison with itself, as all land animals, opp. MICROPHAGOUS.

macro'physics, n. That part of physics which has to do with bodies great enough to be seen and measured without special instruments.

ma'cropodous, a. [Bot.] Having a long HYPOCOTYL; having a long stem.

ma'cropsia, n. [Med.] Condition in which

things seem to the eye greater than they in fact are, an effect of nerve or eye disease.

macro'scopic, a. Great enough to be seen by the eye without the help of an instrument.

'macrosmatic, a. [Zoo., Anat.] Having a very high development of the instruments of the sense of smell.

'macro'splanchic, a. [Zoo.] Having VISCERA of greater than normal size and body greater than normal in relation to arms and legs.

'macrospore, n. MEGASPORE. **macro'sporophore, -phyl,** nn. MEGASPOROPHYLL. **'macrospo'rangium,** n. MEGASPORANGIUM.

macro'structure, n. [Metal.] The design of the CRYSTALS in a solid metal which may be seen without, or with very little help from, a MICROSCOPE.

'macrotherm, n. MEGATHERM.

'macula (maculae), **'macule,** nn. [Biol.] Small coloured mark, hollow, etc. on a part in other ways unmarked or smooth. [Med.] Coloured mark on skin caused by diseased condition. [Astron.] Dark mark on sun or star. **m. 'lutea.** [Anat.] In man and some other higher animals, the small yellow place at the middle of the RETINA of the eye where things are seen most clearly, having the FOVEA at its middle point. **'macular, 'maculate(d),** aa. **macu'lation,** n. The marking, distribution of marks, on a plant or animal.

'madrepore, n. [Zoo.] Any of certain stone-like, branching CORALS.

'madre'poric, a. [Zoo.] To do with a MADREPORE or MADREPORITE. **m. canal.** STONE CANAL.

'madre'porite, n. [Zoo.] In ECHINODERMATA, the plate with holes in it forming the opening at the end of the STONE CANAL through which water goes into it, seen in starfish on the under side of the body, in HOLOTHURIANS more deeply bedded in it.

'mafic, a., n. [Geol.] (Of, to do with) the substances formed of iron and MAGNESIUM (Mg.) present in a ROCK.

Magda'lenian, a., n. [Geol.] (To do with) the latest of the 5 divisions of the PALEOLITHIC stage of man's development.

Magell'anic cloud. [Astron.] One or the other of two masses looking like thin cloud, *the larger* (greater) *M. c.* and *the lesser* (smaller) *M. c.*, made up of stars and NEBULAE at a very great distance away, seen in the night sky near the SOUTH POLE.

ma'genta, a., n. (Of) a sort of orange-red colour with a suggestion of blue mixed with it (*see* SUBTRACTIVE PRIMARY).

'maggot, n. [Zoo.] Insect LARVA with a soft body, no legs, and no clearly marked head, such as that of a number of flies.

magic 'lantern, n. [Optics] Old name for a simple form of PROJECTION LANTERN.

magic numbers. [Phys.] Certain numbers of PROTONS or NEUTRONS in the NUCLEUS of an ATOM which are the cause of increased STABILITY.

'magma, n. [Geol.] Material made liquid by great heat inside the earth, from which, when it makes its way to the outer parts of the earth and becomes cold, IGNEOUS ROCK is formed.

mag'nalium, n. General name for an ALLOY formed chiefly of Mg and Al.

'magnascope, n. In motion pictures, an apparatus for increasing the size of the picture seen.

mag'nesia, n. [Chem.] MAGNESIUM OXIDE (MgO), a white, earth-like substance of very little weight, produced by burning magnesium in air, etc., used medically as an ANTACID.

'magnesite, n. [Chem., Mineral.] Natural MAGNESIUM CARBONATE ($MgCO_3$), used chiefly as a REFRACTORY.

mag'nesium, n. Chemical ELEMENT, at. no. 12, at. wt. 24·32, sign Mg, a bright, white metal, producing a strong white light when burned. present in CHLOROPHYLL and of wide distribution in the earth, but never free—used in mixed metals (sp. in the making of present-day airplanes), fireworks, camera work, etc., and forming important SALTS which are used medically or in industry. **m. 'carbonate.** $MgCO_3$, used medically for acid stomach and as an APERIENT. **m. 'sulphate.** EPSOM SALTS. **mag'nes-ian, -ic,** aa.

'magnet, n. [Phys.] (Mass of) any substance having natural magnetism, or any body or structure which has been given this property, the commonest example of which is a mass of iron in the form of a rod or horseshoe. **'-ize,** v.t. Give the property of magnetism to; make undergo attraction by m. **'magnetized,** a. **'magnetism,** n. The property of having the power of attraction for iron, and of attraction and its opposite for substances like itself, and of producing an effect on anything in the range of its operation through which an electric current is going; the branch of science having to do with these properties and effects.

mag'netic, a. [Phys.] To do with, having, produced by, the properties of a MAGNET. **m. 'axis,** Straight line joining the middle points of a MAGNET's m. poles. **m. 'circuit.** A system of unbroken lines of m. force, gen. produced when MAGNETISM is effected by ELECTRICITY. **m. 'compass.** Instrument for getting directions at and point on the earth by the use of a m. needle or needles or the like (*see* MARINER'S COMPASS and GYRO COMPASS). **m. dip** or **'inclination.** The angle between the plane of the earth's m. field at any point and the HORIZONTAL plane. **m. 'declination** or **vari'ation.** The angle between true North or South and the direction north or south pointed to by a HORIZONTAL m. needle. **m. 'elements.** The three values, m. declination, m. dip and HORIZONTAL INTENSITY, used for giving an account of the earth's m. field at any point. **m. e'quator.** ACLINIC LINE. **m. field.** The space round a MAGNET or a CONDUCTOR transporting electric current in which its m. properties are in operation. **M. flux density. m. flux.** The complete amount of m. force over a given AREA at right angles to a m. field, measured in LINES or MAXWELLS. **m. flux 'density.** The m. flux per unit AREA, measured in GAUSSES. **m. in'duction.** M. flux density; *see* INDUCTION. **m. in'tensity.** The force of attraction or its opposite acting on a unit m. pole or at any point in a m. field, equal to m. flux density. **m. 'iron-ore.** MAGNETITE. **m. 'linkage.** [Elec.] The connection of m. lines of force with electric CONDUCTORS. **m. me'ridian.** Circle round the earth going through the m. poles. **m. mine.** A mine placed on the sea-bed, etc. and caused to go off by any m. body coming near it, used in war for blowing up ships. **m. 'moment.** The turning-force acting on a MAGNET as the effect of the m. field round it. **m. 'needle.** A thin rod of m. steel hanging or supported so as to have the power of turning freely in a HORIZONTAL plane, and so coming naturally to rest in the direction of the earth's m. field, that is, pointing north and south—the acting part of a m. compass. **m. North.** The direction pointed to by the north-turning end of a m. needle. **m. 'permea'bility.** The degree to which a substance takes in m. flux, measured by the RATIO of the m. flux density produced in it to that produced by the same m. field in air. **m. pole.** One or other of the ends of or points on a MAGNET at which its power seems to be strongest, and from which the lines of force mapping its m. field seem to go out, sp., the north or south point on the earth pointed to by a m. needle. **m. pole strength.** Measure of the force acting at a m. pole, the unit being that producing a force of 1 DYNE between two equally strong m. poles at a distance of 1 cm. from one another. **m. South.** The direction pointed to by the south-turning end of a m. needle. **m. storm.** A marked DISTURBANCE in the earth's m. field, freq. causing strong earth currents and electric effects in the sky, seemingly having some connection with SUNSPOTS, which are seen at the same time. **m. sus'cepti'bility.** The RATIO of the m. moment per cm³ produced in a substance to the m. flux density of the field causing

it. **m. tube of force.** LINE OF FORCE. **m. vari'ation.** [Phys.] M. declination. [Meteor.] A change ranging between certain limits in the m. elements at a place, such as takes place regularly through the day or year, possibly caused by changing electric currents in the upper ATMOSPHERE.

'magnetite, n. [Mineral.] An important ORE of iron, Fe_3O_4 (*ferrosoferric oxide*), a black substance which undergoes attraction by a MAGNET and in one form (named *lodestone*) has the properties of one.

mag'neto, n. [Elec.] A MAGNETOELECTRIC machine used for producing the current for firing EXPLOSIVES, or for firing the gas in an INTERNAL COMBUSTION ENGINE, and worked by the engine itself.

mag'neto, a. MAGNETIC. **magneto-.**

mag'neto'chemistry, n. Science of the relations between chemical processes and MAGNETIC effects.

mag'neto'compass, n. EARTH INDUCTOR.

mag'netoe'lectric, a. [Phys.] To do with, using, electric current or effects produced by MAGNETS. **'magnoelec'tricity,** n.

mag'neto-'hydrody'namics. The science of the effects on one another of a MAGNETIC FIELD and a gas or liquid CONDUCTING ELECTRICITY.

magne'tometer, n. [Phys.] Instrument measuring the force and direction of a MAGNETIC FIELD by its effect on a freely turning MAGNETIC NEEDLE. **magne'tometry,** n.

mag'neto'motive force. [Phys.] The force producing a MAGNETIC FLUX.

'magneton, n. [Phys.] The unit of MAGNETIC MOMENT.

mag'neto-'optics, n. Branch of physics having to do with the relation between MAGNETIC FIELDS and light.

mag'neto re'sistance. [Phys.] An increase in the electric RESISTANCE of a metal when placed in a MAGNETIC FIELD.

mag'neto'striction, n. [Phys.] The changing in size of a FERROMAGNETIC body when placed in a MAGNETIC FIELD.

'magnetron, n. [Phys.] THERMIONIC VALVE with a MAGNETIC FIELD acting from out-outside across the current of ELECTRONS and causing them to take a curved line of flight, used for producing OSCILLA-TIONS of high FREQUENCY, sp. in radio.

'magnet(t)ing, n. [Phys.] Getting MAGNETIC materials separate from others by the use of a MAGNET.

magnify, v.t. and i. Make greater, or to seem greater, sp. give the eye a picture which is greater than the true size of the thing seen, so that details become clearer. **magnifi'cation,** n. Sp., magnifying power. **'magnifier,** n. Any instrument for magnifying, sp. [Optics]. [Elec.] AMPLIFIER. **'magnifying glass.** [Optics]. A LENS for magnifying, sp. one put in a frame with a hand-part for use by hand. **'magnifying power.** [Optics] (Of a LENS) the RATIO of the size of an IMAGE formed by it to the size of the thing which it is the image.

'magnitude, n. Size; anything having size of any sort. [Astron.] The measure of the light coming to the earth from a star as given by its position on a fixed scale in which the different degrees are named *first m., second m.,* etc., starting with the brightest star, by comparison with which the others are rated.

mag'nolia 'metal. An ALLOY of lead with Sb and some iron and tin, used for BEARINGS.

'magnum, n. [Anat.] CAPITATUM.

main, 1.a. Chief; to do with a m. 2.n. A chief gas, water, etc. pipe, or electric line, in a distribution system, from which smaller pipes, etc. go off to different parts. **mm.** n.pl. In electric power distribution, all the apparatus transporting current.

'major, a. Great, the greater of two, great in comparison with some other thing, important, opp. MINOR. **m. gene.** [Biol.] Any GENE of a sort whose effects are readily seen in separate plants or animals. **m. in'trusion.** [Geol.] An INTRUSION which is of great size in all directions, such as is formed only and regularly of PLUTONIC ROCK, and so the same thing as a *plutonic intrusion.* **m. ope'ration.** [Med.] Any operation for which a GENERAL ANAESTHETIC is commonly used.

mal-. Badly, bad, not normal, sp. [Med.]: **'-for'mation,** n.

mal, n. Word used for 'disease' in some names of diseases or medical conditions. **m. de mer.** NAUSEA caused by motion of ship.

'mala ('malae), n. [Zoo.] In some insects, a small outgrowth of the MAXILLA, in others a division of the MANDIBLE; in birds, the soft part at the base of the lower mouth-part.

'malachite, n. [Mineral.] A natural, somewhat dark green CARBONATE of copper $(CuCO_3.Cu(OH)_2)$, used for producing copper and as a jewel stone etc. **m. green.** A DYE producing a colour like that of m.

ma'lacia, n. [Med.] Soft condition of a part of the body caused by disease; an unhealthy desire for certain, sp. unnatural, sorts of food. **-malacia,** n. [Med.] A becoming soft through disease.

mala'cology, n. [Zoo.] Science of MOLLUSCA. **mala'cologist,** n.

mala'coma, n. [Med.] MALACIA (of parts of the body).

mala'cophilons, a. [Bot.] (Of flowers) undergoing POLLINATION by HELICIDAE.

mala'copterous, a. [Zoo.] Having soft FIN-RAYS.

mala'cosis, n. [Med.] Condition marked by MALACOMA.

mala'costracous, a. [Zoo.] Having a soft SHELL.

mal'aise, n. [Med.] A general feeling of being ill, not quite in order, without any specially marked pain or other sign of disease.

'malar, 1.a. [Zoo.] To do with the side of the face in back-boned animals; to do with the MALA. 2.n. The ZYGOMATIC bone.

ma'laria, n. [Med.] Disease taking a number of forms, caused by the attacking of the red blood-CELLS by any of certain sorts of very small PARASITES of the PROTOZOA, marked by waves of cold, FEVER, and SWEATING, in that order, and having a tendency to come back time after time. **ma'larial,** a.

male, 1.a. [Biol.] To do with that one of two different sorts of GAMETES which FERTILIZES the other, or with any part, plant, or animal producing m. gametes. 2.n. M. animal.

'malic acid. [Chem.] A complex acid of H, C, and O, present in young fruit and in some wine, forming needle-like CRYSTALS.

ma'lign, ma'lignant, aa. [Med.] (Of diseases) with tendency to become worse until death is caused, causing death; (of a diseased growth) having a tendency to go on increasing and making its way from one part of the body to another till death is caused, frequently coming back again in a different part of the body if cut out. **m. 'tumour.** [Med.] Gen. a CARCINOMA or SARCOMA. **ma'lignancy,** n. The property of being m.

'malleable, a. Able to be formed or stretched by hammering or rolling, as most metals. **mallea'bility,** n.

'malleate, a. Having a hammer-like form.

malle'olus, n. [Anat.] The round outgrowth at the foot end of the two bones of the lower part of the leg. **malle'olar,** a.

'malleus, n. [Zoo.] Any hammer-like structure, sp.: 1. the outer of the 3 bones of the INNER EAR in higher animals; 2. any of the hard site parts of a MASTAX.

Mall'ophaga, n.pl. [Zoo.] An ORDER of small, EXOPTERYGOTE, biting insects without wings, PARASITIC on the bodies of birds and sometimes on other animals.

'malnu'trition, n. [Med.] Condition in which body is not getting, or not making use of, enough food of the right sort.

ma'lonic acid. [Chem.] A white CRYSTALLINE substance, $HOOC.CH_2.COOH$, which may be got from MALIC ACID and is broken up, giving ACETIC ACID, by heating to a higher degree than its MELTING POINT, the ESTER of which (**malonic ester**) is important in the producing of other complex substances, sp. BARBITURATES.

Mal'pighian body or **corpuscle.** [Zoo.] An

expansion at the end of a URINIFEROUS TUBULE with a mass of thin, twisting blood-vessels inside it; a round mass of LYMPHOID TISSUE covering a small blood-vessel in the SPLEEN. **Malpighian 'layer.** The inner side of man's outer skin, made up of CELLS which have not become dry and hard like those of the outside. **Malpighian 'pyramid.** Any of the pointed masses forming the inner part of the KIDNEY in man and other higher animals. **Malpighian tube.** Any of the pipe-like parts opening into the ALIMENTARY CANAL of an insect for the purpose of sending out waste material.

malpos'ition, n. [Med.] Wrong position. The condition of being out of place.

'malpresen'tation, n. [Med.] The coming of offspring to birth in some unnormal position in which it is unable to be sent out of the mother's body without medical help.

malt, n. Grain which has been caused to GERMINATE by making it soft in water and then dried, its STARCH having been in this way changed into sugar, used in the making of beer, etc., and medically for its food value in wasting diseases. **m. sugar.** MALTOSE.

'Malta 'fever. [Med.] UNDULANT FEVER.

'maltase, n. [Biochem.] An ENZYME changing MALTOSE into GLUCOSE.

mal'thusian, a. To do with the theory put forward by Malthus that the rate of increase in the number of men is quicker than that in the amount of food produced for them, and, if not controlled in some other way, will get to a point where it will necessarily be slowed down by need on a great scale, causing crime, disease, war, etc.

'maltose, n. [Chem.] A sugar formed from STARCH by the operation of DIASTASE, sp. in the GERMINATION of grain.

'mamma ('mammae), n. [Zoo.] Milk-producing structure of a female MAMMAL. **m. 'virilis.** RUDIMENTARY m. of a male. **'mammary,** a. **mammary gland.** The complex GLAND of which a m. is chiefly made up. **'mammate,** a. **mamm'iferous,** a. **'mammiform,** a.

Mam'malia, n.pl.]Zoo.] The highest CLASS of back-boned animals, taking in man, marked by having a skin almost completely covered with hair, and, in the female, MAMMAE for giving food to their offspring, which, in all but the MONOTREMES, undergo most of their development in the body of the mother and come to birth living. **'mammal,** n. Animal of the M. **mam'malian,** a.

ma'm(m)illa, n. [Zoo.] The pointed part of a MAMMA, from which milk is taken. **mam'(m)illar(y),** a. [Zoo.] Of, to do with, a m. [Bot.] MAMMIFORM. [Geol.] Made up

of or covered with MAMMIFORM masses. **'mamillary 'process** or **'tubercle.** METAPOPHYSIS. **'mam(m)ilate(d),** aa. [Biol.] Having small m.-like outgrowths. **mammi'lation,** n. A m.-like outgrowth; condition of having m(m). [Med.] Condition of being covered with small points like mm. **ma'm(m)illiform,** a.

M. and B. 693. [Med.] SULPHAPYRIDINE.

'mandible, n. [Zoo.] Hard, biting part of mouth, sp., in back-boned animals, the lower JAW-bone, in ARTHROPODA, one or other of the two front outgrowths of the mouth used for biting. **man'dibular,** a. **mandibular arch.** The first of the VISCERAL ARCHES forming part of the bone-structure of the mouth. **man'dibulate,** a. **mandi'buliform,** a. **man'dibulo-:— -'hyoid,** a. **-max'illary,** a.

'mandu'cation, n. MASTICATION.

'manganate, n. [Chem.] Any SALT having in it the group MnO_4.

'manganese, n. Chemical ELEMENT, at. no. 25, at. wt. 54·93, sign Mn, a hard, readily broken, white metal, chiefly used in making steel. **m. bronze.** [Metal.] An ALLOY of copper and zinc having in it about 4% Mn. **m. di'oxide.** The substance MnO_2, a black powder, present naturally in the earth in the form of PYROLUSITE, used for producing Mn, in making glass, and for a number of other purposes in science and industry. **m. steel** [Metal.] A very hard steel having in it about 13% Mn.

'manganin, n. ALLOY of copper with about 18% MANGANESE and 2% nickel, used for electric RESISTANCES.

mange, n. Skin disease of animals caused by certain ACARINA.

'Mangin 'mirror. [Optics] Hollow MIRROR of thick glass, the front and back of which are differently curved, so as to take away SPHERICAL ABERRATION.

'mania, n. [Med.] Form of mind disease marked by worked-up behaviour, uncontrolled motions and talk tc., strong outbursts of feeling,' alse ideas, and violent tendencies. **'maniac,** n. Person with m. **ma'niacal,** a. **'manic,** a. To do with m.

'manicate, a. [Bot.] Covered with a mass of hairs twisted together like cloth.

'manic-de'pressive, 1. a.[Med.] Said of mind-disease in which person is sometimes in a condition of MANIA, sometimes in one of MELANCHOLIA. 2.n. Person having m.-d. PSYCHOSIS.

'manifold, 1.a. Great in number and of a number of different sorts. [Mach., etc.] Made up of, having to do with, or working, a number of like parts or things. 2.n. [Eng.] A great pipe with a number of branches or holes for connection with other pipes going into or out of it, for example in an INTERNAL COMBUSTION ENGINE for intake and EXHAUST.

'**manna,** n. [Bot.] Sweet sticky substance put out by, and becoming hard on the outside of, certain trees, and having medical uses. [Zoo.] Sweet substance produced by certain APHIDIDAE.

'**mannitol,** n. [Chem.] A white CRYSTALLINE substance of the ALCOHOL group, present in a number of plants and forming the chief part of tree MANNA.

'**mannose,** n. [Chem.] A HEXOSE got by reaction of MANNITOL with O.

'**manograph,** n. [Eng.] An instrument worked by a light-ray, used for making INDICATOR DIAGRAMS on engines whose rate of motion is very high.

ma'**nometer,** n. [Phys.] An instrument for measuring the PRESSURE of a gas, commonly by balancing it against the air pressure on a liquid in a U-formed glass pipe. mano'**metric(al),** aa.

'**mantle,** n. [Zoo.] A loose covering part, sp.:— in MOLLUSCS and like animals, the soft fold of skin inside the SHELL, by which the shell is produced; in ASCIDIANS, the true body-wall under the hard outer cover; in birds, the back together with the folded wings. m. '**cavity.** In MOLLUSCS etc., space between the m. and the body; in ASCIDIANS the space inside the m. m. **lobes.** The back and front divisions of the m. of a BIVALVE.

'**mantle rock.** [Geol.] REGOLITH.

'**manual,** 1.a. Done, used, worked, by the hands. 2.n. [Zoo.] Wing-feather of a bird.

ma'**nubrium,** n. [Zoo.] A part formed as if for gripping with the hand, sp. certain parts of bones, such as the upper part of the chest-bone in man and like animals. [Bot.] A long CELL forming an outgrowth on the inside of every division of the wall of the ANTHERIDIUM in certain THALLOPHYTES.

ma'**nure,** n. Any substance, natural or made chemically, put on land to make it fertile, sp. the solid waste sent out by farm animals such as horses, cows, fowls.

'**manus** (manus), n. [Zoo.] The end division of a front leg or arm, the hand or front foot together with the small bones joining it to the upper part.

'**manyplies,** n. [Zoo.] OMASUM.

'**marble,** n. [Geol.] LIMESTONE (CaCO₃) which has been made CRYSTALLINE by heat, having property of taking a high polish and much used for building and in art. '**marbled.** [Bot.] Having irregular coloured marks as m. frequently has.

'**marcasite,** n. White IRON PYRITES, used for making cheap dress ornaments, jewels.

mar'**cescent,** a. [Bot.] (Of flower, etc.) drying up without falling off plant.

marconigram, n. Old name for RADIOGRAM.

mare, n. [Zoo.] Name given to the female of the horse and certain other like animals.

'**mare** (maria), n. [Astron.] The Latin name for 'sea', given to any flat space on the moon because such places were at one time taken to be seas.

ma'**remma,** n. [Med., Geog.] (Unhealthy air coming from) a low, wet stretch of country, sp. in Italy.

'**margarine,** n. Any of a number of substances like butter and designed to be used in place of it, made from plant or animal fats mixed with milk, the desired VITAMINS, etc.

'**margin,** n. Edge, or flat space banding it, as on an insect's wing, leaf, etc.; a limit to conditions, reasoning, etc. which does not take the form of a sharp line but of a narrow space inside which some range is possible. '**-al,** 1.a. Near, on, coming from, the edge of anything. [Psych.] To do with experiences which are not sharply noted by the mind, but come into it almost unconsciously as a part of those to which it is giving its attention. **marginal placen'tation.** [Bot.] PARIETAL PLACENTATION in an OVARY formed of one CARPEL. '**marginal plates.** [Zoo.] System of plates round edge of hard cover on back of CHELONIA. '**marginal ray cell.** [Bot.] A CELL for some special purpose present with others of the same sort on the edge of a VASCULAR RAY.

margi'**nalia,** n.pl. [Zoo.] Needle-like points round the openings of a sponge for keeping off attackers.

'**marigraph,** n. [Geog., etc.] Instrument recording how high the TIDE is at any place. '**marigram,** n. Record made by a m.

ma'**rine,** a. Of, to do with, living in, the sea. m. **denu'dation.** [Geol.] The rubbing away of the land by the sea. m. **engi'neering.** That branch of engineering which has to do with the building, engines, and apparatus, of ships and harbours.

'**mariner's 'compass.** Sort of COMPASS used at sea in which two or more MAGNETIC NEEDLES are fixed to the middle of a round card marked with the directions (north, north-east, etc.) and delicately balanced on a steel point, and sometimes in part supported by water and alcohol or some other liquid. (*floating-card compass*), inside a glass-covered box or brass bowl.

'**Mariotte's 'bottle** or **flask.** Glass vessel with a pipe running down into it through the cork, and outlets in the side, for giving a current of liquid with an unchanging PRESSURE dependent on the amount by which the base of the pipe is higher than the outlet used. '**Mariotte's law.** BOYLE'S LAW.

marl, n. [Geol.] Any CLAY with more or less chalk in it forming a readily broken earth or soft ROCK. **mar'laceous,** a. **'marlite,** n. A sort of m. not acted on by air.

marma'rosis, n. [Geol.] The changing of LIMESTONE into MARBLE.

marmo'raceous, a. Of, like, MARBLE.

'marmorate, a. [Bot.] Marked with lines or bits of colour, like MARBLE.

'marrow, n. [Zoo.] The soft substance forming the middle part of long bones (*yellow m.*) or present in the spaces in some bone-substances of a network structure (*red m.*).

Mars, n. [Astron.] The fourth PLANET from the sun, coming between the earth and JUPITER, having a mass about $\frac{1}{8}$ that of the earth, two small moons, and a 'year' of 687 days. (*See* p. 331.)

marsh, n. [Geog.] A stretch of low, flat land completely or in part under water which may be anything from an inch or two to two or three feet deep, gen. covered more or less thickly with tall, stiff water-grasses among which water-birds are common, but without trees. **m. gas.** METHANE (CH_4), a gas common over mm. and in mines.

Marsh's test. [Chem.] Very delicate test for ARSENIC in which the liquid to be tested is made to undergo reaction with H, producing AsH_3 which gives a blue flame by which a black coat of As may be formed on a cold glass.

'Marsipo'branchii, n.pl. [Zoo.] CYCLO-STOMATA.

Mar'supialia, n.pl. [Zoo.] An ORDER of MAMMALS whose young are kept in a pocket-like structure on the outside wall of the mother's ABDOMEN, where the MAMILLAE are. **mar'supial,** 1.n. Like, to do with the M. or a marsupium. 2. Animal of the M. **mar'supium,** n. The pocket-like structure of a marsupial; any like structure in lower animals, such as fishes, where eggs or young are kept.

'maser, n. [Phys.] A name made from the first letters of the words 'MICROWAVE AMPLIFICATION by STIMULATED EMISSION of RADIATION' and given to a low-noise AMPLIFIER or OSCILLATOR working by INDUCED EMISSION, but not in fact limited to microwaves, operation on INFRA-RED and longer waves being possible.

mask, n. Anything covering something so as to keep it from view, sp. [Med.] cover put over nose and mouth to keep INFECTION from being taken or given. **-ed,** a. Sp. [Med.] (of a disease) kept from being clearly seen because of other conditions being present with it. **'-ing,** n. Sp., [Acous.] the covering effect of one sound on another sounded with it.

'masochism, n. [Psych.] The getting of pleasure from undergoing pain caused by another, sp. in sex relation. **'masochist,** n. Person with tendency to m. **maso-'chistic,** a.

mass, n. [Phys.] The amount of material substance in a body, measured by its RESISTANCE to a change of motion or by the force of GRAVITY acting on it, which are equal. **m. 'action.** [Chem.] *See* LAW OF MASS ACTION. **m. de'fect.** The amount by which the weight of an ATOM is less than that of the weight of the parts of which it is made up. **m. number** (Of an isotope) the nearest INTEGER to the ISOTOPIC weight. **m. 'spectrograph.** Instrument for producing m. spectra by the use of electric and MAGNETIC FIELDS at right angles to the rays to be broken up. **m. spectrum.** The SPECTRUM of a POSITIVE RAY produced by a m. spectrograph, in which the ray is broken up into PARTICLES ranged in the order of their mm. so that their different at. wts. may be worked out from the spectrum—used in getting knowledge of ISOTOPES.

mass, a. To do with the behaviour, etc. of bodies or groups as such, not with that of the units forming them taken separately. **m. effect.** The tendency for hard steel to become less hard going from the outside to the middle, because of the different rates at which the parts have become cold.

'massage, n., v.t. [Med.] Rubbing and working the body with the hands or an instrument for the purpose of increasing the current of blood to the muscles, etc., so as to make it less stiff, take away pain. **mass'eur,** n. Man whose business is m. **mass'euse,** n. Woman whose business is m.

mass'eter, n. [Zoo.] In the higher back-boned animals, great muscle pulling up the under part of the mouth in the process of crushing food. **masse'teric,** a.

'massicot, n. [Chem., Mineral.] The substance PbO (*lead monoxide*) when it is not FUSED, a yellow-red powder present naturally in the earth or made by heating lead in air.

'massif, n. [Geol.] A mountain mass broken up in the higher part into separate mountains, the chief part or backbone of a mountain range; a large part of the outer earth which has been moved out of its place as one body, and is limited on all sides by FAULTS.

'massive, a. Of great size and weight; solid, of great weight for its size. [Mineral.] Taking the form of a mass without any clear or regular structure, though not necessarily non-CRYSTALLINE.

'massula, n. [Bot.] SPORES or POLLEN grains formed from one CELL and forming one mass.

'mastax, n. [Zoo.] In ROTIFERA, the PHARYNX where the food is crushed between horn-like parts.

mast, n. A tall, thin, upright rod or rod-like structure kept in position by cords, such as those supporting the sails of a ship, sp. [Radio] one supporting or forming the ANTENNA of a radio station.

mast cell, [Zoo., Med.] A sort of LEUCOCYTE full of grains of a strongly BASIPHIL substance, present in CONNECTIVE TISSUE, but in blood only in certain diseases.

mas'tectomy, n. [Med.] The operation of taking off a woman's MAMMARY GLAND.

'master, a. Said of a part or thing controlling, putting in operation, a number of like parts, or used as a guide or test for the design, size, etc, of other things of the same sort. **m. 'factor.** [Bot.] Any condition chiefly responsible for causing an important growth of certain plants in a place. **m. 'matrix.** [Acous.] The first metal copy of a sound record, made by plating the wax on which the sound has been recorded.

'mastic, n. A light yellow RESIN used in making good quality VARNISH.

masti'cation, n. The process of crushing food in the mouth or other part of an animal formed for this purpose; the process of crushing materials in a machine. **'masticate,** v.t. **masti'cator,** n. Sp., a machine for crushing rubber into a smooth mass. **masti'catory,** a.

Masti'gophora, n.pl. [Zoo.] A CLASS of small PROTOZOA having one or more FLAGELLA and without a MACRONUCLEUS.

mas'titis, n. [Med.] INFLAMMATION of a MAMMARY GLAND.

'mastoid, 1.a. [Zoo.] Formed like a MAMMA or MAMMELLA. 2.n. M. process. **m. process** or **bone.** [Zoo.] Somewhat pointed outgrowth on the bone at the back of the ear in higher animals. **m. 'antrum.** The hollow space in the m. bone. **mastoi'ditis,** n. [Med.] INFLAMMATION of a m.

mastur'bation, n. [Med., Psych.] Producing effect of sex-act on self by rubbing sex-parts, etc.

ma'surium, n. Old name for TECHNETIUM.

match, 1.v.t. [Optics] Get a colour (gen., in tests, seen as half the field of view) changed till it is seen to be the same as a given colour (gen. seen as the other half of the field of view). 2.n. A colour which is seen to be the same as another.

mate, 1.n. [Zoo.] (Of a male or female animal) the female (male) which takes part with it in producing offspring, one or other of two animals uniting or living together for this purpose. 2.v.i. and t. Take a m., become mm.; put one animal *with* another, or two animals together, to get offspring produced by them.

ma'terialism, n. Belief or theory that only physical things have existence, and that mind is only a form of behaviour of material substance. **ma'terialist,** n.

Person having this belief. **material'istic,** a

ma'teria 'medica. [Med.] Substances, material, used for medical purposes; the branch of science having to do with the properties of these.

ma'ternal, a. [Zoo.] To do with the mother. **m. in'heritance** The handing down of qualities as effect of the material given to the offspring by the OVUM, not the SPERM, or the qualities so handed down.

ma'ternity, n. Condition of being a mother.

mathe'matics, n. The general science of the properties and relations of space and of numbers, and of the operations by which desired facts about these may be got from given facts, of which arithmetic, geometry, algebra and so on are branches. **mathe'matical,** a. **mathe'matically,** adv.

matri'clinous, a. MATROCLINOUS.

'matrix, n. That inside or round which something is formed and from which it gets its form, as a vessel in which heated metal is let get cold; a mass of substance in which smaller bodies are bedded. [Acous.] A metal print of a wax record, from which other copies are made. [Biol.] The substance between the CELLS of CONNECTIVE TISSUE; UTERUS; the substance on which a FUNGUS or LICHEN has its growth; that part of a TISSUE in which something, such as a tooth or nail, is rooted.

matro'clin-al, -ic, -ous, aa. [Biol.] (Of offspring, INHERITANCE, etc.) having the qualities of the mother more marked than those of the father.

mat(te), n. Liquid made up of mixed SULPHIDES produced in the first stage of the process of getting a metal, for example, copper, from an ORE in which it is present as a sulphide.

'matter, n. [Phys.] Material substance, marked by the properties of GRAVITATION (that is, on earth, weight), and of being INDESTRUCTIBLE. [Med.] PUS.

'matur'ation, n. [Biol.] The process of development in GERM CELLS, male or female, by which they are made ready for uniting with one another for the producing of a fertile OVUM, sp. the later stages of this process. **m. division.** (Any of) the divisions undergone by the NUCLEUS in the process of MEIOSIS forming part of m.

ma'ture, a. [Biol.] Having come to, being at, the stage of complete growth or development. 2.v.t. and i. (Make) become m. **ma'tured,** a. Having become m.

max'illa (maxillae), n. [Zoo.] In back-boned animals, the upper JAW, or the bone supporting all or most of it; in ARTHROPODA one or other of the two outgrowths at the back of the MANDIBLES, formed in different ways for use as a mouth-part. **'maxillary,** 1.a., 2.n. The (chief) bone of the

m.; a maxillary nerve or blood-vessel.
maxillary glands. In some CRUSTACEA, two GLANDS for sending out waste, placed near the bases of the mm. **maxil-'liferous,** a. **max'illiform,** a.

max'illiped(e), n. [Zoo.] In ARTHROPODA, any of the two, four, or six outgrowths at the back of the MAXILLAE used for gripping food and putting it in the mouth.

max'illo-. MAXILLARY (and . . .):— -'**dental,** a.

max'illo'turbinal, n. [Zoo.] In back-boned animals, the right or left of two bones coming from the side walls of the nose and supporting the folds of the MUCOUS MEMBRANE which is the instrument of smell.

'maximum, n. The greatest in amount or highest in degree. **m.** (or **m. and minimum**) **ther'mometer.**[Meteor.]An instrument for recording the highest (or highest and lowest) TEMPERATURE of the air at a given place in a given time, gen. 24 hours.

'maxwell, n. [Phys.] The unit of MAGNETIC FLUX = the FLUX through 1 cm.^{2} at right angles to a field having an INTENSITY of one GAUSS.

'Maxwell's rule or **law.** [Elec.] The law that every part of an electric CIRCUIT has a tendency to motion in such a direction as to make the amount of MAGNETIC FLUX through it as great as possible.

MC, or **Mc,** or **mc** = MEGACYCLE(S).

Mc'Leod gauge. [Phys.] Instrument for measuring very low gas PRESSURES.

MC.P.S., or **Mcps,** or **mcps** or **mc/s** = MEGACYCLES per second.

mean, a., n. (Based on, being) an ARITHMETICAL MEAN; (condition, quality, and so on) equally far from two opposites, taken as representative of what is most normal, generally come across. [Astron.] Based on, measured by, the motion of the m. sun. **m. noon, m. solar day, m. (solar) time,** etc.). **m. 'calorie.** [Phys.] See CALORIE. **m. free path.** [Phys.] The m. distance covered by a MOLECULE of a gas before coming up against another molecule. [Acous.] The m. distance covered by a sound-wave between REFLECTIONS inside something. **m. sun.** The sun pictured as moving at the same rate all the time, so that the year taken for its seeming journey round the ECLIPTIC is made up of equal days, etc.

me'ander, 1.n. [Geog.] Any of the wide curves in a river which meanders. 2.v.i. Be all the time curving, first this way and then that. **m. belt.** Flat stretch of country between mountains in which a river meanders or makes a change in its bed from time to time. **m. line.** [Surveying] The general, straight-line outline of anything with a number of curves, such as a meandering river or land edging the

sea, etc., given by a TRAVERSE SURVEY.

'measles, n. [Med.] An INFECTIOUS disease, commonest in young persons, probably caused by a VIRUS, and marked by breathing-troubles, FEVER, and the covering of the skin with small, round, red SPOTS.

'measurement, n. The process of measuring; a measure of distance, etc.

me'atus, n. [Zoo.] A natural pipe-like opening into the body, as in the ear, nose, etc. **m. audi'torius** or **a'custicus.** The m. of the ear. **m. uri'narius** or **u'rethrae.** The opening of the URETHRA.

me'chanical, a. To do with machines; worked by a machine or engine, automatic. [Phys.] To do with MECHANICS. **m. ad'vantage.** Force produced by a machine ÷ force put on it, sp. by hand. **m. 'energy.** ENERGY as seen in the motion of bodies and the handing on of motion from one to another by material connection. **m. e'quivalent of heat.** The relation between the unit of m. energy and that of heat energy, that is, the amount of the first needed for producing one unit of the second = about 4·183 JOULES per CALORIE. **m. 'mixture.** [Chem.] Substance made up of two or more substances simply mixed together, not united by chemical reaction.

me'chanics, n. Science of the forces acting on bodies and the motions produced by them.

'mechanism, n. The system of parts working together in a machine; any system of parts, steps, processes, by which some purpose is effected; the theory that living processes are controlled by physical and chemical laws. **'mechanist.** Person having belief in the theory of m. **mecha'nistic,** a. To do with the theory of m.; controlled by fixed laws like the working of a machine, so that every event is the outcome of what has gone before. **mecha'nistic 'theory.** The theory of m.

'mechanize, v.t. Make machines take the place of hand-work etc. in (a process, industry, etc.), make MECHANICAL. **'mechani'zation,** n.

'Meckel's (Mec'kelian) 'cartilage or **rod.** [Zoo.] In lower back-boned animals, such as fish, the rod of CARTILAGE supporting the lower JAW; in higher back-boned animals, the arched framework of cartilage round which the jaw-bones are formed.

me'conium, n. [Zoo.] In certain insects, the waste produced by a PUPA as sent out in the form of a liquid from the ANUS of the newly formed complete insect.

'media, n. [Zoo.] Name given to certain middle structures, sp. in insects, the MEDIAL, and in back-boned animals, the part of the wall of a blood-vessel between the outside and the inside.

244

mediad, adv. [Biol.] Near or in the direction of a middle line or plane.

'medial, 1.n. [Zoo.] Middle VEIN of wing of insect. 2.a. At, near, to do with, the middle. **m.** (or **median**) **mo'raine.** [Geol.] The middle MORAINE formed from the moraines edging the sides of two meeting GLACIERS.

' median, 1.a. In the middle (of a thing or a scale), sp. [Zoo.] in the plane cutting an animal into right and left halves. 2.n. A m. line, point, or number. **m. nerve.** [Anat.] The nerve going down the middle of the front of the arm. **m. plane.** Sp., [Bot.] plane going through the middle of a leaf or flower. **m. vein.** Sp., [Anat.] the chief VEIN in the lower part of the arm.

media'stinum, n. [Zoo.] The space in the chest between the two halves of the LUNGS; a structure of CONNECTIVE TISSUE running up the back of the TESTIS and making an incomplete division of it into two sides (**m. testis**). **media'stinal,** a. **'mediastin'itis,** n. [Med.] INFLAMMATION of the m. of the chest.

'medical, a. To do with the science or processes of MEDICINE. **m. my'cology.** The science of FUNGUS diseases in man, for example RINGWORM.

me'dicament, n. Any substance used on or taken into the body for medical purposes. **'medicated,** a. (Of a substance) having a medical substance mixed into it as *m. cotton-wool,* a *m. dressing* for a wound. **'medicate,** v.t.

medi'cation, n. Act or process of giving medical substances to persons who are ill, using medical substances for overcoming disease; substance(s) used in m.; MEDICATING; substance with which another is MEDICATED.

'medicine, n. The science of overcoming disease, putting right any damage to or wrong condition of the body; that branch of m. which has to do with MEDICATION as opp. operations; any substance(s) used against disease, sp. one taken into the stomach for this purpose. **me'dicinal,** a. Having the properties of a m.

'medico-. Medical.

medi(o)-. Middle: **'medio'dorsal,** a., **'medio'ventral,** a.

'medium (mediums or media). 1.n. A thing which is about in the middle of a scale or range; anything used as an instrument for transporting or producing an effect. [Phys.] Substance through which forces or motions, for example, waves, are transported. [Chem.] A substance with which another is mixed to give it the physical properties desired for some purpose, a BASE in this sense, sp. a liquid or near-liquid with which a colouring-substance is mixed to make a paint.

[Biol.] Substance in which a given thing or animal has its being; CULTURE M. 2.a. Of middle size, quality, degree, condition. **m. wave,** Radio wave of WAVE-LENGTH roughly between 100 and 1000 m. **m.-'grained.** [Geol.] Made up of grains of m. size, that is, of a size great enough for the grain-structure to be seen without the help of an instrument, but not great enough for the different grains to be clearly separated by the eye.

'medius, n. [Anat.] The second finger, that is, the middle finger if the thumb is taken as one.

me'dulla, n. [Zoo.] MARROW; the middle or inner substance of a part; m. oblongata. [Bot.] PITH. **m. 'oblon'gata.** [Zoo.] In back-boned animals, the lower back part of the brain, narrowing down to the SPINAL CORD, in which are NERVE-CENTRES controlling breathing, the motion of the heart, and other automatic and necessary processes. **m. spin'alis.** [Zoo.] SPINAL CORD. **'medullate(d),** aa. [Biol.] Having PITH; having a MEDULLARY SHEATH. **'medull'ation,** n. The condition of having or the process of forming PITH or a MEDULLARY SHEATH.

me'dullary, a. [Biol.] To do with the MEDULLA. **m. 'axis** or **'layer.** [Bot.] In LICHENES, the thick ring of substance under the outer skin of the plant body. **m. ca'nal.** [Zoo.] The hollow full of MARROW in a long bone; pipe-like hollow housing the SPINAL CORD together with the hollows in the brain forming expansions of it. **m. folds.** [Zoo.] The edges of the m. groove. **m. groove** or **furrow.** [Zoo.] Hollow line down the middle of the m. plate. **m. plate.** [Zoo.] In the EMBRYO of a back-boned animal, a thick plate of ECTODERM formed down the middle of the back, the first stage in the development of the SPINAL CORD and brain. **m. ray.** [Bot.] VASCULAR RAY. [Zoo.] Any of the parcels of straight pipes going from the middle to the outer part of the KIDNEY in man and like animals. **m. sheath.** [Bot.] The outer coat of the PITH of a stem, of which the CELLS are gen. small and thick-walled and sometimes have been changed into XYLEM. [Zoo.] Coat of MYELIN covering a NERVE-FIBRE and in turn covered by a delicate skin. **m. tube.** Pipe-like hollow formed at a later stage of development by the joining of the edges of the m. groove. **m. 'velum.** In back-boned animals, a thin white plate of nerve-substance in the roof of the hollow in the lower back part of the brain.

me'dusa (medusae), n. [Zoo.] The free-swimming, sexed, and freq. the only form of SCYPHOZOA, an animal of which the body is a jelly-like mass, sometimes

bell-like in form, sometimes like a somewhat arched plate; the like, free-swimming form of the sexed stage of certain
HYDROZOA (commonly named 'jelly-
fish'). me′dusoid, 1.a. Being, like, to do
with, a m. or mm. 2.n. A medusoid
person; in certain COELENTERATA, a
sexed unit which is incomplete in its
development and does not become free
from the COLONY. me′dusoid ′person. A m.
as the sexed stage of a COELENTERATE
having ALTERNATION OF GENERATIONS,
opp. HYDROID PERSON.

meg(a)-. 1. Great, see MACRO-:— mega-
′gamete, n. [Zoo.], mega′lecithal, a. [Zoo.]
′megamere, n. [Zoo.], mega′nucleus, n.
[Zoo.], mega′phyllous, a. [Bot.]. 2. (Before
the names of measuring units, sp. [Elec.])
one million times (the named measure):—
′megohm, n.

′megace′phalic, a. [Med., Anthrop.] Having
a head of greater size than normal.
mega′cephaly, n. The condition of
being m.

′megacycle, n. [Phys.] 1,000,000 CYCLES, one
m. per second being used as a unit of
FREQUENCY, sp. for high-frequency
ALTERNATING CURRENT in radio.

mega′karyocyte, n. [Zoo.] MYELOPLAX
with one great NUCLEUS having in it a
number of small ones, present sp. in
bone, but in blood at an early stage of
development or in certain diseases.

′megalith, n. Great stone used in building
by early man. mega′lithic, a.

megal′(a)esthete, n. [Zoo.] In certain
MOLLUSCS, an instrument of sense somewhat like an eye and possibly giving
reaction to light, present in the MEGALO-
PORES.

′megal(o)-. Great, sp. [Med.] greater than
normal as effect of disease:— ′megalo-
′cardia, n. [Med.].

′megaloblast, n. [Zoo.] Sort of great CELL
present at early stage of development
from which ERYTHROBLASTS are later
produced.

′megalocyte, n. [Med.] ERYTHROCYTE of
more than normal size, present in the
blood in certain diseases.

′megalo′mania, n. [Med.] Condition of a
diseased mind in which a person has the
false belief that he is great and important.

′megalopore, n. [Zoo.] Any of the greater
openings in the hard outer cover of certain
MOLLUSCA in which the MEGALAESTHETES
are placed.

′megalops, n. [Zoo.] The last stage but one
in the development of certain DECAPODA,
in which the legs and like parts are present,
and the eyes are of great size on long
stems. mega′lopic, a.

′megalo′sphere, n. [Zoo.] The great SHELL
formed first by the sexed forms of certain
FORAMINIFERA. megalo′spheric, a. Hav-

ing the first-formed SHELL great in size.

-megaly, n. [Med.] (Of a named part)
growth to an unnormal size, the condition of being over-great in size.

me′gameter, n. An instrument for measuring
LONGITUDE by observation of the stars.

megane′phridium (meganephridia), n. [Zoo.]
In certain worms, any of the common sort
of NEPHRIDIA which come two together in
every ring of the body, as opp. MICRO-
NEPHRIDIUM.

′megaphone, n. Apparatus for making
sound louder, or sending it a greater
distance, sp. an instrument like a great
horn used for talking through.

mega′seism, n. [Geol.] A violent EARTH-
QUAKE. mega′seismic, a.

′megaspore, n. [Bot.] In seed plants and
some FILICALES, the greater of the two
sorts of unsexed SPORES from which come
those producing the sex-CELLS, that is,
the spore producing the female GAMETO-
PHYTE, or, in seed-plants, the EMBRYO
SAC. megaspo′rangium (megospo-rangia),
n. Vessel producing mm. mega′sporophyll,
n. Leaf-like structure producing mega-
sporangia.

′megatherm, n. [Bot.] Any plant needing
great heat and much water, that is,
TROPICAL conditions.

′megaton, n. The unit used in measuring
the EXPLOSIVE force of ATOMIC BOMBS
etc., equal to that of 1,000,000 TONS of
TRINITROTOLUENE.

′megrim, n. [Med.] MIGRAINE.

Mei′bomian glands, n.pl. [Zoo.] The
SEBACIOUS GLANDS of the EYELIDS of
higher animals.

′meioscyte, n. [Biol.] A CELL undergoing
MEIOSIS.

mei′omery, n. [Biol.] Condition of having
less than the normal number of parts,
mei′omerous, a.

mei′ophylly, n. [Bot.] Condition in which
less than the normal number of leaves
are present in a WHORL.

mei′osis, n. [Biol.] The special process of
NUCLEAR division completing the development of a sex-CELL, in which the
NUCLEUS first undergoes division into
two without, as in MITOSIS, having
increased the number of its CHROMO-
SOMES, and then these nuclei undergo a
further division as in mitosis, the outcome being four daughter-nuclei, every
one of which has half the number of
chromosomes present in other cells of the
same plant or animal. mei′otic, a.

meio′stemonous, a. [Bot.] Having STAMENS
less in number than PETALS or SEPALS.

meio′taxy, n. [Bot.] Condition in which a
complete WHORL of leaves or other parts
is not there.

′Meissner's ′corpuscles. [Zoo.] Nerve-endings of special structure to do with the

sense of touch, present in parts of the skin without hair, such as the ends of the fingers. **'Meissner's 'plexus.** A mass of nerve threads between the MUCOUS MEMBRANE and the muscles of the INTESTINES.

'Meissner ef'fect. [Phys.] Effect by which metals, when SUPER-CONDUCTING, have MAGNETIC PERMEABILITY = O.

mela'n(a)emia, n. [Med.] Condition in which grains of MELANIN are present in the blood as effect of the destruction of HAEMOGLOBIN.

melan'cholia, n. [Med.] Condition of mind, present, for example, in MANIC-DEPRESSIVE PSYCHOSIS, in which person is deeply unhappy, given up to sad feelings, unreasoning fears, a desire for death, etc. **melan'cholic,** a. **melan'choliac,** n. Person having m.

mela'niferous, a. [Zoo.] (Of parts) having or producing MELANIN.

'melanin, n. [Biochem.] Any of sorts of dark brown or black colouring-substances present naturally or as effect of disease in skin, hair, or other parts of the bodies of animals.

'melanism, n. [Zoo., Med.] Over-producing of MELANIN causing unnormally dark colour of body or part. **mela'nistic,** a.

melan(o)-. Dark, black: **me'lano-sporous,** a. [Bot.]

'Melano'chroi, n.pl. [Anthrop.] CAUCASIANS of the sort having dark hair and eyes, sometimes light-skinned, sometimes quite dark-skinned.

'melano'cratic, a. [Geol.] (Of IGNEOUS ROCKS, dark-coloured as the effect of having in them a great amount of substances formed of iron and Mg.

'melanocyte, n. [Zoo.] LYMPHOCYTE with MELANIN in it.

mela'noma, n. [Med.] Dark-coloured diseased growth.

'melanophore, n. [Zoo.] A black colour-CELL.

'melanosar'coma, n. [Med.] A small SARCOMA having a dark colour caused by MELANIN, gen. starting in the skin of the CHOROID coat of the eye.

mela'nosis, n. [Med.] Condition in which there is over-much MELANIN in TISSUES. **mela'notic,** a. [Zoo., Med.] Marked by much, sp. over-much, MELANIN, dark-coloured. **mela'notic sar'coma.** MELANOSARCOMA.

mel'anterite, n. [Mineral.] Natural COPPERAS.

mela'nuria, n. [Med.] Condition in which there is MELANIN in person's URINE.

'melli-. [Zoo.] HONEY:— **mell'iferous,** a. **mell'iphagous, mell'ivorous,** aa.

melt, 1.v.t. and i. [Phys.] (Of a solid) make or become liquid as effect of heat. 2.n. Melted substance, or amount melted at one operation. **'melting-point.** TEMPERATURE at which a given solid melts.

'member, n. [Biol.] Any of the unit parts of which a plant is made up; any ORGAN of an animal sp. one forming an addition to the body, such as an arm, leg, feeler; unit of a given group of animals or plants.

mem'brana, n. [Zoo.] A MEMBRANE. **m. granu'losa.** Inner coat of the wall of a GRAAFIAN FOLLICLE. **m. re'ticu'laris** or **m. tec'toria.** A soft net-like MEMBRANE covering CORTI'S ORGAN. **m. tym'pani.** The TYMPANIC MEMBRANE. **m. ves'tibu'laris.** REISSNER'S MEMBRANE.

'membrane, n. (A bit of) thin, skin-like material, sp. made from plant or animal substance, used in science apparatus. [Biol.] (A bit of) very thin CONNECTIVE TISSUE, forming a skin or covering for the walls of plant or animal parts, or making divisions in them or between CELLS, etc. [Zoo.] The thin outer part of the front wings of certain insects. **m. bone.** Bone formed straight from CONNECTIVE TISSUE without going through a CARTILAGE stage, present in the roof of the head and parts of the PECTORAL GIRDLE in most back-boned animals. **membran'aceous,** n. **membran'iferous,** a. **'membranoid, 'membranous,** a. **membranous 'labyrinth.** [Zoo.] *See* INNER EAR. **membranous 'vertebral 'column.** [Zoo.] The covering of MESODERM round the NOTOCHORD and MEDULLARY TUBE.

membra'nella, n. [Zoo.] In some PROTOZOA, a waving band formed by united CILIA.

membra'nula, n. [Zoo.] A CELL ORGAN formed in some CILIOPHORA by the uniting of CILIA.

'Men'deléeff's Table. [Chem.] The PERIODIC TABLE.

mende'levium, n. Chemical ELEMENT, at. no. 101, at. wt. 256, sign Md, a RADIO-ACTIVE substance.

Men'delian, a. [Biol.] To do with, in agreement with, MENDEL'S THEORY, or MENDEL'S LAW. **M. 'character.** A quality which is handed on to offspring in agreement with MENDEL'S LAW, that is, an ALLELOMORPH. **M. unit.** A GENE. **'-ism,** n.

'Mendelism, n. [Biol.] Belief in, or operation of, MENDEL'S THEORY.

'Mendel's 'theory of in'heritance. Theory that the handing on of qualities to offspring is dependent on physical units ('genes') representative of different qualities, and that when two GERM-CELLS are united, their genes are given to their offspring in equal numbers, so that mixed qualities are produced, but that when two producing animals or plants have opposite degrees or forms of certain qualities (for example size, colour of eyes, etc.), a given one of these (the **dominant character**) is regularly present in the offspring in place of the other (the **recessive character**) or anything markedly between the two. **Mendel's Law.** Law that all the offspring produced by two animals or plants, one of which has a dominant and the other a recessive character, will have the dominant character, and that 75% of the offspring produced by uniting these offspring will in turn be like them, the other 25% having the recessive character.

'**menhir,** n. [Archaeol.] A great, upright, rough stone, by itself or one of a line, circle etc. of such stones, put up by early man.

-**menia,** n. [Med.] MENSES.

Ménie´ère's di´sease. [Med.] Disease of inner ear marked by a sense of noise in the ear, a feeling that one's head is going round, trouble in keeping one's balance, and the loss by degrees of the sense of hearing.

me´**ninges,** n.pl. [Zoo.] The three MEMBRANES covering the brain and the SPINAL CORD in back-boned animals. me´**ningeal,** a. menin´**gitic,** a. menin´**gitis,** n. [Med.] INFLAMMATION of the m. or any of a number of diseases causing this. me´**ningocele,** n. [Med.] HERNIA of the m. through some part of the brain-cover or the backbone. me´**ningo-.**

me´**niscus,** n. [Phys., Chem.] The curved top of a liquid in a narrow pipe. [Anat.] Small plate of CARTILAGE between two bones, cushioning them from one another, sp. in knee. [Optics] LENS with one face incurving, the other out-curving. me-´**niscate,** me´**niscoid,** aa.

men(o)-. [Med.]. MENSES:—**meno´sepsis,** n.

meno´**pause,** n. [Zoo., Med.] The natural coming to an end of a woman's power of giving birth, gen. when between 45 and 50 years old, marked by the stopping of MENSTRUATION.

meno´**phania,** n.[Med.] The first taking place of MENSTRUATION in a girl.

menor´**rhagia,** n. [Med.] Unnormally great loss of blood in MENSTRUATION.

menor´**rh(o)ea,** n.[Med.] Normal MENSTRUATION; menstruation with MENORRHAGIA.

meno´**taxis,** n. [Med.] Unnormal increase in the time for which MENSTRUATION goes on. [Zoo.] The motions of an animal in keeping the body in a fixed direction in relation to some sense STIMULUS, as in watching something while walking.

´**mensa,** n. [Zoo.] The biting edge or side of a tooth.

´**menses,** n.pl. [Zoo.] Blood sent out at regular times from the UTERUS of a higher female animal, sp. a woman, as effect of the exchanging of old TISSUE for new inside the uterus, which goes on as long as an animal is in the stage of existence designed for producing offspring.

´**menstrual,** a. [Zoo.] Of, to do with MENSTRUATION. [Astron.] Taking place once a month.

menstru´**ation,** n. [Zoo.] The process of producing the MENSES, which normally takes place in woman every four weeks, going on for between three and five days. ´**menstruate,** v.i.

´**menstruum,** n. SOLVENT.

´**mensual,** a. To do with a month, taking place every month.

mensur´**ation,** n. [Maths.] That branch of geometry which has to do with working out the measure of lines, AREAS and VOLUMES.

´**mental,** a. Of, to do with, taking place in, the mind. [Med.] To do with m. diseases or persons having them. [Zoo.] To do with the MENTUM. **m. age.** [Psych.] A measure of a person's m. development given as the AGE at which a normal person would be at the same stage. **m. de´fective,** n. Person who is mentally deficient. **m. de´ficiency.** [Med.] The condition of being mentally deficient. **m. ´healing.** [Med.] The art or process of attempting to overcome physical diseases or conditions by putting the mind in order or using it as an instrument of control. **m. hy´giene.** [Med.] The science and art of keeping persons mentally healthy. **´-ism,** n. [Psych.] The theory that conscious processes are the right field of psychology and INTROSPECTION its instrument, opp. BEHAVIORISM. **´-ly,** adv. ´**mentally de-´ficient.** [Med.] Not having the power of complete m. development, being stopped at any stage from IDIOCY to MORONITY.

´**menthol,** n. [Chem.] A white CRYSTALLINE COMPOUND of CAMPHOR present in natural oils, $C_{10}H_{20}O$, with a strong but pleasing taste and smell, used medically as an ANTISEPTIC and for rubbing on a part to take away pain.

´**mentum,** n. [Zoo.] The chin; in insects, a plate forming front part of base of LABIUM; in some GASTROPODA, an outgrowth between the head and the foot.

mer´**captan,** n. [Chem.] Any of a group of bad-smelling ORGANIC COMPOUNDS having in them an –SH group, of a like structure to the ALCOHOLS, sp. C_2H_5SH (**ethyl m.**), used in the making of rubber, SULPHONAL, etc.

mer´**captide,** n. [Chem.] Any of the SALTS of MERCAPTANS.

Mer´cator's pro´jection. [Geog.] System of map-making in which the MERIDIANS OF LONGITUDE are placed parallel to one another and the PARALLELS OF LATITUDE are straight lines whose distance from one another is increased with their distance from the EQUATOR, so that at all points the relation between latitude and longitude is the same as it would be on a ball representative of the earth.

´**Mercury,** n. [Astron.] The PLANET nearest to the sun, round which it goes in 88 days, the smallest planet in the sun's system, of mass about $\frac{1}{29}$ of the earth. (See p. 331.)

'mercury, n. Chemical ELEMENT, at. no. 80, at. wt. 200·61, sign Hg, a silver-white liquid metal, a SOLVENT for most other metals, forming with them complex substances named *amalgams.* m. 'fulminate. A white CRYSTALLINE substance formed of mixed ALCOHOL, NITRIC ACID, and m., a violent EXPLOSIVE used in DETONATORS etc. m. 'vapour lamp, Apparatus producing strong blue light with much ULTRAVIOLET RADIATION in it, as the effect of sending an electric current through m. gas in a bulb—used medically, in camera work, and in streetlighting. mer'curial, a. [Chem., Med.] Having in it, or caused by, m. mer'curic, a. [Chem.] Having m. in it, said sp. of complex substances in which m. has a VALENCY of 2. mer'curic 'chloride. CORROSIVE SUBLIMATE. mer'curous, a. [Chem.] Having m. in it, said sp. of complex substances in which m. has a VALENCY of 1. mer'curous 'chloride. CALOMEL.

-mere, n. [Biol.] Part. -meric, -merous, aa. Having parts of the given sort or number. -merism, -mery, n. Condition of being -meric.

meri-. Part.

'mericarp, n. [Bot.] One-seeded part of a dry fruit made up of two or more such parts separating when ready (see CREMOCARP, SCHIZOCARP).

me'ridian, n. [Astron.] Great circle going through the CELESTIAL POLES and the point in the CELESTIAL SPHERE straight overhead at the place of observation. [Geog., etc.] Circle round the earth going through the North and South POLES, sp. any of those circles fixed at certain distances in relation to which LONGITUDE is measured, or any of the lines representative of these on a map (m. of 'longitude). m. 'altitude. [Astron.] The angle measuring the distance on the m. between the highest point at which a star goes across it and the HORIZON. m. circle. [Astron.] An instrument for the observation of the times at which stars go across the m., formed of a scale in the form of a complete circle with a TELESCOPE turning in the plane of the m. m. 'passage [Astron.] TRANSIT. m. plane. [Surv., etc.] The upright plane in the direction of true north and south.

me'ridional, a. [Geog., Astron.] To do with, placed in, the south; to do with a MERIDIAN. m. 'furrow. [Zoo.] Hollow line going from POLE to pole in an egg undergoing division.

'merism, n. [Bot.] The development of a number of like parts, gen. forming a balanced design.

meris'matic, a. [Bot.] To do with MERISTEM, having power of growth like meristem. [Zoo.] METAMERIC.

me'rismoid, a. [Bot.] In FUNGI, having a branched PILEUS.

'merispore, n. [Bot.] One division or SPORE of a complex spore-body.

'meri'stele, n. [Bot.] A separate, outpointing part of a MONOSTELIC stem from which a leaf comes.

'meristem, n. [Bot.] Plant substance made up of like CELLS which have undergone no development for special purposes and all of which have the power of producing new cells by division, present at GROWTH POINTS. 'meriste'matic, a.

me'ristic, a. [Biol.] Made up of, undergoing division into, like parts, sp. METAMERES; to do with such division or the number of such parts. m. vari'ation. A change in the number of divisions.

me'ristoge'netic, a. [Bot.] Having development from a MERISTEM.

'mermaid's purse. [Zoo.] Bag-like cover round the eggs of ELASMOBRANCHI.

mer(o)-. [Zoo.] FEMUR; [Biol.] MERI-.

mero'blastic, a. [Zoo.] (Of eggs) undergoing division only in part, sp. because made up chiefly of food material.

me'rocerite, n. [Zoo.] The fourth division of a feeler in CRUSTACEA.

'merochrome, n. [Chem.] A CRYSTAL made up of two ISOMERS having different colours.

'merocyte, n. [Zoo.] Any of the NUCLEI formed by the division of unused SPERM nuclei in the part of a MEROBLASTIC egg not undergoing division.

mero'gamete, n. [Zoo.] In PROTOZOA, a GAMETE much smaller than the normal CELLS, produced by a process of division after division, opp. HOLOGAMETE. me'rogamy, n. The condition of producing mm.; the uniting of mm.

mero'genesis, n. [Biol.] The producing of, or division into, like parts. meroge'netic, a.

merog'nathite, n. [Zoo.] The fourth division of a mouth-part in CRUSTACEA.

me'rogony, n. [Zoo.] The development into an EMBRYO of a part of a FERTILIZED OVUM not having in it the female NUCLEUS.

mero'hedrism, n. [Cryst.] Condition of having only one-half or one-quarter of the complete number of CRYSTAL FACES, but with balanced structure; loss of some of the normal number of crystal faces by chance, without system. mero'hedral, a.

mero'istic, a. [Zoo.] (Of OVARIES) producing food-forming CELLS as well as OVA.

merome, n. [Zoo.] METAMERE.

mero'morphosis, n. [Zoo.] The forming of the same part again on a smaller scale after its loss.

'meron, n. [Zoo.] Back part of an insect's COXA.

mero′plankton, n. [Zoo.] PLANKTON living for only part of the time near the top of water.

me′ropodite, n. [Zoo.] The 4th division from the base of a walking-leg or MAXILLIPED in some CRUSTACEA.

′merosome, n. [Zoo.] METAMERE.

mero′sthenic, a. [Zoo.] With the back legs much greater and stronger than the front.

me′rotomy, n. [Biol.] Division into parts.

mero′zoite, n. [Bot.] SPORE produced by division of a SCHIZONT in certain SPORO-ZOA.

mero′zoön, n. [Zoo.] Part cut from a one-CELLED animal, having in it a bit of the NUCLEUS.

mes-. MESO-.

′mesarch, a. [Bot.] Forming METAXYLEM all round the first-formed wood, as FILICALES.

mesa′denia, n.pl. [Zoo.] In male insects, ACCESSORY GLANDS formed from MESO-DERM.

′mescal, n. The dried button-like tops of a small plant of the CACTACEAE, having a strong effect on the nerves and used medically by the Indians of Mexico.

mese′ctoderm, n. [Zoo.] In EMBRYOS, the mass of CELLS later undergoing division into MESODERM and ECTODERM.

mes′embryo, n. [Zoo.] BLASTULA.

′mesen′cephalon, n. [Zoo.] Middle part of brain in back-boned animals. **′mesen-cephalic,** a.

mesen′chyma, ′mesenchyme, nn. [Zoo.] In an EMBRYO, that part of the MESOBLAST, made up of somewhat widely-spaced, branching CELLS in a jelly-like substance, from which blood, bone, CARTILAGE, etc. are produced. **mesen′chymal, ′mesen-chy′matic, mesen′chymatous,** aa.

mes′endoderm, n. [Zoo.] In EMBRYOS, mass of CELLS later′becoming MESODERM and ENDODERM.

′mesen′teric(al), aa. [Zoo.] To do with a MESENTERY.

me′senteron, n. [Zoo.] MID-GUT; the middle space of the body-hollow in COELEN-TERATA having MESENTERIES.

′mesentery, n. [Zoo.] In back-boned animals, the fold, or one of the folds, of the material covering the inside of the ABDOMEN, by which the VISCERA are supported and kept in position, and blood-vessels, nerves etc. are transported; in man, sp. the m. of the SMALL INTESTINE; in COELENTERATA a fold of the body-wall forming an upright division in the body hollow. **mesen′teric,** a.

me′sethmoid, n., a. [Zoo.] (Bone in the head of back-boned animals) between the two ETHMOID bones.

mesh, 1.n. (Any of the openings in) a net or network; the number of holes in an inch of wire net, etc., used as a measure of the size of a substance able to be put through such a net. 2.v.i. [Mach.] Of toothed wheels or a wheel and RACK, get into connection with one another, so that the teeth of one are working against those of the other. **m. con′nection.** [Elec.] A SERIES of CONDUCTORS forming a CLOSED CIRCUIT for ALTERNATING CURRENT.

′mesiad, adv. In the direction of the middle plane.

′mesia-l, -n, aa. [Zoo.] In the middle plane. **m. plane.** MEDIAN PLANE. **mesio-.**

′mesmerism, n. [Psych.] HYPNOTISM. **′mes-merist,** n. **′mesmerize,** v.t. **mesmeri′za-tion,** n.

mes(o)-. 1. In the middle:— **meso′phloem,** n. [Bot.], **meso′tarsal,** a. [Zoo.], **meso-′ventral,** a. [Zoo.]. 2. [Zoo.] MESENTERY supporting, etc., what is named:—**meso-′caecum,** n. **meso′colon,** n. **meso′varium,** n.

***meso-.**[Chem.] Having no OPTICAL ACTIVITY because of balanced positions of ATOMS in the MOLECULE.

meso′benthos, n. [Biol.] Plants and animals living on the sea floor between 200 and 1000 metres down.

′mesoblast, n. [Zoo.] The middle GERM-LAYER of a TRIPLOBLASTIC animal, under-going development into muscle, blood, bone, and most other materials between the skin of the body and the inner coat of the ALIMENTARY CANAL. **meso′blastic,** a.

meso′cardium, n. [Zoo.] Skin joining heart of EMBRYO to body wall and INTESTINE; the part of the PLEURA united with the PERICARDIUM.

′mesocarp, n. [Bot.] The middle of the three LAYERS of a PERICARP.

′mesoce′phalic, a. [Zoo.] To do with the middle part of the head; (of man) having a head of middle size.

′mesocoel(e), n. [Zoo.] The hollow of the MESENCEPHALON.

′meso′colloid, n. [Chem.] A COLLOID formed of PARTICLES ranging in size from ·025 to ·25 MICRONS.

meso′cratic, a. [Geol.] (Of IGNEOUS ROCKS) formed of dark and light substances in almost equal amounts, in the middle of the scale between LEUCOCRATIC and MELANOCRATIC.

′mesoderm, n. [Zoo.] MESOBLAST; all the materials having their development from the mesoblast. **meso′dermal,** a.

′mesodont, a. [Zoo.] Having middle-sized teeth, or, of insects, teeth-like parts.

meso′gaster, meso′gastrium, nn. [Zoo.] In back-boned animals, the MESENTERY supporting the stomach.

meso′gloea, n. [Zoo.] A jelly-like substance between the inner and outer walls of sponges and COELENTERATA.

meso′lecithal, a. [Zoo.] Of eggs, having the YOLK in the middle.

Meso'lithic, a., n. (Of) the stage in the history of man's development between PALAEOLITHIC and NEOLITHIC.

'mesomere, n. [Zoo.] In the EMBRYOS of back-boned animals, the middle MUSCLE PLATE.

'mesomi'tosis, n. [Biol.] MITOSIS which takes place inside the skin of the NUCLEUS without any mixing with the substance outside it.

meso'morphous, a. [Chem.] Having a structure which is not completely irregular but not quite CRYSTALLINE.

'meson, n. [Phys.] One of a sort of FUNDAMENTAL PARTICLES whose mass is between that of an ELECTRON and that of a PROTON, present in COSMIC RAYS.

'mesone'phridium, n. [Zoo.] In some animals without backbones, a NEPHRIDIUM formed from MESODERM.

meso'nephros, n. [Zoo.] The middle and first-formed one of the three parts acting as the KIDNEY in the EMBRYO of back-boned animals, which in most lower animals becomes the kidney itself, but in higher animals gives place in the process of development to the METANEPHROS. **meso'nephric,** a.

meso'phi"ic bacteria [Bact.] BACTERIA which have their best growth at a degree of heat between 10° and 40°C.

meso'notum, n. [Zoo.] The back part of the MESOTHORAX of insects.

mesophyll, n. [Bot.] The PARENCHYMA inside a leaf.

'mesophyte, n. [Bot.] Plant living in middle conditions of heat and wet.

meso'plankton, n. [Biol.] PLANKTON living in the middle levels of the sea, from 200 m. down.

meso'podiale, n. [Zoo.] Any one of the bones of the METACARPUS or METATARSUS.

meso'podium (mesopodia), n. [Zoo.] The middle part of the foot of MOLLUSCA; METACARPUS or METATARSUS. **meso'podial,** a.

'mesopr(a)e'scutum, n. [Zoo.] The PRESCUTUM of an insect's MESOTHORAX.

me'sopte'rygium, n. [Zoo.] The middle one of the three base CARTILAGES in the front fins of CHONDRICHTHYES.

mesop'terygoid, n. [Zoo.] A part or outgrowth of the PTERYGOID bone in certain birds and fishes; in higher animals, the space between the pterigoid bones.

mes'orchium, n. [Zoo.] In back-boned animals, the MESENTERY supporting the male sex-part.

meso(r)'rhinal, a. [Zoo.] Between the breathing-holes of the nose.

meso'seismal, a. [Geol.] To do with the middle point of an EARTHQUAKE.

'mesosperm, n. [Bot.] The skin round the NUCLEUS of an OVULE.

'mesospore, n. [Bot.] The middle coat of a SPORE having 3 coats; RESTING SPORE before the start of development; one-CELLED TELIOSPORE.

me'sostasis, n. [Geol.] The chief material of a mixed ROCK.

'mesostate, n. [Zoo., Med.] A middle stage in the process of METABOLISM, or the substances produced in such a stage.

meso'sternum, n. [Zoo.] The middle part of the STERNUM, or, in insects, the sternum of the MESOTHORAX.

meso'thelium, n. [Zoo.] That part of the MESOBLAST forming the wall of the body-hollow in the EMBRYO, and from which the inner coats of the body-hollows (for example, the PERITONEUM), the STRIATED MUSCLES and the heart muscle have their development—different from MESENCHYME in being formed of flat CELLS with little material or space between them.

meso'thorax, n. [Zoo.] The middle division of an insect's THORAX. **'mesotho'racic,** a.

meso'thorium, n. [Chem.] A RADIO-ACTIVE ISOTOPE of Ra used in place of it for some medical and other purposes; a radioactive isotope of Ac.

meso'varium, n. [Zoo.] The fold of the PERITONEUM by which the OVARY is joined to the wall of the body.

Meso'zoic, a., n. [Geol.] (To do with, being) the M. era; the group of ROCK SYSTEMS formed in the M. era. **M. 'era.** The third of the five great divisions of the earth's history, the time of winged and other land and sea REPTILES of very great size, about the middle of which birds and flowering plants first came into existence. (*See* p. 558.)

'met(a)-. [Biol.] (Of a stage or part) coming after, at the back of, higher or later than, or forming the end of, what is named. [Chem.] Being an ISOMER or POLYMER of, or in some other near relation to, what is named; (before names of INORGANIC acids and ANHYDRIDES) formed from the normal or 'ortho-' acid etc. by the loss of water, gen. of one MOLECULE per molecule (*see* ORTHO-, PARA-).

'meta(-). [Chem.] (Before names of BENZENE DERIVATIVES) in which the place of the H ATOM is taken by another substance in two of the groups of the BENZENE RING, between which is one CH group, sign *m*. **m. position.** The position of the changed groups, with one CH group between them, in a m.-DERIVATIVE.

me'tabasis, n. [Med.] A change, for example, in a disease, its effects, the steps taken against it, etc.

meta'batic, a. [Phys.] To do with the handing on from one thing to another of heat or any other form of ENERGY.

'metabi'osis, n. [Biol.] A relation between living things in which one is dependent for its existence on the death before it of the other, by which the right conditions for the second are produced.

me'tabolism, n. [Biol.] All the chemical processes which are all the time going on in a living thing and effecting the building up and the destruction of living substance (see ANABOLISM and KATABOLISM). **meta-'bolic,** a. **me'tabolin, me'tabolite,** nn. Any substance taking part in or produced by m. **me'tabolize,** v.t. Get changed by m.

me'taboly, n. [Bot.] The property of some plant CELLS or one-celled plants of changing their form.

meta'carpus, n. [Zoo.] The part, sp. the bones, of the hand or front foot other than the fingers or toes, in man's hand made up of 5 rod-like bones. **meta-'carpal,** a.

'metacentre, n. (Of a ship, etc.) the meeting-point of the normal PERPENDICULAR through the CENTRE OF GRAVITY and the perpendicular through the CENTRE OF BUOYANCY when the vessel is sloping to one side, important for the working out of STABILITY.

meta'cestode, n. [Zoo.] LARVA with bag-like covering formed by CESTODA.

meta'chemical, a. [Geol.] METASOMATIC. [Chem.] To do with metachemistry. **meta'chemistry,** n. The chemistry of the behaviour of ATOMS and their parts.

Metachla'mydeae, n.pl. [Bot.] SYMPETAL-AE.

meta'chromas-is, -y, nn.[Biol.] The property seen in parts of CELLS of becoming a different colour from that of a BASIC colouring-substance acting on them. **'metachro'matic,** a. metachromatic body or 'granule. Any of the grains of stored food in BACTERIA which are more readily and deeply coloured by colouring-substances than the parts round them.

meta'chromatin, n. [Biochem.] A complex substance of like properties to CHROMATIN present in CELL-substance in the form of small grains, probably a COMPOUND of NUCLEIC ACID. **'metachnoma'tinic,** a.

meta'chromatism, a. [Phys.-Chem.] A change of colour caused by a change in physical conditions, sp. in degree of heat. **'metachro'matic,** a.

meta'chromy, n. [Bot.] A changing of colour.

meta'chrosis, n. [Zoo.] The power of changing colour by the expansion and the opposite of special colour-CELLS, by which some animals keep themselves from being readily seen.

meta'coele, n. [Zoo.] The fourth VENTRICLE of the brain in back-boned animals.

meta'coracoid, n. [Zoo.] The back part of the CORACOID PROCESS.

'metadis'coidal, a. [Zoo.] (Of PLACENTA) of sort seen in man and higher monkeys, having the VILLI at first all over the CHORION but later grouped in the form of a round plate.

me'tadromous, a. [Bot.] (Of leaf, or plant with such leaves) having the chief VEINS of any division coming from the upper side of the middle vein, as in some FILICALES.

meta'genesis, n. [Biol.] ALTERNATION OF GENERATIONS. **'metage'netic,** a.

'metal, n. [Chem.] Any ELEMENT of the sort readily forming POSITIVE IONS and having the marked properties of being DUCTILE and MALLEABLE, of readily transporting heat and electric current, of uniting with O to give BASES, and, in the mass, of having a more or less polished look, all but Hg being solids of CRYSTALLINE structure at normal degrees of heat; and ALLOY. **me'tallic,** a. To do with, made of, producing a m.; like a m. generally, or in some special property; (of sound) like that produced when thin m. is given a blow. **me'tallic lustre.** The look produced by the way in which a m., sp. polished steel, gives back the light, seen in some other substances. **-li'ferous,** a. [Geol.] **metallo-.**

met'aldehyde, n. [Chem.] A white, readily fired, poison solid in the form of long needle-like CRYSTALS, $(C_2H_4O)_3$, produced from ACETALDEHYDE by POLY-MERIZATION and used for burning in small heaters.

metalli'zation, n. [Chem.] Process of getting a substance into a METALLIC form. **'metallize,** v.t. **'metallized,** a. Having undergone m.; coated with a metal.

metal'lography, n. Branch of METALLURGY which has to do with the physical structure of metals and complexes of metals, sp. as far as this is open to observation by the eye with the help of the MICRO-SCOPE, and the relation of this to their properties, and to the ways of working them. **'metallo'graphic,** a. **metal'lo-graphist,** n.

'metalloid, n. [Chem.] Any ELEMENT having some but not all of the properties of a metal, as Si, Sb, As.

me'tallurgy, n. The general science of metals, covering METALLOGRAPHY and the ways of getting metals from the substances with which they are united in the earth. **metall'urgic-(al),** aa. **me'tallurgist,** n.

'metamathe'matics, n. The theory of mathematics.

'metamer, n. [Chem.] A substance which is METAMERIC with another or others.

'metamere, n. [Zoo.] Any of the like parts, most of which are in every way the same, though some may be marked by special developments, coming one after another from end to end of the bodies of some animals, such as worms. **meta'meric.** a. To do with a m. or mm., having mm.

me′tamerism, n. The condition of being made up of mm, metameric structure.

me′tameri′zation, n. The forming of or division into mm. **me′tamerized,** a. Having mm.

meta′meric, a. [Chem.] ISOMERIC as the effect of having the same ATOMS joined to one same atom or group but in the form of different RADICALS. **met′amerism,** n. The property or condition of being m. or the relation between m. substances.

meta′morphism, n. [Geol.] The process in operation inside the earth by which ROCKS are changed in structure etc., or the chemical and physical changes undergone by rock inside the earth, sp. those marked changes effected by great force and heat and with the help of water, by which rocks are given a more solid and CRYSTALLINE structure. **meta′morphic,** a. **metamorphic rock.** ROCK produced by m. from others—one of the three chief groups of rock. (*See* IGNEOUS and SEDIMENTARY).

meta′morphosis, n. [Zoo.] A marked and, more or less sudden, change of form, structure, and way of existence, undergone by an animal in the process of its development after coming out of the egg, as from one stage to another in the development of an insect; a process of development marked by a m. or mm. (*see* COMPLETE M. and INCOMPLETE M.). [Bot.] A change in the normal structure of a plant or flower. [Med.] A change in the structure of a part or substance, sp. a change from a higher and more complex structure to a lower one as effect of disease. [Chem.] Any chemical change producing one substance from another or others. **meta′morphose,** v.i. Undergo m. **meta′morphic,** a.

meta′nauplius, n. [Zoo.] A further LARVA stage in some CRUSTACEA coming after the NAUPLIUS and marked by two further outgrowths representative of the MAXILLAE.

meta′nephros, n. [Zoo.] In back-boned animals, one or other of the two back parts of the KIDNEY undergoing development in the later stage of the EMBRYO, which in the higher forms become the kidney of the fully-formed animal. **meta′nephric,** a.

meta′notum, n. [Zoo.] The back part of an insect's METATHORAX. **meta′notal,** a.

meta′nucleus, n. [Zoo.] The NUCLEOLUS of an OVUM after being sent out of the NUCLEUS.

′metaphase, n. [Biol.] The stage of MITOSIS or MEIOSIS in which the CHROMOSOMES come to the middle of the SPINDLE.

′metaphloem, n. [Bot.] PRIMARY PHLOEM which has undergone complete development.

′metaphos′phoric acid. [Chem.] HPO₃, a glass-like sticky solid formed when P₂O₅ (*phosphorus pentoxide*) is acted on by air.

meta′physics, n. Theory or system of theories as to what existence is and how knowledge is possible, having to do with the first causes of things as opp. the facts about them and their processes, which are the business of science. **meta′physical,** a. **′metaphy′sician,** n.

′metaphyte, n. [Bot.] Plant made up of a number of CELLS.

meta′plasia, n. [Zoo.] The change of one sort of TISSUE into another, as in the forming of bone. **meta′plastic,** a.

me′taplasis, n. [Biol.] The stage of complete growth and development in the history of a living thing.

′metaplasm, n. [Biol.] Any non-living substance in a CELL, sp. food material in an egg-cell. **meta′plas-mic, -tic,** aa.

meta′pleural, a. [Zoo.] At the side of the back.

metap′neustic, a. [Zoo.] (Of insect LARVAE) having only two breathing-holes, placed at the end of the body.

′metaprotein, n. [Biochem.] Substance produced in the first stage of the digestion of PROTEINS.

′metapte′rygium, n. [Zoo.] The inner or farthest back of the three chief CARTILAGES of the opposite FINS of ELASMOBRANCHII.

metap′terygoid, n., a. [Zoo.] (Bone in certain fishes) at the back of the PTERYGOID.

′metasoma′tosis, ′meta′somatism, nn. [Geol.] Change in the make-up of ROCK produced by chemical changes in some of the substances in it as the effect of material coming in from outside. **′metaso′matic,** a. To do with m.

meta′stable state. [Chem.] The condition of a substance in which a change from one PHASE to another is ready to take place but does not do so without some impulse from outside, as SUPERCOOLED water or a SUPER-SATURATED SOLUTION, when a shake or the dropping in of a small CRYSTAL of ice or of the solid about to be formed is necessary to get the process started. [Phys.] The condition of an EXCITED ATOM which does not go back to its normal condition by giving off RADIANT ENERGY till a further impulse is given to it from outside, for example by coming against another atom. **metastable equi-′librium.** [Chem.] M. s.

me′tastasis, n. [Biol.] METABOLISM. [Med.] The transporting of diseased CELLS or BACTERIA from one part of the body to another through the blood-vessels, etc.; the new diseased growth or place caused by m. **meta′static,** a. **me′tastasize,** v.i. [Med.] (Of a diseased condition or growth) be transported to a new place by m.

meta′sternum, n. [Zoo.] In insects, the STERNUM of the METATHORAX; in back-boned animals, the back part of the sternum.

meta′stigmate, a. [Zoo.] Having breathing-openings at back, as ACARINA.

meta′tarsus, n. [Zoo.] The part of the foot of man, or the back foot of other animals, between the toes and the ANKLE, gen. having as its framework five long bones. **meta′tarsal,** a.

Meta′theria, n.pl. [Zoo.] A SUB-CLASS of MAMMALIA made of, of one ORDER, the MARSUPALIA.

me′tathesis, n. [Chem.] DOUBLE DECOM-POSITION. [Philol.] An exchange of place between sounds or letters in a word.

meta′thorax, n. [Zoo.] The third, that is, the back, division of an insect's THORAX.

′metatroch, n. [Zoo.] In a TROCHOPHORE, a band of CILIA ringing the body at the back of mouth.

meta′xylem, n. [Bot.] PRIMARY XYLEM at a fuller stage of development than PROTO-XYLEM, made up of wider, thicker-walled CELLS.

Meta′zoa, n.pl. [Zoo.] (PHYLUM in which are grouped) animals of more than one CELL whose cells are united into TISSUES and which have some system of parts, gen. with nerves and a body-hollow where digestion takes place—that is, all animals of more than one cell but sponges. **meta′zoan,** a., n. **meta′zoic,** a.

meten′cephalon, n. [Zoo.] CEREBELLUM, or cerebellum and PONS.

′meteor, n. [Astron.] A small solid body, freq. formed of iron, coming into the gases round the earth from outer space and giving out light as the effect of heat produced by the FRICTION of its motion through them, sometimes falling to the earth, sometimes completely changed into gas before it gets there—seen as a bright, quick-moving light. **m. ′crater.** [Geog. etc.] Round, unnatural hollow in the earth possibly caused by METEORITES. **m. streams.** [Astron.] Currents of dust moving round the sun, producing meteoric showers when the Earth goes through them. **mete′oric,** a. **mete′oric shower.** A great number of mm. seen when the earth goes through m. streams.

′meteorism, n. [Med.] Expansion of the ABDOMEN caused by over-much gas in the INTESTINES.

′meteorite, n. [Astron., Geol.] A METEOR which has come to earth in the form of a mass of stone or metal. **meteo′ritic,** a. **meteo′ritic hy′pothesis.** [Astron.] The theory that the CRATERS on the moon

were caused by mm. falling in it and not by VOLCANOES.

′meteoro′graph, n. [Meteor.] Apparatus for recording at the same time a number of different METEOROLOGICAL conditions, sp. a group of different instruments sent into the upper air for this purpose. **′meteoro′gram,** n. Record made by m. **′meteoro′graphic,** a.

′meteoroid, n. [Astron.] Any of the great number of small bodies moving round the sun, such as become METEORS when they get near the earth.

meteo′rology, n. Science of the earth's ATMOSPHERE in its relation to weather. **′meteoro′logical,** a. **meteo′rologist,** n.

′meteor′ometer, n. [Meteor.] Apparatus sending automatically to a WEATHER STATION the changes recorded by the BAROMETER and THERMOMETER, etc. [Astron.] An instrument for working out the line of motion of a METEOR.

′meteoro′scope, n. [Astron.] An instrument for measuring the position, distance, and directions of the way taken by a METEOR.

′meter, n. Instrument for measuring and gen. recording automatically, the amount of anything, for example gas, water, electric current, used or going by in a given time, or the rate of a motion or other change. **-meter.**

meter, n. METRE.

met′h(a)emo′globin, n. [Biochem., Med.] Substance formed when blood is united with O, like HAEMOGLOBIN but less readily broken down, present in the blood or URINE after poisoning by NITRATES or CHLORATES.

′methane, n. [Chem.] A gas, CH_4 without colour or smell, which very readily takes fire, present naturally in mines and over MARSHES. **m. ′series.** A HOMOLOGOUS SERIES of OPEN-CHAIN HYDROCARBONS of which m. is the first and representative. **metha′nometer,** n. Instrument measuring the amount of m. in the air, sp. in mines.

′methanide, n. [Chem.] Any of the sub-stances, such as Al_4C_3, which give METHANE when acted on by water.

′methanol, n. METHYL ALCOHOL.

metho′dology, n. System or theory of the rules on which the processes and reason-ing by which knowledge is got in a science are based.

me′thoxl, a. [Chem.] Having or being the group $-OCH_3$.

′methyl, a. [Chem.] Having or being the group $-CH_3$; used in naming different SYNTHETIC substances, sp. DYES (as **m. blue, m. green, m. violet**) having a chemical relation with m. **m. alcohol.** CH_3OH, a readily-burning liquid with no colour and little weight, at one time chiefly produced from wood, having most of the properties and uses of ALCO-

HOL, but a poison, and used most importantly in the making of C COMPOUNDS.
m. 'orange. An orange DYE which is, however, chiefly used as a test for ALKALINITY, its SOLUTION turning light red with acids, light yellow with ALKALIS. **m. sa'licylate.** $C_6H_4(OH)$. CO_2CH_3. **'-ate,** v.t. [Chem.] Put the m. group or m. alcohol into a substance. **'methylated spirit(s).** ALCOHOL with the addition of m. alcohol, making it into a poison, used for burning in cookers, etc
'methyla'mine, n. [Chem.] CH_3NH_2, a gas without colour and with a strong, eye-watering smell. (*See* p. 556.)
'methylene, a. [Chem.] Having the group $-CH_2$.
'metochy, n. [Zoo.] The relation between an insect and another animal or group with which it lives without having any effect on it, bad or good.
me'toecious, a. [Biol.] HETEROECIOUS.
me'toestrum, n. [Zoo.] The time after the OESTRUS of animals in which the sex-parts become normal again and the sex-impulse comes to rest.
me'tonic 'cycle. [Astron.] Stretch of time, 19 years, before the new moon etc. comes round to the same day of the year again.
me'toxenous. a. [Biol.] HETEROECIOUS.
'metre, n. The unit of LENGTH on which the measures in the metric system are based, being that marked on a rod of Pt and Ir kept in Paris, = $39·3701$ in., or $1,650,763·73$ WAVE-LENGTHS of the light produced by the EXCITATION of Kr. **'metre-'kilogram-'second system (of units).** [Elec.] A measuring system based on the m., the kg., and the second, used in some electric work in place of the C.G.S. SYSTEM. **'metric,** a. To do with the metric system. **'metric 'system.** The system of the m. and the kg., in which all other units are got by division or MULTIPLICATION of the base units by 10, 10^2, etc., the higher units being named by putting the Greek, the lower by putting the Latin, word for 10, etc. before that for the base unit, as KILOMETRE, CENTIMETRE. (*See* p. 566.) **'metric ton.** TONNE.
-metric, a. To do with a -METER or with -METRY.
me'tritis, n. [Med.] INFLAMMATION of the UTERUS.
metro-. [Med.] Of, to do with, the UTERUS: **-pa'ralysis.**
me'trology, n. Science or system of units of weight and measure.
'metronome, n. Instrument for marking time, sp. in music, gen, a form of PENDULUM which, by adjustment of a weight, may be given different times of motion. **metro'nomic,** a.
me'tropolis, n. [Biol.] The stretch of country where a given sort of plant or animal is most common.

-'metry. Art, process, science, of measuring what is named.
Mev or **m.e.v.** [Elec.] Sign for 1 million $(1,000,000)$ ELECTRON-VOLTS.
Mg, Sign for MAGNESIUM.
mg. = MILLIGRAM.
mho, n. [Elec.] Unit of CONDUCTANCE, being that of a body having a RESISTANCE of 1 OHM.
'mica, n. [Geol.] Any of a number of natural SILICATES readily separating into very thin, gen. elastic, glass-like leaves. **'m.-schist.** [Geol.] A SCHIST whose structure is produced by parallel plates of m.
mi'cell(e), mi'cella, nn. [Chem.] Very small, somewhat CRYSTALLINE group or chain of MOLECULES, in theory forming a unit of structure in a number of substances, for example CELLULOSE, and playing an important part in living things.
'Michelson-'Morley ex'periment. [Phys.] The first test undertaken in connection with the theory of the ETHER, by which it was made clear that a ray of light goes at the same rate in the direction in which the earth is moving as in any other, so that (a) the ether theory is unsupported, (b) there is no way of measuring the ABSOLUTE motion of the earth, these two outcomes supporting Einstein's RELATIVITY theory.
micr'(a)esthete, n. [Zoo.] In certain MOLLUSCA, one of the very small instruments of sense present in the MICROPORES.
'micro-. Small, sp., so small as to be seen only under a MICROSCOPE:— **-con'stituent,** n. **-'crystal,** n. **-'fossil,** n. **'m.-organism,** n. **-'parasite,** n.; (before names of processes, etc.) to do with MICROSCOPIC things or structures:— **-me'tallurgy,** n.; (before names of measuring units) $\frac{1}{1,000,000}$, sign μ:— **-'ampere,** n., **'microhm,** n.; (before names of instruments) measuring, or recording, or used in connection with, very small amounts, changes, motions, etc.:— **-b'alance,** n. **-'barograph,** n.; [Biol.] small as to the part(s) named:— **-'dont,** a., **-'phyllous,** a.; [Med.] unnormally small as to the part(s) named:— **'cardia,** n.; [Geol.] formed of very small or MICROSCOPIC CRYSTALS:— **-'diorite,** n. **-'syneite,** n.
micro'aerophile, n. [Bot.] A plant which does best without much O.
'microa'nalysis, n. [Chem.] The ANALYSIS of very small amounts of material, needing special processes and very delicate, specially designed apparatus, and gen. the help of a MICROSCOPE.
micro'balance, n. Scales designed for measuring weights less than one mg.
'microbe, n. [Biol.] Any MICROSCOPIC plant or animal, sp. a BACTERIUM. **mi'crobicide,** n. Substance causing death of mm. **'microbi'ology,** n. Science of mm.

'microblast, n. [Zoo.] MICROCYTE.

'microce'phalia, micro'cephal-y, -ism, nn. Condition of having head smaller than normal. 'microce'phalic, 'micro'cephalous, aa.

micre'chemistry, n. Chemistry having to do with very small amounts of substance, using MICROANALYSIS; the chemistry of MICROSCOPIC plants and animals.

'microclima'tology, n. The science of the conditions of heat, wet etc. round special parts of plants, for example among the leaves, where they may be very different from those noted higher up.

micro'conjugant, n. [Zoo.] Micro-GAMETE, sp. of the free-swimming CILIATED sort seen in certain PROTOZOA.

'microcosm, n. A complex system or society complete in itself though forming part of a greater one, sp. man as opp. the MACROCOSM. micro'cosmic, a.

micro'cosmic salt. [Chem.] NaNH₄.HPO₄ (*sodium ammonium hydrogen phosphate*), a white substance changing to a glass-like one on heating.

'microcrypto'crystalline, a. [Geol.] Made up of CRYSTALS so small as not to be seen even under MICROSCOPE.

micro'crystalline, a. [Geol.] Made up of small CRYSTAL grains seen only under the MICROSCOPE.

'microcyst, n. [Bot.] Resting-CELL formed from a zoöSPORE in certain FUNGI.

microcyte, n. [Med.] ERYTHROCYTE of half the normal size, or less, present in certain diseases, 'microcy'th(a)emia, n. Condition of having mm. in blood. 'microcy'tosis, n. Process of producing m.

'microdis'section, n. [Biol.] The taking to bits of very small things, such as CELLS, under the MICROSCOPE.

'microelec'trolysis, n. [Phys.] ELECTROLYSIS using very small amounts of material. 'microe'lectrode, n. ELECTRODE used in m.

micro'farad, n. [Phys.] $\frac{1}{1,000,000}$ FARAD, the everyday unit of electric CAPACITANCE.

micro'gamete, n. [Biol.] The smaller of two uniting GAMETES, looked on as the male. 'microga'metocyte, n. CELL producing mm. by MEIOSIS, or, sp. in PROTOZOA, by simple division. 'microga'meto'genesis, n.

mi'crogamy, n. [Zoo.] MEROGAMY.

mi'croglia, n. [Zoo.] A special sort of CELL of irregular form with branching outgrowths, seen in the grey, and less frequently, in the white nerve-substance of the brain and other parts of the nerve system.

micro'granite, n. [Geol.] A MEDIUM-GRAINED MICROCRYSTALLINE ROCK formed of the same substances as GRANITE (*see* p. 192). 'microgra'nitic, a.

micro'graphic, a. To do with MICROSCOPIC observations, sp. as made clear in camera-pictures. m. 'texture. [Geol.] ROCK structure in which seemingly separate grains of FELDSPAR are fixed in an unbroken network of QUARTZ CRYSTALS.

'micro-inciner'ation, n. [Biol.] The burning away on a SLIDE of all but the MINERAL parts of an animal, plant, or bit of living substance, so as to be able to see the sort and distribution of the minerals in it by looking at and testing the unburned parts under a MICROSCOPE.

'microin'jection, n. [Biol.] The INJECTION of substances into CELLS etc. under the MICROSCOPE, gen. done with automatically controlled instruments.

micro'lecithal, a. [Zoo.] (Of eggs) having little YOLK.

'microlite, n. [Geol.] MICROCRYSTAL; a ROCK substance chiefly formed of Ca₂Ta₂O₇, gen. taking the form of very small yellow or brown CRYSTALS.

micro'mania, n. [Med.] Condition of a diseased mind in which person has the belief that parts of his body have become small or are no longer there.

'microma'nipu'lation, n. [Biol.] MICRODISSECTION and MICROINJECTION.

'micromere, n. [Zoo.] Any of the small CELLS produced in the upper part of an OVUM undergoing division.

'micro-'meteorites, n.pl. METEORITES so small as not to undergo destruction by FRICTION in the ATMOSPHERE, forming dust-like masses and taken to be responsible for rainfall by causing CONDENSATION.

microme'ritic, a. [Geol.] MICROGRANITIC.

mi'crometer, n. An instrument fixed to a TELESCOPE or MICROSCOPE for measuring very small distances, or the distances across bodies very far away. m. (screw) gauge. A measuring-instrument for things of very small size, formed of a U-like metal part, the space between the ends of which may be narrowed by a m. screw coming through one side. m. screw. A screw with a very narrow THREAD designed to go forward only a very small distance with every turn, and having on its head a scale marked with very small degrees by which the distance may be measured. micro'metric(al), aa. mi'crometry, n.

'micro-'micro-. $\frac{1}{1,000,000}$ of a $\frac{1}{1,000,000}$ part, sign $\mu\mu$.

'micro-'micron, n. $\frac{1}{1,000,000}$ MICRON, 10⁻¹² m, or ·01 Å. U. sign $\mu\mu$.

'micron, n. Unit used for measuring MICROSCOPIC bodies = $\frac{1}{1,000}$ mm., sign μ.

'microne'phridium, n. [Zoo.] In certain worms, any of the small pipe-like NEPHRIDIA of which a great number are present in every ring of the body, possibly produced from MEGANEPHRIDIA.

'**micront**, n. [Zoo.] Small CELL formed by division, and producing MICROGAMETES in the same way.

micro'nucleus, n. [Zoo.] The smaller of the two NUCLEI present in the CELLS of most CILIOPHORA, which is REPRODUCTIVE.

'**micro-'organism**, n. [Biol.] Any living thing which is MICROSCOPIC or less in size. '**micro-or'ganic**, a.

'**micro-phage, -'phagocyte**, nn. [Zoo.] A small PHAGOCYTE in the blood, etc. '**microphago'cytic**, a.

mi'crophag-ic, -ous, aa. [Zoo.] Living on small, sp. MICROSCOPIC living things or bits of food-substance, said of fish and other water-animals getting their food by taking in water and sending it out again, keeping back any solid material.

'**microphone**, n. [Acous., Radio] An instrument for changing sound-waves into electric ENERGY. **micro'phonic**, a. Sp., having the properties of a m. in reaction to sound-waves.

micro'photograph, n. A very small camera-print produced from a PHOTOMICROGRAPH of normal size; loosely, a PHOTOMICROGRAPH **micropho'tography**, n.

'**microphyte**, n. [Bot.] Any plant of MICROSCOPIC size, sp. a BACTERIUM. '**microphy'tology**, n.

'**micropore**, n. [Zoo.] Any of the very small openings in the hard outer cover of certain MOLLUSCA in which the MICRAESTHETES are placed.

'**micropyle**, n. [Biol.] Very small opening for letting something in or out, sp. [Zoo.] in the skin of an insect OVUM for letting in a SPERMATOZOÖN, [Bot.] in the coats of an OVULE at the top, letting in the POLLEN TUBE, and, when the seed is starting its development into a plant, water. **micro'pylar**, a.

micro'schizont, n. [Zoo.] Male SCHIZONT of certain PROTOZOA.

'**microscope**, n. Instrument formed of a CONVEX LENS (**simple m.**) or, commonly, two CONVERGING lenses or systems of lenses (**compound m.**), by which the IMAGES formed on the eye by very small things are greatly increased in size, so as to make it possible to see them, or see them more clearly. **micro'scopic(al)**, aa. Sp., of a size to be seen only with the help of a m. **mi'croscopy**, n. The use of, or the art of using, the m.

micro'seism, n. Any of the small, short motions of the earth's outer part, not noted by normal observation but recorded all the time by instruments, probably the effect of motions of the seas. **micro-'seismograph**, n. **microseis'mology**, n. **microseis'mometer**, n.

'**microsome**, n. [Zoo.] Any of the MICROSCOPIC grains of fat, etc. present in CYTOPLASM, probably systems of ENZYMES.

micro'spectroscope, n. A SPECTROSCOPE fixed to a MICROSCOPE for the observation of SPECTRA from very small amounts of any substance.

'**microsphere**, n. [Biol.] CENTROSPHERE. [Zoo.] The very small first-formed SHELL of the unsexed forms of certain FORAMINIFERA. **micro'spheric**, a. Said of FORAMINIFERA of which the SHELL first formed is small.

'**microsplanchic**, a. [Zoo.] Having body very small in relation to the legs, as some insects.

'**microspore**, n. [Bot.] The smaller of the two sorts of unsexed SPORES in seed plants and some FILICALES, that is, the one producing male SEX-CELLS, in flowering plants a POLLEN grain. [Zoo.] The smaller of the two sorts of spores produced by certain PROTOZOA. **microspo'rangium** (microsporangia), n. [Bot.] Walled structure in which mm. are formed, in flowering plants a POLLEN SAC. **micro-'sporic**, a. **micro'sporophore**, n. [Bot.] In FUNGI, any sort of structure producing mm. or microsporangia. **micro'sporophyll**, n. [Bot.] A leaf of changed or unchanged form acting as a microsporophore, in flowering plants a STAMEN.

'**microstome**, n. [Bot.] A very small opening.

micro'structure, n. MICROSCOPIC structure, sp. of metals. **micro'structural**, a.

micro'stylous, a. [Bot.] Having short STYLES.

'**microtherm**, n. [Bot.] Any plant needing only a MEAN heat through the year of between 0°C and 14°C for full growth.

'**microtome**, n. Instrument for cutting very thin plates of TISSUE for MICROSCOPE work. **micro'tomic**, a. **mi'crotomy**, n. The use of, or the art of using, the m.

micro'trichia, n.pl. [Zoo.] Small stiff hairs on the wings of certain insects.

'**microwave**, n. [Radio] ELECTROMAGNETIC wave having a shorter WAVE-LENGTH than 20 cm.

micro'zooid, n. [Zoo.] Any of the sort of very small free-swimming ZOOIDS of certain PROTOZOA having two sorts.

mictu'rition, n. [Med., Zoo.] (Over-frequent) URINATION. '**micturate**, v.i.

mid-. Middle part of, in the middle.

'**mid'brain**, n. [Zoo.] The middle one of the three divisions of the brain in the EMBRYO of back-boned animals, or the MESENCEPHALON which is a development of it, having to do specially with seeing and hearing.

middle ear. [Zoo.] In higher back-boned animals, the hollow part of the ear between the TYMPANIC MEMBRANE and the INNER EAR, full of air and having in it the opening of the EUSTACHIAN TUBE from the throat and the three AUDITORY OSSICLES by which the motions of the tympanic membrane are handed on to the inner ear.

'middle la'mella. [Bot.] In the wall of a plant-CELL, the first-formed substance, made up chiefly of PECTIN, forming a thin plate between two plates of later-formed CELLULOSE material.

'middle piece. [Zoo.] That part of a SPERM-ATOZOÖN between the NUCLEUS and the FLAGELLUM.

mid-gut, n. [Zoo.] In animals without backbones and in the EMBRYOS of back-boned animals, the middle part of the ALIMENTARY CANAL, produced from the ARCHENTERON (*see* FORE-GUT and HIND-GUT).

mid'heaven. [Astron.] The middle line of the sky going from north to south, or the point at which this is cut by the ECLIPTIC.

'midrib, n. [Bot.] The great middle VEIN of a leaf, formed by the stem running on.

'midriff, n. [Anat.] The DIAPHRAGM.

'Miescher's tubes. [Zoo.] RAINEY'S TUBES.

'migraine, n. [Med.] Condition of violent pain in one side of the head, gen. attacking person regularly, freq. causing VOMITING and trouble in seeing.

'migrate, v.t. Go from one place to another, sp. in great numbers. **mi'gration,** n. Sp.:— [Biol.] The change of living-place made regularly at certain times of the year by birds and other animals all together. [Bot.] The moving of plants by natural processes to new living-places. [Phys. Chem.] The motion of IONS in a given direction, as through a gas or liquid, as the effect of a driving force; the moving of an ATOM or atoms from one part of a MOLECULE to another. **mi'gratory,** a. Sp. given to MIGRATING. **mi'gratory cell.** [Zoo.] LEUCOCYTE.

mil, n. Unit used in measuring the distance across wires, $= 0.0254$ mm. or $\frac{1}{1,000}$ inch.

mile, n. British unit of distance $= 1,609.35$ m. **m. ohm.** The weight of a wire 1 m. long having an electric RESISTANCE of 1 OHM. **'-age,** n. Distance in mm.; number of mm. covered in a given time by an automobile etc. (*See* p. 565.)

mili'aria, n. [Med.] PRICKLY HEAT.

milk, n. [Zoo., Chem.] The white or yellow liquid produced by female MAMMALS as food for their offspring, made up of very small drops of fat in a SOLUTION of CASEIN, LACTOSE, ALBUMINS, and some other substances in water. [Biol.] Liquid of m.-like look, such as that present in certain plants. **m. cyst.** [Med.] A pocket-like structure full of m., caused by the stopping up of the m. in a m. DUCT. **m. den'tition.** [Zoo.] The m. teeth. **m. 'fever.** [Med.] A condition of FEVER seen in a woman producing milk for the first time. [Vet.] A disease attacking cows when giving birth to young. **m. 'sickness.** [Med.] A disease marked by VOMITING and shaking of the muscles, caused by taking the m., butter, or meat of cows which have been poisoned by certain plants. **m. tooth.** [Zoo.] Any of the first teeth of MAMMALS, which come out while the animal is young to make way for a second growth.

'Milky Way. [Astron.] The light band seen stretching across the sky at night, made up of stars very far away; the great group of suns, star-groups, etc. of which our sun is part; any of the other star-systems forming a separate unit.

mill, n. A machine for crushing or rubbing anything into small grains or powder; a works with machines for making substances, materials.

mille-. 1,000, or a very great number: **-'florous,** a. [Bot.].

mil'lennium, n. 1000 years. **'millennary,** a.

'millerite, n. [Geol.] Natural nickel SULPHIDE (NiS), a yellow substance gen. in the form of thin hair-like CRYSTALS.

mil'lesimal, 1.n. $\frac{1}{1,000}$. 2.a. Made up of mm. parts; to do with m(m).

milli-. (Before names of measuring-units) $\frac{1}{1,000}$:— **-'ampere,** n. [Elec.], **-'ångstrom,** n. [Optics], **'-bar,** n. [Meteor.], **'-gram(me),** n., **'-lambert,** n. [Light], **-'litre,** n. **-'metre,** n.

'millier, n. TONNE.

'millimicron, n. [Phys.] Unit used in measuring light waves, etc. $= \frac{1}{1,000,000}$ mm., sign mμ.

'milling, n. Process of putting material through a MILL; process of cutting the surface of a metal to give it a desired form, make holes or lines in it, etc., by the use of a turning plate or roller of hard steel with teeth. **m. machine.** Any machine in which the material to be worked on is fixed in position and the instrument working on it is in motion, opp. LATHE.

'milliphot, n. [Optics] Unit of ILLUMINATION $= \frac{1}{1,000}$ PHOT.

'Millon's re'action. [Chem.] The forming of a red substance on heating with Millon's reagent, used as a test for PROTEINS. **Millon's re'agent.** A SOLUTION of MERCURIC NITRATE, $Hg(NO_3)_2$, having in it some free NITROUS ACID, HNO_2.

'Millstone Grit, n. [Geol.] The STRATUM of the CARBONIFEROUS under the coal beds of England, chiefly made up of hard SANDSTONE and SHALE.

mi'mesis, n. [Zoo.] MIMICRY. **mi'metic,** a.

'mimic, 1.v.t. [Biol., Med., Geol.] Be or become like some other living thing or some other structure. 2.n. An animal which makes use of mimicry. **'-ry,** n. Mimicking, sp., [Zoo.] the taking on by an animal of the look of another sort of animal or a thing, for example a leaf or a stick, for the purpose of keeping itself safe (*protective m.*), or helping its designs on other animals, etc. (*see* AGGRESSIVE M., APOSEMATIC M.).

mind, n. [Psych.] In some theories, all the conscious experience of a person, in others, all a person's acts of adjustment to his experience, some of which are conscious and some SUBCONSCIOUS.

'Mindel, n. [Geol.] The second of the four ICE AGES of the PLEISTOCENE PERIOD in Europe. **'Mindel-Biss 'period.** The stage between M. and the coming back of the ice.

'mineral, 1.n. Any INORGANIC substance formed naturally in the earth and having a fixed chemical make-up and special chemical and physical properties making it different from other such substances, sp. [Mineral.] any such solid, other than a natural glass, produced by FUSION. 2.a. To do with mm.; INORGANIC. **m. acid.** [Chem.] Any INORGANIC acid such as HCL or H_2SO_4. **m. 'kingdom.** The group of all non-living things, as opp. plants and animals. **m. oil.** Any oil got from mm., made up chiefly of ORGANIC COMPOUNDS, sp. PETROLEUM—one of the three chief groups of oils. **m. salt.** [Chem.] Any SALT of a m. acid. **m. spring.** A natural spring of m. water. **m. water.** Any water having in it m. salts or gases, sp. one of medical value, **'-iz'ation,** n. Mineralizing. [Bot.] The forming of m. salts or other m. substance in or on a CELL-wall. [Geol.] The forming of new mm. in a ROCK. **'-ize,** v.t. Make the addition of a m. or mm. to a substance so as to get it changed into INORGANIC form; get (sp. ORGANIC material in the earth) changed into stone, or stone-like substance.

mine'ralogy, n. The science of MINERALS. **minera'logical,** a. **mine'ralogist,** n.

'minimum (minima), a., n. (To do with, being) the smallest amount or degree, the lowest unit, opp. MAXIMUM. **'minimal,** a.

'minimus, n. [Anat.] The little finger or toe.

'minor, a. Small in size, amount or degree, or less important (in relation to some other thing), the smaller etc. of two, opp. MAJOR. **m. in'trusion.** [Geol.] An INTRUSION which is not very thick, such as is formed regularly and only of HYPABYSSAL ROCK, and so the same thing as a hypabyssal intrusion.

minus. 1.prep. Made less by, with the loss or SUBTRACTION of, 2.a. [Elec.] NEGATIVE. **m. sign.** The sign ' − ', as in 'a − b'. **m. colour.** A SUBTRACTIVE PRIMARY, as **m. red, m. blue, m. green.**

'minute, n. A unit of time $= \frac{1}{60}$ hour; a unit of angle measure $= \frac{1}{60}$ DEGREE, sign '.

min'utia (minutiae), n. Very small detail.

'Miocene, a., n. [Geol.] (Of, to do with) the M. Epoch. **M. 'Epoch.** The earlier of the two divisions of the later TERTIARY,

running from about 35 to 20 million years back (*see* p. 558).

mi'osis, n. [Med.] Condition in which the PUPIL of the eye is smaller than normal, **mi'otic,** n., a. (Substance) making PUPIL smaller.

mio'stemonous, a. MEIOSTEMONOUS.

mio'taxy, n. MEIOTAXY.

mio'thermic, a. [Geol.] To do with present TEMPERATURE conditions on the earth.

mi'rabilite, n. [Mineral.] Natural GLAUBER SALT, put down by SALT LAKES, heated springs, etc.

mira'cidium, n. [Zoo.] The first-stage LARVA in TREMATODA.

mi'rage, n. [Meteor.] Effect caused by the complete REFLECTION of light from the top of a level stretch of very warm or very cold air touching the earth, and producing to the eye the suggestion of water or the IMAGES of far-away things which are taken to be the things themselves at a short distance away.

'mirror, n. [Optics] A polished surface, such as a metal plate or a glass one backed with silver, having the property of turning back in a certain direction the light-rays falling on it and so forming IMAGES of things on the eye. [Elec.] A metal network turning back electric waves. **m. image.** Sp., a form which is like another in the same way as an IMAGE made by a m. is like the thing, that is, with left and right sides exchanged. **m. 'nucleides .** [Chem.] NUCLEIDES in which the number of PROTONS and NEUTRONS may be exchanged. **m. 'symmetry.** The sort of SYMMETRY seen in a thing and its m. image facing one another.

mis-. Wrong, wrongly.

mis'carriage, n. [Med.] The coming of a FOETUS from the body of the mother before it has had 28 weeks of development, when it has no chance of living.

'miscege'nation, n. [Biol.] The producing of offspring by the uniting of animals or plants of different SUB-SPECIES, sp. RACES of men.

'miscible, a. Able to be mixed so as to make a HOMOGENEOUS substance, as two liquids such as water and alcohol. **misci'bility,** n.

'mispickel, n. [Mineral.] Natural FeAsS, used for producing ARSENIC.

'missile, n. PROJECTILE for use in war. *See* BALLISTIC M., GUIDED M.

mist, n. [Chem.] Any gas full of very small drops of liquid. [Meteor.] A thin FOG formed only of water-drops, and in which the range of view is longer than 1000 m.

mi'stura, n. [Med.] MIXTURE.

mite, n. [Zoo.] Any of the smaller of the two sorts of insects forming the ORDER ACARINA, some PARASITIC on insects or other animals, some on plants, and some living in DECAYING material such as cheese.

mito-. Thread.

mito′chondrium (mitochondria), n. [Biol.] Any of the very small thread-like or grain-like bodies formed of fat and PROTEIN with ENZYMES, present in all CELLS but those of BACTERIA and some ALGAE.

′mitoge′netic, a. [Biol.] Produced by MITOSIS.

mi′tosis, n. [Biol.] The common form of CELL division by which the growth of animals and plants take place, in which, first, twice the normal number of CHROMOSOMES are formed, then there is a division of the NUCLEUS by the development of ASTERS outside it, the loss of the skin covering it, the attraction of the chromosomes to the asters, forming a SPINDLE, the cutting in two of the spindle, and last, the division of the cell itself in the same plane, forming two cells with nuclei having the normal number of chromosomes. **mi′totic,** a. **mitotic ′figure.** The SPINDLE form, **mi′totically,** adv.

′mitra, n. [Bot.] GALEA; pointed top of certain FUNGI.

′mitral, a. [Biol.] Having a wide base and sides curving or sloping to a pointed end. [Zoo.] To do with the m. valve. **m. cell.** Any of the m. cells in the OLFACTORY BULB, to whose bases come thick nerve-threads from the CELLS of the inside of the nose. **m. in′competence** (or **insufficiency** or **regurgi′tation**). [Med.] Condition in which the m. valve is not shutting completely, so letting blood get back into the AURICLE. **m. ′orifice.** [Zoo.] In higher animals, the opening between the left AURICLE and the left VENTRICLE of the heart. **m. valve.** The structure controlling the m. orifice, letting blood through only in one direction, from the AURICLE to the VENTRICLE.

′mitriform, a. [Biol.] MITRAL.

mixed, a. [Bot.] (Of an INFLORESCENCE) in part RACEMOSE and in part CYMOSE; (of a BUD) having in it early forms of leaves and flowers. [Zoo.] (Of a nerve) having SENSORY and MOTOR NERVE-FIBRES. **m. ′crystal.** CRYSTAL formed by two different, sp. ISOMORPHIC, substances.

mixo-. Mixed.

mixo′trophic, a. [Biol.] In part PARASITIC or SAPROPHITIC, but getting or, of a plant, making, food for itself as well.

′mixture, n. The process of mixing or becoming mixed; substance or thing formed of, produced by, mixing two or more substances or things. [Phys., Chem.] Two or more substances having their parts completely mixed together but not chemically united into a new substance (*see* MECHANICAL, PHYSICAL).

M.K.S. (system) = METRE-KILOGRAM-SECOND (SYSTEM).

m.l. = MILLILITRE.

mm. = MILLIMETRE.

m.m.f. = MAGNETOMOTIVE FORCE.

Mn, Sign for MANGANESE.

′mnemic, a. To do with memory. **m. principle.** [Zoo.] The theory that the memory of experience is handed down from offspring to offspring, so accounting for unlearned regular behaviour and adjustments to living-conditions in animals, and for the development of new parts or powers giving the animal a better chance in the fight for existence.

mne′monic, a. [Psych.] Helping or to do with the memory or mnemonics. **′-s,** n.pl. System or science of increasing the power of the memory.

mnemo′taxis, n. [Zoo.] Motion to a place which is dependent on memory, as the going back of an animal to its living place.

-mnesia, -mnesis, nn. [Med., Psych.] Condition of memory.

Mo, Sign for MOLYBDENUM.

′mobile, 1.a. Able to be moved or having power of motion; moving or moved very readily. 2.n. A moving part of a machine. **mo′bility,** n.

mock moon. [Astron.] PARASELENE.

mock sun. [Astron.] PARAHELION.

mo′dality, n. [Med.] Any of a number of physical processes used medically, such as HIGH-FREQUENCY currents, or the apparatus used in connection with them. [Psych.] Any of the chief forms of sense-experience, as seeing, hearing. [Geol.] MODE.

mode, n. Way of doing or being, form, system. [Psych.] MODALITY. [Geol.] The make-up of any example of a sort of ROCK as it is in fact, given as the weights of the substances forming it, as opp. NORM.

′model, n. Anything designed or used as a guide to be copied in making something; a small-scale copy of a machine etc., sp. as used for testing a new design; a design or structure representative of some thing or system, as of an ATOM, the earth moving round the sun, etc. [Zoo.] The animal etc. copied by a MIMIC.

′moderator, n. [Phys., Chem.] Material used to make slower the rate of motion of NEUTRONS while NUCLEAR FISSION is taking place, for example —HEAVY WATER or Be.

modifi′cation, n. (Process, act, of causing or undergoing) some change in form or qualities; a making or becoming less in degree. [Bot.] A change in a plant caused by its living-conditions, which is effected only in these conditions and is not handed on to offspring. **'modifier,** n. Sp., modifying factor. **'modify,** v.t. **'modifying 'factor.** [Biol.] GENE changing the effect of another gene.

'modulate, v.t. Make adjustment(s) in something to get it into agreement with a guide or some other thing. [Acous.] Make a change of FREQUENCY in (sound, sp. [Philol.] that of the voice in talking). [Elec.] Make a change in the frequency of waves by mixing with them others of a different, gen. lower, frequency. **'modulated,** a. **modu'lation,** n. Act of, or change produced by, modulating. [Radio] Modulation of the FREQUENCY, AMPLITUDE, etc. of a high-frequency current in agreement with a SIGNAL CURRENT. **'modulator,** n. [Radio] Apparatus producing modulation.

'modulus, n. [Phys.] Number measuring some property or effect under unit conditions, COEFFICIENT; the fixed number used for MULTIPLYING a measure to get it changed from one system of units into another. **m. of elas'ticity.** The RATIO of the force causing a change in the size of a body without a change in form to the amount of the change.

mo'fette, n. [Geol.] An opening in a VOLCANO through which CO_2, N and O come in the last stage of its working.

Moh's scale of hardness [Mineral.] A scale for measuring how hard a mineral is, formed of 10 minerals, every one of which may be marked by the one over it in the scale, any mineral to be tested being placed under the first one which has the power of marking it: 1. TALC, 2. GYPSUM, 3. CALCITE, 4. FLUORITE, 5. APATITE, 6. ORTHOCLASE, 7. QUARTZ, 8. TOPAZ, 9. CORUNDUM, 10. DIAMOND.

moiré fringes. [Optics]. A regular design of wide, waving, light and dark bands, produced when two DIFFRACTION GRATINGS with the same line-spacing are placed opposite to one another but with the lines not quite parallel, used for very delicate measuring, for example, for automatically putting right errors in MACHINE TOOLS.

mol, n. [Chem.] GRAM-MOLECULE. **m.** or **'molar fraction.** [Chem.] In a mixed group of COMPOUNDS, the RATIO of the number of MOLECULES of any one of them to the number of molecules in the group taken together. **'molal,** a. Molar. **molal so'lution.** A SOLUTION having molality=1. **mo'lality.** The number of mm. of a SOLUTE in 1000 gm. of the SOLVENT. **'molar,** a. To do with a m., having in it one m. of a substance. **molar conduc'tivity.** The electric CONDUCTIVITY of a molar solution. **molar so'lution.** A SOLUTION having molarity=1. **mo'larity,** n. The number of mm. of a SOLUTE per 1000 c.c. of a SOLUTION.

'molar, a. [Phys.] (Of motions and forces) to do with substances in the mass, not with MOLECULES, etc.

'molar, 1.n. [Zoo.] A tooth with a flat (though not smooth) or rounded top used for crushing food, sp. any of the back teeth in MAMMALS, which are not present in the MILK DENTITION; mouthparts in insects etc. used for same purpose. **2.a.** [Zoo.] Used for crushing or rubbing down food; to do with mm. [Med.] To do with, marked by, a MOLE in the UTERUS.

mold, MOULD.

mole, n. [Chem.] MOL.

mole, n. [Med.] Small, round, brown or black, more or less thick, place on the skin, present from birth, sometimes a growth, sometimes a mass of very small blood-vessels; mass of more or less solid substance in the UTERUS formed of an OVUM which has been stopped in its development, parts of a FOETUS after a MISCARRIAGE, or a mass of blood, etc., caused by something going wrong in the development of offspring.

'molecule, n. [Phys., Chem.] The smallest unit making up a chemical ELEMENT or COMPOUND which has the same properties as the substance in the mass, and has the power of independent existence, a structure of two or more ATOMS. **mo'lecular,** a. To do with, made up of, a m. or mm.; to do with a MOL. **mol'ecular 'compound.** A COMPOUND which is looked on as a uniting of mm. as units, still present in the same forms as in the substances of which it is made up, a condition made clear by such a FORMULA as $2CuCO_3.Cu(OH)_2$. **mo'lecular concen'tration.** The CONCENTRATION of a SOLUTION given as the number of GRAM-MOLECULES in a given VOLUME. **mo'lecular conduc'tivity.** MOLAR CONDUCTIVITY. **mo'lecular de'pression** or **'lowering.** The lowering of the FREEZING-POINT of a liquid produced by dissolving 1 MOL of a substance in 100 gm. of it. **mo'lecular ele'vation.** The increase in the boiling-point of a liquid produced by DISSOLVING 1 MOL of a substance in 100 gm. of it. **mo'lecular 'formula.** [Chem.] A CHEMICAL FORMULA giving the number of ATOMS of the different substances making up one m. of a COMPOUND, and so its molecular weight, as H_2O_2 for HYDROGEN PEROXIDE—freq. the same as the EMPIRICAL FORMULA, but not necessarily so, as seen from this example. **mo'lecular heat.** The SPECIFIC HEAT of a substance × its molecular weight. **mo'lecular hy'pothesis.** [Zoo.] The theory that muscles and nerves are made up of mm. having + and − POLES like the mm. of a MAGNET. **mo'lecular 'layer.** [Zoo.] The outer coat of the CEREBRUM and the CEREBELLUM in back-boned animals; one or the other of the two net-like coats of the RETINA. **mo′lecular pump.** AIR-PUMP in which gas is taken out of a vessel by a wheel turning at a very great rate. **mo′lecular so′lution.** [Chem.] A true SOLUTION, in which the mm. of the solid and the liquid are mixed. **mo′lecular ′spectrum.** [Phys.] BAND SPECTRUM produced by ENERGY changes in a m. **mo′lecular ′volume.** [Phys.] The space taken up by 1 MOL of a substance, sp. at its boiling-point under normal PRESSURE. **mo′lecular weight.** The weight of a m. of a substance given in relation to that of O, which is fixed as 16.

Moll′usca, n.pl. [Zoo.] A PHYLUM of soft-bodied animals without back-bones or body divisions, and having no legs, but a development of the underside of the body into a sort of foot, with which the animal gets about—gen. HERMAPHRODITE, freq. covered with a hard SHELL, and for the most part sea-animals. ′mollusc, n. Animal of the M. **mol′luscan,** a. **moll′uscoid,** a.

′Mollus′coida, n.pl. [Zoo.] Name at one time given to a group made up of a number of groups now looked on as separate, for example BRACHIOPODA and POLYZOA.

′molten, n. [Phys., etc.] Made liquid or paste-like by great heat, sp. of metals or MINERALS.

mo′lybdate, n. [Chem.] Any SALT of a MOLYBDIC ACID. **mo′lybdenite,** n. [Mineral.] A natural form of MoS_2, from which Mo is most commonly produced.

mo′lybdenum, n. Chemical ELEMENT at. no. 42, at. wt. 95·95, sign Mo, a hard white metal, somewhat like iron in its physical properties, but in its chemical behaviour more like a non-metal. **mo′lybdic,** a. Having in it m., sp. m. of a higher VALENCY as opp. molybdous. **mo′lybdic acid.** Any of a number of acids formed from MoO_3, of which the simplest is H_2MoO_4. **mo′lybdous,** a. Having in it m., sp. m. of a lower VALENCY, as opp. molybdic.

′moment (of a force). [Phys.] The turning-effect of a force about a point, measured by the force × the distance of the line of operation of the force from the point.

′moment of i′nertia. The measure of a turning body's resistance to a change in the rate of its motion, given by the addition of the amounts got by MULTIPLICATION of the MASS of every part of the body by the SQUARE of its distance from the AXIS.

mo′mentum, n. [Mech.] The amount of motion of a moving body, measured for motion in a straight line by its MASS × its VELOCITY.

′monad, n. [Biol.] Very small and simple living thing or unit part of one. [Zoo.]

A FLAGELLATE PROTOZOAN. [Chem.] An ELEMENT, ATOM, or group having VALENCY 1. **mo′nadic,** a. **mo′nadiform,** a. [Zoo.]

mona′delphous, a. [Bot.] Having the threads of the STAMENS united into a pipe.

mo′nandrous, a. [Bot.] Having (flowers with) only one STAMEN. **mo′nandry,** n.

mon′arch, a. [Bot.] Having only one PROTOXYLEM thread or group of threads, as some roots.

mon′aster, n. [Biol.] The one ASTER formed in an unnormal form of MITOSIS.

mona′tomic, a. [Chem.] Having only one ATOM in the MOLECULE.

mon′axial, a. [Bot.] Having flowers coming straight from the middle, that is the chief, stem.

′monazite, n. [Mineral.] A yellow, red or brown MINERAL frequently present in sand, from which Th is got.

mo′nergic, a. [Biol.] Having one NUCLEUS only.

Mon′golian fold. [Anthrop.] A fold of skin from the upper EYELID, covering the inner angle of the eye and giving it a narrow, sloping look, a mark of the MONGOLIAN RACE.

Mon′golian ′idiocy or **′Mongolism,** n. [Med.] Condition of IDIOCY present from birth, marked by the special physical signs of eyes with a MONGOLIAN FOLD, a great tongue and a wide head short from back to front—probably caused by some GLAND condition. **Mon′golian (′idiot).** [Med.] Person having this condition.

Mon′golian race. [Anthrop.] The division of man of which the Chinese are representative, marked by yellow skin, straight black hair, wide flat faces and eyes with the MONGOLIAN FOLD.

′mongrel, n. [Biol.] Offspring produced by MISCEGENATION.

mo′niliform, a. [Biol.] Having JOINTS or expansions regularly spaced, giving the effect of little balls on a thread, said of roots, insect feelers, etc.

′monimo′stylic, a. [Zoo.] Having the QUADRATE fixed to the SQUAMOSAL in such a way as to have no power of motion. **′monimo′styly,** n. The condition of being m.

′monism, n. The belief that there is only one sort of being or substance in existence, that mind and material substance are one thing.

′monitor, n. [Engin.] An instrument used to keep a changing QUANTITY or quality inside given limits by giving a controlling SIGNAL, used, for example, by a TELEVISION producer.

mon(o)-. One: **′monocar′pellary,** a. [Bot.] **′mono′cellular,** a. [Biol.], **′mono′locular,** a. [Biol.], **′monome′tallic,** a. [Chem.], **′monomo′lecular,** a. [Phys., Chem.], '**mono'stigmatous**, a. [Bot.], '**mono-stylous**, a. [Bot.].

mono'basic, a. [Chem.] (Of acids) having only one H ATOM which may be changed for a metal or a BASIC RADICAL: (of salts) formed from a m. acid.

mono'blastic, a. [Zoo.] Having, produced from, only one GERM LAYER.

mono'branchiate, n. [Zoo.] Having only one GILL or group of GILLS.

mono'cardian, a. [Zoo.] (Having a heart) with only one AURICLE and VENTRICLE, or without any division at all.

mono'carpic, a. [Bot.] Undergoing death after producing fruit once, '**monocarp**, n.

mono'carpous, a. [Bot.] Forming only one OVARY.

mono'cephalous, a. [Bot.] Having only one head of flowers.

mono'cercous, a. [Zoo.] Having only one FLAGELLUM.

mono'cerous, a. [Zoo.] Having only one horn.

mono'chasium, n. [Bot.] Form of flower-grouping in which one branch is produced by the chief stem and by every branch in turn, all ending in a flower.

'**Monochla'mydeae**, n.pl. [Bot.] A SUB-CLASS of DICOTYLEDONS having SEPALS but no PETALS **monochla'mydeous**, a. [Bot.] Of, like, the M., having no PETALS.

'**monochord**, n. [Acous.] An apparatus for measuring the MATHEMATICAL relation of sounds in music, made up of one wire stretched over a sounding-board marked with a scale, on which a support may be moved so as to give any LENGTH of wire desired for testing.

'**monochro'mat**, n. Person by whom all colours are seen as brighter or less bright shades of grey. **mono'chromatism**, n.

'**monochro'matic, mono'chroic**, aa. Having one colour only, all the same colour. [Phys.] (Of light) made up of rays of one WAVE-LENGTH only. [Med.] To do with MONOCHROMATISM. **monochromatic 'filter**. [Photog.] A FILTER letting through light of only one WAVE-LENGTH or of a very narrow range of wave-lengths.

'**monochrome**, 1.a. Monochromic. 2.n. Picture using only shades of the same colour. **mono'chromic**, a. To do with, having, produced with, one colour only.

mono'chronic, a. Being in existence at the same time, of the same time.

monociliated, a. [Zoo.] MONOCERCOUS.

mono'clinal, a. [Geol.] (Of FOLD, etc.) having only one slope, joining two level parts. '**monocline**, n. A m. FOLD.

mono'clinic 'system. [Cryst.] The group of CRYSTAL forms made up of those having the three AXES unequal, two of the angles at which one is cut by another being right-angles, and the third not a right-angle (*see* p. 99). **mono'clinic**, a. Of the m.s.

mono'clinous, a. [Bot.] Having male and female parts in every flower.

'**Monocotyle'dones**, n.pl. [Bot.] The smaller of the two great CLASSES of flowering-plants (*Angiosperms*), made up of plants with only one COTYLEDON, most of which have PARALLEL-VEINED leaves, stems with VASCULAR BUNDLES here and there all through, and flower-parts in groups of three. '**monocoty'ledon**, n. Plant of the M. '**monocoty'ledonous**, a. Sp., having only one COTYLEDON.

mo'nocular, a. To do with, (of instrument) designed for using with, only one eye.

mono'cyclic, a. [Biol.] Forming or having, or made up of, one ring (of parts) only; ANNUAL. [Chem.] Made up of one ring of ATOMS only.

'**monocyte**, n. [Zoo.] Any of the great LEUCOCYTES with one NUCLEUS normally forming a small part of the blood of back-boned animals.

mono'dactylous, a. [Zoo.] Having only one toe or CLAW.

Mono'delphia, n.pl. EUTHERIA.

mono'delphous, a. [Bot.] MONADELPHOUS.

'**monodont**, a. [Zoo.] Having one tooth only, which takes the form of a TUSK.

mo'n(o)ecious, a. [Bot.] Having separate male flowers and female flowers on the same plant or, in FILICALES etc., male CELLS and female cells on different branches of the same plant. [Zoo.] (Of an animal) having male and female sex-parts. **mo'n(o)ecism**, n. [Biol.] **mo'n(o)ecy**, n. [Bot.]

mono'energic, a. [Phys.] (In NUCLEONICS, of a current of PARTICLES) of which all the particles have the same ENERGY.

mo'noestrous, a. [Zoo.] Having one OESTRUS a year.

mo'nogamous, a. [Zoo.] (Of an animal) of which the male has sex-relations with only one female and the other way round. **mo'nogamy**, n. [Zoo.] Condition of being m.

'**monogene**, a. [Geol.] Formed by one ERUPTION or an unbroken chain of eruptions.

mono'genesis, mon'ogeny, nn. [Biol.] The theory that every plant or animal has its development from one CELL. [Zoo.] The producing of offspring by other than a sex process; development without META-MORPHOSIS.

'**monoge'netic**, a. [Biol., Zoo.] To do with, having, MONOGENESIS. [Chem.] (Of DYES) giving only one colour or shade, whatever the process used.

mono'genic, a. [Biol.] Caused by, dependent on, only one GENE. [Zoo.] Producing off-spring of one sex only. [Geol.] (Of ROCKS) made up of one sort of MINERAL. **mo'nogeny**, n.

mono'genous, a. [Zoo.] MONOGENETIC.

'monogono'por-ous, -ic, aa. [Zoo.] Having the same opening for male and female sex-parts, as in some PLATYHELMINTHES.

mo'nogony, n. [Zoo.] MONOGENESIS.

'monograph, n. Book or paper about one special question only.

'monogy'n(o)ecial, mono'gynous, aa. [Bot.] Having only one PISTIL. [Zoo.] Uniting in sex-act with one female only. mo'nogyny, n. Condition of being m.

mono'hybrid, n. [Biol.] HYBRID produced by plants or animals different only in having opposite forms of one quality, so that the offspring will give light on the relation between these forms in HEREDITY.

mono'hydrate, n. [Chem.] Substance in which every MOLECULE is joined to one molecule of water.

mono'hydric, n. [Chem.] Having only one OH group; MONOBASIC.

'monoicous, a. [Bot.] (Of FILICALES and MUSCI) MONOECIOUS.

mono'karyon, n. [Biol.] A NUCLEUS with only one CENTRIOLE.

mono'layer, n. [Chem.] A LAYER of a substance one MOLECULE thick.

'monolith, n. [Archaeol.] One great stone or mass of stone by itself, put up at some time in man's history for some purpose. mono'lithic, a.

mono'mania, n. [Med.] Unbalanced condition of mind in which the person is unnormal on one point only, having, for example, a fixed, unreasoning idea that all those round him are banded together against him. mono'maniac, 1.n. Person having m. 2.a. Of, to do with, m. 'mono-man'iacal, a. Monomaniac.

mono'mastigote, a. [Zoo.] MONOCERCOUS.

'monomer, n. [Chem.] A simple MOLECULE as opp. a POLYMER.

mono'meric, a. [Biol.] Formed from one part only.

'monomero'somatous, a. [Zoo.] Having all the METAMERES united into one, as some insects.

mo'nomerous, a. [Bot.] (Of divisions of a flower) having only one part in place of a ring of parts.

mo'nomial, a. [Biol.] (Of names) formed of one word.

'monomo'lecular re'action. [Chem.] A reaction whose rate is dependent on the amount of only one of the substances taking part.

mono'morphic, a. [Biol.] Having only one form, being all the same in structure, opp. HETEROMORPHIC, DIMORPHIC, POLYMORPHIC. [Zoo.] Keeping the same general form through all stages of development.

mono'morphous, a. [Chem.] CRYSTALLIZING only in one form.

'monont, n. [Biol.] Simple plant or animal producing new ones by simple division of itself.

mono'nuclear, n., a. [Zoo.] (A great LEUCOCYTE) having one NUCLEUS only, without any divisions, as opp. POLYMORPHONUCLEAR. mononucle'osis, n. [Med.] An ACUTE and freq. INFECTIOUS disease marked by a great increase of mm. in the blood.

mono'petalous, a. [Bot.] Having the PETALS united; having one petal only.

mono'phagous, a. [Zoo.] Living on only one sort of food, as insects limited to one sort of plant. mo'nophagy, n.

mono'phonic, a [Phonet.] Representative of one sound, having only one sound.

'monophy'letic, a. [Biol.] Of, to do with, one family line; produced from one common first form or sort.

mono'phyllous, a. [Bot.] Having only one leaf, said sp. of a CALYX.

mono'phyodont, a. [Zoo.] Having only one growth of teeth, keeping the same teeth through all later development.

'monoplane, n. Airplane with one plane only.

mono'plastic, a. [Biol.] Keeping its first form.

mono'plegia, n. [Med.] PARALYSIS of one part of the body only, such as one leg or arm, one muscle or group of muscles.

'monoploid, n. [Biol.] HAPLOID.

mono'podium, n. [Bot.] A middle stem of which the growth keeps on in a straight line, branches being given off first on one side and then the other, which in turn have the same development, as in certain tall evergreen trees. mono'podial, a. To do with, being, a m., or like a m. in structure.

'monopy'renous, a. [Bot.] Having only one stone, said of fruit.

mono'rhinal, a. [Zoo.] Having only one opening in the nose.

mono'sacchar-ide, -ose, nn. [Chem.] Any of the simplest CARBOHYDRATES, having from 3 to 6 C ATOMS, and which it is not possible to get broken down into simpler substances having like properties, sp. SUGARS.

mono'sepalous, a. [Bot.] Having one SEPAL only; having all the sepals united in one.

'monosome, n. [Biol.] The SEX-CHROMOSOME.

mono'sperm-ous, -al, -ic, aa. [Bot.] Having only one seed.

'mono'spermy, n. [Zoo.] The common system of the FERTILIZATION of an OVUM by one male CELL.

'monospon'dylic, a. [Zoo.] (Of VERTEBRAE) having no INTERCENTRA.

'monospore, n. [Bot.] In some ALGAE, a simple unsexed SPORE. monospo'rangium, n. monospo'riferous, a. mono-'sporous, a. [Bot.] Monosporiferous. [Zoo.] Having only one SPORE.

'monostele, n. [Bot.] A solid STELE, as in most roots and the earliest parts of stems. mono'stelic, a.

mo'nostichous, a. [Bot.] Ranged in one line, on one side of an AXIS only.

mo'nostomous, a. [Zoo.] Having one mouth or SUCKER.

'monosy, n. [Biol.] Condition in which parts normally joined are separated.

'monosyl'labic, a. [Philol.] Said of languages having only words of one SYLLABLE, as Chinese.

'monosym'metric(al), aa. [Cryst.] MONOCLINIC. [Biol.] Having BILATERAL SYMMETRY.

Mono'tremata, n.pl. [Zoo.] The lowest ORDER of MAMMALIA, the only ones producing eggs, of which there are only three sorts, all living in or near Australia, all having only one MAMMA without a MAMMILLA, and all very strange-looking, one group being water animals with wide flat BEAKS and WEBBED feet like a water-bird. mono'trematous, a. 'monotreme. Animal of the M.

mo'notrichous, a. [Biol.] Having only one FLAGELLUM.

mo'notrochous, a. [Zoo.] Having the TROCHANTER without division.

mo'notropy, n. [Chem.] The property of a substance of having two or more forms of which only one is STABLE. mono'tropic, a.

'monotype, n. [Biol.] A SPECIES etc. which is the only representative of a GENUS etc. mono'typic, a. Being, to do with, a m.; having only one sort grouped under it.

mono'valent, a. [Chem.] Having a VALENCY of 1. mono'valenc-e, -y, nn.

mono'varient, a. UNIVARIENT.

mono'zoic, a. [Zoo.] (Of a SPORE) producing only one SPOROZOITE.

'monozy'gotic, a. [Biol.] (Of offspring) having development from one egg, as IDENTICAL TWINS.

mon'soon, n. [Meteor.] A regular wind blowing in one direction for one part of the year and in the opposite direction for the other, sp. the m. of south and east Asia, or the time of great rainfall from October to April, when it is blowing from the south-west.

mons 'pubis, n. [Anat.] Rounded structure, covered with hair, over the joining of the PUBES in a man.

mons 'veneris. [Anat.] Rounded cushion of fat over the joining of the PUBES in a woman.

'monster, n. [Biol., Med.] Any plant or animal or FOETUS of unnatural form or structure markedly different from its sort, for example, having more than the normal number of legs. 'monstrous, a.

'montan wax. [Chem.] A wax got from LIGNITE, coal, etc., used in the plates on which sound is first recorded for gramophone records.

mon'ticol-ous, -ine, a. [Biol.] Living on mountains.

'monticule, n. [Geog.] A little mountain, sp. a smaller, second point of a VOLCANO.

'monzonite, n. [Geol.] A COARSE-GRAINED IGNEOUS ROCK made up of almost equal amounts of ORTHOCLASE and PLAGIOCLASE together with different-coloured SILICATES.

moon, n. [Astron.] The earth's SATELLITE, 238,000 miles from it and measuring 2,158 miles across, which, cold itself, sends to the earth light from the sun by REFLECTION, its form as seen from the earth being dependent on its position in relation to the sun and the earth, and changing by degrees in the 28 days it takes to get back to its starting-point, from a thin curve of light at one side (the new m.) to a half-circle (first quarter), to a full-circle (full moon) to the opposite half-circle (third or last quarter) and so to a thin curve on the opposite side, after which, coming into a straight line with the sun, its journey is completely unseen; any satellite. m.-'culminating, a. (Of a star) coming to the MERIDIAN at about the same time as the moon. m.-'culminator, n. Star which is m.-culminating.

mo'raine, n. [Geol.] Stretch or mass of earth, broken stone, etc., put down by a GLACIER (see GROUND, LATERAL, MEDIAN, and TERMINAL).

'moonstone, n. [Mineral.] A sort of OPALESCENT FELDSPAR used as a jewel stone.

'morbid, a. [Med.] To do with disease, (of parts or substance) changed by disease, (of conditions) caused by disease. mor'bidity, n. M. condition; the amount of (a certain) disease in a place, the number of persons attacked in every 100.

mor'biferous, a. [Med.] Producing or transporting disease.

mor'bific, a. [Med.] Causing disease.

'mordant, n. [Chem.] Any substance, gen. a HYDROXIDE of a metal, used on cloth before DYEING because of its property of uniting with the DYE to make an INSOLUBLE substance, in this way giving a fixed colour to materials which would not by themselves take the colour, or, from which it would quickly be washed out, etc. 'mordanting, n. The use or operation of a m. in DYEING.

morgue, n. Public building in which the dead bodies of persons who have come to their death in some public place or by some violent event etc. are kept for a time to give possible friends and relations a chance of coming forward.

'moribund, a. [Med., etc.] Almost dead, in a condition near death.

'moron, n. [Med.] A person having a degree of MENTAL DEFICIENCY which gives him a MENTAL AGE of between 8 and 12 years, needing some care and direction, but able to take part in society and freq. to get a living by work not needing much brain power. mo'ronic, a. mo'ronity, n. The condition of a m.

-morph, n. Form.

morpha'l(l)axis, n. [Biol.] The producing of a new part of smaller size or different form to take the place of a damaged one; slow growth or development of a special part.

'morphia, n. [Chem.] MORPHINE.

-morphic, a. Having a given form. -morphism, -morphy, nn. Condition of being -morphic.

'morphine, n. [Chem., Med.] A bitter, white, CRYSTALLINE substance with NARCOTIC properties, $C_{17}H_{19}NO_3$, the chief substance present in OPIUM, used medically for taking away pain. mor'phinic, a. 'morphinism, n. [Med.] A condition caused by the regular taking of m.

morpho-. Form; forming.

morpho'genesis, mor'phogeny, nn. [Biol.] The process of the development of parts and ORGANS or of any one of them. 'morphoge'netic, a. morphoge'netic 'movements. The changing of the places of groups of CELLS in the process of development of an EMBRYO.

mor'phology, n. [Biol.] The branch of biology which has to do with the form and structure of living things, as opp. their working; the form and structure of a living thing or any of its parts. [Geol.] (The science of) the outer form of the earth or its parts, the forms taken by ROCK, country, etc. morpho'logic(al), aa. morpho'logic 'index. [Anat.] The relation between the size of the body and that of the arms and legs. mor'phologist, n.

mor'phosis, n. [Biol.] The process of development of a living thing or any part of it, sp. TISSUES. mor'photic, a. To do with, taking part in, causing m.

-morphous, a. Formed of or like.

mor'photrop-ism, -y, nn. [Chem.] The change in CRYSTAL form produced by a change in chemical structure.

Morse code. System of short and long signs ('dots' and 'dashes') put together in different ways so as to be representative of different letters, first worked out for and still used in TELEGRAPHY, but used in addition for sending news by flags, or blows on something hard, or in any way in which short and long units are possible.

mor'tality, n. The property of undergoing death; the number of deaths in a given time in a given place, that is, the death rate in a general sense or in relation to special conditions such as a given disease.

'mortar, n. [Chem.] A basin made of pot, glass or some stone-like substance, in which solids are crushed with a PESTLE.

'mortar, n. Any building substance, such as that made by mixing LIME with sand and water, which is used in the form of a paste for uniting bricks etc. and becomes hard on drying.

'mortify, v.i. [Med.] (Of living substance) undergo death and DECAY while part of a living body. 'mortifi'cation, n.

'mortuary, n. [Med.] Out-building in connection with a hospital, etc., in which dead bodies are put for POST MORTEMS or while waiting to be taken away.

'morula, n. [Biol., Med.] Name given to a number of structures having the look of a round mass of small berries, sp. the solid mass of CELLS which is the first outcome of the complete division of an OVUM in a number of animals. moru'lation, n. The forming of a m. by the division of an egg. moruloid, a.

mo'saic, 1.n. Structure made up of a number of irregular bits or small regular units put together, sp. in a way giving a design. [Bot.] The placing of leaves on a plant in such a way that one is not covered by another but the spaces between are narrow, so that as great a number as possible get the rays of the sun with as little waste of space as possible (leaf m.); any of sorts of disease of tobacco and other plants, caused by a VIRUS, in which the leaves become covered with yellow or brown places giving a m. effect (m. disease). 2.a. Being a m., sp. [Geol.] said of the structure of ROCKS. m. de'velopment. [Zoo.] The sort of development in an OVUM or an EMBRYO, when, after the TISSUES are DETERMINED, the development of the different parts goes on for a time independently of one another. m. 'hybrid. [Biol.] An offspring produced by two plants or animals having ALLELOMORPHIC qualities in which these qualities are present together but unmixed, such as an animal of a sort having two sexes which is itself in part male and in part female, or a white flower with red marks produced by a red flower and a white. m. 'image. [Zoo.] The complete IMAGE formed by a COMPOUND EYE when its structure is such that the images formed by the different units are of different parts of the thing seen. m. in'heritance or he'redity. [Biol.] The handing down to offspring of ALLELOMORPHIC qualities. m. 'vision. [Zoo.] Seeing by m. images.

mos'quito, n. Any of a number of sorts of insects of the DIPTERA of which the females have hollow, needle-like mouthparts for SUCKING the blood of other animals and generally put their eggs

266

down on STAGNANT water—important medically because transporting a number of diseases.

moss, n. Any plant of the MUSCI. **'mossy,** a. [Biol.] Said of structures with a branching, thread-like structure or outgrowths, sp. the CELLS of the NEUROGLIA (**mossy cells**).

moss 'agate, n. [Mineral.] A sort of AGATE having in it other substances, such as MnO_2, in the form of brown, black, or green thread-like markings.

'mother cell. [Biol.] Any CELL giving birth to other cells by division.

'mother 'liquor or **liquid.** [Chem.] The liquid from which a substance has been taken by CRYSTALLIZATION.

'mother-of-'pearl, a., n. (Of) the hard, IRIDESCENT substance forming the inner coat of a number of SHELLS.

'motile, 1.a. [Biol.] Having the power of motion from place to place, said of small living things. **mo'tility,** n.

'motion, n. [Med.] (Act of sending out) FAECES.

'motion 'picture. A SERIES of camera-pictures, taken with a special apparatus, representative of very small changes, one after the other, in the position of something in motion, and sent onto a SCREEN at a very quick rate so that the effect on the eye is that of the thing moving.

'motion 'study. TIME AND MOTION STUDY.

'motive 'power. [Phys.] Any power, such as electric, water, or steam power, used for driving a machine.

mo'tivity, n. [Phys.] The power of moving or of causing motion.

moto-. Motion, MOTOR.

'motor, 1.n. [Mach.] A machine producing driving-power, putting anything in motion, sp. an INTERNAL COMBUSTION ENGINE or a machine for changing electric ENERGY into MECHANICAL energy. 2.a. To do with, causing, or handing on motion. [Zoo.] Sp. to do with, causing, motion of muscles, GLANDS, CILIA, etc. [Mach.] Having, worked by, a m. **m. a'phasia.** [Med.] The form of APHASIA in which there is loss of the control of the muscles of the mouth and throat necessary for forming words. **m. 'area.** [Zoo.] A part of the brain controlling motion—in man etc. in the m. cortex. **m. cell.** [Bot.] Any of a group of CELLS which as a group has the power of expansion and the opposite, and so of causing the motion of a part of a plant. **m. con'verter.** [Elec.] A machine changing ALTERNATING into DIRECT current, or the other way round. **m. 'cortex.** [Zoo.] The front divisions of the CEREBRAL HEMISPHERES, controlling the m. nerves. **m. 'end-plate** or **'end-'organ.** [Zoo.] Special structure forming the end of the AXON of a m. neurone,

made up of a branching ending of the axon with a mass of muscle CELL-substance round it, through which the nerve impulses effecting motion are given to the muscle. **m. 'fibre.** [Zoo.] Any NERVE FIBRE by which the CONTRACTION of muscle is effected. **m. 'generator.** [Elec.] A GENERATOR getting from a m. the ENERGY to be changed into current. **m. 'impulse.** [Zoo., Psych.] Any NERVE IMPULSE by which a muscle is moved. **m. nerve.** [Zoo.] Sp. any of the nerves transporting m. impulses from the brain to the muscles. **m. 'neurone.** [Zoo.] A NERVE-CELL making connection between a m. nerve and a muscle. **m. pa'ralysis.** [Med.] Loss of power of moving muscles which are under the conscious control of the brain. **m. root.** [Zoo.] Any NERVE ROOT made up of m. fibres, sp. the VENTRAL ROOT of a SPINAL NERVE.

mo'torium, n. [Zoo.] That part of a nervesystem having to do with motion of the muscles, the MOTOR AREAS.

motor'pathy, n. [Med.] Use of muscle motions against disease. **motor'pathic,** a.

mo(u)ld, 1.n. Vessel in which a soft or liquid substance, such as a heated metal, is put to get solid and from which it takes its form; substance turned out of a m. [Geol.] The print of any animal or plant in stone. 2.v.t. Get formed (as) in a m. **'-ing,** n. Sp., the process of moulding metals.

mo(u)ld, n. [Bot.] A grey or white wool-like growth of FUNGI on the outside of anything, sp. dead plant or animal substance in the process of DECAY; any fungus producing m.; HUMUS.

mo(u)lt, 1.v.i. [Zoo.] Put off outer covering, such as hair, feathers, skin, horns, at regular times. 2.n. The process of moulting; the covering put off. **'moulting,** a., n.

'mountain, n. [Geog.] A mass of land very much higher than the country round it and narrowing up to the top, where it is small in comparison with its base. **m. 'sickness.** [Med.] The ill feeling experienced by persons going up very high on mm. as the effect of the air becoming thinner, so that less O is taken in, marked by quick breathing, pain in the head and chest, and sometimes NAUSEA. **m. winds.** [Meteor.] The regular currents of air blowing to and up the sides of a m. in the daytime and down at night, when the weather is clear, caused by the heating of the upper parts of a m. by the sun to a greater degree than the lower parts.

'mounting, n. Support, that on which an instrument etc. is fixed, sp. [Optics] the non-OPTICAL parts of a TELESCOPE.

'mov(e)able, a. Which may be moved, sp. [Zoo.] (of a connection between bones etc.) joining parts in such a way that they

have some power of independent motion.
'**movement**, n. The working-parts of a watch or clock. [Med.] MOTION.

'**moving-'coil**, a. [Elec.] (Of an instrument) of which the operation is dependent on the motion of a COIL through which current is going in a MAGNETIC FIELD, as a **m.-c. galva'nometer** (see GALVANOMETER).

m.p. = MELTING-POINT.

M shell. [Phys.] The SHELL of an ATOM outside the L-SHELL, having at most 18 ELECTRONS.

mu. The Greek letter μ. **mu'meson**. [Phys.] MESON of REST MASS 215, produced when a PI-MESON is broken-up.

muci-. MUCUS:- **mu'ciparous**, a. [Biol.].

mu'cific, a. [Zoo.] Producing MUCUS. [Med.] Helping the producing of mucus.

'**mucigen**, n. [Biochem.] A substance present in the form of grains in CELLS producing MUCUS.

'**mucilage**, n. [Bot.] Sorts of sticky, jelly-like substances, hard when dry, produced in the CELL-walls of certain plants. **muci'laginous**, a. To do with, like, formed of, or producing m. or MUCIN.

'**mucin**, n. [Biochem.] Any of a group of PROTEINS present in SALIVA or MUCUS.

mu'cinogen, n. MUCIGEN.

mu'civorous, a. [Zoo.] Living on liquids from plants, as certain insects.

muco-. MUCUS or MUCOUS (and . . .); to do with MUCOUS MEMBRANE: -'**fibrous**, a.

'**mucocele**, n. [Med.] A mass of MUCUS inside a hollow part, sp. the LACHRYMAL SAC, stopping it up and causing expansion and INFLAMMATION; any hollow growth with mucus inside it.

muco'cellulose, n. [Bot.] Any of certain substances formed of CELLULOSE mixed with a MUCOUS substance, present chiefly in seeds and fruits.

'**mucoid**, a. [Zoo.] Like MUCUS.

muco'purulent, a. [Med.] Made up of MUCUS mixed with PUS.

Muco'rales, n.pl. [Bot.] An ORDER of PHYCOMYCETES living on dead plant or animal substance or on living plants of the same sort as themselves, taking in most of the MOULDS.

mu'cosa, n. [Zoo.] A MUCOUS MEMBRANE.

mu'coso-. MUCOUS and (. . .): -'**granular**, a.

'**mucous**, a. [Zoo.] Covered with, producing, like, to do with, MUCUS. **m.** '**membrane**. (Any separate part formed of) the sort of TISSUE coating the inside of openings and hollows of the body in back-boned animals, such as the mouth, nose, wind-pipe, UTERUS, etc., formed of an outer very soft and smooth skin having in it m. GLANDS by which it is kept wet, covering a stretch of VASCULAR TISSUE. **m.** '**tissue**. A jelly-like form of CONNECTIVE TISSUE, present in the UMBILICAL CORD and the EMBRYO.

'**mucro**, n. [Biol.] A stiff or sharp point at the end of a part. -'**nate(d)**, -'**niferous**, aa. Ending in a m. said sp. of a leaf. -'**nation**, n. Condition of being mucronate.

'**muculent**, a. [Zoo.] Wet and sticky, covered with or producing MUCUS. [Bot.] Like mucus.

'**mucus**, n. [Zoo.] The thin VISCOUS liquid produced by MUCOUS MEMBRANE: any like substance produced in non-back-boned animals.

mud, n. [Geol.] A very small-grained soft ROCK, sp. CLAY, made paste-like by having much water in it. **m. vol'cano**. Pointed mass of m. formed over a hole in the earth sending out m. and gases. '**m.-flow**, n. A moving mass of almost liquid m. or wet earth caused by rain or sent out by a spring, etc. '**-stone**, n. Sort of stone without clear STRATA, formed of m. put down by a river etc. which has become hard.

Müllerian duct. [Zoo.] In EMBRYOS of back-boned animals, one or the other of two pipes parallel to the WOLFFIAN DUCTS, in the female later freq. becoming OVIDUCTS.

'**Müller's** '**muscle**. [Zoo.] The CILIARY MUSCLE of the eye of a back-boned animal.

mul'tangular bone or **mul'tangulum**, n. [Zoo.] One or the other of two bones of the CARPUS, the **greater mul'tangular**, joined to the first METACARPAL, and the **lesser multangular**, joined to the second metacarpal.

multi.- More than one, a (great) number of:— -'**ar'ticulate**, a. [Zoo.], -'**carinate**, a. [Biol.], -'**cellular**, a. [Biol., Elec.], -'**ciliate**, a. [Zoo.], -col'oured, a., -'**cuspid(ate)**, aa. [Zoo.], -'**florous**, a. [Bot.], -'**foliate**, a. [Bot.], -'**laminate**, a. [Biol.], -'**nodal**, a. [Biol.], -'**nucleate**, a. [Biol.], -'**ovulate**, a. [Bot.], -'**septate**, a. [Biol.], -'**staminate**, a. [Biol.], -'**sulcate**, a. [Biol.].

'**multibreak**, n. [Elec.] Apparatus by which electric current is stopped in a number of places at the same time (freq. **m. switch** or m. '**circuit-'breaker**).

multi'cipital, a. [Bot.] Having a number of branches starting from one point. [Zoo.] Having a number of heads.

'**multicom'ponent**, a. [Phys.-Chem.] Said of a system having two or more COMPONENTS.

multi'costate, a. [Biol.] Having a number of RIBS or RIDGES, sp. of leaf, with VEINS running longways very near together (see picture p. 223).

'**multifid**, a. [Bot.] Having a great number of divisions or parts.

multi'foliolate, a. [Bot.] Having a great number of small leaves.

'**multiform**, a. Having a number of forms; different in form from one another.

multi'jug-ate, **-ous**, aa. [Bot.] Having a great number of small leaves in twos.

multi'lateral, a. Having a number of sides.

multi'locular, a. [Bot.] Having a number of walled spaces.

mul'tiparous, a. [Zoo.] Producing two or more offspring at a birth. [Bot.] Producing a number of side AXES. **multi-'parity,** n. Condition of being m.

'multiped, a. [Zoo.] Having a great number of feet.

'multiple, 1.a. Made up of more than one, or sp. of more than two, things or parts; being or to do with more than one, sp. a great number. 2.n. A number which is a complete number of times a given number, into which a given number goes with nothing over, as '16 is a m. of 4'. **m. a'llelomorph.** [Biol.] Any of three or more GENES or qualities in an ALLELOMORPHIC relation to one another, only two of which may be present together in non-POLYPLOID plants and animals. **m. co'rolla.** [Bot.] A COROLLA formed of more than one ring of parts. **m. 'factor.** [Biol.] M. allelomorph; any of a group of m. factors. **m. 'factors.** [Biol.] Two or more separate GENES acting together as a group, of which the theory is put forward as a way of accounting for BLENDING INHERITANCE. **m. 'fission.** [Biol.] Division of a CELL into more than two parts, sp. the system of division in PROTOZOA, in which the NUCLEUS undergoes division after division before there is any division of the rest of the cell substance, which then becomes separated into the same number of parts, gen. with some substance over. **m. fruit.** [Bot.] A fruit formed from a number of flowers grouped together. **m. 'myeloma'tosis.** [Med.] MYELOMATOSIS in a number of different bones of the same time. **m. neu'ritis.** [Med.] NEURITIS attacking more than one nerve at the same time. **m. per-so'nality.** [Psych.] Condition in which a person's qualities, impulses etc. are formed, not, as normally, into one system, but into two or more than two separate systems, taking control of a person's mind in turn, so that he seems to be a number of different persons in one body. **m. pro'portions.** *See* LAW OF M. PROPORTIONS. **m. scle'rosis.** [Med.] A diseased condition in which there is SCLEROSIS of the brain or SPINAL CORD at a number of different points, the nerve substance there undergoing destruction and giving place to small hard masses of NEUROGLIA, marked by PARALYSIS in a greater or less degree and freq. causing death. **m. star.** [Astron.] Three or more stars having the same sort of connection as the two forming a DOUBLE STAR.

'multiplet, n. [Phys.] A line in a SPECTRUM made up of a number of lines very near together.

'multiplex, a. MULTIPLE. [Elec.] (Of a telegraph etc. system) such that a number of telegrams etc. may be sent at the same time over the same wire. [Radio] To do with the sending out or taking in of a number of independent SIGNALS by one apparatus at the same time.

'multipli'cand, n. [Arith.] The number which is (to be) MULTIPLIED by a given number, as *y* in '*x* times *y*'.

'multipli'cate, a. MULTIPLE. [Zoo.] Made up of a number of folds, as certain SHELLS.

'multipli'cation, n. [Arith.] Act or process of MULTIPLYING. **m. table.** TABLE for use in arithmetic giving the amounts got by the m. of a given number by 2, 3, 4 and so on. **m. 'factor.** [Phys.] The number of NEUTRONS produced in a NUCLEAR REACTOR for the loss of one.

multi'plicity, n. Condition of being MULTIPLE; a great number.

'multiplier, n. [Arith.] The number by which another is (to be) MULTIPLIED, as *x* in '*x* times *y*'. [Phys.] Any instrument for increasing some effect, sp. [Elec.] a RESISTANCE used in connection with an instrument for measuring VOLTAGE to make an adjustment of it to a higher voltage than it is designed to take.

'multiply, v.t. and i. Make or become greater in number, sp. [Biol.] become greater in number by division or the producing of offspring. [Arith.] Get the amount produced by taking a given number, *x*, a given number of times, *y*, that is, by the addition of *x* to itself *y*−1 times ('m. *x* by *y*'); do this process, of which the sign × is representative.

multi'polar, a. [Zoo.] (Of nerve CELLS) having a number of AXONS. [Elec.] (Of GENERATOR etc.) having more than two MAGNETIC POLES.

multi'radiate, a. [Biol.] Having a great number of rays.

multi'seri-al, -ate, aa. [Bot.] Ranged in more than one line; more than one line of CELLS etc. thick.

multi'spiral, a. [Biol.] (Of a SPIRAL structure) having a great number of turns.

'multitu'berculate, a. [Zoo.] Having a (great) number of points or small out growths, said sp. of teeth. **'multi'tubercul-y, -ism,** nn. Sp., the theory that the back teeth of MAMMALS are developments from m. forms.

'multivalent, a. [Chem.] Having a VALENCY of 3 or more.

multi'vincular, a. [Zoo.] (Of the HINGE of a SHELL) formed of a number of cords.

mult'ungulate, a. [Zoo.] Having the HOOF with three or more divisions.

'mummifi'cation, n. [Med.] Process by which a part of the body, sp. arm or leg, becomes dead and dried up through not getting enough blood from the heart. 'mummify, v.i. Undergo m.

mumps, n. [Med.] An ACUTE and INFECTIOUS disease marked by SWELLING and pain in the PAROTID GLAND of the neck, commonest in young persons.

'Munsell colour system. A system of rating colours based on fixed scales for the three properties of HUE, VALUE and CHROMA, every hue being given a letter and a number, every degree of value and chroma a number only, so that any colour may be clearly pointed to by a FORMULA representative of these three.

'mural, a. [Biol., Med.] To do with, near, limited to, the wall of some part.

'muriate, n. [Chem.] A SALT of HCl, sp. KCl, used in farming for making land fertile. 'muriatic acid. Another name for HYDROCHLORIC ACID.

'muricate(d), aa. [Bot.] Covered with short, sharp points.

mu'riculate, a. [Bot.] Covered with very small sharp points.

'muriform, a. [Bot.] Like a brick wall in structure, said of cork substance, the grouping of SPORES, etc.

'murmur, n. [Med.] A sound like that of low rough breathing coming to the ear from a STETHOSCOPE placed over a part of the body, and giving a sign of some unnormal condition, sp. of something wrong with the VALVES of the heart.

'muscae voli'tantes. [Med.] Moving dark points seen in front of the eyes, caused by small solid bits of CELL substance in the liquid part of the eye.

mus'cariform, a. [Biol.] Having the form of a brush.

'muscarine, n. [Chem.] $C_8H_{13}O_3N$, a CRYSTALLINE, ALKALOID poison present in some FUNGI.

'Musci, n.pl. [Bot.] One of the two great divisions of BRYOPHYTA, gen. very small plants of thick growth, forming a soft cover over the earth, stones, trees etc., starting as a branching thread-like structure from which new plants, with a great number of small leaves on a middle stem, undergo development from side BUDS, specially common in woods but of very wide distribution. 'muscoid, a.

'muscle, n. [Zoo.] TISSUE made up of long CELLS having the property of becoming shorter and thicker when acted on by a nerve, by which the motion of parts of the body is effected, and of which most of the FLESH of animals is formed (see STRIATED, UNSTRIATED and CARDIAC); any of the separate masses or structures of m. moving different parts. m. 'column. SARCOSTYLE. m. 'fibre. Any of the long, thick-walled CELLS of m. m. plate. In the EMBRYOS of back-boned animals, a part of the MESODERM undergoing develop-

ment into m. m. 'spindle, n. A structure in m. pointed at the two ends and made up of SENSORY nerve-endings with a cover of CONNECTIVE TISSUE. 'm.-bound, a. [Med.] Having some of the mm. stretched and inelastic from over-use.

mus'cology, n. [Bot.] The science of MUSCI. musco'logical, a. mus'cologist, n.

'muscovite, n. [Geol.] Common form of MICA, light yellow in colour, sometimes named *white mica*.

'muscular, a. [Zoo.] To do with, forming, done by, a muscle or muscles; having good development of muscle. 'musculo-.

'musculature, n. [Zoo.] The system of muscles of an animal or a part, their positions in relation to one another.

'muskeg, n. [Geog.] A BOG of Canada and the north U.S.A. of the sort covered with 'islands' of thickly massed SPHAGNUM MOSS.

'mustard gas. [Chem.] A POISON GAS having a burning effect on the skin, made by the reaction of ETHYLENE and S_2Cl_2.

muta'facient, a. [Biol.] Said of a GENE which has the effect of causing or increasing the MUTATION of another.

'mutagen, n. [Biol.] Any substance increasing the normal MUTATION rate of a SPECIES.

'mutant, n. [Biol.] An animal or plant produced by, or a GENE which has undergone, MUTATION.

'mutaro'tation, n. [Chem.] The change in the OPTICAL ACTIVITY of certain SOLUTIONS, for example those of SUGARS, as they become older.

mu'tation, n. Change. [Biol.] The development by degrees in a SPECIES of plant or animal of a changed structure; the sudden producing in offspring of a quality different, gen. ALLELOMORPHIC, to that normal to its species, which is then handed down in place of the old one, or the sudden change in a CHROMOSOME or GENE by which this new development in a species is effected; the new branch of a species produced by sudden m. mu'tate, v.i. Undergo m. mu'tational, mu'tative, aa.

mute, 1.a. [Phonet.] (Of a letter in writing) not said, representative of no sound in the word as it is said; (of a sound) produced with a short complete stopping of the breath. [Med.] Without power of talking. 2.n. [Phonet.] M. letter or sound, as p or b. [Med.] Person m. from birth.

muti'lation, n. [Zoo., Med.] (Condition of having undergone) loss of a necessary part, making structure incomplete, sp. by having it cut or broken off. 'mutilate, v.t. and i. (Make) undergo m. 'mutilated, a.

'mutism, n. [Med.] Condition, present from birth, of being a MUTE.

'mutual 'character'istic curve. [Radio]

GRAPH representative of the relation between the ANODE current of a THERMIONIC VALVE and the GRID VOLTAGE.

'mutual con'ductance. [Radio] The amount of the increase in the ANODE current in a radio VALVE for a change of one VOLT in the GRID.

'mutual 'coupling. [Elec.] TRANSFORMER COUPLING.

'mutual in'ductance. [Elec.] The property of MAGNETIC LINKAGE between two CIRCUITS as the effect of which MUTUAL INDUCTION takes place; the measure of m.i., that is, of the ELECTROMOTIVE FORCE produced in one circuit by a unit rate of change of current in the other.

mutual in'duction. [Elec.] The producing of an ELECTROMOTIVE FORCE in one electric CIRCUIT by a change of current in a near-by but separate circuit.

'mutualism, n. [Biol.] SYMBIOSIS or any connection between two plants or animals which is of use to the two.

my'algia, n. [Med.] Pain in muscle. my-'algic, a.

my'arian, a. [Zoo.] To do with the system of muscles; (of a system of names) based on the system of muscles.

myas'thenia, n. [Med.] Feeble condition of the muscles. m. 'gravis. A disease marked at first by very quick tiring of the STRIATED muscles and loss of their power of CONTRACTION at times and in the end by its complete loss, caused by the stopping of the chemical reaction at the nerve-endings by which the muscles are put in operation.

my'celium (mycelia), n. [Bot.] The mass or network of thread-like structures of which the plant-body of a FUNGUS is made up, and which is gen. completely bedded in the substance, living or dead, from which it gets its food. my'celi-al, -oid, aa.

my'ceto-. FUNGUS: -'genesis, n., my'cetoid, a.

my'cetoge'n(et)ic, aa. Produced by a FUNGUS.

myce'toma, n. [Med.] A disease of the skin and parts under it, specially attacking the foot, caused by a FUNGUS.

My'ceto'zoa, n.pl. [Biol.] MYXOMYCETES.

myco-. FUNGUS.

Myco'derma, n.pl. [Bot.] The GENUS of FUNGI forming the coating which comes on the top of wine or beer undergoing FERMENTATION; the BACTERIA changing alcohol into ACETIC ACID. myco'derma, n. The coating produced on wine, etc. by M. 'mycoderm, n., a. (FUNGUS) producing mycoderma. myco'derm-ic, -ous, aa.

my'cology, n. The science of FUNGI. myco'logic(al), aa. my'cologist, n.

myco'protein, n. [Biochem.] The PROTEIN substance got from the bodies of BAC-

TERIA. 'mycoprotei'nation, n. [Med.] The process of putting m. into blood.

myco'(r)rhiza, n. [Bot.] SYMBIOSIS between the MYCELIUM of certain FUNGI and the roots of a seed plant, gen. a tree.

my'cosis, n. [Zoo., Med.] Any condition or disease of man or other animals caused by FUNGI in the body. my'cotic, a. m. fun'goides. [Med.] A skin disease of slow development, marked by flat, FUNGUS-like red growths, chiefly on the head, face and chest. -mycosis, n.

myco'trophic, a. [Bot.] Living in SYMBIOSIS with a FUNGUS.

my'driasis, n. [Med.] Condition in which there is a fixed and over-great expansion of the PUPIL of the eye. mydri'atic, n., a. (Substance) causing expansion of the PUPIL of the eye.

my'ectopy, n. [Med.] Condition of a muscle being out of place.

'myelen'cephalon, n. [Zoo.] In back-boned animals, the MEDULLA OBLONGATA. 'myelen'cephalous, a.

-'myelia, n. [Med.] Disease or condition of the SPINAL CORD.

my'elic, a. [Zoo.] To do with the SPINAL CORD.

'myelin, n. [Zoo.] The soft, white, fat-like, material forming the MEDULLARY SHEATH of an AXON. '-(iz)'ation, n. The forming of a MEDULLARY SHEATH.

'myel(o)-. [Zoo., Med.] Bone MARROW: 'myelo'genesis, n., 'myeloid, a.; SPINAL CORD: mye'litis, n. [Med.].

'myelocele, n. [Med.] Condition, present at birth, in which the SPINAL CORD is uncovered and touching the back wall of the body at the lower end, as effect of incomplete forming of VERTEBRAE.

'myeloc(o)el(e), n. [Zoo.] The pipe-like hollow down the middle of the SPINAL CORD.

'myelocyte, n. [Zoo.] A MARROW-CELL. sp. one of the great cells present in the marrow of the long bones of higher animals and possibly producing blood LEUCOCYTES; a nerve-CELL of the SPINAL CORD or brain. 'myelocy'tosis, n. [Med.] A condition in which there is an unnormal increase of mm.

'myelo'gen-ic, -ous, aa. [Med.] Starting or produced in bone MARROW.

'mye'loma, n. [Med.] Diseased growth in bone MARROW, gen. attacking a number of different bones at the same time. '-'tosis, n. The forming of, condition of, having mm.

'myelon, n. SPINAL CORD.

'myeloplast, n. [Zoo.] A LEUCOCYTE of BONE MARROW.

'myeloplax, n. [Zoo.] Any of the great CELLS with a number of NUCLEI present in bone-MARROW and other blood-forming parts, and possibly giving birth to the THROMBOCYTES.

'myelosar'coma, n. [Med.] A MALIGNANT MYELOMA of quick growth.

myen'teric, a. [Zoo.] To do with the muscles of the INTESTINE and their motion.

'mylo-. [Zoo.] MOLAR.

mylo'hyoid, 1.a. [Zoo.] In back-boned animals, to do with the part of the mouth under the tongue. 2.n. Muscle forming the floor of the mouth.

'mylonite, n. [Geol.] A sort of hard ROCK formed of the rock dust produced by FAULTING crushed into a solid mass.

myo-. Muscle:— '-'neural, a., -'sitis, n. [Med.].

'myoblast, n. [Zoo.] CELL which undergoes development into a muscle cell.

myo'cardium (myocardia), n. [Zoo.] That part of the wall of the heart formed of muscle. myo'cardi-ac, -al, aa.

myo'cardiograph, n. [Med.] Instrument making a record of the motion of the heart muscles. myo'cardiogram, n. Record made by m.

'myocar'ditis, n. [Med.] INFLAMMATION of the MYOCARDIUM.

'myocoel(e), n. [Zoo.] The hollow inside a MYOTOME.

myo'comma (myocommata), n. [Zoo.] Any of the parts into which the body muscles of back-boned animals are separated by thin walls; any of the thin, skin-like parts forming walls between mm.

'myocyte, n. [Zoo.] A muscle CELL; in sponges, a cell with the power of CONTRACTION; in certain PROTOZOA, the inner part of the ECTOPLASM in which are the MYONEMES.

'myody'namic, a. [Zoo.] To do with the motion of muscles.

myoepi'cardial 'layer. [Zoo.] The part of the MESOCARDIUM undergoing development into the walls of the heart.

'myoepi'thelial cell. [Zoo.] Very simple form of skin CELL with CONTRACTILE outgrowths, seen in COELENTERATA.

myofi'brilla (myofibrillae), n. [Zoo.] Any of the thread-like parts making up a muscle CELL.

'myofi'broma, n. [Med.] A diseased growth made up chiefly of FIBROUS muscle substance.

'myogen, n. [Biochem.] A PROTEIN of thread-like structure present in muscle PROTOPLASM, from which MYOSIN is produced.

myo'genesis, n. [Zoo.] The development of muscle- or other FIBRES. myoge'n(et)ic, aa. To do with m. [Med.] Starting in a muscle. myogenic theory. The theory that the regular motions of the heart muscle are caused by the muscle CELLS, independently of any impulse given to the muscle by a nerve.

'myograph, n. [Med., etc.] Instrument for recording the rate and force of muscle CONTRACTION.

myo'h(a)ematin, n. [Biochem.] The colouring-material present in muscle, possibly uniting with O like the HAEMATIN of the blood.

'myoid, a. Like muscle.

myo'lemma, n. SARCOLEMMA.

my'ology, n. [Zoo.] The science of muscles. myo'logic(al), aa. my'ologist, n.

my'olysis, n. [Med.] Destruction of muscle substance.

my'oma, n. [Med.] A diseased growth formed of muscle substance. my'omectomy, n.

myomere, n. [Zoo.] MYOCOMMA in the first sense given.

myo'metrium, n. [Zoo.] The muscle wall of the UTERUS.

'myoneme, n. [Zoo.] In a number of PROTOZOA, a very small, muscle-like, CONTRACTILE thread.

myo'nicity, n. [Zoo.] The property or power of CONTRACTION of muscle.

my'opathy, n. [Med.] Any disease of the muscles, sp. any of a number of conditions in which there is an increasing loss of power in the STRIATED muscles as the effect of wasting away from any cause.

'myophore, n. [Zoo.] A part or outgrowth of a SHELL where a muscle is fixed.

my'opia, n. [Med.] A condition of the eye in which a person is unable to see clearly things far from him, caused by an error in the form of the eye by which parallel rays are made to come to a point in front of, and not on, the RETINA. 'myope, n. Person having m. my'opic, a.

'myoplasm, n. [Zoo.] That part of the PROTOPLASM of a muscle CELL which has the power of CONTRACTION.

myo'plasty, n. [Med.] PLASTIC SURGERY on muscles, or using muscle substance.

'myosar'coma, n. [Med.] A MALIGNANT MYOMA of very quick growth.

'myoscope, n. [Med.] Apparatus for watching the motion of muscles.

myo'septum, n. [Zoo.] MYOCOMMA in the second sense given.

'myosin, n. [Biochem.] A GLOBULIN formed in dead muscle from MYOGEN, and said to have something to do with RIGOR MORTIS. myo'sinogen, n. MYOGEN.

my'osis, n. my'otic, a. See MIOSIS, MIOTIC.

my'otasis, n. [Med.] The stretching of a muscle; muscle TONICITY. myo'tatic, a.

'myotome, n. [Zoo.] In back-boned animals, MUSCLE PLATE; in non-back-boned animals made up of METAMERES, the muscles of a metamere.

'myria-. 10,000. (Used in naming units in the METRIC SYSTEM.

Myri'apoda, n.pl. [Zoo.] A CLASS of the ARTHROPODA taking in two groups of small animals having a head and a long body made up of a great number of divisions, with legs (two or four, dependent on the group) on almost every one, living on land and breathing by TRACHEAE.

myrin'gitis, n. [Med.] INFLAMMATION of the TYMPANIC MEMBRANE.

myxa'moeba, n. [Biol.] The AMOEBOID CELL produced by a SPORE of the MYXOMYCETES or of certain simple FUNGI.

myxo-. MUCUS.

'myxocyte, n. [Zoo.] One of the special, freq. star-formed, CELLS present in MUCOUS TISSUE.

myx(o)e'dema, n. [Med.] Disease marked by a very dry condition of the skin, hard SWELLINGS under it, and loss of hair, probably caused by something wrong with the THYROID GLAND. **myx(o)e-'dem-ic, -atous,** aa.

myxofla'gellate, n. [Biol.] A MYXOMYCETE in the stage after a MYXAMOEBA, when it has a FLAGELLUM.

my'xoma (myxomata), n. [Med.] A diseased growth made up of substance like that of MUCOUS TISSUE.

'myxoma'tosis, n. An INFECTIOUS disease of *Lepidae* produced by a VIRUS, gen. causing death.

'Myxomy'cetes, n.pl. [Biol.] A group of very simple living things having some of the properties of a plant and some of an animal (freq. put under THALLOPHYTA), which at full growth are simply uncovered masses of PROTOPLASM with a number of NUCLEI, moving slowly over the earth and taking in food, and at a certain point producing SPORES in a spore-vessel which become MYXAMOEBAE, which in turn become new m.

'Myxophyta, n.pl. [Bot.] The DIVISION of THALLOPHYTA of which MYXOMYCETES is the only CLASS.

Myxo'phyceae, n.pl. [Bot.] CYANOPHYCEAE.

myxo'posium, n. [Zoo.] A branched PSEUDOPODIUM.

'myxospore, n. [Biol.] Any of the SPORES produced by MYXOMYCETES.

N, Sign for NITROGEN.

N., N-, or **N** = NORMAL SOLUTION.

n, Sign for INDEX OF REFRACTION.

n-. [Chem.] *Normal,* that is having an unbranched chain of C ATOMS.

n, Sign for NEUTRON.

Na, Sign for SODIUM.

na'celle, n. Any of the structures housing an engine in an airplane with more than one engine.

'nacre, n. [Zoo.] (A SHELL'S inner coat of)

MOTHER-OF-PEARL. **'nacr-eous, -ine,** aa.

'nacrite, n. [Mineral.] A natural substance having the same make-up as KAOLIN, but different ATOMIC structure and OPTICAL properties.

'nadir, n. [Astron.] The point in the CELESTIAL SPHERE which is straight opposite the ZENITH, that is, where it is cut by a straight line going down through the middle point of the earth from the point of observation.

'n(a)evus, n. [Med.] A MOLE, sp. one present from birth. **'n(a)ev-ose, -oid,** aa.

'naiad, n. [Zoo.] The NYMPH stage of HEMI-METABOLIC insects.

nail, n. [Zoo.] in higher animals, a plate of horn-like substance at end of finger or toe, formed from one of the outer coats of the skin in the same way as a CLAW or a HOOF; a like plate on the end of the BEAK of certain birds. **n. bone.** The end bone of a finger or toe. **n. fold.** The fold of skin at the edge of a nail. **'n.-bed,** n. [Zoo.] The part under a finger- or toe-nail, formed of a deeper skin-substance.

'naked, a. [Biol.] Without a covering or the outgrowths commonly present, such as hair, SHELL, feathers, leaves, PERICARP, etc.; sp. [Bot.] without CALYX and COROLLA. **'n.-'eyed,** a. [Zoo.] Having the sense-structures uncovered, as certain MEDUSAE.

'nanism, n. [Biol., Med.] Condition of being unnormally small in size, opp. GIGANTISM.

nani'zation, n. [Biol.] The producing of NANISM, sp. by design, for example in trees.

'nano-. [Biol., Med.] Of unnormally small size: **'-ce'phalic,** a., **-'som(i)a,** n. **'nanoid, 'nanous,** aa.

nano'plankton, n. [Biol.] PLANKTON of the smallest sizes, seen only with the help of an instrument.

nape, n. [Zoo.] The back of the neck in man. **'napal,** a.

'naphtha, n. [Chem.] Any of a number of liquids which readily become gas and take fire, got from substances with C in them, such as COAL TAR or wood, by DISTILLATION, and used as cleaners or for burning. **'-lene,** n. $C_{10}H_8$, one of the chief substances in COAL TAR, formed of two BENZENE RINGS—a strong-smelling white CRYSTALLINE solid having a number of uses and important specially for the great number of substances produced from it. (*See* p. 392.) **'naphthalene de'rivatives.** Substances produced from NAPHTHALENE by SUBSTITUTION, of which a number are used in the making of DYES. **naphthalene ring.** Ring formed of two BENZENE RINGS with two ADJACENT C ATOMS in common.

naphth(o)-. Having a relation to NAPHTHALENE.

'narcissism, n. [Psych.] Condition of being in love with one's body or oneself, present normally at an early stage in everyone and looked on by Freud as the first stage of sex-development; unnormal stopping of development at this stage, marked direction of love impulses to the self in an older person. narcissi'stic, a.

'narcolepsy, n. [Med.] Condition marked by short attacks of deep sleep.

nar'cosis, nar'coma, nn. [Med.] Unconscious or half-awake condition caused by taking a narcotic, or by certain substances produced in the body as the effect of a diseased condition. nar'cotic, 1.a. Producing n. 2.n. Any substance which, taken into the body, has the effect of producing sleep or causing loss of feeling, and so may be of medical value when rightly used, but which with over-use is the cause of an unbalanced condition of mind, the loss of normal powers, a serious tendency to become unconscious, and possibly CONVULSIONS and death. 'narcotism, n. N.; ADDICTION to a narcotic. 'narcoti'zation, n. 'narcotize, v.t. Put into a condition of n.

'nares, n.pl. [Zoo.] In back-boned animals the openings of the nose, at its outer end (external or anterior n.) or at the back of the mouth (internal or posterior n.). 'narial, a. 'narial septum, The division between the two n. 'nariform, a.

narrow, a. [Phonet.] (Of VOWEL) said with the tongue and muscles somewhat TENSE.

nasal, 1.a. To do with the nose. 2.n. [Phonet.] Sound produced through the nose. n. 'fossa (fossae). One or the other of the pipe-like hollows between the outer and the inner openings of the nose.

nascent, a. In the stage of coming into being, starting growth or development. [Chem.] In a n. state. n. con'dition or state. The condition of an ELEMENT on first being made free by a chemical process, marked by a greater than normal tendency to reaction.

Nasmyth's 'membrane or 'cuticle. [Zoo.] A thin covering present round the hard part of a tooth while it is undergoing development and for a short time after.

'naso-. Nose: '-'antral, a., '-'buccal, a., '-'frontal, a., '-'labial, a., '-'lac(h)rimal, a., '-ma'xillary, a., '-'palat-al, -ine, aa., '-pha'ryngeal, a., '-pharyn'gitis, n., -sinu'sitis, n.

naso'ciliary, a. [Zoo.] Said of that division of the OPHTHALMIC nerve branching to the nose on the one hand and the CILIARY GANGLION of the eye on the other.

naso'pharynx, n. [Zoo.] The upper part of the PHARYNX where the openings from the nose come.

'nastic movement. [Bot.] A motion or change in position of a plant or its parts

in reaction to a STIMULUS but independent of the direction from which it comes, produced by unequal growth or expansion, etc. of certain CELLS, for example the opening and shutting of flowers in different degrees of light, the curving of stems and hanging down of leaves in heat, etc.

'nasus, n. [Zoo.] Nose; CLYPEUS.

'natal, a. [Zoo., Med.] To do with birth; to do with the BUTTOCKS.

'natant, a. [Bot.] Resting on the top of water.

nata'torial, na'tatory, aa. [Zoo.] Formed for swimming.

'nates, n.pl. [Med.] BUTTOCKS.

'native, a. [Geol.] (Of metals) present naturally in the earth unmixed with other substances; in the natural form, not produced by science. [Biol.] Natural to, naturally produced in, a given place, not coming from a different country, etc.

'natural, a. To do with NATURE; produced by processes of nature, not caused or changed by or dependent on man; (of processes or qualities in man) present from birth, not the effect of training; in agreement with the normal workings of man's, or a given man's, body or mind. n. 'frequency. [Phys.] The FREQUENCY of the VIBRATIONS of a body in vibration not kept going by an outside force. n. gas. [Geol.] Gas sent out of the earth through n. openings, as by a VOLCANO, or got by making deep holes down into oil-producing STRATA, sometimes chiefly METHANE, sometimes mixed HYDROCARBONS, used for burning and for producing GASOLENE. n. glass. [Geol.] Glass-like form taken by liquid substances from inside the earth which have become cold very suddenly. n. 'history. Old name for the science of plants and animals. n. 'logarithms. [Maths.] LOGARITHMS using e, or 2·71828 as the BASE, used in working out more complex FUNCTIONS. n. phi'losophy. Old name for n. science, sp. physics. n. scale. DIATONIC SCALE. n. 'science. Those sciences giving an account of material things, living and unliving, astronomy, biology, physics, chemistry, etc. n. se'lection. [Biol.] The tendency for those animals and plants in the best adjustment to their living-conditions to have the best chance of living long and producing offspring, looked on as a controlling force in EVOLUTION.

'naturalist, n. Person having expert knowledge of the different sorts of plants and animals.

'naturalized, a. (Of a sort of plant or animal) having come from another place and become used to its new living-conditions so that it gets on quite naturally in them. 'naturalize, v.t. Get a plant or animal transported to and n. in a new place. **naturali′zation,** n.

′nature, n. All physical things, looked on as a system; all physical things and processes which are not the work of man; the special quality or qualities of a thing conditioning its reactions and behaviour, making it what it is. [Genet.] All those qualities of a plant or animal dependent on GENES and handed on to offspring.

′nauplius, n. [Zoo.] The first LARVA of some CRUSTACEA, having 6 APPENDAGES, one eye, and no body-divisions. **′naupli-al, -oid, -form,** aa.

′nausea, n.[Med.] An ill feeling in connection with the stomach causing a desire to VOMIT. **′nause-ant, -ous,** aa. Causing n. **′-te,** v.t. Give feeling of n. to.

′nautical mile. Measure of distance used at sea equal to 1 MINUTE of LATITUDE, fixed at different values in different countries but all somewhere about 1·852 m., in Britain 6,082 ft.

′navel, n. UMBILICUS.

na′vicular, a. [Biol.] Formed like a boat. 2.n. A n. bone, sp. the small bone at the thumb end of the upper line of CARPAL bones.

navi′gation, n. The science of working out the position of a ship, airplane etc., by astronomy, geometry and so on, and so guiding it in the desired direction; the guiding of a ship or airplane. **′navigate,** v.t. and i. Do the n. of (a ship or airplane).

Nb, Sign for NIOBIUM.

Nd, Sign for NEODYMIUM.

Ne, Sign for NEON.

Ne′anderthal man. [Anthrop.] A sort of early man, named from the place of discovery of the bones, which was in existence from about 100,000 to about 50,000 years back, having a brain of present-day size but a head very long from back to front, sloping back flatly from great RIDGES of bone over the eyes, and little CHIN, and not walking completely upright.

ne′anic, a. [Zoo.] Of, at, a stage before that of full development, between the NEPIONIC and the EPHEBIC.

neap tide, n. [Astron.] The TIDE produced when the moon is at first or third QUARTER, so that the attraction of the sun and moon are working against one another, causing the tide to be lower than at any other time in the month.

ne′arthrosis, n. [Med.] The forming of a new, unnormal JOINT where bones have been broken or damaged by disease.

′nebula (nebulae), n. [Astron.] Any of certain structures in outer space, most of them much farther from us than the stars of our system, formed of great stretches of very thin gas, sometimes with one star in the middle, sometimes joining a great number of stars, and seen as light, mist-like masses in the sky—systems of stars like ours or the material from which will come such systems. (*See* IRREGULAR N., SPIRAL N., PLANETARY N.) [Med.] A clouded place on the CORNEA; an oil to be used in an ATOMIZER for the nose, throat, etc. **′nebular,** a. **′nebular hy′pothesis.** [Astron.] The theory that the SOLAR SYSTEM was produced from a great turning n. which, in the process of getting colder and smaller, sent off rings of gas which in time became the stars and the PLANETS. **′nebulous,** a. Mist-like, cloud-like; not clear, clouded, dark. **′nebulous ′cluster.** [Astron.] A group of stars so great and far away as to seem like a n.

neck, n. [Bot.] The narrowing pipe of an ARCHEGONIUM or PERITHECIUM; the n.-like part of the CAPSULE in MUSCI. [Geol.] The VENT of a VOLCANO; an upright, n.-like mass of IGNEOUS ROCK or solid LAVA by which the n. of a volcano is, or was at one time, stopped up.

necro-. [Med.] NECROSIS; dead TISSUE or dead body.

′necrobi′osis, n. [Med.] The death of a CELL in a living TISSUE, as opp. NECROSIS, which is used of the death of tissues or masses of cells in a living animal.

necro′genic a′bortion.[Bot.]The quick death of plant substance round the point where it is attacked by a PARASITE, keeping it from going further.

ne′crogenous, a. [Biol.] Living or undergoing development in the dead bodies of animals.

ne′crophagous, ne′crophilous, aa. [Zoo.] Living on dead bodies as food.

′necrophile, n. [Psych.] Person having an unnormal attraction to dead bodies. **necro′philia,** n. Condition of being a n. **′necrophilic,** a.

necro′phobia, n. [Psych.] An unnormally great fear of death or of dead bodies. **necro′phobic,** a.

ne′cropsy, ne′croscopy, nn. AUTOPSY.

ne′crosis, n. [Biol., Med.] The death of some part of the substance of a living plant or animal, sp. of bone. **ne′crose,** v.t. and i. (Make) undergo n. **ne′crosed,** a. **ne′crotic,** a.

ne′crotomy, n. [Med.] The DISSECTION of dead bodies; the taking away of dead bone by an operation.

′nectar, n. [Bot.] Sweet liquid produced by plants, gen. by the flowers, as an attraction for the insects by which POLLINATION is effected. **n. guides.** Marks on PETALS guiding insects to n.

nectar′ivorous, a. [Zoo.] Living on NECTAR.

′nectary, n. [Bot.] A special part of a flower for producing NECTAR.

necto-. Swimming.

necto′calyx, n. [Zoo.] In certain SIPHONO-PHORA a bell-like structure moving the COLONY through the water by its motion, formed of a MEDUSOID without a mouth or feelers.

′nectocyst, ′nectosac, nn. The hollow of a NECTOCALYX.

necto′zooid, n. NECTOCALYX.

needle, n. [Bot.] A long, needle-like leaf, designed for keeping in water, seen in certain evergreen trees. [Elec., etc.] MAGNETIC NEEDLE, or like moving MAGNET in certain sorts of GALVANO-METER or VOLTMETER. [Med.] *See* HYPO-DERMIC NEEDLE. [Acous.] The sharp-pointed part of a PICK-UP, today gen. made of SAPPHIRE or DIAMOND, which is put in touch with the record and, moving in the line cut into this, is caused to VIBRATE in such a way as to get the recorded sound produced again.

needle valve. [Mach.] A VALVE formed of a thin pointed rod working in a hole.

negative, 1.a. In relation to some other thing looked on as POSITIVE (which *see*), 'not', 'without', or 'the opposite of' (whatever is in question); (of the outcome of a test, etc.) not giving any sign that a looked-for substance, thing, or condition, is present, not supporting (though not necessarily ruling out) a given theory. [Phys., Maths., etc.] Measured, moving, changing, in the opposite direction to that taken as POSITIVE; (of a number or amount) less than 0, having the sign ' — ' before it. [Elec.] (Of an ELECTRODE, POLE, or PLATE) being the one at a lower ELECTRIC POTENTIAL than the other, and the one away from which the current goes; having a CHARGE of n. electricity. [Chem.] Acid or acid-forming. [Biol.] (Of a motion or growth) in a direction away from a STIMULUS. [Psych.] (Of a reaction) against, marked by a turning away from (a suggestion, argument, etc. [Photog., Television, etc.] (Of a picture) having the dark parts of the thing pictured light, and the light parts dark. [Optics] Having n. rotation. 2.n. The n. picture made on a camera-plate or FILM. **n. after-′image.** [Optics] An AFTER-IMAGE in which light and shade are exchanged as in a camera n., or a COMPLE-MENTARY AFTER-IMAGE—seen when the place of the thing on which the eyes have been fixed is taken by a white plane. **n. cat′alysis.** [Chem.] The slowing of a reaction by a substance which is present with those undergoing it but itself undergoes no change. **n. ′catalyst.** [Chem.] A substance causing n. catalysis. **n. ′crystal** or **′mineral.** [Cryst., Optics] A BIREFRINGENT CRYSTAL or substance in which the INDEX OF REFRACTION for the ORDINARY RAY is greater than that

for the EXTRAORDINARY RAY. **n. elec-′tricity.** The electric property seen in an ATOM, or in a body having some atoms, to which an addition to the normal number of ELECTRONS has been made. **n. glow.** [Elec.] The space of light between the CATHODE DARK SPACE and the FARADAY DARK SPACE in a GAS DIS-CHARGE TUBE. **n. (magnetic) pole.** [Phys.] That end of a straight MAGNET or MAG-NETIC NEEDLE which is pointing to the south when the magnet is hanging freely. **n. po′tential.** [Elec.] A POTENTIAL smaller than that of the earth. **n. re′sistance.** [Radio, etc.] The property of certain VACUUM TUBES and other electric appa-ratus by which as the current gets greater the VOLTAGE necessary to keep it going gets less. **n. ro′tation.** [Phys., Optics] A ROTATION in the opposite direction to the hands of a clock, said sp. of the PLANE POLARIZATION of light. **n. sign.** The sign ' — '. **n. ′transference.** In PSYCHO-ANALYSIS, a TRANSFERENCE in which the deep-rooted feelings which are turned onto the PSYCHO-ANALYST are against him, are those of hate etc.

′negativism, n. [Psych.] The sort of be-haviour sometimes seen in the very young and to a greater degree in DEMENTIA PRAECOX, when a person goes against every suggestion of acting made to him, sometimes by doing the opposite, sometimes by doing nothing at all.

′negatron, n. ELECTRON.

′nekton, n. [Zoo.] The animals swimming in the sea, as opp. PLANKTON.

′nema, n. [Palaeont.] The hollow thread-like outgrowth from the point of the SICULA of a GRAPTOLITE by which it was fixed to something.

nema′thecium, n. [Bot.] Cushion-like, SPORE-producing outgrowth on plant body of sea ALGAE.

′nemato-. [Biol.] Thread-like: NEMATODE. **′nematoid,** a., **ne′matocide,** n., **′nemat-′ology,** n.

′nematoblast, n. [Zoo.] CELL from which a NEMATOCYST is formed.

′nemato′blastic, a. [Geol.] Of ROCK, having a thread-like structure.

′nematocyst, n. [Zoo.] CELL or small bag-like part full of poisoning liquid and having a pipe-like, sharp-pointed out-growth by which this may be sent into the skin of an attacking animal etc., so causing pain, present, for example, in MEDUSAE and in certain worms.

′Nematoda, n.pl. [Zoo.] A PHYLUM of ACOELOMATA made up of worms with round bodies pointed at the two ends, having an ALIMENTARY CANAL with a mouth and end-opening, no CILIA, and separate sexes, a great number being important plant or animal PARASITES. 'nematode, a., n. (Of, like) one of the N.

'nemato'zooid, n. [Zoo.] A ZOOID having NEMATOCYSTS.

'Nemer'tinea, n.pl. [Zoo.] A small PHYLUM of ACOELOMATA made up of flat-bodied worms, chiefly sea-living, having an ALIMENTARY CANAL with a mouth and end-opening, a blood-system, and a long pipe-like feeler which may be put out through an opening over the mouth. 'nemer'tinean, n., a. (Worm) of the N.

'nemorose, a. [Bot.] Living in open spaces in woods.

neo-. New, of late development, young; coming after, or being a later and different form of, what is named.

neo'blastic, a. [Biol.] To do with, being, a new growth.

'Neo-'Darwinism, n. [Biol.] The present-day form of Darwin's theory of NATURAL SELECTION as the chief cause of EVOLUTION, which takes as impossible the handing on of ACQUIRED CHARACTERS.

neo'dymium, n. Chemical ELEMENT, at. no. 60, at. wt. 144·27, sign Nd, one of the RARE EARTH METALS.

'neoen'cephalon, n. [Zoo.] The latest-formed front part of brain

'neofor'mation n. [Anat.] A special form of some part of the body seen only in a small group of men and taken to be of late development.

Neo'gaea, n. The NEOTROPICAL REGION.

ne'ogamy, n. [Zoo.] In PROTOZOA, the uniting of sex-CELLS at an earlier stage than the animal's last stage of development. ne'ogamous, a.

neo'genesis, n. [Zoo.] The forming of new body substance.

'neolau'rentian, a. [Geol.] To do with the early PROTEROZOIC.

neo'lithic, a., n. [Geol., Anthrop.] (Of, to do with) the time in man's history between the PALAEOLITHIC and the ÆNOLITHIC, in which polished stone instruments were in use and farming and the keeping of animals became part of man's existence.

'neomorph, n. [Biol.] A structure which is not normal to the sort of plant or animal, by which it is produced, a new development. neo'morphic, a. neo'morphism, n. 'neo'mor'phosis, n. The development after loss or damage of a new part which is unlike the old or any other part of the body.

'neon, n. Chemical ELEMENT, at. no. 10, at. wt. 20·183, sign Ne, an INERT GAS with no colour and no smell, forming a small part of the air. n. light. [Elec.] A GAS DISCHARGE LAMP in which the gas is n., producing a soft, bright, orange-red light.

'neona'tal, a. [Zoo., Med.] (To do with young which have) newly come to birth.

neo'nychium, n. [Zoo.] The soft covering over the CLAW of a number of higher animals before birth, which keeps the claws from damaging the material round the young animal.

neo'pallium, n. [Zoo.] In higher animals, that part of the roof of the brain which has to do with senses other than the sense of smell, in man forming the chief part of this.

neo'plasia, n. [Zoo., Med.] The development of new living substance, sp. of diseased growths.

'neoplasm, n. [Med.] Any unnormal or diseased growth.

neo'plastic, a. [Zoo., Med.] To do with NEOPLASIA or NEOPLASTY.

neo'plasty, n. [Med.] The GRAFTING of new living substance on to a damaged part.

'neoprene, n. A sort of SYNTHETIC rubber with the property of not being damaged by oil.

neo'te(i)nia, ne'oteny, nn. [Zoo.] The condition in which an animal is, for some special reason or as a regular thing, stopped in its development before coming to the stage of full growth, or in which it still keeps at a later stage some of the structure of an earlier stage. neo'te(i)nic, a.

Neo'tropical, a. [Geog., Zoo.] To do with, coming from, the N. region. N. region. One of the three chief divisions of the earth based on the distribution of sorts of animals, taking in the West Indies and all America south of the north part of Mexico.

neo'vitalism, n. [Zoo.] The theory that the processes which make up living are not fully accounted for by chemical and physical laws, and that some non-material force is needed in accounting for them.

Neo'zoic, a. [Geol.] To do with the time from the end of the MESOZOIC ERA to the present day, = CAINOZOIC (see p. 558).

'neper, n. Unit used for measuring loss of power in telephone or telegraph.

'nepheline, 'nephelite, nn. [Geol.] Natural SILICATE of Al and Na, $NaAlSiO_4$.

neph(el)o-. Cloud, mist.

'nephelo'metric analysis. [Chem.] A way of measuring the amount of solid substance clouding a liquid by the amount of light it lets through. nephe'lometer, n. Instrument used in n. a. [Bact.] An instrument used for getting an idea of the number of BACTERIA in a liquid.

'nephelo'rometer, n. [Meteor.] An instrument for the observation of the rate and direction of the motion of clouds.

'nephograph, n. [Meteor.] An electrically-controlled system of cameras for taking pictures of clouds in such a way as to get a knowledge of their position in the sky. 'nephogram, n.

'**nephoscope,** n. NEPHELOROMETER.
'**nephric,** a. [Zoo.] To do with the KIDNEY(s).
ne'phridiopore, n. [Zoo.] The opening on the outside of the body in a NEPHRIDIUM.
ne'phridium (nephridia), n. [Zoo.] A structure in animals without back-bones for sending out waste in the form of liquid, sp. of the sort taking the form of a small pipe with one end opening to the outside, the other to the COELOM, or a SOLENO-CYTE; any of the small pipes of the KIDNEY in the EMBRYO of a back-boned animal. **ne'phridial,** a.
'**nephrite,** n. [Mineral.] Natural SILICATE of Mg and Ca, a sort of JADE.
ne'phritic, a. [Zoo.] To do with the KIDNEY(s). [Med.] To do with, having, NEPHRITIS.
ne'phritis, n. [Med.] INFLAMMATION of the KIDNEYS.
nephr(o)-. KIDNEY: **neph'rectomy,** n. [Med.] '**nephroid,** a., **ne'phrology,** n.
'**nephrocele,** n. [Med.] HERNIA of a KIDNEY.
'**nephrocoel,** n. [Zoo.] The hollow inside a NEPHROTOME.
'**nephrocyte,** n. [Zoo.] Any CELL with the property of taking up waste from the body and then moving to the outside to let it out, as in insects and sponges.
'**nephrolith'otomy,** n. [Med.] The operation of cutting out a CALCULUS from the KIDNEY.
nephro'mexum, n. [Zoo.] A complex structure formed of a NEPHRIDIUM united with a COELOMODUCT.
'**nephron,** n. [Zoo.] The unit of the KIDNEY in back-boned animals, formed of a MALPIGHIAN CORPUSCLE and a URINARY TUBULE.
'**nephropore,** n. NEPHRIDIOPORE.
'**nephrop'tosis,** n. [Med.] A condition of having the KIDNEY out of its normal position, loose and moving down, gen. with a like dropping of other parts inside the ABDOMEN.
'**nephros,** n. KIDNEY.
ne'phrosis, n. [Med.] DEGENERATION of the small pipes of the KIDNEY.
'**nephrostome,** n. [Zoo.] The opening of a NEPHRIDIUM into the inside of the body, sp. one of the common structure formed like a V and having CILIA for forcing the liquid into the pipe.
'**nephrotome,** n. [Zoo.] That part of the inner coat of every division of a non-back-boned animal which undergoes development into a NEPHRIDIUM. or in the EMBRYO of back-boned animals, the part undergoing development into the KIDNEY.
'**nepi'onic,** a. [Zoo.] Of, at, a very young stage, the one coming straight after the EMBRYONIC.
'**Neptune,** n. [Astron.] The 8th PLANET from the sun, between URANUS and PLUTO, the third greatest in size, having a mass

about 17 times that of Earth, a 'year' of 164·8 years, and one 'moon.' (*See* p. 331.)
nep'tunium, n. Chemical ELEMENT, at. no. 93, sign Np, one of the TRANSURANIC ELEMENTS, produced by man as the outcome of the NUCLEAR FISSION of U and in turn undergoing a RADIOACTIVE charge into Pu.
ne'ritic, a. [Geol., Biol.] To do with, living in, the n. zone. **n. zone.** That part of the sea-floor between low-water mark and the edge of the under-water shelf stretching out from the land, about 180 m. deep.
Nernst distri'bution (or par'tition) law. [Phys.-Chem.] The law that the distribution of a SOLUTE between two touching but unmixed SOLVENTS is in a fixed RATIO so long as the TEMPERATURE is equal and unchanged.
Nernst lamp. An electric-light bulb in which the wire or rod is formed of MgO mixed with OXIDES of the RARE EARTH METALS, such as ZrO_2.
nerve, n. [Zoo.] Any of the cord-like structures of the body, made up of parallel n. fibres and forming a system by which the n. impulses, which are the cause of feeling and of motion, are transported to and from some apparatus of control, sp. the brain and SPINAL CORD; NERVURE. [Bot.] A VEIN of a leaf. **n.block.** [Med.] The stopping of impulses through a n., for the purpose of taking feeling from a part, by INJECTING a medical substance into it. **n. bulb.** END-BULB. **n. ca'nal.** [Zoo.] An opening in the root of a tooth for a n. to go through. **n. cell.** [Zoo.] The special sort of CELL which is the unit of n. substance, present in the brain and SPINAL CORD, the RETINA, and n. GANGLIA, made up of a cell-body, formed of a NUCLEUS and PROTOPLASM, and the thread-like outgrowths, sometimes very long, forming the n. fibres, **n. 'centre.** Any part of the n. system where n. impulses from RECEPTORS are changed into n. impulses acting on muscles, etc.; a group of n. cells controlling or to do with a certain process of the body, for example, breathing. **n. cord.** NEUROCHORD. **n. 'ending.** The outer end or end-structure of a n. fibre, by which it takes in n. impulses or gives them to muscles, etc. **n. 'fibre.** Any of the outgrowths from a n. cell, sp. the long chief outgrowth transporting impulses away from it, formed of a long thread of PROTOPLASM with very small thread-like parts in it, all covered by a delicate skin, with sometimes a thicker outer coat of fat-like substance again covered with a thin skin. **n. 'impulse.** An electric DISTURBANCE which, produced at one point in a n. fibre, goes on from one part to another, and from one FIBRE to another in con-

nection with it, till in the end it has the effect of moving a muscle or causing some change in a GLAND. **n. net.** The simple form of NERVOUS SYSTEM, made up of a network of n. cells, without n. fibres, going all through the body, seen in certain lower animals, such as COELEN-TERATA. **n. 'plexus.** A network of n. fibres **n. root.** The starting-point of a n. in the brain, SPINAL CORD, or other controlling part. **n. trunk.** A group of parallel nn. banded together inside a pipe-like covering.

'nervi-, 'nervo-. Nerve (and . . .): 'n.-'muscular, a.

'nervi ner'vorum. [Zoo.] The very small nerves in the covering of a greater nerve.

'nervous, a. [Zoo.] Of, to do with, caused by, having an effect on, a nerve or nerves. [Med.] Having feeble or unhealthy nn., not well controlled. **n. 'breakdown** or **pros'tration.** [Med.] (The coming on of) NEURASTHENIA. **n. 'system.** [Zoo.] The apparatus of NERVE CELLS, NERVES, special NERVE-ENDINGS, etc., by which the reactions of an animal to things outside itself, and of the different parts of its body to one another, are made possible and controlled. **n. 'tissue.** [Zoo.] The substance made up of NERVE CELLS or NERVE FIBRES together with the material forming a connection between them and the blood-vessels and special CELLS round them.

'nerviduct, n. [Zoo.] A hole in a bone or other stiff structure through which a nerve goes.

'nervule, n. [Zoo.] A small branch, or the thin end, of a NERVURE.

'nervure, n. [Zoo.] Any of the stiff thread-like structures acting as supports for an insect's wing, a branch of the blood- and air-distribution system. [Bot.] VEIN of a leaf. ner'vation, 'nervature, nervu'ration, nn. [Bot., Zoo.] The system of distribution of nn.

'nervus lat'eralis. [Zoo.] The branch of the VAGUS nerve in fishes which goes down the LATERAL LINE.

'Nessler's re'agent or solution. [Chem.] A SOLUTION of HgI_2 in KI mixed with KOH or NaOH used in the Nessler test (or Nessler reaction) to see if AMMONIA (HN_3) is present in water, blood, etc.

nest, n. [Zoo.] The bed or vessel made ready by a bird or other animal, such as an insect or fish, for housing its eggs, and frequently its young till they are able to take care of themselves. [Mach., etc.] A number of like structures grouped together and working as a unit. [Geol.] A small mass of any material bedded inside a mass of different material. [Med.] A small group of CELLS

of a different sort in a mass of cells. '-ling, n. Young bird still living in the n.

'net-knot, n. [Biol.] A small mass of CHROMATIN at the meeting-point of two threads in the network of a NUCLEUS.

'netted, a. [Bot.] Forming, or covered with lines forming, a network.

'nettle-cell, n. [Zoo.] NEMATOCYST.

'nettle rash. [Med.] URTICARIA.

net-veined, a. [Bot.] (Of a leaf) having VEINS running irregularly, forming a network.

'neural, a. [Zoo.] To do with nerves or nerve substance or the nerve system; in back-boned animals, DORSAL. **n. arch.** The arch formed by the NEURAPOPHYSES. **n. axis.** The CEREBROSPINAL AXIS. **n. 'canal.** The hollow space formed by the n. arches down which the SPINAL CORD goes. **n. crest,** or **fold,** or **groove,** or **tube.** MEDULLARY CREST, etc. **n plate.** MEDULLARY PLATE; NEURAPOPHYSIS; the middle line of horn-like plates, gen. 8 in number, in the hard outer cover of CHELONA. **n. spine.** The PROTECTION in the middle line of a VERTEBRA formed by the united edges of the NEURAPOPHYSES and gen. having muscles fixed to it.

neu'ralgia, n. [Med.] Attacks of sharp pain in a nerve which are not caused by any damage to its structure. neu'ralgic, a.

neura'pophysis (neurapophyses), n. [Zoo.] One or the other of the two plates coming from the body of a VERTEBRA and meeting at the back in the form of an arch.

neuras'thenia, n. [Med.] A condition marked by a very tired feeling, loss of force and interest and at the same time of the power to get healthy rest and sleep, pain in the head, trouble with digestion, etc., put down sometimes to overwork and nerves, but now gen. to trouble in the mind—in Freud's system to the forcing down of sex-impulses. neuras'thenic, 1.a. To do with n. 2.n. Person having n.

neu'rax-is, -on, nn. [Zoo.] An AXON or the middle part of it inside the cover.

neuren'teric ca'nal. [Zoo.] In the early EMBRYOS of a number of animals, a connection forming a way through from the lower end of the MEDULLARY TUBE to the lower end of the ARCHENTERON.

-'neuria, n. [Med.] Condition of the nerve system.

-'neuric, a. Having the number of NEURONES named:— 'polyneuric, a.

'neuri'lemma, n. [Zoo.] The thin outer skin of a MEDULLATED NERVE FIBRE. 'neuri-'lemmal, a.

'neurine, n. [Biochem.] A PTOMAINE poison formed in brain substance and in the PUTREFACTION of meat, which may be made into CHOLINE.

'neurite, n. AXON.

neu'ritis, n. [Med.] INFLAMMATION of a nerve. **neu'ritic,** a.

neur(o)-. Nerve: **neu'rectomy,** n. [Med.], **'neuroelec'tricity,** n., **'neuro'genesis,** n., **neuro'muscular,** a., **'neurophysi'ology,** n., **neuro'surgery,** n., **'neurosy'napse,** n.

'neurobio'taxis, n. [Zoo.] The tendency of NERVE CELLS or NERVE FIBRES to be transported, or to make their growth, in the direction from which impulses come most frequently.

'neuroblast, n. [Zoo.] Any of the special ECTODERMAL CELLS from which the development of a NERVE CELL takes place.

neuro'central, a. [Zoo.] To do with, placed between, the NEURAL ARCH and the body of a VERTEBRA.

'neurochord, n. [Zoo.] Any of the solid cordlike structures of nerve substance of which the simplest sort of CENTRAL NERVOUS SYSTEM, as seen in most animals without backbones, is made up.

'neuroc(o)el(e), n. [Zoo.] The system of hollows made up of that running down the middle of the SPINAL CORD together with those in the brain.

neuro'cranium, n. [Zoo.] The part of the bone structure of the head going round the brain and inner ear, and forming the top part of the face, as opp. that forming the mouth-parts.

'neurocyte, n. NEURONE.

neuro'cyton, n. [Zoo.] The body of a NEURONE.

'neuroepi'thelium, n. [Zoo.] The EPITHELIUM of a sense-organ such as the tongue, eye, and nose, whose CELLS have undergone some special development giving them the power of taking in the sense-impulses in question. **neuroepi-'thelial,** a.

neuro'fibril, n. [Zoo.] Any of the very thin thread-like structures forming a complex network in the body of a NERVE CELL and grouped parallel to one another in the NERVE FIBRES.

'neurofi'broma, n. [Med.] A growth made up of FIBROUS substance produced from the fibrous substance of a nerve–covering. **'neuro'fibroma'tosis,** n. A disease in which numbers of nn. are formed.

neuro'genic, a. [Zoo.] (Of the working of a muscle or GLAND) dependent on NERVE IMPULSES to keep it going.

neu'roglia, n. [Zoo.] The TISSUE forming the supporting framework of nerve tissue, sp. in the brain and SPINAL CORD, made up of a network of FIBRES and much-branched CELLS. **'neurogli(o)ma,** n. [Med.] A diseased growth formed from n. **'neurogliosis,** n. [Med.] A condition marked by overgrowth of n. **neu'roglia-c, -l, -r,** aa.

'neurogram, n. [Psych.] The physical print on the brain representative of any conscious experience, by which memory and learning are made possible. **neurohy'pophysis,** n. PARS NERVOSA.

'neuroid, a. [Zoo.] Nerve-like, said sp. of the transporting of impulses through TISSUES without nerves, as in PROTOZOA.

neuro'keratin, n. [Biochem.] A form of KERATIN present in nerve substance.

neuro'lemma, n. NEURILEMMA.

neu'rology, n. [Zoo., Med.] The science of nerves and nerve diseases. **neuro'logical,** a. **neu'rologist,** n.

neu'roma, n. [Med.] A growth formed of nerve-substance or produced from a nerve.**'-tous,** a.

'neuromast, n. [Zoo.] Any of the groups of sense CELLS on the LATERAL LINE in fishes.

'neuromere, n. [Zoo.] The part of the NEUROCHORDS or SPINAL CORD taken in by one METAMERE.

neuro'motor, a. [Zoo.] To do with nerves or NERVE IMPULSES which go from the brain to the muscles.

'neuro'muscu'lature, n. [Zoo.] The system of nerves and muscles taken together.

'neuron(e), n. [Zoo.] A NERVE CELL with its outgrowths. **n. 'theory.** The theory that the nerve system is made up of nn. which are in structure and development separate units, NERVE IMPULSES being forwarded from one to the other at points where they are touching.

'neuroneme, n. [Zoo.] In some CILIOPHORA, a thread running parallel with a MYONEME, probably a NERVE FIBRE.

neu'ronophag(e), 'neurophag(e), nn. [Med.] A PHAGOCYTE causing the destruction of NERVE CELLS. **neu'ronophagia, neurophagia,** nn. The destruction of NERVE CELLS by nn.

neuro'pathic, a. [Med.] To do with nerve diseases; having a disease of the nerves. **'neuropath,** n. N. person. **neuropa'thologist,** n. **'neuropa'thology,** n. The science of nerve diseases. **neu'ropathy,** n. Any disease or unnormal condition of the nerves.

'neuropil(e), nn. [Zoo.] Neuropilem; a delicate branched ending of a NERVE FIBRE. **neuro'pilem, neuropi'lema,** nn. A network of NERVE FIBRES, sp. the thick, soft material, formed of delicate uncovered nerve fibres, between the CELLS of GREY MATTER.

neuro'plasm, n. [Zoo.] The PROTOPLASM between the NEUROFIBRILS. **neuro-'plasmic,** a.

neuro'podium, n. The lower branch of a PARAPODIUM.

'neuropore, n. [Zoo.] The front or upper opening into the NEUROCOELE.

Neur'optera, n.pl. An ORDER of ENDOPTERYGOTA having four thin neuropterous wings of like form, kept upright over the body when at rest, biting mouth-parts and LARVAE living on other insects as food. **neu'ropterous**, a. [Zoo.] Sp., having wings with a network of NERVURES.

neu'rosis (neuroses), n. [Med.] Any unhealthy condition of the nerves, gen. going with marked signs of an ill mind, which is not produced by damage to the nerve system itself but by some physical cause such as overwork, or, more frequently, by some deep division in the mind, such as the incomplete adjustment of the root impulses of the baby to the conditions of existence in society. **neu'rotic**, 1.a. To do with the nerves; to do with n(n).; having n. 2.a. Neurotic person.

neuro'skeleton, n. ENDOSKELETON.

neu'rotomy, n. [Med.] The cutting of a nerve or nerves for medical purposes.

neuro'trophic, a. [Med.] (Of substance) giving food to NERVE CELLS.

neuro'tropic, a. [Med.] (Of poisons, BACTERIA, colouring-substances, etc.) having a special attraction to nerve substance.

neu'rotropism, n. [Zoo., Med.] The property of being NEUROTROPIC; the attraction seen between masses of nerve substance in certain conditions, for example between fully-formed nerve substance and nerve substance in the process of development.

'neuston, n. [Zoo.] Those water animals living in or on the top face of the water.

'neuter, 1.a. [Bot., Zoo.] Without (acting) sex-parts, not male or female. 2.n. [Zoo.] A n. animal.

'neutral, a. Between two opposites, not one or the other, sp.:— [Biol.] NEUTER. [Chem.] (Of solutions) not acid and not ALKALINE, that is, made up of equal numbers of H and HYDROXYL (–OH) IONS. [Elec.] Not POSITIVE and not NEGATIVE; said of a wire, etc. between two others in a system and having a POTENTIAL half-way between theirs in value. [Optics] Without HUE, grey. [Phonet.] (Of the lips) simply open, not rounded or stretched; (of the tongue) resting loosely in the middle of the mouth, as in saying a n. vowel. **n. 'axis** (or **'surface**). [Mech.] That line (or plane) through something on which a force is acting where the STRESS = 0. **n. equi'librium**. [Phys.] The condition of a body which, on being given a small push etc., changing its position in relation to an upright line, comes to rest straight away in the given position, with no tendency to go back to the old one or on to a further new one. **n. 'vowel**. [Phonet.] Any of a number of mixed VOWEL sounds said without force, so that they have no strong, clear outline, as the first '*a*' in '*awake*'. **neu'trality**, n. **neutrali'zation**, n. Sp.:— [Chem.] the reaction of an acid with a BASE by which

a SALT is produced; [Radio] the overcoming of undesired effects caused by the CAPACITANCE current between GRID and PLATE by the use of a balancing CONDENSER. **'neutralize**, v.t. Overcome, take away, the special property or effect of something, sp. by uniting it, or by acting against it, with its opposite.

neu'tret, n. NEUTRINO.

neu'trino, n. [Phys., Chem.] A FUNDAMENTAL PARTICLE having no CHARGE and very small, almost no, mass.

'neutron, n. [Phys., Chem.] A PARTICLE having a little greater mass than a PROTON but no electric CHARGE, forming part of the NUCLEI of all ATOMS but that of H, and able to go readily through solid substances.

'neutrophil(e), 1.a. [Zoo.] Readily coloured by NEUTRAL colouring-substances. 2.n. A POLYMORPHONUCLEAR LEUCOCYTE. **'neutro'philic, neu'trophilous**, aa.

'névé, n. [Geol.] The massed, hard-grained snow, in a condition half-way to becoming solid ice, covering the upper end of a GLACIER, FIRN.

'nevoid, 'nevus, nn. *See* NAEVOID, NAEVUS.

new moon, *See* MOON.

'newton, n. [Elec.] Unit of force in the M.K.S. system.

'Newton's law of 'cooling. [Phys.] Law that the rate of a body's loss of heat to the air etc. round it is PROPORTIONAL to the degree to which its TEMPERATURE is greater than that of the air etc.—good only when the two temperatures are not greatly different.

Newton's laws of 'motion [Phys.] The 3 laws on which DYNAMICS is based:— (1) Every body keeps on in a condition of rest or of regular motion in a straight line till it is acted on by some outside force; (2) The rate of any change in MOMENTUM is PROPORTIONAL to the force acting and the direction of change is in the direction of the force; (3) To every force acting on a body from outside there is an equal and opposite reaction in the body.

'Newton's rings. [Optics] Coloured or light and dark rings round the point where a CONVEX LENS is touching a flat plate etc., caused by INTERFERENCE effects between light-waves REFLECTED by the upper SURFACE of the air between the lens and the plate and light-waves reflected by its lower surface.

'niacin, n. [Biochem.] NICOTINIC ACID.

nib, n. [Zoo.] BEAK (of a bird).

'niccolite, n. [Mineral.] A light coppercoloured natural ARSENIDE of nickel (NiAs), having in it small amounts of iron, copper and S, one of the most important ORES of nickel.

'nickel, n. Chemical ELEMENT, at. no. 28,

at. wt. 58·69, sign Ni, a silver-white metal which does not readily undergo CORROSION, widely used for money, plating, in mixed metals, and as a CATALYST. **nicke′liferous,** a. [Geol.].

Nicol('s) prism. [Optics]. An instrument for producing PLANE-POLARIZED light, formed of a CRYSTAL of ICELAND SPAR cut and then fixed together again in such a way that the ORDINARY RAY is turned out of the crystal at the join and only the EXTRAORDINARY RAY comes through.

′nicotine, n. [Chem.] An ALKALOID poison, $C_{10}H_{14}N_2$, present in tobacco leaves, an oil with a strong smell and no colour.

nico′tinic ′acid. [Biochem.] A substance forming part of the VITAMIN B complex, not having enough of which may be the cause of PELLAGRA.

′nictitant, a. [Zoo.] Nictitating; (of an OCELLUS) having the middle part in the form of a new moon. **′nictitating,** 1.n. Nictitation. 2.a. Doing, or to do with, the act of nictitation. **nictitating ′membrane.** A thin fold of skin which may be pulled across the eye of some animals, such as birds and snakes, for keeping it clean. **′nictitating spasm.** [Med.] A sudden nictitation caused by nerve trouble. **nicti′tation,** n. A quick shutting and opening of the eye.

nida′mental, a. [Zoo.] (Of part, etc.) to do with or producing material for covering eggs or making a NEST.

ni′dation, n. [Zoo.] The development of a new inner coat in the UTERUS between MENSES.

ni′dicolous, a. [Zoo.] (Of birds) living in the NEST for some time after coming out of the egg. **nidi′colae,** n.pl. N. birds.

nidi′fugous, a. [Zoo.] (Of birds) coming out of the egg at a late stage of development and going from the nest very shortly. **nidi′fugae,** n.pl. N. birds.

′nidatory, a. [Biol.] To do with a NEST or NIDUS.

′nidulous, n. [Zoo.] The NUCLEUS forming the starting-point of a nerve.

′nidus, n. [Zoo.] NEST, sp. for the eggs of insects; a group of NERVE CELLS, sp. in the brain. [Biol.] A nest-like hollow. [Bot.] A place for the development of SPORES. [Med.] FOCUS (of INFECTION).

night ′blindness. NYCTALOPIA.

ni′grescence, n. [Biol.] The process of becoming black or dark. **ni′grescent,** a.

′nimbus, n. [Meteor.] Cloud of the level, grey, not sharply outlined sort, from which rain or snow generally comes, sp. that completely covering the sky at times of unbroken rain.

ni′obium, n. Chemical ELEMENT, at. no. 41, at. wt. 92·91, sign Nb, an uncommon light grey metal, of which the older name is, 'columbium'.

′nipple, n. [Zoo.] MAMMILLA. [Mech.] Short rod or pipe used for joining two pipes, gen. by having screw lines on the outer ends for screwing into them.

′Nissl ′granules or **′corpuscles** or **′bodies.** [Zoo.] Small, sharp-angled bodies present in the PROTOPLASM of NERVE CELLS.

′nisus, n. Any strong driving-force in animals, sp.:—[Psych.] The tendency of any healthy animal to make attempts to overcome anything in the way of its desires; a conscious attempt to do something needing some trouble. [Zoo.] The regular MATING impulse coming to certain animals at certain times of the year. [Anat.] The operation of the body muscles for the purpose of driving out FAECES or URINE.

′niton, n. [Chem.] Old name for RADON.

′nitrate, 1.n. [Chem.] SALT or ESTER having in it the group $-NO_3$; $CaNO_3$ or $NaNO_3$, used for making land fertile. 2.v.t. Make undergo reaction with or get changed into a n. **n. bac′teria.** NITROBACTERIA. **ni′tration,** n. Sp., the changing of NITRITES in the earth into nn. as the last stage of NITRIFICATION.

′nitre, n. [Mineral., Chem.] POTASSIUM NITRATE, KNO_3.

′nitric, a. [Chem.] To do with, having in it, producing, N, sp. used of complex substances in which N has one of its higher VALENCIES. **n. acid.** HNO_3, a very CORROSIVE liquid attacking most metals, used in making EXPLOSIVES, DYES, NITRATES for farming, and a number of other processes.

′nitride, n. [Chem.] Substance formed by uniting one ELEMENT with N.

′nitrify, v.t. [Chem.] Get mixed or united with N or a substance having N in it; be the cause of the nitrification of (earth). **′-ing,** a. **nitrification,** n. Sp., [Bact.] the process by which N materials in the earth, are changed, step by step, into NITRATES by the operation of different sorts of BACTERIA.

′nitrile, n. [Chem.] Any of a number of substances having the general form $R.C\equiv N$, where R is an ALKYL group.

′nitro-. [Chem.] Having in it N; formed by putting $-NO_2$ in place of some other group, as **nitroben′zene,** **′nitro′ethane,** **nitro′methane,** **′nitro′propane**—such **nitro** de′rivatives all being liquids with acid properties and no colour.

nitrobac′teria, n.pl. [Bot.] Any of the sorts of BACTERIA in the earth which take part in NITRIFICATION.

nitro′cellulose, n. [Chem.] Any of a group of NITRATES formed by the reaction of CELLULOSE with HNO_3 some of which are used importantly in the making of EXPLOSIVES, others in the making of PLASTICS.

'**nitrogen,** n. Chemical ELEMENT, at. no. 7, at wt. 14·008, sign N, a gas without colour or smell not readily taking part in chemical reactions, forming more than 75% of air, and present, united with other substances, in earth and in all living substance. **n. 'cycle.** The process by which N in some form is taken from the air, earth, and sea and made into more complex substances by plants, then goes into the bodies of animals in the form of food, is given back to the earth in the form of animal waste or dead bodies, and in the end is again changed into free N going back to the air, or into INORGANIC material forming part of earth and sea, by the operation of BACTERIA. **n. fi'xation.** The producing of N COMPOUNDS from free N for purposes of industry; the producing of ORGANIC N compounds from the N of the air by certain BACTERIA in the earth. **n. 'fixers, 'n.-'fixing bacteria.** Any of the sorts of BACTERIA having the power of n. fixation. **ni'trogenous,** a.

nitro'glycerin(e), n. [Chem.] Any NITRATE of GLYCEROL, sp. $C_3H_5(ONO_2)_3$, an oil made by the reaction of H_2SO_4 and HNO_3 with GLYCERINE, not SOLUBLE in water, becoming solid when cold, burning quietly in the open air, but EXPLODING with great force when given a blow or heated quickly in a shut vessel.

ni'trophilous, a. [Bot.] Living in NITROGENOUS earth.

ni'troso compounds, [Chem.] Complex substances having in them the group —NO.

'**nitrous,** a. [Chem.] To do with, having in it, producing, N, sp. used of complex substances in which N has one of its lower VALENCIES. **n. 'acid.** HNO_2, forming substances having in them the group $-NO_2$, but itself having existence only in a SOLUTION of $Ba(NO_3)_2$ in H_2SO_4. **n. 'oxide.** N_2O, a gas used as an ANAESTHETIC, sometimes named 'laughing gas'.

ni'vation, n. [Geol.] The effects produced by NÉVÉ on ROCKS, etc.

'**noble gas.** [Chem.] INERT GAS.

'**noble 'metal.** Any metal, such as silver and gold, which is not readily united with non-metals or attacked by acids or the O of the air.

nocti-. Night.

nocti'lucent, a. [Zoo.] Giving out light at night. **nocti'lucence,** n.

noc'turnal, a. [Zoo.] To do with, taking place in, the night. [Zoo.] Sleeping in the day and coming out, getting food, etc., at night.

node, n. A meeting or joining-point, or the middle point of a system. [Geom.] Point where a curve goes across itself, that is, point common to two parts of a curve. [Biol., Med.] A hard round mass or place on something, as on a diseased JOINT; a point of narrowing between two wider parts. [Bot.] The place on a stem where a branch or leaf is joined to it. [Phys.] The point, line, or plane in a VIBRATING body where little or no motion is taking place, a point of least AMPLITUDE in a system of STATIONARY WAVES. [Astron.] One or other of the two points where the way taken by a PLANET etc. is cut by the ECLIPTIC. [Radio] A point in a CIRCUIT where the current is greatest and the VOLTAGE least. '**nodal,** a. '**nodal point.** [Radio] Node. '**nodal points (of a lens).** [Optics] Two points on the AXIS of a LENS or system of lenses such that a ray sent in through one will come out as a parallel ray through the other.

'**nodical month.** [Astron.] The time between the moon's being at a NODE and coming round to it again.

'**nodose,** a. [Biol.] Having small, round, knot-like outgrowths. **no'dosity,** n.

'**nodule,** n. [Biol., Med.] A small round outgrowth or thick place, sp. [Bot.] such a structure on the root of a plant where BACTERIA have their living-place. [Astron.] GRANULE. '**nodul(at)ed,** aa. **nodu'lation,** n. '**nodular,** a. **nodu'liferous,** a. '**nodulose,** a.

noe'genesis, n. [Psych.] The development of knowledge by the mind, ranging from conscious experience to the point of producing new ideas, the highest operation of the mind.

no'esis, n. [Psych.] The operation of the mind in becoming conscious of things not given to it by sense, for example, ABSTRACT relations, sp. at first view, without any process of reasoning; more generally, the working of the mind or reason as opp. the conscious experiencing of things outside, which is the first stage in the development of knowledge. **no'etic,** a. To do with n. or the higher powers of mind, not a part of sense experience.

noise, n. [Elec.] Undesired effect caused in any ELECTRONIC CIRCUIT, chiefly by the heat motion of ELECTRONS.

'**noma,** n. [Med.] A serious ULCERATION of the side of the face in young boys and girls who have become very feeble, sp. after an INFECTIOUS disease.

'**nomenclature,** n. System of naming.

-nomy. System of knowledge or rules.

non-. Not:—**n.-e'lectrolyte,** n. [Chem.], **n. -'viable,** a. [Biol. etc.].

non(a)-. Nine.

nona'gesimal, n. [Astron.] The middle point (90°) of the half of the ECLIPTIC limited by the HORIZON.

'**nonagon,** n. [Geom.] Plane form having 9 straight sides and 9 angles.

non-'arcing, a. [Elec.] (Of a metal) not readily keeping up an electric ARC.

non-con'ductor, n. [Phys.] A substance not normally transporting heat, electric current or whatever is in question.

non-'con'junction, n. [Biol.] Condition in which two CHROMOSOMES do not come together in the early stage of MEIOSIS.

non-dis'junction, n. [Biol.] Condition in which two CHROMOSOMES do not become separated at the ANAPHASE.

'non-'ego, n. [Psych.] Anything or everything outside, not a part of, the self.

non-'ferrous, a. (Of a substance) having no iron in it, based on, to do with, metals other than iron.

'nonius, n. VERNIER.

non-'metal, n. [Chem.] Any ELEMENT which is not a metal, gen. readily forming NEGATIVE IONS and not readily transporting electric current.

non-'polar, a. Not having, not having to do with, POLES. **n. bond.** [Phys.-Chem.] COVALENT BOND, **n. liquid.** Any liquid in which the MOLECULES give no signs of opposite electric CHARGES.

non-'protein, n. [Biochem.] Any substance in a plant or animal which is not a PROTEIN, sp. of those having N in them but simpler in structure than proteins.

'nonsense 'syllable. [Psych.] A group of letters forming a word to the eye and ear but having no sense, used in memory or hearing tests.

non-'sensi'bility, n. [Bot.] The power of a plant to undergo the attack of a PARASITE without any marked damage.

non-'sequence, n. [Geol.] A smaller and less important change from the order of history than an UNCONFORMITY.

non'valent, a. [Chem.] Of VALENCE = 0, that is, having no power of uniting with other ATOMS, as He.

noon, n. [Astron.] Time of sun's CULMINATION at any place, the middle of the day.

nor- [Chem.] Used before the name of a substance as a way of naming: (a) the substance from which it comes; (b) a NORMAL substance ISOMERIC with it.

'Nordic, a. [Anthrop.] Of, to do with, the N. race. **N. race.** A RACE of tall, long-headed, blue-eyed, yellow-haired men living in North Europe, for example in Norway, Scotland and the north of England.

norm, n. A rule or law, a representative example, by their agreement or non-agreement with which things are judged to be regular—unsurprising, healthy, natural—or the opposite—uncommon, special, unhealthy, incomplete, etc. [Geol.] The make-up of an IGNEOUS ROCK as it is worked out from the make-up of the MOLECULES of the substances forming it, as opp. to its make-up as given by simply getting the weights of the different substances present in a fixed amount of it.

'norma, n. [Anat.] A view of some structure,

sp. the bone-structure of the head, from a given point, for example, as seen when looking down on it.

'normal, 1.a. In agreement with a NORM, as most commonly come across, marked by no special qualities, regular, natural healthy etc. [Psych.] Of AVERAGE, brain power and development; not having any disease or unhealthy condition of the mind, not unbalanced, in good adjustment to living. [Geom.] At right angles (*to* a line or plane). **2.n.** That which is n. [Geom.] Line or plane which is n. to another. **n. e'lectrode.** [Elec.] A metal ELECTRODE in a SOLUTION of a salt of the same metal, so that the POTENTIAL DIFFERENCE between them is unchanging. **n. 'element.** [Elec.] STANDARD CELL. **n. fault.** [Geol.] A sloping FAULT in which there has been a slipping down of material on the line of the slope. **n. 'pressure.** [Chem.] A PRESSURE = 760 mm. of Hg. **n. salt.** [Chem.] A SALT formed by all the H of an acid being exchanged for metal. **n. 'saline so'lution.** [Biochem., Med.] Common salt in water in such amount as to be ISOTONIC with the blood and other body liquids and in which CELLS etc. may be kept living for some time, about 0·6%. **n. so'lution.** [Chem.] A SOLUTION having a weight of the SOLUTE equal to 1 GRAM-ATOM of H in every LITRE. **n. 'syllable.** [Phonet.] A SYLLABLE of a word said with STRESS so that its sound is given its full value, as opp. a REDUCED SYLLABLE. **n. 'temperature and 'pressure.** [Chem.] 0°C and 760 mm. of Hg.

'normal, a. [Chem.] Having an unbranched chain of C ATOMS.

nor'mality, n. Condition, degree, of being normal.

'normalize, v.t. [Metal.] Get (a metal, sp. steel) heated to a point at which the CRYSTAL structure is broken down, and then let get cold in the air, for the purpose of making the crystals finer and taking out any DEFECTS.

'normoblast, n. [Zoo., Med.] In MAMMALS, an incompletely formed ERYTHROCYTE, from which the NUCLEUS of the ERYTHROBLAST has not quite gone.

'normocyte, n. [Zoo.] ERYTHROCYTE.

north ce'lestial pole. [Astron.] The ZENITH of the NORTH POLE.

North Pole. [Geog.] That point of the earth which is farthest north. [Phys.] (Of a MAGNET) the POSITIVE POLE.

'northern lights. AURORA BOREALIS.

nosepiece, n. The part of a MICROSCOPE to which the OBJECTIVE is fixed, sp. one supporting more than one objective and able to be turned round to whichever is desired.

'nostril, n. [Zoo.] One or other of the two

outside openings of the nose.

note, n. [Acous.] A TONE as used in music.

'notifiable, a. [Med.] (Of a disease) of which any example has to be noted to the government medical authorities.

'notochord, n. [Zoo.] Rod made up of great CELLS inside a stiff covering taking the place of a back-bone in certain animals without back-bones and in the EMBRYOS of back-boned animals. **noto'chordal,** a.

'nototribe, a. [Bot.] Said of a flower of which the ANTHERS and STIGMA are so placed as to be touched by an insect going into it, so as to get CROSS-FERTILIZATION.

'notum, n. [Zoo.] The top side of a division of the THORAX in an insect. **'notal,** a.

'nova, n. [Astron.] A DARK STAR of which the light output is suddenly greatly increased, so that a new star seems to have come into the sky, and which then, after a time, becomes dark again as before.

novem-. Nine.

'nozzle, n. A short outlet pipe at the end of a pipe or at the side etc. of a vessel, for narrowing, and sometimes controlling, the outgoing current of liquid or gas.

Np, Sign for NEPTUNIUM.

Nt, Sign for NITON.

N.T.P. = NORMAL TEMPERATURE AND PRESSURE.

nu'becula, n. [Med.] Cloud-like mass or mark, sp. in the URINE or on the CORNEA. [Astron.] NEBULA. **N.** major (minor). LARGER (LESSER) MAGELLANIC CLOUD.

nu'bi-. Cloud: -'**ferous,** a., -**form,** a.

nu'cellus, n. [Bot.] Mass of thin-walled CELLS forming the middle part of a seed in the process of development, having one or two coats of cells round it and the EMBRYO SAC inside it.

nucha, n. [Zoo.] The back of the neck; in insects, the back part of the THORAX. **'nuchal,** a.

nuci-. Nut: **nu'ciferous,** a.

nu'civorous, a. [Zoo.] Using nuts as food.

'nuclear, a. To do with, forming, like, a NUCLEUS; (of ATOMS) joined to the NUCLEUS. **n. 'budding.** [Biol.] The narrowing and parting of a NUCLEUS at some point, producing a smaller separate nucleus. **n. disc.** [Biol.] The wheel-like form made by the CHROMOSOMES in the n. plate. **n. di'vision.** [Biol.] See AMITOSIS, MITOSIS, MEIOSIS. **n. 'energy.** [Phys.] ENERGY freed in n. fission. **n. 'fission.** [Phys.] The division of the NUCLEUS of an ATOM of great weight, such as U, into two almost equal parts by a process of BOMBARDMENT with NEUTRONS, freeing great energy. **n. 'fragmen'tation.** [Biol.] AMITOSIS. **n. 'isobars.** [Chem.] ISOTOPES of different ELEMENTS having the same number of PROTONS and NEUTRONS taken together but different numbers of the two taken separately. **n.**

'isomers. [Chem.] ISOTOPES of any ELEMENT having the same number of PROTONS and NEUTRONS but different RADIOACTIVE properties. **n. i'somerism.** [Chem.] The existence of n. isomers, the condition or property of being, or the relation between, n. isomers. **n. 'membrane.** [Biol.] The delicate skin round a NUCLEUS. **n. 'physics.** The branch of physics having to do with the NUCLEI of ATOMS. **n. plate.** [Biol.] EQUATORIAL PLATE; wall of division formed in the NUCLEUS in certain sorts of AMITOSIS. **n. re'action.** [Phys., Chem.] A reaction causing changes in the NUCLEI of ATOMS, by which ISOTOPES or different ELEMENTS are produced. **n. re'actor.** [Phys.] A structure in which n. fission is made use of in a controlled way for producing ENERGY, RADIOACTIVE ISOTOPES, etc. **n. sap.** [Biol.] The more liquid part of the substance forming a NUCLEUS, which in plants takes up almost all the space inside the n. membrane. **n. 'spindle.** [Biol.] See SPINDLE. **n. transmu'tation.** The changing of the ATOMS of one ELEMENT into those of another by n. reaction.

'nucleate(d), a. [Biol.] Having a NUCLEUS or nuclei.

nucle'ation, n. The forming of a NUCLEUS.

'nuclei, n.pl. See NUCLEUS.

nu'cleic 'acid. [Biochem.] Any of a number of very complex acids made up of NUCLEOTIDES, present in NUCLEO-PROTEINS and probably taking an important part in the SYNTHESIS of proteins and in the process of HEREDITY—grouped into two divisions, RIBONUCLEIC acids, having in them the sugar *deribose,* and DEOXY-RIBONUCLEIC acids having in them the sugar *deoxyribose*

'nuclein, n. [Biochem.] Any of a group of substances with much P in them, got by incomplete HYDROLYSIS of NUCLEO-PROTEINS and formed of a PROTEIN MOLECULE united to one of NUCLEIC ACID.

'nucle-o, -i, To do with, in relation to, a NUCLEUS or nuclei: **'nucleiform,** a., **'nucleoid,** a.

nucle'olo-'centrosome, n. [Bot.] A NUCLEO-LUS which undergoes division like a CENTROSOME, seen in some lower plants.

nucle'olus, n. [Biol.] A body of some size, gen. round, seen in the NUCLEUS of most CELLS. **nucle'olar,** a. **'nucleo'lated(d),** a. Sp., [Bot.] (Of a SPORE) having one or more OIL-DROPS.

nucle'olysis, n. [Biol., Med.] The destruction of a NUCLEUS, the process by which it becomes broken up into the substances of which it is formed, as in a dead CELL.

'nucleo'microsome, n. [Biol.] A CHROMATIN grain in a NUCLEUS.

'nucleon, n. [Phys.] PROTON or NEUTRON.

nucle'onics, n. [Phys.] The science of the NUCLEUS of the ATOM, its parts and ENERGIES.

'nucleoplasm, n. [Biol.] The substance forming a network structure in a NUCLEUS.

'nucleo'protein, n. [Biochem.] Any of a group of substances made up of PROTEINS and NUCLEIC ACID, forming an important part of the NUCLEI of most CELLS.

'nucleotide, n. [Chem.] Any substance made up of RIBOSE or DEOXYRIBOSE, PHOSPHORIC ACID, and a BASE produced from PURINE, PYRIDINE, or PYRIMIDINE.

'nucleus, n. Mass forming the middle, and commonly the chief, part of certain things, part round which other parts are formed or grouped, sp.:— [Biol.] A mass of living substance with a delicate skin round it and CHROMOSOMES in it, present in almost all living CELLS and seen as a clear liquid with one or more NUCLEOLI and (when STAINED) a complex network of more solid, PROTEIN substance running through it, necessary to the existence and healthy working of its cell, and controlling the process of REPRODUCTION and the system of INHERITANCE. [Phys., Chem.] The middle mass of an ATOM, round which ELECTRONS are moving, itself formed of one or more PROTONS and (in all ELEMENTS but H), NEUTRONS, and having a POSITIVE CHARGE equal to the NEGATIVE CHARGE of the electrons round it. [Zoo.] The earliest formed part of a SHELL or like structure; a little knot of NERVE CELLS, sp. in the brain or SPINAL CORD of back-boned animals. [Bot.] The small grain in the middle of a STARCH grain. [Astron.] The small middle and brightest part of the head of a COMET; a bright mass of grouped stars in a NEBULA.

nu'dation, n. [Bot.] The producing, as the effect of natural or other processes, of a part of the earth without any plants.

nudi-. [Biol.] Uncovered, not in a vessel or covering.

nudi'branchiate, a. [Zoo.] Having GILLS without a cover.

nudi'caul(ous), aa. [Bot.] Having stems without leaves.

nudi'florous, a. [Bot.] Having flowers without GLANDS or hairs.

null'ipara, n. [Med.] Woman who has never given birth. nul'liparous, a.

'nulliplex, a. [Biol.] (Of a POLYPLOID) having only the RECESSIVE GENES for a given ALLELOMORPH.

null 'method. [Physl.] A way of measuring something, for example an electric current, by balancing it against a measured thing or effect of the same sort till the reading on the instrument used, for example a GALVANOMETER, is 0.

nume'ration, n. System, act, of numbering. 'numerative, a.

'numerator, n. [Arith.] That part of a FRACTION which in writing is put over the line, as 2 in $\frac{2}{3}$.

'nummulite, n. [Geol., Zoo.] (FOSSIL of) an animal of a group of FORAMINIFERA, most sorts of which have now gone out of existence, having a flat round or long SHELL formed of separate hollows ranged or twisted round the middle point. 'nummu'litic, a.

'nuptial, a. [Zoo.] To do with MATING. n. flight. The flight of the female of a society of bees with a number of males after her, for the purpose of being FERTILIZED by one of them in the air. n. 'plumage. [Zoo.] Bright etc. feathers produced by some male birds at MATING time for the attraction of the female.

nurse cells. [Zoo.] CELLS round an egg-cell, probably for the purpose of producing food for it.

'nurture, n. [Biol.] The conditions acting on an animal or plant from birth as effecting its structure or qualities, opp. NATURE.

nut, n. [Bot.] A dry, gen. one-seeded, fruit with a very hard cover not bursting open at full development, formed from a SYNCARPOUS OVARY.

'nutant, a. [Bot.] Hanging down, pointing to the earth.

nu'tation, n. [Bot.] A regular change in the direction taken by the point of a plant such as a stem or root in the process of growth. [Astron.] A short (about 19 years long) side-to-side motion of the earth's POLE in the motion of PRECESSION, causing the motion of the CELESTIAL POLES to be a little irregular. '-al, a.

nut'gall, n. [Bot.] A nut-like GALL produced on certain trees, and having in it GALLIC ACID.

'nutricism, n. [Biol.] Condition in which two animals or plants are living together with only one of them profiting by the connection.

'nutrient, 1.a. [Med.] Having (much) food-value, being a food which is of (great) use for healthy growth and development. 2.n. A n. food.

'nutriment, n. [Biol.] Food or food-value.

nu'trition, n. [Biol.] The taking in and digestion of food, and its use in the chemistry of plants and animals; the science or process of giving the necessary food to (an animal, plant, or part), or the process of being given it. nu'tritious, n. NUTRIENT. nu'tritive, a. To do with n.; NUTRIENT.

nycta-, nycti-, nycto-. Night.

nycta'lopia, n. [Med.] Condition in which a person who sees quite well in a bright light is more than normally poor at seeing in the dark or a bad light, freq. caused by not enough VITAMIN A in his food. **nycta'lopic**, a. **'nyctalope**, n. Person having n.

nyc'tanthous, a. [Bot.] (Of flowers) opening at night.

nycti'nastic 'movements. [Bot.] Motions of plants in connection with the change from day to night, caused by different amounts of light and heat. **nycti'nasty**, n. The fact, or the reaction, of n.m.

'nyctipe'lagic, a. [Zoo.] Coming to the top part of the sea only at night.

'nyctitate, a. NICTITATE.

nyc'titropism, n. [Bot.] The tendency of parts of plants to take up special positions at night, for example the up-curving of leaves while sleeping.

nycto'phobia, n. [Med.] An unnormal fear of the dark.

'nylon, n. [Chem.] Any long-chain POLY-MERIC AMIDE, produced by a chemical process, of such a structure that it may be pulled into threads and made into materials for clothing, cords, etc., which are noted for their strong and elastic quality.

nymph, n. [Zoo.] The stage before that of full growth in certain insects with INCOM-PLETE METAMORPHOSIS, sp. in EXOPTERY-GOTA, when only the wings and sex-parts are still waiting development. **'-al**, a.

nympho'mania, n. [Med.] A condition of unnormal and uncontrolled sex-desire in woman. **'nympho'maniac**, 1.a. To do with n. 2.n. Woman having n.

nys'tagmus, n. [Med.] An automatic quick rolling of the eye from side to side, taking place when the body has been turning round and round or as the effect of nerve trouble, damage to the brain or ear, etc. **nys'tagmic**, a.

O, Sign for OXYGEN.

o- = ORTHO- [Chem.].

Ω, Sign for OHM.

'oar-feather, n. REMEX.

o'asis, n. Fertile, watered place in a great stretch of dry, infertile country, sp. a sand waste.

ob-. [Bot.] (Of a given form) turned round, upside down, fixed to stem etc. at the end opposite to the normal one for that form: -'**conic(al)**, aa., -'**cordate**, a., -'**cuneate**, a., -'**lanceolate**, a., -'**ovate**, a., -'**ovoid**, a. (For leaf-forms given such names, see picture, p. 223.)

obcom'pressed, a. [Bot.] Flat from front to back.

obdipto'stemonous, a. [Bot.] Having two rings of STAMENS, with those of the outer ring placed opposite the PETALS.

o'bese, a. [Med.] Having an overdevelopment of fat all over the body. **o'besity**, n.

'object, n. Thing under observation, etc. [Psych.] That which is outside the self, sp. that part of it to which the self has a reaction of sense or feeling at any given time; any group of sense experiences having a regular connection with one another and forming what is looked on by the mind as a material thing; that which is viewed by the mind in the experience of having knowledge, the thing of which a person is conscious as opp. the experience or event of being conscious of it. **o. 'blindness**. [Med.] A condition of mind in which a person, though able to see in a physical sense, is without the power of putting his sense experiences together so as to be conscious of oo. as such. **o. glass** or **lens**. OBJECTIVE. **o. space**. [Optics] In connection with an OPTICAL SYSTEM, the space from which the rays forming the IMAGE come or seem to come.

ob'jective, 1.a. To do with facts open to common observation, not with the private experiences of any mind; (of observations, etc.) uncoloured by, independent of, the feelings or opinions of the person making them. [Psych.] To do with, being, things outside the self, sp. outside a person's body; (of reactions, etc.) able to be measured by physical instruments; (of OBJECTS of sense experience) seen or in any way sensed as being in a space outside the body. [Med.] (Of the effects of a disease) open to observation by persons other than the one undergoing them. 2.n. [Optics] the LENS or lenses in an instrument nearest to the thing under observation. **o. psy'chology**. That branch of psychology which has to do only with reactions (of behaviour or body processes) which are open to observation by persons other than the self. **objec'tivity**, n.

'oblate, a. [Geom.] Of a SPHEROID, flat at the POLES; having the form of a spheroid markedly wider than it is long.

'obligate, o'bligatory, aa. [Biol.] Being what is named in all conditions, not having the power of changing its way of existence, as an o. PARASITE.

o'blique, 1.a. Sloping, not level or upright, placed at an angle other than a right angle to a given direction, sp. [Biol.] to the AXIS of an animal, plant, or part, as muscles, body-divisions, etc. [Bot.] (Of leaves) not SYMMETRICAL, a.n. Any of certain o. muscles, sp. of two muscles working the eyeball. **o'bliquely**, adv. **o'bliquity**, n. **o'bliquity of the e'cliptic**. [Astron.] The angle between the plane of the earth's EQUATOR and that of its ORBIT, which is at present about 23°26' and is getting less at the rate of 0·47" a year.

oblite′ration, n. [Biol., Med.] The process of taking away some part or causing it to go out of existence or use, as the complete closing of a pipe-like part by the force of the parts round it. **o′bliterate,** v.t. **o′bliterated,** a.

′oblong, n., a. [Four-sided form) with sides roughly parallel and longer than it is wide. [Bot.] (Of leaf) more than twice as long as it is wide, with sides parallel and ends rounded (*see* picture p. 223).

′oboe, a. A RADAR system for giving an airplane its position by SIGNALS from two stations.

′obovate, a. [Bot.] (Of a leaf) somewhat egg-like in form, with the narrow end fixed to the stem (*see* picture p. 223).

obscur′ation, n. [Optics etc.] That amount of the light or other RADIATION falling on a body which is taken away in going through it.

ob′scure, a. [Biol.] (Of markings, etc.) not clear, not readily seen, said, for example, of the VEINS of a leaf.

ob′sequent, n., a. [Geog.] (River) branching from a SUBSEQUENT river in the opposite direction from the CONSEQUENT river out of which this comes.

ob′servatory, n. [Astron.] Building in which observations of stars and other bodies in the sky are made.

ob′server, n. Person making observations. **ob′serve,** v.t. Make observation of. **ob′served,** a. Got by observation, noted.

ob′session, n. [Psych., Med.] Idea, feeling, or impulse which is all the time present in or coming back to a person's mind, keeping him from giving normal attention to other things, sometimes to such a degree as to be a sign of a diseased mind; the condition of being or becoming obsessed by an idea, etc. **ob′sess,** v.t. (Of idea, etc.) have an obsessive grip on a person's mind. **ob′sessed,** a. Gripped by an o. **ob′sessional, ob′sessive,** aa. **ob′sessional neu′rosis.** [Med.] A NEUROSIS marked by oo., sp. of a sort driving the person to go through certain forms of behaviour, such as hand-washing or some more complex and unnatural train of acts, over and over again or at certain fixed times.

ob′sidian, n. [Mineral.] Sorts of natural glass chemically like GRANITE, produced by a VOLCANO, gen. black or very dark in colour, used as jewel-stone (*see* p. 192).

′obsolete, a. Gone out of use or existence, sp. [Biol.] not clearly marked or no longer present, said of parts or processes at one time common to the family from which a sort of plant or animal comes, or present in itself at an earlier stage in its development. **obso′lescence,** n. Process of becoming o. or condition of being almost o. **obso′lescent.** a.

ob′stetric(al), aa. [Med.] To do with ob-

stetrics. **obstet′rician,** n. Person trained in obstetrics. **ob′stetrics,** n. That branch of medical science which has to do with the care of women in the process of becoming mothers and with the event of giving birth.

ob′struct, v.t. Get, be, in the way of something. [Med.] Get (hollow part) stopped up. **′-ion,** n. Sp., anything stopping up a pipe-like part. **′-ive.** a.

′obturator, n. [Zoo.] Any structure shutting an opening or hollow, sp. any of a number of parts near or having a connection with the o. foramen, for example the **o. nerve. o. fo′ramen.** The great opening formed by the ISCHIUM and the PUBIS which is almost completely shut by the **o. ′membrane. o. canal.** The narrow opening not covered by the o. membrane through which go the **o. nerve** and the o. blood-vessels (the **o. artery** and the **o. vein**).

ob′tuse, a. Rounded at the end, not sharp or pointed. [Geom.] (Of an angle) greater than 90° and less than 180°. **obtusi-.** [Biol.] Obtusely. **obtusi′lingual,** a. [Zoo.] Having a short, rounded tongue.

ob′verse, a. Having the base, or the end at which it is fixed, narrower than the top, said of plant and animal parts, instruments, etc.

′obvolute, a. [Bot.] CONVOLUTE.

occi′dental, a. Of, in, the west, where the sun goes down.

′occiput, n. [Zoo.] The back part of the head or its bone-structure in back-boned animals; like parts in insects. **oc′cipital,** 1.a. To do with the o. 2.n. The great chief bone of the o., formed of a number of more or less united parts. **oc′cipital ′condyle.** Rounded outgrowth of bone on the base of the division of the skull by which it is fixed into the top division of the backbone in such a way as to make possible the motion of the head up and down or from side to side. **′occipi′talia,** n.pl. The occipital bones. **oc′cipito-.**

occ′lusion, n. [Biol., Med.] The shutting or stopping up of a pipe or hole. [Chem.] The taking in of a liquid or sp. a gas by a solid. [Phonet.] A complete shutting of the breath outlets, as in forming the letter *p*. **occ′lude,** v.t. **occ′ludent,** a. **occ′lusive.** 1.a. 2.n. [Phonet.] A sound formed with o., or the letter representative of such sound.

occ′lusor, a. [Zoo.] Any muscle used for shutting an opening by pulling a cover over it.

occul′tation, n. [Astron.] The keeping from view of a body in the sky by another such body coming between it and the point of observation, as the o. of a star by the moon. **oc′cult(ate),** vv.t. and i. (Make) undergo o. **oc′culting,** a. [Astron.,

Optics] Said sp. of instruments used for cutting off light from a body.

occu'pational, a. [Med.] (Of a disease) caused by a person's work.

'ocean, n. [Geog.] The great body of salt water covering over 70% of the earth; any of the five great divisions into which the o. is separated by the great land masses. oce'anic, a. Sp., [Biol.] Living in the open sea where it is over 200 m. deep. 'ocea'nography, n. The science of the o., its geography, history, motions, physical and chemical behaviour, etc. 'ocea'nographer, n. oceano'graphic(al), aa.

o'cellus (o'celli), n. [Zoo.] A small place present on the outside of a number of lower animals giving a reaction to light and forming a simple sort of eye; [Biol.] a coloured marking of eye-like form. o'cellar, 'ocellate(d), aa. ocel'lation, n. Condition of having oo. ocelli-.

'ochre, 'ocher, n. [Mineral.] A natural earth substance made up chiefly of Fe_2O_3, in colours from yellow to dark red and brown, widely used in making paints. 'ocherous, a. Sp., yellow or yellow-brown.

'ochrophore, n. [Biol.] Yellow colour-CELL; IRIDOCYTE.

'ocrea, n. [Bot.] A cup-like structure round the base of a leaf-stem. [Zool] A boot-like cover at the base of the leg in some birds. ocre'aceous, a. ocreate, a.

oct(a)-, octo-. 8:- -oc'tandrous, a.

'octagon, n. [Geom.] Plane form with 8 straight sides and 8 angles, oc'tagonal, a.

octa'hedron, n. [Geom.] A solid having 8 plane faces, which are gen. three-sided and with three equal angles. octa-'hedral, a.

octa'hydric, a. [Chem.] Having in it 8 –OH groups.

oc'tamerous, a. [Bot., Zoo.] Having certain parts in groups of 8.

'octan, a. [Med.] (Of attacks of a disease) coming back every 8th day.

'octane, n. [Chem.] Any of a group of ISOMERIC PARAFFINS present in PETROLEUM, the most common of which, a liquid without colour, gen. named iso-octane, has ANTI-KNOCK properties which make it important in connection with the producing and rating of PETROL for engines.

octa'valent, a. [Chem.] Having a VALENCY of 8.

'octave, n. A group of 8. [Phys.] In any scale of VIBRATIONS, as light or sound waves, the part of the scale between any two whose FREQUENCIES are to one another in the relation of 1 to 2; sp., in music, a range of 8 notes forming an o.

oc'tennial, a. Taking place every 8 years; going on for 8 years.

oc'tet, n. [Chem.] A group of 8 ATOMS not readily separated.

'octopod, n., a. (Animal) having 8 feet or arms. Oc'topoda, n.pl. [Zoo.] An ORDER of CEPHALOPODS having 8 arms with lines of SUCKERS for gripping food or fixing themselves to any support, etc.—sea animals living gen. on the sea-bed in cracks between stones, but swimming when necessary.

octo'radiate, a. [Biol.] Having 8 rays or arms.

'ocular, 1.a. [Zoo.] To do with the eye or the sense of seeing; eye-like. 2.n. [Optics] The part of an instrument to which the eye is put. o. spot. [Zoo.] A place on the skin of an animal which gives a reaction to light.

'oculist, n. Medical expert on the eyes.

'ocul(o)-. [Zoo.] Eye, to do with the eyes and . . .): ocu'liferous, a., 'oculo'nasal, a.

oculo'motor, a. [Zoo.] To do with or causing motions of the eye, said sp. of the nerve going to the muscles by which the eye-ball is controlled.

'oculus, n. [Zoo.] Eye.

odd, a. (Of a number) into which 2 goes with 1 over, as the number 3, opp. EVEN. o.-'pinnate, [Bot.] (Of leaves) PINNATE with the middle stem ending in one small leaf, so that there is an o. number of divisions, opp. ABRUPTLY PINNATE (see picture p. 223).

Odo'nata, n.pl. [Zoo.] An ORDER of EXOPTERYGOTE insects, some of great size, with 4 long narrow wings of almost equal size, two great COMPOUND EYES, and strong biting mouth-parts, undergoing the first stage of their development in water.

-odont, a. [Zoo.] Having teeth of the given sort. -odontia, n. Condition of being -odont.

odont(o)-. Tooth: odon'togeny, n.

odon'talgia, n. [Med.] Pain in a tooth. odon'talgic, a.

o'dontoblast, n. [Zoo.] Any of the DENTINE-forming CELLS present round the soft inner mass of a tooth.

o'dontoclast, n. [Zoo.] Any of the great CELLS responsible for the destruction of the roots of the MILK TEETH when the time comes for them to come out.

o'dontoid, a. [Biol.] Like a tooth; to do with the o. process. o. 'process. The tooth-like part of the second VERTEBRA of a back-boned animal on which the first ring-like vertebra is slipped, so as to make possible a turning motion of the head.

odon'tology, n. The science of teeth. o'donto'logical, a. odon'tologist, n.

odon'toma, n. [Med.] Any diseased growth in connection with a tooth, or of tooth-like substance or structure.

o'dontophore, n. [Zoo.] The complete structure of parts round and supporting the teeth of a MOLLUSC. odon'tophorous, a.

o'dontoplast, n. [Zoo.] ODONTOBLAST; odontoblast-forming CELL.

odonto'stomatous, a. [Zoo.] Having mouth-parts with teeth.

o'doriphore, n. [Chem.] A group of ATOMS forming part of the MOLECULE of a substance and responsible for its special smell.

odo'rometry, n. The science of measuring smells.

'odour, n. [Psych.] The sense-experience given by the nose; that property of a substance causing a sense of smell; any of the different sorts into which attempts have been made at grouping smells as sense-experiences.

-odynia, n. [Med.] A condition of pain in a given part or from a given cause: **neuro-'dynia,** n.

oe'cology, n. [Biol.] ECOLOGY.

oe'dema, n. [Bot.] The expansion of parts of a plant through the over-development of CELLS as the effect of having much water in the wrong conditions of heat and light. [Med.] DROPSY. **'-tous,** a.

'Oedipus 'complex. [Psych.] In Freud's system, unconscious sex-love of a boy for his mother and hate of, or desire for the death of, his father, normal in the very young, and frequently having some after-effect in the older person, sometimes unhealthy, a common cause of NEUROSES etc.

'Oedogoni'acae, n.pl. [Bot.] A small FAMILY of branching thread-like green ALGAE producing lines of narrow CELLS of special form at certain points in the threads, male plants frequently being very small and PARASITIC on the female.

'oersted, n. [Phys.] The unit of MAGNETIC intensity in the C.G.S. system, $=1$ LINE/cm^2.

(o)e'sophagus, n. [Zoo.] The pipe going from the PHARYNX to the stomach. **oeso'phageal,** a. oeso'phag(o)-.

oestra'diol, n. [Zoo., Biochem.] The important OESTROGEN present in the OVARY, $C_{18}H_{24}O_2$, of greater power than OESTRONE and, in addition to controlling MENSTRUATION etc., being responsible to a great degree for female SECONDARY SEX CHARACTERS.

'oestrin, 'oestrone, nn. [Biochem.] An important OESTROGEN, $C_{18}H_{22}O_2$, present in female URINE, sp. in PREGNANCY.

'oestrogen, n. [Zoo., Biochem.] Any HORMONE having an effect on the OESTROUS CYCLE and other female sex-processes in MAMMALS. **oestro'genic,** a.

'oestromania, n. [Zoo.] Unnormal sex-desire in female animals.

'oestrous, a. [Zoo.] To do with the OESTRUS. **o. 'cycle.** In female MAMMALS, the train of changes in the UTERUS and other parts having a connection with sex and giving birth, which takes place regularly over a fixed time in four stages marked by: 1. the forming of GRAAFIAN FOLLICLES, 2. the freeing of the egg-CELLS, 3. adjustments for the producing of offspring, 4. (if no offspring undergo development) the changing back by degrees to the same conditions as at the starting-point.

'oestrum, 'oestrus, nn. [Zoo.] Second stage of the OESTROUS CYCLE, in which the sex-impulse of the female comes into operation, the only time at which sex-connection is possible in animals with a marked oestrous cycle. **'oestrual,** a. **'oestru'ation,** n. The condition of being in the o.

'offset, n. [Bot.] A branch of a plant running sideways over or under the earth and putting out a new root at its end.

'offshoot, n. [Bot.] A side branch of a chief stem.

ohm, n. [Elec.] The commonly used unit of electric RESISTANCE $= 10^9$ C.G.S. units. **'ohmic,** a. **'ohmic 'heating.** In PLASMA PHYSICS, the ENERGY given to CHARGED PARTICLES in reaction to an electric field and their COLLISIONS with one another. **'ohmic re'sistance.** True electric RESISTANCE, marked by the changing of ENERGY into heat, as opp. forces acting against a current which are not in fact caused by this property of the CONDUCTOR but by other things, such as INDUCTANCE. **'ohm-meter,** n. Instrument for measuring RESISTANCE.

Ohm's law. [Elec.] The law that the RATIO of the POTENTIAL DIFFERENCE between two ends of a given CONDUCTOR and the size of the current going through it is unchanging, generally given in the form: VOLTAGE $=$ the current in AMPERES $\times$ the RESISTANCE in OHMS.

oil, n. [Chem.] Any of a great group of NEUTRAL liquids got from plants, animals or MINERALS, having in common a marked smooth VISCOSITY, the properties of burning and of being SOLUBLE in ETHER and ALCOHOL but not in water, and the fact that H and C are present in them. (*See* ESSENTIAL O., FIXED O. and MINERAL o.). **o. gland.** [Zoo.] UROPYGIAL GLAND, **o.-imm'ersion lens** or **objective.** [Optics, etc.] An OBJECTIVE having a drop of o. with the same power of REFRACTION as glass between it and the thing looked at, used in a high-powered MICROSCOPE to give a clearer picture. **o. of 'vitriol.** [Chem.] Old name for SULPHURIC ACID. **'oily,** a. Covered with, having in it, like, an o.

ointment, n. [Med.] Soft wax or fat mixed with medical substances, used for dressing wounds, rubbing on skin, etc.

Old Red 'Sandstone. [Geol.] A thick SERIES of ROCKS representative of the DEVONIAN SYSTEM in parts of Great Britain and Europe.

Old Stone Age. PALEOLITHIC.

ole′aginous, a. Having in it, producing, oil.

o′lecranon, n. [Anat.] Outgrowth of bone at the top end of the ULNA, forming the point of the ELBOW, to which the muscle pulling the lower arm straight is fixed. [Zoo.] A like part of the front leg of a four-legged animal.

′olefin(e), n. [Chem.] Any OPEN-CHAIN HYDROCARBON having one DOUBLE BOND, for example ETHYLENE, a sort of substance readily undergoing chemical reaction.

o′leic, a. [Chem.] To do with, having in it, produced from, oil. **o. ′acid.** [Chem.] An acid OLEFIN, $C_{18}H_{34}O_2$, present in the form of OLEIN in most animal and plant fats and oils, readily uniting with O in the air, turning yellow and becoming strong and unpleasing in smell and taste.

ole′iferous, a. Producing oil.

′olein, n. [Chem.] A substance produced by the reaction of OLEIC ACID with GLYCERINE.

′oleine, n. [Chem.] The liquid part of any fat, as opp. STEARINE.

′oleo-. Oil, OLEIN: **-refrac′tometer,** n., **-′resin,** n.

′oleo ′margarine, n. MARGARINE made from OLEO OIL.

′oleo oil. A yellow, butter-like oil got by crushing animal, sp. beef, fat.

′oleosome, n. [Biol.] A mass of fat-like substance in the CYTOPLASM of a CELL.

oleo′stearin(e), n. The white solid separated from OLEO OIL by crushing animal fat, used in cooking.

′oleum, n. [Med.] Oil. [Chem.] FUMING SULPHURIC ACID.

ol′factory, 1.a. [Zoo., etc.] To do with the sense of smell. 2.n. O. nerve. **o. bulb.** The rounded mass at the end of the o. lobe in man, where the nerves coming from the nose are rooted. **o. cell.** [Zoo.] A CELL specially designed to give a reaction to smells, in back-boned animals any of the nerve-cells ending in a hair-like outgrowth (**o. hair**) which are bedded in the roof of the nose. **o. lobe.** In back-boned animals, one or other of the two parts, in man long and narrow, coming forward from the lower front of the brain and having to do with the sense of smell. **o. pit.** [Zoo.] In animals without back-bones, a small hollow with o. sense CELLS; in the EMBRYOS of back-boned animals, a small hollow which will later become an outer opening of the nose. **ol′faction,** n. The sense of smell or the act or process of smelling.

olfac′tometer, n. [Psych.] A measuring-instrument used in olfactometry. **olfac-′tometry,** n. The science or process of measuring a person's sense-reactions to smells and the different INTENSITIES of the smells used.

oli′g(a)emia, n. [Med.] A condition of the body in which the amount of blood becomes less.

olig(o)-. [Biol., Med.] Small in size or number or amount: **oli′gandrous,** a., **oligo′carpous,** a., **oligo′sporous,** a., etc.

′Oligocene, n. [Geol.] The third PERIOD or ROCK system of the TERTIARY (*see* p. 558).

Oligo′chaeta, n.pl. [Zoo.] An ORDER of CHAETOPODA without PARAPODIA or clearly marked head and with only a small number of CHAETAE on every body division, HERMAPHRODITE, and living in earth or inland water, for example the earthworm. **′oligo′chaete,** n., a. [Animal] of or like the O. **oligo′chaetous,** a.

oligo′clase, n. [Mineral.] A sort of FELDSPAR made up of SILICATES of Ca, Na, and Al.

′oligody′namic, a. [Chem., Med.] (Of certain substances) producing their effects in very small amounts; (of effects) produced by very small amounts of some substance.

oli′gomerous, a. [Bot.] (Of flowers) having one or more rings of parts with less parts than the others.

′oligo′trophic, a. [Ecol.] (Of bodies of inland water) having high sharp edges with almost no trees or plants.

′oliv-a, -e, n. OLIVARY BODY.

′olivary ′body. [Zoo.] The rounded mass on the MEDULLA OBLONGATA formed by the pushing up from inside of the olivary nucleus. **′olivary ′nucleus.** A band of grey nerve substance in the MEDULLA OBLONGATA with a wave in it pushing up the substance over it.

′olive, oli′vaceous, aa. [Bot.] Grey-green with a suggestion of yellow.

′olivine, n. [Mineral.] A common natural SILICATE of iron and Mg, gen. a soft green in colour, but of which there are light-green and yellow TRANSPARENT sorts valued as jewel stones.

-oma, n. [Med.] Diseased condition or growth. **-omatous,** a.

o′masum, n. [Zoo.] The 3rd division of the stomach of a RUMINANT.

ombro-. Rain: **′-graph,** n., **om′brometer,** n., **′-phil(e),** n. [Bot.].

o′mentum, n. [Zoo.] A fold of PERITONEUM, sp. one joining VISCERA. **o′mental,** a. **omento-.**

omma′teum, n. [Zoo.] A COMPOUND EYE.

omma′tidium, n. [Zoo.] Any of the units or simple eyes of which a COMPOUND EYE is formed.

omni-. All.

om′nigenous, a. Of all sorts.

om′nivorous, a. [Zoo.] Using animals and plants for food, not limited to one or the other.

omo-. Shoulder: **-′hyoid,** a.

'omo ideum, n. [Zoo.] The PTERYGOID bone of a bird.

omo'sternum, n. [Zoo.] The front part of the chest-bone in AMPHIBIA; in certain higher animals, a CARTILAGE or bone joining the chest-bone and a CLAVICLE.

omphal(o)-. [Zoo.] UMBILICUS:— om'phalic, a., ompha'litis, n. [Med.], omphaloid, a., 'omphalomesen'teric, a.

'omphalos, n. UMBILICUS.

'onanism, n. [Med.] MASTURBATION by a man, 'onanist, n. ona'nistic, a.

'onc(h)osphere, n. [Zoo.] The stage in the development of a CESTODE worm before it becomes a CYSTICERCUS.

on'cology, n. The branch of medical science having to do with diseased or unnatural growths in the body.

'ondograph, n. [Elec.] An instrument for recording ALTERNATING-current wave-forms.

'onomato'mania, n. [Psych., Med.] A condition in which there is a loss of memory of certain words together with a strong impulse to keep on saying other words over and over.

'ontocycle, n. [Biol.] A process of development in which a plant, animal, or sort goes back in its later stages to forms like that of its earlier stages.

onto'genesis, on'togeny, nn. The history of the growth and development of one animal or plant, as against that of a family or group. 'ontoge'netic, a.

onych(o)-. [Zoo.] Nail or CLAW or the substance of which they are formed: 'onchyo'genic, a.

'onyx, n. [Mineral.] A sort of natural SILICA (SiO₂) formed of straight parallel bands of different colours, sp. black, white, and red, used for ornament.

oö-. [Biol.] Egg or OVUM: oö'genesis, o'ogeny, nn. o'oif, a.

'oöcyst, n. [Zoo.] Bag-like structure formed round two uniting SEX-CELLS in certain PROTOZOA.

'oöcyte, n. [Zoo.] Female CELL from which an OVUM is produced by division; in PROTOZOA a cell producing female GAMETES.

oö'cytin, n. [Zoo.] A substance got from male sex-CELLS which has the effect of FERTILIZING female sex-cells from the same sort of animal.

o'oecium, n. [Zoo.] Bag-like part or hollow in the body of an animal in which eggs undergo development.

oö'gamete, n. [Zoo.] Female GAMETE in SPOROZOA.

o'ogamy, n. [Biol.] The system of producing offspring by the uniting of male and female CELLS of which the female cell is much greater than the male and without the power of motion, the male making its way to it. o'ogamöus, a.

oö'gonium (oögonia), n. [Bot.] Female sex-part of certain ALGAE and FUNGI, having in it one or more OÖSPHERES. [Zoo.] CELL producing oöCYTES. oö'gonial, a.

'oöki'nete, n. [Zoo.] A worm-like stage of the ZYGOTE of certain PROTOZOA.

'Oölite, n. [Geol.] (Any stone of) the higher part of the JURASSIC system in England and some other parts of Europe, freq. marked by OÖLITIC LIMESTONES.

oölith, n. [Geol.] Small ball-like mass of CaCO₃, (Ca, Mg)CO₃, or a SILICATE, seen on sea-floor etc. or massed together in SEDIMENTARY ROCKS, sp. LIMESTONES. 'oölitic, a. Formed chiefly of oo.

o'ölogy, n. Science of bird's eggs. oö'logical, a. o'ologist, n.

'Oömy'cetes, n.pl. One of the two divisions of PHYCOMYCETES, white MOLDS of different sorts, etc.

'oöphore, n. [Bot.] OÖPHYTE.

'oöphor(o)'. [Med.] OVARY: o'öphorectomy, n., o'öphoritis, n.

'oöphyte, n. [Bot.] The sexed stage in the history of BRYOPHYTA and PTERIDOPHYTA.

'oöplasm, n. [Biol.] The CELL substance of an OVUM. oö'plasmic, a.

oösphere, n. [Biol.] An OVUM or female GAMETE before being made fertile, sp. one great in size, round in form, and without power of motion.

'oöspore, n. [Bot.] In lower plants, a RESTING SPORE formed from an OÖSPHERE when it has been made fertile.

o'östegite, n. [Zoo.] A plate-like structure on the lower part of a leg in some higher CRUSTACEA, which is used as a vessel for the eggs.

'oös'tegopod, n. [Zoo.] A leg having an OÖSTEGITE.

'oö'theca, n. [Zoo.] A vessel for the eggs seen in some insects and MOLLUSCA.

'oötype, n. [Zoo.] The part of the OVIDUCT in certain worms where the eggs are given their outer covering.

ooze, n. [Geol.] Soft, small-grained material on the bed of the deep sea made up chiefly of hard parts of very small animals.

oö'zoid, n. [Zoo.] An animal produced from an OVUM.

o'pacity, n. Condition or quality of being OPAQUE. [Phys., Astron.] The measure of a body's power of stopping by ABSORPTION any sort of waves, for example, light, sound, or electric.

'opal, n. [Mineral.] Natural, non-CRYSTALLINE SiO₂ having more or less water in it, a number of sorts of which are valued as jewels. opa'lescent, 'opaline, aa. Beautifully IRIDESCENT like most oo., sp. milk-like and iridescent like the commonest of the jewel oo. opa'lescence, n.

o'paque, a. Not letting light or given rays through.

'**open,** 1.a. Opp. CLOSED, sp.: [Med.] Not covered by new growth etc., as *an o. wound.* [Bot.] Of a VASCULAR BUNDLE, having CAMBIUM in it so that it is able to go on getting thicker. [Elec.] (Of CIRCUIT) not complete, with an opening in the CONDUCTING part or parts, so that the current is stopped. [Phonet.] (Of VOWELS) said with a wide opening between the tongue and the roof of the mouth; (of CONSONANTS) formed without completely stopping the breath. 2.v.t. [Med.] Make (the BOWELS) undergo EVACUATION.

'**open-cast,** a. (Of a mine) not under the earth, forming an open hole in it.

open chain. [Chem.] *See* CHAIN. '**open-chain,** a.

'**open 'channel hy'draulics.** *See* HYDRAULICS.

open-'hearth 'process. The process of making steel from PIG IRON in an apparatus in which the materials are placed on a structure like a great hollow plate and heated by flame being sent over them under a low roof.

'**operable,** a. Which it is possible to put into operation. [Med.] (Of a condition or part) for or on which an operation would be possible or of help.

ope'rameter, n. An instrument for numbering the complete turns made by a wheel or other part of a machine.

ope'ration, n. An act, process, bit of work, sp. one done for the purpose of producing a certain effect; (of a machine, chemical substance, system, etc.) the condition of acting, working; the act of working a machine, system, etc. [Med.] An o. on the body, gen. with instruments, making a physical change in it, sp. that of cutting some part out or off. '**operate,** 1.v.i. Do some o., have some effect, 2.v.t. Put and/or keep (machine, system) in o. '**operating,** a. Sp., [Med.] Used for oo. '**operative,** a. Having, or strong enough to have, the effect designed; to do with the oo. of hands or machines. [Med.] To do with, using, oo. '**operator,** n. Sp., person operating a machine. [Math.] A sign to be representative of an operation to be done.

o'**perculum,** n. [Biol.] A cover by which a part may be opened or shut, for example that of certain seed-vessels or of the SPORE-vessel in MUSCI, or the hard plate on the foot of some GASTROPODA for shutting the opening of the SHELL when the animal is inside; in fish, the stiff overhanging fold covering the breathing-apparatus, and in some ARACHNIDA, a small plate having a like purpose; in the brain of higher animals, the part covering the INSULA. o'**percular,** 1.a. To do with, having the purpose of, an o. 2.n. The chief bone of the o. in fish, at the back upper end. o'**perculate,** a. Having an o.

O'**phidia,** n.pl. [Zoo.] The SUB-ORDER of SQUAMATA made up of snakes—long-bodied animals without legs or clearly marked-off tails, noted for the power of opening the mouth very wide, for having a thin MEMBRANE covering the eye but no moving EYELIDS, and for being without EARDRUMS. o'**phidian,** 1.a. Of, like, to do with the O. 2.n. Snake.

'**ophio'pluteus,** n. [Zoo.] Free-swimming LARVA of OPHIUROIDEA.

o'**phitic 'structure** or '**texture.** [Geol.] The structure of a ROCK in which long, narrow, flat CRYSTALS of FELDSPAR are framed in AUGITE, forming a design which gives the suggestion of the markings on a snake.

Ophiu'**roidea,** n. pl. [Zoo] A CLASS of ECHINODERMATA of star-like form with long waving arms, simple or branched, clearly marked off from the middle body and readily broken off to get out of the grip of another animal. **ophi'uroid,** 1.n. Animal of the O. 2.a. To do with, of, like in form to, the O.

oph'**thalmia,** n. [Medl] INFLAMMATION of the eyeball or the CONJUNCTIVA.

oph'**thalmic,** a. [Zoo.] To do with the eye or parts near it. **ophthalmo-.**

ophthal'**mology.** The branch of medical science having to do with the eye. **oph'thalmo'logic(al),** aa. **ophthal'molo-gist,** n.

ophthal'**mometer,** n. [Med.] Instrument for measuring different parts of the eye, sp. the curve of the LENS with a view to the discovery of errors of REFRACTION. **oph'thalmo'metric(al),** an. **ophthal'mo-metrist,** n. **ophthal'mometry,** n.

oph'**thalmo'plegia,** [Med.] Loss of power of eye muscles.

oph'**thalmoscope,** n. [Med.] An instrument for the observation of the inner parts of the eye using an in-curving circle of looking-glass for sending light into the eye, with an opening in the middle through which the eye is viewed.

-'**opia,** n. [Med.] Condition of the eye or the power of seeing. -'**opic,** a.

'**opiate,** n. [Med.] Any substance causing sleep, sp. one with OPIUM in it.

opi'**someter,** n. An instrument for measuring curved lines on a map, formed of a wheel which may be rolled over them recording by a needle the distance covered, used in SURVEYING.

opisth(o)-. [Biol.] (At the) back.

o'**pistho'c(o)elous,** a. [Zoo.] Curving in at the back and out at the front, said of the units of the backbone.

o'**pistho'glossal,** a. [Zoo.] Having the tongue fixed at the front and free at the back.

o'**pistho'gnathous,** a. [Zoo.] Having the JAWS sloping back from the rest of the face, as opp. PROGNATHOUS.

o'pistho'tonos, n. [Med.] A condition in which the back is arched violently forward and the head and legs pulled back, caused by a SPASM of the muscles of the back in certain diseases or as the effect of certain poisons.

'opium, n. [Med.] A dried milk-like liquid got from certain plants of Asia or east Europe which has very strong NARCOTIC properties, used medically or smoked for pleasure with very damaging effects.

op'ponens, n. [Zoo.] Name given to certain muscles of the hand or foot by which a finger or toe is pulled round so as to be opposite another, for example in placing the little finger opposite the thumb. op'ponent, a. Causing to be opposite, said of an o.

'opposite, a. [Bot.] (Of leaves) placed in two's level with and opposite to one another on the stem; (of STAMENS) placed opposite the middle points of the PETALS.

oppo'sition, n. [Astron.] The condition of the moon or other PLANET when it is in a straight line with the earth and the sun, the earth being between the other two.

-opsia, -opsis, -opsy, nn. -OPIA.

opsi'ometer, n. OPTOMETER.

op'sonin, n. [Zoo., Med.] A substance present in the blood which has the effect of increasing the destruction of CELLS, such as disease BACTERIA, by LEUCOCYTES. op'sonic, a. op'sonic 'index. The relation of the number of given BACTERIA undergoing destruction in the blood of an ill person after being INOCULATED against his disease to the number undergoing destruction in a healthy person.

'optic, 1.a. [Zoo.] To do with the eyes or the sense of seeing. [Phys.] OPTICAL (only in one or two fixed uses with certain words). 2.n. [Zoo.] O. nerve. o. 'angle. [Cryst.] The angle between the o. axes of a CRYSTAL having two. o. 'axis (axes). [Cryst.] That direction through a BIRE-FRINGENT CRYSTAL in which there is no separating of the ORDINARY and EXTRA-ORDINARY rays. [Optics] The line round which the rays of light in a system of LENSES are SYMMETRICAL, sp. the straight line from the middle of the back wall of the eye through the middle of the CRYS-TALLINE LENS. o. 'capsule. [Zoo.] The covering structure round the eye of ELASMOBRANCHII and of the EMBRYOS of back-boned animals. o. cup. [Zoo.] The later form of the o. vesicle. o. disc or pa'pilla. [Zoo.] The light-coloured, round, and somewhat thick place on the RETINA where the o. nerve comes into the eyeball, forming the BLIND SPOT. o. lobe. [Zoo.] In back-boned animals, one or the other of two rounded parts on the top of the middle division of the brain which has to do with the sense of seeing and from which the o. nerves come; in lower animals, the part of the brain in connection with the eyes. o. 'vesicle. [Zoo.] In the EMBRYOS of back-boned animals, one or the other of two outgrowths of the front part of the brain, in form at first like a hollow ball on a stem, then changing into a cup-like structure, which undergoes development into the RETINA, the stem forming the o. nerve.

'optical, a. [Phys.] To do with, acting on, measuring, worked by, light, forming part of the science of OPTICS. [Zoo.] OPTIC. o. ac'tivity. [Chem., Phys.] The property of certain substances of turning through an angle the plane of POLARIZATION of PLANE-POLARIZED light going through them. o. bench. An apparatus formed of a long straight rail or two like parallel structures on which parts of o. instruments may be fixed and moved about on a scale for testing. o. 'centre (of a lens). [Optics] The point on the AXIS of a LENS or system of lenses such that any ray going through it comes out of the lens etc. in a direction parallel to that in which it went in. o. 'double. [Astron.] A DOUBLE STAR which is in fact not one, but only two separate stars seen as very near together because their distance and position are such as to put them almost in the same line from the eye. o. glass. Specially made glass, smooth and regular in the highest degree possible, used for eye-glasses and o. instruments. o. 'instrument. Any instrument designed as a help in seeing, or by which light is broken up or changed in direction, for example, a MICROSCOPE, TELESCOPE, SPECTROSCOPE. o. i'somerism. [Chem.] The existence of o. 'isomers, that is ISOMERS different from one another only in turning the plane of PLANE-POLARIZED light in opposite directions, a form of STEREOISOMERISM. o. ro'tation. [Chem., Phys.] O. activity or the effect produced by it on PLANE-POLARIZED light; SPECIFIC ROTATION. o. square. A hand-instrument for marking off a right angle with the help of two looking-glasses at an angle of 45°, used in SURVEYING. o. 'system. A system of LENSES, looking-glasses, etc. by which light-rays are made to take desired directions, as in an o. instrument.

'opticon, n. [Zoo.] The innermost part of the OPTIC LOBE in insects.

'optics, n. The science of light, its properties, behaviour, and effects, taken from every point of view (see PHYSICAL O., GEO-METRICAL O.).

'optimum. n., a. (The point at which any condition, for example, of heat, is) best for some purpose, sp. [Biol.] for growth and development. 'optimal, a.

'optogram, n. [Med.] Picture of thing seen,

fixed for a short time on the RETINA by the operation of light on the VISUAL RED.

op′tometer, n. [Med.] An instrument for measuring the power of the eyes, their range of clear seeing and limits of adjustment etc. **op′tometrist.** n. **op′tometry,** n. The measuring and testing of the eyes for the purpose of giving persons glasses.

′optophone, n. An instrument by which light-waves are changed into sound-waves, so that by its use a person unable to see may be given the power of recording different degrees of light, and even of reading print by ear.

′ora, n.pl. *See* os.

′oral, a. Said, as opp. given in writing, etc. [Zoo.] To do with, near, in, on the same side as, the mouth. [Med.] (Of medical substances) taken through the mouth. [Phonet.] (Of sounds) made through the mouth with the nose shut, as *l*.

orb, n. Anything in the form of a ball or circle, sp. any of the round masses present in orbicular ROCKS. **or′bicular,** a. In the form of an o. [Bot.] (Of leaves) round, with the stem at the middle point. [Zoo.] Placed round an opening, sp. of the muscles round the eye or mouth. [Mineral.] (Of ROCK structure) full of round masses formed of coat after coat of different substances.

or′bicu′laris (orbiculares), n. [Zoo.] A muscle of which the FIBRES go round an opening.

or′biculate, a. [Bot.] (Of leaves) almost completely round in outline (*see* picture p. 223).

′orbit, n. [Zoo.] The hollow in the bone-structure of the head in which the eye of back-boned animals is placed; the skin round the eye of a bird. **′orbito-.**

′orbit, n. The line of motion of one body moving round another, sp. [Astron.] the o. of a body in the sky kept moving round another by attraction, as the o. of the earth round the sun or the moon round the earth, or of any SATELLITE sent up by man. [Phys.] In Bohr's theory of the ATOM, the o. of an ELECTRON round the NUCLEUS.

′orbital, a. [Zoo., Astron., Phys.] To do with an ORBIT, sp. the orbit of the eye; (of ELECTRONS) in motion round the NUCLEUS of an ATOM. **o. ′index.** [Zoo.] The number giving the relation between the measure across the ORBIT of an eye from left to right and its widest measure from top to base, used in CRANIOMETRY.

′orbito′sphenoid, a., n. [Zoo.] (Of, being) a bone forming part of the side wall of the head near the eye in back-boned animals, in man the smaller wing of the SPHENOID.

Orchi′daceae, n.pl. [Bot.] An important FAMILY of MONOCOTYLEDONS, some of which are EPIPHYTIC, noted for the

special structure of their frequently very beautiful EPIGYNOUS flowers, which have three PETAL-like SEPALS and three true petals, one of which is gen. markedly different from the others, forming a great lip-like part, sometimes with a long SPUR at the back.

′orchis, n. TESTICLE. **orch(i)-, orchid(o)-.**

order, n. Degree, position in some sort of scale, for example, of size, order of development, etc., as used, for example, in naming the RADII of a RADIOSYMMETRICAL animal. [Biol.] In the grouping of plants and animals, a group whose divisions are FAMILIES, and which is itself a division of a CLASS (*see* p. 560).

′ordinal, n., a. [Arith.] (Number) giving the order of a thing, as *first, second, third*, etc., as opp. CARDINAL.

′ordinary ray. [Optics] Of the two rays into which light is broken by BIREFRINGENCE, the one whose behaviour is in agreement with the normal law of REFRACTION.

′ordinate, n. [Math.] *See* CARTESIAN COÖRDINATES.

Ordo′vician, a., n. [Geol.] (Of) the ROCKS of the second PERIOD of the PALAEOZOIC (*see* p. 559).

ore, n. A MINERAL of which some part (gen. a metal) is of value, and for which it is mined, etc.

o′rexis, n. [Psych.] Feelings, desires and purposes taken together as one side of experience, the processes having to do with knowledge forming the other side.

′organ, n. [Biol.] A part of a plant or animal which is clearly marked off from other parts as a unit having special structure and doing special work, for example the root of a plant, the heart or brain of an animal. **o. of ′Corti.** [Zoo.] CORTI'S ORGAN. **organo-. orga′nelle,** n. [Biol.] A part of a CELL, or of a simple one-celled plant or animal, doing special work.

or′ganic, a. Forming, forming part of, to do with, something having an organization of parts, sp. dependent on one another and working together. [Biol.] Living, to do with living substance or living things; formed of, or having, or to do with, an ORGAN or organs. [Chem.] To do with o. chemistry. [Med.] (Of disease, change, etc.) to do with, having an effect on, the structure of an organ or organs. [Psych.] To do with, coming from, the inner oo. of the body, as an o. sense-experience. [Geol.] (Of materials) formed by the operation of plants or animals or made up of parts of their substance. **o. ′chemistry.** That branch of chemistry which has to do with **o. compounds.** that is, substances formed of C united with H, or with H and other substances, such as are produced by living things and present in all living substance.

'organism, n. [Biol.] Any living thing; a living thing of the more complex sort having true ORGANS. orga'nismal, a.

'organize, v.t. Get units, such as the different parts of a group or structure, into relation with one another, forming a system or working together as one thing, that is, give organization to. orga'nizable, a. Sp., [Biol.] Able to be formed into living substance. 'organized, a. Sp., [Biol.] Being an ORGANISM. organizer, n. Sp., [Zoo.] Any part of an EMBRYO which has an effect on the development of other parts by sending into them substances causing or conditioning it.

or'gano'genic, a. [Geol.] ORGANIC. [Biol.] To do with ORGANOGENESIS.

or'gano'genesis, organ'ogeny, nn. [Biol.] The development of ORGANS in plants and animals.

orga'nography, n. [Biol.] The branch of ORGANOLOGY which has to do with giving an account of the most clearly marked ORGANS of plants and animals, their form, position, and purpose, sp. the outer parts of a plant.

orga'nology, n. [Biol.] The science of the ORGANS of plants and animals. 'organo-'logical, a. orga'nologist, n.

'organome'tallic 'compound. [Chem.] Any substance formed of a metal united with an ORGANIC group.

orga'nomony, n. [Biol.] The system of laws controlling the process of living.

orga'nophyly, n. [Biol.] The PHYLOGENY of ORGANS.

or'ganosol, n. [Chem.] A COLLOIDAL SOLUTION in which the liquid is an ORGANIC COMPOUND.

or'gano'therapy, n. The use as medical substances of animal ORGANS or substances made or got from them, sp. the DUCTLESS GLANDS.

'organo'trophic, a. [Biol.] To do with the process of forming and giving food to ORGANS.

organo'tropic, a. [Zoo., Med.] (Of substances) acting on the ORGANS of the body.

'orgasm, n. [Med.] The condition of expansion of an ORGAN; (the very strong complex of physical feelings experienced at) the CLIMAX of COPULATION, when the SEMEN is sent into the UTERUS. [Psych.] Violent uncontrolled feeling, worked-up condition, sp. that taking place in connection with the physical o. of the sex-act. or'gas-mic, -tic, aa.

ori'ental, a. Of, in, the east, where the sun comes up. o. 'region. One of the chief divisions of the earth from the point of view of the distribution of animals and plants, taking in the south part of all Asia and the islands of the Indian Ocean and the South China Sea.

'orien'tation, n. Position, direction, in relation to other things; act or process of orienting, condition or fact of being oriented. [Biol.] The position or change of position of a plant, animal, or part, sp. as a reaction to something acting on it from outside. [Chem.] The positions and order of the ATOMS or groups in a MOLECULE. [Cryst.] The position of the planes of a CRYSTAL in relation to certain fixed planes. [Psych.] (The power of) getting things in relation to one another in space, seeing where they are, or of being clearly conscious of one's position in relation to other things; the condition of seeing clearly one's relations to the persons round one, to society. 'orient, 'orientate, vv.t. Put a thing or things in a certain position in relation to other things or to one another; get a knowledge, be conscious, of the position of something. sp. [Psych.] of oneself, or [Chem.] of the positions of ATOMS or groups in a MOLECULE. [Chem.] Have the effect of causing an atom or group to take a certain position in a molecule. [Cryst.] Put a CRYSTAL in such a position that its AXES are pointing in certain given directions. [Surveying] Get a map on a table, etc. turned round so that the lines and directions on it are parallel to those of the country before it, of which they are representative.

'orifice, n. An opening in something, an outlet, a mouth, sp. one letting through liquid etc.

'origin, n. The process of coming into being; that in which anything has its start or starting-point, from which it is a development, or from which it comes. [Anat.] The more fixed or greater or inner end of a muscle. [Maths.] See CARTESIAN COORDINATES, POLAR COÖRDINATES.

'ormolu, n. [Chem.] A sort of BRASS with much copper in it so that it has the look of gold, used for ornamenting wood-work such as seats, table, clocks.

'ornis, n. [Zoo.] The birds living in a certain stretch of country.

or'nithic, a. To do with birds.

ornitho-. Bird.

orni'thology, n. The science of birds. 'ornitho'logical, a. orni'thologist, n.

orni'thopter, n. ORTHOPTER.

oro-. [Zoo.] Mouth:— oro'nasal, a. [Geol.] Mountain:— or'ography, n., o'rology, n.

oro'anal, n. [Zoo.] Joining, to do with, or acting as, mouth and ANUS.

o'rogeny, oro'genesis, nn. [Geol.] The forming of mountains, sp. the stage in which their material becomes crushed together causing FAULTS and FOLDS. oro'genic, oroge'netic, aa.

oro'graphic rain. [Meteor.] The rain caused by currents of air with water in it meeting mountain slopes and being turned up into colder air.

oro'heliograph, n. Special camera taking a picture of the complete circle of view from a point.

'orohy'drography, n. The science of the relation between mountains and the draining of a country by rivers.

o'rometer, n. [Meteor.] A BAROMETER having a second scale recording how high the instrument is from sea-level. **oro'metric,** a.

'orpiment, n. [Mineral.] Natural As_2S_3, used as a colouring-substance, ranging from light yellow to orange-red.

'orrery, n. [Astron.] An apparatus of balls representative of the sun and the PLANETS, worked by wheels, for making clear their sizes, positions and motions in relation to one another.

'Orsat appa'ratus. An apparatus for the ANALYSIS of gases coming from engines, etc.

ortho-. Straight; regular; upright; right, normal; in the right relation. [Chem.] (Before the names of INORGANIC ACIDS and ANHYDRIDES) being the normal form having in it more (less) water than some other sort for which the sign META(PARA) is used.

ortho-. [Chem.] Put before names of substances produced from BENZENE as a sign that a BENZENE RING is present in the first and second positions.

'orthoce'phalic, ortho'cephalous, aa. [Craniometry] Having a SKULL with a VERTICAL INDEX of between 70 and 75, that is, not markedly long-headed or wide-headed.

orthochro'matic, a. (Of a camera-plate or FILM) giving a picture in which the light and shade are more truly representative of the degrees of light in the view itself than in the earlier plates or films, but not as truly so as in PANCHROMATIC ones, because less SENSITIVE to the colour red.

'orthoclase, n. [Mineral.] One of the commonest sorts of FELDSPAR, having in it Al and K or Na, an important part of a great number of sorts of ROCK (see p. 192).

ortho'clastic, a. [Mineral., Cryst.] Readily broken in two directions at right-angles to one another.

ortho'diagraph, n. [Med.] An apparatus for recording the size and form of structures inside the body by outlining their edges with X-RAYS.

ortho'genesis, n. [Biol.] The development of a sort of plant or animal in a fixed direction over a very long time, independently of any outside forces or conditions, as the effect of the working out of its INHERITANCE, which is clearly seen in the parallel development of different groups having a common ANCESTOR; the theory that EVOLUTION takes place only by o. and

that development is limited by fixed tendencies. **orthoge'netic,** a.

or'thognathous, a. [Craniometry] Having a FACIAL ANGLE of between 85° and 93°, that is, with the chin almost in a straight line with the upper part of the face.

'orthogneiss, n. [Geol.] GNEISS formed from IGNEOUS ROCK.

or'thogonal, a. Right-angled; (of parts) at right-angles. **o. com'ponent.** [Astron.] The force having a tendency to the pulling of a moving body out of its ORBIT.

'orthograde, a. [Zoo.] Walking with the body upright.

ortho'graphic(al), aa. To do with right angles.

'ortho-'hydrogen, n. [Chem.] A H MOLECULE in which the SPINS of the two ATOMS are parallel.

or'thology, n. INVESTIGATION of the use of language, with the purpose of making clear the limits of the senses of words, and the right way of using them. **ortho'logical,** a.

ortho'metric, a. [Cryst.] Having the AXES at right-angles to one another.

ortho'p(a)ed-ics, -ia, nn. [Med.] That branch of medical science which has to do with the putting right, by operations, physical adjustments, the use of apparatus for training muscles, etc., of parts of the body, such as arms, legs, feet, which are wrongly-formed or have become so as the effect of disease or damage on bones or JOINTS. **ortho'p(a)edic,** a. **ortho-'p(a)edist,** n.

ortho'phoria, n. [Med.] The normal condition of balance of the muscles of the two eyes, causing their lines of view to come together at whatever they are looking at. **ortho'phoric,** a.

orthop'n(o)ea, n. [Med.] A diseased condition in which breathing is possible only when the body is upright, a sign of very serious heart trouble.

ortho'praxy, n. ORTHOPAEDICS.

or'thopter, n. A flight machine supported by wings moving like a bird's.

Or'thoptera, n.pl. [Zoo.] An ORDER of EXOPTERYGOTE insects with biting mouth-parts, narrow, stiff front wings and wider, MEMBRANOUS, back wings folding longways in a straight line (when wings are present)—strong jumpers and quick runners living chiefly in or near the earth, in grass etc. **or'thopterous,** a. [Zoo.] Sp. having back wings like the O.

or'thoptic, a. [Med.] To do with, having, designed for producing, ORTHOPHORIA.

ortho'radial, a. [Zoo.] Said of the division of an OVUM in which the lines of division are SYMMETRICAL in relation to the OVUM'S AXIS.

ortho'rhombic, a. [Cryst.] Of the o. system. **o. system.** The system of CRYSTAL forms in which the crystal has 3 unequal AXES at right-angles to one another. (*See* p. 99.)

'ortho**scope**, n. [Med.] An instrument for looking at the eye, sp. the IRIS.

'orthosympa'**thetic** 'nervous 'system. [Zoo.] Name sometimes given to the SYMPA-THETIC, as opp. the PARASYMPATHETIC, NERVOUS SYSTEM.

ortho'**stichous**, a. [Biol.] Ranged in a straight line, or straight over one another, said of leaves on a stem, the FIN RAYS in certain fish, etc. ortho'**stichy** (ortho-stichies), n. Sp., [Bot.] An upright line of leaves etc. on a stem, or the straight line joining them.

or'**thotropism**, n. [Bot.] Growth straight up or down, as of most chief stems and roots. ortho'**tropic**, a.

or'**thotropous**, a. [Bot.] (Of an OVULE) having a straight NUCELLUS. or'**tho-tropy**, n.

Os, Sign for OSMIUM.

os (ora), n. [Zoo.] A mouth or opening.

os (ossa), n. [Zoo.] A bone.

'os**cheal**, a. [Zoo.] Of, to do with, the SCROTUM. osche(o)-.

'os**cillate**, v.t. Be in motion forward and back between two points; be changing regularly from a higher to a lower value and back, or from a condition to its opposite and back. 'os**cillating**, a. 'os**cill**-lating 'current. [Elec.] ALTERNATING CURRENT of a FREQUENCY of hundreds or thousands of CYCLES per second, as used in radio. os**cill'ation**, n. The act or condition of oscillating; one complete motion or change of an oscillating body etc. from one limit of its motion or value to the opposite limit. [Radio] The producing of oscillation currents in a CIRCUIT.

'os**cillator**, n. [Elec.] Any apparatus for producing oscillating current, sp. [Radio] a system of THERMIONIC VALVES and oscillating circuits. os**cill'atory**, a. oscil-latory 'circuit. [Radio] An electric CIRCUIT having an INDUCTOR and a CONDENSER joined in SERIES, causing oscillating current.

'os**cillograph**, n. [Elec.] An instrument, gen. using a CATHODE RAY TUBE, for recording in the form of a curve the wave-forms of an ALTERNATING electric current or other OSCILLATING electric force. 'oscillo-'**graphic**, a. 'oscill'**ography**, n. 'oscil-logram, n.

oscil'**lometer**, n. An instrument for measuring the angle through which a ship is rolled at sea. [Med.] An instrument for measuring the OSCILLATIONS of BLOOD-PRESSURE.

'os**cilloscope**, n. [Elec.] A CATHODE-RAY OSCILLOGRAPH.

'os**culant**, a. [Biol.] (Of a group) forming a bridge between two other groups, being in between them, in part like one, in part

like the other. [Zoo.] Fixed tightly together, gripping tightly. 'os**culate**, v.i. [Biol.] (Of a group) be o.

'os**culum** ('oscula), n. [Zoo.] Any of the openings in a sponge through which the water taken in is sent out. oscu'li-**ferous**, a.

-osis, n. [Med.] Ending used as a sign of a diseased or unnatural condition, sp. one caused by over-much, over-producing, of the substance etc. named, as in *leucocytosis, acidosis* .-otic, a. and n.

'os**mic**, a. [Chem.] Of, to do with, having in it Os, sp. Os with a high VALENCY. o. 'acid. Common name for OsO_4, a CRYSTALLINE substance giving off a bad-smelling poison gas, used mixed with water as a STAIN for fat in Biology—better named OSMIUM TETROXIDE.

'os**mious**, a. [Chem.] Having in it Os with a lower VALENCY.

osmi'**ridium**, n. [Mineral.] A very hard, white, natural ALLOY of Os and Ir with small amounts of other metals.

'os**mium**, n. Chemical ELEMENT, at. no. 76, at. wt. 190·2, sign Os, a hard blue-white or grey metal not attacked by acids, of greater weight than any other substance.

osmo-. [Psych.] Smell. [Chem.] OSMOUS. [Phys.] OSMOSIS, OSMOTIC.

'os**mograph**, n. [Phys.] An instrument for recording OSMOTIC PRESSURE.

os'**mometer**, n. [Psych.] An instrument for measuring the sense of smell. [Phys.] An instrument for measuring OSMOTIC PRESSURE.

'os**mophore**, n. ODORIPHORE.

os'**mosis**, n. [Phys.-Chem., Zoo.] The motion of a SOLVENT, gen. water, through a MEMBRANE, sp. a SEMI-PERMEABLE membrane, separating a stronger SOLUTION from one less strong or from clear water, which goes on till the solutions on the two sides of the membrane are equally strong and have the same osmotic pressure—a very important process in living things, the CELL walls of which are semi-permeable membranes. os'**motic**, a. osmotic pressure. The force of the liquid making its way through the MEMBRANE in o., which is the same as that of a gas in the same conditions.

osmo'**taxis**, n. [Biol.] TAXIS in reaction to changes in OSMOTIC PRESSURE.

os'**phradium**, n. [Zoo.] A sense ORGAN near the breathing-apparatus in certain sea MOLLUSCA, probably used for testing the amount of sand coming in in the water.

'ossa, n.pl. *See* os.

'ossein, n. COLLAGEN.

osseo-. (Of)bone substance:— '-al'**bumin**-**oid**, n.:— OSSEOUS and ...:— '-carti-'laginous, a.

'os**seous**, a. [Zoo.] Formed of, like, producing, to do with, bone.

'ossicle, n. [Zoo.] Any small bone or bone-like part, sp.:— AUDITORY OSSICLE; in some birds and REPTILES, any of the ring of small plates of bone in the outer coat of the eyeball; in ECHINODERMATA, any of the bits of hard substance bedded in the body wall; in some CRUSTACEA, any of the hard plates in the stomach. os'sicular, a.

os'siculum, n. [Zoo.] OSSICLE.

'ossifi'cation, n. [Zoo.] The forming of bone; the condition or process of becoming changed into bone. 'ossified, a. 'ossify, v.t. and i. (Make) become changed into bone, get bone formed; (make) become very hard, bone-like.

'ossiform, a. Like bone.

'osteal, a. OSSEOUS.

Os'teichthyes, n.pl. [Zoo.] The group of fishes of which, in some systems, ACTINO-PTERYGII and CHOANICHTHYES are looked on as divisions, taking in all those whose hard inner framework is made of true bone.

oste'itis, n. [Med.] INFLAMMATION of bone.

oste(o)-. Bone:— 'osteo'genesis, n., osteo-ge'netic, a., 'osteoid, a., oste'ology, n., osteo'logical, a.

'osteoar'thritis, n. [Med.] CHRONIC disease in which there is INFLAMMATION and, in time, destruction of the CARTILAGES, and the parts of the bones nearest to them, at a JOINT.

'osteoblast, n. [Zoo.] A bone-forming CELL. 'osteo'blastic, a.

'osteo'clasis, n. [Med.] The operation by which a wrongly-formed bone is broken and put together again; the destruction of bone substance by OSTEOCLASTS.

'osteoclast, n. [Zoo.] Any of the great CELLS by which the destruction of bone sub-stance is effected in the forming of the hollows in bones, or for the purpose of keeping the form of a bone from being changed in the process of growth.

'osteo'cranium, n. [Zoo.] A brain-cover formed of a structure of bones, as in the higher animals, as opp. the softer CHON-DROCRANIUM of lower animals.

'osteo'dentine, n. [Zoo.] A sort of tooth substance, forming the teeth of fish, which is very like bone in structure.

'osteo'derm, n. [Zoo.] A plate of osteo-dermis on the skin of an animal. '-is, n. Skin which has been changed or almost changed, into bone; an o.

oste'ology, n. [Zoo.] The science of bones.

oste'olysis, n. [Zoo., Med.] The destruction or death of bone-substance. osteo'lytic, a.

oste'oma, n. [Med.] A diseased growth formed of bone-substance or in a bone.

'osteoma'lacia, n. [Med.] A disease in which the bones slowly become soft as the effect of the loss of Ca, seen sp. in PREGNANT women, very infrequent in boys and girls. osteoma'lac-ial, -ic, aa.

'osteomye'litis, n. [Med.] INFLAMMATION of the soft inner substance of bones.

oste'opathy, n. [Med.] The system of work-ing against disease by the adjustment of bones, effected by rubbing, twisting, pulling, etc. parts of the body, based on the theory that any wrong position of a bone, muscle, etc. will not only be the cause of special troubles, but, by its effect on the nerves and blood, will make the system more open to attack by disease generally. 'osteopath, osteo-'pathist, nn. osteo'pathic, a.

'osteophone, n. [Med.] An apparatus fixed on the head so as to send sound waves through the bones to the inner ear, used by persons whose hearing is bad.

osteo'plastic, a. [Zoo.] Producing bone. [Med.] To do with the process of taking away diseased parts of bones, building up bones which have undergone loss with new material, etc.

osteo'porosis, n. [Med.] An increase in the spaces in bone-substance as the effect of destruction of CELLS.

'osteoscle'rosis, n. [Med.] The process by which bone-substance becomes un-naturally hard and tightly massed; the condition of having undergone o.

oste'otomy, n. [Med.] The operation of cutting a bone. 'osteotome, n. Instrument for o.

'ostiole, n. [Biol.] Small opening, sp. [Bot.] that forming the outlet for the SPORES in certain FUNGI. 'ostiolar, a. 'ostiolate, a.

'ostium (ostia), n. [Zoo.] A mouth-like opening, sp:— in sponges, any of the openings through which water is taken into the body; in ARTHROPODA, that in the wall of the heart through which the blood comes in; in MAMMALIA, that at one end or the other of the FALLOPIAN TUBE. 'ostial, a. 'ostiate, a.

'Ostwald 'system. The system of naming colours and shades by signs based on the amounts of white, black and colour which, mixed together, give the colour or shade in question.

o'talgia, n. [Med.] Pain in the ear. o'talgic, a.

'otic, n. [Zoo.] Of, to do with, near, the ear, sp. the INNER EAR.

-otic, a. and n. See -OSIS.

ot(o)-. To do with the ear: o'titis, n., o'tology, n. [Med.].

oto'conium (otoconia), n. [Zoo.] Any of the small, chalk-like grains present in the INNER EAR of higher animals, some of which are fixed to hair-like outgrowths of sense-CELLS so that their change in position when the balance of the animal is changed is straight away telegraphed to the brain.

'otocyst, n. [Zool.] In animals without back-bones, a bag-like part having to do with the sense of balance, which has in it a liquid and OTOLITHS.

'otolith, n. [Zoo.] Any of the stone-like masses or sand-like grains in an OTOCYST. which, when the animal is moving, are themselves moved and give impulses to sense-CELLS in the form of small hairs; OTOCONIUM.

'o'tology, n. [Med.] The science of the ear and its diseases. **oto'logical,** a.

'otorhino'laryng'ology, n. The branch of medical science having to do with the ear, nose and throat.

oto'sclerosis, n. [Med.] The forming of bone-like substance in and about the INNER EAR, by degrees causing loss of hearing.

'otoscope, n. [Med.] An instrument for the observation of the outer pipe of the ear and the TYMPANUM, sp. one having a rubber TUBE, one end of which is pushed into the ear under observation and the other into that of the medical man, through which sounds giving signs of a hole in the tympanum may be noted. **oto'scopic,** a. **o'toscopy,** n.

'Otto 'cycle. FOUR-STROKE CYCLE.

ounce, n. British unit of weight:— in AVOIRDUPOIS WEIGHT $=\frac{1}{16}$ of a pound or 28·3495 gm.; in TROY and APOTHECARIES' WEIGHT $=\frac{1}{12}$ of a pound or 31·10352 gm.; in liquid measure=FLUID OUNCE.

-ous, a. [Chem.] Ending put onto Latin names of ELEMENTS as a sign that in COMPOUNDS so named the element has its lower or lowest VALENCY, as in *ferrous oxide,* Fe O. (*See* -IC.)

'outbreeding, n. [Biol.] The producing of offspring by two animals of one sort which are not relations, or by animals and plants of different sorts.

'outcrop, 1v.i. [Geol.] (Of a STRATUM) come up through the top of the earth, be uncovered at some point, 2.n. An out-cropping; that part of a stratum which outcrops.

'outer ear. [Zoo.] The part of the ear of back-boned animals outside the TYMPANUM when this is not at skin level, made up of a short pipe opening to the outside, to-gether with, in higher animals, an out-growth of skin or CARTILAGE framing or covering the opening.

'outlier, n. [Geol.] An OUTCROP of a higher STRATUM which has been cut off from the rest by the weathering away of the parts between and is now completely ringed by outcrops of lower strata.

'ova, n.pl. *See* OVUM.

'oval, a. Roughly egg-like in outline. [Bot.] (Of leaf) about half as wide as long, and widest in the middle, narrowing by degrees to rounded ends.

oval'bumin, n. [Biochem.] An ALBUMIN forming the chief substance in the white of a bird's egg.

'ovarian, a. [Zoo.] Of, to do with, an OVARY. **o. 'follicle.** GRAAFIAN FOLLICLE.

'ovarian, n. [Med.] The OVARIES of pigs made into a medical substance for use in diseases of women.

ovari(o)-. OVARY, of the ovary (and . . .):— **o'vario-ab'dominal,** a., **ovari'otomy,** n. [Med.] **ova'ritis,** n. [Med.].

o'variole, n. [Zoo.] In insects, any of the pipe-like parts of which the OVARY is made up.

o'vario'testis, n. OVOTESTIS.

'ovary, o'varium, nn. [Zoo.] That part of a female animal, in back-boned animals gen. two in number, in which OVA are produced. [Bot.] The hollow part at the base of a CARPEL, or formed from two or more carpels united, in which OVULES are produced.

'ovate, a. [Bot.] Having the outline of an egg, with the wider end forming the base, said sp. of leaves. **ovate-.** In form between o. and . . .:—**'-'lanceolate,** a. O. and . . .:—**'-a'cuminate,** a.

'overcor'rect, v.t. Go further than necessary in making an adjustment to overcome an error in (an instrument, sp. a LENS), so as to give it another, gen. the opposite, error. **'-ed,** a. **'-ion,** n.

'overfold, n. [Geol.] A FOLD with one LIMB overturned so that the two are sloping more or less in the same direction, giving it roughly the form of an '*S*'.

over'lap, 1.v.t. and i. (Of a flat structure) have its edge resting on the edge of, and in part covering, another flat structure. [Geol.] (Of a STRATUM, in a group of strata formed regularly one after the other) go further than the edge of the stratum under it, so as to be resting in part on strata of an older group, produc-ing an UNCONFORMITY. 2.n. A condition of overlapping. [Geol.] The part of a stratum which overlaps the one under it onto older strata.

'overshot wheel. [Eng.] A water-wheel turned by a current of water going across the top of it.

over'step, 1.v.t. [Geol.] (Of a STRATUM) com-pletely OVERLAP an older stratum or a number of older strata. 2.n. The condi-tion of, or structure produced by, over-stepping, or that part of a stratum which oversteps others.

'over'thrust fault. [Geol.] A THRUST FAULT.

'over'tide, n. [Geog., etc.] A TIDE which takes place in addition to, and more fre-quently than, the two normal tides at a place.

'overtone, n. [Acous.] Any of the sounds of higher FREQUENCY than the FUNDA-MENTAL TONE in a complex tone.

'over'voltage, n. [Phys.-Chem.] The VOLT-AGE needed to get a gas free from an

ELECTROLYTE, less the voltage which would in theory be needed if the ELECTRODE was made of the gas.

ovi-. Egg:— '-**form**, a., o'**vigenous**, a.

ovi'capsule, n. [Zoo.] Any structure for housing eggs in the body of the mother.

'**ovicell,** n. [Zoo.] In POLYZOA, an expansion of the body-wall in which the eggs are kept.

'**oviduct,** n. [Zoo.] A pipe transporting OVA or eggs from the OVARY or body-hollow to the outside, or from the ovary to the UTERUS, etc.

'**ovine,** a. [Zoo.] To do with, like, sheep.

o'**viparous,** a. [Zoo.] Producing eggs which undergo most of their development into young outside the body of the mother, as birds. **ovi'parity, o'viparousness,** nn.

ovi'positor, n. [Zoo.] In insects and some fish ,a pipe-like and sometimes sharp part at the back by which the eggs are put down in the necessary position for development, for example in holes in the earth, inside trees, or under the skin of other animals, etc. **ovi'posit,** v.t. (Of insect) put down eggs.

'**ovisac,** n. [Zoo.] Bag-like or pocket-like OVICAPSULE.

'**ovism,** n. [Zoo.] Old theory that the egg has in it the complete EMBRYO together with the GERMS of all future offspring.

ovo-. Egg, OVUM:— -'**genesis,** n.

'**ovoid,** a. Like an egg in form, sp. [Bot.] o. and with the stem, etc. at the greater end, as some fruits.

ovo'testis, n. [Zoo.] A part in certain animals which have sex processes but not separate males and females, which is at the same time an OVARY and a TESTIS.

'**ovovi'viparous,** a. [Zoo.] Producing eggs which undergo full development, and from which the young come, inside the body of the mother, but which keep a strong cover till the process is complete. '**ovovivi'parity,** n.

ovu'lation, n. [Biol.] The forming of OVA or OVULES; the freeing of ova or ovules from an OVARY.

'**ovule,** n. [Bot.] The structure in seed plants, fixed to a CARPEL, inside which is the female CELL which after FERTILIZATION becomes a seed. [Biol.] An OVUM or seed at an early stage of development. '**ovular,** a. '**ovulate,** a. **ovu'liferous,** a. **ovu'liferous scale.** [Bot.] One of the o.-producing SCALES of a female CONE in CONIFERAE.

'**ovum** (ova), n. [Zoo.] A female sex-CELL, of great size in comparison with the male cell and without the property of motion, which has the power of development into a new animal after uniting with the male sex-cell—this name being sometimes limited to the stage before the o. is made fertile, but very commonly used for it up to the point when the EMBRYO is clearly formed.

oxolate, n. [Chem.] Any SALT or ESTER of OXALIC ACID.

ox'alic 'acid, [Chem.] An ORGANIC acid of which OXALATES are present in a great number of plants, used in DYEING and BLEACHING.

'**oxidase,** n. [Biochem.] Any of a group of ENZYMES present in plant and animal substance and helping OXIDATION.

oxi'dation, n. [Chem.] The act or process of OXIDIZING. **o.-re'duction po'tential.** [Phys.-Chem.] In ELECTRO-CHEMICAL CELLS, the POTENTIAL at which o. takes place at the ANODE and REDUCTION at the CATHODE.

'**oxide,** n. [Chem.] Any substance formed by uniting one ELEMENT with O.

'**oxidize,** 1.v.t. [Chem.] Get (a substance) united with O; take ELECTRONS from (an ATOM or ION), and so give (an ELEMENT) a higher POSITIVE VALENCY. 2.v.i. [Chem.] Become oxidized in any sense. '**oxidizing,** a. Causing OXIDATION. '**oxidant,** a., n.

ox'onium, n. [Chem.] The UNIVALENT POSITIVE ION H_3O^+

oxy-. [Biol.] Sharp or pointed. [Chem.] OXYGEN; having an O ATOM united to two different atoms.

oxya'cetylene flame. The flame produced by C_2H_2 burning in O. '**oxya'cetylene 'blowpipe** or **torch.** An instrument for producing an oxyacetylene flame, used in WELDING (**o. 'welding**).

oxy'chromatin, n. [Biol.] A form of CHROMATIN not STAINING deeply and having in it little NUCLEIC ACID.

oxy'chloride, n. [Chem.] Substance formed of O and Cl united with a given ELEMENT.

'**oxygen,** n. Chemical ELEMENT, at. no. 8, at. wt. 16·0, sign O, a gas without colour or smell uniting with most other elements, necessary for the process of burning and for the breathing of most living things— the commonest of all the elements, forming about $\frac{1}{5}$ of the earth's ATMOSPHERE.

oxy'genotaxis, oxy'taxis, nn. [Biol.] TAXIS in reaction to O. **oxy(geno)-'tactic,** a.

'**oxyhaemo'globin,** n. [Biochem.] HAEMOGLOBIN united with O.

'**oxy-'hydrogen 'blowpipe.** An instrument like the OXYACETYLENE BLOWPIPE but burning mixed H and O and not producing quite as high a degree of heat, used in WELDING.

oxy'luminescence, n. [Phys.-Chem.] LUMINESCENCE caused by OXIDATION.

o'**xyntic,** a. [Biol.] Producing acid. **o. cells.** [Zoo.] CELLS in the inner coat of the stomach by which HCl is produced.

'**oxy-phile, -'philic,** aa. [Biol.] Readily coloured by acid STAINS.

oxy'tocin, n. [Zoo.] A HORMONE produced by the PITUITARY GLAND and helping the motion of the UTERUS in the process of giving birth. **oxy′tocic**, a.

oxy′tropism, n. [Biol.] TROPISM in reaction to, and gen. in the direction of, O.

oz. = ounce.

o′zokerite, n. [Mineral.] A form of PARAFFIN wax present in the earth.

o′zone, n. [Chem.] A form of O of which the MOLECULE is O_3, present in small amounts in the upper air, made chiefly by the DISCHARGE of ELECTRICITY into O or air, used in AIR-CONDITIONING, etc. **′ozonizer**, n. Apparatus for making o.

P, Sign for: [Chem.] PHOSPHORUS; [Biol.] PARENTAL GENERATION.

p- = PARA- [Chem.].

π, the Greek letter 'pi', used as a sign of some special property in physics and chemistry. [Geom.] Sign for the RATIO of the CIRCUMFERENCE of any circle to its DIAMETER, = 3·14159, or, roughly $\frac{22}{7}$. **π ′meson**. [Phys.] *See* PI-MESON.

Pa, Sign for PROTOACTINIUM.

pace maker. [Zoo., Med.] In back-boned animals, that part of the heart from which the impulse starting the strong CONTRACTION of the heart muscles is sent out at every BEAT.

pachy-. [Biol., Med.] Thick.

′pachyderm, n., a. [Zoo.] (Animal) having a very thick skin. **pachy′derm(at)ous**, aa. **pachy′dermia**, n. [Med.] Condition in which the skin becomes unnormally thick. **′pachy′dermatocele**, n. [Med.] A soft TUMOUR hanging over the face or ears.

pachy′nema, n. PACHYTENE STAGE.

′pachytene stage. [Biol.] The stage in MEIOSIS after the uniting of the CHROMOSOMES in twos, at which the threads become thicker and shorter.

Pa′cinian ′bodies or **corpuscles**. [Zoo.] In back-boned animals, thickly-covered expansions forming the endings of certain sense-nerves, as in the skin of the feet and hands.

′packing ef′fect. [Phys., Chem.] MASS DEFECT.

′packing ′fraction. [Phys., Chem.] The RATIO of the MASS DEFECT of an ATOM to its MASS NUMBER, which gives a sign of the STABILITY of the NUCLEUS.

pad, n. [Zoo.] The cushion-like part formed of thick skin on the under side of the foot or toe of some animals. [Med.] A soft cushion-like dressing for supporting a part or keeping a wound well-covered, etc.

′paddle, n. [Zoo.] FLIPPER.

p(a)ed(o)-. Boy; baby; young person or animal.

′p(a)ederasty, n. [Med.] Sex-act between a man and a boy. **′p(a)ederast**, n. Man given to p. **p(a)ede′rastic**, a.

′p(a)edi′atric, a. [Med.] To do with paediatrics. **′-s**, n.pl. That branch of medical science having to do with the care and diseases of babies and young persons. **′p(a)edia′trician**, **′p(a)ediatrist**, nn.

′p(a)edo′genesis, n. [Zoo.] The producing of offspring without a sex-process by an animal before its sex-development is complete, for example, in the LARVA stage.

pair, n. Two things or parts of like form and purpose which go together, sp. balancing one another in position. as the ears, legs, etc.[Zoo.] A male and female animal which have come together for MATING. **p. for′mation**. [Phys.] The forming of an ELECTRON and a POSITRON when high-ENERGY PHOTONS come against a solid or gas. **-ed**, a. Forming a p., ranged in pp. **′-ing**, n. (Of two animals or moving structures such as CHROMOSOMES) the act of coming together, becoming united, sp. SYNAPSIS.

′pal(a)e(o)-. [Anthrop., Geol., etc.] Old, to do with very early stages in the earth's history or the development of living things: **′pal(a)eo′ethnic**, a. **′pal(a)eoge′ography**, n.

Pal(a)e′arctic, a. Of, in, to do with, the P. region. **P. ′region**. A division of the earth for purposes of Zoology, taking in Europe, North Asia, and North Africa.

′pal(a)eo′botany, n. The science of FOSSIL plants. **′pal(a)eobo′tanical**, a. **′pal(a)eo-′botanist**, n.

′Pal(a)eocene, a., n. [Geol.] (Of) the earliest PERIOD of the TERTIARY (*see* p. 558).

′pal(a)eocli′matic, a. To do with weather conditions on the earth in times before the existence of man.

′pal(a)eo′cranium, n. [Zoo.] An early form of bone-structure of the head, or an early stage in its development.

′pal(a)eoden′drology, n. The science of FOSSIL trees.

′pal(a)eoen′cephalon, n. [Zoo.] The earliest form of brain in back-boned animals.

′Pal(a)eogene, a., n. (Of) the earlier part of the TERTIARY ERA, up to the end of the OLIGOCENE PERIOD (*see* p. 558).

′pal(a)eoge′netic, a. [Zoo.] Said of qualities or structures handed down unchanged from the early form of an animal to its present-day representatives, seen chiefly in the EMBRYO.

′pal(a)eo′lithic, a., n. [Anthrop., etc.] (Of, to do with, being) the time in man's history between the EOLITHIC and the NEOLITHIC, about the middle of the PLEISTOCENE PERIOD, when stone instruments were in use but farming had not been started.

'pal(a)eon'tology, n. The science of the living things present on the earth in times long past and their relation to later forms, based on the knowledge got from FOSSILS. 'pal(a)eonto'logic(al), aa. 'pal(a)-eon'tologist, n.

'pal(a)eovol'canic, a. [Geol.] Of, to do with, or being, IGNEOUS ROCKS formed before the TERTIARY PERIOD.

'Pal(a)eo'zoic, a. [Geol.] Of, to do with, the P. era. P. 'era. The great division of the earth's history from the first signs of living things through the development of fish to that of land-and-water animals and land plants of the earliest sort (see p. 559).

'pal(a)eozo'ology, n. The science of FOSSIL animals.

'palama, n. [Zoo.] The MEMBRANE joining the toes of water birds.

'palatal, 1.a. [Zoo., Phonet.] To do with the PALATE. 2.n. [Phonet.] Sound made with the front part of the tongue near the PALATE. pa'latalize, 'palatize, vv.t. [Phonet.] Give a PALATAL sound to (a letter) by putting the tongue to or near the PALATE in saying it.

'palate, n. [Zoo.] The roof of the mouth in back-boned animals; the EPIPHARYNX of an insect. [Bot.] That part of the lower lip of a PERSONATE COROLLA by which the opening into the throat of the flower is shut. 'palatine, 1.a. [Zoo.] To do with the p. 2.n. Bone forming part of the p. of back-boned animals. 'palato-. [Zoo.] (Of) the p. (and …):— 'palato-'nasal, a. [Phonet.] Palatal (and …):— 'palato-'dental, a.

'palatogram, n. [Phonet.] Picture of the points where the tongue comes against the PALATE in making different sounds.

pale, 'palet or 'palea (paleae), nn. [Bot.] The small, thin, SCALE-like inner leaf forming, together with the flowering GLUME, the covering of a grass flower; a like thin, dry scale on other plants. pale'aceous, a. [Bot.] Having pp. or like a p., thin and dry and of little weight.

pale(o)-. PALAE(o)-.

palin'genesis, n. [Zoo.] The handing down of parts and qualities unchanged from the earliest form of any sort of animal to all later ones, so that these undergo in themselves in short form the same process of development which the sort has undergone in its history up to that point. [Geol.] The changing of ROCK back into liquid as the effect of heat inside the earth, and the forming of new rock from it. 'palinge-'netic, a. To do with p., handed down from earlier forms.

pali'sade cell. [Bot.] Any of the long pipe-like CELLS placed at right-angles to the face of a leaf and forming the palisade layer. pali'sade layer. A stretch of p. cc. under the top skin of a leaf having a special connection with PHOTOSYNTHESIS. pali'sade tissue or parenchyma. The material formed of p. cc.

pal'ladium, n. Chemical ELEMENT, at. no. 46, at. wt. 106·7, sign Pd, a silver-white metal looking like Pt, with which it is frequently united.

'pallaes'thesia, n. [Med.] The SENSITIVITY of bone to VIBRATION.

'pallet, n. [Zoo.] The hard plate on a SIPHON in some BIVALVE MOLLUSCS.

'pallium, n. [Zoo.] In MOLLUSCA or BRACHIO-PODA, the MANTLE; in back-boned animals, the wall of the upper part of the brain. [Meteor.] An unbroken stretch of cloud. 'pallial, a. 'palliate, a. pallio-.

palm, n. [Zoo.] The somewhat hollow under-side of the hand, between the fingers and the base, or the like part of an animal's front foot. 'palmar, a.

'palmate(d), aa. [Bot.] Having a number of divisions stretching out from a middle part, like the fingers of a hand, said sp. of leaves (see picture p. 223). [Zoo.] Having the toes joined by skin, as most water-birds; in form somewhat like a hand with fingers outstretched, as certain horns. 'palmately, adv.

pal'matifid, a. [Bot.] (Of leaves) PALMATE, with the divisions narrow or pointed and starting about half-way to the base.

pal'matisect, a. [Bot.] Of leaf, with deep divisions almost to the base, giving a PALMATE effect (see picture p.

pal'mitic 'acid. [Chem.] $C_{15}H_{31}.COOH$, a wax-like FATTY ACID present in the form of GLYCERIDES in a great number of plant and animal fats.

palp, n. PALPUS.

'palpable, a. Which may be experienced by touch or PALPATED.

pal'pate, v.t. [Med.] Put the hand on (a part of the body) to get knowledge of its condition by touch, feeling it with the fingers. pal'pation, n.

'palpi-fer, -ger, nn. [Zoo.] That part of the lower lip or other mouth-part supporting the PALPI in insects.

palpi'tation, n. [Med.] A conscious feeling of the heart coming violently against the chest wall, gen. at an unnormally quick rate, caused by overtaxing one's physical force, by some violent shock or reaction, or by disease. 'palpitate, v.i. (Of heart) be pumping with very quick, strong rhythm, or jumping irregularly, causing p.

'palpus, (palpi), n. [Zoo.] In insects and CRUSTACEA, any of the JOINTED feelers, sometimes used for other purposes in addition to touch, on or near the mouth-parts; in some worms, one or the other of two small sense-structures on the head; in some MOLLUSCS, any of 4 leaf-like outgrowths at the sides of the mouth, used for making currents to send the food in. 'palpal, a. 'palpate, a. 'palpiform, a.

'palsy, n. PARALYSIS.

pa'ludal, a. Of, to do with, low, wet places or stretches of not very deep water covering low land.

palu'dicolous, a. [Biol.] Living in, having growth in, PALUDAL places.

'paludism, n. [Med.] The condition of having MALARIA in the system, of being given to attacks of the disease from time to time.

'paludous, a. To do with, causing, p.

'paludose, a. [Bot.] PALUDICOLOUS.

pan-. To do with all or every, complete(ly), general: '-hyste'rectomy, n. [Med.].

panchro'matic, a. (Of camera FILM, etc.) giving a reaction to light of all colours so as to make an uncoloured picture which is representative of the different degrees of light in the differently coloured parts of the view.

'pancreas, n. [Zoo.] A great GLAND present in higher back-boned animals near the DUODENUM into which it sends the pancreatic juice and which is, in addition, the producer, through special groups of CELLS, of INSULIN for sending into the blood. pancre'atic, a. pancre'atic duct. The opening through which the pancreatic juice is sent into the DUODENUM. pancre'atic juice. The substance produced by the p. and sent into the DUODENUM for the purpose of helping digestion, a clear ALKALINE liquid having in it a number of ENZYMES for acting on different sorts of food substance. pan-'creatin, n. Any ENZYME of the pancreatic juice or a group of these, got from animals and used medically as a help to digestion.

pan'demic, n., a. [Med.] (Disease) attacking a very great number of persons over a great stretch of country, an EPIDEMIC of very wide distribution.

pan'duriform, a. pan'durate, a. [Bot.] (Of leaf) OBOVATE with the sides hollowed in (see picture p. 223).

pan'gamic, a. [Zoo.] (Of MATING, or the animals taking part in it) uncontrolled by any form of selection.

'pangen, n. [Biol.] One of the units of which PROTOPLASM is said to be made up in some theories.

pan'genesis, n. [Biol.] The theory that PANGENS from all parts of the body make their way to and become part of the GERM CELLS, put forward as a way of accounting for the handing on of qualities to offspring. pange'netic, a.

'panicle, n. [Bot.] A flowering-structure in which the flowers are produced on branches of branches, sp. a RACEME of which the side branches are in turn racemes (see picture p. 199). pa'niculate, 'panicled, aa.

pa'nidio'morphic, a. [Geol.] (Of ROCK made up of different substances) with all its substances in the form of complete and well-formed CRYSTALS.

pan'mixia, n. [Zoo.] The producing of offspring without the operation of NATURAL SELECTION, said to take place when certain parts or qualities are no longer needed and to have as its outcome their loss by degrees.

'pannus, n. [Med.] (The forming of) a network of blood-vessels covering part of the CORNEA in certain eye diseases.

pan'optic, a. Giving a general view over all parts of any field, '-on, n. An instrument made up of a MICROSCOPE and a TELESCOPE; name given to the Basic 'Word Wheel', an apparatus for teaching how to put words together into statements in English.

'panphoto'metric, a. [Bot.] (Of leaves) so placed and formed as to get as little strong sunlight falling straight on them as possible, that is, gen., narrow and upright.

pan'psychism, n. The theory that all material things have some non-material part or force in them, and that every physical motion is to some degree at the same time a mind process.

pan'sporoblast, n. [Zoo.] In some SPOROZOA, a CELL-complex producing SPORES and SPOROBLASTS.

'pantachromism, 'pantochromism, nn. [Chem.] The property seen in certain SALTS of having two or more differently-coloured forms.

panto-. PAN-: -'phobia, n. [Med.].

'pantograph, n. An instrument for copying maps, pictures, etc. to any desired scale. panto'graphic, a.

'pantothenic acid. [Biochem.] A substance of the VITAMIN B complex.

'papier-'mâché, n. A material made of paper crushed up with some sticky substance, or pasted thickly together, forming a hard substance like thin wood, etc.

pa'pilio'naceous, a. [Bot.] (Of a flower, or a plant having such a flower) in form somewhat like a great-winged insect, having 5 PETALS, one, much the greatest, upright at the back, two united into a boat-like point at the front and base of this, and the other two forming small wings at the sides.

pa'pilla (pa'pillae), n. [Zoo.] MAMMILLA. [Biol.] Any very small, rounded or pointed outgrowth, sp.:— round the root of a feather, hair, or tooth; of those going from the DERMIS into the EPIDERMIS in MAMMALS, freq. an instrument of touch; of those on the tongue of back-boned animals, supporting the TASTE-BUDS; at the inner angle of the eye in higher animals; at the base of a GLANDULAR hair on a flower or leaf. pa'pillar(y), aa. 'papillate, a. papill'iferous, a. pa'pilliform, a. 'papillose, a.

papill'oma, n. [Med.] Hard or soft growth on skin or MUCOUS MEMBRANE caused by over-growth of PAPILLAE.

'pappus, n. [Bot.] Circle or group of hairs or SCALES topping the fruit of certain seed plants, causing the seed to be readily transported by the wind. papp'iferous, a. 'pappose, a.

'papula (papulae), n. [Zoo.] Any of the small, finger-like, thin-walled outgrowths of the body-wall forming the breathing-apparatus of ECHINODERMATA. [Med.] PAPULE.

'papule, n. [Med.] Small solid PAPILLA on the skin, caused by some unhealthy condition. 'papular, a. 'papulose, 'papulous, aa.

papy'raceous, a. [Bot.] Thin, dry, paper-like.

'para-. [Biol., Med.] At the side of, near:— -'central, a., -'mastoid, a.; (of diseases) not the true or full form but very like it:— -'typhoid, n.; second, smaller, acting as an addition:— '-fla'gellum, n. [Chem.] Being some special form of the substance named, or having some other important relation to it, for example, an ISOMER or a POLYMER; having in it more water-MOLECULES than certain other forms of the same substance for which the sign 'ORTHO-' or 'META-' may be used.

'para-'an(a)es'thesia, n. [Med.] ANAESTHESIA of the two sides of the lower half of the body.

para'basal appa'ratus. [Zoo.] In certain MASTIGOPHORA, a structure round the base of the FLAGELLA.

para'basal body. [Zoo.] In MASTIGOPHORA, a CELL-body having a connection with the BLEPHAROPLAST. 'parabi'osis, n. [Zoo.] The condition of the physical joining of two animals seen naturally in SIAMESE TWINS; the producing of this condition in two animals for science purposes by so joining their bodies that their two blood systems become one; the form of connection seen among certain ants, in which two or more sorts are living together but keep their offspring separate. 'parabi'otic, a.

par'abola, n. [Geom.] The CONIC SECTION got by cutting a CONE by a plane parallel to the line of its side, or a curve of this form. para'bolic, a. To do with, in the form of, a p. [Bot.] Having a wide base curving by degrees to a rounded end. para'bolic 'mirror. A looking-glass whose SURFACE is a PARABOLOID, used in a TELESCOPE to make parallel rays of

light come to a FOCUS. para'bolic re'flector. An instrument of like structure to a parabolic mirror for REFLECTING radio waves from a star etc. onto an AERIAL, used in RADIO TELESCOPES.

par'aboloid, n. [Geom.] The SURFACE produced by turning a PARABOLA about its AXIS, p. of revo'lution. P.

para'bronchi, n.pl. [Zoo.] The smaller branches of the breathing-pipes of birds, with their endings in the LUNG substance.

para'casein, n. [Chem.] The solid INSOLUBLE form of CASEIN produced when milk COAGULATES and from which cheese is made.

paracen'tesis, n. [Med.] The process of putting a hollow needle through the wall of a body-hollow to take out liquid.

'parachor, n. [Chem.] A number giving the VOLUME of a MOLECULE of a liquid in relation to the SURFACE TENSION, equal to the surface tension × the MOLECULAR WEIGHT, DIVIDED by the DENSITY of the liquid MINUS the density of its gas, and based on certain fixed values for every ATOM of those making up the molecule and every VALENCY BOND uniting them, so giving a key to the make-up and structure of the molecules of liquids.

para'chordal, n., a. [Zoo.] (One or the other of two flat, curved, opposite plates of CARTILAGE in the head of an EMBRYO) at the side of the NOTOCHORD.

'parachute, n. [Bot.] Seed with PAPPUS or like apparatus for helping its distribution by the wind.

par'acme, n. [Zoo.] The time in the history of an animal or sort when the point of highest development is past and it is moving to death or destruction.

'paracoele, n. [Zoo.] In back-boned animals the inner hollow of a CEREBRAL HEMISPHERE.

'paracone, n. [Zoo.] The outer front CUSP of an upper MOLAR tooth.

para'conid, n. [Zoo.] The outer front CUSP of a lower MOLAR tooth.

'paraco'rolla, n. [Bot.] Any outgrowth, such as a CORONA, forming an addition to a COROLLA.

para'cusi-s, -a, nn. [Med.] Anything wrong with the hearing.

par(a)es'thesi-a, -s, nn. [Med.] Any unnormal feeling in connection with the skin, for example a sense as of ants walking over it, wool brushing against it, etc.

'paraffin(e), n. [Chem.] Any HYDROCARBON of the general form C_nH_{2n+2}. p. oil. Any of a number of oils having pp. in them and burned for heating and lighting, got from PETROLEUM, or in the DISTILLATION of wood, coal etc., in England the name being limited to KEROSENE. p. 'section. [Biol.] A SECTION of a TISSUE which has been bedded in p. wax so as to keep it together for cutting and observation. **p. wax.** Wax-like substance, without colour, smell, or taste, made up of mixed HYDRO-CARBONS, chiefly pp., and sometimes named 'solid p.', got from PETROLEUM etc.

'**paraform, 'paraform'aldehyde,** nn. [Chem.] A solid white substance, $(H.CHO)_2$, produced from FORMALDEHYDE by POLYMERIZATION, used as a DISINFEC-TANT.

para'ganglion (paraganglia), n. [Zoo.] In higher back-boned animals any of a number of small masses having a structure like that of the chief part of the SUPRARENAL GLAND, present in the body, sp. near the AORTA, and probably producing ADRENALIN.

para'gaster, n. [Zoo.] The middle hollow in a SPONGE. **para'gastric,** a. **para'gastric ca'nals.** The pipes opening into the p.

para'genesis, 'parage'nesia, nn. [Biol.] Condition in which HYBRIDS have the power of producing offspring by uniting with father's or mother's SPECIES, but not with one another. [Geol.] The forming of MINERALS touching one another so that they have an effect on one another's development; the order of the development of minerals present together in ROCKS. '**parage'netic,** a. '**parage'netic twins.** TWIN CRYSTALS, the twin structure of which was present from the start of their development.

para'geusia, n. [Med.] An unnormal condition of the sense of taste.

para'globulin, n. [Zoo.] Any of the GLOBU-LINS present in blood-SERUM and other body liquids.

para'glossa, n. [Zoo.] One or the other of two small structures on the opposite sides of the LIGULA of insects.

para'gnatha, n.pl. [Zoo.] Two structures on the MAXILLA of certain ARTHROPODA.

para'gnathous, a. [Zoo.] Having the two JAWS equally long, meeting at the end, as certain birds.

para'gneiss, n. [Geol.] Sort of ROCK produced by METAMORPHISM acting on a SEDIMENTARY rock.

'**paragoge,** n. [Philol.] The addition of a sound to the end of a word, in the normal process of the development of the language or by chance. **para'gogic(al),** aa.

pa'ragonite, n. [Mineral.] A MICA having in it Na in place of K.

'**para'graphia,** n. [Med.] A condition in which the wrong letters or words are used in writing, as the effect of some mind disease or damage to the brain.

paraheli'otropism, n. [Bot.] The tendency of leaves to put themselves in a position parallel to the sun's rays by turning or curving, so as not to get overmuch light.

para'hormone, n. [Zoo.] Any substance

having effects like a HORMONE but not produced for this purpose by a special part of the body, being simply the outcome of its general processes.

'**parahy'pophysis,** n. [Zoo.] A structure under the PITUITARY GLAND which has come down from the past but no longer has any purpose and does not undergo complete development.

'**parallax,** n. [Phys., Astron.) A seeming change in the position of anything in relation to another thing or to the general view when seen from different places, named in astronomy **diurnal** or **geocentric p.** when the seeming change is caused by the turning of the earth on its AXIS, and **annual, stellar,** or **heliocentric p.** when it is caused by the motion of the earth round the sun. '**parall'actic,** a. **parallactic angle.** [Astron.] The angle between the DECLINATION CIRCLE and the VERTICAL CIRCLE going through a star. **parall'actic 'motion.** [Astron.] That part of the recorded motion of a star which is accounted for by the motion of the point of observation as part of the SOLAR SYSTEM. **parall'actic 'orbit.** [Astron.] The curve in which a star seems to move round every year because of the earth's motion round the sun.

'**parallel,** n. [Elec.] The form of connection in an electric system, such as a system of CELLS or other units, in which all the POSITIVE ELECTRODES, etc. are joined to one CONDUCTOR and all the NEGATIVE ones to another, when the units are said to be *in p.* [Geog.] Any of the circles round the earth p. to the EQUATOR, or the lines on a map representative of those circles, at fixed and equal distances from one another, in relation to which LATI-TUDE is measured (freq. **p. of latitude**).

'**paralleli'nervate,** a. PARALLEL-VEINED.

'**parallelism,** n. Quality or condition of being parallel, in the physical sense or, sp., in the sense of being like, taking the same line of development, pointing in the same direction, etc.

para'llelodrome, a. PARALLEL-VEINED.

para'llelogram, n. [Geom.] A 4-sided plane form with opposite sides parallel. **p. law.** The rule that if a p. is formed of which two meeting sides are representative in direction and amount of two forces acting at the same point, the line from the angle of meeting to the opposite angle of the p. will be representative in direction and amount of the force produced by the two forces acting together. **p. of forces.** The p. used in agreement with the p. law for getting the measure and direction of the force produced by two separate forces acting together at the same point.

'**parallel pro'jection.** PROJECTION of the

form of a body onto a flat SURFACE by
taking parallel lines from the points of
the body.

'parallel-veined, a. [Bot.] (Of a leaf) with
VEINS running roughly parallel from base
to end or at least for some part of the way.

'parallel ve'nation. [Bot.] Of a leaf, the
condition of being parallel-veined.

pa'ralysis, n. [Med.] Loss of power of reaction, motion, or feeling in any part of
body. **p. 'agitans.** A disease of the CENTRAL
NERVOUS SYSTEM marked by the uncontrolled shaking of parts of the body, a
feeble condition of the muscles, a somewhat bent position, and, in the later
stages, a tendency for the walk to get out
of control and become a run, commonest
in older persons. **para'lytic,** 1.a., 2.n.
Paralytic person. **'para'lyzant,** n., a.
(Substance, etc.). causing p. **'paralyse,**
v.t. Make undergo p. **'paralysed,** a.

'paramag'netic, a. [Phys.] (Of substances)
having a MAGNETIC PERMEABILITY a little
greater than 1. **para'magnet,** n. A p.
substance or thing. **'para'magnetism,** n.
The properties seen in a paramagnet
when put into a MAGNETIC FIELD.

para'metrium, n. [Zoo.] The mass of FIBROUS
TISSUE round the UTERUS, sp. near the
narrow part.

par'ameter, n. [Maths.] A VARIABLE which
is kept fixed for the purpose of getting
knowledge of the effects of other vari-
ables; a variable of which two other vari-
ables are FUNCTIONS, used in making
clear their relation to one another. **para-
'metric,** a. **para'metric e'quations.** EQUA-
TIONS making clear the relation of x to y
by the use of a p. (in the second sense) t,
as $x=at$ and $y=bt$.

param'nesia, n. [Med.] Unnormal behaviour
of the memory, as the loss of the memory
of the sense of words, or the feeling of
having been to a place before on going
there for the first time.

Para'm(o)ecium, n. [Zoo.] A common GENUS
of CILIOPHORA in form somewhat like
the under-part of a shoe, with the body
completely covered with CILIA. **para-
'me(o)cium** (param(o)ecia). An animal of
the GENUS P.

para'morphism, n. [Geol.] The changing of
one sort of MINERAL into another by a
change in the structure of the MOLECULE,
without any change in its chemical
substance. **'paramorph,** n. A MINERAL
which has the property of undergoing p.

para'nephric, a. [Zoo.] At the side of the
KIDNEY.

para'nephros, n. SUPRARENAL GLAND.

para'noia, n. [Med.] A diseased condition of
the mind marked by the building up of a
completely false picture of one's relations
to others (for example, the fixed idea that
one is being regularly wronged), without

loss of the power of reasoned thought or
of normal behaviour generally. **para'-
'noic,** 1.a., 2.n. Person having p. **'paranoid,** a. Of, to do with, or like p. or a
paranoiac. **'paranoid schizo'phrenia.** A
form of SCHIZOPHRENIA having some of
the marks of p. but with less system in
one's false ideas and greater loss of reason
and control. **'paranoid state.** A condition
in which a person has a tendency to p. but
is not completely in the grip of it.

para'nucleus, n. [Biol.] A second NUCLEUS
or a nucleus-like body in a CELL.

para'phasia, n. [Med.] Condition in which a
person in talking makes use of the wrong
words, caused by some damage to the
brain or some mind trouble. **para-
'phasic,** a.

para'phrenia, n. [Med.] Mind-disease, sp.
SCHIZOPHRENIA of the sort in which by
degrees the person's belief that he is great
overcomes all other ideas, ending in a
complete loss of reason.

pa'raphysis (paraphyses), n. [Bot.] Any of
the non-fertile thread-like outgrowths
commonly seen among the fertile parts
of a great number of CRYPTOGRAMS. [Zoo.]
In a great number of back-boned animals,
a hollow outgrowth of the roof of the
brain in front of the PINEAL GLAND.
para'physate, a.

'parapi'neal 'body. [Zoo.] In CYCLOSTO-
MATA, LACERTILIA and some fish, an outgrowth in front of the PINEAL BODY which
in some forms has the structure of an eye.

para'plegia, n. [Med.] PARALYSIS of the legs
and lower half of the body.

para'podium (parapodia), n. [Zoo.] In a
number of worms, one or the other of two
short outgrowths on every ring of the
body, used as feet and sometimes as
feelers or in connection with breathing;
in some GASTROPODS, one or the other of
two outgrowths on opposite sides of the
foot, making it of use in swimming.

para'pophysis (parapophyses), in. [Zoo.]
A TRANSVERSE PROCESS of the sort seen
in lower back-boned animals, coming
from the lower part of the CENTRUM

par'apter-on, -um, nn. [Zoo.] A small hard
plate on the THORAX of an insect, for
example, where the wing is joined to the
body; a group of small feathers at the
JOINT of the wing in birds.

para'quadrate (bone), n. [Zoo.] SQUAMOSAL.

'parase'lene (paraselenae), n.[Meteor.] A ball
of feeble light, freq. one of a number, seen
near the moon, and looking like another
moon, a part of its ice HALO which in some
conditions becomes brighter than the rest.

'parasite, n. [Biol.] An animal or plant living,
fixed or moving about, on, or inside, or
with, another living thing and getting
food from its body, freq. causing its
death in time, but sometimes doing little

damage, though never any good. **para-'sitic(al)**, aa. **parasitical 'current**. [Elec.] Undesired current in an electric instrument causing trouble in use. **'parasitism,** n. [Biol.] The condition of living as a p. [Med.] Diseased condition, sp. of the skin, caused by pp. **parasi'tology,** n. The science of pp., sp. from the point of view of overcoming them in plants, animals, and man. **parasi'tosis,** n. [Med.] The condition of having pp. on or in the body.

para'sphenoid (bone), [Zoo.] In some lower back-boned animals, a bone forming the floor of the brain-cover.

'parasympa'thetic, a. [Zoo.] The name given to that part of the AUTONOMIC NERVOUS SYSTEM starting in the brain and the lower part of the back-bone.

'parasy'napsis, para'syndesis, nn. [Biol.] The uniting of like CHROMOSOMES side by side in MEIOSIS, opp. TELOSYNAPSIS.

pa'rately, n. [Biol.] The development of seemingly like parts by plants or animals having no family relation to one another.

para'thormone, n. [Biochem.] The HORMONE produced by the PARATHYROID GLAND, controlling the amount of Ca in the blood, and without which the system becomes poisoned and death takes place.

para'thyroid, n. [Zoo.] Any of a number of, gen. 4, small ENDOCRINE GLANDS in or near the THYROID, producing PARATHORMONE.

para'tonic, a. [Bot.] (Of plant motions) caused by outside STIMULI.

para'trophic, a. [Biol.] Completely PARASITIC.

'paratype, n. [Biol.] An example of a new SPECIES of animal or plant put forward with the HOLOTYPE as representative to a somewhat less degree.

para'typhoid, n. [Med.] Disease having much in common with TYPHOID but less serious.

par'axial, 1.a. [Zoo.] By the side of. near to, the AXIS of the body. [Optics] Said of the space near the axis of an OPTICAL system, or of a ray parallel to such an axis. 2.n. P. ray.

Para'zoa, n.pl. [Zoo.] A SUB-KINGDOM of animals between PROTOZOA and METAZOA in their degree of development, having a number of CELLS but with little organization among them, no separate parts, and only one group of representatives, the sponges. **para'zoan,** a., n.

paren'chyma, n. [Bot.] A sort of TISSUE made up of thin-walled CELLS with rounded ends, with air-spaces between them, forming the chief substance of plant leaves, fruit, the middle part of stems, etc. [Zoo.] The chief substance of an ORGAN, sp. a GLAND, as against its framework etc.; soft sponge-like tissue with spaces full of liquid or jelly-like substance forming the greater part of the body in PLATYHELMINTHES. **paren-'chymal,** a., **paren'chymatous,** a.

'parent, n. [Biol.] A father or mother, or any plant, animal, or CELL etc. by which another is produced in any way. **pa'rental,** a. **pa'rental gene'ration**. In MENDEL's THEORY of INHERITANCE, the first GENERATION by which HYBRIDS are produced, taken as the starting-point in working out the inheritance of later generations by Mendel's law.

par'enteral, a. [Zoo.] Placed or taking place outside the INTESTINES. [Med.] Said of the putting of medical substances into the system in any way other than through the digestion.

pa'resis, n. [Med.] Incomplete PARALYSIS; GENERAL PARALYSIS of the INSANE (freq. **general p.**). **pa'retic,** a.

par'focal, a. [Optics] (Of different EYE-PIECES used with the same instrument) having the lower FOCAL points all in same plane.

par'helion (parhelia), n. [Meteor.] A ball of bright light, freq. one of a number, seen near the sun and looking like another sun, an effect produced by its ice HALO in certain conditions.

pari'drosis, n. [Med.] Condition in which the SWEAT-producing system is out of order.

pa'rietal, 1.a. [Zoo.] To do with or forming part of the wall of a structure; to do with, or near, the p. bones. [Bot.] (Of PLACENTA or OVULES) fixed to or near to the wall round the OVARY, not in the middle. 2.n. A p. bone. **p. bone**. One or the other of two MEMBRANE BONES forming the top and sides of the head between the FRONTALS and the OCCIPITALS in back-boned animals. **p. cell**. [Zoo.] Any of the great acid-producing CELLS in the inner wall of the stomach in back-boned animals. **p. 'layer**. [Zoo.] The part of the PERITONEUM or PLEURA covering the body wall, as opp. the part going round what is inside. **p. lobe**. [Zoo.] The middle division of a CEREBRAL HEMISPHERE.

pari'pinnate, a. [Bot.] (Of leaf) PINNATE without a leaf at the point of the branch, that is, with an even number of small leaves.

'parity, n. The condition of being level or equal. [Med.] The condition or fact of having given birth to offspring.

Parke's process. The process of getting silver away from lead by the addition of zinc to the liquid mixed metal, zinc and silver forming a solid which becomes separated from the lead.

'Parkinson's dis'ease. PARALYSIS AGITANS. **'Parkinsonism,** n. P. d.

paro'nychia, n. [Med.] An INFLAMMATION at the base or side of, or under, a finger-nail. **paro'nychiac,** a.

par'osteal, a. [Med.] Of, to do with, PAR-OSTOSIS; of ‚in, the substance on the outside of the PERIOSTEUM.

'parost(e)'osis, n. [Med.] The forming of bone in an unnormal place or outside the PERIOSTEUM.

pa'rotic, a. [Zoo.] Near the ear. **p. 'process.** In some fish and REPTILES, an outgrowth of bone where a bone of the ear is united to another bone of the head.

pa'rotid, a., n. (To do with) a SALIVARY GLAND, in man the greatest, placed at the side of the face in front of and lower than the ear, in higher animals; in some ANURA, a group of poison-producing glands on the side of the neck. **paro'titic**, a. **-parous**, a. [Biol.] Giving birth to; (of GLANDS, etc.) producing.

'paroxysm, n. [Med.] Sudden violent attack of a disease, or increase in its effects; a CONVULSION. **parox'ysmal**, a.

pars (partes), n. [Zoo., Med.] A part, sp. of an ORGAN. **p. ner'vosa.** In higher animals, part of the back division of the PITUITARY GLAND.

'parsec, n. [Astron.] The chief unit used for measuring the distances of stars = 206265 ASTRONOMICAL UNITS, or $19 \cdot 16 + 10^{12}$ miles, or $3 \cdot 26$ light years.

'parted, a. [Biol.] Of LOBATION etc., with divisions cut in almost to the base, middle stem etc.

'parthen(o)-. [Biol.] Produced or producing by other than a sex process.

'partheno'carpy, n. [Bot.] The development of fruit without the POLLINATION of the producing flower, such fruit having no seed. **'partheno'carpic**, a.

'partheno'genesis, n. [Biol.] The producing of offspring by female CELLS without uniting with male cells. **'partheno-ge'netic**, a. **'parthenoge'netically**, adv.

'parthenospore, n. [Bot.] SPORE produced without a sex process.

'partial, 1.a. Not complete, in part. 2.n. [Acous.] Any of the simple TONES of different FREQUENCIES into which a sound may be broken up by ANALYSIS.

'particle, n. A very small bit or grain. [Phys.] A body having mass, but so small that it may be looked on as having no size; an ATOM in a special electric condition and moving quickly; a FUNDAMENTAL P. **par'ticulate**, a. In the form of very small pp.

par'tition, n. The process of division, separating; a wall or like structure forming a division between parts. **p. coeff'icient.** [Chem.] DISTRIBUTION CO-EFFICIENT.

partu'rition, n. [Zoo.] The process of giving birth to offspring. **par'turient**, a. To do with p.; about to give birth, in the act of giving birth. **par'turi'facient**, n., a. [Med.] (Substance) helping p.

'passage bed. [Geol.] A STRATUM put down at a time when conditions on the earth were changing from one EPOCH to another, and so having a connection with two SYSTEMS.

'passage cell. [Bot.] Any of the thin-walled CELLS among the cork cells round the middle part of a root or stem, through which water may go.

Passeri'formes, n.pl. [Zoo.] The greatest ORDER of birds, taking in more than half the recorded SPECIES, with feet specially formed for gripping branches, three toes pointing forward and one back. **'passerine.** 1.a. Of, to do with, the P. 2.n. A passerine bird.

'passive, a. [Psych., Med., Elec. etc.] (Of thing) not acting, letting itself be acted on without doing anything in support of or against the process; (of a development, effect, process) coming in, started from, outside the thing or system in question, not caused or helped by any force inside it. [Chem.] (Of a substance) in the condition of giving little or no reaction, not in a condition to be readily acted on [Metal.] Having the property of passivity. **p. con'gestion.** [Med.] CONGESTION caused by something stopping the blood from getting away from a part, not by an unnormal amount of blood going into it. **p. e'lectrode.** [Elec.] The ELECTRODE upon which a substance is put down when PRECIPITATED by an electric current. **p. imm'unity.** [Med.] IMMUNITY produced by p. immunization. **p. 'immuniz'ation.** [Med.] IMMUNIZATION by putting into an animal ready-made ANTIBODIES from another animal by which they have been produced in reaction to disease or INOCULATION. **p. iron etc.** [Chem., Metal.] Iron or other metal which has become p. as the effect of the ready forming of a coat of OXIDE on the outside of it. **pas'sivity**, n. The condition of being p., sp. [Chem.] the property of certain metals, normally giving a reaction to acids etc., of becoming p. in certain conditions, probably as the effect of the forming of a very thin coat of some COMPOUND of the metal on the outside of it.

'pastern, n. [Zoo.] The part of the foot of a horse, and like animals between the FETLOCK and the HOOF.

pasteuri'zation, n. [Med.] The process, named after Pasteur, of making liquids, sp. milk, safe as food by heating them to a degree at which their chemical and food properties are little changed, but the destruction of disease BACTERIA is effected. **'pasteu'rize**, v.t. Make undergo p. **'pasteurized**, a.

pa'tagium, n. [Zoo.] Stretch of skin between the front and the back leg forming a wing of those MAMMALS having the power of flight, or giving support and balance to certain tree-animals given to making very long, flight-like jumps; like stretch of skin on a bird's wing; one or the other of two small outgrowths on the front part of the body.in some LEPIDOPTERA. **pa'tagial,** a. **pa'tagiate,** a.

pa'tella, n. [Zoo.] A thick, flat, moving bone formed on a TENDON and covering the point of the knee in higher animals; like bone in the ELBOW. [Bot.] A plate-like APOTHECIUM, unstemmed, and with a clearly marked edge. **pa'tellar,** a. **pa'tel-late,** a. **pa'telliform,** a.

patent, a. [Bot.] PATULOUS.

'**patent,** v.t. Get a patent for (an invention). **paten'tee,** n. The owner of, or person who is attempting to get, the p. for an invention. **p. log.** *See* LOG.

path, n. The line of motion of any moving body, as the p. of the earth round the sun, the p. of a ray, etc.

pa'thetic, n., a. [Zoo.] (The muscle) by which the eyeball is turned out and down in higher animals; to do with the **p. muscle,** as the **p. nerve.**

'**pathogen,** n. [Med.] Any substance or organism causing disease. **patho'genic,** a. To do with pp., causing disease. **patho-'genesis,** n. The causing or development of a disease.

patho'logical, a. [Med.] Diseased, unhealthy; to do with PATHOLOGY.

path'ology, n. That branch of medical science which has to do with diseases, their causes and properties and their effects on the body. **path'ologist,** n.

-pathy, n. [Med.] Disease. **-pathic,** a.

'**patina,** n. [Chem.] A thin, freq. coloured, coat formed naturally on certain metals, such as copper, as the effect of having been long out in the air, or produced on them by the operation of acids; the look given to the SURFACE of other polished materials, such as wood, or certain sorts of stone, by long use, rubbing, operation of the air, etc.

patro'clin-al, -ic, -ous, aaa. [Biol.] (Of offspring, INHERITANCE, etc.) in which the qualities of the father or male producer are more marked than those of the mother or female producer.

patro'genesis, n. [Zoo.] Condition in which the CHROMOSOMES of an offspring come only from the male sex-CELL.

'**pattern,** n. Design formed by something, for example a wave-p.

'**Pattinson's 'process.** The process of separating silver from lead by heating the mixed metal till it is liquid, then letting it get cold and taking away the first part which becomes solid, the process being done over and over till the liquid is unmixed silver.

'**patul-ent, -ous,** aa. [Bot.] Stretching out widely, as the branches of a tree; opening widely and loosely, as the CALYX of some flowers.

'**Pauli's (ex'clusion) 'principle.** EXCLUSION PRINCIPLE.

paunch, n. RUMEN.

'**pavement epi'thelium.** [Zoo.] EPITHELIUM made up of flat, thin CELLS joined edge to edge.

pawl, n. [Mach.] A tongue-like structure or a rod on one part of a machine which by falling or slipping between teeth on another moving part, such as a wheel, keeps it from moving in the opposite direction or has some other desired effect on its motion.

Pb, Sign for lead.

Pd, Sign for PALLADIUM.

p.d. or **P.D.** = POTENTIAL DIFFERENCE.

peak, n. A more or less pointed top, as of a mountain; the highest point, sp. in a process of development or any other process which may be pictured by a line or curve. **p. (of the) load.** [Eng.] The greatest amount of power given out or taken in by a machine or power distribution system etc., in a given time. **p. value.** [Elec.] The greatest + or − value of an ALTERNATING CURRENT.

pearl, n. [Zoo.] Round mass of NACRE formed in thin leaves, one over the other, round a grain of sand or some other undesired body inside the SHELL of some MOLLUSCA, **p. ash,** [Chem.] POTASH. '**pearly,** a. P.-like, sp. in having the special, softly bright look of a p. and the milk-like colour which is most common to it.

pearl disease. [Med.] TUBERCULOSIS in cows etc.

'**pearlite,** n. [Metal.] An ALLOY of iron and iron CARBIDE present in certain sorts of steel and in CAST iron.

peat, n. [Geol.] Dead plant material which has become formed into a solid mass in the hollows of wet or water-covered land, in not very warm countries, and, in place of undergoing complete destruction, is in the first stage of changing into coal— used for burning when dried.

'**pebble,** n. [Geol.] A small stone (from 2 mm. to 50 mm. across) made round and smooth by rubbing against others in a river or sea.

'**pecten** (pectines), n. [Zoo.] Any comb-like structure; structure, sometimes pectinate, on the inside of the RETINA in the eye of most birds and some REPTILIA; in some ARACHNIDA, an apparatus for making a noise by the rubbing of parts; in other Arachnida, one or the other of two parts on the under side of the body at the back of the legs which are said to be instruments of the sense of touch.

[Bot.] STERIGMA. 'pectinal, a. 'pectinate, a. [Biol.] Comb-like, in botany used sp. of a PINNATIFID leaf whose divisions are very narrow. pecti'nation, n. Condition of being pectinate; toothed part.

'pectin, n. [Biochem.] Any of a group of complex CARBOHYDRATES, white, non-CRYSTALLINE substances, present in the CELL-walls of fruit and other plant food, and forming a jelly when heated with acid fruit and sugar. 'pectic, a. 'pectinous, a. 'pectize, v.i. [Chem.] (Of a liquid COLLOIDAL SOLUTION) become jelly. pecti-'zation, n.

pec'tineus, n. [Zoo.] A flat, four-sided muscle on the inside front of the top part of the leg. pec'tineal, a.

'pectoral, 1.a. [Zoo.] To do with the chest. 2.n. A p. muscle, p. arch or 'girdle. The framework of bone or CARTILAGE by which the arms or front legs or front FINS of a back-boned animal are supported. p. fins. The front PAIR of FINS of a fish. pecto'ralis (pectorales), n. Any of the muscles joining the wall of the chest to the bones of the upper arm, front leg, or wing, the chief muscles used by a bird in flight.

'pectus, n. [Zoo.] The chest, sp. of a bird; in ARTHROPODA, a hard plate formed by the united under- and side-walls of a body division.

ped(i)-. Foot: 'pedal, 'pedial, aa., 'pediform, a.; PAED-.

'pedate, a. [Zoo.] Having a foot or feet. [Bot.] Foot-like, sp. (of leaf) PALMATE with three divisions, of which the two side ones are again cut into smaller divisions.

pedes, n.pl. See PES.

'pedicel, n. [Bot.] A small short stem having on it one leaf, flower, or fruit. [Zoo.] A short stem-like part supporting another part, as the eye in some animals, or used as a foot; the middle division of an insect's feeler. pedi'cellate, a.

'pedicel'laria (pedicellariae), n. [Zoo.] Any of the small gripping structures present in great number on the outside of certain ECHINODERMATA.

pedi'celus, n. [Biol.] A (small) PEDICEL.

'pedicle, n. [Biol.] PEDICEL; in some ARACHNIDA, a narrow part joining the front and back divisions of the body.

pe'dicular, a. [Zoo.] To do with LICE. [Med.] Having PEDICULOSIS.

pe'diculosis, n. [Med.] The condition of having LICE on the body.

'pedicure, n. [Med.] Care of the feet and toe nails. 'pedicurist, n. Expert in p.

'pedigree, n. [Bot.] Family tree (of the ANCESTORS) of an animal, sp. as giving light on HEREDITY.

pedi'palp, n. [Zoo.] The second leg-like part on the head of ARACHNIDA, in some formed for walking, in others for gripping, in others for use as an instrument of touch, and in others for (male) sex purposes.

pe'dology, n. The science of SOIL in its relation to the growth of plants.

pe'dometer, n. An instrument used in SURVEYING for recording the number of steps taken in walking a certain distance and so measuring the distance covered.

'pedrail, n. A sort of wheel with 'feet' at fixed distances on the outer band, used in farming machines, etc.

pe'duncle, n. [Bot.] The chief stem of a group of flowers. [Zoo.] PEDICEL, sp. one supporting an animal which is fixed in one place with no, or little, power of moving about; a narrow white band joining different parts of the brain in back-boned animals. pe'duncular, a. pe'dunculate(d), aa.

peel, v.i. [Med.] (Of skin) come off in bits as the effect of sunburn or certain other conditions or diseases, (of body or part) undergo the peeling of the skin.

'pegmatite, n. [Geol.] A sort of IGNEOUS ROCK with grains of specially great size, taking the form of VEINS or DYKES.

'Peking man. SINANTHROPUS.

'pelage, n. [Zoo.] The hair or wool coat of an animal.

pe'lagic, a. To do with the deep sea. [Biol.] Living in the p. zone. [Geol.] (Of material, etc.) forming the bed of deep water, sp sea. p. zone. [Biol.] The upper part of the open sea, further out than any under-water shelf of land, as far down as light gets.

Pelecy'poda, n.pl. LAMELLIBRANCHIA. pe-'lecypod, n., a. (Animal of the P. pele-'cypodous, a.

'pelite, n. [Geol.] Any ROCK formed chiefly from CLAY. pe'litic, a. (Of ROCKS) produced by the effect of heat and force on CLAY material.

pell'agra, n. [Med.] A CHRONIC disease, seen sp. in Italy, Spain, the south of France and south U.S.A., marked by stomach, nerve and skin trouble, and probably caused by living on food not having in it enough VITAMIN B2. pell'agrous, a.

'pellicle, pel'licula, nn. A very thin delicate skin or covering, for example that round PROTOZOA, or the outer skin of a PILEUS, or formed on the top of a liquid. pel'-'licular, a. pel'liculate, a.

pe'loria, n. [Bot.] A condition in which flowers of regular structure are produced by a sort of plant normally having flowers of irregular structure.

'pelta, n. [Bot.] The almost flat, cover-like APOTHECIUM of certain LICHENS.

'pellate, a. [Bot.] Almost flat and with stem etc. fixed on the under side in place of on the edge at the base, as certain leaves (see picture p. 223).

'**Peltier ef'fect.** [Elec.] The producing or taking up of heat at the point where two metals through which electric current is going are joined.

'**pelvis,** n. [Zoo.] The basin-like structure formed by the lower end of the backbone and the bones joining it to the pelvic girdle; loosely, the pelvic girdle itself; the basin-like hollow inside the KIDNEY in connection with the upper end of the URETER. '**pelvic,** a. **pelvic arch** or **girdle.** The arch or ring of bones to which the legs or back-legs or back FINS of a back-boned animal are joined. '**pelvic cavity.** The hollow of the p., forming the lower part of the ABDOMEN. **pelvic 'fascia.** The skin coating the inside of the pelvic cavity. '**pelvic fins.** The back PAIR of FINS in a fish. '**pelvigraph,** n. [Med.] An apparatus for making an outline of the form of the p. **pel'vimeter,** n. [Med.] An instrument for measuring the distances between different points on the p. **pel'vimetry,** n. [Med.] The measuring and recording of the size and form of the female p. in connection with the process of giving birth.

pelvi'sternum, n. EPIPUBIS.

pen, n. [Bot.] MIDRIB. [Zoo.] The narrow structure of horn-like substance bedded in the bodies of certain DIBRANCHIA and representative of the SHELL.

'**pencil,** n. [Phys.] A group of rays, sp. of light, by degrees coming together at a point. **pen'cilliform,** a.

'**pendulous,** a. Hanging down, bent over from the point of support, as [Bot.] a p. OVULE. '**-ness,** n.

'**pendulum,** n. [Phys.] A weight on the end of a thread, wire etc. hanging freely from a fixed point, so that when given an impulse it is kept moving regularly from side to side through a middle point by the force of the earth's attraction.

'**peneplain,** n. [Geol.] A stretch of country which has become almost flat as the effect of wind and water.

'**penetrance,** n. [Biol.] (Of a GENE) the number of plants or animals in a given number to which a gene has been handed on in which its effect is clearly seen.

'**penetrate,** v.t. and i. Go into, through (a thing, substance, etc.). '**penetrable,** a. Which may be penetrated. '**penetra-'bility,** n. **pene'trating,** a. '**penetrating ray.** COSMIC RAY. **pene'tration,** n. **pene-'tration twins.** [Mineral.] CRYSTALS united in such a way that one seems to have gone through the other.

'**penial,** a. [Zoo.] To do with, near, the PENIS. **p. 'setae,** In male NEMATODA, two needle-like bodies at the sex-opening.

peni'cill-ate, -iform, aa. [Biol.] Pencil-like in form; having hairs at end like a painter's brush.

peni'cillin, n. [Chem., Med.] Any of a group of acid substances made from the MOULD *Penicillium,* which by their power of stopping the growth of disease BACTERIA are of great value against a wide range of diseases such as PNEU-MONIA and MASTOIDITIS.

'**penis,** n. [Zoo.] The structure in a male animal by which the SPERM is put into the body of the female.

pen'naceous, a. [Zoo.] Feather-like, having feathers; (of feather) having hooked structures on the BARBULES.

penni-. Feather: '**-form,** a.

'**pennyweight,** n. *See* TROY WEIGHT.

pe'nology, n. The science of punishment for crime, of the best ways of managing prisons and training prisoners into a respect for the law and a desire to go straight.

penta-. 5. **pent'angular,** a., '**-'carpellary,** a. [Bot.].

'**pentad,** n. [Chem.] PENTAVALENT ATOM.

penta'dactyl(e), a. [Zoo.] Having 5 fingers or toes, or 5 finger-like parts. **p. limb.** The sort of LIMB seen in four-footed animals, which has three divisions, for example, the upper leg, lower leg, and foot, with five toes etc., complete or VESTIGIAL, on the end division, **penta'dactylism,** n.

'**pentagon,** n. [Geom.] A plane form with 5 straight sides and 5 angles. **pent-'agonal,** a.

pen'tamerous, a. [Biol.] Made up of 5 parts, sp. [Bot.] (of a flower) having 5 parts in every ring.

'**penta'methylene,** n. CYCLOPENTANE.

'**pentane,** n. [Chem.] Any of three ISOMERIC HYDROCARBONS, C_5H_{12}, of low boiling-point, one of which is normally a gas and the others liquids, got from PETRO-LEUM.

'**pentaploid,** a. [Biol.] Having 5 times the HAPLOID number of CHROMOSOMES. **penta'ploidy,** n.

'**pentarch,** a. [Bot.] Having 5 XYLEM groups, as some roots.

penta'valent, a. [Chem.] Having a VALENCY of 5.

'**pentode,** n. [Elec.] A THERMIONIC VALVE having 5 ELECTRODES, that is with three GRIDS between the ANODE and the CATHODE.

'**pentosan,** n. [Chem.] Any of a group of complex CARBOHYDRATES very common in plants, from which PENTOSES are produced by HYDROLYSIS.

'**pentose,** n. [Chem.] Any of a group of MONOSACCHARIDES with 5 ATOMS of O.

pento'suria, a. [Med.] A condition in which PENTOSES are present in the URINE.

pen'toxide, n. [Chem.] An OXIDE with 5 ATOMS of O.

pe'numbra, n. [Optics, Astron.] The lighter part round the edge of a shade where the light coming from a body of great size is not completely cut off.

'people, n. [Anthrop.] A RACE of men; a group of men, not necessarily limited to one race or nation, united by common ways, beliefs, and language, and gen. living in the same general division of the earth.

'pepo, n. [Bot.] A one-CELLED fruit with a great number of seeds inside a thick, soft wall, formed from an INFERIOR OVARY, a sort of berry.

'pepsin, n. [Biochem.] An ENZYME produced by the inner coat of the stomach in higher animals, together with HCl, and effecting the digestion of PROTEINS.

'peptic, 1.a. [Zoo., Med.] To do with, or helping, digestion; to do with or like PEPSIN. 2.n. Any substance helping digestion. p. glands. The GLANDS in the coat of the stomach by which PEPSIN and HCl are produced. p. 'ulcer. [Med.] An ULCER of the stomach or DUODENUM, caused by the damaging of the MUCOUS MEMBRANE by the produce of the p. glands.

pepti'zation, n. [Chem.] The forming of a COLLOIDAL SOLUTION of a substance, sp. from a GEL. 'peptize, v.t.

'peptone, n. [Biochem.] Any of a group of substances produced in the end from PROTEINS by the operation of ENZYMES in digestion or by other forms of HYDROLYSIS. 'peptoni'zation, n. pepto'nuria, n. [Med.] Condition in which a p. is present in the URINE.

per-. [Chem.] Put before the name of a COMPOUND as a sign of one having in it:—1. two O ATOMS joined together; 2, a greater amount of O than the normal compound.

'Peracarida, n.pl. [Zoo.] A SUBCLASS of CRUSTACEA in which the first division of the THORAX is united with the head and the legs have TWO-JOINTED PROPODITES.

pe'rambulator, n. An instrument for measuring distance formed of a great wheel with a hand-part by which it is rolled over the country, automatically recording the distance covered, used in SURVEYING.

per'ceive, v.t. and i. [Psych.] Become conscious of, get knowledge of (something) through the senses.

per cent. (Used in giving rates) in every 100 parts or units of whatever is in question, sign %. per'centage, n. Amount or number p.c.

per'ception, n. [Psych.] The power or process of PERCEIVING; one act or event of perception; a percept. 'percept, n. The knowledge made present to the mind by an act of p.; that into which a complex of sense-effects is changed by the act of the mind in becoming conscious of it in

relation to something outside the self and to other experiences. per'ceptible, a. Of which knowledge may be got by p.; having a great enough effect on some sense or senses to make a person conscious of it. percepti'bility, n. -al, a. To do with the science of p. per'ceptive, a. To do with the act or power of p., using p. per'ceptual, a. (Of knowledge, etc.) given by p.

per'chlorate, n. [Chem.] Any SALT having in it the group –ClO₄.

per'chloric acid. [Chem.] HClO₄, a liquid without colour, damaging to the skin, forming PERCHLORATES.

per'cipienc-e, -y, nn. [Psych.] The power of PERCEPTION. per'cipient, n., a. (Person) having p.; (person) PERCEIVING something; in TELEPATHY, etc., the person to whom knowledge comes in some other way than by sense.

'percolate, 1.v.i. (Of a liquid or gas) make way slowly *through* something with very small holes or spaces between its parts, as a mass of solid substance; 2.v.t. Send (liquid) slowly through a substance etc. to get the liquid clear or, sp. [Med.] to get the desired medical substances washed out of the substance (for example, crushed plant material) into the liquid. 'percolation, n. 'percolator, n. [Med.] An apparatus for making medical substances by percolation.

per'current, a. [Bot.] (Of MIDRIB) going from the base to the end of the leaf, but not further. [Zoo.] Going from one end to the other of the body or any part.

per'cussion, n. The coming together of two solid bodies with force, the giving of blow(s), shock by one to another. [Med.] The act of percussing. p. cap. A small cover having in it some violent EXPLOSIVE which will go off on receiving a blow, used in fire-arms for causing the EXPLOSION of the chief CHARGE. per'cuss, v.t. and i. [Med.] Give quick blow(s) with the finger or an instrument to a part of the body with a view to judging the condition of the parts inside it from the sound made by the blow. per'cussive, a.

percu'taneous, a. [Med.] (Of a process, such as the use of an electric current on muscles, etc.) effected through the skin without cutting it.

perenn'ation, n. [Bot.] (Of plants) the condition or process of living for a number of years.

pe'rennial, n., a. [Bot.] (A plant) living for three or more years, normally flowering and producing fruit the second year and every year after, sometimes with the loss of all its top growth every Fall, starting completely new growth again from the root in the Spring, sometimes only stopping growth for the Winter and going on from the same point again, as a tree.

'perfect, a. [Biol.] With all its parts complete and in working order. [Bot.] (Of a flower) having male and female sex parts; (of a FUNGUS) at the stage of producing SPORES by a sex process. **p. 'die'lectric.** [Phys.] In theory, a DIELECTRIC in which all the ENERGY needed for producing an electric field is given back when the field is no longer in being. **p. 'fluid.** [Phys.] A liquid or gas which is not compressible, has the same DENSITY all through, and has no VISCOSITY. **p. gas.** IDEAL GAS. **p. state** [Biol.] That stage in the LIFE-CYCLE of a plant or animal in which SEX-CELLS are produced.

per'flation, n. [Med.] The act of blowing through a space, opening, pipe, to get it clear.

per'foliate, a. [Bot.] (Of leaf) with base going round the stem in such a way that the stem seems to go through the leaf.

'perforate, 1.v.t. Make a small hole or holes through, go through a substance or thing in this way. 2.a. [Biol.] Having a number of small holes, or [Bot.] small marks looking like holes. [Zoo.] (Of SPIRAL SHELLS) having a small hollow in the middle of the outside, with the turn(s) of the shell going round it. **'perfor'ation,** n. The act of perforating or condition of being perforated; a small hole going through something from one side to the other.

per'fuse, v.t. [Zoo., Med.] (Of a liquid) go through (a part); send liquid through an ORGAN or TISSUE, sp. by way of the blood-vessels. **per'fusion,** n.

peri-. [Biol., Med.] (Part) going round, about, the named part:— **-'anal,** a., **-ar'terial,** a., **-ar'ticular,** a., **-'petalous,** a., **-pharyn'geal,** a., **-'visceral,** a.

'perianth, n. [Bot.] The outer leaf-like parts of a flower circling the sex-parts, the SEPALS and PETALS together, in flowers which have the two.

peri'astron, n. [Astron.] That point in the motion of a DOUBLE STAR at which the two are nearest to one another.

'periblast, n. [Zoo.] The outer skin of an insect EMBRYO. **peri'blastic,** a.

'periblem, n. [Bot.] The MERISTEM at the growth point in the stem and root of a plant, from which the CORTEX is formed.

peri'cardium, n. [Zoo.] The cover of skin-like substance round the heart, made up of an outer and an inner coat, the space between which is full of thin liquid; the pericardial cavity. **peri'cardia-c, -l,** aa. **peri'cardial 'cavity.** In the back-boned animals, the division of the space inside the body taken up by the heart, and of which the outer coat of the p. is the inner covering; in other animals, the space in which the heart is, sometimes having in it blood for the heart's use. **'pericar-**

'ditis, n. [Med.]. **pericardio-. pericardi'o-tomy,** n. [Med.].

'pericarp, n. [Bot.] The wall of a seed-vessel or fruit formed by the development of the wall of the ovary.

'pericentre, n. [Astron.] The point in its motion at which a body moving round another is nearest to it. **peri'central,** a. **peri'central cell.** [Bot.] AUXILIARY CELL.

peri'chondrium, n. [Zoo.] The cover of FIBROUS material round a CARTILAGE. **peri'chondrial,** a. **'perichond'ritis,** a. [Med.].

peri'chordal, a. [Zoo.] Going round, covering, the NOTOCHORD.

peri'chylous, a. [Bot.] Having a system of water-storing CELLS outside the CHLORO-PHYLL cells, said of certain thick-leaved plants.

'periclase, n. [Mineral.] Natural OXIDE of Mg, MgO.

peri'clinal, a. [Bot.] (Of CELL walls) parallel to the SURFACE of a part. **p. chi'maera.** [Bot.] A CHIMAERA in which the TISSUE of one sort of plant goes completely round that of the other.

'pericline, n. [Mineral.] A sort of ALBITE in the form of long white CRYSTALS, freq. TWINS.

peri'clinium, n. [Bot.] The INVOLUCRE of a COMPOSITE FLOWER.

peri'cranium, n. [Zoo.] The TISSUE over the structure of bones or CARTILAGE covering the brain in back-boned animals.

peri'cycle, n. [Bot.] The thin coat of PAREN-CHYMA on the outside of the STELE in most plants.

peri'cyclone, n. [Meteor.] The ring of increasing PRESSURE round a CYCLONE.

'periderm, n. [Bot.] The cork-forming ring of substance in a tree together with the outside covering formed from it. [Zoo.] The outside skin of HYDROZOA. **peri-'derm-ic, -al,** aa.

'peridesm, n. [Bot.] The TISSUE round a VASCULAR BUNDLE.

peri'desmium, n. [Zoo.] The delicate skin covering a LIGAMENT.

pe'ridium, n. [Bot.] The outer coat of the fruit body in FUNGI, when this is designed as a cover. **pe'ridial,** a.

peri'dotite, n. [Geol.] A sort of COARSE-GRAINED IGNEOUS ROCK present gen. in small INTRUSIONS.

'periente'ritis, n. [Med.] INFLAMMATION of the inner coat of the INTESTINES.

peri'foliary, a. [Bot.] Round the edge of a leaf.

peri'gastric, a. Round the VISCERA.

'perigee, n. [Astron.] That point in the moon's motion round the earth at which it is nearest the earth. **peri'gea-l, -n,** aa.

peri'gonium (perigonia), n. [Bot.] PERIANTH; the ring of leaves round the base of the ANTHERIDIUM in Musci. [Zoo.] GONO-THECA.

peri'gynium, n. [Bot.] Skin-like cover of the ARCHEGONIUM in some BRYOPHYTA.

pe'rigynous, a. [Bot.] (Of flowers) having the PISTIL in the middle of a basin, round the edge of which the other flower-parts are ranged. (*See* picture p. 151.) pe'rigyny, n.

peri'helion, n. [Astron.] That point in the motion of any body going round the sun at which it is nearest to the sun.

peri'karyon, n. [Zoo.] The body of a nerve-CELL.

'perilymph, n. [Zoo.] The liquid in the space between the bone structure and the pipe of MEMBRANE inside it, in the inner ear of higher animals.

pe'rimeter, n. The outer edge of anything; CIRCUMFERENCE. [Med.] An instrument for measuring how far sideways from the AXIS of the eye different colours may be seen, gen. in the form of a band of metal bent into a half-circle, on which coloured circles are moved round before the eye.

peri'me'tritis, n. [Med.] INFLAMMATION of the PERIMETRIUM.

peri'metrium, n. [Zoo.] The part of the PERITONEUM covering the UTERUS.

'perimorph, n. [Mineral.] A CRYSTAL of one substance having inside it one of another substance.

peri'mysium, n. [Zoo.] The material going round muscles or parts of muscles and keeping them together.

peri'n(a)eum, n. [Zoo.] The outer part of the body between, or taking in, the ANUS and the VAGINA or SCROTUM. peri'n(a)eal, a.

peri'neurium,n. [Zoo.] The covering material uniting a parcel of nerve threads.

'period, n. Stretch of time, sp. the time taken by some stage of development or some event. [Phys., Elec., Astron.] (Of a motion or change taking place regularly, over and over, or the body etc. undergoing such motion or change) the time from any given point to that same point again, that is, the time of a complete CYCLE, as the p. of the earth's motion round the sun, the p. of an ALTERNATING electric current, the p. of a PENDULUM, etc. [Chem.] Group of ELEMENTS taking up one line (*short p.*) or sometimes, two lines (*long p.*) across the periodic table, ranging from an ALKALI METAL to the first INERT GAS coming after it. [Geol.] The second longest division in the system of time used in geology, that is, a division of an ERA, made up of EPOCHS. [Med.] The regular p. of MENSTRUATION.

peri'odic, a. To do with a p. in any sense; taking place regularly, over and over, through a fixed time or range; periodical.

peri'odic law. [Chem.] The fact that like chemical and physical properties are seen to be present periodically in the scale of chemical ELEMENTS ranged in the order of their ATOMIC NUMBERS. periodic

'system. [Chem.] The grouping of the chemical ELEMENTS in the order of their ATOMIC NUMBERS in such a way that the periodic law is made clear and the change of properties from one element to another is seen to be part of a regular rhythm.

periodic 'table. The TABLE in which the periodic system is pictured. peri'odical, a. Taking place, coming again, from time to time, as p. outbursts of a disease. perio-'dicity, n. The property of being periodic, sp. of having a regular rhythm.

per'iodate, n. [Chem.] Any of a number of substances having in them the group –IO_4.

peri'odic 'acid. [Chem.] The acid H_5IO_6, a feebler acid than IODIC ACID but with a stronger OXIDIZING effect.

'perio'dontal, a. [Zoo.] Round a tooth.

peri'osteum, n. [Zoo.] The skin-like material tightly covering bones, to the outer part of which muscles etc. are fixed, and in the inner part of which are bone-forming CELLS and blood-vessels taking blood to the bone. peri'osteal, a. periosteo-.

peri'ostracum, n. [Zoo.] The horn-like outer part of the SHELL in MOLLUSCA.

peri'otic, 1.a. [Zoo.] To do with, or being part of, the part of the head round the inner ear, said of bones. 2.n. A p. bone or CARTILAGE.

pe'riphery, n. The outer SURFACE, edge, or outline, of a body or form. pe'ripheral, a. Of, on, in the direction of, the p. [Zoo.] Of, to do with, the peripheral nervous system. pe'ripheral e'lectron. VALENCY ELECTRON. pe'ripheral 'nervous 'system. [Zoo.] In higher animals all the system of nerves outside the CENTRAL NERVOUS SYSTEM.

'periplasm, n. [Bot.] The part of an oöGONIUM outside the oöSPHERE. [Zoo.] Coat of PROTOPLASM round an insect's egg inside the VITELLINE MEMBRANE.

peri'pneustic, a. [Zoo.] Having breathing-holes in a line down opposite sides of the body, said of insects.

'perisarc, n. [Zoo.] The outer horn-like covering of a COLONY of HYDROZOA.

'periscope,n. Instrument making it possible, by a system of REFLECTIONS, to see from one level the view that would be before the eye at a different level, sp. a pipe-like structure used on under-water boats for looking over the top of the sea, etc. peri'scopic, a.

'perisome, n. [Zoo.] The body-wall of animals without back-bones. periso'matic, a.

'perisperm, n. [Bot.] Food material present in some seeds outside the EMBRYO SAC, formed from the NUCELLUS.

'perisphere, n. [Biol.] The outer part of an ATTRACTION SPHERE.

'perispore, n. [Bot.] The covering of a SPORE; the mother-CELL of SPORES in ALGAE.

Per'isso'dactyla, n.pl. [Zoo.] An ORDER of HOOVED MAMMALS made up of animals (for example, the horse) most of which have 3 or 5 toes, and all of which, whatever the number of toes, have the third much greater than the rest, pointing straight forward and taking the weight in walking. **pe'risso'dactyle(e),** 1.a. Having 3, 5, etc. toes, or toes of very unequal development; of, to do with, the P. 2.n. Animal of the P. **per'issodactylism,** n.

peri'stalsis, n. [Zoo.] Wave-like motion of a pipe-like part produced by the CONTRACTION of its walls one part after the other from end to end, and having the effect of forcing through it whatever is inside it, sp. this motion of the INTESTINES. **peri'staltic,** a.

'peristome, n. [Biol.] The part round a mouth or opening, sp. [Bot.] ring of teeth round the SPORE-VESSEL in MUSCI, [Zoo.] the lip of a SPIRAL SHELL. **peri'stom(e)al, peristo'matic,** aa.

peri'thecium, n. [Bot.] Bottle-like ASCOCARP, gen. with an opening in the end, in certain FUNGI.

'perito'neum, n. [Zoo.] The MEMBRANE of which part makes the inner coat of the peritoneal cavity and part is folded round the different ORGANS inside it. **'perito'neal,** a. To do with the p. **'perito'neal 'cavity.** The space inside the body of higher animals from the base of the chest to the PELVIS, inside which are the stomach and most of the apparatus of digestion. **'periton'itis,** n. [Med.] INFLAMMATION of the p.

peri'trichous, a. [Zoo.] (Of PROTOZOA) with a twisting line of CILIA round the mouth. [Bot.] (Of BACTERIA) having a regular distribution of FLAGELLA all over the body.

'peritroch, peri'trochium, nn. [Zoo.] A band of CILIA; a LARVA with a p. round it. **peri'trochous,** a.

peri'vascular, a. [Zoo.] Going round blood-vessels.

peri'vitelline, a. [Zoo.] Round the YOLK, said of space between the yolk of an egg and the outer part.

'perlite, n. PEARLITE.

'Perm'alloy, n. (Trade name of) an ALLOY, at one time made only of iron and nickel (in the relation of about 1 to 4) but now with other metals, which is very readily MAGNETIZED and has low HYSTERESIS loss, used importantly for under-water telegraph lines.

'permanent, a. Unchanging, fixed in the same condition or place for ever, or for whatever part of time is in question, opp. TEMPORARY. **p. 'cartilage.** [Zoo.] CARTILAGE which does not become bone at a later stage. **p. den'tition or teeth.** [Zoo.] The second growth of teeth, taking the place of the MILK TEETH, in MAMMALS. **p. 'hardness.** The HARDNESS of water which is still present after long boiling, caused by Ca and Mg CHLORIDES or SULPHATES. **p. 'hybrid.** [Biol.] A HYBRID the offspring of which go on having the same hybrid qualities, because of some LETHAL FACTOR working against the development of such offspring as would, by MENDEL'S LAW, have the qualities of one or the other of the mixed SPECIES. **p. 'magnet.** [Phys.] A body or substance which, after having been given MAGNETIC properties, keeps them. **p. 'tissue.** [Biol.] Material formed of CELLS which have undergone their full development into special sorts and will make no further change till the time comes for their death. **p. set.** [Phys.] (The amount of) the p. change in size or form undergone by a substance as the effect of a force which has overcome its ELASTICITY. **p. 'water 'table.** [Geol.] See WATER TABLE. **permanence, 'permanency,** nn. Condition or property of being p.

per'manganate, n. [Chem.] Any SALT of permanganic acid. **p. of 'potash.** POTASSIUM PERMANGANATE. **perman'ganic acid.** HMnO$_4$.

'permeable, a. Having the property of letting something through, as a MEMBRANE etc. which lets through it a liquid or gas. **'permea'bility,** n. The quality of being p. or the degree to which a thing is p. [Phys.] The degree to which a substance becomes MAGNETIZED in a MAGNETIC FIELD (see MAGNETIC PERMEABILITY).

perme'ameter, n. [Elec.] An instrument for measuring MAGNETIC PERMEABILITY.

'permeance, n. 1 ÷ RELUCTANCE.

'Permian, a., n. [Geol.] To do with the latest PERIOD of the PALAEOZOIC ERA (see p. 559).

per'mitted, a. [Phys.] Not ruled out by the EXCLUSION PRINCIPLE.

per'mittance, permit'tivity, nn. DIELECTRIC CONSTANT.

permu'tation, n. A change in the order or grouping of a number of things. **permu'tations,** n.pl. [Maths.] The different orders in which a given number of things may be put.

per'nicious, n. [Med.] (Of disease) very serious, causing, or with a tendency to be the cause of, death. **p. a'naemia.** [Med.] A p. disease in which the red blood-CELLS become smaller and smaller in number and of an unnormal size or form, marked by a very feeble condition of the muscles and damage to the digestion and nerve system, and caused by the need of something normally present in the LIVER.

'peronate, a. [Bot.] Covered with wool-like hairs or with a meal-like substance, said of the stems of some FUNGI.

pe′ron(a)eus, n. [Zoo.] The FIBULA, or any of a number of muscles having a connection with it. **pero′neal**, a. **peroneo-**.

per′oral, a. [Zoo.] Round the mouth, as the **p. ′membrane** of INFUSORIA.

pe′roxidase, n. [Biochem.] Any of a group of ENZYMES, present chiefly in plants, causing the giving up of O to another substance by a PEROXIDE, sp. H_2O_2.

per′oxide, n. [Chem.] Any OXIDE having a greater amount of O than is united with the other ELEMENT in the normal OXIDE, sp. one in which two ATOMS of O are joined together and which gives H_2O_2 by reaction with acids; HYDROGEN p., H_2O_2.

perpen′dicular, a. Upright, at right angles to the earth. **perpendicu′larity**, n.

per′petual, a. Unending, going on all the time. **p. motion**. The condition of an impossible machine which after being put in motion would go on for ever without any further ENERGY being given to it from outside. **p. night (day)**. The time of almost six months in the year at the NORTH or SOUTH POLE when the sun does not come up (go down).

per′radius, n. [Zoo.] Any of the 4 chief RADII of COELENTERATA.

perse′cution mania. [Med., Psych.] See DELUSION OF PERSECUTION.

′perseve′ration, n. [Biol., Psych.] The going on, or coming back over and over, of a physical reaction or a feeling etc. after the STIMULUS by which it was started has come to an end. [Med.] The saying of a word or words, or the doing of an act, over and over without sense. **per′severative**, a.

per′sistent, a. [Biol.] (Of a part) keeping its place to the end of an animal's or plant's development, or longer than normally, said, for example, of leaves which, though dried up, do not come off in the Fall, or of parts special to the early stage of an animal which are still present, though no longer needed, in the later stages. **per′sistence**, n. **per′sistence of ′vision**. [Zoo.] The fact that the sense-effect produced by light acting on the eye goes on for a little time after the STIMULUS has been changed or taken away, on which is said to be based the effect of motion-pictures, in which the eye, because of this fact, sees as an unbroken development the separate pictures of different positions which are unrolled quickly before it.

′person, n. [Zoo.] A separate animal or unit of a society or group, sp. a unit of a COLONY of HYDROZOA, etc. [Psych.] A HUMAN BEING looked on as having special qualities and a private experience, as being separate and different from all other human BEINGS, but at the same time conditioned by its relations with the group. **′-al**, a. [Psych.]. **personal e′quation**. In science observations, an error caused by some special and freq. regular tendency in the person making the observation. **personal i′dentity**. [Psych.] The connection which keeps a person one and the same through all his existence, however greatly he may be changed in the process of development, of which memory is the chief instrument. **person′ality**, n. [Psych.] The complete system of qualities making up a person, sp. viewed in connection with his effect on or relations with others; the condition of being a p., of having personal identity. (See DUAL P., MULTIPLE P.)

′personate co′rolla. [Bot.] A COROLLA whose PETALS are united into a throat-like structure with two lips round the opening, the throat being almost shut by an outgrowth from the base of the lower lip.

per′sorption, n. [Chem.] The very complete taking in of a gas by a solid, in which an almost MOLECULAR MIXTURE is formed

per′spective, n. The art or science of picturing solid things on a flat or curved plane in such a way that the eye is given the same signs of distance, size, or form as it would have in looking at the things themselves, in other words, a natural picture.

perspi′ration, n. [Zoo.] The liquid, made up chiefly of salt water, given off by the SWEAT GLANDS in the skin of higher animals; the process of perspiring. **per′spire**, v.i. Give off p., a process designed chiefly to keep the body from getting overheated.

′pertur′bation, n. [Phys., Astron.] A change in the regular motion of a body produced by some change in the force acting on it, sp. in the motion of a PLANET caused by the GRAVITATIONAL force of another body. **per′turb**, v.i. Be the cause of p. in. **′pertur′bational, per′turbative**, aa. **per′turbed**, a.

per′tussis, n. [Med.] An INFECTIOUS disease chiefly of the very young, attacking the breathing-pipes and marked by violent outbursts of coughing ending in a long intake of breath making a strange, loud, high sound.

per′version, n. Act of perverting or thing perverted. [Med., Psych.] An unhealthy change or development in any natural tendency, sp. any way of getting sex-pleasure by some act other than normal sex-connection, or the desire to do this. **′pervert**, n. [Med.] Person given to some form of sex p. **per′vert**, v.t. Put (something) to a wrong use, get it turned away from its right or natural purpose.

′pervious, a. PERMEABLE. [Zoo.] Open, having a hole through it.

pes (pedes), n. [Zoo.] The TARSUS and foot of the (back) leg of a back-boned animal; a foot-like structure.

'**pessary,** n. [Med.] An instrument for placing in the VAGINA as a support for the UTERUS or to keep some other part in the right position; a medical substance formed into a small solid mass to be put into the vagina.

pest, n. An insect causing great damage or destruction to plants.

'**pestle,** n. [Chem., Med.] Small solid instrument, gen. of glass or pot, with a rounded end, for crushing substances to a powder or paste in a MORTAR.

'**petal,** n. [Bot.] Any one of the ring of leaf-like, but gen. not green and freq. bright-coloured, parts of a flower round the STAMENS and/or CARPELS and inside the ring of SEPALS. (*See* p. 151.) **petall'iferous,** a. **pe'taliform,** a. Sp., almost OVAL. '**-ine,** a. To do with, fixed to, or like, a p. '**-(l)ed,** a. '**-oid,** a. Sp., [Zoo.] petaliform, said of the foot-like expansion at the end of an AMBULACRUM in certain ECHINODERMS, or of an ambulacrum having such an end. **peta'lloideous,** a. Said sp. of MONOCOTYLEDONS having the parts of the PERIANTH p.-like, as against those in which they are green and leaf-like or thin, dry, and brown. **-petalous,** a. Having the number of sort of pp. named. '**petalo-**.

'**petalody,** n. [Bot.] The changing of other flower-parts, sp. STAMENS, into PETALS.

'**petiole,** n. [Bot.] The thin, short stem of a leaf. [Zoo.] The narrow stem-like part joining the back division of the body to the rest in certain insects, for example, ants. '**petiolar,** a. '**petiolate,** a. '**petiolule,** n. The p. of a small leaf forming part of a complex leaf.

pe'tit mal. [Med.] A less serious form of EPILEPSY, without CONVULSIONS.

petri-. PETRO.

'**Petri dish.** Flat vessel of thin glass with a cover, used for the growth of BACTERIA.

petri'faction, n. [Geol.] The changing of plant and animal bodies or parts in the earth into stone or a hard, stone-like material, as the effect of the operation of water having in it substances such as Si or Ca, which get between the MOLECULES of the dead substance and by degrees take their place, freq. keeping the very same structure. **petri'factive,** '**petrifying,** aa. Causing p. **petrified,** a. '**petrify,** v.t. and i.

petro-. [Geol.] Stone, ROCK. [Zoo., Med.] PETROUS.

petro'genic, a. [Geol.] To do with the forming of ROCKS.

pe'trography, n. [Geol.] That part of PETROLOGY giving an account of the qualities of ROCKS and their place in the system in which rocks are grouped. **pe'trographer,** n. **petro'graphic(al),** aa.

'**petrol,** n. A liquid formed of mixed HYDROCARBONS of low boiling-point, readily taking fire, got from PETROLEUM or by uniting hydrocarbons, and used for driving automobile engines. **p. 'engine.** Engine in which p. is burned.

petro'latum, n. [Med.] A white or yellow oil, gen. in an almost solid form like soft fat or jelly, formed of mixed HYDROCARBONS and produced from PETROLEUM, used medically as, or as part of, an OINTMENT.

pe'troleum, n. [Chem., Mineral.] A very complex liquid MINERAL formed chiefly of HYDROCARBONS, present in pockets under the earth, from which are produced by FRACTIONAL DISTILLATION a great number of different oils for different purposes, for example, for burning for heat or light, for driving engines, LUBRICATING machines, medical uses, and so on.

pe'trology, n. That branch of Geology which has to do with ROCKS, how they come into being, their physical and chemical structure, the forces acting on them, the changes they undergo, their relations to one another in space, time, and qualities, etc. **petro'logic(al),** aa. **pe'trologist,** n.

'**Petromy'zontia,** '**Petromy'zontidae,** nn.pl. [Zoo.] A division of CYCLOSTOMATA having the hollow in which the mouth is placed very well-marked and the GILLS near the head—sea and inland-water animals.

'**petrophyte,** n. [Bot.] Any plant living on stone.

pe'trosa, n. [Zoo.] The specially hard part of the TEMPORAL bone in man, forming the hollow for the inner ear.

pe'trosal, 1.a. [Zoo.] Formed of very hard, solid bone; to do with the PETROSA. 2.n. A bone in other animals taking the place of the petrosa in man.

'**petrous,** a. Very hard, stone-like, sp. [Zoo.] said of very solid bone; to do with the PETROSA or the PETROSAL.

'**pewter,** n. A mixed metal, formed chiefly of tin, with lead and/or copper, ANTIMONY and BISMUTH making up almost 20% of it, in old times much used for plates, spoons, etc. but now of little use.

-pexy, -pexia, -pexis, nn. [Med.] The operation of fixing a part to another or in the desired position by stitching, etc.

Peyer's glands or **patches.** [Zoo.] Massed groups of LYMPH pockets in the walls of the INTESTINE.

phaco-. LENS: **pha'coid(al),** a. [Zoo., Med.] The CRYSTALLINE LENS of the eye: '**-cyst,** n., '**-scle'rosis,** n., **-'therapy,** n.

'**phacolity,** n. [Geol.] A small INTRUSION of LENS-like form at the top of an ANTICLINE.

phaco'malacia, n. [Med.] A condition in which the LENS of the eye becomes soft.

'**phaeic, phae'ochrous,** a. [Zoo.] Dark, sp.

grey-brown, in colour, said sp. of LEPI-
DOPTERA.

ph(a)eo-. [Biol.] Brown, dark.

'phaeophyll, n. [Bot.] The brown colouring-
substance of PHAOPHYCEAE.

Phaeo'phyceae, Phaeo'phyta, nn.pl. [Bot.]
A great group of dark yellow-brown
ALGAE, most of which are sea-plants,
freq. of very great size, fixed to stones or
the sea-bed by a HOLDFAST, and having
leaf-like, waving bands, sometimes
branched, on a stem, the special colour
of which is caused by their having in them
the yellow colouring-substance, FUCO-
XANTHIN, as well as CHLOROPHYLL.

'phaeoplast, n. [Bot.] A brown CHROMATO-
PHORE of PHAEOPHYCEAE.

'phaeospore, n. [Bot.] Any SPORE having
PHAEOPLASTS in it.

phage, n. BACTERIOPHAGE. **-phage,** n.
[Biol.] Animal or plant taking as food,
or sp., CELL causing the destruction of,
the named thing. **-phagic, -phagous,** aa.
-phagia, -phagy, nn.

phage'daenia, n. [Med.] An ULCERATION
quickly covering more and more of the
skin etc. and causing destruction.

'phagocyte, n. [Zoo.] Any of different sorts
of LEUCOCYTE having the power of
changing their form and taking in
BACTERIA, bits of waste material, etc.,
which are present in the blood or other
body-liquids, by simply overrunning
them. **phago'cytable,** a. Said of BACTERIA
which readily undergo phagocytosis.
phago'cytic, a. **'phagocy'tolysis, pha-
'golysis,** nn. The destruction of pp.
'phagocy'tosis, n. The taking in of small
bodies by pp., sp. the destruction of
BACTERIA in this way.

'phalange, n. [Bot.] A group of STAMENS
joined by their threads. [Zoo.] PHALANX.

'phalanx (phalanges), n. [Zoo.] Any of the
bones of the fingers or toes. **pha'lan-
g(e)al,** a.

'phallus, n. [Zoo.] The PENIS in higher
animals; the part in an EMBRYO which
undergoes development into the penis or
CLITORIS. **'phallic,** a. **'phallic 'symbol.**
[Psych.] Any form giving a suggestion of
an upright PENIS, present in a DREAM
etc., and representative of some sex
desire etc. which has been forced back
into the SUBCONSCIOUS mind.

'phanero-. Open to view, readily seen.

'phanero'crystalline, a. [Mineral.] Formed
of CRYSTALS of a size to be clearly seen.

'phanerogam, n. [Bot.] A seed- or flowering-
plant, opp. CRYPTOGAM. **Phanero'gamae,
Phanero'gamia,** nn.pl. The old name for
SPERMATOPHYTA, or flowering plants,
based on the fact that in such plants the
apparatus of REPRODUCTION is readily
seen. **phane'rogamous,** a.

'phanerophyte, n. [Bot.] Tree or plant whose

DORMANT BUDS are not covered by earth
but produced on branches out in the air.

'phantasy, n. FANTASY.

'phantom, a. Seeming, not being what is
named in the true, full sense. **p. 'tumour.**
[Med] A TUMOUR-like expansion in
some part of the body, caused by gas,
the knotting of muscles, etc., seen in
HYSTERIA.

pharma'ceutics, n.pl. [Med.] The science of
the use of medical substances; the art or
business of making, mixing, measuring
out, etc. medical substances. **pharma-
'ceutical,** a. **pharma'ceutical chemist.**
Expert in p., sp. one who makes up
medical substances ordered for ill persons
by a medical man.

'pharmacist, n. PHARMACEUTICAL CHEMIST.

'pharmaco-. (To do with) medical substances: **-'therapy,** n.

pharma'cology, n. The science of medical
substances and their effects.
'pharmaco'logic(al), aa. **pharma'cologist,** n.

'pharmaco'p(o)eia, n. [Med.] A book listing
DRUGS, chemicals, and medical substances with directions for making, testing, and using them, and an account of
their properties, etc., sp. one put out by
medical or other authorities, such as the
British P., which is backed by the
British government; a store of medical
substances. **'pharmaco'p(o)eal,** a.

'pharmacy, n. [Med.] PHARMACEUTICS; a
store trading in medical substances.

pharyn'geal, a. [Zoo., Med.] To do with the
PHARYNX.

pharyng(o)-. PHARYNX (and . . .): **pharyn-
'gitis,** n. [Med.], **pha'ryngo-b'ranchial,** a.
[Zoo.], **pharyn'gology,** n. [Med.], **pha-
'ryngo'plegia,** n. [Med.].

pha'ryngoscope, n. [Med.] An instrument for
looking into the PHARYNX.

'pharynx, n. [Zoo.] In back-boned animals,
the thick-walled pipe joining the mouth
and the OSEOPHAGUS, the inside of the
throat; in lower animals the first part of
the ALIMENTARY CANAL going from the
mouth.

phase, n. Any of a number of possible
stages or conditions. [Astron.] Any of the
different forms of the moon as seen from
the earth at different times in the moon's
journey round it (*see* MOON, CRESCENT,
GIBBOUS); any of the like changes in the
look of any PLANET caused by changes in
position cutting off the light from some
part of it. [Phys.] A stage or point in a
PERIODIC motion, freq. given as they
measure of an angle, 360° being taken as
representative of a complete PERIOD.
[Phys.-Chem.] Any of the physically
different parts of a group of forms of
material substance, as a gas, a liquid, and
a solid, which are together in space,
touching but not mixing; all the pp. of

the same sort, physically and chemically, in such a system. [Biol.] A stage in MEIOSIS or MITOSIS. [Zoo.] COLOUR PHASE. **p. 'angle.** [Astron.] The angle between the earth and the sun as seen from a PLANET. **p-'contrast 'microscope.** A MICROSCOPE in which small DIFFERENCES of DENSITY in the thing being viewed are put into sharp CONTRAST by the use of special LENSES etc., causing light INTERFERENCE effects and so making it possible to see TRANSPARENT parts, for example, of a TISSUE. **p. 'difference** or **dis'placement.** [Phys.] The amount by which two motions, currents, etc., are different in p., that is, by which any p. of one is earlier or later than the parallel p. of the other. **p. 'meter.** [Elec.] An instrument for measuring the p. difference between two electric currents or forces. **p. rule.** [Phys.- Chem.] The rule that in a system having P pp., F DEGREES OF FREEDOM, and C COMPONENTS, $P + F = C + 2$. **p. 'splitter.** [Elec.] An apparatus by which two electric currents different in p. may be got from one machine, **p. ve'locity.** [Phys.] The VELOCITY of a wave forming part of a complex of waves.

-phasia, n. [Med.] Talking.

'phellem, n. [Bot.] CORK.

'phelloderm, n. [Bot.] The inner coat of the PHELLOGEN, formed of PARENCHYMA.

'phellogen, n. [Bot.] The substance round a root or stem in higher plants, under the outer covering, forming CORK on its outside and PHELLODERM on its inside.

'phen'acetin(e), n. [Chem., Med.] The substance $C_{10}H_{13}NO_2$, used medically for overcoming FEVER.

'phenocryst, n. [Geol.] Any of the greater CRYSTALS in a stone of PORPHYRITIC TEXTURE.

'phenoge'netics, n.pl. [Biol.] The science of the operation of GENES in the process of an animal's or a plant's development. **'phenoge'netic,** a.

'phenol, n. [Chem.] A CRYSTALLINE substance, C_6H_5OH, with acid properties and a special smell, produced by DISTILLATION from ORGANIC substances such as wood and coal, and from the middle FRACTION of COAL-TAR—a strong, burning poison, used, mixed with water, as an ANTISEPTIC, and in making other chemicals, BAKELITE, etc.; any of a group of substances having an –OH group joined in a BENZENE RING, like p., and having the properties of ALCOHOLS and feeble acids. **phe'nolic,** a. Of, like, having in it, or produced from, p.

phe'nology, n. [Biol.] The science of the relations between CLIMATE and the regular behaviour of plants and animals, such as the time of flowering, MATING, etc. **pheno'logical,** a. **phe'nologist,** n.

phe'nomenon (phe'nomena), n. Any fact or event open to observation by the senses and of interest to science; any very strange or uncommon fact or event. [Psych.] Anything experienced through the senses at a given time. **phe'nomenal,** a. Sp., very uncommon, surprising. **phe'nomenalism,** n. [Philos.] The theory that all knowledge is of pp. only and that no knowledge of anything further is possible; the theory that only pp. have existence. **phe'nominalist,** n. **phenome'nology,** n. The observation and recording of pp., or that branch of a science limiting itself to this without attempting any theory of their cause, deeper relations, etc.

'phenotype, n. [Biol.] The qualities a plant or animal has in fact, as opp. those it would have if conditioned completely by its INHERITANCE independent of its conditions of existence; a TYPE produced by the reaction between a given GENOTYPE and given living-conditions; a group of plants or animals having like pp. though different genotypes, or an animal or plant of such a group. **pheno'typic,** a. **phenotypic 'character.** Quality produced in a plant or animal by its condition of living.

'phenyl, a., n. [Chem.] (Having in it) the AROMATIC MONOVALENT group –C_6H_5. **p. group.** P.

-phil(e), n., a. [Biol.] Plant or animal which is —PHILOUS.

-philia, n. [Med.] The condition of having a tendency to, or an unhealthy desire or love for, what is named.

phi'lology, n. The science of language, covering the history, development, grouping, sounds and structure of languages, and their relation to the general development of those nations etc. whose mother-tongues they are.

phi'losophy, n. The general name for reasoned attempts to give answers to the deeper questions of existence which are outside the range of science, covering theories of the cause and purpose of all things, of right and wrong, of knowledge and art, of the relation of mind to body, etc.; in relation to any science or body of knowledge, the general ideas on which it is based, the beliefs forming its starting-point and conditioning its reasoning. **phi'losopher,** n. Writer on or teacher of p. in the first sense. **philo'sophic(al),** aa.

-philous, a. [Biol., Biochem.] Having a love for, forming a connection with, having its growth or living in or on. **-philly,** n.

phleb(o)-. VEIN.

phle'bitis, n. [Med.] INFLAMMATION of the wall of a VEIN, producing a THROMBUS inside it.

'phlebograph, n. [Med.] An instrument for

recording PULSATION taking place in a VEIN.

'phleboscle'rosis, n. [Med.] SCLEROSIS of the wall of a VEIN.

phle'botomy, n. [Med.] The act or system of opening a VEIN and letting out blood from a person as a way of stopping BLEEDING inside or for a number of other medical purposes. **phle'botomize,** v.i. Do the operation of p. **phle'botomist,** n.

phlegm, n. [Med.] A thick MUCUS produced in the throat, nose, and upper breathing-pipes in over-great amount in certain diseases, and freq. coughed up.

'phlegmon, n. [Med.] INFLAMMATION of a TISSUE, with the producing of PUS, pain, and SWELLING. **'phlegmonous,** a.

'phloem, n. [Bot.] In higher plants, the TISSUE by which food substances produced by the leaves are taken about the plant, made up of SIEVE TUBES, PARENCHYMA, and gen. COMPANION CELLS, sometimes with other sorts in addition, such as FIBRES, which are freq. very long and strong and of use in industry.

phlo'giston, n. [Chem.] In the theory widely current in the 1700's, a substance said to be present in all bodies able to be burned, the process of burning being the separating of p. from the rest of the body. **phlo'gisticated air.** Priestley's name for N.

'phlycten, phlyc't(a)ena, nn. [Med.] A small PUSTULE, sp. on the CONJUNCTIVA. **phlyc-'t(a)en-ar, -ous,** aa. **phlyc'tenul-e, -a,** nn. A small p. **phlyc'tenular,** a.

-phobe, n., a. (One) having a PHOBIA for what is named. **-'phobia,** n. PHOBIA.

'phobia, n. [Med., Psych.] A very great and unreasoning fear and hate of some special thing, for example, of being shut in.

phobo'taxis, n. [Biol.] Motion of a plant or animal away from a damaging STIMULUS.

phon-. PHONO-.

phon, n. [Acous.] Unit measuring how loud a sound is, equal to the INTENSITY in DECIBELS of a sound having a FREQUENCY of 1000 which is as loud as the sound to be measured.

pho'nation, n. [Zoo.] Act or process of producing sound by some apparatus in the body.

phon'autograph, n. [Acous.] An early form of recording machine in which sound-waves are sent into a horn, causing the motion of a DIAPHRAGM to be recorded by a needle fixed to it and touching a smoked roller.

-phone. Sound, voice (used in names of instruments for transporting sound, or giving out recorded sound).

phone, n. [Philol.] A language sound.

pho'neidoscope, n. [Phys.] An instrument for the observation of the motion of sound-waves as seen in their effect on a thin FILM of soap and water.

'phoneme, n. [Philol.] The group of sounds of which what is commonly looked on as the same sound, is seen to be made up when the little changes made by different voices, or dependent on the place of the sound in a word, etc., are taken into account.

pho'nendoscope, n. [Med.] A form of STETHOSCOPE making the sounds under observation louder.

pho'nesis, n. PHONATION.

pho'netic, 1.a. To do with the sounds made by the voice in talking, or with the science of PHONETICS; (of letters or other signs) representative of sounds. **p. 'symbols.** The special signs, truly representative of language sounds, used in place of letters in PHONETICS, or, in word-lists, teaching, etc., to make clear the sound of a word. **-'ally,** adv. **pho-'netico-.**

pho'netics, n. The general science of the sounds made in talking, the way in which they are produced by the voice apparatus, their relations to one another, their relations to letters, the changes they undergo in the history of a language, etc.; the system of sounds of a given language; PHONETIC SYMBOLS. **phone'tician,** n. One expert in p.

'phonic, a. Of, to do with sound, sp. with language sounds. [Phonet.] VOICED.

phon(o)-. Sound, language-sound, talk.

phono'chemistry, n. The science of the effect of sound-waves on chemical reactions.

'phonodeik, n. [Acous.] An instrument for making camera pictures of sound-waves in air.

'phonogram, n. [Acous.] A GRAMOPHONE record. [Phonet.] A sign representative of the sound of a word, a group of letters, or one letter.

'phonograph, n. [Acous.] An early name for a GRAMOPHONE, now no longer used. **phono'graphic,** a.

pho'nography, n. [Phonet.] The art of writing in signs representative of the way words are sounded (other than PHONETIC SYMBOLS), or such a system of writing, such as shorthand; an account of language-sounds and the phonetic symbols representative of them.

'phonolite, n. [Geol.] A sort of FINE-GRAINED IGNEOUS ROCK, a form of TRACHYTE (see p. 192).

pho'nology, n. [Phonet.] The science of language sounds, sp. the history and theory of sound-changes, in a language or family of languages; the PHONETICS of a language.

pho'nometer, n. [Acous.] An instrument for measuring the INTENSITY of a sound or the FREQUENCY of a sound-wave.

-phore, [Chem.] Group of ATOMS responsible

for the property named. [Biochem., Biol.] A part or CELL producing or responsible for what is named. [Bot.] A supporting stem or other structure on which what is named has its place. -**phoric, -phorous,** aa.

'**phosgene,** n. [Chem.] $COCl_2$, a poison gas of great weight, readily made liquid, having a very strong smell, and specially damaging to the breathing-apparatus, used in DYE-making.

'**phosphagen,** n. [Biochem.] A substance with PHOSPHORIC ACID in it present in the muscles of back-boned and other animals and freeing ENERGY for their use by its ready reactions.

'**phosphate,** n. [Chem.] Any SALT or ESTER of a PHOSPHORIC ACID, a group having great value as FERTILIZERS. **p. rock.** [Geol.] ROCK having in it a great amount of $Ca_3(PO_4)_2$, from which P may be got.

phos'phatic deposits. [Geol.] Great beds of PHOSPHATE ROCKS, present sp. in places with little rainfall.

'**phosphene,** n. [Physiol., Med.] A sense of light produced in a way other than by light falling on the eye, for example, by PRESSURE on the eyeball.

'**phosphide,** n. [Chem.] Any substance formed by uniting P with one other ELEMENT or one RADICAL.

'**phosphine,** n. [Chem.] PH_3, a poison gas with a disgusting smell.

'**phosphite,** n. [Chem.] Any SALT or ESTER of PHOSPHORIC ACID.

'**phospho'lipid(e),** n. [Biochem.] A fat having in it N and P.

'**phospho'protein,** n. [Biochem.] Any of a group of PROTEINS in which P is part of the MOLECULE.

'**phosphor,** n. [Phys.] Any substance which gives out light as the effect of BOMBARDMENT by X-RAYS, ULTRA-VIOLET rays, quickly-moving ELECTRONS, etc.

'**phosphor bronze.** A sort of BRONZE made specially hard, strong, and elastic by the addition of P.

phospho'rescence, n. [Chem.] The property or condition of giving out light with little or no heat, as seen in P, sp. the property of certain substances of giving out light for a short time after light or other rays falling on them have been stopped; the soft light given out by P when slowly uniting with O in air, or by any form of p. [Zoo.] The giving out of light by an animal, such as certain insects. **phospho'rescent,** a. **phos'phoroscope,** n. Instrument for making observations of p.

'**phosphoreted 'hydrogen.** PHOSPHINE.

phos'phoric acid. [Chem.] Any of the acids H_3PO_4, $H_4P_2O_7$, HPO_3 and H_2PO_3, sp. the first of these (*orthophosphoric acid*).

'**phosphorous acid.** [Chem.] H_3PO_3, formed by the reaction of cold water with an OXIDE of P, P_4O_6.

'**phosphorus,** n. Chemical ELEMENT, at. no. 15, at. wt. 30·98, sign P, in its common form a white or yellow, wax-like, CRYSTALLINE substance, giving out a very feeble light in air and an unpleasing smell, present in earth, natural water, a great number of MINERALS, and all living substance, and, though itself a poison, necessary to all living things.

phot, n. [Optics] C.G.S. unit of ILLUMINATION = 1 LUMEN/cm^2.

'**photic,** a. To do with light, sp. [Biol.] with the producing of light by, or the effects of light on, plants and animals. **p. 'region.** The top part of the sea, which gets the most light.

'**photism,** n. [Psych.] A sense or idea of light or colour produced by, or going with, a sense-experience got through a sense-ORGAN other than the eyes, for example the connection of different colours with different sounds.

photo-. Light, in relation to light, produced by light, of light and . . . :— **pho'tophilous,** a. [Bot.] **pho'tophily,** n. [Bot.] '**-polymerization,** n. [Phys.-Chem.], '**-'thermic,** a. [Phys., Chem.]; PHOTOGRAPHIC.

'**photoac'tinic,** a. (Of light rays) having the power of producing chemical effects, said sp. of blue or ULTRA-VIOLET rays.

'**photo'active,** a. PHOTOSENSITIVE.

'**photobi'otic,** a. [Biol.] For the (healthy) existence of which light is necessary.

'**photoca'talysis,** n. [Chem.] The increasing (or the opposite) of the rate of a chemical reaction by light. **photo'catalyst, photo-'catalyzer,** nn. A substance acting as a go-between in p., the effect of light on it being to make it a CATALYST. **photocata'lytic,** a.

'**photocell,** n. PHOTOELECTRIC CELL.

'**photo'chemical,** a. Of, to do with the chemical effects of light. **p. cell.** [Elec.] An electric CELL having an ELECTROLYTE and two ELECTRODES of like metal between which a POTENTIAL DIFFERENCE is produced by sending light onto one of them. **p. in'duction.** The fact that a p. process takes time; the time between the direction of light to anything and the producing of a chemical reaction in it.

'**photo'chemistry,** n. The branch of chemistry to do with the chemical effects of light.

'**photo'chronograph,** n. [Astron.] An instrument for recording the time of an event, such as the TRANSIT of a star, PHOTOGRAPHICALLY.

'**photoconduc'tivity,** n. [Elec.] The property of certain substances, for example, SELENIUM, of undergoing a change in the degree to which they let electric current through when there is a change in the amount of light falling on them. '**photocon'ductive,** a.

'photo con'trol. The control of the reactions of plants by the use of light.

'photo'current, n. [Elec.] The current produced by a PHOTO-ELECTRIC CELL when acted on by light.

'photody'namics, n. [Biol.] Science of the effects of light in causing the motion of living things, sp. plants and their parts.

'photoelas'ticity, n. [Mech.] The property seen in TRANSPARENT substances under STRAIN of producing colours on the lines of strain when POLARIZED light is sent through them; a way of seeing where the strains are in a body by sending polarized light through a transparent copy of it.

'photo-e'lectric, a. Of, to do with, the electric effects of light, sp. the giving off of ELECTRONS by a metal, or the lowering of the electric RESISTANCE of a substance, when acted on by light. p. cell. [Elec.] Any electric CELL whose electric properties are changed by the operation of light, sp. one producing a current by the p. effect. p. current. A current of photoelectrons. p. effect. Sp., the freeing of ELECTRONS from a metal by light. 'photoelec'tricity, n. Electric current or properties produced as the effect of light: PHOTO-ELECTRONICS. 'photo-'electron, n. An ELECTRON made free from the SURFACE of a substance, sp. a metal, by light.

'photo-elec'tronics, n. The science of the effects on one another of ELECTRICITY and light, sp. those having to do with free ELECTRONS.

'photo-e'mission, n. [Elec.] The giving out of PHOTOELECTRONS. photo-e'missive, a.

'photo-en'graving, n. The process of making a picture on a copper plate for printing from by covering it with a coat of GELATIN, on which the thing to be pictured has been PHOTOGRAPHED, and then burning the SURFACE of the plate away with acid acting through the GELATIN.

'photogen, n. [Zoo.] A light-producing apparatus or substance in animals.

photo'genic, a. In PHOTOGRAPHY, having qualities which come out well in a camera picture. [Biol.] Light-producing.

photo'grammetry, n. The making of maps and SURVEYS by PHOTOGRAPHY. photo-'grammeter, n. Sort of camera used for this purpose. 'photogram, n. Picture made by a photogrammeter.

pho'tography, n. The science of making pictures of things by causing, with a LENS, the rays coming from the things to make an IMAGE on a plate etc. coated with a chemical giving a reaction to light, the picture then being uncovered by washing the plate with another chemical producing a dark DEPOSIT wherever the light has had its effect, so that prints may be made from it (by a like operation of light on SENSITIZED paper). 'photograph, 1.n. Picture made by p. 2.v.t. Make picture of by p. pho'tographer, n. Person making photographs. photo'graphic(al), aa.

'photograv'ure, n. The process of printing from copper plates or rollers on which a picture has been produced by PHOTO-ENGRAVING; a picture so made.

photo'halide, n. [Chem.] Any HALIDE which is acted on by light.

photo'heliograph, n. [Astron.] A form of TELESCOPE for making camera-pictures of the sun. 'photoheli'ography, n.

'photo-ioni'zation. [Phys.] The IONIZATION of an ATOM or a MOLECULE as the effect of a blow from a high-ENERGY PHOTON.

photo-'isomerization, n. [Chem.] ISOMERIZATION effected by light.

'photoki'nesis, n. [Zoo.] Motion in reaction to light. 'photoki'netic, a.

'photolumi'nescence, n. [Phys.] LUMINESCENCE caused in a substance by the falling on it of light or ULTRA-VIOLET rays. 'photolumi'nescent, a.

pho'tolysis, n. [Chem.] Process by which the MOLECULES of a substance are broken up as the effect of light or other rays. [Bot.] The effect on the grouping of CHLOROPLASTS in plants of changes in the amount of light.

photo'magnetism, n. MAGNETO-OPTICS.

pho'tometer, n. [Optics] An instrument for measuring LUMINOUS FLUX, LUMINOUS INTENSITY, ILLUMINATION, etc., by comparison with a light of fixed value. photo'metric(al), aa. pho'tometry, n.

photo'micrograph, n. A picture of normal size of something very small, made by a camera joined to a MICROSCOPE. 'photo-micro'graphic, a. 'photomi'crography, n.

'photon, n. [Phys.] One QUANTUM of light or RADIANT ENERGY.

'photonasty, n. [Biol.] The reaction of a plant to changes in the general amount of light, such as shutting or opening at nightfall.

pho'topathy, n. PHOTOAXIS.

photo'period, n. [Bot.] The best number of daylight hours for the normal growth and flowering of a given plant, some doing best with a shorter day, others with a longer. photo'peri'odic, a. To do with the p. or with photo-periodism. '-ism, n. [Bot.] The reaction of plants to a greater or smaller number of daylight hours, the fact that plants have pp.

'photophobe, n. [Biol.] An animal, plant, or part which does best in the dark or takes a position turned away from the light. photo'phobia, n. The condition of being photophobic, sp. [Med.] The normal reaction of the eye, causing an automatic shutting of it, against a strong light; the condition of being unnormally SENSITIVE to light, unable to be in the light without pain. **photo′phobic,** a.

′photophore, n. [Zoo.] A light-producing part in certain fish, sp. any of a number of places in the skin. [Med.] ENDOSCOPE with electric light.

′photopho′resis, n. [Phys.-Chem.] The motion of very small bodies, such as dust grains in the air, away from, or in the direction of, a strong light.

′photoph′thalmia, n. [Med.] OPHTHALMIA produced by being for some time in very strong electric light, the effect of ULTRA-VIOLET rays.

pho′tophygous, a. [Bot.] Shade-loving. **pho′tophygy,** n.

photo′product, n. [Chem.] Any substance produced by the chemical effect of light.

pho′topic, a. [Zoo.] (Said of eyes) in a condition to see in a good light, opp. SCOTOPIC. **pho′topia,** n.

pho′topsia, n. [Med.] The sense of experiencing sudden rays of light, stars, etc., before the eyes, as the effect of some unhealthy condition of the RETINA or nerves.

′photore′ceptor, n. [Zoo.] A nerve-ending or sense-apparatus designed to give a reaction to light. **′photore′ceptive,** a.

′photo′sensitive, a. [Phys., Chem.] Giving a physical or chemical reaction to light or any like form of RADIANT ENERGY. **p. cell.** [Phys.] PHOTOELECTRIC CELL. **′photo-sensi′tivity,** n.

′photosphere, n. [Astron.] The light-giving outer part of the sun, that is, as far into the sun as it is possible for us to see. [Zoo.] Any of the light-giving structures in CRUSTACEA.

photo′stable, a. [Phys., Chem.] Not acted on by light.

′Photostat, 1.n. Trade name for an apparatus for making copies of flat things such as pages of print or writing, designs, maps, etc., straight onto SENSITIZED paper by the operation of light; picture made by a p. 2.v.t. and i. Make copy of (book, etc.) with P.

′photosur′veying, n. SURVEYING with a PHOTOTHEODOLITE.

′photo′synthesis, n. [Bot.] The building up, in the green parts of plants, of CARBOHYDRATES from CO_2 and water, which is possible only with the help of ENERGY got from sunlight and coming into operation through CHLOROPHYLL. **′photosyn′thetic,** a.

′photo′taxis, n. TAXIS in reaction to light. **photo′tactic,** a.

′photote′legraphy, n. The telegraphing of a camera or other non-motion picture by SCANNING it with light-rays, using these for MODULATION of the current, and doing the process the other way round at the other end of the telegraph line.

′photothe′odolite, n. A form of camera used in SURVEYING, by which a number of pictures are taken of the same point at the same time from different angles, so that its position may be worked out by comparison.

′photo′therapy, **′photothera′peutics,** nn. [Med.] The use of light or ULTRA-VIOLET rays on the body for medical purposes, as in skin diseases. **′photothera′peutic, photo′therapic,** aa.

′photo′tonus, n. [Bot.] The condition of a plant or part which is able to give its normal reaction to light. **photo′tonic,** a.

′photo′tropism, n. [Biol.] TROPISM in reaction to light. [Phys.-Chem.] PHOTOTROPY. **′phototrope,** n. Plant or chemical substance having p. **photo′tropic,** a.

pho′totropy, n. [Phys.-Chem.] Loss or change of colour caused by light or like rays, sp. the property, seen in certain substances, of having different colours in light of different WAVE-LENGTHS.

′photovol′taic, a. [Elec.] To do with the producing of a POTENTIAL DIFFERENCE, and so an electric current, between two bodies by light.

′phragma, n. [Biol.] A division separating two parts of a vessel, two masses of substance, etc., sp.:— [Zoo.] Any infolded part or ingrowth of the body wall of an insect, etc.; [Bot.] a division of an OVARY formed by an ingrowth from the wall.

′phragmacine, n. [Geol.] The thin pointed, inner SHELL of a BELEMNITE.

′phragmoid, a. [Bot.] Having divisions at right angles to the long AXIS.

′phrenic. a. [Zoo.] To do with the DIAPHRAGM of higher animals.

phreno-. PHRENIC (and . . .).

′phrenograph, n. [Med.] An instrument for recording the motion of the DIAPHRAGM in breathing.

phre′nology, n. The theory, not taken seriously by science, that the outline of the head at any point gives signs of the degree of development of the part of the brain under it, or the process, based on this theory, of feeling the head to get an idea of a person's qualities and powers.

′phthisis, n. [Med.] A wasting away of the body, a process of becoming very thin and feeble; disease marked by p., sp. TUBERCULOSIS of the LUNGS. **′phthisical,** a.

***p*H-value.** [Chem.] The measure of the CONCENTRATION of H IONS in a SOLUTION, given as a number on the scale of the

LOGARITHMS of $\dfrac{1}{\text{H concentration}}$, used as

a sign of the degree to which the solution is ACID or ALKALINE, 0, or the greatest H-ion concentration, being the most acid end of the scale and 14, or the least H-ion concentration being the most alkaline.

'**phycochrome**, n. [Bot.] The colouring-substance of blue-green ALGAE, formed of CHLOROPHYLL and PHYCOCYANIN.

'**phyco'cyanin**, n. [Bot.] The blue colouring-substance giving PHYCOCHROME its blue-green colour.

'**phycoe'rythrin**, n. [Bot.] The red colouring-substance of red ALGAE.

phy'cology, n. [Bot.] The science of ALGAE.

'**Phycomy'cetes**, n.pl. [Bot.] A great CLASS of lower FUNGI ranging from very simple ALGA-like forms to forms with some sort of sex development and a normal, but not SEPTATE, MYCELIUM.

'**phyco'phaein**, n. [Bot.] The brown colouring-substance of brown ALGAE.

'**phyco'xanthin**, n. [Bot.] The yellow-brown colouring-substance of DIATOMS.

'**phyla**, n.pl. See PHYLUM.

phy'letic, a. See PHYLUM.

-**phyll**, n. Leaf.

'**phyllade**, n. [Bot.] A very small SCALE-like leaf produced before the true leaves.

'**phyllary**, n. [Bot.] Any of the small leaves round the base of the flower-head in COMPOSITAE.

'**phyllite**, n. [Geol.] An ARGILLACEOUS ROCK representative of a stage in METAMORPHISM between SLATE and MICA SCHIST, having a softly bright look caused by very small mica CRYSTALS.

'**phyll(o)-**. Leaf: 'phylloge'netic, a.; phyll'ogeny, n., 'phylloid, a., phyll'ophagous, a. [Zoo.] 'phyllophore, n.

'**phyllo'branchia**, n. [Zoo.] A GILL formed of a number of thin plates.

'**phylloclad(e)**, phyllo'cladium, nn. A green stem acting as a leaf, freq. so flat and wide as to have the look of one, but sometimes round-bodied.

'**phyllody**, n. [Bot.] The changing of flower-parts into leaves.

'**phyllome**, n. [Bot.] A general name for all leaves and leaf-like structures.

'**phyllomor'phosis**, n. [Bot.] The changing of leaves at different times of the year; PHYLLODY.

phyl'lophorous, a. [Bot.] Having on it, producing, leaves.

'**phyllopode**, n. PHYLLOPODIUM.

phyllo'podium, n. [Bot.] The stem and AXIS of a leaf, sp. of a plant of the FILICALES.

phyl'lopodous, a. [Zoo.] Having leaf-like swimming-feet, as BRANCHIOPODA.

'**phylloquinine**, n. VITAMIN K.

'**phyllosi'phonic**, a. [Bot.] (Of stem) having LEAF GAPS.

-**phyllous**, a. [Bot.] Having leaves of the number or sort named, -leaved.

'**phyllo'tax-is, -y**, nn. [Bot.] The system of the distribution and order of leaves on a stem. **phyllo'tactic**, a.

'**phyllo'xanthin**, n. XANTHOPHYLL.

-**phylly**, n. [Bot.] The condition of being -PHYLLOUS.

'**phylo-e'phebic**, a. [Zoo.] To do with time of greatest VITALITY of a group or SPECIES.

'**phylo'genesis, phy'logeny**, nn. [Biol.] The history of the development of a sort or division of animals or plants, opp. ONTOGENESIS. 'phyloge'netic, phyl'ogenic, aa.

'**phylum** (phyla), n. [Biol.] A chief division of animals (or, in less common use, plants for which the parallel grouping is generally named a DIVISION) made up of forms of like general structure and having as its divisions, if any, CLASSES (see pp. 560 and 562). **phy'letic**, a. To do with pp. or with the line of development from a common form. **phy'letic 'classifi'cation**. [Biol.] A system of plant grouping based on development from early forms.

phy'siatrics, n. [Med.] The science of the body's ways and power of fighting disease naturally without medical help; the use of p. as a medical instrument.

'**physic**, 1.n. Any medical substance taken by mouth sp. an APERIENT. 2.v.t. Give p. to. **phy'sician**, n. A person whose business is the medical care of those who are ill, sp. one expert in the use of p. etc., as opp. a SURGEON.

'**physical**, a. To do with material things or forces, sp., to do with the body as opp. the mind; to do with, controlled by the laws of, physics as opp. those of chemistry, psychology, etc. **p. as'tronomy**. ASTROPHYSICS. **p. change**. A change not caused by a chemical reaction, as a change of form or structure produced by a physical force. **p. 'chemistry**. The science of the relation between physical and chemical properties and changes. **p. 'culture, p. edu'cation**. Training in the development and care of the body, its muscle power, etc. **p. ge'ography**. That branch of geography giving an account only of the physical conditions in different countries, as against that having to do with their produce or trade, or with the political divisions of the earth. **p. ge'ology**. That branch of geology which has to do with the outer physical condition of the earth and the changes taking place in it, the development of mountains, rivers, waste lands, the effects of weathering and earth-shocks etc. **p. 'mixture**. A complex of two or more substances which, though the substances are not chemically united, may not be broken up into them by simply sorting or draining one from another, for example, a SOLUTION. **p. optics**. That branch of the science of light which has to do with it as based on a physical event, a wave-motion, etc., see GEOMETRICAL OPTICS. **p. 'property**. Any property of a material thing or substance which has nothing to do with its chemical reactions, for example weight, size, colour, power of letting light through, etc. **p. 'spectrum**. [Phys.]

A range of RADIATIONS grouped in the order of their FREQUENCIES. **p. 'therapy.** [Med.] The use against disease of p. operations, such as rubbing, baths, sunbaths, electric current, etc. **physico-.**

physics, n.pl. The science having to do with the properties and effects of material things, and the changes in them not caused by chemical processes, that is, chiefly with the motion of bodies and their parts and the producing of ENERGY, covering the sciences of MECHANICS, heat, light, sound, and electric and other RADIATIONS. **'physicist,** n. Expert in p. [Biol.] One having the belief that living processes may all be accounted for by physics and chemistry.

physio-. PHYSIOLOGICAL:— **'-patho'logic-al,** a.

'physio'chemical, a. BIOCHEMICAL.

physi'ognomy, n. [Bot.] The special look of a plant society, from which even at a distance it is clear of what sort of plants it is made up. **physiog'nomica**(l), aa.

physi'ography, n. PHYSICAL GEOGRAPHY, sp. GEOMORPHOLOGY.

physi'ology, n. [Biol.] That branch of biology which has to do with the processes going on in living things and the working of their different parts, as opp. their structure. **physio'logic(al),** aa. **physio'logical a'natomy.** [Biol.] The science of the relation between the structure of a living thing or part and its purpose, way of working. **physiological 'antidote.** [Med.] Any medical substance undoing the effects of a poison by causing an opposite physiological effect, such as increasing the rate of a process which the poison has the effect of slowing down, etc. **physiological 'chemistry.** BIOCHEMISTRY. **physiological 'optics.** That branch of OPTICS having to do with the eye and seeing. **physiological 'primary.** [Optics, Psych.] Any of the three colours of light (red, green and blue of a certain WAVE-LENGTH) by the uniting of which a TRICHROMAT makes all other colours. **physiological psy'chology.** That branch of psychology which has to do with the relation between the working of the nerves, muscles, etc. and sense-experience or other events in the mind. **physiological race.** [Biol.] A group of plants or animals forming part of a SPECIES from the point of view of structure, but different from the rest in their food, their reactions to certain things, their way of living, or (of PARASITES) their power of causing disease, etc. **physiological 'saline** (or **salt so'lution**). [Zoo., Med.] NORMAL SALINE. **physiological (race) 'specializ'ation.** [Biol.] The existence in a SPECIES of a number of physiological races. **physiological 'zero.** [Biol.] The lowest TEMPERA-TURE at which the METABOLISM of a living thing or substance is able to go on.

'physio'therapy, n. [Med.] PHYSICAL THERAPY.

phy'sique, n. The special structure and physical qualities of the body of a person or RACE of men.

'physocele, n. [Med.] A TUMOUR having in it gas or air.

physo'clist-ic, -ous, a. [Zoo.] (Of fish) having no pipe joining the AIR-BLADDER and the ALIMENTARY CANAL.

'physo'gastry, n. [Zoo.] The condition of having an ABDOMEN of great size, as certain insects.

'physo'stigmine, n. [Chem., Med.] A CRYSTALLINE ALKALOID, $C_{15}H_{21}O_2N_3$, got from the seeds of a plant, which has an effect on the PARASYMPATHETIC NERVOUS SYSTEM, and is used medically for slowing the heart-rate, etc., and for CONTRACTING the PUPIL of the eye.

'physo'stom(at)ous, aa. [Zoo.] (Of fish) having at all stages the AIR-BLADDER joined to the ALIMENTARY CANAL by a pipe.

-phyte, n. [Bot.] Plant having the property, or living in the places, etc., named.

'phytic acid, n. [Biochem.] An acid, $C_6H_6(PO_4H_2)_6$ present in plants, sp. the outer parts of grain, which makes INSOLUBLE SALTS with Ca, Fe and Mg, and so keeps these substances from being taken into the blood from the INTESTINE.

'phyto-. Of, to do with, plants, sp. PARASITIC plants. **'-bi'ology,** n., **'-chemistry,** n., **'-'genesis,** n., **'-'hormone,** n., **'phytoid,** a., **phy'tology,** n., **'-physi'ology,** n.

'phytochrome, n. [Bot.] Any colouring substance of a plant necessary for its chemical processes, as CHLOROPHYLL.

phy'togenous, a. Coming from, produced by, plants.

'phytoge'ography, n. The science of the distribution of plants on the earth.

phy'toma, n. [Bot.] That part of a plant's substance other than that forming the sex-apparatus.

'phytomer, n. [Bot.] A unit of plant structure; a bit of a plant producing a BUD, the smallest part of a stem, root, or leaf which has the power, it cut off, of growth into a new plant.

'phyto'morphic, a. [Biol.] Having a plant-like structure.

'phyton, n. PHYTOMER.

phy'tonomy, n. [Bot.] Laws of the development of plants.

'phytopa'thology, n. [Bot.] The science of plant diseases and unnormal forms, sp. as caused by PARASITES. [Med.] The science of diseases caused by plant parasites.

phy'to-phagous, -philous, aa. [Zoo.] Using plants as food.

'phyto'pharmacy, n. [Bot.] The science of the use of chemical substances to overcome plant diseases or PARASITES.

'phyto'plankton, n. [Bot.] Plant PLANKTON.

phy'tosis, n. [Med.] Any disease caused by a plant PARASITE.

phy'totomy, n. [Bot.] The cutting up of plants to get a knowledge of their structure.

'phyto'toxin, n. Any poison produced by a plant.

pi. The Greek letter π, which *see*.

'pia 'mater. [Zoo.] The delicate skin round the brain and SPINAL CORD in higher animals.

'pica, n. [Med.] A desire for unnatural food, such as coal or chalk, seen in man and other animals in certain diseases or conditions.

'piceous, a. Of, to do with, or like PITCH, sp. [Zoo.] of the colour of pitch.

'pick-up, n. [Elec.] The apparatus in connection with the NEEDLE on a RECORD PLAYER by which the VIBRATIONS of the needle moving in the lines in the record are taken to an AMPLIFIER.

pic'ramic acid., [Chem.] A red CRYSTALLINE solid, got by the REDUCTION of PICRIC ACID and used in the making of DYES.

'picric 'acid, n. [Chem.] $C_6H_2(NO_2)_3OH$, a yellow CRYSTALLINE solid with strongly acid properties, used to make EXPLOSIVES, in DYEING, and medically as an ANTISEPTIC, sp. in dressing burns.

pi'ezo-, pieso-. PRESSURE; PIEZO-ELECTRIC.

pi'ezo-chemistry, n. The science of the effects of great pressure on chemical reactions.

pi'ezo-crystalli'zation, n. [Geol.] The forming of CRYSTALS under great PRESSURE, as in OROGENESIS.

pi'ezo-elec'tricity, n. Electric properties produced by the piezo-electric effect. pi'ezo-electric. a. Of, to do with, producing or produced by, having the property of undergoing, the piezo-electric effect. pi'ezo-e'lectric 'crystal. [Radio] A CRYSTAL of some p.-e. substance such as QUARTZ cut to a special size and form and used as an OSCILLATOR or RESONATOR in radio apparatus. pi'ezo-e'lectric effect. The effect produced by an ELECTRIC FIELD on certain CRYSTALS of causing their expansion in one direction and CONTRACTION in another, or the parallel effect by which PRESSURE on such a crystal is the cause of opposite ELECTRIC CHARGES on its different faces.

pie'zometer, n. [Phys.] An instrument for measuring to what degree the amount of space taken up by a liquid may be made smaller by PRESSURE. pi'ezo'metric, a. pie'zometry, n.

pig iron. CRUDE iron produced by SMELTING, gen. in the form of long CASTS named 'pigs'.

'pigment, n. A colouring-substance, for example, one used for coating SURFACES (as paint or the powder which gives a paint its colour), or [Biol.] one present in the form of a solid or liquid in the CELLS of a plant or animal, so that they are seen as coloured. 'pigmentary, a. 'pigmentary colour. [Zoo.] A colour given to an animal by the ABSORPTION of certain light-rays by p. in the skin, as opp. SURFACE COLOUR. pigmen'tation, n. [Biol.] The condition of being coloured by p.; the distribution of p. in an animal, plant, or part, its system of colouring, pig-'mented, a.

pile, n. [Phys.] ATOMIC PILE. [Elec.] VOLTAIC PILE, or any BATTERY of like structure, used for producing a DIRECT CURRENT of high VOLTAGE. [Med.] HAEMORRHOID.

'pileo'rhiza, n. [Bot.] A root covering.

'pileum, n. [Zoo.] The top of the head of a bird.

'pileus, n. [Bot.] The umbrella-like structure forming the top of the fruit-body of some FUNGI. [Zoo.] The like part of a MEDUSA. [Meteor.] CAP.

pi'lidium, n. [Zoo.] The LARVA of NEMERTINEA, in form somewhat like a hat with a group of CILIA on the top point and the young worms undergoing development inside.

pi'liferous, a. [Bot.] Having hairs on it, covered with hairs; ending in a thin hairlike point. p. 'layer. That part of the outer skin of a young root producing the ROOT HAIRS.

'pilose, a. [Bot.] Covered with hairs, sp. not very stiff hairs.

'pilot, n. [Aeronautics] Person driving an airplane; (used only before another n.) something done on a small scale acting as a guide, or as a test operation, before putting the chief operation into effect. p. ba'lloon. [Meteor.] A rubber ball full of H sent into the upper air for the purpose of getting, by the observation of its motion, a knowledge of the direction and force of air-currents. p. 'burner or jet. In a boiler etc., a small gas-flame kept burning all the time so that a greater burner may be lighted from it. p. cell. [Elec.] A CELL of a BATTERY whose condition is taken as a sign of the condition of the rest of the battery. p. lamp or 'signal. [Radio, Telegraph, etc.] A small light in connection with an electric system or apparatus which comes on as a sign, sometimes that the current is on, sometimes that something is needing attention.

'pilotax itic, a. [Geol.] Having, or being, a ROCK structure formed of a network of threads of FELDSPAR with other materials in very small grains between them, seen in certain LAVAS.

'pilus (pili), a. [Biol.] A hair-like structure.

'pi-'meson, n. A MESON of REST MASS 273 when + or −, 264 when NEUTRAL, producing MU-MESONS and ELECTRON on DECAY.

'pimple, n. [Med.] Any small PAPULE or PUSTULE of a not very serious sort.

'pinaco'cyte, n. [Zoo.] Any of the flat, plate-like CELLS forming the outer coat of the skin of sponges.

Pi'nales, n.pl. CONIFERAE.

'pincers, n.pl. An instrument, gen. scissors-like in structure, with two short curved arms meeting at the end, used for gripping things. [Zoo.] A p. -like gripping apparatus as seen in some CRUSTACEA and insects.

'pinchbeck, n. Metal made of copper with between 10% and 15% of zinc, used in cheap jewels as a copy of gold.

'pinchcock, n. A gripping instrument for putting on a rubber pipe so that the opening through it may be made smaller or completely shut to keep back the liquid coming through it.

pinch ef'fect. [Elec.] The narrowing of a body of liquid metal when a strong electric current (of about 10^5 AMPERES) is sent through it, caused by MAGNETIC attraction between the parts of the metal.

pi'neal eye. [Zoo.] The PARAPINEAL or PINEAL BODY when it has an eye-like structure and is still used as an eye, or at least is clearly representative of a part which at one time in the history of the animal was used as an eye.

pi'neal gland or 'body. [Zoo.] In back-boned animals, a small hollow outgrowth on the middle line of the top of the front part of the brain, in man and most animals having no clear purpose but possibly producing a HORMONE, but in certain REPTILIA and CYCLOSTOMATA forming an eye-like structure at the top of the head. pineal'oma, n. [Med.] A TUMOUR of the p. g.

'pin-eyed, a. [Bot.] (Of a GAMOPETALOUS flower) having the STIGMA tall enough to be seen like a pin-head in the opening of the narrow pipe formed by the united lower parts of the PETALS, with the STAMENS shorter and out of view.

'pinhole 'camera. A camera having a very small hole in a thin metal plate in place of a LENS.

'pinion, n. [Mach.] A small toothed wheel turning against a greater one and giving or getting motion from the push of the teeth as they come, one after another, into the spaces between the teeth on the other wheel.

'pink, v.i. KNOCK.

'pinkeye, n. [Med.] A form of CONJUNCTIVITIS readily given by one person to another.

'pinna, n. [Bot.] Any of the small leaves of a PINNATE leaf. [Zoo.] A bird's feather or wing; a FIN; in MAMMALS, the outer ear.

'pinnate, a. [Biol.] Feather-like in having parts or branches on two opposite sides of a middle structure, sp. [Bot.] (of a COMPOUND LEAF) having the separate leaves or branches ranged in this way on opposite sides of the chief stem (see picture p. 223). pinn'ately, adv.

pinn'atifid, a. [Bot.] (Of a leaf) cut PINNATELY, about half-way to the stem, into narrow divisions.

pinn'atiped, a. [Zoo.] Having the toes united by skin or more solid substance, sp. to make them of use in swimming.

pinn'atisect, a. [Bot.] (Of leaf) cut PINNATELY almost to the middle stem into a number of narrow divisions (see picture p. 223).

pinni-. Feather:— '-form, a.

Pinni'pedia, n.pl. [Zoo.] A division of the CARNIVORA made up of PINNATIPED water animals. 'pinniped, n., a. (Animal) of the P.

'pinnule, n. [Bot.] Any of the divisions of a PINNA. [Zoo.] Any of the further divisions of a PINNATE part; any of the side-branches edging the arms of CRINOIDEA. 'pinnular, a. 'pinnulate, a.

pint, n. Unit of liquid or dry measure, =0·568 l. (G.B.) or 0·4732 l. (U.S.A.), or in APOTHECARIES' MEASURE = 20 British or 16 U.S.A. FLUID OUNCES.

'pintle, v. [Mach.] A pin or rod in a machine or structure, sp. an upright pin, on which some part is turning. p. chain. SPROCKET CHAIN.

'pio'note, n. [Bot.] A flat stretch of unsexed SPORES, freq. jelly-like, produced in LAYERS by some FUNGI.

'pipeclay, n. [Geol.] A grey-white CLAY, almost free from iron.

pi'pette, n. [Chem.] A small instrument for taking up small amounts of liquid or gas for measuring, changing them from one vessel to another, etc.—in its simplest form a thin glass pipe marked with a scale, into which a liquid is forced by SUCTION effected by a rubber bulb or the user's mouth.

Pi'rani gauge. [Phys.] An instrument for measuring a very high degree of VACUUM by the effect of the gas which is still present on the electric RESISTANCE of a wire.

'Pisces, n. [Astron.] The 12th SIGN of the ZODIAC, the 'fish'.

'Pisces, n.pl. [Zoo.] A SUB-PHYLUM or CLASS of back-boned water animals, in old groupings made up of all fish, in some present-day groupings of all fish but ELASMOBRANCHS, and in others limited to those with a framework of true bone, breathing only by GILLS and having

FINS in PAIRS, gill-covers supported by bone, and a skin covered with SCALES, that is, most present-day fish.

pisc(i)-. Fish: **'pisciform,** a., **pis'civorous,** a.

pi'scicolous, a. [Zoo.] (Of PARASITES) living inside fish.

'pisciculture, n. Fish farming, the producing of fish for food.

'pisiform, a. [Geol.] In the form of round grains of some size. **p. bone.** [Zoo.] A small round bone of the CARPUS in some back-boned animals. **'pistil,** n. [Bot.] A separate CARPEL of a group of carpels; GYNOECIUM, sp. when formed of one carpel, or of two or more carpels united; separate carpels taken as a group. **'-late,** a. (Of a flower) having a p. but no or incomplete STAMENS, female.

'piston, n. In a machine, a part moving forward and back or up and down as the effect of, or against, the force of a liquid or gas—gen. in the form of a CYLINDER, or a round plate etc., on the end of a rod, working tightly inside a pipe, as in a pump. **p. head.** In a steam engine, the part of the p. fixed to the rod by which it is moved. **p. ring.** An elastic ring of metal going round a p. and springing out against the wall of the pipe so as to keep any liquid etc. from getting through the space between the p. and the wall. **p. valve.** A p. working in a pipe with openings, and controlling them as a VALVE.

pit, n. [Biol.] A small hollow in a SURFACE. [Med.] The p. marking the place where a PUSTULE has been. [Bot.] A small, clearly marked-off, place in the wall of a plant CELL which does not become thicker as the parts round it do, so forming a small hollow with a thin base (the **p. 'membrane),** designed to come opposite a like place in another cell touching it so as to make a way for liquids to go from one to the other. **p. of the stomach.** The hollow on the front of man's body under the chest. **'pitted,** a.

pitch, n. [Chem.] A thick black or very dark, sticky liquid, becoming solid when cold, produced from TAR, PETROLEUM, etc., or got from the earth in the form of ASPHALT.

pitch, n. (Angle of) slope, such as that of a roof, part of an instrument or machine, etc., or [Geol.] of a BED. [Mach.] The distance between any two of a number of regularly spaced like parts, as the teeth on a wheel, the THREADS of a screw. [Acous.] That property of a TONE which is dependent in part on the sound PRESSURE but chiefly on the number of VIBRATIONS per second of the sound waves, the greater this number being, the higher the p.

'pitchblende, n. A brown or black MINERAL with a somewhat glass-like look, formed chiefly of URANIUM OXIDE without regular CRYSTAL structure, from which Ra and U are got.

'pitcher, n. [Bot.] A leaf or part of a leaf of special form, like a water-vessel, produced by certain plants and acting as a sort of mouth in which small insects are kept and acted on by water or substances produced by the plant till they are ready for digestion by it.

pith, n. [Bot.] The loose, sponge-like material forming the middle part of the stem in DICOTYLEDONS and GYMNOSPERMS. **p. ball.** [Phys.] A ball of p. used, because of its little weight, in apparatus designed for giving examples of the operation of electric attraction, etc.

Pithe'canthropus, n. [Anthrop., Zoo.] The sort of early man of the later TERTIARY PERIOD of which our knowledge is based on bones unearthed in Java in 1891, very like a great APE in bone-structure, sp. of the face, with a man-like but small brain and walking upright.

pi'tocin, n. [Zoo., Med.] A HORMONE produced by the PITUITARY GLAND and causing the reaction of the muscles of the UTERUS by which offspring are forced from the body of the mother.

pi'tometer, n. An instrument for automatically recording changes in the rate of a current of water, of which the chief parts are two PITOT TUBES.

'Pitot(:s) tube. [Phys.] A pipe, shut at one end and bent into a short arm at right angles at the open end, which is placed in moving air with its mouth facing the current for measuring the rate of it, used in airplanes etc. **'Pitot comb.** A group of small P.tt. for taking readings of the PRESSURE of moving air at different points at the same time.

pi'tressin, n. VASOPRESSIN.

pi'tuitary, n. [Zoo.] A small body fixed to the INFUNDIBULUM of the brain in back-boned animals, having two divisions, the **anterior p.** at the front, and the **posterior p.** at the back, which have different purposes, controlling between them, through the substances produced by them, a number of very important processes of the body, such as growth. **p. gland** or **body.** P. **p. membrane.** The MUCOUS MEMBRANE of the nose.

pi'tuitrin, n. [Med., Zoo.] A substance got from the POSTERIOR PITUITARY of cows etc. and having in it PITRESSIN and OXYTOCIN.

'pivot, 1.n. [Mach.] A point, short pin, etc., on which a part is turning, a FULCRUM. 2.v.i. Be turning on a p. **p. joint.** [Zoo.] A JOINT at which only ROTARY motion is possible. **'-al,** a.

pla'centa (placentae or placentas), n. [Zoo.] The flat structure to which the EMBRYO of a VIVIPAROUS animal is fixed in the body of the mother, in which its TISSUES and those of the mother are very near together, or to some degree united, so that O and food substances from the blood of the mother make their way into that of the embryo, and waste substances of the blood of the embryo make their way out into that of the mother, by OSMOSIS. [Bot.] The part of an OVARY wall producing the OVULES. **pla′cental**, a. **pla′centate, a. ′placen′tation**, n. [Bot.] The way in which pp. are placed in an OVARY (see PARIETAL, MARGINAL, AXILE, and FREE CENTRAL). [Zoo.] The development of the p.; the form and structure of a p., and the way in which it is joined to the UTERUS (see DECIDUATE, DIFFUSE, COTYLEDONARY, ZONARY, DISCOIDAL, METADISCOIDAL). **′Placen′talia**, n.pl. Animals having a p., EUTHERIA.

placer, n. [Geol., Mining] A DEPOSIT of sand or small stones put down by a river, etc. with which there is mixed a great amount of gold or some other metal or ORE of value.

′placode, n. [Zoo.] Any plate-like structure; in the EMBRYO of backboned animals, a thick part of the outer covering forming the first stage in the development of nerve GANGLIA in the head.

Placo′dermi, n.pl. [Zoo.] A group, in some systems, a CLASS, of EXTINCT fish covered with great plates of bone, and having an AUTOSTYLIC JAW.

′placoid, a. [Zoo.] Plate-like. **p. scale**. A tooth-like SCALE formed of a plate-like base of DENTINE with a sharp, hard point coming out from it, such as those with which the body of an ELASMOBRANCH is completely covered.

plagi(o)-. Sloping.

′plagioclase, n. [Min.] A general name for the group of TRICLINIC FELDSPARS made up of the SILICATE of Al and Na mixed in different amounts with the silicate of Al and Ca.

plagio′clinal, a. [Geol.] Said of structures which are not parallel to the general direction of the STRIKE in any place.

′plagio′tropic, plagi′otropous, aa. [Bot.] (Of a root, branch, etc.), sloping in the direction of its growth, making an angle other than a right angle with the upright, in reaction to the earth's pull. **plagio-′tropism**, n.

plague, n. [Med.] Any death-causing EPIDEMIC disease which has a tendency to get out of control, sp. BUBONIC PLAGUE.

plain, n. [Geol.] A great stretch of level or almost level land, gen. not much higher than sea-level.

plain muscle. [Zoo.] UNSTRIATED MUSCLE.

pla′nation, n. [Geol.] The development by a

river of its FLOOD-PLAIN by the putting down of material in certain places and the taking away of it in others.

Planck's ′constant, Planck's ′quantum of action. [Phys.] The fixed number giving the RATIO of the ENERGY of a QUANTUM of a RADIATION to its FREQUENCY, sign *h*, value $6·624+10^{-27}$ ERG-SECS. **Planck's (radiation) law.** The QUANTUM THEORY.

plane, n. A flat SURFACE, physical or as pictured by geometry; any of the chief supporting surfaces of an airplane, sp. the level stretch of two opposite wings. **p. of polari′zation.** [Optics.] The plane to which the VIBRATIONS of p.-polarized light are limited. **p. of ′symmetry.** The p. cutting anything, sp. a CRYSTAL, into two SYMMETRICAL halves. **p.-′polarized.** [Optics] (Of light) so POLARIZED that all the VIBRATIONS are in straight lines in the same p. **p. polari′zation.**

′planet, n. [Astron.] A body going round the sun like the Earth, that is, Mercury, Venus, Earth, Mars, Jupiter, Saturn, Uranus, Neptune or Pluto. **plane′tarium**, n. A working copy of the planetary system, in which small balls or circles of light are put in motion by a machine, sp. a room with an arched roof against which the pp. are seen in motion. **′-ary**, a. **′planetary e′lectron.** [Phys.] Any of the ELECTRONS moving round the NUCLEUS of an ATOM. **′planetary ′nebula.** [Astron.] Any of certain small NEBULAE of a regular form which have a round structure in the middle.

plane′tesimal, n. [Astron.] See p. hypothesis; a small solid body in space going round a middle mass like the PLANETS. **p. hy′pothesis.** The theory that the sun's system was formed by the effect on a great mass of gas of a star coming near it, causing it to put out two opposite arms of gas and at the same time to be given a turning motion, as the effect of which parts were broken off the out-stretching arms and the PLANETS were formed by the uniting of the greater masses with numbers of very small bits named pp.

′planetoid, n. Any of the very small p.-like bodies moving round the sun in a wide band, chiefly between MARS and JUPITER.

plani-. Plane, flat, level.

′planiform, a. [Zoo.] (Of a JOINT) having the meeting SURFACES almost flat.

plan′imetry, n. The measuring of the AREAS of plane curved forms. **plan′imeter**, n. Instrument for p. made up of a moving arm with a point on it which is moved round the edge of the form to be measured supported by a small wheel having a scale from the readings on which the AREA may be worked out.

′planisphere, n. [Astron.] A plane picture

THE PLANETS

Symbol	Name	Distance from sun (million miles)	Axial rotation	Orbit time	Equatorial diameter (miles)	Synodic period of orbit (days)
☿	Mercury	36·0	88 days	88 days	3,100	115·88
♀	Venus	67·2	23 hrs. 56 mins.	224·75 days	7,700	583·92
⊕	Earth	93·0	23 hrs. 56 mins.	365·25 days	7,927	—
♂	Mars	141·5	24 hrs. 27 mins.	687 days	4,200	779·94
♃	Jupiter	483·3	9 hrs. 51 mins.	11·86 years	88,700	398·88
♄	Saturn	886·1	10 hrs. 14 mins.	29·46 years	75,100	378·09
♅	Uranus	1783	10 hrs. 49 mins.	84·01 years	29,300	369·66
♆	Neptune	2793	14 hrs. 0 mins.	164·79 years	27,700	367·49
♇	Pluto	3660	6 days 9 hrs.	248·43 years	3,600	366·74

SUN

MERCURY   VENUS   PLUTO   MARS

JUPITER

NEPTUNE   URANUS

EARTH

SATURN

Name	Mean surface temperature (°C)	Number of satellites	Volume (Earth = 1)	Mass (Earth = 1)	Density (g/cm³)	Escape velocity (Km/sec)
Mercury	191	0	0·055	0·053	5·3	4·2
Venus	69	0	0·91	0·815	4·95	10·3
Earth	17	1	1·00	1·000	5·52	11·2
Mars	−37	2	0·15	0·107	3·95	5·0
Jupiter	−146	12	1317	318·0	1·33	61·0
Saturn	−179	9	762	95·22	0·69	37·0
Uranus	−207	5	50·0	14·55	1·56	22·0
Neptune	−220	2	42·0	17·23	2·27	25·0
Pluto	−226	0	1·0(?)	0·9	5·0(?)	10·0(?)

representative of the CELESTIAL SPHERE and its bodies.

'plankton, n. [Biol.] The plants and animals, most of which are very small, living in the water of seas, rivers etc., chiefly near the top, and moving freely with it but having little or no power of swimming, very important as food for fish and other sea animals.

'plan(o)-. [Biol.] With the power of moving about: 'planospore, n., 'plano'zygote, n.

plano-. PLANI-.

'planoblast, n. [Zoo.] A free-swimming HYDROID PERSON.

'plano'concave, a. (Of a LENS) flat on one side, hollow on the other.

'plano'convex, a. (Of a LENS) flat on one side, curved out on the other.

'plano'gamete, n. [Biol.] A GAMETE with the power of moving about, sp. one of the CILIATED SPORES seen in some ALGAE.

plano'gamic, a. [Bot.] Having pp.

'planosome, n. [Biol.] A CHROMOSOME in addition to the normal ones, or one not forming part of a PAIR.

plant, n. [Biol.] Any of that group of living things which have little or no power of digestion of solids and so get all or most of their food in the form of gas or of SOLUTIONS of chemical substances in water, further marked off from animals, though not completely, by the fact that they have no power of moving from place to place and that their reactions all seem to be automatic.

'planta, n. [Zoo.] The under side of the foot in back-boned land animals; the flat end-part of a PROLEG; the end-division of the leg in insects. 'plantar, a.

'plantigrade, n., a. [Zoo.] (Animal) walking on all the under part of the foot, not on the toes only.

'plantula, n. PULVILLUS.

'planula, n. [Zoo.] The form of LARVA seen sp. in COELENTERATA, free-swimming, flat with an egg-like outline, and having an outer coat of CILIATED CELLS. 'planular, a. 'planulate, a. 'planuliform, a. 'planuloid, a.

'planum, n. [Zoo.] A flat SURFACE of bone, or a flat part of a bone, sp. in the head of higher animals.

plaque, n. [Med.] Small, flat mass, mark, or place, on the skin or other part of the body. [Zoo.] THROMBOCYTE.

-plasia, -plasis, nn. [Biol., Med.] Development, forming.

-plasm, n. [Biol.] PLASMA.

'plasm(a), n. [Biol.] PROTOPLASM; the clear, water-like, liquid part of blood, milk, and other body substances. [Phys.] That condition of material substance, somewhat like that of a gas, in which there are great distances between the MOLECULES and great amounts of ENERGY stored in the PARTICLES, producing

NEUTRAL particles, IONIZED particles and free ELECTRONS all moving freely and COLLIDING with one another—the condition of most of the material in our UNIVERSE, for example in the IONOSPHERE and INTERSTELLAR space, and of special interest for the different uses which are made of it under controlled conditions in GAS DISCHARGE TUBES; in a gas discharge tube, that part of the gas in which the IONS of opposite sign are almost equal in number so that there is no CHARGE. [Mineral.] A green TRANSLUCENT form of CHALCEDONY, used as a jewel stone. p. or plas'matic 'membrane. [Bot.] The very thin skin, formed of fat and PROTEIN, covering the PROTOPLASM of all plant CELLS under the cell-wall and round any VACUOLE. [Zoo.] The very thin skin covering the PROTOPLASM of animals such as AMOEBAE which have no other covering. p. 'physics. The science of material substance in the p. condition. 'plas'matic, 'plasmic, aa. plasm(o)-.

plasma'gen(e), nn. [Biol.] A body in the PROTOPLASM of a CELL outside the NUCLEUS by which some property of a cell is handed on to its offspring, a physical unit of INHERITANCE which is not transported by the CHROMOSOMES.

'plasma'lemma, n. [Biol.] PLASMA MEMBRANE.

'plasmocyte, n. LEUCOCYTE.

'plasmoderma, n. [Bot.] A very thin skin of PROTOPLASM round a VACUOLE.

'plasmodesm (plasmodesmata), n. [Biol.] A delicate thread of PROTOPLASM forming, with a number of others, a connection between two CELLS.

plas'modiocarp, n. [Bot.] A long, sometimes branched, body with SPORES undergoing development inside it, formed from the PLASMODIUM in some MYXOMYCETES.

plas'modium (plasmodia), n. [Biol.] A mass of uncovered PROTOPLASM with a number of NUCLEI and the power of moving and taking in solid food like an AMOEBA, formed by the uniting of separate amoeba-like CELLS without the uniting of their nuclei. [Bot.] The plasmodial plant body of MYXOMYCETES. plas'modial, a. Of, to do with, like, a p.

plas'mogamy, n. [Biol.] The uniting of PROTOPLASM without the uniting of NUCLEI; PLASTOGAMY. plas'mogamous, a.

'plasmoid, n. [Phys.] A light-giving body seen in a GAS DISCHARGE TUBE when the current is of very high FREQUENCY.

plas'molysis, n. [Biol.] The loss of water from a living CELL as the effect of OSMOSIS, causing the mass of PROTOPLASM to become smaller. 'plasmolyse, v.t. and i. (Make) undergo p. plasmo'lytic, a.

'plasmon, n. [Biol.] The CELL-substance outside the NUCLEUS as an instrument of

HEREDITY, the PLASMAGENES taken together.

'plasmosome, n. [Biol.] A small grain of CYTOPLASM; a NUCLEOLUS formed of cytoplasm and going away in the process of CELL-division without mixing with the CHROMOSOMES, said to be a *true nucleolus* as opp. a KARYOSOME or like body.

plas'motomy, n. [Zoo.] In certain PROTOZOANS, the division of a PLASMODIUM into two or more.

-plast, n. [Biol.] A CELL or small unit of living substance.

'plaster, n. A paste, commonly made by mixing sand and water with CaO, $Ca(OH)_2$, or $CaSO_4.2H_2O$, which becomes hard when dry and is used in building for coating inside walls, etc. [Med.] (A bit of) cloth coated with medical substances made into a sort of paste which becomes tightly fixed to the skin when put onto a part of the body, used for covering wounds, keeping other dressings in place, or to take away INFLAMMATION of the muscles etc. by producing heat, etc. **p. cast.** [Med.] A stiff dressing made by coating thin material with p. of Paris and used for covering damaged parts of the body, sp. where bones have been broken, so as to keep them from moving. **p. of Paris.** $2CaSO_3H_2O$, a white powder forming a very hard substance when mixed with water and dried, used for MOULDED ornament in building and medically for p. casts.

'plastic, 1.a. [Phys.] Paste-like in the property of being able to undergo change of form in any direction without being broken or damaged, and of keeping the form given to it if not acted on by any other force. [Biol., Med.] Able to undergo, in the condition of undergoing, growth, development, or adjustment, by natural processes; to do with, causing, the building up of TISSUES. 2.n. [Phys., Chem.] Any p. substance, natural or man-made. **plastics,** n.pl. Sp., the great group of pp. now produced by the POLYMERIZATION of ORGANIC substances, which may be THERMOSETTING or THERMOPLASTIC, and are used as materials for making a wide range of MOULDED things, such as electric INSULATORS, radio etc. chests, floorcoverings, raincoats, and things for use in the house, etc. **p. 'surgery.** That branch of medical work which has to do with changing the form of parts of the body or building them up again after loss or damage, by GRAFTING etc. **plas-'ticity,** n. **plasti'cize,** v.t. Make (more) p., sp. by the addition of some other substance. **'plasti'cizer,** n. A substance mixed with another, sp. with a CELLULOSE coating, to make it more p., more readily

formed or worked, or to keep its p. properties.

'plastid, n. [Bot.] Any of certain small bodies in the CYTOPLASM of plants which have to do with the producing of PIGMENTS (and are then named CHLOROPLASTS or CHROMOPLASTS), or which give signs of this property when light gets to them (LEUCOPLASTS).

plasto'chondria, n. MITOCHONDRIA.

plas'togamy, n. [Zoo.] PLASMOGAMY of PROTOZOA.

plas'tometer, n. An instrument for measuring PLASTICITY.

'plastosome, n. MITOCHONDRIUM.

'plastron, n. [Zoo.] The hard plate covering the under side of an animal of the CHELONIA. 'plastral, a.

'plastron respi'ration. [Zoo.] A system of breathing in some underwater insects in which a store of air is kept under a network of delicate hairs.

-plasty, n. [Biol.] Process of development, growth. [Med.] PLASTIC SURGERY having to do with what is named by the first part of the word.

plate, 1.n. Metal made into flat, smooth stretches, equally thick at all points; square etc. of metal p., or like bit of glass or other hard material, sp. a metal p. with writing, design, etc. cut into or stamped on it for printing from, or a p. of glass, metal, or other hard material, coated with a substance which is acted on by light, for use in a camera. [Phys.] An ELECTRODE having the form of a thin p., as the ANODE of a VACUUM TUBE. [Bact.] A flat, open glass vessel, sp. a PETRI DISH, used for CULTURES, or the material in it. [Biol., Med.] A structure or growth which is p.-like in any way, as the separate units of a PLASTRON; a THROMBOCYTE; the structure to which false teeth are fixed for putting into the mouth, or this with its teeth. 2.v.t. Get covered with pp. of metal, or, sp., with a thin coating of metal (*see* ELECTROPLATING). **p. current.** [Elec.] The current going between the CATHODE and ANODE in a VACUUM TUBE. **p. glass.** A specially smooth and level sort of glass, gen. made by CASTING into great pp. and then rolling and polishing. **'plated,** a. **'-let,** n. Sp. a THROMBOCYTE.

'plateau (plateaux), n. [Geog.] A great stretch of high, level (or chiefly level) land, gen. with lower land all, or almost all round it, but sometimes walled in by mountains (*see* TABLELAND).

'platen, n. The flat plate or roller backing the paper and forcing it against the letters in a printing- or writing-machine; the moving table on which the material to be cut by certain sorts of machine is fixed.

'platinate, n. [Chem.] A SALT of PLATINIC ACID.

pla'tinic, a. [Chem.] Of, to do with, having in it Pt, said sp. of those substances in which the VALENCY of Pt is 4. **p. acid.** Pt(OH₄), a feeble acid.

'plat'inise, v.t. Get coated, united, or IMPREGNATED, with Pt.

platinite, n. An ALLOY of iron and nickel sometimes used in place of Pt in electric light bulbs.

'platinum, n. Chemical ELEMENT, at. no. 78, at. wt. 195·23, sign Pt, a hard silver-white metal, readily worked and able to be pulled out into thin wires, not readily attacked by chemicals, noted for its high MELTING-POINT and the fact that it undergoes an expansion when heated about equal to that of glass. **p. black.** Pt in the form of a soft black powder got from a SOLUTION of p. TETRACHLORIDE (PtCl₄) by PRECIPITATION. **p. group, p. metals.** [Chem.] The group of ELEMENTS which are like Pt in their chemical and physical properties, separated into the *light platinum group*, made up of Rh, Ru, and Pd, metals of SPECIFIC GRAVITY about 12, and the *heavy platinum group*, Os, Ir, and Pt, metals of much greater weight (s.g. over 21). **p. sponge.** Pt in the form of a grey sponge-like mass, having a marked power of OCCLUSION for H, O, and some other gases, and used as a CATALYST. **p. ther'mometer.** An apparatus for measuring TEMPERATURE by changes in the electric RESISTANCE of Pt wire. **'platinize,** v.t. Give (a body) a thin coating of Pt or get (a substance) mixed with small grains of Pt.

'platy-. Wide and/or flat: **'-ce'phalic,** a.

'platy'dactyle, a. [Zoo.] Having fingers or toes with flat ends.

'Platyhel'minthes, n.pl. [Zoo.] A PHYLUM of METAZOA made up of flat worms without COELOM or ANUS, waste being sent out through branching pipes with FLAME-CELLS—gen. small, HERMAPHRODITE, and PARASITIC. **platy'helminth,** n. Animal of the P. **'platyhel'minthic,** a.

pla'tysma, n. [Zoo.] A wide flat stretch of muscle at the right and left sides of the neck in higher animals, having a connection with the muscle and nerve of the side of the face.

plax, n. [Zoo.] A flat, plate-like structure.

play, [Mech.] (Of a part of a machine) condition of having space for motion, of not being so tightly fixed into another part as to be unmoving; the motion of a part in this condition.

-plegia, n. [Med.] PARALYSIS.

plei-, pleio-, pleo-. More or greater (than is common), a great number of: **plei'androus,** a. [Bot.], **pleio'sporous,** a. [Bot.]. **plei'omerous,** a. [Bot.] Having a great

number of, or more than the normal number of, PETALS or SEPALS. **plei-'omery,** n.

pleio'morph-ic, -ous, a.[Bot.] Having two or more forms in one CYCLE of existence. [Zoo.] POLYMORPHIC. **pleiomorphism,** n.

'pleion, n. [Meteor.] A part of a country where something such as rainfall, degree of heat, etc., is much greater than that normal for the other parts.

'ple(i)opod, n. [Zoo.] Swimming-leg of CRUSTACEA.

'pleio'tropism, n. [Biol.] The condition in which one GENE has an effect on more than one quality in the offspring.

'Pleistocene, 1.a. [Geol.] Of the P. Period. 2.n. The P. Period. **P. Period.** The latest stage in the earth's history before the present, in which most of N. Europe and N. America was from time to time covered with ice, named the *Great Ice Age* (*see* p. 558).

'plenum, n. [Phys.] A space full of material of some sort, opp. VACUUM.

pleo'cholia, n. [Med.] The forming of over-much BILE PIGMENT.

pleo'chroism, pleo'chromatism, nn. [Min.] The property of some MINERALS of being different in colour when looked at in the direction of different CRYSTAL AXES. **pleo'chroic,** a. **pleochroic 'halo.** A pleochroic dark edging round a bit of RADIO-ACTIVE substance present inside a MINERAL CRYSTAL. **'pleochro'matic,** a.

'pleocy'tosis, n. [Med.] A condition in which the number of LEUCOCYTES is increased, sp. in the CEREBROSPINAL FLUID.

pleo'morphic, a. [Biol.] PLEIOMORPHIC. [Cryst.] The property of CRYSTALLIZING in two or more quite different forms. **pleo'morphism,** n.

'pleonaste, n. [Mineral] Natural OXIDE of Me, Fe and Al, a dark green, brown or black sort of SPINEL

'pleo'phagons, a.[Biol.] PARASITIC on more than one sort of plant.

pler'ergate, n. [Zoo.] REPLETE.

'plerome, n. [Bot.] The middle part of the MERISTEM at the growth-points of stems and roots, from which the STELE is later formed.

ple'rosis, n. [Med.] The forming of new body substance after loss or wasting. **ple-'rotic,** a.

plesio'morph-ous, -ic, aa. [Cryst.] Very like in CRYSTAL form but different chemically. **plesio'morphism,** n.

'plessigraph, n. [Med.] A form of PLEXI-METER.

'plessor, n. [Med.] A small hammer used in PERCUSSION.

'plethora, n. [Med.] (The condition of having) an unnormally increased amount of blood in the body, with or without an

increase in the number of red blood-CELLS.
ple'thoric, a.

ple'thysmograph, n. [Med.] An instrument for recording changes in the size of a part of the body caused by changes in the amount of blood in it. plethys'mography, n.

'pleura, n.pl. See PLEURON.

'pleura (pleurae), n. [Zoo.] The bag-like structure of delicate skin forming the outer covering of a LUNG and the inner coating of the side of the body where the lung is.

'pleural, a. [Zoo.] To do with the PLEURA(E) or with the side(s) of the body; to do with a PLEURON. p. 'cavity or sac. The space in the body where a LUNG is, or that narrow part of it between the PLEURA and the body-wall in which is a small amount of thin liquid to keep the two from rubbing in the process of breathing.

'pleurisy, pleu'ritis, nn. [Med.] INFLAMMATION of the PLEURA(E). pleu'ritic, a.

'pleurite, n. PLEURON.

pleur(o)-. To do with, near, a side of the body or the PLEURA(E).

pleuro'branchiae, n.pl. [Zoo.] Breathing-apparatus of certain ARTHROPODA, coming out of the side walls of a SOMITE.

'pleurodont, a. [Zoo.] Having the teeth fixed by their sides to the side of the JAW bone.

'pleuro'dynia, n. [Med.] FIBROSITIS of the muscles near or in connection with the RIBS, causing pain in the chest, sp. when breathing or coughing.

'pleuron (pleura), n. [Zoo.] The side wall, gen. in two parts, of a division of the THORAX in an insect; a side outgrowth of the SHELL covering a division of the thorax in CRUSTACEA.

'pleuroperito'neum, n. [Zoo.] The skin coating the inside of all the body and forming a covering for the parts inside it, in animals having no DIAPHRAGM.

'pleurotribe, a. [Bot.] (Of flowers) having the ANTHERS and STIGMA so placed that they are touched or rubbed by the sides of insects coming in.

'plexal, a. [Zoo.] Of, to do with, a PLEXUS.

'plexiform, a. [Zoo.] Like a network, of very complex structure.

plex'imeter, n. [Med.] A small, hard, flat plate put against the body to take the blow in PERCUSSION.

'plexus, n. [Zoo.] A network, sp. of blood-vessels or nerves. plex'itis, n. [Med.] INFLAMMATION of a nerve p.

'plica, n. [Zoo.] A fold of skin or like material, or a fold-like structure or part. 'plical, a.

'plicate, a. [Biol.] Having a number of parallel folds, or marks as of folds, as a leaf. plicato-.

'plicatile, a. Able to be folded, sp. [Zoo.]

(of the wings of insects) folding from end to end.

pli'cation, n. A folding or fold, sp. [Geol.].

plici-. Fold:— plic'iferous, a., '-form, a.

plio-. PLEI-.

'Pliocene, a., n. [Geol.] (Of) the latest PERIOD of the TERTIARY ERA, which came to an end about 1,000,000 years back (see p. 558).

'plosive, n., a. [Phonet.] (Sound) made with a sudden letting out of the breath at the end, as 'p', 't'. 'plosion, n. The sudden letting out of breath in saying a p.

plot, v.t. Make a map to scale of (land), a design for (a building, machine, etc.), or (p. a curve) make a GRAPH representative of the relation between certain things by the use of CO-ÖRDINATES.

pluck, v.t. [Geol.] Get (ROCK) broken loose and take it away in great masses, said of GLACIERS.

'Plücker tube. [Elec.] A GEISSLER TUBE in which the part where the DISCHARGE takes place is very narrow, producing a much brighter light.

plug, 1.n. [Mach., Med.] A bit of wood, metal, or any material, used for pushing into a hole so as to get it stopped up. [Elec.] A part with pins or a screw structure for pushing or screwing into another part so as to make an electric connection, for example on the end of a cord fixed to some electric apparatus. 2.v.t. Put a p. in, get stopped up with a p.

'pluma (plumae), n. [Zoo.] Any of the outer feathers of a bird, with a stiff middle stem and a strongly-designed structure, which give the bird its outline.

'plumate, a. PLUMOSE.

plumb, a. Truly upright. p. bob. A small mass of lead or other weight at the end of a cord, which when let go will be hanging straight down, used in building etc. for testing if something is p. p. line. The cord of a p. bob, or the two taken together.

plum'bago, n. GRAPHITE.

plumbi-, plumbo-. Lead, having in it lead and . . .:— plum'biferous, a.

'plumbous, a. To do with, having in it, lead, sp. [Chem.] lead with a low VALENCY.

'plumbum, n. Lead.

'plumbism, n. [Med.] Lead poisoning.

plume, n. [Zoo.] A feather, sp. a PLUMA, or feather-like structure. [Bot.] A feather-like structure or group of hairs etc. on a fruit or seed, helping its distribution by the wind. plu'maceous, a. plu'migerous, a.

'plumiped, n. [Zoo.] Bird with feathered feet.

'plummet, n. A PLUMB BOB.

'plumose, a. [Biol.] Having feathers or feather-like parts; having a feather-like structure, with hairs or other parts ranged on two sides of a middle line.

'plumula (plumulae), n. [Bot.] PLUMULE. [Zoo.] Any of the soft, delicate under-feathers of a bird at full growth. plumu-'laceous, a. 'plumular, a. 'plumulate, a. plum'uliform, a.

'plumule, n. [Bot.] The first BUD, at the point of the AXIS, produced by the EMBRYO of a seed plant, and responsible for the development of the chief stem. [Zoo.] PLUMULA.

'plunger, n. [Mach.] A PISTON; any part working like a piston.

'plural gel, n. [Chem.] GEL formed of two or more substances GELLING at the same time.

plur(i)-. More, more than one, a number of:— pluri'cellular, a. [Biol], pluri'glandular, a. [Med.], pluri'sporous, a. [Bot.].

pluri'axial, a. [Bot.] (Of plants) having the flowers on stems other than the chief stem, opp. MONAXIAL.

pluri'locular, a. [Bot.] (Of an OVARY) having two or more divisions.

plus, 1. prep. Increased by, with the addi-tion of (sign +), opp. MINUS. 2. adj. Being an addition, making greater or of more value, helping. [Elec.] POSITIVE. p. lens. [Optics] A LENS causing rays to come to a point. p. strain. [Bot.] In HETEROTHALLIC FUNGI uniting without a normal sex-process, that one of the two sorts which seems to have male properties, being of stronger growth, etc.

'pluteus, n. [Zoo.] The free-swimming LARVA of ECHINOIDEA and OPHIUROIDEA. 'pluteal, a.

'Pluto, n. [Astron.] The outermost of the PLANETS, about 3,671 million miles from the sun, with a 'year' of about 248 years, and a mass about equal to that of the earth. (See p. 331.)

plu'tonic, a. [Geol.] Coming from, formed, deep inside the earth. p. in'trusion. An INTRUSION of p. rock, regularly of great size in all directions, and so the same thing as a MAJOR INTRUSION. p. rock. IGNEOUS ROCK which has become solid deep down in the earth, completely made up of CRYSTALS of a size to be readily seen but freq. badly formed as the effect of being pushed together with not enough room to take their normal forms.

'plutonite, n. [Geol.] General name used in U.S.A. for all ROCKS forming PLUTONIC INTRUSIONS, sp. those of the COARSE-GRAINED group.

plu'tonium, n. Chemical ELEMENT, at. no. 94, sign Pu, one of the TRANSURANIC ELEMENTS produced in the RADIOACTIVE DECAY of Np, having a number of ISOTOPES, the most important of which is Pu239, in which FISSION may be produced by BOMBARDMENT by slow NEUTRONS.

pluvial, -o-us, aa. To do with rain.

pluvio-. [Meteor.] To do with rain: pluvi-'ography, n. pluvi'ometer, n.

P.M. = POST MORTEM.

pneo-. Breath, breathing: 'pneody'nam-ics, n.

'pneograph, n. [Med.] Instrument for record-ing the force etc. of air-current in breathing.

pne'ometer, n. [Med.] SPIROMETER.

'pneoscope, n. [Med.] An instrument for measuring the motions of the breathing-apparatus.

'pneum(a)-. Air, gas.

pneu'matic, a. To do with PNEUMATICS. [Mach.] Using, full of, air or other gas, said of any elastic structure into which air or gas is pumped to keep it stretched and give it the properties of a rubber cushion; worked by the force of air or gas, as a p. brake. [Biol.] Full of air, or having hollows or pockets full of air, as certain bones in birds having the power of flight. p. 'trough. [Chem.] A vessel of water or Hg with glass vessels full of water upside down in it, used in the chemical LABORATORY for taking in gases. '-ally, adv. pneuma'ticity, n. The condi-tion of being p., sp. [Zoo.] of having air-spaces. 'pneumatized, a. [Zoo.] Having air spaces.

pneu'matics, n. [Mech.] The branch of MECHANICS having to do with forces acting on or produced by air or other gases, their weight, PRESSURE, and so on, and effects caused by these.

pneumat(o)-. Air; breath.

'pneumatocele, n. [Med.] A SWELLING with air or gas in it; PNEUMONOCELE.

'pneumatocyst, n. [Zoo.] The AIR-BLADDER in a fish; any air-pocket which keeps an animal up in the water, sp. in SIPHONO-PHORA.

'pneumatograph, n. [Med.] An instrument for recording the motion of the chest in breathing.

pneuma'tolysis, n. [Geol.] The operation on the ROCK round it of steam or highly heated gas given off by a MAGMA in the process of becoming solid. 'pneumato-'lytic, -'litic, a. To do with, effected by, p.; (of MINERALS) formed by p.

pneuma'tometer, n. [Med.] An instrument for measuring the force with which the LUNGS send out breath. pneuma'tometry, n. Sp., the use of the p. as a help in DIAGNOSIS.

'pneumatophore, n. [Bot.] A sponge-like root or outgrowth going up into the air for the purpose of taking air to the roots, formed by plants living in wet sticky earth through which little air gets. [Zoo.] PNEUMATOCYST. pneuma'tophorous, a.

'pneumatopyle, n. [Zoo.] A small opening to the outer air in the PNEUMATOPHORE of SIPHONOPHORA.

pneumo-. LUNG; PNEUMONIA and ...); PNEUMATO-.

pneumo'coccus, n. [Bact., Med.] The BACTERIUM which is the cause of LOBAR PNEUMONIA. **pneumo'cocc-al, -ic, -ous,** aa.

'pneumo'coniosis, pneu'mono'coniosis, nn. [Med.] Any of certain diseases of the LUNGS caused by breathing in dust of some sort, for example coal-dust in mining.

pneumo'gastric nerve. [Zoo.] VAGUS.

pneu'molysis, n. [Med.] An operation to get the PLEURA free from the chest wall, or to get its outer part free from the inner part covering the LUNG, for the purpose of COLLAPSING a lung.

'pneumon'ectomy, n. [Med.] The operation of taking out a LUNG.

pneu'monia, n. [Med.] Any disease marked by INFLAMMATION of any part of the LUNG(s), causing the lung substance to become hard; sp. an acute p. attacking one or more of the greater divisions of the lung and caused by the PNEUMO-COCCUS. **pneu'monic.**

pneu'monocele, n. [Med.] HERNIA of the LUNG through the chest-wall.

pneumo'tax-is, -y, nn. [Biol.] TAXIS in reaction to CO_2 present in water. **pneumo'tactic,** a.

pneumo'thorax, n. [Med.] The condition in which there is air or gas in the PLEURAL CAVITY; the putting of air or gas into the pleural cavity for the purpose of sending the air out of a diseased LUNG.

-pn(o)ea, n. [Med.] Breathing.

Po, Sign for POLONIUM.

pock, n. [Med.] A PUSTULE, sp. one of those caused by a disease such as VARIOLA.

pod, n. [Bot.] A dry seed-vessel or fruit, sp. a LEGUME.

-pod, n., a. (Animal) having the given number of sort of feet. **-poda,** n.pl.

'podal, po'dalic, aa. To do with the feet.

'pode-on, -um, nn. [Zoo.] The PETIOLE in HYMENOPTERA.

po'detium (podetia), n. [Bot.] The stem-like, cup-like, or branching plant-body in some LICHENES.

'podex, n. [Zoo.] The part of the body round the ANUS. **'podical,** a. **podical plates.** In insects, two small hard plates near the p.

'podite, n. [Zoo.] A walking-leg of CRUS-TACEA.

'podium (podia), n. [Zoo.] A hand or foot; any foot-like structure, sp. one of the tube-feet of ECHINODERMATA. [Bot.] A base structure or support, sp. the stem of a leaf. **'podial,** a. **'-podium.**

pod(o)-. Foot.

'podobranch, podo'branchia (podobran-chiae), nn. [Zoo.] A GILL fixed to the upper part of the end one of the chief divisions of a leg in CRUSTACEA.

-podous, a. [Zoo.] Having the given number or sort of feet.

'pod-sol, -zol, n. White or grey ASH-like earth, formed under evergreen trees or the sort of plants covering waste places in colder countries, sp. in N. Russia.

'Poggendorff bridge. POTENTIOMETER.

poiki'litic, a. [Geol.] Said of the TEXTURE of IGNEOUS ROCKS made up of CRYSTALS of one substance with very small crystals of another present in them here and there.

poikilo'blastic, a. [Geol.] Said of the TEXTURE of METAMORPHIC ROCKS made up of CRYSTALS of one substance with very small crystals of another present in them here and there.

'poikilo'cyte, n. [Med.] A red blood-CELL of irregular form, seen in certain diseases. **'poikilocy'tosis,** n. Condition in which pp. are present in the blood, as in serious ANAEMIA.

poikilo'therm-al, -ic, aa. [Zoo.] COLD-BLOODED.

point source. [Optics, Acous.] A SOURCE of light or sound having no size—an idea used in the theory of light or sound as a way of getting down to the most general laws of RADIATION and as a base for units of measure, and roughly true for sources whose size is very small in comparison with their distance from the point of observation.

poise, n. [Phys.] Unit of VISCOSITY in the C.G.S. system = 1 DYNE-SEC./cm^2.

Poi'seuille's equation or **formula,** or **law.** [Phys.] The law that the VOLUME of a liquid of VISCOSITY η which goes in one second through a hair-like pipe L units long and $2R$ units across under a PRESSURE $P = \dfrac{\pi P R^4}{8 L \eta}$.

poison gas. [Chem.] Any gas which is or might be used in war for causing death or serious damage to men.

Pois'son('s) 'ratio. [Phys.] In a pulled wire, the RATIO of the CONTRACTION sideways to the expansion longways.

'polar, a. Of, to do with, near, at, a POLE or the poles of anything; having poles, having polarity. **p. 'axis.** [Astron.] (Of a SPHERE) the straight line through its two POLES, sp. that on which the earth is turning or that on which the CELESTIAL SPHERE seems to be turning; that AXIS of an instrument, such as an EQUATORIAL, pointing to the CELESTIAL POLE. **p. body** or **cell** or **globule.** [Zoo.] One of other of the two small CELLS, made up almost completely of NUCLEUS, which become separated from an OÖCYTE in the process of MEIOSIS. **p. bond.** [Chem.] ELECTRO-VALENT BOND. **p. cap.** [Biol.] A group of delicate STRANDS formed at the POLE of a NUCLEUS at the start of a process of division and becoming part of the SPINDLE.

[Astron.] One or other of the two white spaces round the poles of the PLANET MARS, which are seen to become greater when it is winter there and taken to be formed of ice and snow as are the like parts of the earth. **p. circle.** [Geog., Astron.] One or other of the two PARALLELS OF LATITUDE at a distance of about 23°27′ from the NORTH or SOUTH POLE. **p. coördinates.** [Maths.] The COÖRDINATES giving the position of a point P in a plane by its distance, r, from a given point O in the plane (the *origin*) and the angle ϕ which the line from P to O (the *radius vector*) makes with any given line going through O. **p. distance.** [Astron.] The ANGULAR DISTANCE of a star etc. from the POLE of the CELESTIAL SPHERE. **p. field** or **plate.** [Zoo.] One or other of two CILIATED parts forming part of the apparatus having to do with the sense of balance in CTENOPHORA. **p. 'molecule.** [Phys.] A MOLECULE whose structure makes it a DIPOLE. **p. 'nucleus.** [Bot.] One or other of the two NUCLEI at the two ends of the EMBRYO SAC in flowering plants which are later united to become the female nucleus. **p. pro-'jection.** A way of mapping the earth on paper, etc. in which the point of view is at the middle of the earth and the plane of PROJECTION goes through one of the p. circles. **p. ray.** [Biol.] ASTER RAY as opp. SPINDLE FIBRE. **po'larity,** n. [Phys., Chem., Biol.] The condition of having POLES, or of being different, sp. opposite, in properties, powers, or form in opposite parts or directions, as the two ELECTRODES of an electric CELL, the two ends of a MAGNET, the head and tail of an animal, or the root and top of a plant. [Bot.] The tendency of a plant to undergo growth in the direction of its poles, one end going down into the earth, the other up into the light.

pola'rimeter, n. [Optics, Chem.] An instrument for measuring some property of a substance sp. a liquid, based on the angle through which the plane of POLARIZED light is turned by it. **polari'metric,** a. **pola'rimetry,** n. The measuring of the OPTICAL ACTIVITY of a substance by the use of the p.

po'lariscope, n. [Optics] Any of a number of forms of instrument for the observation of the properties of POLARIZED light or the effects of different substances on it.

polari'zation, n. The process of coming to have, or of causing something to have, POLARITY. [Chem.] The separating of the POSITIVE and NEGATIVE CHARGES of a MOLECULE. [Elec.] The effect on a DIELECTRIC of an ELECTRIC FIELD, by which the positive charge on every ATOM is moved a little in relation to the negative charge, causing a turning force in the direction of the field; an increase in the electric RESISTANCE of a CELL and loss of E.M.F. caused by the coating of the ELECTRODES with gases produced by ELECTROLYSIS. [Optics, Radio, etc.] The process of limiting the VIBRATIONS making up light or other ELECTRO-MAGNETIC rays (which normally are in all directions at right angles to that of the ray) to one or two fixed directions, effected by the REFLECTION of normal light from a plane at the ANGLE OF POLARIZATION, or by sending it through a substance having the property of BIREFRINGENCE (*see* PLANE P. and CIRCULAR P.). **'polarize,** v.t. Make undergo p. **'polarized,** a. (Sp. of light) which has undergone p. **polarized 'relay.** [Elec.] A RELAY working by MAGNETIC POLARIZATION, gen. produced by a PERMANENT MAGNET, so that the operation is dependent on the direction of the current as well as on its size. **'polarizer,** n. Sp., the part of a POLARISCOPE where the light coming in is polarized.

po'larograph, n. [Chem.] An instrument for the ANALYSIS of SOLUTIONS by ELECTROLYSIS, of which the CATHODE is formed by falling Hg.

'Polaroid, n. [Optics, etc.] The trade name of a material used for producing POLARIZED light, formed of two thin skins of CELLULOSE NITRATE with BIREFRINGENT CRYSTALS between them.

pole, n. One or the other of the two ends of an AXIS or line of direction, sp. when these are opposite to one another in position (as the pp. of a SPHERE) or are representative of opposite or markedly different properties. [Astron., Geog.] *See* CELESTIAL and TERRESTRIAL POLES; (of a GREAT CIRCLE) one or other of the two points at which a line through the middle of the sphere at right angles to the great circle is cut by the outline of the sphere. [Biol.] In living things or their structures or CELLS, sp. egg-cells, one or the other of the two parts at opposite ends of a middle line which are different in structure or purpose (*see* ANIMAL and VEGETATIVE POLE); one or the other end of the SPINDLE in MITOSIS; the point where some line-like part, such as a NERVE FIBRE, has its start or end. [Phys.] One or the other of the two points or parts between which an electric or MAGNETIC force is acting, as the parts (gen. the ends) of a MAGNET) from which the lines of force are rayed out or where they come together again, or the TERMINALS of an electric CELL; *see* UNIT POLE. **p. plate.** [Zoo.] A plate-like body formed at the two ends of the SPINDLE in the MITOSIS of PROTOZOA. **p. strength.** [Elec.] (Of a given MAGNETIC p.) the force in DYNES which would be produced by it on a unit magnetic p. at unit distance from it.

'poliomye'litis, n. [Med.] INFLAMMATION of the GREY MATTER of the SPINAL CORD, sp. INFANTILE PARALYSIS.

po'litical e'conomy. ECONOMICS.

po'litical science. That branch of the SOCIAL SCIENCES which has to do with the organization and government of countries or other political units.

'pollen, n. [Bot.] The dust-like or sticky substance produced by the ANTHERS of seed-plants, made up of a mass of MICRO-SPORES (p. grains) inside which male GERM-CELLS undergo development, de-signed to be transported to the female flower-parts by wind, insects, etc. p. brush. [Zoo.] A brush-like structure on the leg or body of a bee for transporting p. p. sac. [Bol.] A hollow in an ANTHER in which p. is formed. p. tube. [Bot.] A pipe-like out-growth produced by a p. grain after it has become fixed on a STIGMA, which goes down through the STYLE into the OVARY and by which the male NUCLEUS is taken to the female nucleus for the purpose of uniting with it.

'pollex, n. [Zoo.] The thumb, or the toe having the same position on a front foot.

'pollin(i)-. POLLEN: 'pollin'iferous, a., 'pollinoid, a.

polli'nation, n. [Bot.] The transporting of POLLEN from ANTHER to STIGMA, the dropping etc. of pollen on a stigma as the first stage in the producing of seed. 'pollinate, v.t. Take POLLEN to (flower or STIGMA).

poll'inium (pollinia), n. [Bot.] A united mass of POLLEN grains designed to be trans-ported all together in POLLINATION, freq. by having a sticky stem-like or plate-like part which becomes fixed to insects.

pol'lute, v.t. [Med.] Make anything, sp. food or drink, unclean, unhealthy, by the addition of some substance, for example make water unhealthy for drinking or for the animals living in it by sending waste into it. pol'lution, n. [Med.] The act of polluting (water, etc.) or the condition of being polluted; the sending out of SEMEN at times other than when in the act of sex connection.

'polocyte, n. [Biol.] POLAR BODY.

po'lonium, n. Chemical ELEMENT, at. no. 84, at. wt. 210, sign Po, a RADIO-ACTIVE element with a HALF-LIFE of 136·5 days forming the last stage before lead in the DECAY of Ra.

poly-. A (great) number of, more than one, more than the normal number:— '-'car-pellary, a., '-'centric, a., '-'cephalous, a., '-'nuclear, a., '-'phyllous, a., '-'sperm-ous, a.

'polya'delphous, a. [Bot.] Having the

STAMENS united by their FILAMENTS into three or more groups.

poly'andry, n. [Zoo.] The condition in which a female has sex connection with a number of males, as in certain fish. [Bot.] The condition of having 20 or more free STAMENS. poly'androus, a.

'polyarch, a. [Bot.] Having a great number of threads or parcels of XYLEM, as certain roots.

'polya'tomic, a. [Phys., Chem.] (Of a sub-stance) having more than one ATOM in the MOLECULE; having more than one atom able to be exchanged for an atom of another substance.

poly'basic, n., a. [Chem.] (An acid) having in the MOLECULE more than one H ATOM for which a metal atom may be exchanged. 'polyba'sicity, n.

'polycarp, n. [Zoo.] A GONAD on the inside of the body-wall in some ASCIDIACEA.

poly'carp-ic, -ous, aa. [Bot.] Having two or more separate OVARIES.

poly'cercous, a. [Biol.] Having a number of heads, said of worms.

Poly'chaeta, n.pl. [Zoo.] An ORDER of CHAETOPODA, having PARAPODIA with a great number of SETAE and gen. a well-marked head with special outgrowths, sea-animals in which the sexes are sepa-rate and the uniting of SEX-CELLS takes place outside the body.

poly'chotomous, a. [Biol.] Branching again and again into a number of divisions.

poly'chrest, n. [Med.] A medical substance which is of use for a number of purposes. -ic(al), aa.

poly'chroism, poly'chroic. See PLEOCHRO-ISM, PLEOCHROIC.

poly'chromas-y, -ie, n. [Biol.] The quality of being able to be coloured by different sorts of STAIN; the producing of different shades or colours with the same stain.

'polychro'matic, poly'chromic, aa. [Biol., Chem., Optics] Having a number of colours, having differently coloured forms or changing colour.

'polycoty'ledon, n. [Bot.] Plant with more than two COTYLEDONS. -ous, a. 'poly-coty'ledony, n. Unnormal increase in the number of COTYLEDONS.

'polycoty'ledonary, a. [Zoo.] With a PLACENTA having a number of divisions.

poly'cyclic, a. [Chem.] Having more than one RING of ATOMS (in a MOLECULE). [Biol.] (Of a STELE or SHELL) made up of two or more rings.

poly'dactyl-e, -ous, aa. [Med., Zoo.] Having more fingers or toes than normal. poly-'dactyl-ism, -y, nn.

polydis'perse, a. [Phys.-Chem.] (Of a COLLOID) DISPERSED in grains of dif-ferent sizes.

poly'embryony, n. [Biol.] The forming of

two or more plants or animals from one seed or egg.

poly'ethylene, n. [Chem.] POLYTHENE.

po'lygam-ous, -ic, aa. [Zoo.] Having sex-connections with more than one of the opposite sex at the same MATING time, opp. MONOGAMOUS. [Bot.] Having male, female, and HERMAPHRODITE flowers. **po'lygamy**, n. The condition of being p. or the system of p. MATING among animals.

'polygene, n. [Biol.] A GENE of the sort whose effects are not great enough to be seen in the INDIVIDUAL but which, acting together with other genes whose effect by themselves would be unimportant, has a part in fixing the tendencies of a family group.

poly'genesis, n. The process of producing, or the condition of being produced, by the uniting of a number of causes, or as the effect of developments from more than one starting-point, etc., sp. the theory that man is not the offspring of only one sort of early man, but of two or more independent developments. **polyge'netic**, a. Produced by, to do with, p., sp. [Biol.] produced by the uniting of opposite sexes. [Chem.] (Of DYES) giving different colours or shades with different MORDANTS. [Geol.] (Of a mountain range) made up of two or more ranges of independent development.

poly'genic, a. [Chem.] Forming two or more substances with the same MONOVALENT ELEMENT. [Biol.] POLYGENETIC; controlled by, to do with, POLYGENES.

po'lygenous, a. Made up of a number of different sorts. [Chem.] POLYGENIC.

'polygon, n. [Geom.] A plane form made up of a number of straight sides, sp. more than 4. **po'lygonal**, a. **p. of forces**. FORCE POLYGON.

po'lygyny, n. [Zoo.] The condition of being polygynous or the system of polygynous MATING. **po'lygynous**, a. [Zoo.] (Of males only) POLYGAMOUS. [Bot.] Having a number of separate STYLES.

poly'hedron, n. [Geom.] A solid formed by a number of plane POLYGONAL faces.

poly'hydric, a. [Chem.] (Of a substance) having more than two –OH groups in the MOLECULE.

'polymer(e), nn. [Chem.] Any of two or more polymeric COMPOUNDS, sp. one produced from another by polymerization. **poly'meric**, a. [Chem.] (Of two COMPOUNDS or one in relation to another) made up of the same ELEMENTS in the same relation by weight, but different in MOLECULAR weight. **polymeric gene**. [Biol.] a non-ALLELOMORPHIC GENE whose effect is the same as, and makes stronger, the effect of another. **po'lymerism**, n. [Chem.] The condition or quality of being polymeric.

'polymeri'zation, n. [Chem.] The changing of a substance into one polymeric with it, and freq. having different properties, by the uniting of its MOLECULES in two's, three's, etc. **'polymerize**, v.t. and i. (Make) undergo polymerization.

'polymere, n. [Geol.] Any IGNEOUS ROCK made up of two or more sorts of substance.

po'lymerous, a. [Bot.] Having a great number of parts (said of WHORLS, or of flowers having such whorls).

'polymorph, n. [Cryst., Biol.] A polymorphous substance, plant, or animal. [Zoo.] A POLYMORPHONUCLEAR LEUCOCYTE. **poly'morphism**, n. [Cryst.,Mineral.] The property of certain chemical substances of CRYSTALLIZING in two or more different ways, forming substances which are seemingly different. [Biol.] The condition in which an animal or plant has two or more quite different forms, for example the CASTES of certain insects, or the stages in METAMORPHOSIS. **poly'morph-ic, -ous**, aa. Having or to do with polymorphism.

'polymorpho'nuclear 'leucocyte. [Zoo.] A sort of LEUCOCYTE in back-boned animals (forming 65–75% of those in man) having an irregular NUCLEUS, gen. with deep divisions, which takes a dark colour on staining, and clearly marked, deeply-staining grains in the CELL–substance—PHAGOCYTIC, produced in bone MARROW, and most commonly NEUTROPHIL, though some sorts are EOSINOPHIL or BASOPHIL.

poly'nomial, a. [Biol.] Made up of 3 or more words (said of certain systems for naming plants and animals).

poly'nucleate, a. [Biol.] Having a number of NUCLEI.

poly'oestrous, a. [Zoo.] Having a number of OESTROUS CYCLES in one MATING time.

'polyp, n. [Zoo.] The commonest form of COELENTERATE, having a pipe-like body, with one end shut and fixed to some support and a mouth at the other ringed with feelers for pulling in food, freq. forming COLONIES, as the CORAL pp., and some sorts having a MEDUSA stage. [Med.] A soft growth, or a growth-like mass of INFLAMED TISSUE, on a stem, sp. one formed on a MUCOUS MEMBRANE, as inside the nose. **'-oid**, a.

'poly'peptide, n. [Biochem.] Any of the substances produced in the later stages of the digestion of PROTEINS by the uniting of MOLECULES of AMINO ACIDS.

'Poly'petalae, n.pl. [Bot.] A SUB-CLASS of DICOTYLEDONS in which PETALS are present and all separate.

poly'petalous, a. [Bot.] (Of a flower or COROLLA) having the PETALS separate from one another.

po′lyphagous, a. [Zoo.] Living on different sorts of food, said sp. of insects attacking a great number of different sorts of plant. [Bot.] (Of a PARASITIC FUNGUS) attacking a number of CELLS of the HOST at the same time. **po′lyphagy,** n.

′polyphase, a. [Phys.] (Of an electric current, system, etc.) formed of, using, two or more currents different in PHASE.

poly′phydont, a. [Zoo.] Having more than two growths of teeth one after the other.

′polyphy′letic, a. [Biol.] (Of a group of SPECIES, etc.) uniting groups which, having no common ANCESTOR, have had quite different histories; CONVERGENT.

′polypi-de, -te, n. [Zoo.] A unit of a COLONY of POLYZOA.

poly′plastic, a. [Biol.] Able to take a number of forms.

′polyploid, a. [Biol.] Having three or more times the HAPLOID number of CHROMOSOMES.

polyp′neustic, a. [Zoo.] Having a great number of breathing-holes.

′polypod, n., a. [Zoo.] (Animal) having a great number of feet or legs, said sp. of insect LARVAE when the development of the body-divisions with their legs etc. is complete.

′poly′propylene, n. [Chem.] A PLASTIC which is like POLYTHENE but has greater RESISTANCE to heat, SOLVENTS, and NUCLEAR RADIATION.

′polypus (po′ypi), n. [Med.] POLYP.

poly′rhiz-al, -ous, aa. [Bot.] Having a great number of roots.

poly′saccharide, polysaccharose, nn. [Chem.] Any of the group of natural CARBOHYDRATES whose MOLECULES may be broken up by HYDROLYSIS into two or more molecules of a MONOSACCHARIDE.

poly′sepalous, a. [Bot.] (Of flower or CALYX) having the SEPALS separate from one another.

poly′somic, a. [Biol.] DIPLOID but for the fact that one (or more) of the CHROMOSOME-groups has three or four HOMOLOGOUS units in place of the normal two. **poly′somy,** n.

′polyso′mitic, a. [Zoo.] Having a great number of SOMITES; formed by the uniting of a number of somites.

poly′sperm-ia, -y, nn. [Zoo.] The sending of more than one male CELL into the female cell, even when only one will become united with it.

poly′spermous, a. [Bot.] Having a number of seeds.

poly′sporous, a. [Bot.] Having a great number of seeds or SPORES.

′polyspory, n. [Bot.] The forming of more than the normal number of SPORES.

′polystele, n. [Bot.] DICTOSTELE.

poly′stelic, a. [Bot.] Having more than one STELE. **poly′stely,** n. [Bot.] The condition

of having the VASCULAR substance grouped into a number of STELES, of which every one has more than one VASCULAR BUNDLE.

poly′stemonous, a. [Bot.] Having more than twice the number of STAMENS as of PETALS or SEPALS.

po′lystichous, a. [Bot.] Grouped in a number of lines.

poly′stomatous, a. [Zoo.] Having a great number of openings or mouths.

poly′stylar, a. [Bot.] Having a number of STYLES.

′polysym′metrical, a. [Biol.] Having more than one plane of division into like halves.

′poly′synthesism, n. [Philol.] The system, seen for example in the languages of American Indians, by which words and parts are united into complex words having the sense of a complete statement. **polysyn′thetic,** a. (Of a language) having p.

poly′thalamous, a. [Biol.] (Of a fruit, SHELL, etc.) made up of a number of divisions formed one after another.

′polythene, n. [Chem.] A strong THERMOPLASTIC material with a wax-like look, used widely as an INSULATING material in electric apparatus and for paper-thin water-tight food bags etc.

po′lyto-cous, -kous, a. [Zoo.] Producing a number of eggs or offspring at one time. **poly′to-cy, -ky,** n.

poly′tonic, a. [Philol.] Said of languages in which the same root-sounds are given different senses by using different PITCHES.

po′lytrichous, a. [Zoo.] (Having the body) covered with a thick, regular coat of hairs or CILIA.

poly′trophic, a. [Zoo.] Using as food more than one substance, said sp. of disease BACTERIA; (of insects or their OVARIES) having a food-CELL joined to every egg-cell.

poly′uria, n. [Med.] The producing of URINE in over-great amount or over-frequently.

poly′valent, a. [Chem.] Having a VALENCY greater than 1. [Med.] Acting against a number of different BACTERIA or other disease bodies. **poly′valence,** n.

Poly′zoa, n.pl. [Zoo.] A PHYLUM of METAZOA made up of small water-animals, gen. fixed and COLONIAL, somewhat like the HYDROZOA in form but more complex, having a COELOM, an ANUS placed near the mouth, and a LOPHOPHORE round the mouth. **poly′zoan,** n., a. (Animal) of the P.

poly′zoic, a. [Zoo.] Made up of a number of ZOOIDS; (of a SPOROCYTE) producing a number of SPORES.

pome, n. [Bot.] A fruit with the seeds inside a thin, paper-like structure with two or more divisions, formed of the walls of the united CARPELS, bedded in a thick mass of substance which is a development of the RECEPTACLE, for example, the apple.

po'mology, n. [Bot.] The science of fruit-trees and fruit-producing.

'pondero'motive, a. [Phys.] (Of a force, sp. electric or MAGNETIC) having a tendency to put a material body in motion.

pons (pontes), n. [Zoo.] A bridge-like structure or other connection between two parts. [Anat.] P. Varolii. **p. Va'rolii.** A mass of nerve threads at the front end of the under side of the MEDULLA OBLONGATA. **'pont-al, -ic, -ile, -ine,** aa.

pop'liteal, a. [Zoo.] To do with the back of the upper part of the leg near the knee.

'poppet, n. In machines, an upright support or guide fixed at the lower end only. **p. 'valve.** A VALVE formed of a round or pointed head on a rod by which it is lifted into the opening to be covered, used sp. as an inlet or outlet valve in INTERNAL COMBUSTION ENGINES.

popu'lation, n. The number of persons living in a place. [Biol.] All the animals or plants living in a given place taken together. [Statistics] The complete group of persons, things, etc., from which examples are taken for measuring purposes. **'populate,** v.t. Be living in numbers in (a place). **'populated,** a. (Of place) having persons living in it, used as a living place *by* (named plants or animals).

'porcelain, n. A specially white, hard sort of pot material which is to some degree TRANSLUCENT, the best quality of which is made of KAOLIN, FELDSPAR, and QUARTZ, and used for false teeth, etc.

pore, n. A very small opening, such as those between the grains of a stone, or in the skin of plant or animal. **p. plate.** [Zoo.] The part of the middle structure in certain RADIOLARIA which is full of small holes; MADREPORITE. **po'riferous, 'poriform,** aa.

-pore, n. [Zoo.] A small opening, sp. to the outside of the body.

'poren'cephaly, n. [Med.] A condition in which hollows having in them liquid are formed in the brain-substance.

pori'cidal, a. [Bot.] (Of ANTHERS) having POROUS DEHISCENCE.

Po'rifera, n.pl. [Zoo.] The only PHYLUM of PARAZOA, the sponges.

'porocyte, n. [Zoo.] In sponges, a sort of pointed CELL going through from the inner hollow to the outside with a pipe running through it for taking in water.

po'rogamy, n. [Bot.] The going of the POLLEN TUBE through the MICROPYLE, the commonest system of FERTILIZATION in seed plants.

po'rometer, n. [Phys.] An instrument for the comparison of the size of the openings in POROUS substances, based on the rate at which a given gas goes through them in given conditions. [Bot.] An instrument for measuring the degree to which the STOMATA of a leaf are open by sending air through the leaf and measuring the rate at which it goes.

'poroscope, n. An instrument for testing POROSITY or looking at PORES.

po'rosity, n. The property or condition of being POROUS; the degree to which a substance is porous, sp. [Geol.] given as the PERCENTAGE of the VOLUME of a ROCK taken up by the PORES.

'porous, a. Full of PORES, and so (of a substance) having the property of taking in or letting through liquids. **p. cell** or **cup** or **pot.** [Elec.] A p. pot used in an electric CELL formed of two liquids, to keep them from getting mixed over-quickly. **p. de-'hiscence.** [Bot.] The sending out of POLLEN or seeds through small openings made in the ANTHER or seed-vessel. **p. 'plaster.** [Med.] A medical PLASTER for putting on the body, having in it a great number of small holes for the purpose of helping it to keep flat and smooth. **'-ness,** n.

'porphyrite, n. [Geol.] A PORPHYRY without QUARTZ (*see* p. 192).

'porphy'ritic, a. *See* PORPHYRY.

'porphyro'blastic, a. [Geol.] (Of ROCKS) having what seems to be a PORPHYRITIC TEXTURE, but in which the greater CRYSTALS have been formed after the rock became solid.

'porphyro'phore, n. [Zoo.] A red or red-blue colour-CELL.

'porphyry. n. [Geol.] A general name for smaller-grained IGNEOUS ROCKS with separate CRYSTALS of greater size (*see* p. 192). **porphy'ritic,** a. Of or like p., having porphyritic texture. **porphyritic 'texture.** The special structure of greater CRYSTALS bedded in a small-grained mass for which p. is noted.

por'rect, a. [Bot.] Outstretched, coming out in a direction parallel to the earth.

'Porro 'prism. [Optics] A structure of two PRISMS which by the use of REFLECTION has the effect of turning round an IMAGE seen through it, so that the right side is seen as the left and the top as the base, used in TELESCOPES, etc. as a way of putting right the images formed by the LENS without making the instrument as long as would be necessary if a lens-system was used for the purpose.

'portal, a. [Zoo.] Of, to do with the p. system. **'p. system.** [Zoo.] In back-boned animals a system of VEINS, branching into CAPILLARIES at the two ends, taking the blood from the ALIMENTARY CANAL, SPLEEN and PANCREAS into the LIVER (*hepatic p. system*), and in lower back-boned animals, a further like system taking blood from the back part of the body to the KIDNEYS (*renal p. system*).

p. vein. The great VEIN formed by the united veins of the p. system near the LIVER.

'posit, v.t. To take or put forward as true, as a fact needing no support from reasoning and which may be used as a starting-point for it.

po'sition circle. [Astron., etc.] The circle on the earth joining all the points of observation from which the ALTITUDE of the sun, a given star, etc., is the same as that from where the person making the observation is at the time, used in NAVIGATION. **position line.** A part of a p.c. which goes through the point where the person making the observation is, and which, because of the great size of the circle, generally has on a CHART the form of a straight line, used for fixing his position.

po'sitional as'tronomy, The oldest branch of astronomy, having to do with the position of the stars etc. viewed as points on the CELESTIAL SPHERE as seen from the point of observation, and giving a knowledge of all the motions of the bodies in the sun's system from day to day and month to month.

po'sition effect. [Biol.] The effect on the qualities produced by a GENE of a change in its position in relation to other genes, as when part of a CHROMOSOME is moved to another place in the same or a different chromosome.

'positive, 1.a. Said of that one of two opposite things, qualities etc., which is taken as the point of view and in relation to which the other thing etc. is said to be NEGATIVE, sp. (of the outcome of a test, etc.) giving a sign that a certain thing, substance or condition is present, giving support to a theory. [Phys., Maths., etc.] Measured, moving, or changing, in a direction which is in fact, or is looked on as, the direction of increase, of going up a scale; (of a number or amount) greater than 0, which may be given the sign +. [Elec.] (Of an ELECTRODE, POLE, etc.) being the one at a higher ELECTRIC POTENTIAL than the other and so the one from which the current goes; having a CHARGE of p. electricity. [Biol.] (Of a motion or growth) in the direction of the STIMULUS. [Psych.] (Of reaction, feeling) made clear in some act, moving the person to do something, not to do nothing; giving sign of agreement, approval, attraction, not of a turning away. [Optics] Having a p. rotation. [Photog.] (Of a camera picture) having the light and shade in the same positions as in the thing pictured, not exchanged, as in a NEGATIVE. **2.n.** A p. camera-picture got by printing from a negative. **p. 'after-image.** [Psych.] The AFTER-IMAGE in the

same colours as the thing on which the eyes have been fixed, seen when the eyes are shut or the place of the thing is taken by a dark plane. **p. 'column** or **glow.** [Phys.] The long line of light going from the ANODE to the FARADAY DARK SPACE in a GAS-DISCHARGE TUBE. **p. elec'tricity.** [Elec.] (The electric) property seen in an ATOM, or in a body having some atoms, from which one or more ELECTRONS have got away. **p. 'mineral** or **'crystal.** [Cryst., Optics] A MINERAL or CRYSTAL having BIREFRINGENCE in which the INDEX OF REFRACTION for the EXTRAORDINARY RAY is greater than that for the ORDINARY RAY. **p. (mag'netic) pole.** That POLE of a straight MAGNET which is pointing to the North when the magnet is hanging freely. **p. po'tential.** [Phys.] An electric POTENTIAL greater than that of the earth. **p. ray.** [Phys.] A line of p. IONS going from the ANODE to the CATHODE in a GAS-DISCHARGE TUBE. **p. ray an'alysis.** The separating of p. rays so as to give a MASS SPECTRUM, for the purpose of getting knowledge of the masses of the PARTICLES. **p. ro'tation.** [Phys., Optics] A ROTATION in the same direction as the hands of a clock, said sp. of the PLANE POLARIZATION of light. **p. sign.** The sign +.

'positivism, n. The teaching that physical things and events and their relations in time and space are the only things of which knowledge is possible.

'positron, n. [Phys.] A very short-living PARTICLE having the same MASS as the ELECTRON and an equal but opposite CHARGE, a POSITIVE ELECTRON.

post-. 1. (The part, sp. a bone) at the back of, (part) forming the back part of, chiefly [Zoo.]:— **'-'abdomen,** n., **'-'anal,** a., **'-'branchial,** a., **'-'centrum,** n. [Zoo.], **'-'clavicle,** n., **'-'clypeus,** n., **'-'cranial,** a., **'-'frontal,** a., n., **'-'hepatic,** a., **'-'renal,** a., **-'thyroid. 2.** Coming straight after in time: **'-embry'onic,** a. [Zoo.] **'-'fertili'za-tion** a. [Bot.], **'-'glacial,** a. [Geol.,] **'-mei'otic,** a. [Biol.] .**P.-'Pliocene,** a., n, [Geol.], **'P.-'Tertiary,** a., n. [Geol.].

post'axial, a. [Zoo.] On the back side of the AXIS, sp. of the body or of an arm or leg, that is, on the same side as the ULNA or the FIBULA.

post'cardinal, a. [Zoo.] At the back of the heart.

post'caval vein. [Zoo.] The great VEIN which takes the blood back to the heart from the legs of man or birds or the back legs of other animals, and from almost all the body between them and the arms, wings, or front legs, in air-breathing back-boned animals. **post'cava,** n. P.v.

pos'terior, 1.a. At, near, nearer, or nearest the back. [Zoo.] At or nearer the tail-end of the body; in man, freq. at or near the back. [Bot.] At or on the back of another part. 2.a., n. [Bot.] (That part of a flower at the side of a chief stem which is) nearest to the stem.

'postero-. At the back and . . .:— '-'lateral, a. '-'medial, a.

post'gangli'onic, a. [Zoo.] (Of NERVE FIBRES) going away from the GANGLION, taking NERVE IMPULSES out to other parts of the body.

pos'tic-ous, -al, aa. [Biol.] On the outer side, (on the side) turned away from the AXIS.

post-'mortem, 1.a. [Med.] Formed, done, etc., after death; to do with a p.-m. 2.n. AUTOPSY.

post'notum, n. POSTSCUTELLUM.

post'orbital, n., a. [Zoo.] (In some back-boned animals, one or the other of two bones) at the back of the hollow in which the eye has its place.

'post-'partum, a. [Med.] To do with the condition of a woman straight after giving birth.

postpa'tagium, n. [Zoo.] In birds, a small fold of skin stretching between the upper part of the arm-structure, that is, of the wing, and the body.

'postscu'tellum, n. [Zoo.] In the division of an insect's body by which the wings are supported, a narrow plate at the back of the SCUTELLUM.

'postulate, 1.v.t. Put (statement) forward as a fact, take (consciously or unconsciously) as true, and make use of as a base for reasoning. 2.n. Theory postulated.

'postzyga'pophysis, n. [Zoo.] A ZYGAPO-PHYSIS (gen. one of two) on the back (or, in man, the lower) face of a NEURAL ARCH.

'potable, a. (Of water, medical substance, etc.) right, designed for, drinking.

'potam(o)-. River(s): **po'tamic,** a., **'potam-'ology,** n., **'potamo'plankton,** n.

'pot'amous, a. [Biol.] Living in rivers.

'pota_.h, n. [Chem.] Any COMPOUND whose chief ELEMENT is POTASSIUM, sp. POTAS-SIUM CARBONATE and CAUSTIC POTASH.

po'tassium, n. Chemical ELEMENT, at. no. 19, at. wt. 39,096, sign K, a silver-white, soft metal, very readily uniting with other substances, present in all living material, and necessary to the existence of all living things, of little use as a metal, being chiefly valued for its SALTS, which are used for making land fertile, in glass and gunpowder making, and for a great number of chemical and medical pur-poses. **p. 'alum.** See ALUM. **p. 'bromide.** KBr, used medically as a SEDATIVE and in making camera pictures. **p. 'carbonate.** K_2CO_3 or $KHCO_2$ (**p. bicarbonate**), white CRYSTALLINE substances strongly ALKA-LINE when mixed with water, used in making glass and soap. **p. 'chloride.** KCl,

a white CRYSTALLINE substance of wide natural distribution in MINERALS and waters, used as a FERTILIZER and for making other p. SALTS. **p. 'cyanide.** KCN, a white CRYSTALLINE substance which is a strong poison, used in chemical ANALYSIS, in ELECTROPLATING, and in the CYANIDE PROCESS. **p. di'chro-mate,** $K_2Cr_2O_7$, a bitter, orange-coloured, CRYSTALLINE substance, used in DYEING, in camera work, and as a cleaner, sp. for LABORATORY vessels. **p. hy'droxide.** A white solid readily taking up water from the air and becoming wet and in the end liquid, and forming in less than its weight of water a CAUSTIC and strongly ALKA-LINE SOLUTION, used in soap-making. **p. 'nitrate.** KNO_3, a white CRYSTALLINE substance present naturally in the earth, sp. in warm dry countries, a strong OXIDIZER when heated, used in making gunpowder, fireworks, etc., as a PRE-SERVATIVE for meat, and for medical purposes. **p. per'manganate.** $KMnO_4$, dark red-blue CRYSTALS used, mixed with water, as an OXIDIZER and DISINFECTANT.

'potency, n. [Med.] (Of a medical substance or an ORGAN etc. of the body) power of producing an effect, doing its work; (of a male) power of having sex-connections.

'potent, a. Having p. or great p.

po'tential, 1.a. [Phys., Chem., Biol., etc.] Present but not acting; possible as a development but not, so far, in being. 2.n. [Elec.] Of a point in an ELECTRIC FIELD or CIRCUIT, the level of ELECTRIFICATION in comparison with the earth, measured by the amount of work needed to take a unit POSITIVE CHARGE to that point from an INFINITE distance. **p. 'difference.** [Elec.] The condition in which, or the amount by which, the p. of one point is different from that of another, causing a tendency for an electric current to go from the one having the (*at the*) higher p. to the other, measured by the work done in the motion of a unit CHARGE from one point to the other. **p. di'vider.** An apparatus for the division of a p. difference into parts. **p. 'energy.** [Phys.] The ENERGY which a body has the power of producing as the effect of its position or its condition of being stretched or forced into a smaller space than it normally takes up, for example, the energy which may be freed by it in falling from a high place or in undergoing expansion when the force acting on it is taken away.

po'tentiometer, n. [Elec.] An instrument used in electric engineering for measuring POTENTIAL DIFFERENCES; loosely, POTEN-TIAL DIVIDER, VARIABLE RESISTOR.

'pothole, n. [Geol.] A great rounded hollow formed in the bed of a river by the rubbing of small stones sent round and round by the current; a deep CAVE going down into the earth.

pot'ometer, n. [Bot.] An instrument for measuring the rate at which a plant gives off water in the form of gas.

potter's clay, [Geol.] A FINE and very PLASTIC sort of CLAY with no or little iron in it, used in CERAMICS.

Pott's 'fracture, [Med.] A FRACTURE of the FIBULA near the foot, with damage to the ANKLE JOINT, causing the foot to be pushed out sideways.

pouch, n. [Biol.] A bag-like structure sp.:— [Zoo.] one for taking the young about in, as in MARSUPALIA, or for storing food, as in the mouth of some RODENTIA; [Bot.] a SILICLE; [Med.] a CYST with liquid in it.

'Poulsen arc. [Radio]. An electric ARC produced between C and Cu in a tight vessel through which H goes without stopping, placed in a MAGNETIC FIELD— used for producing unending waves of very high FREQUENCY.

'poultice, n. [Med.] A dressing for putting on the skin to take away INFLAMMATION, etc. made of some soft mass, such as bread and water, or meal, heated and put on a cloth.

pound, n. British and American unit of weight and mass:— in AVOIRDUPOIS WEIGHT = 16 ounces or 453·592 grams; in TROY WEIGHT = 12 ounces or 373·2418 grams.

'poundal, n. [Phys.] Unit of force in the foot-pound-second system, being that force effecting the ACCELERATION of a mass of 1 pound at the rate of 1 foot per second per second = 13825·5 DYNES.

'Poupart's 'ligament. [Anat.] The strong thick LIGAMENT on the lower side of the muscle of the GROIN.

'powder-down 'feather. [Zoo.] A sort of DOWN feather in certain birds of which the end is all the time being broken up into a powder-like substance so that it gets no longer though growth from the root keeps on.

'powder 'pattern, n. [Cryst.] Design produced in a powder when a narrow PENCIL of X-rays is sent through it for the purpose of getting light on its CRYSTAL STRUCTURE.

'power, n. Loosely, MECHANICAL or electric force or ENERGY. [Phys.] The rate at which WORK is done by an electric current or mechanical force, gen. measured in WATTS or HORSE-POWER. [Optics] Of a LENS or instrument, the degree to which the size of things seen through it is increased, commonly measured in DIAMETERS. [Maths.] Of a number, 1 + the number of times it is MULTIPLIED by itself to give a certain amount, given as an EXPONENT of the number, which is

then said to be *raised to that p.*, for example, 2×2 is 2^2, or 2 *to the second power*. **p. 'factor**. [Elec.] The RATIO of the p. present in an A.C. electric CIRCUIT measured in WATTS to the VOLT-AMPERES (the volts × the amperes) produced in it.

pox, n. [Med.] Word used in forming the names of diseases marked by the producing of POCKS, as SMALLPOX.

'p-p. 'factor. [Biochem.] The 'PELLAGRA PREVENTIVE' VITAMINE, NICOTINIC ACID.

Pr, Sign for PRASEODYMIUM.

'practical, a. (Of a science or branch) to do with practice. **'practice**, n. Work in the field, observation, the use of knowledge, as opp. theory. [Med.] Sp. the work of a medical man, the number of persons he has to look after, who go to him for attention. **-ly**, adv.

'practical 'system. [Elec.] The system in general use for measuring electric amounts, of which the units are DECIMAL MULTIPLES or FRACTIONS of the centi-metre-gram-second units, based on an adjustment to everyday measuring needs and on the relation of the units to one another. **practical 'unit**, A unit of the p.s., as the OHM, AMPERE, JOULE, etc.

pr(a)e-. PRE.

prae'coces, n.pl. [Zoo.] Birds whose young have a cover of DOWN and are able to go about and take care of themselves on coming out of the egg.

prae'tarsus, n. [Zoo.] An outgrowth at the end of the TARSUS in some insects.

'pragmatism, n. The system of PHILOSOPHY started by the American C. S. Pierce, the chief teaching of which is that thought is an instrument for bettering existence, and that knowledge is to be judged true only if it is in agreement with experience and may be put to use, all reasoning which may not be tested by facts and has no effect on living being of no value. **'pragma-tist**, n. **prag'matic**, a. To do with p.; To do with facts and events as opp. theories and ideas.

'praseo'dymium, n. Chemical ELEMENT, at. no. 59, at. wt. 140·9, sign Pr, one of the RARE EARTHS, very like NEODYMIUM and present in the same MINERALS.

pre-. (The part, sp. a bone) in front of, (part) forming the front part of, chiefly [Zoo.]:— **'-'abdomen**, n., **'-'axial**, a., **'-'coracoid**, n., **'-'oral**, a., **-sphenoid**, a., n., **'-'sternum**, n.; (thing or time) coming before a given thing or time:— **'-'human**, a., n.

pre-'Cambrian, a., n. [Geol.] (Of) the great division of earth's history. (the 'era') coming first in the time-scale of Geology, from almost 6,000 to 600 years back. (*See* p. 559).

pre'caval vein. [Zoo.] One or other of the two great VEINS (or in man, the one great vein) taking the blood from the head and front legs (or arms) of air-breathing back-boned animals back to the heart. **pre-'cava, n., P.v.**

pre'cession, n. The condition of coming before some other thing in time, or coming earlier than before. [Phys.] Of a body turning on its AXIS, a CONTINUOUS change in the direction of this axis (*axis of spin*) as the effect of a force acting at right angles to it so that the axis is turning about its first position. [Phonet.] The forming of a VOWEL sound at a point further forward than that at which it is normally formed. **p. of the 'equinoxes.** [Astron.] The coming of the EQUINOXES to the MERIDIAN a little earlier every time because of the p. of the earth's AXIS caused by the attraction of the sun and moon on the part of the earth near the EQUATOR, where there is a greater expansion of the earth's form than there would be if it was a quite regular SPHERE. **pre'cess, v.i.** [Phys.] Undergo p. **pre'cessional, a.**

'pre-'Chellean, a., n. (Of, to do with, being) the time in man's history when the EOLITHIC was ending and the PALAEOLITHIC starting

'precious 'metal. Any of the NOBLE METALS, sp. gold, silver, and PLATINUM, highly valued for purposes of ornament, and the first two of which are freq. used as money.

'precious stone. Any of the jewel stones of the highest range of value, all having a position in the HARDNESS SCALE higher than that of TOPAZ.

pre'cipitant, n. [Chem.] Any substance causing PRECIPITATION on addition to a liquid.

precipi'tation, n. [Phys., Meteor.] (Of a VAPOUR, or a liquid mixed with and supported by a gas) the process of becoming massed into drops and falling, as when rain or snow comes down; the operation of causing (a vapour, etc.) to do this; snow, water, etc. sent down on to the earth by p. [Chem.] The forming in or separating from a liquid of a powder or like form of solid substance as the effect of some chemical or physical change; the operation of causing (a solid) to become separated from a liquid in this way. **pre-'cipitate, 1.v.t. and i.** [Phys., Meteor., Chem.] (Make) undergo p. 2.n. [Chem.] The precipitated substance in a liquid. **pre'cipitated, a. pre'cipitative, a., pre-'cipitator, n.** [Chem., Phys., Meteor.] An apparatus for causing p.

pre'cipitin, n. [Med.] An ANTIBODY formed in the blood of an animal after INOCULATION with a plant, animal, or BACTERIAL PROTEIN, which has the property of forming a wool-like PRECIPITATE on addition to a clear SOLUTION of the protein in reaction to which it is formed.

pre'cipi'tinogen, n. [Med.] A PROTEIN in reaction to which a PRECIPITIN is formed.

pre'cision, a. (Of an instrument) with the smallest possible error in its readings or working.

pre'cocity, n. [Biol., Med., Psych.] The condition of coming to development much earlier than normal, used sp. of the development of the mind. **pre'cocious, a.** Sp. of a boy or girl, very forward in mind development, knowledge of how older persons go on, etc.

pre'conscious, n. [Psych.] That part of the mind of whose workings a person is not conscious at a given time but of which he readily becomes conscious when questioned, etc.

pre'cordial, a. [Zoo.] In front of the heart.

pre'cursor, n. Something of the same sort coming before some other thing and forming a step to its development, an early form of something which gives place to some later and better form. [Chem., Biochem.] A substance forming a stage in the development of another substance which is later formed from it.

pre'dacious, 'predatory, aa. [Zoo.] Living by attacking other animals for food; causing destruction to grain, fruit, buildings etc.

predi'gestion, n. [Med.] The putting of food through some of the processes of digestion by the use of chemicals etc., before it is taken—sp. for persons of delicate digestion. **predi'gested, a.** (Of food) having undergone p.

preen gland. UROPYGIAL GLAND.

pre'ferred number. [Phys.] Any of certain numbers of PROTONS or NEUTRONS which are seen in those NUCLEI having the greatest degree of STABILITY.

'prefix, n. [Philol.] A letter, SYLLABLE or syllables, with a certain sense, put at the front of a word and united with it to make a new word having their united sense, as 'un' in 'uncommon'.

'prefoli'ation, n. [Bot.] The grouping of plant leaves in the BUD.

prefor'mation ('theory). [Biol.] The old theory that the complete organization of fully-formed parts of an animal or plant is present in the EMBRYO from the start, and that development is only a process of the growth of these in size.

pre'frontal, 1.a. [Zoo.] At the front of the brain, or bone structure of the head. 2.n. One or other of two PAIRED bones in this position over the eyes.

'pregangli'onic, a. [Zoo.] To do with, or said of, the NERVE FIBRES going from the SPINAL CORD to the GANGLIONS of the SYMPATHETIC NERVOUS SYSTEM.

pregnan'diol, n. [Zoo.] A female sex-HORMONE produced together with PROGESTERONE.

'pregnant, a. [Med., Zoo.] (Of a female

animal) with young undergoing development inside the body. ′pregnancy, n. The condition of being p.

pre′hallux, n. [Zoo.] An incompletely formed sixth toe on the inner side of the back foot, seen in a number of MAMMALS and AMPHIBIANS.

pre′heated, a. Heated before being used in some process, sp. of air, gas, or water going into an engine.

pre′hens-ile, -ory, aa. [Zoo.] Made for gripping, or twisting round things, as a p. tail.

′prehis′toric, a. Of, to do with, the time in man's history before records were kept, and of which there are no histories. pre-′history, n. P. times; p. ARCHAEOLOGY and ANTHROPOLOGY.

pre-ig′nition, n. [Engin.] The taking fire of the mixed gases in an INTERNAL COMBUSTION ENGINE before the right time, as the effect of overheating, etc.

pre′liminary, a. Coming at the start of some process or before some event, and making ready for or giving a sign of what is to come. p. ′tremor. The first motion in an EARTHQUAKE, a LONGITUDINAL WAVE going through the deeps of the earth and water.

pre′lithic, a. To do with a stage in man's history before the use of stone instruments.

′premax′illa(ry), nn. [Zoo.] One or the other of the two bones supporting the front upper teeth, or, in man, the two parts of the upper MAXILLAE, or, in birds, united into the upper part of the BEAK.

′premise, ′premiss, nn. A statement (gen. one of two) taken as the base or starting-point of a chain of reasoning.

pre′molar, 1.a. [Zoo.] Said of those teeth in certain MAMMALS which come in front of the MOLARS at the side of the mouth and which, like them, are used for crushing food, but, unlike them, are present as MILK TEETH as well as in the second growth. 2.n. A p. tooth.

pre′natal, a. [Zoo., Med.] To do with, taking place in, the time between the start of the development of offspring and its birth.

pre′nuptial, a. [Zoo.] Done, coming, etc., before the act of MATING, and having a connection with it.

prepa′ration, n. [Chem., Med., Biol.] A substance which has been got ready for some purpose, sp. a medical substance, or one made ready for use or testing in the LABORATORY.

prepa′tagium, n. [Zoo.] A fold of skin between the upper and the lower arm in a bird's wing.

pre′penna (prepennae), n. [Zoo.] A soft, PLUMULA-like feather on a baby bird which will later give place to a PLUMA.

pre′potency, n. [Biol.] The power of pro-

ducing offspring more like the self than like the other PARENT. pre′potent, a. Having p.

pre′plumula (preplumulae), n. [Zoo.] A DOWN FEATHER on a baby bird which will give place to a down feather on the older bird.

′prepuce, n. [Zoo.] The fold of skin covering the end of the PENIS in MAMMALS. pre-′putial, a.

pre′pupa, n. [Zoo.] A resting-stage before the PUPA stage in the development of some insects.

pre′putium, n. PREPUCE.

presby′opia. n. [Med.] A condition of the eyes, normal in old persons, in which a person is unable to see things near to the eyes as clearly as things far away because of the loss of the power of adjustment of the CRYSTALLINE LENS.

pre′scutum, n. [Zoo.] The front bit of the TERGUM of an insect.

presen′tation, n. [Med.] The position of a baby in relation to the mouth of the UTERUS in the process of birth, see BREECH P.

pre′servative, n. A substance used to keep anything from undergoing natural change or destruction, sp. one put into bottled, tinned etc.food to keep it from going bad.

press, n. [Mach.] Any machine or apparatus doing its work by PRESSURE, as in cutting out metal parts with a stamp, printing, crushing, forcing material into smaller space, stamping designs on it, etc.

′pressor, a. [Zoo.] Causing an increase in the PRESSURE of the blood in the ARTERIES, as p. nerves, etc.

′pressure, n. [Phys.] Pushing force, force pushing against some opposite force, the sort of force which, acting on a body from outside has a tendency to get it moved in the direction in which it is acting, or to get its parts forced together into smaller space, sp. such a force acting over a SURFACE; measure of p. on a surface, given as units per cm². [Meteor.] P. of the atmosphere. [Elec.] ELECTROMOTIVE FORCE, measured in VOLTS, p. gauge. [Engin.] An instrument for measuring the p. of a liquid or gas, for example, that of the steam in a steam boiler. p. of the atmosphere. Sp., the p. of the earth's ATMOSPHERE as measured by the BAROMETER. p. sen′sation. [Psych.] The sense-experience given by a p. on the skin changing the form of its SURFACE somewhat, as in touching anything, or by p. acting somewhere inside the body. p. spot or point. [Psych.] Point on skin at which p. is sensed. p. suit. Air-tight clothing, designed to keep the air-p. on the body about normal, necessary for an airman when flying higher than 60,000 ft.

'**pressurized**, a. (Of a room in some plant, a space-RESEARCH CAPSULE, etc.), having an apparatus for keeping the air-PRESSURE inside almost normal.

pre'ventive, 1.a. Keeping something from coming about, sp. [Med.] keeping off disease or certain developments, such as CONCEPTION. 2.n. Anything, such as a medical substance, having or used for a p. effect. **p. 'medicine.** That branch of medical science having to do with keeping persons from getting diseases.

'**prezyga'pophysis**, n. [Zoo.] ZYGAPOPHYSIS on the front face or, in man, the upper face, of a NEURAL ARCH.

'**prickle**, n. [Biol.] A small, sharp point, sp. [Bot.] one coming up through the outer skin of a stem from the part under it. **p. cell.** [Zoo.] The sort of CELL present in the deeper STRATA of EPITHELIUM, having small p.-like outgrowths joining it to the other cells. '**prickly**, a. **prickly heat.** [Med.] A non-CONTAGIOUS outburst of small red points on the skin causing a great desire for rubbing, common in babies in warm weather, the effect of INFLAMMATION of the SWEAT GLANDS.

pri'm(a)eval, a. Of the very early stages of man's or the earth's history, still the same as in those times, very old, as p. ROCKS, p. impulses. **p. 'atom.** [Astron.] The first, highly CONDENSED, mass of material substance from which the UNIVERSE is said to have come by certain astronomy experts.

'**primal**, a. PRIMARY in time or order.

'**primary**, 1.a. First in time or order, forming or to do with a starting-point, first-formed, oldest; chief, most important; to do with, being, a p. [Chem.] Produced by the SUBSTITUTION of only one ATOM or group (as **p. 'amine**). [Elec.] Being or to do with the INDUCING current in an apparatus, as a **p. current, p. coil**, etc. [Geol.] Sp., of, being, the PALAEOZOIC or earlier; (of ROCKS) formed deep in the earth and having undergone no change. See SECONDARY. 2.n. [Optics, Psych., etc.] A p. colour. [Zoo.] Any of the long feathers with a stiff middle structure on the outer or hard part of a bird's wing. [Elec.] A p. COIL. [Astron.] The brighter star of a DOUBLE STAR; a star etc. viewed in relation to its SATELLITE(s). **p. acid.** [Chem.] Any acid in which the CARBOXYL group is joined to the end C ATOM of a chain. **p. 'alcohol.** [Chem.] Any of the sort of ALCOHOLS having the group –CH$_2$OH, which have the property of forming acids with the same number of C ATOMS. **p. body.** [Bot.] That part of a plant body formed of p. meristem. **p. body cavity.** [Zool.] BLASTOCOELE. **p. cell.** [Elec.] An electric CELL in which the chemical reaction is IRREVERSIBLE

so that it is not possible to give it back its power, when this has been used up, by sending an electric current through it in the opposite direction. **p. colour.** [Psych.] Any of a group of colours or STIMULI by mixing which all other colours may be formed or produced, but which themselves are not formed of any others, see PHYSIOLOGICAL, PSYCHOLOGICAL and SUBTRACTIVE P. **p. e'lectron.** In THERMIONICS, any of the ELECTRONS falling on a body as against those given out by it. **p. growth.** [Bot.] Growth effected by p. meristem, causing the part to become longer and producing outgrowths. **p. host.** [Biol.] The plant or animal on which a PARASITE is living at full growth or in its sexed stage. **p. 'increase.** [Bot.] Increase in the size of a stem or root caused by p. growth. **p. me'dullary ray.** [Bot.] A VASCULAR RAY going from the middle to the outside of a stem or root. **p. 'meristem.** [Bot.] The MERISTEM produced by development straight from PROMERISTEM, of which the chief structure of the plant is formed. **p. 'phloem.** [Bot.] The PHLOEM of a p. vascular bundle made up of PROTOPHLOEM and METAPHLOEM. **p. sere.** [Bot.] A SERE starting on land which has had no plants on it before in the present division of the earth's history. **p. 'thickening.** [Bot.] The first coats of CELLS by which the young cell wall is made thicker. **p. 'tissue.** [Bot.] Material formed from p. meristem. **p. 'vascular 'bundle.** [Bot.] A VASCULAR BUNDLE formed straight from a PROCAMBIAL STRAND. **p. wood** or '**xylem.** [Bot.] The XYLEM of a p. vascular bundle, made up of PROTOXYLEM and METAXYLEM. '**primarily**, adv. '**primacy**, n. The condition of being first or chief.

'**Primates**, n.pl. [Zoo.] The highest ORDER of MAMMALS, among which are monkeys and man, marked by a very high development of the brain and of the power of using the hands and/or feet for gripping and guiding instruments etc., gen. having the power of turning the thumb and/or first toe opposite to the other fingers or toes, freq. with nails in place of CLAWS. '**primate**, n. Animal of the P.

prime, a. Chief, most important. **p. 'mover.** [Mech.] Any natural force used by man for producing power; an engine or machine for turning some natural force into machine power, as a steam-engine, a water-wheel, an INTERNAL COMBUSTION ENGINE, etc. **p. 'number.** [Arith.] An INTEGER such that no integer but itself and 1 will go into it with nothing over. **p. 'vertical.** [Astron.] The VERTICAL CIRCLE at right-angles to the MERIDIAN.

'**primine**, n. [Bot.] The outer coat of an OVULE having two coats.

pri'mipara, n. [Med.] A woman giving birth

for the first time or who has only once given birth, **pri'miparous,** a.

'primitive, a. [Anthrop.] Of the earliest stages of man's history; (of forms of existence, society, etc.) still at an early stage of development, very little or no further forward than in p. times. [Geol.] Earliest formed. [Biol.] To do with the first stage in the development of a structure, material, or part, being the earliest form of, first-formed, sp. simple in comparison with later developments; (of a sort of animal or plant) low in the scale of EVOLUTION (generally or in relation to other sorts in the same chief grouping), still very near to the starting-point of its line of development; of p. times, no longer in existence. **p. groove.** [Zoo.] A hollow line running down the middle of the p. streak. **p. streak.** [Zoo.] A thicker band formed on the top side of the BLASTODERM in the GASTRULATION stage of some backboned animals, taking the same direction as the AXIS of the future EMBRYO.

pri'mordial, a. In existence at or from the start, very old, unchanged from its earliest condition. [Biol.] PRIMITIVE. **p. cell.** [Bot.] A CELL before the forming of the cell-wall. **p. leaf.** [Bot.] The first leaf formed after the COTYLEDONS; the very small rounded PROJECTION which is the start of the development of a leaf. **p. 'meristem.** PROMERISTEM. **p. 'ova.** [Zoo.] Great CELLS in the EMBRYO which later become egg-cells. **p. 'utricle.** [Bot.] The skin of PROTOPLASM forming the inner coating of the CELL-wall, together with the hollow inside it, in a cell at full growth.

pri'mordium, n. [Biol.] The earliest stage in the development of any part at which it becomes clear what it is going to be.

'principal, n. Chief, most important. **p. 'axis (of a lens).** [Optics] The straight line through the CENTRES OF CURVATURE of the faces of a LENS. **p. 'focus.** [Optics] Of a LENS or SPHERICAL MIRROR, the point at which rays of light parallel to the p. axis are made to come together, or from which they are made to seem to go out, by the instrument. **p. plane.** [Optics, Cryst.] Of a LENS, one or other of the planes through the p. points and at right-angles to the p. axis; of a BIREFRINGENT CRYSTAL, a plane having in it the OPTIC AXIS and the ORDINARY or the EXTRAORDINARY RAY. **p. points.** [Optics] (Of a LENS or system of lenses) two points on the p. axis such that if v is the distance of a thing from one of them and u that of its IMAGE from the other, the FOCAL LENGTH, f, is given by

$$\frac{1}{v} - \frac{1}{u} = \frac{1}{f}$$

— the same as the NODAL POINTS when the two sides of the lens are of the same material **p. 'section.** [Cryst.] Of a BIREFRINGENT CRYSTAL, a plane going through the OPTIC AXIS and at right-angles to one of the crystal faces.

'principle, n. A general law or rule, or something taken as such, on which some reasoning or some process, machine etc. is based; the chief property of any thing or substance, or that part of it giving it this property, that is, responsible for the effect it has, said sp. of medical substances. **p. of inde'terminacy.** [Phys.] UNCERTAINTY PRINCIPLE. **p. of least time.** [Optics] FERMAT'S PRINCIPLE.

prism, n. [Optics] A body of glass, etc. having parallel and equal three-sided ends and three plane sides, two of them making equal angles with the third, used for the REFRACTION or REFLECTION of light rays. [Cryst.] A hollow and unended CRYSTAL form made up of three or more plane faces parallel to one of the AXES. **pris'matic,** a. To do with, in the form of a p.; made up of pp.; (of OPTICAL INSTRUMENTS) using a PORRO PRISM; (of colours) formed by the REFRACTION of light through a p.; having the colours of the SPECTRUM, like light broken up by a p.; loosely, having a number of colours, IRIDESCENT. [Cryst.] ORTHORHOMBIC. **prismatic 'spectrum.** [Optics] A SPECTRUM produced by a p. as opp. one produced by a DIFFRACTION GRATING.

pro-. Part in front of, or forming the front of:— -'amnion, n., -'atlas, n.; to do with the PROTHORAX:— '-sternum, n.; (being) an early form or stage of, EMBRYONIC:— -'cartilage, n., -'chorion, n., -'embryo, n.,

pro'angiosperm, n. [Bot.] Any of the FOSSIL plants of which ANGIOSPERMS are probably developments.

proba'bility, n. The condition of being probable; the degree to which something is probable, sp. the chance of the coming about of any special form of a certain event, given as the RATIO of the number of ways in which it is possible for this form to come about to the number of ways in which all the different forms of the event may come about; probable event, etc.

'probable 'error. Of a group of observations of a measure or amount, an error whose amount is such that in any given observation the chances of the error being greater or less than this are equal.

probe, 1. n. [Med.] A long thin instrument with a rounded point used for putting into wound etc. to see how deep it is or if there is anything inside it which has to come out, such as bits of bone, CALCULI, lead from a gun, etc.; any instrument etc., for example an ELECTRODE, used for the like purpose of discovery. [Astronautics] A VEHICLE sent up by a ROCKET for taking instruments and possibly man far out into space for purposes of discovery, commonly named a *space p.* or a *deep-space p.*, as opp. the 'capsule' of those rocket-fired vehicles which become earth SATELLITES. 2.v.t. Make use of a p. on (wound or part).

Pro'bosci'dea, n.pl. [Zoo.] An ORDER of MAMMALS, animals of great size with very thick legs, a thick, leather-like skin almost without hair, two upper INCISOR teeth which have undergone development into great curved TUSKS, and gen. (in all present-day representatives) a very long pipe-like nose with the openings at the end, having the power of gripping things by twisting itself round them or by a special gripping-apparatus at the end, and used for putting food into the mouth and for drinking through.

pro'boscis, n. [Zoo.] Any long pipe-like outgrowth from the face or mouth of an animal, sp., in some insects the SUCKING apparatus formed by the mouth-parts, in some worms the PROTRUSIBLE front part of the ALIMENTARY CANAL, in NEMERTINEA a protrusible part coming out of an opening over the mouth, probably a feeler, in PROBOSCIDEA the long waving nose. probos'cidiform, a.

pro'cambium, n. [Bot.] The material formed of long, narrow CELLS, present at the back of the growth points in roots and stems, from which the development of VASCULAR TISSUE takes place. pro-'cambial, a. procambial strand. A long narrow group of p. CELLS which undergo division into ZYLEM, PHLOEM and sometimes CAMBIUM, forming a VASCULAR BUNDLE.

'procarp, n. [Bot.] The female sex-part in red ALGAE, made up of a CARPOGONIUM and a TRICHOGYNE.

pro'cercoid, n. [Zoo.] An early LARVA stage in some CESTODA.

'process, 1.n. [Biol.] An outgrowth, a part coming out from the parts round it. 2.v.t. In industry, make (a substance or material) undergo some special process, freq. chemical, to make it better for marketing, for example, by increasing the time for which it will keep, giving it the property of not being damaged by water and so on; get facts, observations, e.g. the instrument-readings sent back by radio from a space PROBE, sorted and ANALYSED. '-ed, a. '-ing, n.

pro'coelous, a. [Zoo.] With an incurving front face (and gen. an outcurving back face), said of the divisions of the backbone.

'procreate, v.t. and i. [Zoo.] Have offspring; (of male) be the cause of a female's producing (offspring), become the father of (offspring). procre'ation, n. 'procre'ator, n. Father or, less freq., mother. 'procre'ative, a. Sp., having the power or tendency to p., sp. frequently.

'proctal, a. [Zoo.] Near the ANUS.

proct(o). RECTUM or ANUS: proc'talgia, n. [Med.], proc'tectomy, n. [Med.], proctitis, n. [Med.]

procto'deum, n. [Zoo.] The end part of the ALIMENTARY CANAL in the EMBRYO where the ECTODERM round the opening is turned in over the ENDODERM of the canal. procto'deal, a.

pro'cumbent, a. [Bot.] (Of stems) flat on the earth.

pro'dentine, n. [Zoo.] The soft substance covering the points of a tooth before the DENTINE is formed.

'prodrome, n. [Med.] An early sign of the coming on of a disease. 'prodrom-al, -ic, -ous, aa. Giving a sign of the future development of a disease.

pro'ducer, n. [Engin.] An apparatus for producing gas for burning, driving gas engines, etc., by forcing air and steam through a bed of heated COKE. p. gas. The gas made in a p., formed chiefly of CO, H, and N.

'product, n. What is produced, thing, substance, etc. produced by a process, for example, by a chemical reaction. [Arith.] (Of two or more numbers) the number got by MULTIPLYING one by the other.

pro'ethnic, a. [Anthrop.] To do with man, or with the men of a certain part of the earth, at an early stage, before the division into well-marked RACIAL groups.

'profile, n. The outline of any body, sp. of a person's face seen from the side; a GRAPH, sp. [Psych.] one representative of the qualities of a person's mind so far as it is possible to get these measured and give them certain values in numbers (psychic or mental or psychological p.). [Surveying, etc.] An outline to scale on paper of the changes in the level of the earth at a certain place, as they would be seen by looking sideways at a long cut at right-angles to the level plane; a like outline of some engineering structure.

proga'mete, n. [Biol.] An oöcyte or SPERMATOCYTE. [Biol.] In certain FUNGI, a HYPHA from which GAMETES are separated by the forming of walls across the hypha.

pro'gamic, a. [Biol.] Taking place, present, before FERTILIZATION.

pro'genitor, n. [Biol.] Plant, animal, or sort, by which another has been produced or from which it has come down.

'progeny, n. [Biol.] Offspring.

pro'geria, n. [Med.] A diseased condition in which young persons become like very old ones, getting very small and dried up with loss of hair, deeply lined skins, and feeble minds—probably as the effect of damage to the PITUITARY GLAND.

pro'gesterone, pro'gestin, nn. [Zoo.] A HORMONE produced by the CORPUS LUTEUM in female MAMMALS by which a number of the changes in the UTERUS making ready for the producing of off-spring, and other changes in the body for the same purpose (such as an increase in the size of the milk-producing GLANDS) are effected.

pro'glotti-s, -d, (proglottides) nn. [Zoo.] Any of the divisions making up the body in CESTODA, having in them male and female sex-parts and able to go on living for a time after being broken off, produced by BUDDING from the neck.

prog'nath-ous, -ic, aa. [Zoo.] With JAWS coming further forward than the rest of the face, sp., of man, having a FACIAL ANGLE of between 70° and 80°. **'prognath-ism, -y,** nn.

prog'nosis, n. [Med.] The act or art of seeing at the start how a disease will go on in an ill person, or a statement as to its probable future development. **prog'nostic,** 1.a. Of, to do with, p., or on which a p. may be based. 2.n. Any sign pointing to the probable future development of a disease. **prog'nose, prog'nosticate,** vv.i. and t. Give a p. or the p. of (a disease).

'progress, n. Motion forward or development to a higher point. **pro'gress,** v.i. Undergo p., go forward from place to place or from a lower or worse to a higher or better stage, get on well, **pro'gression,** n. The act or condition of progressing; a line or chain of things, events, steps, coming after one another, sp. progressing to some point or condition. [Astron.] The motion of the PLANETS through one division of the ZODIAC after another from west to east. [*See* ARITHMETICAL PROGRESSION and GEOMETRICAL PROGRESSION]. **pro'gressional,** a. **pro'gressive,** a. Going forward, becoming better from stage to stage; to do with, marked by, a progression of stages etc., coming about or having its effect by increasing degrees, not all at one time, sp [Med.] (of a disease) getting worse, increasing its grip, by degrees. **progressive meta-'morphism.** [Geol.] The changes taking place by degrees in ROCKS in touch with, or near to, IGNEOUS INTRUSIONS.

pro'hibited, a. [Phys.] In the theory of ATOMS, said of ORBITS or STATES in which the existence of an ELECTRON is not normally possible.

prohy'drotropism, n. [Bot.] TROPISM in the direction of water.

pro'ject, 1.v.t. Send or put out, forward, as (of an animal) p. the tongue, (of a body or apparatus) p. heat, light, etc. (sp. *onto* some other thing). [Map-making, Optics, etc.] Make (a picture of a body etc.) on a plane or curved SURFACE such as would be made if straight lines from all or some of the points of the body were cut by the plane, take forward (the points, outline, of the body etc.) in one's mind, or by some process of light rays, so that a picture of them is formed on a surface cutting the lines, as when the shade of a body is formed on some surface. [Psych.] Give to a sense-experience the position from which the STIMULUS comes or is judged to come, for example, take pain caused by a tooth to be present in the tooth, see colours as present in space outside the body, etc.; take as being events outside the self, or the properties of other persons, certain experiences, ideas, desires, purposes etc. which are in fact unconscious processes in the self, as freq. in diseases of the mind. 2.v.i. (Of a part or thing) be further forward than, come out into space from, the mass or parts round it. **'-ing,** a. Coming out from, being further forward than, what is round it. **'-ion,** n. Act, process, or condition of projecting; a map etc. or an IMAGE made by projection; a projecting part. **projection 'lantern.** [Optics, etc.] A simple apparatus for projecting onto a SCREEN an IMAGE of increased size of a picture on a glass etc. plate through which light is sent by the use of two LENSES, one at the back of the plate to send the light equally to all parts of it, and one in front of the plate by which the rays are given their direction. **'-ive,** a. [Optics, etc., Psych.) To do with or produced by projection. **'-or,** n. Sp., [Optics] An apparatus for sending a strong pencil or band of light for a great distance in a certain direction; an apparatus by which an IMAGE is projected onto a SCREEN, sp. a motion-picture projector to which is gen. joined an apparatus for sending out at the same time recorded sound.

'project, n. An undertaking designed for some purpose of science.

pro'jectile, 1.a. Giving an impulse to, sending forward with force. [Zoo.] (Of part) able to be pushed forward. 2.n. A body given a forward impulse with great force and then going on by itself, as a ball from a gun.

pro'lactin, n. [Zoo.] The chief LACTOGENIC HORMONE.

pro'lamin(e), n. [Chem.] Any of a group of PROTEINS not SOLUBLE in water or strong ALCOHOL, but soluble in a 70–80% SOLUTION of alcohol.

pro'laps-e, -us, nn. [Med.] The falling down or slipping out of place of some part inside the body.

'prolate, a. Of a SPHEROID, not as fully curved round its EQUATOR as at the POLES, measuring more from top to base than from side to side; having the form of a p. spheroid.

'proleg, n. [Zoo.] One of the short soft legs without divisions of an insect LARVA.

pro'liferate, 1.v.t. [Biol.] Get (new like parts, or offspring) produced quickly by the division of CELLS or BUDDING, over and over. 2.v.i. Undergo quick growth, or get offspring produced, by proliferation. 'prolife'ration, n. The act of proliferating; a growth formed by proliferating. pro-'liferative, a. [Biol.] Having the property of proliferating; to do with proliferating. [Med.] (Of a process or disease) marked by the proliferation of new CELLS, the quick forming of new TISSUE. pro'liferous, a. Proliferative, sp. [Bot.] sending out, or producing new plants by, outgrowths of all sorts, such as OFFSETS. 'prolifi'cation, n. Proliferation, sp. [Bot.] the development of a new branch from the inside of a flower or fruit, or the new branch produced in this way.

pro'lific, a. [Biol.] Producing offspring freely, in great numbers. '-acy, n.

pro'meristem, n. [Bot.] The MERISTEM of growth points and EMBRYOS, made up of CELLS of regular form undergoing quick division, and from which the PRIMARY MERISTEM is formed.

pro'methium, n. Chemical ELEMENT, at. no 61, at. wt. 146–157, sign Pm, one of the RARE EARTH METALS which first came to light in the FISSION of U in 1926 and of the natural existence of which there is still no knowledge.

'prominence, n. A PROJECTING part; the condition of projecting. [Astron.] One of the great tongues of flame seen round the edge of the sun in an ECLIPSE, or at any time by the use of the SPECTROSCOPE. [Phonet.] Of a word, SYLLABLE etc., the condition of being said in a way to make it seem more important or marked than the other words of a group or syllables of a word, for example, by the use of ACCENT or STRESS. 'prominent, a. PRO-JECTING. [Phonet.] Having p.

'promontory, n. [Zoo.] A PROJECTING structure sp. on a bone, as p. of the sacrum, the p. formed by the angle between the upper end of the SACRUM and the part of the backbone to which it is joined.

pro'moter, n. [Chem.] A substance increasing the effect of a CATALYST.

promy'celium (promycelia), n. [Bot.] The short, thread-like pipe put out by RESTING SPORES in UREDINALES and USTILA-GINALES on which smaller spores are produced.

pro'nation, n. [Zoo.] The position in which the hand or front foot is turned so that the PALM is facing down, or the turning of the hand, etc. into this position; the act of getting into, or the condition of being in, a PRONE position. 'pronate, pro'nated, aa. (Of the hand or foot) in the position of p.;

bent forward, almost PRONE. pro'nator, n. [Zoo.] Any of the muscles effecting p. of the hand or foot.

prone, a. [Zoo.] (Of men or animals or body parts) placed with the face or front part flat on or parallel to the earth. '-ness, n.

pro'nephro-s, -n, nn. [Zoo.] Front part of KIDNEY in the EMBRYO of backboned animals, freq. having no use or no longer present at full growth. pro'nephric, a.

'pronograde, a. [Zoo.] Walking with the body parallel to the earth, walking on four legs.

pro'notum, n. [Zoo.] The plate on the top of the PROTHORAX of an insect.

'Protonsil, n. [Med., Chem.] Trade name for a substance of the SULPHONAMIDE group, the first of them to be used medically.

pro'nucleus, n. [Zoo.] The male or the female NUCLEUS in a FERTILIZED OVUM at the stage when they have undergone MATURA-TION but are still separate.

'pronymph, n. [Zoo.] Form or stage before the NYMPH stage in DIPTERA.

pro'oestru-s, -m, nn. [Zoo.] The first stage of the OESTRUS CYCLE, when the body is getting ready for MATING.

proof, 1.n. A test, or an argument based on fact, making it so clear that something is true that it is impossible for the mind not to have belief in it; fact(s) or observation(s) on which a p. is based; the giving of p. 2.a. Used for testing purposes, acting as a test; having the property of not being attacked or damaged by something (p. against a disease, etc.), or of not letting a liquid or gas through; in agreement with the condition fixed by law for p. spirit. p. plane. [Elec., Engin.] An apparatus made of CONDUCTING material on a non-conducting hand-part used for taking a charge from a body. p. 'spirit. Alcohol for drinking which is in agreement with a STANDARD fixed by law, in England made up of about 49·3% by weight of ETHYL ALCOHOL in water. p. stress [Metal.] The STRESS needed for producing PERMANENT SET in metals.

-proof, a. Not attacked or damaged by, not letting through:— 'fireproof, a., gasproof, a., rainproof, a., waterproof, a.

pro'ostracum, n. [Zoo.] In present-day DIBRANCHIA the PEN; the long thin front part of a BELEMNITE.

pro'otic, a., n. [Zoo.] (To do with, near) the front bone of the framework of the ear in back-boned animals.

'propagate, 1.v.i. [Biol.] Have, go on having, offspring, (of a sort or group) become greater in number as the effect of the producing of offspring, (of plants) sp. by OFFSETS etc. 2.v.t. (Of plants or animals) make the numbers of (their sort) greater by producing offspring; get (a sort of plant or animal) to p., keep it in being in this way; take about, make a distribution of (seeds, etc.), take (a disease) from person to person; take forward or send on the effects of (wave motions, impulses, etc.) from point to point. **propa'gation,** n. **'propa'gative,** a. **'propagator,** n.

'propane, n. [Chem.] C_3H_8, a gas without colour readily taking fire, the third of the PARAFFIN SERIES.

pro'pel, v.t. Send (a body, ship, etc.) forward by pushing or giving a forward impulse to, or keeping propelling parts in motion. **pro'pellant,** n., a. (Anything) propelling, or with a tendency to p., sp. any EXPLOSIVE used for this purpose, as gunpowder or any of the materials firing a ROCKET. **pro'peller,** n. Sp. a bladed, turning structure by which an airplane or ship is forced forward, or any part of different form having the same purpose, as an AIRSCREW or SCREW PROPELLER.

'proper, a. Special, natural, *to* a thing, being its special property; right for a given purpose. **p. 'motion.** [Astron.] The motion of a star in relation to the CELESTIAL SPHERE as it seems to observation.

'prophase, n. [Biol.] The first part of the process of MITOSIS or MEIOSIS from the time when the CHROMOSOMES are seen to the forming of the SPINDLE.

prophy'laxis, n. [Med.] The art or process of keeping off disease. **prophy'lactic,** n., a. (Anything) which keeps off, or is a help in keeping off, disease, sp. a medical substance taken for this purpose.

'propio'nic 'acid, [Chem.] A FATTY ACID, $C_2H_5.COOH$, produced in the DISTILLATION of wood. (*See* p. 557.) **propion-, propiono-,** Of, to do with, p. a.

pro'pode-on, -um, nn. [Zoo.] In some HYMENOPTERA, the first division of the ABDOMEN which has become united with the THORAX in front of the PETIOLE. **pro'podeal,** a.

propodite, n. [Zoo.] The 6th division from the body of the walking-legs or MAXILLIPEDS in some CRUSTACEA; the 4th division from the body of the legs in ARACHNIDA.

pro'podium, n. [Zoo.] The small front part of the foot in GASTROPODA.

'propolis, n. A wax-like material taken by bees from the BUDS of certain trees, and used by them for fixing together parts of their HONEYCOMBS, etc.

pro'portion, n. The relation in size, amount, number, or degree of one thing or group of things to another, sp. of one part of a structure or substance to another or to the complete structure or substance; (of a structure) balance, right p., harmony of size between the parts. [Math.] RATIO; (of ratios) the condition of being equal, or a group of equal ratios (of which the TERMS are said to be *in p.*). **pro'portional,**

a. To do with p., based on some fixed p.; (of amounts, etc.) having a fixed p. (*to* some other amount or to one another); having the right or natural p. (*to* some other thing or to one another); (of RATIOS) equal. **pro'portional 'counter.** [Phys.] A special sort of IONIZATION CHAMBER in which ALPHA-PARTICLES may be measured with BETA-PARTICLES present. **'-ally,** adv. **'-'ality,** n. **-ate,** a. Proportional, sp. *to* something. **'-ately,** adv.

propo'sition, n. A statement of a fact for which arguments are to be given.

pro'prietary, a. (Of medical substances) patented, or of which the FORMULA or process of making is special to some maker and not public property. **p. name.** The special name under which a p. substance is marketed.

'proprio'ceptor, n. [Zoo.] Any RECEPTOR giving a sense of something taking place inside the body (other than changes caused by substances taken into the ALIMENTARY CANAL or the breathing apparatus), sp., and sometimes limited to, those sensing changes of position in muscles etc., or in the balancing apparatus of the inner ear. *See* INTEROCEPTOR. **'proprio'ceptive,** a.

'proprio'genic, a. [Zoo.] Said of an EFFECTOR other than muscle, or of one which is at the same time a RECEPTOR.

'prop root. [Bot.] A root starting from the stem outside the earth and going down to it, giving support to the plant.

pro'pulsion, n. [Mech.] The act of PROPELLING. [Med.] A tendency to be bent forward in walking. **pro'pulsive,** a. PROPELLENT.

pro'pupa, n. [Zoo.] Form or stage in the development of an insect before the PUPA.

'propyl, a. [Chem.] Having in it the ALKYL group $-C_3H_7$ of which PROPANE is the HYDRIDE. **p. 'alcohol.** $C_3H_7.OH$, a liquid without colour having two ISOMERS, of which the normal one is got from FUSEL OIL.

pro'scolex, n. [Zoo.] An early stage in the development of a CESTODE in which it has the form of a bag-like structure full of liquid.

prose'cretin, n. [Zoo.] The substance producing SECRETIN.

prosen'cephalon, n. [Zoo.] The front part of brain in back-boned animals.

prosen'chyma, n. [Bot.] One of the two chief materials making up plants, formed of long CELLS with pointed ends and freq. little or no substance inside them, whose chief business is giving support to the plant or transporting liquids, etc. **prosen'chymatous,** a.

'prospect, 1.v.i. Go over (a country etc.) looking for MINERALS of value with a view to mining, oil-producing, etc. 2.n.

A place giving hope of minerals of value in an amount great enough for mining, etc. **pro'specting,** n. **pro'spector,** n.

'prostate gland, [Zoo.] A GLAND forming part of the male sex-ORGANS in higher back-boned animals, the produce of which is sent to be mixed with outgoing SPERM, making it more liquid and possibly having other effects. **'prostate,** n. P. g. **pro'static,** a. To do with the p. g. **'prostatism,** n. [Med.] A condition common in older men in which the p.g. becomes over-sized and gives trouble.

'prosthesis, n. [Med.] The addition to the body of some false part to take the place of one which has been taken off or out, as a leg, eye, tooth, etc.; false part made to take the place of one which the body no longer has. [Philol.] The addition of one or more sounds or letters to a word, sp. at the start. **pros'thetic,** a. **pros'thetics,** n.pl. [Med.] The branch of medical science which has to do with p.

'prosthion, n. In CRANIOMETRY, a point on the upper JAW at the middle of the front teeth.

pros'tomium, n. [Zoo.] In worms and MOLLUSCA, the part of the head in front of the mouth. **pros'tomiate,** a.

'prostrate, a. [Bot.] PROCUMBENT. [Zoo.] PRONE on the earth etc.

pros'tration, n. [Med.] A condition in which a person's forces are almost completely drained away, very feeble condition sp. of nerves or muscles. **prostrated,** a. [Med.] In a condition of p.

'protamine, n. [Chem., Biochem.] Any of a group of simple PROTEINS, strongly BASIC, which are never present naturally by themselves, but only united with acid proteins in the SPERM of fish.

pro'tandrous, a. [Biol.] (Of plants) producing and sending out POLLEN before the STIGMA of the same flower is in a condition to take it in, or (of HERMAPHRODITE animals) producing the male sex-CELLS before the female sex-cells, so that the female sex-cells are not FERTILIZED by male cells from the same plant or animal. **prot'andry,** b.

protan'omaly, n. [Optics, Psych.] A form of DEFECTIVE COLOUR VISION in which a person, though normal in being TRICHO-MATIC, sees the red part of the SPECTRUM more feebly than a normal person.

'protan'opia, n. [Optics, Psych.] DICHRO-MATISM in which a person is unable to see different CHROMATIC colours in the red-yellow-green part of the SPECTRUM, and in which, as opp. DEUTERANOPIA, the LUMINOSITY of the red end is much less than for a normal person (earlier named *red blindness*). **'protanope,** n. Person having p.

Pro'targol, n. [Med.] Trade name for a

PROTEIN powder having silver in it, and forming in water a COLLOIDAL SOLUTION of silver, used as an ANTISEPTIC.

pro'taxis, n. [Geog., Geol.] The line of the first 'uplifting of a mountain range, its middle part.

'protease, n. [Chem., Biochem.] Any of a group of ENZYMES by which PROTEINS are broken up or AMINO ACIDS are made into proteins, present in all living things.

pro'tective, a. [Biol., Chem., Elec., etc.] Designed to keep off danger or damage, as **p. colouring** in animals, a **p. coating** on a metal, keeping it from chemical attack, or a part of an electric apparatus cutting off the current, etc., if anything goes wrong. **p. 'colloid.** [Chem.] A COLLOID which when mixed with a non-REVERSIBLE or UNSTABLE colloid in small amount makes it reversible or STABLE. **p. 'layer.** [Bot.] A coat of cork CELLS covering the place on the stem where a leaf has come off in the Fall, to keep water in and insects etc. out. **p. 'mimicry,** [Zoo.] The copying by an animal of the form or colouring of things round it for the purpose of keeping safe by making itself hard to see. **pro'tect,** v.t. Keep safe, keep from damage, etc.

'proteid, n. Old name for PROTEIN.

'protein, n. [Chem., Biochem.] Any of a great and important group of complex natural substances, forming a great part of all living material, made up of H, O, N, and C, and sometimes P, S, or Fe, in the form of long CHAINS of AMINO ACIDS, into which they may be broken up by HYDROLYSIS—needed in food for body-building and got chiefly from meat, cheese, eggs, and fish. **p. shock.** [Med.] A strong reaction of the SMOOTH MUSCLE of the body caused, sometimes on purpose, by putting a p., such as any BACTERIAL VACCINE, into the blood. **p. 'therapy.** [Med.] The putting of p. into the blood for the purpose of overcoming disease.

pro'tentomon, n. [Zoo.] The first or general form of which, in theory, winged insects are a development.

prote(o)-. PROTEIN.

'proteo'clastic, a. [Biochem.] Causing PRO-TEINS to be broken down.

prote'olysis, n. [Biochem.] Any process by which PROTEINS are broken down chemically, as in digestion. **'proteo'lytic,** a. Sp., effecting p., as a **p.** ENZYME.

'proteose, n. [Chem., Biochem.] Any of the group of substances formed from PRO-TEINS as a step in the process of digestion.

'proter-'androus, -'ogynous, etc. *See* PRO-TANDROUS, PROTOGYNOUS.

'proterotype, n. [Biol.] Any TYPE which is made the, or a, representative type of a new SPECIES.

'Protero'zoic, a., n. [Geol.] (Of, to do with)

the third division ('period') of the PRE-CAMBRIAN ERA, when the development of living things got as far as ringed worms and some ALGAE (*see* p. 559).

pro'thallus (prothalli or prothalluses), **pro'thallium** (prothallia), nn. [Bot.] A very small, thin, green plant-body produced from a SPORE and producing ANTHERIDIA and/or ARCHEGONIA, forming the sexed stage in PTERIDOPHYTA, gen. flat on the earth and fixed to it by hair-like roots, but sometimes under the earth. **pro'thalloid**, a.

pro'theca, n. [Zoo.] The first-formed part, the base, of a CALYCULUS in CORAL.

pro'thesis, n. PROSTHESIS.

pro'thorax, n. [Zoo.] The front division of an insect's THORAX. **'prothor'acic**, a.

pro'thrombin, n. [Zoo., Chem.] The substance in the blood from which THROMBIN is formed, that is, thrombin itself before it is put into operation by THROMBO-PLASTIN.

Pro'tista, n.pl. [Biol.] A general name for all one-CELLED living forms which might be grouped as plants or as animals, but are not clearly one or the other, as BACTERIA. **protis'tology**, n. The science of P.

proto-. [Zoo.] First, most forward (part or division). [Biol., Geol.] First, or before in time, first-formed, an early form of, being present in the EMBRYO, LARVA, etc., being the PROTOTYPE of, being that from which the named thing is produced. [Chem.] The first COMPOUND in a SERIES, that having in it the smallest amount of the chief ELEMENT.

'protoac'tinium, n. Chemical ELEMENT, at. no. 91, at. wt. 231, sign Pa, a RADIOACTIVE element which gives birth to Ac.

'protoba'sidium, n. [Bot.] A BASIDIUM having 4 divisions, every division producing a SPORE.

proto'cephalon, n. [Zoo.] The front division of an insect's head.

proto'cercal, a. [Zoo.] (Of fish) having the two divisions of the tail FIN equal.

'Protochor'data, n.pl. [Zoo.] A general name for the lower divisions of the CHORDATA, that is CEPHALOCHORDA, HEMICHORDA and UROCHORDA.

'protocone, n. [Zoo.] The front inner CUSP of a top MOLAR tooth (*see* TRITUBERCULY).

proto'conid, n. [Zoo.] The front outer CUSP of a lower MOLAR tooth (*see* TRITUBER-CULY).

proto'cranium, n. [Zoo.] The back part of an insect's EPICRANIUM.

proto'epiphyte, n. [Bot.] An EPIPHYTE which gets all its food from the SURFACE of the plant to which it is fixed and from the air.

proto'genic, a. [Biol.] Present from the start of development. [Chem.] Able to give out a PROTON.

prot'ogynous, a. [Biol.] (Of plants) with the CARPEL becoming ready for FERTILIZA-TION before POLLEN is produced in the same flower; (of HERMAPHRODITE animals) producing the egg-CELLS earlier than the SPERM, opp. PROTANDROUS.

Proto'lithic, a. EOLITHIC.

pro'tolysis, n. [Bot.] The process by which CHLOROPHYLL is broken up into simpler substances by light.

'proton, n. [Phys.] A body forming part of the NUCLEUS of every ATOM and having a POSITIVE CHARGE equal to the NEGATIVE charge of an ELECTRON and a MASS about 1840 times that of an electron. **proton-alpha** (or *p*, *α*), **proton-deuteron** (or *p*, *d*), **proton-'gamma** (or *p*, *γ*), **proton-neutron** or (*p*, *n*) **reaction**. [Phys.] The taking in of a p. and giving out of an ALPHA PARTICLE (DEUTERON, GAMMA RAY, or NEUTRON) by the NUCLEUS of an ATOM.

proto'nema, n.[Bot.] The branching thread-like plant produced from a SPORE and forming the first stage in the development of MUSCI, the full growth of the plant being produced by BUDDING from the p. **proto'nem(a)al**, aa. **proto'nematoid**, a.

'proto-ne'phridium, -'nephros, nn. [Zoo.] The simplest sort of structure for sending out waste from the body in METAZOA, formed of a pipe-like part going from the inner hollow of the body to the outside and having one or more FLAME-CELLS, present in certain worms and LARVAE. **'protone'phridial**, a.

proto'pathic, a. [Zoo.] (Of RECEPTORS) giving a reaction only to strong PRESSURE or a marked change from heat to cold or cold to heat, having no power of delicate or clear sense-experience; to do with, having an effect on, p. nerves. [Med.] Said of the first, limited working of a nerve again after it has been damaged and for a time put completely out of operation.

'protophloem, n. [Bot.] The PHLOEM first formed from the PROCAMBIUM, so far not very complex in structure but ready for quick development into fully formed phloem.

'protophyte, **pro'tophyton** (protophyta), nn. [Bot.] Any one-CELLED plant. **proto-'phytic**, a.

'protoplasm, n. [Biol.] The substance of all living CELLS, made up of a grey, jelly-like material of complex chemical structure forming the NUCLEUS, the mass round it, and the PLASTIDS and MITOCHONDRIA inside it, the base of all living forms; the cell-substance other than the NUCLEUS. **proto'plasmic**, a.

'protoplast, n. [Biol.] The PROTOPLASM of a CELL, sp. [Bot.], as opp. the complete plant-cell with its CELL WALL. [Zoo.] A one-CELLED animal.

proto′podite, n. [Zoo.] The division of a leg nearest the body in ARTHROPODA. **′protopo′ditic,** a.

′protostele, n. [Bot.] The sort of STELE present in most roots, in the stems of PTERIDOPHYTA, and in the earliest stems in other plants, having solid wood in the middle with PHLOEM round it.

Proto′theria, n.pl. A SUB-CLASS of MAMMA-LIA having in it only the ORDER, MONO-TREMATA.

proto′trophic, a. [Bot.] Using chemical ELEMENTS as food, sp. (of BACTERIA) living on only one element.

′prototype, n. The first form of something, of which later forms are copies or developments, sp. [Biol.]; PROTEROTYPE.

proto′xylem, n. [Bot.] The earliest XYLEM formed in a plant, made up of very narrow vessels having thin walls with lines of the thicker wood-substance running through them in separate rings or one long twist.

Proto′zoa, n.pl.[Zoo.] The SUB-KINGDOM and PHYLUM of animals in which there is no division of the body into CELLS, ranging from the lowest animals (very like BACTERIA but for the fact that they have at least one clearly-marked NUCLEUS) to more complex forms with special parts for special purposes, most of them very small and living in water, some of them PARASITES. **proto′zo-al, -an, -ic,** aa. **proto′zo-an, -on,** nn. Animal of the P.

proto′zoaea, n. [Zoo.] A stage in the development of certain ARTHROPODA before the ZOAEA, when there is still no sign of the forming of the body rings.

′protozo′ology, n. That branch of Zoology having to do with the simplest animal forms.

pro′tractile, a. [Zoo.] Able to be PROTRUDED.

pro′tractor, n. [Geom., etc.] An instrument put down on paper for measuring or marking off angles on it. [Zoo.] Any muscle used for pushing or pulling out a part.

pro′trude, v.t. and i. Put out (a part), sp. from an opening, as p. the tongue; (of a part) PROJECT. **pro′trusible,** a. Able to be protruded.

pro′tuberance, a. A PROJECTING part, sp. a rounded one; (of a part) the property or condition of projecting. **pro′tuberant,** a. (Of part, etc.) PROJECTING, sp. not sharply but as a rounded mass.

′protyle, n. In old chemistry and astronomy, a first substance from which, in theory, all the ELEMENTS had been produced.

proud flesh, n. [Med.] An overgrowth of GRANULATION TISSUE in a wound or damaged tissue.

Prout's hy′pothesis. An old theory that all chemical ELEMENTS are formed from H, based on the belief that all ATOMIC WEIGHTS are MULTIPLES of that of H.

prove, v.t. Give PROOF of.

proven′triculus, n. [Zoo.] The front part of the stomach of a bird where the digestion GLANDS are, as opp. the GIZZARD; in earthworms, the thin-walled, bag-like part in front of the gizzard; in insects and Decapoda, the gizzard.

′province, n. [Geol.] A stretch of country marked by a common structure or a common history.

pro′vitamin, n. [Biochem.] A substance with the property of becoming or producing a VITAMIN, sp. ERGOSTEROL (*p.D.*) from which VITAMIN D is produced by the operation of ULTRA-VIOLET rays.

′proximal, a. (Of parts of a structure or system) nearest to the middle or to the chief part or body, at the inner end, sp. [Biol.] (of the end of a part, such as an arm, leg, muscle, etc.) nearest the point at which it is fixed to the body or to a greater part.

′proximate, a. Nearest to some other thing, with nothing between. [Chem.] To do with p. ANALYSIS. **p. an′alysis.** [Chem.] The ANALYSIS of a complex substance into other complex substances making it up, *see* ULTIMATE ANALYSIS. **p. cause.** The end-cause in a chain of causes, that whose effect is the end-effect itself, not some other cause in the chain, a cause acting straightforwardly, not through a second cause. **p. ′principle** or **′substance** [Chem.] Any complex substance which is present naturally as such in plants and animals and may be looked on as a unit in ANALYSIS, for example water. **prox′imity,** n. The condition of being nearest or very near to something.

pro′zymogen, n. [Zoo.] A substance producing a ZYMOGEN.

′pruinose, a. [Bot.] Covered with delicate powder-like white grains, as certain fruits or leaves.

pru′ritus, n. [Med.] A condition of the skin causing a strong desire for rubbing. **pru′ritic,** a.

′prussic acid. [Chem.] HCN in water, a strong poison.

psal′terium, n. OMASUM.

psammite, n. [Geol.] Any ROCK made up chiefly of sand grains. **psam′mitic,** a. Sp. produced by METAMORPHISM from psammitic SEDIMENTARY rocks.

psamm′oma, n. [Med.] A TUMOUR of the MENINGES having in it BRAIN SAND.

′psammophyte, n. [Bot.] A plant living in sand.

′psammous, a. [Med.] Sand-like or having sand in it.

′pselism, pse′lismus, nn. [Med.] STUTTERING or other trouble in talking, such as is caused by badly-formed mouth-parts.

pse′phicity, n. [Geol.] The degree to which sand grains are rounded.

′psephite, n. [Geol.] Any ROCK made up of

rounded bits of stone of a greater size than grains. **pse′phitic,** a.

pseud-. PSEUDO-.

pseudam′nesia, n. [Med.] A loss of memory for a short time.

pseud′annual, n. [Bot.] Any plant completing its growth and flowering in one year, but living on from year to year in the form of a bulb or like structure.

pseuda′pogamy, n. [Bot.] The producing of offspring by the uniting of two unsexed NUCLEI or an unsexed and a female nucleus, as in certain FUNGI.

pseuda′pospory, n. [Bot.] The producing of DIPLOID SPORES, as in certain FILICALES.

pseudar′throsis, n. [Med.] The forming of a false JOINT between bones which have been broken and not united.

pseud′haemal, a. [Zoo.] Said of the blood and blood-vessels of CHAETOPODA and ECHINODERMATA.

pseudo-. Seemingly the same as what is named but not truly so, false:— **-scien-′tific,** a. [Biol., Med.] False, copying, sp. (of conditions of the body) like those caused by changes of structure or disease bodies, but produced by other causes, such as HYSTERIA; (of a part, etc.) not normal. [Zoo.] (Of a part, etc.) like in structure or purpose to the named part in other animals. [Chem.] Like, having a near relation to, ISOMERIC with.

′pseudo ′acid, n. [Chem.] A substance which, though not itself an acid, is readily changed into an ISOMER which is one.

′pseudoa′quatic, a. [Biol.] Living in wet places but not in water.

′pseudobase, n. [Chem.] A substance which, though not itself a BASE, is readily changed into an ISOMER which is one.

′pseudobulb, n. [Bot.] A bulb-like structure on the stem in ORCHIDACEAE for storing water, etc. **pseudo′bulbous,** a.

pseudo′bulbil, n. [Bot.] An out-growth, bulb-like in form, of some FILICALES in the sexed stage, taking the place of SPORANGIA.

′pseudocarp, n. [Bot.] Any fruit not formed from the OVARY only, but taking in other parts, as the apple and some berries.

pseudo′cellus, n. [Zoo.] Any of certain sense-ORGANS present here and there in some insects, whose use is not clear.

pseudo′centrum, n. [Zoo.] The body or base of a VERTEBRA when it is formed by the uniting of ARCUALIA, as in some land-and-water animals. **pseudo′centrous,** a. (Of a VERTEBRA) having a p.

pseudo′cilium, n. [Bot.] A very thin, thread-like, unmoving outgrowth from a CELL in ALGAE.

′pseudocone, a. [Zoo.] (Of the eyes of certain insects) having in place of true CRYSTALLINE CONES, cone-like CELLS full of a thin jelly-like substance.

′pseudoconju′gation, n. [Zoo.] In some SPOROZOA, a joining of two units end to end or side to side for a time without any uniting of their substance.

′pseudodont, a. [Zoo.] Having teeth made of horn, as MONOTREMATA.

pseu′dogamy, n. [Biol.] The development of offspring from a female CELL as the effect of being in touch with a male cell, but without any uniting of their NUCLEI.

pseudo gaster, n. [Zoo.] In certain sponges, a hollow opening to the outside, with the true body-hollow opening into it.

′pseudogyne, n. [Zoo.] A worker ant looking like a female, specially in the form of the THORAX.

′pseudoi′somerism, n. TAUTOMERISM.

pseu′domerism, n. [Chem.] A condition in which, though the behaviour of a substance in forming COMPOUNDS is TAUTOMERIC, it has not so far been possible to get it broken up into two ISOMERS.

′pseudome′tamerism, n. [Zoo.] A structure of the body looking like METAMERISM but without true divisions.

pseudo′mixis, n. [Biol.] PSEUDOGAMY; the uniting and producing of offspring by two unsexed CELLS or two cells of the same sex.

′pseudo′monocoty′ledonous, a. [Bot.] Having two COTYLEDONS so united as to seem like one.

′pseudomorph, n. A false or irregular form. [Mineral.] A MINERAL having the outer, CRYSTAL form of a substance other than that of which it is made up, as the effect of having been forced etc. into the place first taken in a ROCK by the substance having that form. **pseudo′morph-ous, -ic,** aa. **pseudo′morphism,** n.

′pseudonavi′cella, n. [Zoo.] A sort of very small boat-like SPORE with SPOROZOITES in it produced by some SPOROZOA.

′pseudoparen′chyma, n. [Bot.] In FUNGI a mass of HYPHAE so twisted together as to have the look of PARENCHYMA.

pseudo′perianth, n. [Bot.] A cup-like part formed round the ARCHEGONIUM after FERTILIZATION in some HEPATICAE.

′pseudoplas′modium, n. [Bot.] A group of small AMOEBAE massed together but not united in substance.

′pseudo-pod, -′podium (pseudopodia), nn. [Zoo.] In one-CELLED animals or free cells, any bit of the cell substance pushed out from the cell at need, forming a roughly arm-like or leg-like part with no fixed outline, used for taking in food or effecting motion from place to place; a foot-like outgrowth of the body-wall seen in some insect LARVAE. [Bot.] In some MUSCI, a thin stem or branch without leaves supporting the SPOROGONIUM or producing GEMMAE; in MYXOMYCETES, any of the p.-like parts put out by a PLASMODIUM. **pseu'dopodal,** a.

pseudo'pregnancy, n. [Zoo.] In certain animals, changes in the body like those at the start of PREGNANCY coming on after the OESTRUS when there has been no sex-connection, or after sex-connection without FERTILIZATION. [Med.] Signs like those of pregnancy caused by some growth in the UTERUS, etc., or by a NEUROTIC desire on the part of a woman to have a baby.

pseu'dopsia, n. [Med.] A condition in which the eyes see things which are not present or see present things as different from what they are.

pseudo salt. [Chem.] A substance which is like a SALT, and freq. has that name, but is without the property of becoming IONIZED in SOLUTION.

pseudo'septate, a. [Biol.] Seeming to have divisions.

pseudo'sessile, a. [Zoo.] Of certain HYMEN-OPTERA, having the PETIOLE so short that the two parts of the body seem to be joined into one.

pseudo'skeleton, n. [Zoo.] In sponges, a system of SPICULES formed of hard material taken in by the animal, not produced by it.

pseudo'symmetry, n. [Mineral.] Seeming SYMMETRY, as in CRYSTALS whose structure is near enough to that of crystals in a different system to be taken for it, or which are given the look of a different structure from their true one by TWIN-NING. **'pseudosym'metric,** a.

pseudo'trachea, n. [Zoo.] Any of a number of pipes in the LABELLA of DIPTERA through which liquids are taken in.

pseudo'varium, n. [Zoo.] An OVARY producing PSEUDOVA.

pseu'dovum (pseudova), n. [Zoo.] An egg undergoing development into a new animal without FERTILIZATION.

pseudo'zoaea, n. [Zoo.] A LARVA-stage in STOMATOPODA which is like the ZOAEA stage in DECAPODA.

Psilo'tales, n. pl. [Bot.] An ORDER of PTERIDOPHYTA having a stem forking into two, with no or very small leaves, no true roots, and a GAMETOPHYTE, free from CHLOROPHYLL, under the earth.

psitta'cosis, n. [Med.] A BACTERIAL disease of certain birds, sp. of the ORDER *Psittacideae.* which may be taken by man, on whom it has a serious effect like TYPHOID FEVER with INFLAMMATION of the LUNGS.

'psoas, n. [Zoo.] One or the other of two muscles of the LOIN.

pso'riasis, n. [Med.] A CHRONIC skin disease, marked by the forming of rough red places, later becoming covered with white SCALES, sp. on the JOINTS. **'psori-'asic, psori'atic,** aa.

psychas'thenia, n. [Med.] A serious NEUROTIC condition marked by the loss of the power of decision, unreasoning doubts and fears and trouble of mind, fixed ideas, etc.

'psyche, n. [Psych.] The mind taken as all that is not physical in a person, thought, feeling and driving-force, conscious and unconscious, or the thing or part in man responsible for and undergoing all these processes. **'psychic,** a. To do with the p., sp. with the higher powers of the mind, reason, etc.; of, to do with, the operations of minds without bodies; (of forces, events) non-physical and outside normal experience, independent of the laws of time and space and of the every-day relations between mind and material things; (of a person) open to the effects of, with the power of getting in touch with, psychic forces. **'psychic 'blindness (deafness, etc.).** Loss of the power of seeing (hearing, etc.) as the effect of some damage to the sense-apparatus in the brain, the eye (ear, etc.) being normal. **'psychical,** a. Psychic, sp. in the second sense. **'psychical re'search.** The attempt at building up a body of knowledge about events which seem to give support to the idea of the existence of psychic forces.

psy'chiatry, n. The branch of medical science having to do with diseases and unnormal conditions of the mind. **psychi'atric,** a. **psy'chiatrist,** n.

psych(o)-. Mind; PSYCHOLOGICAL (and . . .).

'psychoa'nalysis, n. [Med.] The system started by Freud of uncovering by a process of questioning, and by the recording and comparison of his DREAMS, and so on, the workings of a person's unconscious mind—the fears, desires etc. stamped on him in his earliest years and still having power over him without his knowledge—with a view to helping him to a healthy and balanced condition of mind. [Psych.] The body of knowledge or detailed theory based on this system, or, and sp., the general theory that the tendency of the mind to get pushed into its unconscious part those early impulses and reactions which are at war with the later development of the self is the chief cause of all mind troubles not coming from any physical damage to the brain. **'psycho'analyst,** n. [Med.] A person whose business is helping ill persons by p.

'psychody'namic, a. [Psych.] To do with the forces by which the mind is moved. **'psychody'namics,** n. The side of psychology having to do with the moving forces in the mind, such as purpose, desire, etc.

'psychogal'vanic, a. [Psych., Zoo.] Of, to do with, electric changes in the body in connection with feelings experienced in the mind. **p. 'reflex.** A lowering for a

short time of the seeming electric RESIST-
ANCE of the skin as a reaction to certain
sense-effects or suggestions made to the
mind, probably caused by the behaviour
of the SWEAT GLANDS; an increase in the
ELECTROMOTIVE FORCE of the skin in like
conditions.

psycho'genesis, n. [Psych.] The history of
the birth and development of the mind,
or of any quality of the mind or any
condition of the body caused by the mind.

psycho'genic, a. [Med.] Starting in, caused
by, the mind.

psy'chology, n. The general science of the
mind, covering all sense-experience,
reasoning, and feeling, normal and unnormal, in themselves and in their
effects on behaviour, from the point of
view of the self, of society generally, or
of any special apparatus of society such
as education or industry; the qualities
and way of working of the mind, feelings
etc. of a person, or sp. a sort of person, as
'the p. of the actor'. 'psycho'logical, a. To
do with p.; to do with, experienced,
caused by, the mind. psychological
'primary. Any of the six colours, red,
yellow, green, blue, black, and white by
which all other colours may be painted
in words. psy'chologist, n.

psy'chometry, n. [Psych.] The art or process
of measuring qualities of mind, for
example the time taken for reactions or
mind-processes, or the degree of brain
power as given by INTELLIGENCE TESTS.
psycho'metric(al), aa. psy'chometer, n. A
timing and measuring instrument used in
p. psy'chometrist, n.

psycho'motor, a. [Psych.] Of, to do with, the
motion of muscles taking place as the
effect of a process of the mind.

'psychoneu'rosis, n. [Med.] NEUROSIS, or, in
Freud's system, a condition like a neurosis which has no physical cause at all,
but is dependent only on warring impulses in the unconscious mind.

'psycho'nomic, a. To do with the laws of
PSYCHOLOGY; to do with psychonomics.
'psycho'nomics, n. That branch of
PSYCHOLOGY having to do with the
reactions of a person to his physical
living-conditions and to society.

'psychopath, n. [Med.] A person who is in
very poor adjustment to others or to
society, being unbalanced to a marked
degree in his feelings, making much of
small troubles, readily wounded or overcome by doubts and fears, feeble in
decision, given to strange tastes, irres-
ponsible acts, loss of self-control, etc.,
but not to the point of having any clear
NEUROSIS or of undergoing any loss of
reasoning power; person whose mind is
unbalanced. psycho'pathic, a. Of, to do

with, a p. or psychopathy. psy'chopathy,
n. Diseased or unnormal condition of the
mind, sp. the condition of a p.

'psychopa'thology, n. That branch of
PSYCHOLOGY which has to do with unnormal or diseased conditions of the
mind. 'psychopatho'logical, a. 'psychopa'thologist, n.

'psycho'physical, a. To do with PSYCHO-
PHYSICS; of, to do with, mind and body,
or with non-material and material
things, forces. p. 'parallelism. [Psych.]
The theory that for every event in the
mind there is a parallel change in the
body, sp. the brain, taking place at
the same time.

'psycho'physics, n. PSYCHOPHYSIOLOGY;
that branch of PSYCHOLOGY which has to
do with reactions to physical STIMULI, sp.
with the relations of degree or amount
between a sense-experience and a
physical stimulus, or with the measuring
of the INTENSITY of sense-experiences.
'psycho'physicist, n.

'psychophysi'ology, n. Science of the relations between mind and body processes.

psy'chosis, n. [Med.] Any disease or very
unbalanced condition of the mind, sp.
one more serious than a NEUROSIS and
caused by some disease of or damage to
the nerve-system; (in old use) any process
of the mind, sp. as parallel to a brain
process.

'psycho'somatic, a. [Zoo., Med., Psych.]
To do with mind and body acting together as a system.

'psycho-thera'peutics, -'therapy, nn. The
use of processes working on the mind,
such as PSYCHOANALYSIS, SUGGESTION,
reasoning, attraction to new interests,
etc., to overcome diseases or unhealthy
conditions of the body, sp. those caused
by or going with some PSYCHOLOGICAL
trouble, some division in the mind itself.

'psychro-. Cold:— -'phobia. [Med.]

'psy'chrometer, n. [Meteor.] An instrument
for measuring the amount of water in the
ATMOSPHERE, made up of two THERMO-
METERS side by side, the bulb of one of
them being kept wet, so that, as its reading will be lower than that of the other
because of its being kept cold by EVAPORA-
TION, and the rate of evaporation is
dependent on the amount of water in
the atmosphere, this may be worked out
from comparisons of the two readings.

'psychro'philic, 'psychrophile, aa. [Biol.]
(Of living things, sp. BACTERIA) doing
best in cold.

'psychrophyte, n. [Bot.] A PSYCHROPHILIC
plant, a plant of very cold countries.

Pt, Sign for PLATINUM.

pteri'dology, n. [Bot.] The science of
PTERIDOPHYTA, sp. FILICALES.

'Pterido'phyta, n.pl. [Bot.] A great DIVISION

of ARCHEGONIATAE made up of the highest sorts of plants other than seed-plants, having, in the unsexed GENERATION, a clear division of the plant-body into root, stem and leaf, together with special VASCULAR TISSUE, the sexed generation being small, THALLOID and little seen—one of the oldest groups of plants, which came to their highest development in the CARBONIFEROUS PERIOD. 'pterido'phyte, n., a (Plant) of the P. pterido'phytic, a.

ptero'carpous, a. [Bot.] Having winged fruit.

'ptero'dactyl, a. [Zoo.] Any of an ORDER of REPTILIA with the power of flight living in the middle and later part of the MESOZOIC ERA, of great size, with MEMBRANE wings supported on the framework of the hand and arm. ptero'dactyloid, a. ptero-'dactylous, a.

'pteroid, a. [Bot.] Wing-like or feather-like, as the leaves of FILICALES.

ptero'paedes, n.pl. [Zoo.] Birds able to make use of their wings in flight when newly out of the egg.

Pter'opoda, n.pl. [Zoo.] A group of GASTROPODA living near the top of the sea with the front part of the foot in the form of two great thin wings, used for swimming. 'pteropod, n., a. (Animal) of the P.

ptero'podium, n. A winged foot, as in PTEROPODA and certain CHIROPTERA.

ptero'spermous, a. [Bot.] Having winged seeds.

ptero'stigma, n. [Zoo.] A thick place or CELL not letting light through, near the front edge of the wing in certain insects.

pte'rotic, 1.a. [Zoo.] Of, to do with, like, a wing or wing-like part. 2.n. A p. bone of the inner ear in higher animals and fish.

-pterous, a. [Zoo.] Having the named number or sort of wings or wing-like parts.

pte'rygial, 1.a. [Zoo.] To do with a wing, FIN, or PTERYGIUM. 2. A p. bone or CARTILAGE, sp. an ACTINOST.

pte'rygiophore, n. [Zoo.] ACTINOST.

pte'rygium (pterygia), n. [Med.] A wing-like mass of CONJUNCTIVA coming over the eyeball from the side, caused by wind, dust, etc. [Zoo.] A general name for an arm, leg, wing, or FIN of a back-boned animal.

pterygo'branchiate, a. [Zoo.] Having feather-like GILLS, as some CRUSTACEA.

'pterygoid, 1.a. Wing-like, said sp. of the outline of an airplane shorter from nose to tail than across the wings. [Zoo.] Of, near, to do with the p. bone(s) or process. 2.n. P. bone, muscle, blood-vessel, etc. p. bone. In lower back-boned animals, one or the other of a PAIR (or, in fish, two or more pairs) of bones of the upper part of the mouth, going from the

PALATINE to the QUADRATE. p. 'process. In man and higher back-boned animals, a structure (one of two) formed of two plates stretching down, one from the inside and one from the outside of the base of the SPHENOID BONE. 'pterygo-.

Ptery'gota, n.pl. [Zoo.] A division of the CLASS of insects made up of all but the APTERYGOTA, that is of all winged insects or insects which, though themselves without wings, are developments from winged forms.

'pteryla (pterylae), n. [Zoo.] Any of the parts of the skin of a bird on which there are feathers, opp. APTERIUM. ptery'losis. n. The growth of feathers on a bird in fixed places; the distribution or system of pp. in a bird.

pti'linum, n. [Zoo.] In certain flies, a bag-like structure on the front of the head used in pushing a way through the cover of the PUPA, later wasting away.

Ptole'maic system. [Astron.] The Greek theory of the relations of the earth, sun, and PLANETS as worked out by Ptolemy of Alexandria, in which the earth was taken to be fixed in the middle of the system, with the sun and stars moving round it.

'ptomaine, n. [Biochem.] Any of a group of ALKALOIDS, a number of which are poisons, formed in the process of PUTREFACTION, sp. of meat. p. 'poisoning, [Med.] The name given to poisoning caused by bad food, sometimes, but not necessarily, by pp.

-ptosis, n. [Med.] the dropping of (the named part) into a lower position.

'ptyalin, n. [Biochem.] An ENZYME present in the SALIVA of man and some other animals, by which STARCH is changed into sugar.

'ptyalism, n. [Med.] Condition in which over-much SALIVA is produced.

'ptyxis, n. [Bot.] The form in which a young leaf is folded or rolled in the BUD.

Pu, Sign for PLUTONIUM.

'puberty, n. [Zoo.] The time of existence at which sex-development is complete and a male or female is first able to PROCREATE or give birth to offspring, or, in lower animals, to eggs.' puberal, 'pubertal, a.

'pubes, n. [Zoo.] The part of the body over the PUBIS, which in man becomes covered with hair at PUBERTY. [Bot.] PUBESCENCE.

pu'bescence, n. [Biol.] A covering of soft short hair, as on some leaves, stems, insects. pu'bescent, a. Covered with soft short hair; to do with, having come to the stage of, PUBERTY.

'pubic, a, [Zoo.] To do with the PUBES or the PUBIS. p. bone. PUBIS.

pubi'otomy, n. [Med.] The operation of

cutting through the PUBIS at one side, sp. for the purpose of helping the birth of a baby.

'pubis (pubes), n. [Zoo.] The front bone of the 3 forming a side of the PELVIS. **p. sym'physis.** The join between the right and left pp. where they come together in the middle line of the body.

pu'dendum (pudenda), n. [Anat.] The outer sex-parts in man, sp. of the female (gen. pp.) pu'dendal, 'pudic, aa. Used sp. of nerves and blood-vessels having a connection with the pp.

pu'erperal, a. [Med.] To do with, coming after, the act of giving birth. **p. 'fever.** A disease marked by FEVER attacking women in the puerperium, caused by some form of SEPSIS. **puer'perium,** n. [Med.] The time, about 6 weeks, between the act of giving birth and the point at which the UTERUS has gone back to its normal size and condition.

'pulley, n. [Mach.] A wheel fixed in a frame and turning on a pin, with a hollow etc. outer edge made to take a band, cord, or chain, used for increasing, or changing the direction of, a pulling force at one end of the cord etc., and so lifting a weight at the other; any more complex structure, such as a system of pp., based on the same idea, and used for like purposes. [Anat.] A structure over or through which a TENDON goes for the purpose of changing the direction of its motion.

pullu'lation, n. [Bot.] GEMMATION.

'pulmo-. LUNG: -'gastric, a., '-nitis, n.

'pulmonary, a. [Zoo.] Of, to do with, like, effected by, the LUNGS. **p. sac** or **'cavity.** In some land or inland-water MOLLUSCA, a development of the hollow between the MANTLE and the body acting as a LUNG, having a network of blood-vessels in its walls and a narrowed and CONTRACTILE opening.

pulmo'branchia, n. [Zoo.] An air-breathing GILL; a LUNG-BOOK. **pulmo'branchial,** a. **pulmo'branchiate,** a.

pul'mometry, n. [Med.] The process of measuring the amount of air which a LUNG is able to take in. **pul'mometer,** n. Instrument used in p.

Pulmo'nata, n.pl. [Zoo.] The group of MOLLUSCA having a PULMONARY SAC.

'pulmonate, a. [Zoo.] Having LUNGS.

pul'monic, 1.a. [Zoo., Med.] PULMONARY; to do with PNEUMONIA. 2.n. A person having a disease of the LUNGS.

pulp, n. A soft, wet mass, anything crushed to a powder and then wetted, sp. plant or animal FIBRES, as the 'wood-p.' used in paper making. [Biol.] A soft, freq. sponge-like, mass of animal or plant substance inside a structure, for example a tooth, or forming part of a fruit. **p. 'cavity.** [Zoo.] The inner hollow of the

tooth of a back-boned animal, full of a p. of CONNECTIVE TISSUE, with nerves and blood-vessels running through it, and in connection by a narrow opening with the substance in which the tooth is rooted. **'pulpy,** a.

pul'sation, n. [Phys.] The process of moving forward and back between two points or becoming greater and then less, stronger and then feebler, in regular rhythm; a motion, change, or effect undergoing p., or one unit in such a motion etc.; sound made by anything in p. [Zoo., Med.] Sp. the regular CONTRACTION of the heart or expansion of an ARTERY; a sense of p. in some part, such as the ears. **p. 'theory.** [Astron.] The theory that certain stars undergo a regular expansion and CONTRACTION, being brightest when at their smallest. **pul'sate,** v.t. **pul'sating,** a. **'pulsatory,** a. **'pulsatory e'lectric 'current.** A current changing regularly in amount but not in direction. **pul'sating 'vacuole.** CONTRACTILE VACUOLE. **'pulsat-ive, -ile,** aa.

pulse, 1.v.i. [Phys., Zoo., Med.] Be in a condition of PULSATION. 2.n. PULSATION, sp. that of the ARTERIES; p. rate. [Phys.] A small amount of ENERGY produced from time to time, as in RADAR. **p. rate.** [Med.] The number of PULSATIONS of the ARTERIES in a minute, gen. got by feeling the artery on the inner side of the arm near the hand. **p. wave.** [Zoo., Med.] The wave of increased PRESSURE sent down the ARTERIES by every CONTRACTION of the heart. **pul'simeter,** n. [Med.] An instrument for measuring the force and rate of the p.

pul'someter, n. [Mach.] A pump without a PISTON, in which steam, let first into one of two vessels and then into the other by an automatic VALVE, is used for making and forcing out water.

'pulverize, q.v.t. Get crushed into powder, 2.v.i. Become pulverized. **'pulverable,** a. Which may be pulverized. **'pulveriza-tion,** n.

pul'villus (-villi), pul'vinulus (-vinuli), nn. [Zoo.] A small, gen. cushion-like part under the CLAW of an insect, freq. having the power of becoming fixed to things. **pul'villar,** a. **pul'villiform,** a. Like a small cushion.

'pulvinate, a. [Biol.] Cushion-like. [Bot.] Having a PULVINUS.

pul'vinus (-vini), n. [Bot.] Cushion-like expansion of a leaf-stem at the place where it is joined to a plant stem, freq. having the property of moving the leaf by changing its form. **pul'vinar,** a.

'pulviplume, n. [Zoo.] POWDER-DOWN FEATHER.

'pulvis, n. [Med.] Powder (used only in names of medical substances).

'pumice, n. [Geol.] A substance, gen. grey, of the same make-up as glass but having a sponge-like structure, formed on the top of a LAVA with much gas in it, used, sp. powdered, as an ABRASIVE. p. stone. P.

pump. n. [Mach.] A machine for lifting, or taking away, or forcing into smaller space, liquids or gases, by the operation of unequal PRESSURES through one-way VALVES.

puncta, n.pl. See PUNCTUM.

'punctate(d), aa. [Biol., Med.] Covered with small round holes, hollows or points. punc'tation, n. The condition of being, or the process of making something, p.; a small hole or point.

'punctiform, a. Point-like.

'punctule, n. [Biol.] A very small round hollow, hole, or mark. 'punctulate, a.

'punctum (puncta), n. [Biol.] A point (in the sense of a place, a pointed end, or a small round mark) or a pin-point hole, used chiefly in names of special points.

'punctum, n. [Biol.] A point (in the sense of a place, a pointed end, or a small round mark), a pin-point hole, used chiefly in names of special points.

'puncture, 1.n. A small hole, as a pin-hole; the act of puncturing. [Zoo.] Small hollow, as if made by pin-point. 2.v.t. Make a p. in.

'pupa (pupae or pupas), n. [Zoo.] A resting-stage or form between the LARVA and the IMAGO in the development of an insect, when it is gen. rolled up in a COCOON (*p. obtecta*), but sometimes covered by the outer larva skin (*p. coarctata*), and sometimes uncovered (*p. libera*). 'pupal, a. pupate, v.i. Become a p.

pu'parium, n. [Zoo.] The outer covering of a PUPA when formed from the skin of the LARVA.

'pupil, n. [Zoo.] The opening, changing in size, at the middle of the IRIS, by which light comes into the eye. [Zoo.] P.-like dark mark at the middle of an OCELLUS. pu'pillary, a. pu'pillary reflex. The automatic narrowing of the p. in reaction to light. pupill'ometer, n. An instrument for measuring the p. of the eye.

pu'piparous, a. [Zoo.] Giving birth to young whose development has got to the PUPA stage, as some two-winged insect PARA-SITES.

pure, a. Unmixed with any other thing at all, or unmixed with any undesired or damaging thing, sp.:— [Chem.] free from any other substance; [Biol.] coming from, made up of, one SPECIES only; [Acous.] (of a TONE) produced by a simple sound-wave, with only one FREQUENCY; [Phonet.] (of a sound) said with the tongue, lips, etc. in the one position special to it, so as to be unmixed with any sound formed differently; (of science

or a science) having to do only with the discovery of knowledge, not with any use which may be made of knowledge in living, for example, in the invention of machines, medical work, industry, etc. p. line. [Zoo.] A family line of plants and animals which are all the same in the quality, number, and order of their GENES, being the offspring of one HOMOZYGOUS and self-FERTILIZING plant or animal or produced by INBREEDING from two completely like and homozygous plants or animals. 'purification, n. The process of purifying something or the condition of undergoing this. 'purify, v.t. Sp., [Med., etc.] make free from damaging things or substances, as purify water, purify the blood. 'purifying, a. 'purity, n. The condition of being p., of which in Chemistry three signs are:—an unchanging boiling-point, an unchanging MELTING-point, and an unchanging CRYSTALLINE form.

'purge, 1.v.t. [Med.] Get, have the effect of getting, waste cleared from (the BOWELS). 2.n. A medical substance with the property of purging the bowels. pur'gation, n. The clearing of the BOWELS by the use of a p. 'purgative, 1.a. Acting as a p. 2.n. A p.

'purine, n. [Chem.] Any of a group of COMPOUNDS, of which the representative is $C_5H_4N_4$, got from URIC ACID.

Pur'kinje cell. [Zoo.] Any of the great nerve CELLS of somewhat bottle-like form, with thick DENDRITES and one thin AXON, present in the middle of the outer CERE-BELLUM in higher animals. Pur'kinje ef'fect or phe'nomenon. [Zoo.] The fact that when the light is feeble the colours red, orange, and yellow are seen as less bright than blue and green.

'purpura, n. [Med.] A disease or diseased condition in which dark blue marks are formed under the skin and MUCOUS MEMBRANES by blood coming through the walls of blood-vessels.

purpur(eo)-. Dark red-blue in colour.

pus, n. [Med.] The thick yellow-white liquid formed in poisoned wounds, made up of dead TISSUE undergoing destruction by substances sent out by LEUCOCYTES attacking BACTERIA, of the bodies of the leucocytes and bacteria themselves, and of SERUM. 'purulence, n. [Med.] P.; the forming of p.; the condition of being purulent. 'purulent, a. Of, to do with, like, formed of, producing, p. 'purulently, adv.

'pusher, n. In an airplane, a PROPELLER or AIR-SCREW which is further back than the engine and so has the effect of pushing the machine forward, as opp. TRACTOR.

'push-pull, a. [Elec.] Having a push-pull connection. push-pull connection. [Elec.] A parallel connection of two electric VALVES etc. of such a sort that current goes through them in opposite directions.

'**pustule,** n. [Med.] A small SWELLING on the skin with PUS in it. [Biol.] A small outgrowth or p.-like structure on the skin of an animal, or some part of a plant, sp. one caused on a leaf by a FUNGUS. '**pustulant,** 1.a. [Med.] Causing the forming of pp. 2.n. A pustulant medical substance. '**pustul-ar, -ous,** aa. To do with, like, covered with, pp. '**pustulate,** 1.v.i. [Med.] become covered with pp. 2.a. [Med., Biol.] Having, covered with, pp.

pu'**tamen,** n. [Bot.] The hard covering of the seed in a DRUPE. [Zoo.] The outer grey substance of the LENTICULAR NUCLEUS; the skin coating the inside of the SHELL in a bird's egg.

putre'**faction,** n. [Biochem., Biol.] The process by which dead plant or sp. animal substance, sp. PROTEIN, is broken up and formed into other chemical substances, a number of which have a very bad smell, by the operation of BACTERIA and FUNGI. '**putrefy,** v.t. and i. (Make) undergo p. '**putrefying,** a. pu'**trescence,** n. The condition of being putrescent; putrescent material, pu'**trescent,** a. (Of material) in the process of p. '**putrid,** a. (Of material) at a late stage of p., sp. as having a very bad smell.

pu'**trescine,** n. [Biochem.] A PTOMAINE, $H_2N.(CH_2)_4.NH_2$, produced in the PUTREFACTION of meat and fish.

py-. PYO-.

py'**(a)emia,** n. [Med.] A diseased condition marked by the forming of ABSCESSES in different parts of the body, caused by PUS-forming BACTERIA getting into the blood from a wound or other point of attack. py'**(a)emic,** a.

pyc'**nidia,** n.pl. See PYCNIDIUM.

pyc'**nidiophore,** n. [Bot.] A structure producing PYCNIDIA.

pyc'**nidiospore,** '**pycnospore,** '**pycno-co'nidium, -go'nidium,** nn. [Bot.] A SPORE produced in a PYCNIDIUM.

pyc'**nidium** (pycnidia), nn. [Bot.] A small bottle-like part of certain FUNGI and LICHENES producing CONIDIA on the inside. pyc'**nidial,** a.

'**pycnium,** n. [Bot.] A SPERMOGONIUM in UREDINALES. '**pycnial,** a. '**pycniospore,** n. A SPERMATIUM in UREDINALES.

pycn(o)-. Thick in substance.

pyc'**nometer,** n. SPECIFIC GRAVITY BOTTLE.

pyc'**nosis,** n. [Bot., Med.] (Of a part or a liquid) the process of becoming thick, sp. a damaging change of this sort in the substance of a CELL-NUCLEUS, by which it becomes smaller and the CHROMOSOMES are massed into a deeply STAINING knot, a sign of the death of the cell. pyc'**notic,** a.

py'**gidium,** n. [Zoo.] The end-part or last division of the body, or some addition to it, in a number of lower animals, as the last division of a worm, the plate on the top of the last division in an insect. py'**gidial,** a.

'**pygostyle,** n. [Zoo.] An upturned plate of bone forming the tail end of the backbone in most birds, formed by the uniting of the last backbone divisions.

'**pyic,** a. PURULENT.

'**pyknic,** a. (In Kretschmer's system of physical TYPES) having the physical structure which gen. goes with a happy outlook, more interest in things outside than in the self, and a tendency, if anything goes wrong with the mind, to a MANIC-DEPRESSIVE condition—short and somewhat square, with short arms, legs, and neck, a round face and a thick body. See ATHLETIC, ASTHENIC.

pykn(o)-. See PYCN(O)-.

'**pylon,** n. A high, gen. steel, structure supporting a wire or wires.

py'**lorus,** n. [Zoo.] The opening of the stomach into the DUODENUM in higher animals; the back end of the stomach in some lower animals. py'**loric,** a. py'**loro-.**

pyo-. PUS:— '**-genic,** a., '**pyoid,** a., py-'**ophagus,** a.

pyo'**genesis,** n. The forming of PUS. pyo-'**gen-ic, -ous,** aa.

pyor'**rh(o)ea,** n. [Med.] A disease of the soft material round the teeth, marked by INFLAMMATION, the forming of PUS, and the coming loose of the teeth. pyor-'**rhoeal,** a.

py'**osis,** n. [Med.] The forming of PUS.

'**pyramid,** n. A solid having a flat base with three or more three-sided sides meeting at a point. [Zoo.] A pointed, somewhat p.-like structure. [Cryst.] A CRYSTAL form with three or more sloping faces cutting all three AXES. py'**ramidal,** a. py'**ramidal cell.** [Zoo.] Any of the great CELLS of irregular, more or less p.-like outline and having a number of DENDRITES, forming the chief substance of that part of the brain controlling motion.

'**pyran,** n. [Chem.] C_5H_6O, a RING COMPOUND (see p. 392).

py'**rene,** n. [Bot.] PUTAMEN, sp. the small stone in a DRUPELET. [Chem.] $C_{16}H_{10}$, a white, CRYSTALLINE substance formed of 4 BENZENE RINGS, got from COAL TAR.

pyren'**(a)emia,** n. [Med.] The existence of NUCLEATED ERYTHROCYTES in the blood. pyren'**ematous,** a.

py'**renocarp,** n. DRUPE.

'**pyrenoid,** 1.a. [Bot.] Like a PYRENE. 2.n. [Biol.] A small grain of PROTEIN round which a coating of STARCH is formed in some simple animals and plants, sp. in the CHROMATOPHORES of ALGAE.

pyret(o)-. [Med.] FEVER. py'**retic,** a.

py'**rexia,** n. [Med.] An increase in the body's heat over the normal. py'**re(c)tic,** a.

pyreto-:— 'pyreto'genic, a., 'pyreto-genesis, n., 'pyreto'genetic, a., pyre'to-genous, a.

'**pyrhelio'meter,** n. [Meteor.] An instrument for measuring the heat and ENERGY given out by the sun. **pyr'heliometry,** n.

'**pyridine,** n. [Chem.] C_5H_5N, a liquid without colour and with strong unpleasing smell, in which the C and N ATOMS are in the form of a ring with an H atom joined to every C atom, present in COAL TAR, tobacco, etc. (*See* p. 392.)

pyri'doxine, n. [Biochem.] One of the substances making up VITAMIN B.

'**pyriform,** a. [Biol.] In form somewhat like an electric light bulb, rounded, longer than it is wide, and narrowing at one end, used in naming certain parts in animals.

pyri'formis, n. [Zoo.] A muscle going from the SACRUM to the head of the FEMUR.

py'rimidine, n. [Chem.] Any of a group of substances based on a ring of 4 C and 2 N ATOMS, covering NUCLEIC ACIDS and BARBITURIC ACID.

'**pyrite** or **py'rites,** n. [Mineral.] A general name for MINERALS in which metals are united with S, as FeS_2 (*iron p.*).

pyri'tology, n. [Chem.] The science or art of BLOWPIPE ANALYSIS.

pyro-. Fire, great heat (-'**genic,** py'ro-genous, aa., '-'**genesis,** n.). [Chem.] Produced by heating the substance named (-'**boric acid**). [Geol.] Produced by fire or great heat ('-meta'morphism, n.). [Med.] PYRETO ('-'**genic,** a.).

'**pyrobi'tuminous,** a. [Chem.] Giving BITUMENS when heated, like coal.

pyro'chemical, a. To do with chemical work at a high degree of heat.

pyro'clastic, a. [Geol.] (Of ROCKS) made up of broken bits produced by a VOLCANO.

pyro'crystalline, a. [Geol.] CRYSTALLIZED from MAGMA.

'**pyroelec'tricity,** n. [Phys., Mineral.] The development of opposite electric charges in certain CRYSTALS as the effect of heating; the science of this effect. **pyroe'lec-tric,** a. To do with, having, p. [Elec.] (Of effects) caused by the producing of heat through DIELECTRIC LOSS.

pyro'gallol, n. [Chem.] A white CRYSTALLINE poison, with a bitter taste and acid properties, got by the operation of heat on GALLIC ACID, used in DEVELOPERS and for taking up O in gas ANALYSIS, sometimes named **pyro'gallic acid.**

pyrog'nostic, a. [Mineral.] To do with, made clear by heating, sp. by BLOW-PIPE tests. **pyrog'nostics,** n.pl. [Mineral.] The properties of a MINERAL made clear by BLOWPIPE tests.

pyro'ligneous, a. [Chem.] Produced by the PYROLYSIS of wood.

pyro'lusite, n. [Mineral.] Natural MnO_2, a black or dark-grey solid with a metal-like look, but not hard, from which Mn is got.

py'rolysis, n. [Chem.] The separating of a substance into its parts by heat. **pyro-'litic,** a.

'**pyromag'netic,** a. [Phys.] Produced or working by heat and MAGNETISM together.

py'rometer, n. [Phys.] An instrument for measuring very high degrees of heat, outside the range of a THERMOMETER, sp. from a distance by electric effects, rays given out, etc. (*see* PYROPHOTOMETER). **pyro'metric(al),** aa. **py'rometry,** n.

pyro'ph-eric, -oric, -orous, aa. [Chem.] Taking fire when put out in the air, as the powdered forms of certain metals, such as lead and iron, or one of those mixed with the powdered OXIDE of the metal.

'**pyropho'tometer,** n. [Phys.] A PYROMETER based on a comparison of the INTENSITY of the light of a given colour, gen. red, sent out by a given heated body, with the intensity of that sent out by the flame to be tested.

py'rosis, n. HEARTBURN.

'**pyrostat,** n. Apparatus for keeping anything from getting on fire by automatically cutting off current, giving some sign, etc., when put into operation by conditions representative of danger, such as overheating, smoke, etc. [Phys.] THERMO-STAT for keeping up a very high degree of heat.

pyro'technics, '**pyrotechny,** nn. The science of fireworks. **pyro'technic(al),** aa.

pyro'therapy, n. [Med.] The producing of PYREXIA as a way of fighting disease.

py'rotic, a. [Med.] Burning, biting, with the property of causing destruction of TISSUE, as an acid; of, to do with, PYROSIS.

py'roxylin, n. [Chem.] Any of a group of substances like GUN-COTTON but formed of CELLULOSE NITRATES which are poor in N.

py'roxene, n. [Mineral.] A natural SILICATE of Ca, Mg, Fe and sometimes other substances such as Al or Mn, one of the commonest substances present in IGNEOUS ROCK; any substance of the p. group. **p. group.** A group of near relations of p., very like in make-up and structure though representative of different CRYS-TAL SYSTEMS.

'**pyrrole,** n. [Chem.] C_4H_5N, a liquid without colour and with a special smell, having BASIC properties, in which the C and N ATOMS are in the form of a ring with an H atom joined to every one—present in COAL TAR but got chiefly from BONE OIL, and forming part of or giving birth to a great number of important substances, for example CHLOROPHYLL and HAEMO-GLOBIN. (*See* p. 392.)

Py'thagorean 'system. [Astron.] The early form of the COPERNICAN SYSTEM, based on the idea that the earth goes round the sun, put forward by the Greek Pythagoras. **Py'thagorean or Pythagoras' 'theorem.** [Geom.] The THEOREM that the square of the HYPOTENUSE of a right angled TRIANGLE is equal to the squares of the other two sides taken together.

py'xidium, n. [Bot.] A CAPSULE opening by forming a crack all round so that the top part comes off like a hat or the cover of a box. **'pyxidate,** a.

Q. [Radio] Sign for the RATIO of REACTANCE to RESISTANCE in a COIL used for TUNING.

Q10. [Chem., Biol.] Sign for the increase in the rate of a process produced by increasing the TEMPERATURE by 10°C, given as the number of times the old rate goes into the new rate.

Q-level. *See* ENERGY LEVEL.

Qu, Sign for the QUININE MOLECULE.

Q-value, [Phys.] The amount of ENERGY, gen. given in MEV, freed by a NUCLEAR REACTION.

'quadrangle, n. QUADRILATERAL.

'quadrant, n. A curve which is one-quarter of a circle, or the plane form made by joining the ends of such a curve to the middle of the circle; anything in the form of a q. [Surveying, etc.] An instrument for measuring angles, sp. ANGLES OF ELEVATION, having a scale of 90° in the form of a q. and some apparatus, such as a LEVEL TUBE, for getting it level. [Zoo.] The part of an OVUM produced from any one of the first 4 BLASTOMERES. **q. elec'trometer.** [Phys.] An ELECTROMETER in which a hanging needle is put into operation by a POTENTIAL DIFFERENCE between two PAIRS of metal qq. in a round box.

'quadrat, n. [Bot.] A square space of country marked out for observation as representative of the plant growth in that part.

'quadrate, 1.a. (Roughly) square in form. 2.n. [Zoo.] In back-boned animals other than MAMMALS, the bone of CARTILAGE at the inner end of the upper mouth-bone, fixing it to the brain cover, and gen. forming the connection between the upper and lower mouth-bones. **quad-'ratic,** a. Square. **quadratic e'quation.** [Algebra] An EQUATION in which the SQUARE of the QUANTITY to be worked out is present but no higher POWER of it, as $x^2 - 4\,x + 4 = 0$. **quadrato-.**

'quadrature, n. [Astron.] The relation of position between two bodies in the sky when they are at a distance of 90° from one another as measured from the earth, at which time one is said to be *in q. with* the other. [Phys.] Of two VIBRATIONS, sp. electric currents, the relation of being different in PHASE by a ¼ of a CYCLE.

qua'dratus, n. [Zoo.] Name given to a number of muscles, gen. of somewhat square form, as the q. **'femoris,** by which the upper part of a man's leg is turned.

quadr(i)-. 4: **quadri'carpellary,** a., **quadri'locular,** a. [Bot.].

'quadriceps, n. [Zoo.] Any muscle rooted at four points, sp. **q. ex'tensor,** the great muscle with four heads going down the front of the upper part of the leg in higher animals.

'quadrifid, a. [Biol.] Cut into 4 parts by deep divisions.

quadri'foliate, a. [Bot.] (Of a leaf) made up of 4 leaves coming from a common middle part.

quadri'geminal, a. [Biol.] Having 4 like parts, or two PAIRS of like parts. **q. 'bodies.** CORPORA QUADRIGEMINA.

quadri'jugate, a. [Bot.] (Of a PINNATE leaf) made up of 8 small leaves in twos.

quadri'lateral, n., a. [Geom.] (A plane form) having 4 straight sides.

quadri'pennate, a. [Zoo.] Having 4 wings.

quadri'plegia, n. [Med.] PARALYSIS of the two arms and two legs.

'quadritu'bercular, a. [Zoo.] (Of teeth) having 4 CUSPS.

quadri'valent, a. [Chem.] Having a VALENCY of 4.

qua'drumanous, a. [Zoo.] Having all 4 feet formed like hands, as monkeys, etc.

'quadruped, n., a. [Zoo.] (Animal) having 4 feet, sp. of which none are like hands, gen. used only of MAMMALS. **qua'drupedal,** a.

'quadruple, a. Made up of 4 parts or units, grouped in 4's; 4 times as great. **q. point.** [Phys.-Chem.] A point on a DIAGRAM representative of the conditions of CONCENTRATION, TEMPERATURE, and PRESSURE, under which 4 PHASES of a SYSTEM of two substances may be present together and in EQUILIBRIUM.

'quadruplet, n. A group of four things of the same sort. [Zoo.] Any of 4 babies produced at one birth.

'quadruplex, a. [Biol.] Having twice the HAPLOID number of CHROMOSOMES with the DOMINANT of a certain GENE present 4 times.

'qualitative, a. To do with qualities. opp. QUANTITATIVE. **q. (chemical) an'alysis.** The process of testing a substance or separating it into its parts with a view to the discovery only of what substances make it up, not of the amounts in which these are present.

'quality, n. [Acous.] That property which makes one TONE different from another having the same PITCH and LOUDNESS, dependent on the number and loudness of the OVERTONES present in it. [Optics] CHROMA. [Phonet.] The property special to any VOWEL sound as the effect of the way in which it is formed, and independent of the time for which it is kept up and the force with which it is produced, etc. [Psych.] The property special to any of the different sorts of simple sense-experience, for example that in which taste is different from smell.

'quanta, n.pl. *See* QUANTUM.

quanti'zation, n. [Phys.] Division into QUANTA; the putting of relations in physics into the language and mathematics of the QUANTUM THEORY. **'quantize,** v.t.

'quantitative, a. To do with QUANTITY; able to be measured or numbered. **q. (chemical) a'nalysis.** The process of testing a substance or separating it into its parts with a view to the discovery of what amounts of different substances are present in it.

'quantity, n. Amount, number, measure; (anything having) the property of being able to be measured or numbered, or to be greater or less while still the same in every other property. [Phonet.] The time for which a language-sound goes on, its measure in time in comparison with that of other language-sounds, that which makes it 'long' or 'short'.

'quantum (quanta), n. [Phys.] A fixed smallest physical unit of some sort, sp. the unit of ENERGY in the q. theory, dependent on the FREQUENCY of the VIBRATIONS by which the energy is produced, and equal, when the vibrations are ELECTRO-MAGNETIC, to the frequency × PLANCK'S CONSTANT. **q. mech'anics.** [Phys.] A theory of ATOMS and ATOMIC effects in which WAVE MECHANICS is united with the q. theory. **q. of 'action.** PLANCK'S CONSTANT. **q. state.** ENERGY LEVEL. **q. theory.** The theory first put forward by PLANCK, together with all the developments based on it, that ENERGY taken in or given out in the form of RADIATION is in amounts of one or more qq., that is, that such energy is never produced in an amount less than a q. **q. number.** A number given to every ENERGY LEVEL in an ATOM.

'quarantine, 1.n. [Med.] Time for which a ship etc. having, or in danger of having, a serious INFECTIOUS disease among those on it, is kept by the authorities from landing at a place; time for which a person having such a disease and those looking after him are kept away from others; the place where a ship is put while waiting for the end of q.; the act of causing a ship or person to be kept away from others till the danger of giving them a disease is

over, or the condition of being controlled in this way. 2.v.t. Put in q.

quart, n. Unit of liquid or dry measure, $=2$ pints, or G.B. 1·1365 l., U.S.A. ·9463 l.

'quartan, n., a. [Med.] (A FEVER, sp. a form of MALARIA) attacking again every 4th day with two days' rest between the end and the start of the attacks.

quar'tation, n. In ASSAYING, the lowering of the PROPORTION of gold in an ALLOY, gen. to about a $\frac{1}{4}$, by the addition of silver, because it is impossible to get the gold separated by the normal simple process when the proportion is very high.

'quarter, n. [Astron.] One or the other of the two positions of the moon when in QUADRATURE to the sun (*see* MOON); any quarter of the moon's journey round the earth.

'quarter-wave plate, 'quarter-undu'lation plate. [Optics] A thin plate of some BIREFRINGENT substance, e.g. QUARTZ, so designed that there is a PHASE DIFFERENCE of $\frac{1}{4}$ WAVELENGTH between the 2 rays into which a PLANE-POLARIZED ray is broken up in going through it, making possible the changing of plane-polarized into CIRCULARLY POLARIZED light.

quartz, n. [Mineral.] Natural SiO_2, chiefly in the form of clear, uncoloured CRYSTALS but having some coloured and some CRYPTO-CRYSTALLINE forms, the commonest of all solid substances present in the earth. **q. clock.** A clock controlled by the VIBRATION of a q. crystal, having great ACCURACY, used in Astronomy and for fixing STANDARDS etc. **q. 'crystal.** [Phys.] A bit of q. cut in such a way as to have PIEZO-ELECTRIC properties so that it vibrates with a fixed FREQUENCY. **q. glass.** A hard, glass-like substance made by FUSING q. —of great value for chemical and electric apparatus because it is not readily damaged by heat, cold, or chemicals, has high electric RESISTIVITY, and lets through ULTRA-VIOLET rays. **'quartzose,** a. To do with, formed of, like, q.

'quasi, a. Like, almost the same as, copying, seeming, sp. not truly what is named. **q.-'optical waves.** [Phys.] Short ELECTRO-MAGNETIC waves PROPAGATED in a like way to light waves.

qua'ternary, a. Having 4 parts (said sp. of the WHORLS of a flower), grouped in fours; coming 4th. [Chem.] Made up of 4 substances. [Geol.] Being, to do with, the Q. era. **Q. Era.** [Geol.] The time in the earth's history from the end of the TERTIARY about a million years back to the present day (*see* p. 558).

queen, n. [Zoo.] The fertile female of insects living in societies having a distribution of work, for example bees and ants.

quench, v.t. [Metal]. Make (metal) hard by

making it suddenly cold, used sp. of putting steel at red heat into water, oil.
quick, n. [Med.] A part of the FLESH feeling pain very readily and sharply, sp. that under a finger- or toe-nail.
'quickening, n. [Med.] The first feeling by a PREGNANT woman of the FOETUS moving in her body, between the 4th and 5th months of its development. **'quicken,** v.i. Undergo the experience of q., get to that stage in the producing of offspring; (of FOETUS etc.) become living.
'quicklime, n. LIME which has not been SLAKED.
'quicksand, n. [Geol.] Stretch of sand mixed with water which seems solid to the eye but has very little power of supporting weight, so that a person etc. stepping on it is pulled down into it.
'quicksilver, n. MERCURY.
qui'escent, a. In a condition of rest, not in motion, or, of forces, etc., not in operation.
quill, n. [Zoo.] Any of the great stiff feathers of a bird's wing or tail; the hollow middle stem of a q.; any of the stiff, sharp-pointed outgrowths mixed with the hair on the bodies of certain animals and put up by them in time of danger.
'quinary, a. Made up of 5 parts, grouped in fives.
'quinate, a. [Bot.] QUINARY, said sp. of leaves formed of 5 smaller leaves.
'quincunx, n. A grouping of 5 things such that there is one at every angle of a square and one in the middle. [Bot.] The folding of 5 flower-parts in the BUD in such a way that two are on the outside, two on the inside, and one has one edge outside and one inside. **quin'cuncial,** a.
qui'nine, n. [Chem.] An ALKALOID, $C_{20}H_{24}O_2N_2$, present in certain South American trees, a bitter, white, CRYSTALLINE substance forming a number of SALTS. [Med.] Any of the salts of q. used for lowering FEVER, sp. in MALARIA, and as a TONIC.
'quinoline, n. [Chem.] C_9H_7N, a substance formed of a BENZENE and a PYRIDINE RING with 2 C ATOMS in common, an oil-like liquid without colour present in COAL TAR and BONE OIL, from which are produced a great number of substances of value medically or in industry.
qui'none, n. [Chem.] Any of a group of substances made from BENZENE and like HYDROCARBONS by putting two O ATOMS in the place of two H atoms, used in DYEING, TANNING, etc.
'quinqu(e)-. 5: **-'foliate,** a. (see picture p. 223), **-'partite,** a., **-'valent,** a.
'quinsy, n. [Med.] Violent INFLAMMATION of the TONSIL(s) with the forming of PUS.
'quintal, n. A unit of weight in the METRIC system = 100 kg.
'quintan, a., n. [Med.] (A FEVER) attacking again every 5th day, with three days rest between the end and the start of the attacks.
quin'triple, a. Made up of 5 parts or units, grouped in fives; 5 times as great.
'quintuplet, n. A group of 5 things of the same sort. [Zoo.] Any of 5 babies produced at one birth.
'quotient, n. The number got by the division of one number by another, the number of times one number will go into another.

r- = RACEMIC [Chem.].
r, Sign for ROENTGEN.
R, Sign for:— the GAS CONSTANT; RYDBERG'S CONSTANT.
R.A. = RIGHT ASCENSION.
Ra, Sign for RADIUM. **RaA, RaB,** etc., Sign for RADIUM A, RADIUM B, etc.
'rabies, n. [Med.] An ACUTE disease of dogs and like animals which may be given to man by a bite from a diseased animal, and is then named HYDROPHOBIA— produced by a FILTER-PASSING VIRUS and attacking the brain and SPINAL CORD, causing a violently worked-up condition, PARALYSIS and gen. death. **'rabid,** a. (Of an animal) having r.
race, n. [Biol.] A group of animals or plants inside a SPECIES which have enough special points in common to be grouped together, but are not different enough from the rest to make a separate species. [Zoo.] Sp., any of the natural divisions of men, having in common fixed qualities different from those of other groups pointing to their having come from a common early ANCESTOR; a family line, a group of persons with a common ancestor. **'racial,** a.
race, n. [Mach.] A GROOVE, hollow, etc. in which some rolling or slipping machine-part has its motion, sp. that housing a BALL-BEARING; a narrow way taking water to or from a machine by which it is worked.
race'mation, n. [Bot.] A mass of berries, etc. on one chief stem.
ra'ceme, n. [Bot.] An INDEFINITE flower-grouping in which stemmed flowers are produced first on one side and then on the other of a chief stem, the order of development being from the base up (see picture. p 199). **racemi'ferous,** a. **ra'cemiform.** a. **'racemose,** a. [Bot.] (Having the flowers-grouping in the form of a r., said not only of true rr., but of unstemmed flowers grouped in the same way. [Zoo.] Having a great number of divisions grouped in a way giving a sug-

gestion of a mass of small berries, said sp. of GLANDS. 'racemule, n. [Bot.] A small r.

ra'cemic, a. [Chem.] Naming or to do with substances formed by the mixing or uniting of equal numbers of MOLECULES of two OPTICAL ISOMERS, into which they may be separated, which have themselves no optical properties. r. acid. The r. form of TARTARIC ACID. 'racemi'zation, n. [Chem.] The changing of a substance having OPTICAL ACTIVITY into its r. form, sometimes taking place naturally (*autoracemization*), sometimes effected by boiling or by a chemical operation.

'rachianaes'thesia, n. [Med.] (ANAESTHESIA caused by) putting an ANAESTHETIC into the backbone.

ra'chilla, n. [Biol.] A small RACHIS, sp. [Bot.] the middle stem of a grass SPIKE-LET.

rachi(o)-. [Zoo., Med.] (Of) the backbone:— 'rachiomyelitis, n., 'rachioparalysis, n.

'rachis, n. [Biol.] Chief or middle stem or supporting, stem-like structure, sp.:— [Bot.] the chief stem of a flower-group or of the small leaves of a complex leaf; [Zoo.] the backbone; the stiff middle stem of a feather. 'rachial, ra'chidial, aa. 'rachiform, a.

ra'chitis, n. [Med.] A bone disease common in the young, in which the bones become soft and freq. bent, etc., caused by not getting enough VITAMIN D in the food. ra'chitic, a. ra'chitomous, a. [Zoo.] Temnospondylous.

'racial, a. [Biol.] *See* RACE.

rack, n. [Mach.] A straight or curved rod with teeth on one side for working in connection with a toothed wheel, etc. (*see* PAWL, PINION). '-work, n. Any machine-part or apparatus using a r.

'radar, n. [Phys.] The system of getting a knowledge of the position and distance in relation to a point of observation of any body (for example, an airplane), and the direction in which, if moving, it is going, by sending out all round bursts of ELECTROMAGNETIC WAVES of very short WAVE-LENGTH from a radio apparatus, and working out the desired facts from the time taken for any waves meeting the body to be sent back by it together with the direction in which such waves were sent out—used for guiding airplanes in landing at an air-station etc., and on ships.

'radial, 1.a. To do with, on, in the position of, a RADIUS; (of parts, motions, forces) raying out from a middle point. [Biol.] Having r. symmetry. [Zoo.] Of, near, to do with, the RADIUS of the arm or front leg, or with any of the ray-like arms of ECHINODERMS. 2.n. [Zoo.] A blood-vessel, nerve, etc. having to do with the RADIUS; the bone supporting the base of a front

FIN in a fish. r. ca'nal. [Zoo.] In ECHINO-DERMS, any of the pipes of the WATER-VASCULAR SYSTEM which go out from the middle to the TUBE-FEET; any of the very small pipe-like openings going out from the middle hollow almost to the outside in certain sponges. r. 'symmetry. A form of structure such that it is cut into two like and equal halves by any plane at right-angles to it and going through the middle point, sp. [Biol.] used of the bodies of animals, such as starfish, or of flowers made up of like parts ranged in a regular way about a round middle part. r. ('vascular) 'bundle. [Bot.] A VASCULAR BUNDLE with the XYLEM and PHLOEM ranged in different lines raying out from the middle, as in most roots. r. wall. [Bot.] A division-wall at right angles to the SURFACE of a part and placed across a RADIUS. 'radially, adv. 'radially sym'metrical. Having r. sym-metry.

'radiale, n. [Zoo.] That bone of those at the join of the hand and arm (or foot and front leg) which is nearest to and has a connection with the RADIUS.

'radian, n. [Geom.] Unit of angle measure equal to the angle made at the middle point of a circle by joining it to the ends of an ARC having the same measure as the RADIUS, or about 57·3°.

'radiant, 1.a. [Phys.] Sending out RADIA-TIONS; sent out in the form of radiations, transported by WAVES. 2.n. [Astron.] The far point in the sky from which the lines of motion of two or more METEORS produced at the same time seem to come, though in fact they are parallel. r. 'energy. [Phys.] ENERGY transported or given out in the form of WAVES, sp. that given out by ATOMS and MOLECULES as the effect of changes in their structure, as in light rays, X-RAYS, etc. r. heat. Heat trans-ported, like light, by ELECTROMAGNETIC WAVES, r. 'umbel. [Bot.] An UMBEL having the outer flowers much greater in size than those in the middle.

'radiate, 1.a. Having RADIAL SYMMETRY. [Bot.] Having RAY FLORETS. 2.v.i. and t. Come or send out in different directions from a common point, as or like rays. [Phys.] Send out ENERGY, or (of energy) go out, in the form of WAVES; send out in all directions, sp. (heat, light, etc.) in the form of waves. 'radiating, a. Sp., coming out from a common point in different directions, as 'radiating lines'. 'radiator, n. Any apparatus for radiating some-thing, sp. a structure by which the heat from a steam or hot-water heating system is given out, an electric fire, etc. for heating a small space, or the system of pipes in an automobile through which water is sent to radiate the heat from the engine and keep it from getting over-heated. **r. 'veined.** [Bot.] (Of leaves) with the VEINS starting from a common point.

radi'ation, n. The act of RADIATING or process of being radiated, or the condition of having a radiating structure; a radiating structure. [Phys.] The r. of ENERGY, sp. in the form of ELECTROMAGNETIC WAVES; the transporting of heat from one point to another by electromagnetic waves so that no heat is given up to the substance, if any, between, as in the heating of the earth by the sun; what is given out by r., as energy, sp. in the form of electromagnetic waves, or the PARTICLES given off in RADIOACTIVITY. [Biol.] In the development of a group of plants or animals, their distribution into different places causing different adjustments to different living-conditions and so producing new forms. **r. 'capture.** THE CAPTURE of NEUTRONS or PROTONS by a NUCLEUS, producing GAMMA rr. **r. po'tential.** [Phys.] The ENERGY, given in ELECTRON-VOLTS, needed for transporting an ELECTRON from its normal position in an ATOM to some other position. **r. 'pressure.** [Phys.] The PRESSURE of RADIANT ENERGY sp. light, on SURFACES in its line of motion. **r. 'sickness.** [Med.] The condition caused in the body by being acted on over-much by X-RAYS or RADIOACTIVE rays. **r. 'survey meter.** [Phys.] An apparatus, such as a GEIGER COUNTER, with which r. is measured. **r. 'temperature.** [Phys.] BLACK-BODY TEMPERATURE. **r. 'therapy.** The medical use of any sort of rr. on the body. **'-al.** a. [Phys.] **'radiative,** a. [Phys.] Of to do with, marked by, the process of r. **'radical,** 1.a. To do with, coming from, going to, the root or base of a fact, question, etc. [Bot.] Of, to do with the root, coming from a root or a stem under the earth, or from the level of the earth. 2.n. [Chem.] a group of ATOMS which takes part in chemical reactions as an unbroken unit but does not normally have a separate existence. [Philol.] ROOT. **'radically,** adv. In a way having to do with the root, chief part, of some fact, thing or [Philol.] word. **radi'cation,** n. [Bot.] The form of root system of a plant.

'radicle, n. [Bot.] A very small root; the root part of an EMBRYO plant. [Zoo.] A root-like part, the end of a vessel etc. which is fixed into some other part, its starting point.

'radicose, a. [Bot.] Having a great root.

ra'dicular, a. [Bot.] To do with a root or RADICLE.

'radicule, n. [Bot.] A small root. **ra'diculose,** a. Having a great number of rr.

'radio, 1.n. [Phys.] The use of ELECTRO-MAGNETIC WAVES longer than those of

RADIANT HEAT for sending signs, sounds, and pictures through space; instrument for taking in r. programmes etc. 2.a. To do with, produced by, used in, r. **r. as'tronomy.** The use of r. waves sent out or sent back by the stars and other bodies in space in getting a knowledge of them, the instrument of which is the r. telescope or the INTERFEROMETER. **r. 'beacon.** Structure near sea or on airfield from which regular r. beams are sent out in certain directions as a guide to ships or airplanes. **r. beam.** Trains of ELECTROMAGNETIC WAVES kept together by special apparatus so as to go out in one limited direction in place of raying out all round. **r. con'trol.** The controlling of apparatus at a distance by ELECTROMAGNETIC WAVES, for example the guiding of an airplane in this way. **r. 'frequency.** The range of FREQUENCIES used in radio, ranging from about 100 KILOCYCLES per second up. **r. link.** A complete system of r. apparatus in operation between two or more places. **r. 'station.** Building and apparatus from which r. TRANSMISSION is effected. **r. te'legraphy.** The system of telegraphing without wires, using r. to send the SIGNALS, gen. in MORSE CODE. **r. te'lephony.** The system of telephoning without wires, using r. for transporting the voice. **r. 'telescope.** An instrument for taking in r. waves from outer space, of which there are two sorts, one using an INTERFEROMETER, the other a PARABOLIC REFLECTOR (which *see*) which may be turned so as to be pointing at any part of the sky. **r. wave.** An ELECTROMAGNETIC WAVE having r. frequency, that is, a HERTZIAN WAVE. **'-gram,** n. A telegram sent by radiotelegraphy; an apparatus for taking in r. programmes which has a record-player joined to it so that its LOUD-SPEAKER may be used, when desired, for playing records.

'radio-. RADIAL or RADIALLY (**'-sym-m'etrical,** a., **'-'symmetry,** n.). [Zoo.] To do with the RADIUS (and . . .) (**'-'carpal,** a., **'-'ulnar,** a.). [Med.] To do with, using, effected by, RADIANT ENERGY (**'-diag-'nosis,** n.). [Phys.] RADIATION (**radi-'ometry,** n.). [Phys., Chem.] RADIO-ACTIVE (**'-'chemistry,** n.; **'-'element,** n.).

radioac'tinium, n. Chemical ELEMENT in the U-Ac RADIOACTIVE SERIES, an ISOTOPE of Th having a HALF-LIFE of 18·9 days, sign RdAc.

'radio'active, a. [Phys., Chem] Of, to do with, marked by, caused by, RADIO-ACTIVITY. **r. (disinte'gration) 'series.** Any of the three groups of naturally r. ELEMENTS formed of a mother element and the elements into which it is changed, one after the other, by RADIO-ACTIVITY. **r. 'tracing,** [Biol.., Med.] The discovery of the position or line of motion of an unseen ELEMENT in a plant or animal body, by putting into the body a small amount of the r. ISOTOPE of the element, which will go the same way, and whose motions may be recorded by instruments such as a GEIGER COUNTER.

'radioac'tivity, n. [Phys., Chem.] The undergoing by certain ATOMIC NUCLEI (chiefly those of Ra, U, Th, and Ac) of SPONTANEOUS changes in which RADIANT ENERGY and GAMMA RAYS are given off, the changed or daughter nucleus forming an ISOTOPE of the mother element and in turn undergoing like changes, till at last the process comes to rest with the producing of an isotope of lead.

'radio'genic, a. [Chem.] Produced by RADIOACTIVITY.

'radiogoni'ometer, n. [Radio] An apparatus giving the direction from which electric waves are coming.

'radiograph, n. [Phys., Med.] An instrument for measuring and recording the sun's RADIATION; a picture produced on a camera plate or FLUORESCENT SCREEN by waves shorter than light-waves, sp. X-RAYS sent through the thing to be pictured. **radi'ographer,** n. Expert in radiography. **radio'graphic,** a. To do with radiography or with the fact that X-RAYS, etc. sent into a body are let through in different degrees by different substances. **radi'ography,** n. The science or process of taking r. pictures.

radio'isotope, n. [Phys.] Any RADIOACTIVE ISOTOPE of an ELEMENT which may be produced by science but has no natural existence.

Radio'laria, n.pl. [Zoo.] A great ORDER of sea RHIZOPODA having a middle mass of PROTOPLASM walled in by a thin, horn-like substance and an outer mass from which come great numbers of thread-like PSEUDOPODIA and which is gen. supported by small, hard, pointed bodies, sometimes forming a complex network. **radio'larian,** n., a. [Animal] of the R. **radiolarian ooze.** A red CLAY on the sea-bed formed of the framework of radio-larians.

radi'ology, n. The science of X-RAYS and RADIOACTIVITY, sp. that branch of medical science making use of RADIOGRAPHY inside the body, or of X-RAYS, other rays, or RADIUM as a way of fighting disease. **radio'logical,** a. **radi'ologist,** n.

'radiolumi'nescence, n. [Phys., Chem.] LUMINESCENCE caused by BOMBARDMENT with ALPHA-PARTICLES, ELECTRONS, etc. **'radiolumi'nescent,** a.

'radio'meteorograph, n. [Meteor.] A METEOROGRAPH whose reactions are

sent back to the station in the form of radio waves.

radi'ometer, n. [Phys.] An instrument designed for recording or measuring RADIANT ENERGY, formed of a small circle or leaved structure of MICA, one side or certain faces of which are made black, hanging in a glass vessel without air, the taking in of radiant energy (for example, from the sun) by the black parts causing an increase in the heat of those parts, the outcome of which is the turning of the mica round and round.

'radiomi'crometer, n. [Phys.] A very delicate instrument for measuring heat RADIATION, made up of a THERMOCOUPLE in SERIES with a GALVANOMETER.

radio'paque, a. [Phys.-Chem.] Not letting through X-RAYS or other waves shorter than light.

'radiophone, n. [Phys.] Any apparatus for producing sound by the operation of light or other rays. [Radio] A RADIO-TELE-PHONE, sp. a TRANSMITTER or RECEIVER.

radiopho'tography, n. [Radio] The sending of camera pictures from one place to another by ELECTROMAGNETIC WAVES.

'radio'strontium. STRONTIUM 90.

radio'therapy, n. [Med.] The use of RADIATIONS, sp. X-RAYS and those of RADIOACTIVE substances, such as Ra, in fighting disease.

radio'thorium, n. A chemical ELEMENT in the Th RADIOACTIVE SERIES having a HALF-LIFE of 1·9 years.

'radium, n. Chemical ELEMENT, at. no. 88, at. wt. 226·05, sign Ra, an uncommon ALKALINE EARTH METAL, white in colour, noted for its very high degree of RADIOACTIVITY and got chiefly, in very small amounts, from PITCHBLENDE and CARNOTITE, but sometimes present in sea-water and in springs. **r. ema'nation.** RADON.

'radius (radii), n. (The measure of) a straight line from the middle point of a circle or SPHERE to its outer limit; a r-like part. [Zoo.] In back-boned land animals, the front bone of the two long bones of the lower part of the front leg or arm; any of the chief planes of division of the body in a RADIOSYMMETRICAL animal, the 4 chief planes being named simply **rr.,** those coming half-way between them, '**rr.** of the second order', and so on; the third greatest VEIN of an insect's wing, near the middle line of the wing; any of the lines raying out from the base in the FIN of a fish; any of the five ray-like plates in an ARISTOTLE'S LANTERN. **r. of 'curvature.** [Phys.] The r. of the circle or SPHERE of which a given curve or SURFACE is part. **r. 'vector.** [Astron.] The straight line joining the middle point of a body to the middle point of a body moving round it, for example the sun and the earth.

'**radix**, n. [Bot.] Root. [Zoo.] The root or starting-point of a structure, sp. of a nerve.

'**radon**, n. Chemical ELEMENT, at. no. 86, at. wt. 222, sign Rn, a RADIOACTIVE INERT GAS, the first daughter-element produced by Ra, having a HALF-LIFE of 3·82 days, first named *niton*, used medically against CANCER.

rado'needle, n. [Med.] A hollow needle with RADIOACTIVE material inside, commonly RADON, used for putting into CANCERS.

'**radula**, n. [Zoo.] In most MOLLUSCA, a moving band of horn-like substance covered with very small teeth on the floor of the mouth, used for getting food broken up and moved on. **r. sac.** The part of the mouth in which the r. is formed. '**radular**, a. '**radulate**, a. '**raduliform**, a.

'**raies ul'times.** [Phys., Chem.] The strongest lines in the SPECTRUM of an ELEMENT, which are still present when the amount of the substance is so small that no other lines are seen.

'**rainband**, n. [Meteor.] A dark band in the yellow part of the sun's SPECTRUM caused by water VAPOUR in the earth's ATMOSPHERE.

'**rainbow**, n. [Meteor.] An arch formed of the colours of the sun's SPECTRUM in bands, seen on the opposite side of the sky to the sun and caused by the REFRACTION and REFLECTION of the sun's rays by rain-drops.

rain, n. [Meteor.] Water falling from the clouds in drops, caused by the CONDENSATION of water-VAPOUR as the effect of the air becoming colder, and the massing together of drops till their weight is great enough to overcome the FRICTION of the air supporting them. '**rainy**, a.

'**rainfall**, n. [Meteor.] The amount of water falling in a place as rain (or snow) in a given time, gen. measured by the number of inches or cm. deep it would be if not drained away.

rain 'forest. [Geog. etc.] A great wood in those warmer parts of the earth having a very high rainfall, marked by a great number of very tall evergreen trees with a thick growth of lower sorts and EPIPHYTES.

rain gauge. [Meteor.] An instrument for measuring the amount of RAINFALL in a given time, gen. in the form of a FUNNEL going down into a narrow-necked vessel marked with a scale.

rain prints. [Geol.] Small holes in the natural upper sides of certain STRATA probably made by hard rain falling on them when they were still soft enough to take the prints, before being covered by other strata.

rain wash. [Geol., Geog.] The washing away or into different positions of earth or loose material by rain; material which has been so moved or massed.

'**Rainey's 'corpuscles.** [Zoo.] SPORES of SARCOSPORIDIA seen in walled masses in the muscles of sheep, cows, etc. **Rainey's tubes.** Narrow pipe-like bodies covering SARCOSPORIDIA in the later stages of development present in the muscles of sheep, cows, etc.

'**raised beach.** [Geol.] Material put down by a body of water, such as a river or the sea, which is now higher than the water's highest level as the effect of an uplift of the land or a fall in the river bed, etc.

râle, n. [Med.] A rough or cracking sound made by the breath going over or through material produced in a diseased LUNG and noted when the ear or a hearing instrument is put against the chest.

'**ramal**, a. [Bot.] To do with, formed on, a branch.

'**Raman ef'fect.** [Optics] The addition of certain lines to the SPECTRUM of light of one colour which has been sent through a TRANSPARENT substance, caused by a loss of ENERGY to, or the getting of energy from, some MOLECULES of the substance, the effect of which is a change in the FREQUENCY of some of the light. **Raman lines.** The new lines produced in the SPECTRUM of a light by the R.e.

'**rambler**, n. [Bot.] Any plant whose stems are not stiff enough to keep it upright unsupported, and which makes great growth by going from one support to another, up walls, or over the plants round it, etc.

ra'mentum (ramenta), n. [Bot.] Any of the small, thin, brown SCALES seen on the stems and leaves of FILICALES. **ramen'taceous**, a. Covered with or like rr. **ramen'tiferous**, a.

rami-. Branch, branches: **ram'iferous**, a. [Bot.] '**ramiform**, a., **ra'migerous**, a.

'**ramicorn**, a. [Zoo.] (Of insects) having branched feelers.

'**ramifi'cation**, n. The process of branching; a branch or branched structure; an outcome or development. [Bot.] The system of branching of a plant, the order of its branches. '**ramify**, v.i. Send out branches, undergo development by branching.

rami'florous, a. [Bot.] Having flowers on branches.

ram jet. [Engin.] The simplest form of JET ENGINE, in which the air forced in at the front is COMPRESSED simply as the effect of the great rate of the plane's motion.

'ramous, a. [Biol.]. To do with, like, a branch; RAMOSE.

'ramose, a. [Bot.] Much branched. **ra'mosity,** n.

'Ramsay-'Young law or **rule.** [Chem.] The law that the RATIO of the boiling-points of two chemically like substances is roughly the same at all PRESSURES.

'Ramsden 'eyepiece. [Optics] An EYEPIECE used sp. in TELESCOPES etc. when CROSS-WIRES are made, made up of two LENSES CONVEX on one side and flat on the other, placed with the convex sides facing one another at a distance equal to ⅔ of their common FOCAL LENGTH, a structure designed to give very low SPHERICAL ABERRATION.

'ramular, a. [Bot.] To do with a branch or branches.

'ramulus (ramuli), a. [Biol.] A very small branch. **ramu'liferous,** a.

'ramus (rami), n. [Biol.] A branch or branch-like structure, sp. [Zoo.]: a branch of a nerve, blood-vessel, or bone structure. [Zoo.] In back-boned animals, the right or left lower JAW BONE, or the back division of this; a BARB of a feather; one or the other of two branch-like parts of a MASTAX.

range, n. [Biol.] The country over which a sort of animal or plant is present in its natural condition. [Phys.] (Of an ALPHA RAY) the distance, sp. in air, to which it is sent out by Ra. **'r.-'finder,** n. An instrument for measuring the distance away of a seen thing, sp. used in connection with guns.

'ranine, a. [Zoo.] To do with the under side of the tongue.

'Ranvier's nodes, n.pl. [Zoo.] Rings round a MEDULLATED NERVE FIBRE where MYELIN is not present and the NEUROLEMMA is narrowed.

Ra'oult's law. [Chem.] The law that when a small amount of a substance is DISSOLVED in a great amount of a liquid, the lowered VAPOUR PRESSURE of the liquid is to its normal vapour pressure as the number of MOLECULES dissolved is to the number of molecules of the dissolving liquid, whatever the TEMPERATURE.

rape oil, 'rapeseed oil. COLZA OIL.

raphe, n. [Biol.] A line-like or band-like join, gen. between two halves of a part, as in some fruits, or between the right and left halves of the brain or the roof of the mouth etc. [Bot.] A line running down the VALVE of a DIATOM marking the place of a narrow opening; in an ANATROPOUS OVULE, the part of the FUNICLE running down the side of it.

'raphide, n. [Bot.] A needle-like CRYSTAL, gen. of CALCIUM OXALATE, formed in a plant CELL, freq. one of a mass or group of such crystals.

rap'torial, 'raptatory, aa. [Zoo.] (Sp. of birds) getting their food by attacking other animals; designed for the purpose of gripping, wounding, transporting other animals, as the BEAKS and CLAWS of r. birds.

rare earth. [Chem.] Any OXIDE of a rare earth element. **rare earth 'element** or **'metal.** [Chem.] Any of the 15 elements having at. nos. from 57 to 71 (La, Ce, Pr, Nd, Il, Sm, Eu, Gd, Tb, Dy, Ho, Er, Tm, Yb, Lu), all being metals with very like properties, all of wide distribution in the earth but not in great amounts, all forming OXIDES of the general form M_2O_2, and all got from their 'earths' by a long and complex process—together with which are gen. grouped the like metals of lower at. wt., Sc and Y.

rare gas. INERT GAS.

'rarefy, v.t. and i. Make (a substance) or (of a substance) become, thinner, as in undergoing expansion without addition, opp. COMPRESS. **rare'faction,** n. Act or process of rarefying or the condition of being rarefied. [Med.] The development of spaces in the substance of bone, making it less hard and solid, as the effect of a loss of Ca SALTS caused by certain diseases.

rash, n. [Med.] A mass of small points, gen. red, coming out suddenly on the skin, as in certain diseases.

ra'sorial, a. [Zoo.] Getting food by turning the earth over with the feet, as fowls; designed for the purpose of cutting into, turning over, the earth etc., as the feet of fowls.

rasp, 1.n. A steel instrument in the form of a rod or flat blade covered with sharp points, used for rubbing away material. 2.v.t. Get rubbed (as) with a r.

'raspatory, n. [Med.] A sort of RASP used for rubbing down rough places on bones or taking the outer skin off them.

'ratchet, n. [Mach.] A PAWL on a moving arm driving a toothed wheel when the arm is moved; the complete apparatus of r., r. wheel, and another pawl for keeping the wheel from turning back, **r. wheel.** The toothed wheel worked by a r.

'Rathke's pouch or **pocket.** [Zoo.] In back-boned EMBRYOS, the small pocket-like part at the back of the mouth-hollow which undergoes development into the ANTERIOR PITUITARY.

'rating, n. [Mach.] The place of a machine or apparatus on a scale of work-power etc., as given by the maker, the limit of its operation.

'ratio, n. The relation between two numbers seen in the division of one by the other, gen. put in the form $\frac{a}{b}$ or $a:b$, for example, the r. of 10 and 2 is $\frac{5}{1}$ or 5:1. Any such relation between things or qualities which may be measured.

'ratioci'nation, n. Reasoning, the step by step development of one bit of knowledge from another by the use of those rules by which a normal mind is forced to be guided, sp. the process of reasoning from general statements to facts of experience; a train of r. **rati'ocinative,** a.

'rational, a. In agreement with, to do with, having, using, reason.

'rational calorie. [Phys.] *See* CALORIE.

'rationalism, n. The theory that knowledge may be got by reasoning from ideas seen by the mind to be necessarily true independently of experience. opp. EMPIRICISM. **'rationalist,** a.

'rationalize, v.t. Give reasons for (a fact, event, etc.). [Psych.] Put forward reasons for an opinion or act which is in fact not based on reasoning but is the outcome of deeper forces or impulses of which the person attempting the rationalization is, or may be, unconscious. **rationali'zation,** n. The act of rationalizing (a fact, an opinion, act, etc.); an account of an opinion or act which is the outcome of rationalization.

'ratite, 1.a. [Zoo.] (Of birds) having a flat chest-bone without a KEEL. 2.n. A bird of any of the sorts without the power of flight, having small wings, no KEEL for the support of wing muscles, and no BARBULES on the feathers.

'rattle, n. [Zoo.] A structure formed of horn-like parts at the end of the tail in certain snakes, by shaking which the snake makes a sharp noise when troubled. [Acous.] A great number of separate ECHOES produced very quickly one after the other.

raw, a. (Of materials for industry) in the natural condition before being worked on, or having gone through only the first stages of being made ready for further processes, as *r. cotton,* cotton as it comes from the plant before being made into thread, *r. brick,* brick before it has been made hard by fire. [Med.] (Of a wound, etc.) open, with the skin off, with the parts normally covered by skin uncovered, and so feeling pain at the least touch. **r. ma'terial.** The material (not necessarily r.) from which anything is made.

'ray, n. Any of a number of straight lines going out in different directions from a common point. [Biol.] Any of a number of parts going out from a common part like rr., sp. [Zoo.] a r.-like division of the body, as an arm of a starfish. [Zoo.] Any of the rods of bone-like or horn-like material supporting the FIN of a fish; any of the long VEINS of an insect's wing; *see* MEDULLARY RAY. [Bot.] R. floret; a branch of an UMBEL; *see* VASCULAR RAY.

[Phys.] A line representative of the direction in which light or RADIANT ENERGY is going, at right angles to the WAVE FRONT; a line of light or radiant energy of the smallest possible DIAMETER, the unit of a BEAM; a line of PARTICLES going one after the other in the same direction, as sent out, for example, by a RADIOACTIVE substance. **r. flower** or **'floret.** [Bot.] Any of the flat, band-like flowers of a COMPOSITE FLOWER, sp. of those forming an outer ring round a mass of flowers of pipe-like form; any of the greater flowers on the outside of an UMBEL in certain plants.

'Rayleigh disc. [Acous.] An apparatus for measuring the force of sound-waves, formed of a small plate of some thin material hanging by a thread of glass in a vessel, the plate being turned by the sound-waves in a direction at right angles to them and their force being worked out from the twisting-force put on the thread, as recorded by the motion of a ray of light sent back from a small looking-glass on the thread and moving over a scale.

'Rayleigh line. [Optics] In the RAMAN EFFECT, the ray sent out which is of the same FREQUENCY as the light used.

'rayon, n. Any of a great number of silk-like or cotton-like man-made materials for clothing etc., made from thread formed by forcing a sticky SOLUTION of VISCOSE or CELLULOSE ACETATE through very small holes and drying and twisting the threads of cellulose or cellulose acetate so produced.

Rb, Sign for RUBIDIUM.

R.B.A. = RIBO-NUCLEIC ACID.

RdAc, Sign for RADIOACTINIUM.

RdTh, Sign for RADIOTHORIUM.

R.D.X., Sign for HEXOGEN.

Re, Sign for RHENIUM.

re-. Again:— **'-com'pression,** n., **'-distil-l'ation,** n., **'-evaporation,** n., etc.

re'actance, n. [Elec.] That part of the IMPEDANCE of an electric system caused by its INDUCTANCE, $= 2\pi nL$, where n is FREQUENCY and L the inductance. [Acous.] IMPEDANCE.

re'actant, n. [Chem.] Any of the substances taking part in a chemical reaction.

re'action, n. [Psych.] A turning against (something) in thought or feeling. [Mech.] The opposite force produced in a body by a force acting on it from outside. [Biol.] Any change of condition, any act or behaviour, caused in a living thing or substance by a STIMULUS. [Chem.] Any chemical change, any process in which two or more substances have a chemical effect on one another causing other substances to be formed or freed. [Radio] The system of turning back into the RADIO-FREQUENCY CIRCUIT of radiofrequency ENERGY still present in the AUDIOFREQUENCY circuit after DETECTION. **r. time.** [Biol., Psych.] The time between the start of the operation of a STIMULUS and the start of such part of the r. as is open to observation. **r. type.** [Psych.] The sort of r. given to a certain STIMULUS (that is, SENSORY, MOTOR or mixed), or which a person has a general tendency to give, and by which he is grouped. **re'act,** v.i. Undergo or give a r. (*against, to* [Mech., Biol., etc.] or *with* [Chem.]). **'-al,** a.

re'activate, v.t. Give back its special property, power of acting or reaction, to something which has undergone the loss of it by use etc., as [Med.] a SERUM, [Phys.] an ATOM or MOLECULE, [Phys.-Chem.] an ABSORBENT, a CATALYST etc., [Radio] an ELECTRON TUBE. [Med.] Make (a disease) come back, become worse, again. **re'activation,** n.

re'active, a. [Chem.] Having the power of, or sp. a strong tendency to, chemical reaction. [Elec.] Having REACTANCE. **reac'tivity,** n.

re'actor, n. [Chem.] REACTANT. [Zoo., Psych.] Person or animal giving a reaction, sp. one being used for testing the effects of a STIMULUS. [Phys.] NUCLEAR R. [Elec.] Any structure forming part of an electric apparatus which is used because of its great REACTANCE for stopping the current or changing its PHASE or value.

re'agent, n. [Chem.] Any substance which, because of its reactions, is used in testing for, or measuring amounts of, other substances, or for causing a desired chemical process to come about.

real, a. Having true existence, not a fiction or ILLUSION. **r. 'focus.** [Optics] The point at which light rays come together, or would come together if not stopped, after REFRACTION or REFLECTION by a CONVERGENT LENS or lens system or a CONCAVE REFLECTOR (*see* VIRTUAL FOCUS). **r. image.** A picture produced by rays REFRACTED or REFLECTED to a r. focus, that is, one which may be sent onto a SCREEN or camera PLATE, etc. **re'ality,** n.

re'algar, n. [Mineral.] Natural As_2S_2, an orange-red CRYSTALLINE substance burning with a blue flame.

'realism, The theory that material things have a true existence independent of mind, and that sense-experience gives us a knowledge of these material things themselves, not simply of events taking place in our minds which may or may not be representative of events outside them.

'Rèau'mur scale. [Phys.] A scale of TEMPERATURE on which the point at which water becomes ice is 0° and the boiling-point of water is 80°, now little used.

reca'lescence, n. [Phys.] A sudden development of heat by a metal when it gets to a certain TEMPERATURE, different for different metals, in the process of becoming cold after being heated to a higher temperature. **reca'lescent,** a.

'recapitu'late, v.t. Go over shortly the chief points of (an argument, line of reasoning, etc.) again. [Biol.] (Of an EMBRYO) go through in its development in much shorter form (the chief stages in the development of its sort). **recapitu'lation,** n. **recapitulation theory.** The theory that all animals and plants recapitulate in their development the history of their sort. **'recapitu'lat-ive, -ory,** aa.

re'ceive, v.t. and i. Get, be given, take in, sp. (of a radio, telephone etc., instrument) take in ELECTROMAGNETIC WAVES or electric currents and get them changed back into sound or into SIGNALS of some sort. [Zoo., Psych.] Be acted on by a STIMULUS. **re'ceiver,** n. Any vessel, sp. one forming part of a machine or apparatus, which receives material, sp. gas or liquid, for or produced by some process; the plate of an AIR-PUMP with the glass vessel covering it; the receiving part of a telephone, telegraph, or radio apparatus. **re'ceiving,** a., n.

'Recent, a. [Geol.] Being or to do with the division of the earth's history from the end of the PLEISTOCENE to the present day (*see* p. 558).

re'ceptacle, n. Any vessel for putting or storing things in, a RECEIVER. [Bot.] In flowering plants, the end of a flower-stem, freq. a clearly-marked expansion, sometimes bulb-like, sometimes taking the form of a hollow plate, a deep cup or an almost shut vessel, on which the flower is resting, or the like part of a stem supporting a group of small flowers; in non-flowering plants, any of a number of structures, sp. cup-like or plate-like, supporting SPORES or SEX-PARTS (*see* pictures p. 151). **recep'tacular,** n. [Bot.] Sp., (of fruits) formed chiefly of the r.

recep'taculum, n. RECEPTACLE, sp. [Zoo.] name given to a number of bag-like structures or hollows in which liquids, etc. are stored, as CHYLE (**r. 'chyli**) or OVA (**r. 'ovorum**). **r. 'seminis.** SPERMOTHECA.

re'ception, n. The act of RECEIVING anything or the process of being received.

re'ceptor, n. [Med.] *See* SIDE-CHAIN THEORY. [Zoo., Psych.] A CELL or structure, such as a nerve-ending or sense-ORGAN, designed to be acted on by STIMULI and to send impulses through nerves to the brain. **re'ceptive,** a. Having the property of taking in or being acted on by a certain thing, sp. readily. [Zoo., Psych.] To do with rr. or the RECEPTION of STIMULI. **re'ceptive spot.** [Bot.] A clear place on the outside of a female CELL in certain plants, where the male cell gets in. [Zoo.] The point on the outside of a female cell where the male cell gets in. **recep′tivity,** n.

re′cess, n. [Biol.] A small hollow, freq. one in which some part has its place.

re′cessive, 1.a. [Biol.] *See* RECESSIVE CHARACTER under MENDEL'S THEORY OF INHERITANCE; said in addition of the GENE responsible for a r. CHARACTER or of an offspring having a r. character. 2.n. A r. GENE or CHARACTER.

re′ciprocal, 1.a. (Of a relation, effect, operation etc., between two things) working in the two opposite directions, from the one to the other and the other to the one, (of things) having such a relation; being in a r. relation to another thing, opposite in direction and equal or balancing in effect, as a force *r. to* another. [Math.] Being a r. or rr. 2.n. Thing, effect, in a r. relation to another. [Math.] A number a (or b) having a relation to a number b (or a) such that $a \times b = 1$, that is, the r. of 10 is $\frac{1}{10}$. **r. ′hybrids.** [Biol.] Two HYBRIDS, of which one is the offspring of a male of one SPECIES and a female of another, the other of a female of the first species and a male of the second. **r. ′inner′vation.** [Zoo.] The INNERVATION of a part by two nerves or groups of nerves putting opposite effects into force, as those effecting at the same time the CONTRACTION of certain muscles of an arm or leg and the RELAXATION of others, so that the part may be freely bent at the JOINT. **r. Law.** [Chem.] The law that the chemical effect of light is unchanging when the INTENSITY × the time of operation is unchanged. **reci′procity,** n. The condition of being r.

re′cipro′cate, 1.v.t. Be RECIPROCAL to, do something reciprocal to. 2.v.i. [Mech.] Have motion, be moving, forward and back, first in one direction and then in the opposite. **re′ciprocating,** a. Sp., [Mech.] **re′ciprocating ′engine.** Any engine in which the PISTON has reciprocating motion. **recipro′cation,** n. **re′-′ciprocat-ory, -ive,** aa.

′reclinate, re′clineal, aa. [Bot.] Bent down, sp. back, so that the point (as of a leaf) is lower than the base.

re′clining, a. [Bot.] Curving or sloping back; RECUMBENT.

recog′nition, n. [Psych.] PERCEPTION together with the knowledge that the perception of the same thing has taken place before. **′-al,** a. **re′cognitive,** a. **′recognize,** v.t. PERCEIVE (something) and at the same time be conscious that one has had the experience of perceiving it before.

re′coil, 1.n. [Mech.] Sudden jump back, change to motion in the opposite direction, as of a ball on meeting a solid with force, or a spring when the force pushing it together is taken off; the force causing, or giving a tendency to, this effect. 2.v.i. Give a r. **r. e′lectron.** [Phys.] An ELECTRON freed from an ATOM by a blow from one QUANTUM of a GAMMA RAY or X-RAY.

recol′lection, n. [Psych.] The act or process of putting the memory into operation, of producing memories; a memory; or sp. a train or system of memories. **recol′lect,** v.t. and i. Make a memory of (something) come to mind, be conscious of a memory. **′-al,** a. To do with the psychology of r. **recol′lective,** a. To do with the act of r.

′recombi′nation, n. The process of becoming united or of putting (things, substances) together again after being separated; the process of putting the units or simple substances into which two or more groups or complex substances have been broken up together again in a different way, so as to make new groups or substances; group or substance formed by r. [Biol.] The forming in offspring of new groups of GENES, different from the groupings in the father or mother, as the effect of the separating or exchange of CHROMOSOMES or GAMETES in MEIOSIS or FERTILIZATION. [Phys.] In PLASMA PHYSICS, the loss of CHARGED PARTICLES to others with which they recombine, inside the plasma or on near-by SURFACES. **recom′bine,** v.t. and i. (Make) undergo r.

re′constitute, v.t. RECONSTRUCT; give back its qualities to something, for example to a dried substance, such as dried milk, by the addition of water, or [Med.] to wasted TISSUES by giving them medical help. **recon′stituent,** 1.a.. 2.n. [Med.] A substance effecting reconstitution. **reconsti′tution,** n.

recon′struct, v.t. Put (something no longer in existence) together again, make a complete copy or picture of (an animal or part, a time in history, etc.) by putting together its parts or the knowledge of them. **′-ion,** n. Sp., a copy or picture so formed. **′-ive,** a.

′record, 1.n. [Acous.] Any structure stamped, marked, cut, by a process started by sound waves, so that these sounds are given out again when the process is made to take place in the opposite direction by putting this structure in a machine designed for the purpose, sp. a GROOVED plate used on a GRAMOPHONE or r. player. 2.v.t. Make a r. of (sound). **r. player.** An electric instrument used for TRANSMITTING sound from a r. through an AMPLIFIER to a LOUD-SPEAKER. **re′corder,** n. A machine for making sound rr. **re′cording,** n. The process or science of making sound rr.

recru′descence, n. The starting or becoming stronger or more violent again, of something which has for a time been stopped or feebler, sp. [Med.] of diseases. **recru′desce,** v.i. Undergo a r., become stronger or worse again. **recru′descent,** a.

′recrystalli′zation, n. [Chem.] The process of forming CRYSTALS again after having been made liquid, or the operation of causing a substance to do this for the purpose of getting undesired substances away from it or of getting better-formed crystals. **re′crystallize,** v.t. and i. (Make) undergo r.

′rectal, a. [Zoo.] Of, to do with, near, the RECTUM. **r. gland.** A small, bag-like branch of the RECTUM in some fish. **′rectally,** adv.

′rectangle, n. [Geom.] A plane form with 4 straight sides meeting at 4 right angles. **rec′tangular,** a.

rect(i)-. Straight.

′rectify, v.t. Put right, take away (an error); make an adjustment in (an instrument) so that its reading etc. will be true, sp. to overcome the effect of some special condition. [Chem.] Get (a liquid) free from other substances by DISTILLATION, sp. get alcohol (almost) free from water in this way. [Elec.] Get an ALTERNATING CURRENT changed into a DIRECT CURRENT. [Radio] DEMODULATE. **rectifi′cation,** n. **′rectified,** a. **′rectified spirit.** Alcohol which has been rectified to the point of having in it no more than 10% by measure of water. **′rectifier,** n. [Elec.] An instrument for changing an ALTERNATING into a DIRECT CURRENT. [Radio] DEMODULATOR. [Chem.] The part of a DISTILLING apparatus where the substances first given off in the form of gas are separated and changed back into liquid. **′rectifying,** a.

recti′line-ar, -al, aa. Formed of, having, straight lines; (moving) in a straight line. **r. ′propagation of light.** The seeming motion of light in straight lines not taking account of DIFFRACTION. **′recti′line′arity,** n. **r. lens.** [Optics] A LENS so designed that all parallel lines are kept parallel by it.

recti′serial, a. [Bot.] Grouped one under the other in straight lines, said sp. of leaves.

recto-. RECTUM, RECTAL (and ...), chiefly [Med.]:— **′-′ab′dominal,** a., **′-co′litis,** n., **′-′genital,** a., **′-vaginal,** a.

′rectrix (rectrices), n. [Zoo.] Any of the stiff tail feathers of a bird, used in guiding flight.

′rectum, n. [Zoo.] The end-part of the INTESTINE with an opening to the outside through which the solid part of the waste from digestion is sent out.

′rectus, n. [Zoo.] Name given to any of a number of muscles in the form of a straight band in different parts of the body in higher animals, sp. to the 4 outer muscles by which the eyeball is moved (the SUPERIOR r., INFERIOR r., EXTERNAL (or LATERAL) r., and INTERNAL (or MEDIAL) r.).

re′cumbent, a. Resting on the side, back or front, not upright, sp. [Biol.] (of parts) resting on something from end to end. **r. ′anticline.** [Geol.] An overturned ANTICLINE with its chief plane almost flat.

re′cuperate, v.t. and i. [Phys., Biol., Med.] Get back (properties, powers, good condition) again after loss; become strong or normal again by degrees, sp. (of person) after being ill. **recupe′ration,** n. **re′cupera-tive,** a. Sp., [Med.] Helping recuperation. [Mach.] Having a recuperator. **re′cu-perator,** n. [Mach.] REGENERATOR. **re′cuperatory,** a.

re′cur, v.i. Take place, come back, again. **re′curring,** a. Taking place, coming back, again and again.

re′current, a. Taking place, coming back, again and again. [Biol.] Turning back in the direction of the starting point, said of nerves, blood-vessels etc., and sp. of the smaller VEINS of a LEAF. **r. sensi′bility.** [Zoo.] SENSIBILITY of the MOTOR roots of the nerves in the SPINAL CORD caused by FIBRES of the SENSORY roots being mixed with them.

re′curvate, ′re′curved, aa. [Bot.] Bent or curved back.

red, a. [Optics] (Of light rays) of the group having the longest WAVELENGTHS of light which may be seen. **r. ′algae.** RHODO-PHYCEAE. **r. ′arsenic.** REALGAR. **r. blindness.** PROTANOPIA. **r. body or gland.** [Zoo.] A knot of hair-like blood-vessels on the inner wall of the AIR-BLADDER in some fish, possibly controlling the distribution etc. of the gases inside the bladder. **r. (blood-) cell** or **′corpuscle.** [Zoo.] ERY-THROCYTE. **r. clay.** [Geol.] A sort of soft CLAY present only in the deepest parts of the sea (r. clay ABYSSES), formed chiefly of material from volcanoes and METEORITES and so slow in growth (be-cause most sorts of solid substance undergo destruction before getting so far down) that bits of the hardest parts of EXTINCT and present-day animals are sometimes present together on the top of it. **R. ′Giant.** [Astron.] Any of certain stars of very great size giving out a feeble r. light. **r. lead.** [Chem.] Pb_3O_4, a red or yellow powder formed by heating PbO to a very high degree in air, used in making paint, glass, etc., and in OXIDA-TION. **r. ′marrow.** [Zoo.] The sort of

MARROW present in the spaces of bones, which is of a sponge-like structure, with very little fat in it, and has to do with the forming of blood. **r. mud.** Soft substance covering the sea-bed in certain parts, formed of dust from the land transported by wind and coloured r. by iron OXIDE. **r. 'nucleus.** [Zoo.] One or the other of two masses of nerve-CELLS, one at one side and the other at the other of the middle line of the TEGMENTUM in higher animals, **r. shift,** [Phys., Astron.] A change in the position of the lines in a SPECTRUM, sp. of a star etc., in the direction of the red end, caused by the DOPPLER EFFECT. **r. snow.** [Bot.] Snow covered with a growth of one-CELLED ALGAE coloured with HAEMATOCHROME, seen on mountains; the algae producing this effect.

'redinte'gration, 'reinte'gration, nn. [Psych.] The coming back to the mind of a complete earlier experience, in the form of a memory or idea, when any part of it becomes present again; the producing of the same reaction earlier caused by a complex STIMULUS or group of stimuli by some part of the old stimulus.

'redia (rediae), n. [Zoo.] A second LARVA form of TREMATODA, producing itself again or CERCARIAE, by an ASEXUAL process.

re'duce, 1.v.t. Make smaller in size or less in number, amount or degree; make (a liquid) less strong by the addition of water, etc.; get (a substance) broken up into smaller parts by crushing, rubbing, etc., as **r.** a substance *to* powder; get (any complex thing, from a material substance to an idea) broken up into its chief parts, free from unnecessary or undesired additions. [Mining] Get (a metal, sp. gold) free from its ORE. [Chem.] Make (a substance) undergo reduction. [Med.] Put (a part) back into its right place or get it back to its right size or form. [Psych.] Get to the root of (desires, tendencies, etc.) by uncovering the unconscious impulses on which they are based. 2.v.i. [Biol.] Undergo MEIOSIS. **re'duced,** a. Sp. [Biol.] (Of a part) smaller and simpler in structure than the normal, or than the like part in earlier stages of development of the same sort of plant or animal. **reduced a'pogamy.** [Bot.] The producing of a SPOROPHYTE by a GAMETOPHYTE without the uniting of GAMETES. **reduced 'fertili'zation.** [Biol.] The uniting of two NUCLEI other than a male and a female nucleus for the purpose of producing offspring, for example, the uniting of two female nuclei, or of a female and an unsexed nucleus. **reduced 'mechanism.** [Mech.] A simpler form of a complex MECHANISM, made by putting in only those parts which are necessary for the simplest form of the operation. **reduced 'pressure ('temperature, 'volume).** [Phys.] The RATIO of the PRESSURE (TEMPERATURE, VOLUME) of a gas to its CRITICAL PRESSURE (CRITICAL TEMPERATURE, CRITICAL VOLUME). **reduced 'syllable.** [Phonet.] A SYLLABLE without STRESS and so freq. not given its full sound-value (*see* NORMAL SYLLABLE). **re'ducer,** n. [Chem.] A reducing agent; a vessel in which reduction takes place. [Mach.] A part used for putting a greater part into connection with a smaller part, for example a reducing coupling; any of a number of parts for reducing PRESSURE. **re'ducible,** a. Which may be reduced. **re'ducing,** a. **re'ducing 'agent.** [Chem.] A substance used for, having the property of causing, chemical reduction. **reducing 'coupling** (or 'socket or 'pipe-joint). [Mach.] A short pipe the inside measure across which is less at one end than the other, for joining a narrower pipe to a wider one, end to end. **reducing valve.** [Mach.] An automatic VALVE for reducing the PRESSURE of a gas in an engine. **re'duction,** n. The act or process of reducing or the condition of being reduced; the amount by which something is reduced. [Biol.] Reduction division. [Chem.] Any process by which the ELECTRONEGATIVE part of a COMPOUND or the POSITIVE CHARGE of an ELEMENT is reduced, the opposite process to OXIDATION, sp.:—1. the taking away of O from (a substance); 2. the uniting of H with (a substance); 3. the addition of an ELECTRON to (an ATOM or ION). **reduction division.** [Biol.] MEIOSIS, sp. the first division, in which the CHROMOSOME NUMBER is reduced by half. **re'ductive,** a.

re'ductase, n. [Biochem.] Any ENZYME effecting or helping in the chemical REDUCTION of ORGANIC COMPOUNDS.

re'duplicate, 1.a. [Bot.] (Of AESTIVATION) with the edges of the flower-leaves turned out where they come together, [Philol., Biol.] Reduplicated or marked by reduplication. 2.v.t. [Philol.] (Of a language or word-form) put (the ROOT or part of it) in twice, sp. at the start of a word. **redupli'cation,** n. [Philol.] The act of reduplicating or the condition of being reduplicated, sp. as a way of INFLECTION. [Biol.] (Of a part) the fact of there being one or more other such parts in the same plant or animal.

reed, n. [Acous.] A tongue of wood or metal, producing sound when caused to VIBRATE by blowing, forming part of a number of instruments of music.

reef, n. [Geog.] A line etc. of ROCKS in the sea at or not far under the level of the water, gen. near land and freq. uncovered when the sea goes out, for example those made by CORALS. [Mining] A VEIN, sp. one of QUARTZ with gold in it.

reel, n. [Mach., etc.] A CYLINDER round which wire, thread, etc., is rolled, sp. one turning in a machine, for example one on which silk or cotton thread is rolled as it is made, or one on which the FILM of a moving picture is rolled.

re-'entrant, a. [Elec.] (Of a WINDING) having the ends joined so as to make a CLOSED CIRCUIT.

re'fer, v.t. Take (a condition, etc.) as being the effect of the cause named, or sp. [Psych.] take (a sense-effect) as being present in the place named (r. the effect *to* the cause, place). **'reference,** n. The act of referring something, or the condition of being referred, to some cause or place; relation to, connection with; what a law, theory etc., has r. to, its range. **re'ferred,** a. **referred pain.** [Psych.] Pain which seems to be in a part of the body other than that where it is being caused.

re'fine, v.t. [Chem., Metal.] Get (a substance) free, or as free as possible, from other substances (in METALLURGY said only of the further refining processes used after a metal has been got from its ORE). **'-ment,** n. The process of refining anything. **'-ry,** n. A works for the refining of sugar, oil, or metals. **re'fining,** a. Sp., used in refining.

re'flect, 1.v.i. [Phys., Optics] (Of a thing or substance) have the effect of turning RAYS (of WAVES or PARTICLES) of a given sort meeting its SURFACE so that they do not go into it, sp. send back light in this way; r. light in such a way as to make an IMAGE, as a looking-glass does [Psych.] Be giving one's mind to reflection. 2.v.t. Get (rays, light, sound, etc.) turned back; give an IMAGE of (a thing) by reflecting light. **'-ing.** a. Sp., (of instruments, for example, a GALVANOMETER) using as a pointer a ray of light reflected from the moving part onto a scale. **reflecting 'telescope.** [Astron.] A form of TELESCOPE used for overcoming CHROMATIC ABERRATION, in which the IMAGE is formed by the reflection of the light coming into the instrument by a hollow looking-glass or polished SURFACE, and not by its REFRACTION through a LENS. **reflection, re'flexion,** nn. [Phys., Optics] The property or act of reflecting, or the process of being reflected; an IMAGE formed by reflection. (*See* LAWS OF REFLECTION.) [Biol.] The condition of being REFLECTED; a reflected fold. [Psych.] The process of giving attention to, of picturing to oneself, one's past experiences. **reflection 'factor** or **'coeff'icient.** [Optics] A measure of a substance's power of reflecting light, gen. given as the RATIO of the INTENSITY of the light reflected by the substance to that of the light falling on it at right angles (*see* TOTAL, DIFFUSE, DIRECT, SPECULAR). **re'flective.** a. [Psych.] To do with reflection. **reflec'tivity,** n. [Phys., Optics] The property of reflecting; the EXTINCTION COEFFICIENT of a body of substance so thick that no change in this coefficient is effected by making it thicker. **reflec'tometer,** n. [Optics] An instrument for measuring the reflection factor of a substance. **re'flector,** n. [Phys., Optics] Any instrument or apparatus for reflecting light, heat, sound etc., gen. for the purpose of causing a wider and more equal distribution; a reflecting telescope. [Radio] A part of an ANTENNA ARRAY by which a certain part of the waves sent out are turned in the opposite direction. **re'flected,** a. [Phys., Optics] *See* REFLECT. [Biol.] (Of a part) folded back on itself.

'reflex, 1.a. Bent or turned back. [Zoo.] (Of an act) produced automatically as a reaction to a STIMULUS, without the operation of the WILL. 2.n. A r. reaction, the simplest sort of reaction produced by a nerve-system, in which there is an automatic physical connection between a certain ingoing nerve and a certain outgoing one, so that the same stimulus is regularly answered straight away by the same reaction. **r. 'action.** [Zoo.] A r. process or act. **r. 'angle,** [Geom.] An angle greater than 180° and less than 260°. **r. arc** or **'circuit.** [Zoo.] The complete apparatus of a r., or the way taken by the NERVE IMPULSE producing a r., made up of a nerve-ending acted on by the STIMULUS, an ingoing nerve through which the impulse is transported to a r. centre, an outgoing nerve to which it is there handed on, and the muscle or GLAND put in operation by this nerve and producing the reaction. **r. 'camera.** A CAMERA in which the picture formed by the LENS is REFLECTED by a looking-glass so as to be viewed through a glass plate in the top before the picture is taken. **r. 'centre.** Any of the groups of NERVE CELLS, in higher animals placed in the SPINAL CORD or BRAIN STEM, where the NERVE IMPULSE ending in a r. is handed on from the incoming to the outgoing nerve. **r. 'circuit.** [Radio]. A CIRCUIT used in radio RECEIVERS in which one or two VALVES are used for HIGHFREQUENCY and low-frequency AMPLIFICATION at the same time. **re'flexive,** a. R. or to do with rr. **'reflex'ology,** n. [Zoo.] The science of rr. [Psych.] The belief that all behaviour is made up of simple or complex rr. without any control by a mind, **'reflex'ologist,** n.

re'flexed, a. [Biol.] (Of a part) bent, curved, or folded back.

'refluent, a. REFLEX.

'reflux, 1.n. A running back again of a liquid or gas after moving the other way, a back-coming current, or the sudden change of a current from one direction to the opposite. 2.a. Of a current of liquid or gas, moving back, moving in the opposite direction to its earlier motion. **r. con'denser.** [Chem.] A CONDENSER in a DISTILLATION apparatus so placed that the liquid formed in it goes back into the boiling liquid.

re'fract, v.i. and t. [Phys., Optics] Make (rays, sp. of light) undergo refraction. **'-ile, '-ing,** aa. **re'fracting 'angle of a prism.** The angle of a PRISM between the two sides through which a refracted ray goes. **refracting 'telescope.** [Astron.] The earliest form of TELESCOPE, in which the IMAGE is formed by the refraction of the light coming into it by an OBJECTIVE. **'-ion,** n. [Phys., Optics] The changing of the direction of a ray of waves of any sort when it goes, at an angle other than a right angle, from one substance into another in which its rate of motion is different, for example, from air into glass. [Astron.] The refraction of light from a star, etc. on coming into the earth's ATMOSPHERE, causing the body from which it comes to be seen in a different place in the sky from that where it in fact is. **'-ive,** a. Sp., having the property or power of refracting rays, sp. of light. **refractive 'index.** INDEX OF REFRACTION. **refrac'tivity,** n. The property of refracting, sp. light; the measure of the refractive power of a substance for light, which is equal to its INDEX OF REFRACTION less 1. **refrac'tometer,** n. Any instrument for measuring the INDEX OF REFRACTION of a substance or the amount of refraction undergone by given rays, sp. of light, in a given substance in certain conditions. **refrac'tometry,** n. **'-or,** n. Sp., a refracting telescope; any refracting apparatus used for changing the direction of light rays.

re'fractoriness, n. The condition or quality of being REFRACTORY in any sense.

re'fractory, 1.a. (Of substances) hard, not readily worked or changed; able to be heated to a very high degree without changing chemically or becoming soft. [Zoo., Psych.] (Of a part) in the condition of giving no reaction to STIMULI. [Med.] (Of a disease or condition) very hard to overcome. 2.n. Any material used, because of its REFRACTORINESS, for making apparatus which has to undergo heating to a high degree, coating the inside of FURNACES, etc.

re'fractory period or **phase.** [Zoo., Psych.]

The short space of time after a muscle, nerve, etc. has given a reaction before it has the power of giving a reaction again.

re'frangible, a. [Phys., Optics] Able to be REFRACTED. **refrangi'bility.** n. Sp., the amount of REFRACTION undergone by a given sort of ray, the angle through which it is turned.

refrige'ration, n. The producing of a condition of great cold by some physical or chemical process, for the purpose of keeping food from going bad, gen. based on the sudden, heat-using EVAPORATION of some liquid or the expansion of a COMPRESSED VAPOUR. **re'frigerant,** n. Any substance on whose behaviour some system of r. is based, such as liquid air, AMMONIA or CARBON DIOXIDE. **re'frigerate,** v.t. Make or keep (food) cold by r. **re'frigerating,** a. **refrigerating engine** or **machine.** An engine using MECHANICAL ENERGY for the operation of all or part of the process of r. **re'frigerative,** a. Making cold, taking away heat; to do with r. **re'frigerator,** n. A complete apparatus of any sort used for r.; a chest, room etc. kept cold by r. for keeping food in.

re'fringent, a. REFRACTING or REFRACTIVE. **re'fringen-ce, -cy,** nn. REFRACTIVITY.

rege'lation, n. [Phys.] The process by which ice which has been changed into water as the effect of force being put on it, without any change in its TEMPERATURE, becomes solid again when the force is taken off.

re'generate, v.t. Give back to (something) its full properties or power after their loss or using up, for example, r. a substance by the addition to it of some substance which has gone or been taken from it. **regene'ration,** n. The process of regenerating or being regenerated. [Biol.] The producing of new materials or parts to take the place of those which have been used up, damaged, broken off, etc.; the natural uniting again of the parts of something which has been broken or cut, such as a nerve, so that it becomes as good as before. [Mach., Elec.] the automatic turning back into use, by a machine or system, of ENERGY, such as heat, or some substance, such as water, produced by it in the process of its working, and normally wasted. [Radio] REACTION. **re'generative,** a. **regenerative 'cycle.** [Mach.] A CYCLE in a steam-engine by which heat which would normally be wasted is turned back into use again. **re'generator,** n. [Mach.] A structure of parallel pipes used in FURNACES, gas-burning engines, etc., by which the outgoing heated air is used for heating the incoming cold air.

'regimen, n. [Med.] A system of medical rules for a person about the sort of food and drink to be taken, the amount of rest necessary, etc., in order to get or keep well, or to overcome some undesired tendency, such as the tendency to become over-fat.

'region, n. A part of space or of a body, a place or division, sp. one not sharply marked off. [Zoo., Geol.] Any of the chief divisions of the earth based on the animals living there. 'regional, a. 'regional meta'morphism. [Geol.] All the changes in the structure and make-up of ROCKS produced by PRESSURE etc., and by heat caused by motions of the earth, in the part of the country where they are, as opp. CONTACT METAMORPHISM.

'regma, n. [Bot.] A SCHIZOCARP whose one-seeded divisions are round. (See p. 158.)

'regolith, n. [Geol.] The covering of loose material made up of earth, sand, broken stones, etc. on the outside of the earth.

re'gression, n. RETROGRESSION. [Biol.] The tendency for the offspring of any group of animals or plants to be less and less different from one another, as the effect of the working of HEREDITY, than their PARENTS were, so that wide VARIATION is ruled out and development goes on regularly in a fixed direction. [Psych.] The process of going back to the desires and impulses of an early stage of development as a reaction to troubles of adjustment at a later stage, sp. as the cause of a FIXATION; the loss by degrees in old persons of the memory of, or the power to do, things learned earlier, starting with the loss of the memory of later events while memories of things further back are still clear. re'gress, v.i. Undergo r., go back to an earlier condition, etc. 'regress, n. A regressing.

'regular, a. [Bot.] (Of a flower) RADIALLY SYMMETRICAL. [Cryst.] Of the CUBIC SYSTEM. r. re'flection. [Optics] SPECULAR REFLECTION. r. trans'mission. [Optics] The going of light through a body in such a way that it is seen from the other side as coming from the point from which it is in fact coming. regu'larity, n. The condition of being r.

'regulate, v.t. Make or keep (an amount, process, motion, machine, etc.) regular, or in fixed adjustment to some other thing. 'regulating, a. regu'lation, n. The act or process of regulating. [Elec., Engin.] The fall (regulation down) or increase (regulation up) in VOLTAGE in an electric machine produced by changing from no LOAD to full load or the other way round. [Zoo.] The process of adjustment by which normal development of an egg or EMBRYO is effected even though it has undergone some loss or change in structure in the early stages. 'regulative, a. 'regulator, n. Sp., a thing or part used

for regulating, as [Chem.] a substance used in a reaction for controlling the amount of some other substance produced, [Mach.] a part for changing the rate of the hands of a clock or watch, or for the control or adjustment of such things as electric current, the rate of motion of machine parts, the amount of steam, gas etc. let into an engine; a very delicate clock, gen. with separate hands for hours, minutes, and seconds, by which other clocks and watches are timed or regulated.

re'gurgi'tation, n. The coming back of a current of liquid in a pipe or like part, the changing of its normal direction to the opposite, sp. [Zoo., Med.] the coming back into the mouth of food which has been down the throat; the running of the blood in the heart in the opposite direction to the normal as the effect of the wrong working of the VALVES. re'gurgitant, a. re'gurgitate, 1.v.t. (Of an animal) send back (food) into the mouth, as the effect of being ill, or in certain animals, for the purpose of giving it to the young, etc. 2.v.i. (Of liquid or food) undergo r.

re'heat, n. AFTERBURNING.

re'heating, n. [Engin.] In a steam TURBINE, the process of sending used steam back to undergo further heating and expansion.

'Reimer-'Tiemann re'action. [Chem.] The reaction by which PHENOLIC ALDEHYDES are produced as the effect of $CHCL_3$ acting on PHENOLS with strong KOH present.

'Reissner's 'membrane. [Zoo.] The delicate MEMBRANE forming the roof of the outer lower part of the COCHLEA.

'reimplan'tation, n. [Med.] REPLANTATION.

rein'fection, n. [Med.] (The process of getting) a further INFECTION of the same sort as one still present in, or only newly overcome by, the body.

rein'force, v.t. Make stronger by the addition of other material, for example, in the form of a covering, support, etc. rein-'forced, a. reinforced 'concrete. CONCRETE with metal, gen. steel rods, bedded in it, giving it support. rein'forcement, n. Sp., material or structure reinforcing another.

re'jector, n. [Radio] A CIRCUIT designed to let through all SIGNALS but one.

Reinsch test. [Chem.] A test for As, in which a bit of bright copper leaf is put in the liquid to be tested and goes grey with a coating of $CuAs_2$ if As is present.

rejuven'ation, n. [Biol., Med.] The process of giving or getting back earlier powers, making or becoming as strong, etc., as when younger. [Geol., Geog.] The starting again, by an old river or river system, of the downcutting process seen where young rivers are first making their way through a country, as the effect of an uplifting of the land drained by it and its attempt to get down to the new base level made possible by this; the development in a stretch of country which has been almost levelled by the operation of a river system, of the irregular look of a young country, as the effect of the r. of rivers. **re′juvenate,** v.t. Make undergo r. **re′juvenated,** a. **re′juvenative,** a.

re′juve′nescence, n. [Biol.] REJUVENATION; the starting of new growth from old or damaged parts; the forming of new CELLS from old ones by the bursting of the PROTOPLASM from its walls and its organization again into new and more ACTIVE units.

re′lapse, 1.n. [Med.] A coming back of a disease when a person is getting over it, seems to have overcome it. 2.v.i. Undergo a r.

′relative, a. Viewed, measured, in relation to or comparison with some other thing of the same sort, not independently in itself, opp. ABSOLUTE. **r. ′density.** [Chem.] (Of a gas) the RATIO of its DENSITY to that of H under the same conditions. [Phys.] SPECIFIC GRAVITY. **r. hu′midity.** [Meteor.] The RATIO of the amount of water VAPOUR present in the air to the greatest amount which might be present in it at the same TEMPERATURE, or the ratio of the PRESSURES of these two. **rela′tivity,** n. The condition or fact of being r. [Phys.] The body of mathematical laws having to do with space and motion, and making it clear that space and time are to be taken together as forming a 4-DIMENSIONAL CONTINUUM, worked out by Einstein—the keystone of which is the fact that only r. motion is open to our observation and that all measures of time and space are r. to some FRAME OF REFERENCE, so that there is no one independently true answer to any such question; (one or other of) the two theories covering these laws:— (1) **the special (or restricted) theory of relativity,** giving an account of events from the point of view of two systems moving at a fixed and regular rate r. to one another, two of the chief discoveries of which are that the MASS of a body is dependent on its rate of motion, and that the FITZGERALD-LORENZ CONTRACTION is a natural outcome of this new way of looking at things; (2) **the general theory of relativity,** taking up the point of view of systems whose motions r. to one another are not fixed and regular, and offering an important new outlook on the question of GRAVITATION.

re′lax, 1.v.i. (Of a force or motion) become less, undergo a loss of driving power and by degrees come to a stop. [Biol., Med.] Go from a condition of acting, or being ready for acting, to one of rest, sp. let muscles which have been in a stretched condition go loose. 2.v.t. Make (a force or motion) r. [Biol., Med.] Let (the body, muscles, etc.) go loose; make (the BOWELS) relaxed. **re′laxed,** a. Sp. [Med.] (Of BOWELS) in a condition to send out waste readily and frequently, or (of person) having the bowels in this condition. **relax′ation,** n. **relax′ation ′oscillation.** [Elec.] An OSCILLATION increasing slowly to its greatest degree and then suddenly going back to its starting-point. **relax-′ation time.** [Phys.] The time needed for any relaxing force or motion to get to $\frac{1}{2.718}$ of its value. **re′laxing,** a. Sp. [Med.], causing relaxation of the BOWELS; (of weather, place, etc.) causing a tired feeling, taking away a person's desire to do things.

′relay, n. [Elec.] A bit of apparatus using a small electric force for controlling a greater one in the same or a different CIRCUIT, for example in a telegraph system, where feeble incoming impulses are handed on by a r. to a current strong enough to have an effect on a sounding apparatus. **r. cell.** [Zoo.] INTERNUNCIAL NEURONE.

re′lease, 1.v.t. [Mach.] Let (a part, etc.) go. 2.n. [Mach.] A part designed for keeping another part unmoving or in a certain position and then letting it go to do its work when needed, as that by which the SHUTTER is opened in a camera; the act of letting out the substance working an engine, such as steam, at the end of the STROKE.

′relict, n. [Biol.] A SPECIES or other group of plants or animals which has come down from a time when conditions in the earth were very different and is still living today, though its sister species etc. have gone out of existence. **r. mountain** [Geog.] A mountain which has been produced by the weathering or washing away of the land round it.

re′lief, n. [Mach.] A making less of PRESSURE or FRICTION on a part of a machine to give smoother working, for example by the cutting down or adjustment of an edge, or by putting in some special part between others, etc. [Med.] A making less or stopping of pain or some other condition causing unrest. [Geog.] The different levels marking any part of the land, its ups and downs, taken together; the distance of the highest points of any land from its base level. **r. map.** [Geog.] A map made of some solid material with its SURFACE formed into mountains and hollows like that of the country of which it is representative; a map on paper giving the r. of a country by some system of shading etc. the different levels.

re′lieve, v.t. [Mach., Med.] Give r. to (part, machine, person); make (PRESSURE, pain, etc.) less.

re′liquiae, n.pl. INDUVIAE.

re′luctance, n. [Elec.] In a MAGNETIC CIRCUIT, the RATIO of the MAGNETO-MOTIVE FORCE in operation to the MAG-NETIC FLUX produced by it.

reluc′tivity, n. [Elec.] $\dfrac{1}{\text{PERMEABILITY}}$.

REM or **rem** = RÖNTGEN EQUIVALENT MAN.

′remanence, n. [Elec.] The MAGNETIC FLUX DENSITY still present in a FERROMAG-NETIC substance when the MAGNETIZING force is stopped. **′remanent**, a. RESIDUAL.

′remedy, n. [Med.] Any substance or process used against a diseased condition or other trouble of body or mind. **re′medial**, a. To do with overcoming a diseased condition, putting right damage to the body or mind; used as a r.

′remex (remiges), n. [Zoo.] Any of the great feathers of a bird's wing, a PRIMARY or a SECONDARY. **re′migial**, a.

re′mission, n. [Med.] A sort of rest in a disease or pain, a short time when it is less violent. **re′mittent**, a. [Med.] Becoming less violent for a time at regular stages, as **r. fever** (another name for MALARIA).

re′montant, a. [Bot.] Flowering more than once a year.

′renal, a. [Zoo.] To do with, near, the KIDNEYS. **′r.-′portal system.** In some lower back-boned animals, chiefly fish and AMPHIBIA, a part of the blood-vessel system by which some of the blood going back to the heart is taken through the KIDNEYS.

′reniform, a. [Bot.] (Of a leaf, etc.) having the form of a man's KIDNEY or the outline of a kidney cut longways.

′rennet, n. [Zoo.] The inner coat or part of the stomach of an animal still taking its mother's milk, sp. of the ABOMASUM of a young cow; a substance made from the r., having in it RENNIN and used for making milk go solid.

′rennin, n. [Biochem.] An ENZYME present in GASTRIC JUICE and in certain lower animals and plants, which has the effect of changing the CASEIN or CASEINOGEN in milk into an INSOLUBLE substance, so causing the milk to go more or less solid.

reno-. [Zoo.] KIDNEY, of the kidneys (and . . .): **-′gastric**, a.

REP or **rep** = RÖNTGEN EQUIVALENT PHY-SICAL UNIT.

re′pand, a. [Bot.] (Of leaf, etc.) having a somewhat waving edge.

re′pel, v.t. Keep (something) off, as r. insects, r. heat, r. a disease, r. water.

[Phys.] (Of a body or CHARGE) keep (another body or charge) at a distance from itself, put out a force driving it back when it comes near, have on it the effect opposite to that of attraction. **re′pellent**, n., a. Sp. [Med.] (A substance) stopping the development of diseased growths, skin troubles etc., getting them broken up and taken back into the system.

′repent, a. [Zoo.] Moving over the earth, etc. with the body touching or very near to it, as worms etc. [Bot.] Running over the earth and rooting at different points, not making upright growth.

repe′tition com′pulsion. [Psych.] The COM-PULSION caused in a person undergoing expert PSYCHO-ANALYSIS to go through again the experiences of his earlier development. so that the workings of his SUBCONSCIOUS come to light and the memory of past reactions comes back in the process of experiencing them again.

re′place, v.t. Put (something) back again in the same place; take the place of, or put some other thing in the place of (a given thing). **re′placeable**, a. Of which the place may be taken by some other thing. **r. ′hydrogen.** [Chem.] The H ATOMS in an acid which, by reaction with a BASE, may be exchanged for metal atoms, forming a metal SALT. **re′placement**, n. Sp. something which replaces another thing. **replacement de′posit, replacement vein**, etc. [Geol] A DEPOSIT etc. formed of material which has taken the place of material at one time there.

re′placing bone. [Zoo.] CARTILAGE BONE.

replan′tation, n. [Med.] The putting back again in their places in the mouth of teeth which have been pulled out, for example, to undergo the cleaning off of diseased material round the roots.

re′plenish, v.t. Keep (a material or force which is being used up) up to the amount needed by making additions to make up for losses. **′-er**, n. Sp. [Elec.] A small electric machine used in connection with certain old-time ELECTROMETERS or like instruments for keeping up their CHARGES.

re′plete, n. [Zoo.] A sort of worker ant with an INGLUVIES designed for storing food to be REGURGITATED for the use of the group.

′replicate, a. [Bot.] Folded over on itself, as a r. leaf.

re′plicatile, a. [Zoo.] (Of a bird's wing) folding over on itself when at rest.

′replum, n. [Bot.] A division separating the two parts of some MONOCARPELLARY fruits, formed by an ingrowth from the PLACENTA.

re′press, v.t. [Psych.] Keep feelings, etc. from taking their natural outlet, sp. get them pushed out of the conscious mind. **-′ion**, n. Sp., the unconscious process by which a desire, impulse etc., unpleasing to the self is pushed out of the conscious mind and kept from working itself out normally, so that it becomes a cause of trouble in the SUBCONSCIOUS; a repressed desire, impulse, etc. **'-ed,** a. Sp., (of person) having repressions. **'-ive,** a. Repressing or causing repression.

'reproduce, 1.v.t. Get (a certain sort of thing) produced again, make or be a copy of (something), make another thing, do another act, etc., of the same sort as (the one in question), sp. [Biol.] (of a plant, animal, or part) r. (itself, its sort) by having offspring or forming new parts like itself by any process, such as division or GEMMATION. 2.v.i. [Biol.] R. its sort, have offspring. **re'producer,** n. Sp., an apparatus for reproducing sound. **repro'duction,** n. The act or process of reproducing or the condition of being reproduced, sp. [Biol.] the producing of offspring; a copy. [Psych.] The process of experiencing again an earlier experience, or some part of it, as the effect of memory; the doing of an act after learning it, being caused to do it by a teacher, etc. **repro'duction 'factor.** In a NUCLEAR REACTOR the AVERAGE number of NEUTRONS freed in one process of FISSION which go on to give birth to further fission, sign k. **repro'ductive,** a. To do with reproduction, sp. [Biol.] with the producing of offspring. **repro'ductiveness, 'reproduc'tivity,** nn. The property of reproducing or the tendency to r., sp. [Biol.] the degree of this tendency in any sort of animal or plant.

Rep'tilia, n.pl. [Zoo.] CLASS of air-breathing back-boned animals with moving JAWS, 4-legged when legs are present and gen. covered with SCALES or hard plates, of which a great number of ORDERS have gone out of existence and those living today are all COLD-BLOODED, egg-producing, and have no or very short legs, for example, snakes. **rep'tilian,** a. Of, to do with, like, a reptile. **'reptile,** n. An animal of the R.

re'pugnatorial, a. [Zoo.] (Of structures) designed to keep other animals off, as the **r. glands** in ARTHROPODA, which give off a substance with a very unpleasing smell, or the property of burning anything touching it, etc.

re'pulsion, n. The act of REPELLING or the condition of being REPELLED. [Phys.] A force opposite to that of attraction acting between bodies or CHARGES and keeping them at, or driving them to, a certain distance from one another. [Biol.] The tendency of certain GENES, sp. two DOMINANT GENES, to go into separate CHROMOSOMES and not to be handed on together to the offspring, opp. LINKAGE. **re'pulsive,** a. Effecting r., to do with r.

ré'seau, n. [Astron.] A system of delicate lines forming a network of squares on a camera plate on which a picture of stars is taken, for help in measuring their position, etc.

re'section, n. [Med.] The cutting off of part of a structure in the body, for example, the end of a bone, for medical purposes.

re'serve, n., a. (Amount of anything) over, in addition to, the amount normally necessary, and kept in store to be used when needed, as r. CELLULOSE, that stored in a plant for later use.

'reservoir, n. Great basin where the water for the use of a town etc. is stored, and from which it undergoes distribution, or this body of water itself. [Zoo.] In some MASTIGOPHORA a space with liquid in it opening into the GULLET. [Bot.] A space between CELLS, gen. where something produced by the plant, such as oil, is stored. [Geol.] A body of ROCK of sponge-like structure forming a natural storing-place of oil, or water, or gas.

re'sidual, 1.a. Being or to do with a RESIDUE, produced by taking away other parts; present after its cause has come to a stop; being a residue which it is impossible to get away, as the **r. gas** which is still present in a VACUUM TUBE after as much has been pumped out as possible. 2.n. The amount by which a value got by observation in a given test is different from the value of the same thing as worked out from theory. [Psych.] Any after-effect of, or mark made on the mind by, an experience, which has an effect on later behaviour. **r. a'ffinity** or **'valency.** [Chem.] The power of attraction which the ATOMS forming a MOLECULE have in addition to that taken up in uniting them to one another, and whose operation keeps the molecules themselves together in the normal way and is sometimes the cause of the forming of more complex molecules or of CHEMISORPTION. **r. air.** [Med.] The (amount of) air still present in the LUNGS after breathing out with as much force as possible. **r. 'boulder.** [Geol.] A mass of specially hard stone which at one time was part of a greater mass of which the softer parts have been weathered away. **r. de'posit.** [Geol.] The INSOLUBLE parts of ROCK which are still present in the same place after the rock masses themselves have been broken up and washed or weathered away, ranging in size from r. boulders to small-grained earth material such as, and specially, CLAY. **r. 'error.** An error which no amount of care is able to keep out of an observation. **r. ioni'zation.** [Phys.] The IONIZATION which takes place in a gas independently of the operation on it of X-RAYS or other special causes. **r. 'magnetism** or **induc-**

tion. The MAGNETIC FLUX still present in a FERROMAGNETIC substance when the MAGNETIZING force is stopped. **r. 'product** Any substance of independent use produced in the process of producing some other substance. **r. radi'ation** or **ray.** The INFRA-RED rays, or one of these, separated from the others given out by a heated body by causing the mixed rays to be REFLECTED again and again from the polished face of a certain substance.

'residue, re'siduum, nn. That which is over, unused, untaken, after a part has been used, taken away, given an account of, etc., the rest of something. [Chem.] The substance present in the vessel at the end of a process such as EVAPORATION. [Geol.] RESIDUAL DEPOSIT.

re'siduent, n. [Chem.] A waste substance produced in the process of producing another substance; a RESIDUAL PRODUCT.

re'silience, n. [Phys.] Resiliency. [Mech.] The stored ENERGY of an ELASTIC body under a STRESS, or the WORK used by it per unit VOLUME in going back to its normal form and size when the stress is taken off. **re'siliency,** n. The property or power of jumping back on coming with force against another body; the property of going back to its normal size and form after being changed for a time by an outside force not greater than its ELASTIC LIMIT. **re'silient,** a. Having resiliency. **resili'ometer,** n. An instrument for testing resiliency.

re'silium, n. [Zoo.] The elastic part joining the two halves of a BIVALVE SHELL, made of CHITIN.

'resin, n. [Chem.] Any of a number of solid or almost solid ORGANIC substances, becoming sticky liquids on heating, given off by, or got by chemical processes from, certain plants and trees—SOLUBLE in alcohol and some other liquids, but not in water, made up chiefly of POLYMERIZED acids mixed with TERPENES, and used in paints and VARNISHES, soaps, etc.; any of a number of r.-like substances made chemically by POLYMERIZATION and used as PLASTICS. **r. soap.** Any of the soaps formed of the ALKALINE SALTS of rr., such as common yellow soap. (*See* SOAP.) **'resinate,** n. Any SALT or ESTER produced from a r., sp. a ROSINATE. **'resinous,** a. **'resinous elec'tricity.** Old name given to NEGATIVE ELECTRICITY because it was first produced by rubbing AMBER etc.

re'sistance, n. The power or process of acting against a force put upon it, of (completely or to some degree) keeping off some effect or attack, of not being acted on or moved or damaged by something, as the r. of a substance to blows, fire, cold, weather, chemicals, the attacks of insects, etc. [Phys.] Sp., a body's power of stopping or slowing the motion of something through it, as the r. of water to the motion of a ship, of air to that of an airplane, of a pipe to a current of liquid going through it. [Elec.] Sp., the force put up by a CONDUCTOR against an electric current going through it, as the effect of which a certain amount of electric ENERGY is changed into heat, the value of which is got by OHM'S LAW; a resistor. [Biol., Med.] Sp., the power of a plant or animal to keep off or overcome the attacks of disease. [Psych.] Sp., the fight put up by a person against being made conscious of his SUBCONSCIOUS processes when he is undergoing PSYCHOANALYSIS. **r. coil.** [Elec.] A COIL of wire put into a CIRCUIT to make its r. greater. **r. ther'mometer.** A THERMOMETER or PYROMETER in which TEMPERATURE is measured by measuring the electric r. of a twist of wire, gen. of Pt, based on the fact that the degree of electric r. of metals has a fixed relation to the temperature. **r. 'welding.** [Metal.] Any of a number of different WELDING processes in which the necessary heat is produced by sending a strong electric current through the parts to be joined. **re'sist,** v.t. and i. Give, have the property of, r. to (something). **re'sistant,** a. Offering r., sp. [Biol., Med.] to disease. **resisti'bility,** n. The property of being resistible; the power of resisting. **re'sistible,** a. Which may be resisted. **re'sisting,** a. **re'sistive,** a. Sp., to do with electric r. **resis'tivity,** n. Sp., [Elec.] (of a given substance) the measure of the electric r. of 1 cm^3. **re'sistor,** n. [Elec.] A bit of electric apparatus put into a system because of its power of r., which may be used for a number of purposes, such as control.

reso'lution, n. The process of getting something separated into its parts physically or in thought. [Mech.] The discovery of the power and direction of two or more forces whose united operation is the cause of a force under observation, the process of getting a given force broken up into the forces of which it is the outcome, opp. COMPOSITION OF FORCES. [Optics, etc.] The process of getting clear and separate from one another the parts of something seen, sp. through an instrument, as the r. of a NEBULA into different stars, the r. of the parts of a SPECTRUM, etc. [Chem.] Sp., the separating of a complex substance not having OPTICAL ACTIVITY into two substances having equal and opposite optical activity of which it is formed. [Med.] The going away by degrees of some unnormal condition, sp. INFLAMMATION, or the causing of this process. **re'solve,** v.t. and i. (Make) undergo r. **re'solving 'power.** [Optics etc.] The power of an instrument, for example a TELESCOPE or the eye itself, to give clear and separate pictures of details or of things so small in themselves, or at such a great distance, as to make a very small angle at the eye; like power of a RADIO TELESCOPE in taking in sound-waves from the stars etc.; (of a SPEC-TROSCOPE) the power of separating rays whose WAVE-LENGTHS are only to a small degree different from one another; (of a camera PLATE or FILM) the power of copying clearly the small details of the thing pictured.

'resonance, a. [Acous.] The effect caused when a body having the power of VIBRA-TION is put in motion by sound-waves from another body having the same FRE-QUENCY as the natural frequency of the body's vibration, causing a greater AMPLITUDE of vibration and so a louder sound. [Elec.] The effect on an OSCIL-LATORY electric CIRCUIT of an incoming current having the same, or almost the same, FREQUENCY as the circuit; the condition *in* which an electric system is said to be when it is in adjustment with an electric current causing r. in it. [Phonet.] That quality in a sound made by the voice caused by vibration of the air in the nose, throat, etc. 'resonant, a. Having or to do with r. [Elec.] (Of an electric system) in adjustment to, having the same FREQUENCY as, an electric force coming from outside, so as to be in r. with it. 'resonant 'circuit. [Radio] OSCIL-LATORY CIRCUIT. 'resonant 'frequency. A FREQUENCY at which r. is caused. 'resonate, v.i. [Acous., Elec.] Give out r., give the reaction of r. 'resonator, n. [Acous.] An apparatus, such as an open pipe or hollow ball with two openings, designed for increasing a sound by r., sp. with a view to the discovery of what TONES make up a given complex sound. [Elec.] Any of a number of apparatuses for causing or using the effect of r. [Phonet.] Any hollow in the nose, throat, etc. where VIBRATIONS causing r. are pro-duced.

re'sorption, n. The ABSORBING again of something which has for a time been free, sp.:—[Med.] the taking back into the system of the material forming something, for example, a diseased growth; [Geol.] the DISSOLVING again in liquid MAGMA of solid substance which has been formed from it. re'sorb, v.t. re'sorbent, re'sorp-tive, aa.

respiration, n. [Biol.] The process, or one act of, breathing, that is, of pumping air through the LUNGS or water through the GILLS of an animal (*external r.*); the complex physical and chemical processes by which plants and animals take in O from the air and give off CO_2 etc., or, in ANAEROBIC living things, by which some substance other than free O is taken in and broken down, for the purpose of producing the ENERGY needed for other living processes (*internal* or *cell* or *tissue* r.). 'respirator, n. An apparatus put over the mouth and nose for breathing through, used for keeping out dust, poison gases etc. or for breathing in medical gases. respi-'ratory, a. To do with r. respiratory 'centre. [Zoo.] That part of the MEDULLA OBLONGATA controlling breathing. res-piratory 'enzyme. [Biol.] Any CATALYST helping the reactions of OXIDATION and REDUCTION. respiratory heart. [Zoo.] The right half of the heart in animals in which this is cut off from the left side (that is, in birds and higher animals), by which blood is sent to the LUNGS. respiratory 'move-ments. [Zoo.] Those motions of the body of an animal, such as breathing, by which air or water is kept going through or over the breathing apparatus. res-piratory 'organ. [Zoo.] A structure in an animal specially designed for taking O into the blood etc. through its walls and sending out CO_2 and other waste gas, that is, a LUNG or GILL. respiratory 'pig-ment. [Zoo.] Any of a number of coloured substances present in the blood of animals which readily become united with O, transporting it in this way from the respiratory organ to other parts of the body to which it is given up by another reaction, for example HAEMOGLOBIN. respiratory 'quotient or 'ratio. [Biol.] The RATIO between the amount (by measure) of CO_2 given off and the amount of O taken in by a plant or animal in a given time. respiratory tree. [Zoo.] In HOLO-THUROIDEA, a much-branched pipe-like outgrowth of the CLOACA, gen. one of two, having to do with r. respiratory 'trumpet. [Zoo.] In the PUPAE of certain DIPTERA, one or the other of two pipe-like out-growths from the forward division of the body by which air gets into the breathing-system. res'pire, 1.v.i. [Biol.] Do the motions of breathing, get air or water pumped in and out of the breathing-apparatus; (of respiratory organs or TISSUES etc.) take up O etc. and send out CO_2, go through the process of r. 'respirometer, n. [Med.] An instrument for the observation of a person's breath-ing.

re'sponse, n. Any event or change produced in a thing or substance as a reaction to something acting on it, as [Biol.] the behaviour of a living substance or thing caused by a STIMULUS, sp. a motion in reaction to a sense stimulus. r. type [Psych.] REACTION TYPE. res'pond, v.i.

Give a r. (*to* anything acting on it).

'restiform, a. [Zoo.] Like thick cord. **r. body.** [Zoo.] One or the other of two masses of nerve threads on the MEDULLA OBLONGATA.

rest mass. [Phys.] Mass which a body has when at rest, its mass, by the theory of RELATIVITY, changing with its rate of motion.

'resting, a. [Biol.] (Of a stage) in which growth or other marked change is not taking place, has been stopped for a time; (of a living thing) in a r. stage. **r. cell** or **'nucleus.** A CELL or NUCLEUS which is not undergoing division. **r. spore.** [Bot.] A SPORE with specially thick walls to keep it from being damaged by cold, heat etc., designed to undergo a somewhat long r. stage before GERMINATION. **r. stage.** Sp., in MITOSIS the stage before the start of the process, in which the CHROMOSOMES are not seen but are probably being made ready and DUPLICATED.

resti'tution, n. [Phys.] The process of going back to an earlier condition, sp. of an ELASTIC body after being changed by a force.

re'store, v.t. Put back in its place or into its normal condition (something taken away or damaged), as r. a person's hearing by an operation. [Med.] Put (a person) in a healthy, normal condition again after he has been ill or unconscious etc. **'resto-'ration,** n. **res'torative,** n., a. [Med.] (Substance, etc.) with the power of making an unconscious person conscious again, or helping him quickly back to a normal condition after having been overcome by a sudden shock or attack of some sort, or after being ill.

'Reststrahlen, n.pl. RESIDUAL RAYS.

re'strainer, n. The name freq. given to a RETARDER in camera work.

resu'blimed, a. [Chem.] SUBLIMED again.

re'sultant, 1.n. [Mech.] That force which is the outcome of a number of forces acting on the same body, that is, the force which, acting on the body by itself, would have the same effect on it, such as causing motion in the same direction and at the same rate, as the given forces acting together have. [Chem.] A substance produced by a reaction as opp. those taking part in it. **2.**a. Being a r. or outcome.

re'supinate, a. [Bot.] Turned round so as to be upside down, as a flower or the fruit-body of a FUNGUS in which the HYMENIUM is at the top.

re'suscitate, v.t. Make (person) become conscious again after having been unconscious or near death, or give to (a plant, a system etc.) a new power of living, get it going again. **re'susci'tation,** n.

retain, v.t. *See* RETENTION.

re'tard, v.t. Make (a motion or moving thing, a process or development) slower, keep (an event) back so as to make it later. **'-ed,** a. Sp. [Psych.] (Of person) slow in mind-development, still only at the level of development normal to persons younger than himself; having slow mind processes, reactions, **retar-'dation,** b. Act of retarding or condition of being retarded. [Phys.] Sp., the rate at which a VELOCITY becomes slower. **'-er,** n. Sp. [Chem.] Any substance which, when present with other substances taking part in a reaction, makes the rate of reaction slower.

'rete (retia), n. [Zoo.] A network structure, for example of blood-vessels, nerves, etc. **r. Mal'pighii** or **mu'cosum.** MALPIGHIAN LAYER. **r. mirabile.** [Zoo.] A small but very thick network of blood-vessels formed by the branching of a greater vessel and gen. uniting again into one, as the RED GLANDS of fish. **'retial,** a.

re'tention, n. The act or fact of keeping something, not letting it go, or the condition of being kept, sp. [Med.] the keeping in the body of something, such as URINE which is normally sent out. [Psych.] The r. of effects of experience, of some mark of it which has its effect on later reactions, the base of conscious memory and of HABIT. **re'tain,** v.t. Keep. **re'taining,** a. Sp. (of structures) keeping something in place, supporting. **re-'tentive,** a. Sp., [Psych.] with good power of r. **re'tentiveness,** n. **reten'tivity,** n. Sp., [Phys.] a body's power of retaining MAGNETISM when the MAGNETIZING force is no longer in operation; REMANENCE.

'reticle, 'reticule, nn. [Optics] A system of lines, hairs, wires, in the EYEPIECE of a TELESCOPE, etc., used as a help in marking the position of the parts of the thing viewed.

re'ticular, a. Net-like. [Zoo.] To do with a RETICULUM. **r. 'theory.** [Biol.] The old theory that PROTOPLASM is made up of a network of more solid threads with liquid in the spaces. **r. 'tissue.** [Zoo.] A sort of TISSUE made up of a network of RETICULIN threads with LYMPH in the spaces between the CELLS, present in muscles, nerves, and GLANDS of higher animals.

re'ticulate, 1.a. Net-like, having a network structure or marking, sp. [Biol.] having NERVURES etc. forming a network, as a r. leaf or wing. **2.**v.i. and t. Be or make r.; put a RETICULE onto an instrument. **re'ticulated,** a. R. (sp. in fields other than biology). **re'ticu'lation,** n. Sp., a net-like structure.

re'ticulin, n. [Chem., Zoo.] A substance very like COLLAGEN and sometimes changing into it, but less readily acted on by heat or chemicals, present in the bodies of animals. **r. 'fibres**, [Zoo.] Very thin threads of r. forming a network supporting and uniting RETICULAR TISSUE.

re'ticulocyte, n. [Zoo., Med.] An ERYTHRO-CYTE in an incomplete stage of development, in which a network structure of thicker material is seen on STAINING, present sp. in the blood of young animals or after a serious loss of blood or erythrocytes. **re'ticulocy'tosis**, n. [Med.] A condition marked by an unnormal number of rr. in the blood, seen in certain forms of ANAEMIA.

re'ticulo-endo'thelial system. [Zoo., Med.] A system of PHAGOCYTES coming in touch with the blood or LYMPH in different parts of the body of a backboned animal, for example in the bone-MARROW, LIVER, LYMPH-NODES, etc., and taking up from those liquids any small unnormal bodies, such as BACTERIA, which have got into them.

reticu'lose, a. Having a network structure.

re'ticulum, n. Any network or net-like structure, sp. [Biol.] RETICULAR TISSUE; the network of thicker substance seen in the PROTOPLASM of a great number of CELLS when STAINED, but not now looked on as part of its natural structure. [Zoo.] The second division of the stomach in RUMINANTS.

'retiform, a. Net-like. **r. 'tissue**. [Zoo.] RETICULAR TISSUE, sp. of the LYMPHATICS.

'retina, [Zoo.] The back wall of the eyeball in back-boned animals, which is acted on by light and on which pictures of things seen are formed, having an outer coloured coat covering a complex of nerve-endings of two sorts, RODS and CONES, joined to the brain by the OPTIC NERVE. **'retinal**, a. **retinal fa'tigue**. [Med.] A condition caused by chemical effects in the r. in which pictures of things seen are still present after the things have gone, when the eye is no longer being acted on. **'retino-**.

retin'aculum (retinacula), n. [Zoo.] A band or other structure keeping parts together or a certain part in position, sp.:— in LEPIDOPTERA, the part on the front wing locking with the FRENULUM; in certain unwinged insects the structure keeping a FURCULA to the under side of the body; in certain CRUSTACEA, a hook keeping the egg-vessel in its place. [Bot.] The sticky mass at the base of a POL-LINIUM.

'retinophore, n. [Zoo.] Any of the group of CELLS round the body of clear, REFRAC-TIVE substance at the front of a unit of a COMPOUND EYE, and by which this substance is produced, **reti'nophoral**, a.

reti'noscope, n. [Med.] An instrument used for retinoscopy. **'retinoscopy**, n. Observa-

tion of the RETINA, sp. a way of testing the REFRACTION of the eye by sending light onto it from a looking-glass and watching the motion of light and shade across the eye when the glass is turned.

re'tinula, n. [Zoo.] The group of sense-CELLS at the back of a unit of a COMPOUND EYE.

reto'nation wave, n. [Phys.] A wave sent back through the burned gases from the starting-point of an EXPLOSION wave.

re'tort, n. A vessel in which substances are heated for the purpose of DISTILLATION (in Chemistry commonly a glass vessel with a long stem and a ball-like expansion at the end, somewhat like a smoker's pipe; in gas-making or a metal industry, a great vessel of iron, FIRE-CLAY etc.).

re'tract, v.t. and i. [Mech., Zoo., etc.] Get (a part, etc.) pulled in or back, as r. the tongue; undergo retraction or be retractile. **re'tractile**, a. Able to be retracted. **re'traction**, n. **re'tractive**, a. Retracting or having the property of retracting. **retrac-'tivity**. n. The property of being retractile. **re'tractor**, n. An instrument or part effecting the retraction of something, sp. [Zoo.] a muscle. [Med.] An instrument or band for parting the lips of a wound so that the deeper parts may be seen, or for keeping the edges away from the knife in an operation.

'retral, a. At, near, or to the back.

'retro-. At, or to the back, in a back direction:— **'-'caecal**, a., **'-cer'vical**, a., **'-curved**, a., etc.

retro'action, n. [Radio] REACTION. [Psych.] The effect of an act or experience on the RETENTION of one which took place earlier. **retro'active**, a. Having an effect to do with past experiences, as **retroactive as'sociation**, the ASSOCIATION of an event with one going before it, **retroactive am'nesia**, the loss of memory of events which took place at or near the time of a shock, etc. but not of those further back.

retro'bulbar, a. [Zoo.] At the back of the eye-ball.

'retrocede, v.i. [Med.] (Of a disease) go from the outside to the inside of the body. **retro'cession**, n. Act or process of retroceding. **retro'cedent**, a.

retro'flected, a. Turned or bent back on itself. **'retroflex(ed)**, aa. [Zoo., Med.] RETRO-FLECTED, said sp. of the UTERUS when its body is bent back on the CERVIX. [Phonet.] (Of the tongue) in a position with the end lifted and turned back. **retro'flexion**, n.

'retrograde, a. Going back, having a direction opposite to forward, said of a motion, or of a development back to a lower form or condition; having a r. motion or development. [Zoo.] (Of an animal) walking or swimming with the back end pointing in the direction of motion.

[Astron.] Going from east to west, opposite to the normal direction of the bodies in the sun's system, said sp. of the seeming motion of a PLANET in this direction produced by the motion of the earth in relation to it. **r. am′nesia.** RETRO-ACTIVE AMNESIA. **r. evo′lution.** [Biol.] Development of a sort of plant or animal back to a simpler form. **r. ray.** [Phys.] A ray moving away from the CATHODE in a DISCHARGE TUBE but made up of ATOMS which have, or seem to have, a POSITIVE CHARGE. **′retrogra′dation,** n. [Astron.] The act of moving with, or the condition of having, a r. motion.

retro′gress, v.i. Have a RETROGRADE motion or development, go back. **′-ion,** n. [Astron., Biol.] The act of retrogressing or the condition of being RETROGRADE. [Med.] The changing of a part, sp. a living substance, back to a simpler organization with loss of its special properties and power to do its work; the changing back of a part to its normal size and condition after being used for its special purpose, for example, of the UTERUS after the birth of a baby. **′-ive,** a. Sp., [Biol.] To do with or undergoing retrogression. **retro′gressive meta′morphism.** [Geol.] The changing back of a ROCK which has undergone a complex process of development to one of its earlier stages, as the effect of an undoing of the conditions by which it was produced.

retro′morphosis, n. [Zoo.] RETROGRADE development in the stages of an animal's existence, METAMORPHOSIS in which the end stage is lower than the first. **retro-′morphosed,** a. Having undergone r.

′retroposed, a. [Med.] (Of a part) pushed back, being out of place in a back direction, without being bent or turned. **retropo′sition,** n. The process by which something becomes r., or the condition of being r.

retro′pulsion, n. [Med.] The turning or pushing back of a baby's head while birth is taking place; the condition of walking seen in PARALYSIS AGITANS, in which a person is forced to go running in a back direction.

′retro-′rocket, n. A ROCKET apparatus used in space-ships etc. for the purpose of slowing down the VEHICLE, gen. for helping it to make a change of direction, e.g. in order to come back to earth.

re′trorse, a. [Biol.] Pointing or facing back, or opposite to the normal direction for such a part, or to that of other like parts, as feathers.

retro′serrate, a. [Biol.] Having teeth or tooth-like parts (as those of the toothed edge of a leaf) sloping or pointing back.

retro′stalsis, n. [Med.] PERISTALSIS in the wrong direction, opposite to the normal one. **retro′staltic,** a.

′retrovacci′nation, n. [Med.] VACCINATION with a retrovaccine. **retro′vaccinate,** v.t. **retro′vaccine,** n. A VACCINE got from a cow which has first had SMALLPOX VACCINE from a diseased person put into it.

′retroverse, a. RETRORSE. **retro′version,** n. Condition of being or process of becoming r. [Med.] Condition in which the UTERUS is sloped back or turned upside down without being RETROFLEX. **′retrovert,** v.t. Get turned or bent back, make r.

re′turn, a. Coming or going or transporting anything back to the starting-point, etc., as a r. pipe, the **r. electrons** in a CATHODE RAY TUBE, etc.

re′tuse, a. [Biol.] (Of the end of a part) with a rounded or flat outline having a small hollow in the middle, sp. of an EMARGINATE leaf as opp. OBCORDATE.

re′verberate, 1.v.t. [Phys.] (Of a body, etc.) send back (waves, sp. sound-waves); get substance heated in a reverberatory furnace. 2.v.i. (Of waves, sp. sound waves) be turned back, sp. again and again. [Acous.] (Of waves or a body) make a further sound, keep a sound going, by reverberation. **re′verberating,** a. **reverber′ation,** n. Sp., sound produced in a walled-in space by the turning back of sound waves again and again, and going on after the first cause of the sound has come to an end. **reverber′ation time** or **′period.** [Acous.] The time needed for a sound to come down to $\frac{1}{1,000,000}$ of its power after the producing of it has been stopped. **re′verberative,** a. To do with reverberation; having a tendency to r., reverberating. **re′verberator,** n. Thing or apparatus causing the reverberation of heat, light, or sound. **re′verberatory,** a. Sp., working, producing an effect, by reverberation. **re′verberatory furnace.** A FURNACE in which the flame is sent back from the roof onto the material to be heated.

re′verse, 1.v.t. Get (thing) turned completely round, put back to front, upside down, inside out, make (the order or position of things) opposite to what it is, get the places of (two things) exchanged, etc.; make (a motion or thing) go in the opposite direction; make (a process) take place in the opposite order, starting at what was the end and going back to what was the start. 2.v.i. R. itself. 3.n. The opposite side to the one in question, gen. to the one normally on top or outside etc.; the opposite effect, fact, process, etc. 4.a. Reversed. **re′versal,** n. The act or process of reversing or the condition of being reversed. **re′versed,** a. Sp., in a position or direction opposite to the

388

normal. [Bot.] Sp., RESUPINATE. [Zoo.] (Of a turning structure or motion, as in SHELLS or SPIRAL CLEAVAGE) in the opposite direction to the hands of a clock. 'reversed 'drainage. [Geol.] The running of rivers in a direction opposite to their earlier one, or to that natural to the structure of the land, as the effect of the forming of a WATERSHED across rivers cut in two by RIVER CAPTURE. re'verse(d) fault. [Geol.] A FAULT in which the STRATA have been forced up on the upper side of the line of slope of the fault or forced down on the under side. reversed 'image. [Optics] An IMAGE which is upside down in relation to the thing pictured by it, or turned round so that the right side becomes the left and the left, the right; an image with the colours reversed, as in a camera NEGATIVE. '-ment, n. Reversal. re'versible, a. Which may be reversed, has the property of working in one or the other of two opposite directions. reversible cell or 'element. [Chem., Elec.] An electric CELL whose chemical reaction may be reversed by sending through it a current opposite in direction to that produced by it, or which may be used for changing chemical ENERGY into electric energy or electric energy into chemical energy. reversible 'colloid. [Phys., Chem.]. LYOPHIL. reversible heat-'engine. [Mech.] An engine which may be given one or the other of two opposite motions. [Phys.] An engine which, if made to go through its process the other way round, gives up the same amount of heat etc. as was in the first place given to it, or takes up the same amount as, in the first place, was produced by it. reversible re'action. [Chem.] Sp., a reaction which takes place in two directions, in the same conditions, at the same time, uniting given substances into a more complex one and getting this complex substance broken up into the given substances, so that it is only possible to get it completed in one direction or the other by taking away the desired substance as quickly as it is formed to keep the amounts unbalanced. re'versing, a. Sp., effecting a reversal, as a reversing electric SWITCH. reversing 'layer. [Astron.] The coat of gas, some hundred miles thick, round the sun, in which takes place that ABSORPTION of its light causing the FRAUNHOFER LINES.

re'version, n. Going back to an earlier condition, sp. of chemical substances or living things. [Biol.] An animal or plant which has undergone r. r. to type. [Biol.] The producing in a plant or animal of the qualities of some early ANCESTOR which have for some time not been present in the later developments of its sort; RETRO-GRESSION. '-ary, a. re'vert, v.i. Undergo r.

'revolute, a. [Bot.] Rolled back, sp. onto the under side, as the edges of some leaves.

revo'lution, n. [Phys., Astron.] The motion of a body round a point outside itself, as that of the moon round the earth. re'volve, v.t. and i. (Make) undergo r. re'volving, a.

revo lution, n. [Geol.] Any of the times in the earth's history when there were sudden and violent changes in its outer structure.

re'vulsion, n. [Psych.] A violent disgust or turning from, or a sudden, violent reaction against. [Med.] The process of turning a disease from one part of the body to another by sending the blood back from the first part. re'vulsant, re'vulsive, nn. aa. [Med.] (Substance) causing r. '-ary, a. To do with, marked by, r.

'Reynolds 'number. A measure of the RATIO of the KINETIC ENERGY transported in a liquid or gas to the energy DISPERSED as heat.

r.f. = RADIO-FREQUENCY.

Rh, Sign for RHODIUM.

rhabd(o)-. A rod-like structure: 'rhabdoid, a.

'rhabdite, n. [Zoo.] Any of the very small, smooth, rod-like bodies in the skin-CELLS of most TURBELLARIA and some TREMATODA; one or the other of two like outgrowths forming the apparatus by which the eggs are put down by some insects.

rhab'ditiform, a. [Zoo.] (Of the LARVA of NEMATODA) having a short, straight OESOPHAGUS with two bulb-like parts.

rhab'ditis, n. [Zoo.] The free-living sexed LARVA of certain NEMATODA. 'rhabditoid, a. Like a r., sp. in having a narrow, pipe-like, mouth hollow.

'rhabdolith, n. [Zoo.] A very small, hard, rod-like supporting structure in certain PROTOZOA, present in great numbers at the top and on the bed of the sea.

'rhabdom(e), n. [Zoo.] A rod-like REFRACTING structure framed by the CELLS of the RETINULA and made up of RHABDOMERES.

'rhabdomere, n. [Zoo.] A unit of REFRACTIVE substance, produced by a CELL of the RETINULA and forming part of a RHABDOME.

'rhachis, rhachitis, etc. See RACHIS, RACHITIS, etc.

'rhagon, n. [Zoo.] A form of sponge having a wide flat base by which it is fixed to its support and only one opening through which water is sent out, placed at the highest, middle, point of the upper side.

'rhamphoid, a. In form like a bird's BEAK.

'rhenium, n. Chemical ELEMENT, at. no. 75, at. wt. 186·31, sign Re, a hard, grey-white, very uncommon metal, with a very high MELTING-point, used in electric engineering, sp. in THERMOCOUPLES. 'rhenic, a.

rhe(o)-. Current, sp. [Elec.]

'rheobase, rheo'basis, nn. [Zoo., Med.] The smallest electric current necessary for producing an effect on a nerve or muscle, given unlimited time.

rhe'ology, n. The science of the change of form and the FLOW of substances, such as CLAY, butter etc., covering ELASTICITY, VISCOSITY and PLASTICITY.

rhe'ometer, n. Any instrument for measuring a current, sp. [Med.] an apparatus for measuring the rate of the blood-current.

rheo'pexy, n. [Chem.] The process of increasing the rate at which a THIXOTROPIC SOL becomes a GEL by regular smooth motion.

rhe'ophily, n. [Biol.] The tendency of certain water animals or plants to put themselves in, gen. facing, the current of a river, etc. 'rheophile, n., a. (Animal or plant) marked by r., or living in running water.

'rheophore, n. [Elec.] A wire transporting a current.

rheo'caul, n. HYDRORHIZA.

'rheostat, n. [Elec.] A RESISTOR whose RESISTANCE may be changed as desired. rheo'static, a. rheo'static con'troller. A part controlling a current by the use of a r.

rheo'taxis, n. [Biol.] TAXIS in reaction to a current of air or water. rheo'tactic, a.

rheo'tropism, n. [Biol.] TROPISM in reaction to a current of air or water. rheo'tropic, n.

'Rh(esus) 'factor. [Zoo., Med.] A complex of ANTIGENS present in the blood of the RHESUS monkey and of a great number of men and women, and not present in the rest, which is independent of the regular BLOOD-GROUPING and important in BLOOD TRANSFUSION and CHILDBIRTH. Rh-'positive, a. Having the R. f. Rh-'negative, a. Being without the R. f.

rheum, n. [Med.] A thin water-like liquid coming from a MUCOUS MEMBRANE when INFLAMED, for example from the nose when a person has a cold. 'rheum-ic, -y, aa. To do with, marked by, r.

'rheumatism, n. [Med.] Name given to any of a number of CHRONIC diseases causing pain in and a stiff condition of JOINTS or muscles, freq. seemingly caused by getting very cold and wet. rheu'matic, a. rheu'matic 'fever. An ACUTE disease, clearly caused by some MICRO-ORGANISM, chiefly attacking young persons and marked by rheumatic pains, FEVER, and a tendency to INFLAMMATION of the heart. 'rheumatoid, a. 'rheumatoid ar'thritis. A CHRONIC disease, sometimes starting with an ACUTE attack, commonest in older persons, in which there is great SWELLING at the JOINTS, which in the end may become completely stiff and DEFORMED.

'rhexis, n. [Med.] RUPTURE (of a blood-vessel, etc.).

'rhinal, a. [Zoo.] To do with the nose.

rhinen'cephalon, n. [Zoo.] The part of the brain having to do with the sense of smell in back-boned animals.

rhin(o)-. Nose:— rhi'nitis, n. [Med.]. rhi'nology, n., 'rhinopharyn'gitis, n.

'rhinoscope, n. [Med.] An instrument with a looking-glass for looking inside the nose.

rhino'theca, n. [Zoo.] The hard cover of the upper half of the BEAK of a bird.

rhi'zanthous, a. [Bot.] Producing flowers which seem to come straight from the root.

rhiz(o)-. Root:— 'rhizo'genic, a., 'rhizoid, a., rhiz'ophorous, a.

rhizo'carp-ic, -ous, aa. [Bot.] Having roots living through a number of years, but producing new outer plants, stems and leaves, etc., every year; producing small self-POLLINATING flowers on the roots under the earth, as well as normal flowers. 'rhizocarp, n. A r. plant.

rhizo'caul, n. HYDRORHIZA.

'rhizocorm, n. [Bot.] A short, thick, RHIZOME.

'rhizoid, n. [Bot.] Any of the thin root-like outgrowths in MUSCI, FILICALES, and certain FUNGI and ALGAE, by which the fruit-producing plant is fixed to the earth.

'rhizome, n. [Bot.] A thick root-like stem under the earth, freq. parallel to the top of it, sending roots down from its lower side and stems up from its top side, and living from year to year. rhiz'omatous, a.

'rhizomorph, n. [Zoo.] A root-like mass of HYPHAE in some FUNGI. rhizo'morphic, a. rhizo'morph-oid, -ous, aa. [Bot.] Root-like, having the form of a root.

'rhizophore, n. [Bot.] In some MUSCI, a thin forked branch without flowers, going down into earth and producing roots from the ends.

'rhizoplast, n. [Zoo.] In certain PROTOZOA, a delicate root-like or thread-like outgrowth joining a BLEPHAROPLAST or PARABASAL BODY to the NUCLEUS.

Rhi'zopoda, n.pl. [Zoo.] The division of SARCODINA made up of animals producing RHIZOPODIA. 'rhizopod, n., a. (Animal) of the R.

rhizo'podium (rhizopodia), n. [Zoo.] A thread-like PSEUDOPODIUM, branching like a root, or forming part of a network of pseudopodia looking like roots.

'rhizo'tax-is, -y, nn. [Bot.] The system of growth of the root of a plant, the sort of design formed by its roots.

'rhodium, n. Chemical ELEMENT, at. no. 45, at. wt. 102·91, sign Rh, a hard, silver-white metal like Pt, and forming with it an ALLOY used in THERMOCOUPLES.

'rhodophane, n. [Zoo.] A red, oil-like colouring substance present in parts of the RETINA of birds, fishes, snakes, etc.

Rhodo'phyceae, Rhodo'phyta, nn.pl. [Bot.] The group of ALGAE having a red or red-blue colour as the effect of PHYCOERYTHRIN or PHYCOCYANIN being present with the CHLOROPHYLL, chiefly sea-plants, with waving thread-like or band-like plant bodies, and a complex system of producing offspring, having no GAMETES with the power of motion. rhodo'phyceous, a.

'rhodophyll, n. [Bot.] The complex colouring material of RHODOPHYCEAE, in which the chief substance is PHYCOERYTHRIN.

rho'dopsin, n. VISUAL PURPLE.

rhomb, n. RHOMBOHEDRON, sp. [Cryst.]

rhomben'cephalon, n. HIND-BRAIN.

'rhombic, a. Having the form of a RHOMBUS. [Cryst.] ORTHORHOMBIC.

rhombo'hedron, n. [Geom.] A 6-sided solid of which every face is a 4-sided form with its opposite sides equal and parallel, sp. [Cryst.] a CRYSTAL of this form. rhombo-'hedral, a. rhombo'hedral system or class. [Cryst.] A grouping of CRYSTALS, looked on by some authorities as a separate CRYSTAL SYSTEM, by others as a division (class) of the TRIGONAL SYSTEM, in which the r., or some form based on it, is the unit of structure.

'rhomboid, 1.n. [Geom.] A 4-sided plane form whose angles are not right-angles and of which the opposite sides are equal but the sides forming the angles are not. 2.a. Rhomboidal; see RHOMBUS. rhom-'boidal, a. Having the form of a r. [Bot.] Rhomboidal and fixed to something by one angle.

rhom'boideus, n. [Zoo.] In higher animals, a muscle joining the SCAPULA to the back-bone.

'rhombus, n. [Geom.] A plane form with 4 equal sides, the angles of which are not right-angles. 'rhomboid, a. Having the form of a r.; see RHOMBOID, n.

'rhonchus, n. [Med.] A whistling sound made in breathing, noted on putting the ear or an instrument to the chest, caused by the air going through material formed in the greater BRONCHI as the effect of INFLAMMATION. 'rhonch(i)al, a.

rH-value. [Chem.] A number given to a system based on the OXIDIZING power of a system based on the LOGARITHM of the HYDROGEN PRESSURE.

'rhyncho-. [Zoo.] SNOUT or PROBOSCIS or BEAK.

'Rhynchoceph'alia, n.pl. An ORDER of REPTILIA in looks somewhat like the LACERTILIA, most sorts of which are now no longer in existence having been among the earliest forms.

'rhynchocoel, n. [Zoo.] In NEMERTINEA, the pipe-like hollow into which the PROBOSCIS is pulled when not in use.

rhyncho'daeum, n. [Zoo.] In NEMERTINEA, the part of the animal in front of the brain.

'rhynchodont, a. [Zoo.] Having a toothed BEAK.

rhyn'chophorous, a. [Zoo.] Having a BEAK.

'rhynchostome, n. [Zoo.] In NEMERTINEA, the opening through which the PROBOSCIS is put out.

'rhyolite, n. [Geol.] A general name for small-grained IGNEOUS ROCKS of the same make-up as GRANITE but with some glass mixed in, chiefly LAVA FLOWS (see p. 192). rhyo'litic, a.

rhy'simeter, n. An instrument for measuring the rate of a current of liquid or gas, based on PITOT'S TUBE.

'rhythm, n. The quality given to a motion, or to any SERIES in time or space (for example, a series of sounds, or the units of a design), by the regular coming again of all or certain of its parts; a rhythmic motion or condition. '-ic(al), aa. rhyth-mic de'posit or 'sedimen'tation. [Geol.] The putting down of two or more different sorts of SEDIMENT in a rhythmic order so that a regular design of STRATA is formed, freq. as the effect of a regular r. of weather conditions. rhythmic pre-'cipitation. [Chem.] The forming of LIESEGANG RINGS. rhyth'micity, n. The property of being rhythmic.

'ria, n. [Geog., Geol.] A long narrow inlet of the sea, becoming deeper as it goes to its opening, caused by a lowering of the land through which at one time a river went.

rib, n. [Biol., Mach., etc.] Any structure giving a suggestion of an animal's r., as the rr. of an airplane; a RIDGE. [Zoo.] In back-boned animals, any of the narrow arched bones curving round the upper part of the body from the back-bone and supporting the body wall. [Bot.] Any of the greater VEINS of a leaf. 'ribbed, a. Sp., having RIDGES.

ribo'flavin, n. [Biochem.] VITAMIN B_2, a vitamin helping growth, necessary to man and other higher animals and of wide distribution, present in plant-seeds, fruit, YEAST, eggs, milk, LIVER and a great number of other foods.

rice grain. [Astron.] GRANULE.

'ribo'nucleic 'acid. [Chem.] That sort of NUCLEIC ACID having in it the sugar deribose, and present in the substance of living cells.

'ribose, n. [Chem.] A PENTOSE, $C_5H_{10}O_5$.

'rickets, n. [Med.] RACHITIS. 'rickety, a. Having, or having been changed in form by, r.

Ric'kettsia, n.pl. BACTERIAL ORGANISMS of very small size transported by PARASITES such as SIPHONAPTERA and seen in

HOMOCYCLIC ORGANIC RING COMPOUNDS

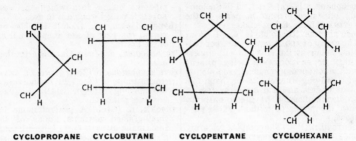

CYCLOPROPANE   CYCLOBUTANE   CYCLOPENTANE   CYCLOHEXANE

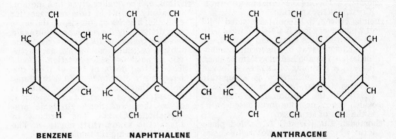

BENZENE   NAPHTHALENE   ANTHRACENE

HETEROCYCLIC ORGANIC RING COMPOUNDS

FURAN   PYRROLE   THIOPHENE

THIAZOLE   PYRIDINE   PYRAN

the blood etc. of persons having TYPHUS and like diseases.

'rictus, n. [Zoo.] The GAPE of a bird's mouth; a deep division opening widely at the top. 'rictal, a.

'rider, n. A small weight put on the arm of a BALANCE, sp. [Chem.] a bit of Pt wire put on a CHEMICAL BALANCE to make a true adjustment to the smallest division of weight.

ridge, 1.n. A part coming out from, higher than, the parts round it, in the form of a line, or cord, or narrow wave, such, for example, as is made in the earth by a plough; the top of a wave-like r., such as the meeting-line of two slopes of a roof. [Meteor.] A long narrow arm of high ATMOSPHERIC PRESSURE pushing into other parts from a greater stretch, gen. given its full name **r. of high pressure.** 2.v.t. Make rr. on. 'ridged, a.

rift, n. A long, narrow crack or opening. [Geol., Mining] The direction, roughly at right-angles to the GRAIN, in which stone etc. is most readily parted. **r.'-valley,** n. [Geog., Geol.] A long, narrow, hollow formed by the slipping down of the land between two roughly parallel FAULTS.

'rigging, n. The process of getting the parts of an airplane into adjustment; a system of cords, wires, etc. supporting something, as those working the sails of a ship and their supports, or those which go over a BALLOON or airship, supporting, and making a distribution of, the weight of its under parts.

right as'cension. [Astron.] Of a star, etc. the ANGULAR distance to the east on the CELESTIAL EQUATOR between the FIRST POINT OF ARIES and the body's HOUR CIRCLE, sometimes measured in degrees, but freq. in time. **r. a. of me'ridian.** The SIDEREAL TIME at any place.

'right-angled 'triangle. [Geom.] A plane form having 3 straight sides meeting in 3 angles, one of which is 90°.

'rigid, a. The property of being completely stiff, unable to be bent or forced into a different form. [Mech.] (Of a body) viewed as having the property of being completely unchanged in form or size by any force; to do with the science of r. bodies. **ri'gidity,** n. The condition or property of being r. **rigidity 'modulus.** [Mech.] Of a material undergoing SHEAR, the RATIO of the INTENSITY of the STRESS to the STRAIN, given in DYNES per cm².

'rigo(u)r, n. [Biol.] The condition of the loss of the power of reaction caused by CELLS or parts becoming stiff sp., [Bot.] this condition seen in plants when the conditions are not good for growth, [Zoo.] the death-like condition produced in some animals as a reaction to a sudden

shock. [Med.] A sudden feeling of cold and attack of shaking, a sign of oncoming FEVER. **rigor 'caloris.** R. produced in a plant or animal by heat (named sometimes **heat r.**). **rigor 'mortis.** [Med.] The very stiff condition of a dead body caused by r. of the muscles, which comes about shortly after death and goes on for a certain time.

rill(e), n. [Astron.] Any of the long, narrow, deep cuts on the face of the moon.

rim, n. Edge of a vessel, hollow, etc., sp. a RIDGE, thicker band, or overhanging structure on the edge of anything, as [Bot.] of the wall round a BORDERED PIT.

'rima (rimae), n. [Biol.] A long, narrow opening, a deep crack. **r. 'oris.** [Zoo.] The space between the lips. 'rimate, a. 'rimi- form, a. ri'mose, a. Having a great number or a network of rr. 'rimula, n. A little r. sp. in the brain and SPINAL CORD. 'rimulose,

rime, n. [Meteor.] A mass of ice-grains produced on something by mist or cloud, as the effect of cold, sp. on the side of something facing the wind.

rind, n. [Bot.] The outer skin or covering, sp. of a tree or a fruit.

'rinderpest, n. An acute disease of sheep, cows and goats, readily given by one to another, causing INFLAMMATION of the MUCOUS MEMBRANES, sp. of the INTES- TINES.

ring, n. [Chem.] A chain of ATOMS of which every one is united to two others so that the chain has no end, pictured in GRAPHIC FORMULAE in the form of a ring. **r. 'compound.** Any complex substance having one or more rr. in the MOLECULE.

ring bark. [Bot.] The hard outer covering of a tree stem when it may be taken off in the form of complete rings round the stem, the distribution of the PHELLOGEN being regular.

ring ca'nal. [Zoo.] The pipe-like hollow running round the edge of the 'umbrella' of a MEDUSA; the water-pipe going round the throat in ECHINODERMS.

ring cell. [Bot.] The sort of thick-walled CELL forming the ANNULUS in FILICALES.

ring 'complex. [Geol.] A number of ring dykes one inside the other with other material between, and having roughly the same middle point. **ring dyke.** A very wide DYKE formed in a FAULT having the outline of an upright pipe, the OUTCROP of which is in the form of a circle.

'ringent, a. [Biol.] (Of a flower, etc.) having widely opened lips, (of a SHELL) having openings or a crack between the two parts when shut.

'Ringer's so'lution or fluid. [Zoo., Med.] A liquid made up of NaCl₂, KCl, and CaCl₂ and some other SALTS in water, used for putting parts taken from animals for the purpose of observation or testing in, to take the place of the normal body liquids needed to keep the CELLS living.

'ringless, a. Not having a ring or ANNULUS.

ring 'vessel. [Zoo.] The vessel in the form of a ring joining the four long waste-pipes in the head of CESTODA.

'ringworm, n. [Med.] A skin disease, readily given to other persons or animals by touch, caused by certain FUNGI and marked by diseased places on the skin, sp. of the head, taking the form of rings or rounds (other name *Tinea*).

ri'parian, ri'parious, ri'parial, aa. [Biol.] Living on the edges of rivers or currents of water.

'ripple, n. [Phys.] A train of very small waves on the top of a liquid caused by a troubling of the SURFACE TENSION; a very small change coming and going in the INTENSITY of a regular electric current. r. marks. [Geol.] Narrow parallel RIDGES seen on a stretch of sand or on SEDIMENTARY ROCK, caused by the operation on it of a current of water or wind before it became hard.

rise, v.i. [Astron.] (Of a star, etc.) get to a position on top of the HORIZON east of the point of observation.

ri'sorius, n. [Zoo.] A band of muscle going across the side of the face to the angle of the mouth, used in laughing.

'risus sar'donicus. [Med.] A pulling back of the lips giving the look of a fixed smile, caused by a SPASM of the face muscles in certain diseases, for example TETANUS.

river 'capture or 'piracy. [Geog., Geol.] The cutting into or across a river of another river (or one of its incoming branches) of stronger current and deeper bed, so that the water of the upper part of the first river is now drained into the second.

'rivulet, n. A small river.

'riv(ul)ose, aa. Marked with irregular, waving or bent lines or cuts, like rivers as pictured on a map, sp. [Bot.].

R.M.S. = ROOT MEAN SQUARE.

Rn, Sign for RADON.

RNA = RIBONUCLEIC ACID.

'roasting, n. The process of heating metals or ORES in air for the purpose of driving off gases or getting undesired substances united with O, used sp. for getting ores free from S. roast, v.t.

'Rochelle salt. [Chem.] COOK.(CH.OH)$_2$. COONa.4H$_2$O (*sodium potassium tartrate*), a CRYSTALLINE substance without colour, used medically as an APERIENT, in making BAKING POWDER, as a CEMENT, and as PIEZO-ELECTRIC CRYSTALS in radio and other sound apparatus.

rock, n. [Geol.] Any of the solid materials of which the outer part of the earth is chiefly formed, made up sometimes of one sort of MINERAL, but gen. of different sorts mixed with one another and with dead plant and animal substances, and having no fixed chemical structure but looked on as a separate material because of its general make-up and its physical properties, as sand, stone, earth, etc.: more loosely, any of these materials forming hard masses, such as what is generally named stone; a great mass of hard r. r. 'crystal. [Mineral.] QUARTZ when it is uncoloured and glass-like, being formed of nothing but SiO$_2$. r. flour. [Geol.] The substance like wet powdered earth produced by the rubbing of a GLACIER on its bed. r. salt. [Mineral.] Natural CRYSTALLINE NaCl, common salt.

'rocker, n. [Mach.] A part of a machine supported on or turning about a point near the middle and moving first up at one end and down at the other and back again, or turning first one way then the other, as that part in a DYNAMO to which the BRUSHES are fixed. 'rocking, n., a. (The process of) moving like a r., up and down, from side to side, or first one way and then the other, about a middle point.

'rocket, n. A PROJECTILE sent through the air by its reaction to an EXPLOSION produced inside it, used as a firework, as a way of SIGNALLING, or for taking something to a distance, for example, a line to a ship in trouble, or a BOMB to a place to be damaged in war, or, in Astronautics, a CAPSULE up into space. r. bomb. A BOMB taken through the air by a r.

rod, n. [Zoo.] One of the two sorts of NERVE-CELL (rr. and CONES) present in the RETINA of the eye of higher animals, rod-like in form and having a very delicate reaction to light, so making it possible to see when the light is feeble. r. 'fibre, The NERVE FIBRE to which a r. is joined. r. 'granule. The NUCLEUS of a r. fibre.

rod epi'thelium. [Zoo.] A sort of EPI-THELIUM in which the CELLS seem to be formed of parallel bands.

Ro'dentia, n.pl. [Zoo.] An ORDER of small MAMMALS living on plant food, with teeth and JAWS specially formed for biting away hard substances little by little, for example, rats. 'rodent, 1.n. An animal of the R. 2.a. Of, like, a rodent. 'rodent 'ulcer. [Med.] A CANCER coming from the base of the skin, gen. on the face, causing an open wound which does not get better, but is of very slow growth, so not of great danger to other parts.

'roentgen, 'Röntgen, n. [Phys.] The international unit for measuring X-RADIA-TION, equal to that amount producing one ELECTROSTATIC UNIT of electric force in 1 cm of dry air. R. e'quivalent man. That amount of any RADIATION which has in man's body the same effect as 1 r. of X-RAYS or GAMMA-RAYS. **R. e′quivalent′physical unit.** That amount of any RADIATION other than X-RAYS or GAMMA-RAYS which is the cause in man's body of the same amount of IONIZATION as is produced by 1 r. of X-rays or gamma-rays in air. **R. rays.** X-RAYS.

rolls, n.pl. [Mach.] Two parallel steel rollers near together and turning in opposite directions, used for crushing material between them, or making metal flat, etc.

root, 1.n. [Bot.] The part of a plant, freq. stem-like and branching with its chief part in a straight line with the chief stem of the plant, which gen. goes down into the earth, fixing the plant in its place and taking in water and the food-substances present in earth with the ends of its branches—different from a stem in not producing leaves and SHOOTS, in having a r. cap, and in some points in its inner structure, for example, the fact that the PROTOXYLEM is outside the METAXYLEM [Zoo.] Any part like a r. in position or purpose, forming the base or support of something, the starting-point of its development, or its fixed inner end, as the r. of a nail, a diseased growth, a tooth, or a nerve. [Philol.] A FUNDAMENTAL unit of language which, though frequently not a word in itself, is the base on which words are formed by INFLECTION or the addition of independent PREFIXES or endings, and which gives to all words of which it is part a connection of sense—that part of any word, frequently representative of a word or part in an older language, which is still there when all special additions or form-changes have been taken away and which it is not possible to get broken up into simpler sense units. **2.**v.i. (Of a seed, a cutting from a plant, a bulb, etc.) send out a r. or rr., get fixed in the earth, etc. and make a start on the process of growth **r. ′borer.** [Zoo.] Any insect or LARVA forcing its way into the rr. of plants. **r. cap.** [Bot.] A cover of CELLS over the end of a r. keeping it from damage as it is forced down by growth into the earth. **r. cell.** [Bot.] The RHIZOID of an ALGA. **r. ′climber.** [Bot.] A CLIMBER fixing itself to its support by rr. produced from time to time. **r. hair.** [Bot.] Any of the hollow, hair-like outgrowths from the skin of a r. which take in liquid food-substances from the earth through their walls, gen. produced in great numbers near the end of a r. **r. ′nodule** or **′tubercle.** [Bot.] A small rounded outgrowth on the rr. of certain plants produced by NITROGEN-FIXING BACTERIA. **r. ′parasite.** [Bot.] A plant producing rr. which go into the rr. of other plants and take food from them.

r. ′parasitism. The operation of r. parasites, or the condition of being a r. parasite. **r. ′pocket.** [Bot.] A bag-like structure covering the rr. of certain water-plants. **r. ′pressure.** [Bot.] The force by which water is sent up into the stems of plants from the rr. **r. ′process.** [Bot.] A branching structure fixing the plant-body of an ALGA to a support. **r. sheath.** [Bot.] A covering structure, gen. of dead CELLS, over some rr. which are produced outside the earth, as by a r. climber; the cover of an EMBRYO r. in grass plants. [Zoo.] The skin covering the inside of the small hole in which a hair is rooted, formed of two coats of CELLS, an inner and an outer one. **r. ′tuber.** [Bot.] A TUBER formed of a r. **′-age,** n. [Bot.] Rooting. **′-less,** a. Having no rr., sp. [Zoo.] of teeth. **′-let,** n. [Bot.] Any of the smaller branches of a r. **roots,** n.pl. [Bot.] The r. of a plant when it has a great number of branches. **′-stalk. -stock,** nn. [Bot.] RHIZOME.

root, n. [Arith.] (Of a number) the number of which it is the SQUARE (*square root*), or the CUBE (*cube root*), or any other POWER. **r.-mean-square,** n. The square r. of the ARITHMETICAL MEAN of the SQUARES of a group of numbers. **r. mean-square-value.** [Elec.] Of an ALTERNATING CURRENT or VOLTAGE, the r.-mean-square of its values over one complete CYCLE, which is equal in heating effect to the same number of units of DIRECT CURRENT.

′ropy, a. (Of a liquid) sticky enough to be pulled out into thick threads. **r. ′lava.** [Geol.] LAVA of which the face has the look of thick cords formed into loose turns round and round.

ro′sette, n. [Biol.] Flower-like structure with parts or material forming a circle, or a number of circles one inside the other, round a middle point, sp. a thick r. of leaves at the base of a flower stem or forming the end of a chief stem, as in some TROPICAL trees.

′rosin, n. [Chem.] The hard RESIN got by taking the oil from TURPENTINE, commonly yellow in colour, but sometimes red, brown, or black, formed chiefly of ABIETIC ACID, used in VARNISH, paint, soap, and as a FLUX in SOLDERING. **′-ate,** n. Any SALT or ESTER produced from r.

ros′tellum, n. [Bot.] A small BEAK-like outgrowth, sp. the small outgrowth under the RETINACULA in ORCHIDACEAE. [Zoo.] A rounded outgrowth with hooks on it in CESTODA. **′ros′tellar,** a. **ros′tellate,** a. **ros′telliform,** a.

rostrate, a. [Zoo.] Having a BEAK or beak-like part. [Bot.] Ending in a long, gen. hard, point. **rostr(i)-.** BEAK:— **ros′triferous,** a., **′rostriform,** a., **′rostroid,** a.

'rostrum (rostra), n. [Biol.] An outgrowth like a BEAK in form or position, sp. on an animal's SHELL or the head of an insect. [Zoo.] The beak of a bird. 'rostral, a.

rot, 1.v.t. and i. DECAY, said sp. of dead plant material. 2.n. DECAY. 'rotten, a. Having undergone rotting, DECAYED.

'rotary, a. Turning round like a wheel. [Mach.] (Of an engine, pump, VALVE, etc.) worked by a r. motion or by parts having such a motion. r. con'verter. [Elec.] SYNCHRONOUS CONVERTER.

ro'tate, 1.v.t. and i. [Make] undergo ROTATION. 2.a. Formed like a wheel, with flat, outstretched parts, sp. [Bot.] of a flower, ro'tating, a. ro'tative, a.

ro'tation, n. The motion of a body turning round a line going through it, as a wheel or the earth; one complete turn of this sort, going through 360°; the coming about or causing to come about of different things in a fixed order, one after the other, again and again. r. of crops. In farming, the growth of different food plants one after another in a certain order year after year on the same land, to keep it fertile. '-al, a. To do with, produced by, based on, r. ro'tational fault. [Geol.] A FAULT in which the THROW becomes less and less till it gets to 0 and at that point goes on increasing again with a throw in the opposite direction. ro'tational 'quantum number. [Phys.] A number representative of the ANGULAR MOMENTUM in QUANTA of a FUNDAMENTAL PARTICLE.

ro'tator, n. [Mach.] A part causing the ROTATION of another part. [Zoo.] A muscle turning a part round, sp. any of a number of small muscles coming out of the TRANSVERSE PROCESS of a backbone division and going into the LAMINA of the division on top of it.

ro'tatory, a. ROTARY or to do with or causing ROTATION, sp. of POLARIZED light. r. 'power. [Phys.] Of a substance, the angle through which the plane of POLARIZATION of light is turned in going through 1 cm. of it.

Ro'tifera, n.pl. [Zoo.] A CLASS of TROCHELMINTHES made up of very small water-animals moving and getting food by the instrument of a wheel-like band of CILIA at one end of the body, the other end gen. forming a pointed tail or 'foot' by which the animal is able to get itself fixed to some support, commonest in inland water where there is no current. 'rotifer, n. Animal of the R.

'rotiform, a. Wheel-like or in the form of a circle.

'rotor, n. [Mach.] A part which ROTATES in another part which is unmoving, as the moving wheel or system of wheels in a steam TURBINE, or sp. [Elec.] the turning part in a DYNAMO etc.

'rotoscope, n. [Elec., Eng.] A STROBOSCOPE for the observation of quickly turning machine parts.

'rotten, a. See ROT.

'rotula, a. [Anat.] PATELLA.

rotundi'folious, a. [Bot.] Having round leaves.

rouge, n. [Chem.] A light red powder formed of Fe_2O_2, gen. got by heating $FeSO_4$, used for polishing glass, metal etc., and as red colouring material.

'roughage, n. [Med.] The part of food, made up chiefly of CELLULOSE, which is not acted on by the digestion but has the important effect of helping PERISTALSIS by its mass.

'rouleau (rouleaux), n. [Zoo.] A grouping of ERYTHROCYTES looking like a number of round plates one on top of the other.

round-headed, a. BRACHYCEPHALIC.

roundworm, n. [Zoo.] A NEMATODE worm.

Rous'seau 'diagram. [Optics] A curve PLOTTED in relation to CARTESIAN CO-ORDINATES giving the amount of light sent out by an electric bulb or a flame in different directions.

row, n. A line (of things, numbers, letters, etc.) on the same level, going across a page, sp. in a TABLE, as opp. COLUMN.

'royal 'jelly. [Zoo.] The liquid food, formed of food which has undergone part of the process of digestion in the stomach of a WORKER bee, given by the workers to the LARVA of the QUEEN.

Ru, Sign of RUTHENIUM.

'rubber, n. An elastic solid got from a milk-like liquid produced by certain TROPICAL trees, formed chiefly of a HYDROCARBON POLYMER $(CH_2.CH:C(CH_3:CH_2)_n$; any substance with the properties of natural r. produced by chemical reactions, sp. by POLYMERIZATION of certain hydrocarbons.

ru'bella, n. [Med.] A disease marked by dark red places on the skin, very like MEASLES but caused by a different VIRUS, and less serious.

ru'bidium, n. Chemical ELEMENT, at. no. 37, at. wt. 85·48, sign Rb, a soft white metal with properties very like those of K, RADIOACTIVE to a small degree and bursting into flame in air—of wide natural distribution but only in small amounts, got chiefly from CARNALLITE.

ru'bigin-ous, -ose, aa. Brown-red in colour. [Bot.] Having a RUST disease.

'rubro'spinal tract. [Zoo.] That part of the SPINAL CORD formed of NERVE FIBRES coming from the RED NUCLEUS.

'ruby, n. [Mineral.] A clear, deep, red, natural form of Al_2O_3, highly valued as a jewel stone.

rudaceous, a. [Geol.] (Of DEPOSITS) made up of bits of broken material of some size, not small grains, e.g. SCREE and GRAVEL— naming one of the chief groups of SEDIMENTARY ROCKS.

'rudder, n. FIN-like structure fixed to the back of a ship and turning from side to side, used for guiding a ship; like structure used for guiding an airplane.

'rudiment, n. [Biol.] A part at the start of its development; a part of which the development has been stopped at an early stage; a part no longer of any use to a plant or animal, which has been kept on from an earlier stage of its development or from that of the development of its sort, and has become smaller or incomplete. **rudi'mentary,** a. Being a r. in any sense.

ruff, n. [Zoo.] A sort of collar of stiff or long hair or feathers round the neck of an animal.

'rufous, a. Of a bright, strong, yellow-red or brown-red in colour.

'rugose, 'rugous, aa. [Biol.] Of skin etc., with a (great) number of folds or deep lines; having a r. skin. **ru'gosity,** n. The condition of being r.; a fold or a r. place. **'rugulose,** a. Having or covered with very small folds.

'rumen, n. [Zoo.] The first stomach of a RUMINANT, having a connection with the others only through the throat.

'ruminant, 1.n. [Zoo.] A MAMMAL of the sort which ruminates, having gen. 4, but sometimes only 3, stomachs or stomach-divisions, food going no further than the first of these the first time it goes down the throat. 2.a. Being a r.; to do with rumination. **'ruminate,** v.t. and i. Take (food) down the throat and then get it back later in small masses for more complete crushing before sending it through the apparatus of digestion, as a cow does. **rumi'nation,** n. The process of ruminating. [Med.] Rumination of food by persons, sp. babies, in certain diseases.

rump, n. [Zoo.] The lower or tail end of the back in man and higher animals, the BUTTOCKS etc.

'runcinate, a. [Bot.] (Of a leaf) PINNATELY cut, with the divisions pointing back to the base.

'runner, n. [Bot.] A stem running over the earth, putting out roots and forming a new plant at the end of every division.

'run-off, n. [Geog.] That part of the rain-water falling in a stretch of country which goes into the rivers and is not taken up by the earth.

'runway, n. Bed or way made for a current of liquid or by a river; a hard level place made for the landing and taking flight of airplanes.

ru'pestrine, ru'picoline, ru'picolous, aa.

[Biol.] Living, having its growth, on or among stones.

'rupture, 1.n. Hole or parting made in anything, for example in a blood-vessel, as the effect of bursting, being over-stretched, or undergoing other force; the act of rupturing or the condition of being ruptured. [Med.] Sp., HERNIA. 2.v.t. and i. (Make) become ruptured. **'ruptured,** a. Having a r., broken open. [Med.] Sp., having a HERNIA.

rust, n. The red or orange coating formed chiefly of $Fe_2O_3.H_2O$ produced on iron as the effect of being in water or in air with water in it; any of like coatings formed on other metals. [Bot.] R. fungus; plant disease caused by a r. 2.v.t. and i. (Make) become rusty. [Bot.] Be attacked by a r. **r. 'fungus.** [Bot.] Any of the UREDINALES, so named because of the r.-like places caused by them on the stems and leaves of plants. **'rusty,** a.

rut, n. [Zoo.] OESTRUS in higher animals, such as cows.

ru'thenium, n. Chemical ELEMENT, at. no. 44, at. wt. 101·7, sign Ru, a hard silver-white, readily broken metal, present in OSMIRIDIUM. **ru'thenic,** a.

'Rutherford 'atom. Rutherford's picture of the ATOM as made up of a POSITIVE NUCLEUS, round which ELECTRONS are moving.

'rutile, n. [Mineral.] A natural form of TiO_2, a red-brown CRYSTALLINE substance with a look of bright metal, used for producing Ti, and sometimes as a jewel stone.

'Rydberg('s) 'constant. [Phys.] A CONSTANT forming part of a FORMULA for getting the WAVE-NUMBERS of the lines in the SPECTRUM of an ATOM, based on a value for the H atom of 109,678 cm.-1.

S, Sign for SULPHUR.

s. = second (of time).

s. ele'tron or **'state** or **'level.** [Phys.] ELECTRON or ATOM for which AZIMUTHAL QUANTUM NUMBER is 0.

'sabin, n. [Acous.] The unit of sound ABSORPTION, equal to the effect of 1 sq. ft. of a material giving complete absorption.

'Sabouraud pas'tille. [Med.] An instrument for measuring the amount of X-RADIATION by which a SURFACE has been acted on.

sac, n. [Biol.] Any bag-like part or structure. **'saccate,** a. Having, forming or, sp. of a fruit, covered by, a s. **sac'ciferous,** a. **'sacciform,** a.

'saccharase, n. SUCRASE.

'saccharated, a. (Of medical substances) mixed or united with sugar.

saccha'riferous, a. Producing sugar.

sac'charify, v.t. and i. [Chem., etc.] (Make) become changed into sugar. **sac'charifi-'cation,** n. **sac'charifier,** n. An apparatus for changing other CARBOHYDRATES, such as STARCH, into sugar.

saccha'rimeter, n. [Chem.] Any instrument for measuring the amount of sugar in a SOLUTION, sp. a special sort of POLARI-METER used for this purpose, **saccha'rimetry,** n.

'saccharin, n. [Chem.] $C_6H_4SO_2CONH$, a white CRYSTALLINE powder, from 300 to 550 times as sweet as common sugar and used in place of it, but with no food value, made from TOLUENE. **'saccharine** a. Of, to do with, like, producing, sugar.

'saccharoid, a. Like sugar.

saccha'rimeter, n. [Chem.] Any instrument for measuring the amount of sugar in a SOLUTION, sp. a sort of HYDROMETER used for this purpose.

'saccharose, n. [Chem.] Any SUGAR, sp. SUCROSE.

'sacculus, 'saccule, nn. [Biol.] A small bag-like part, sp. [Zoo.] the lower of the two divisions of the INNER EAR in back-boned animals, having a connection with CORTI'S ORGAN. **'sacculate(d),** aa. Having, forming, or sp. being inside, a small bag-like structure. **saccu'lation,** n. **sac'culiform,** a.

'sacrum, n. [Zoo.] That part of the backbone forming part of or joined to the PELVIS, made up of one or more VERTE-BRAE, gen. united into one bone. **'sacral,** a. **'sacral 'index.** The RATIO of 100 times the measure of man's s. from end to end to its measure across the wide top edge (named its *base*). **sacral ribs.** Separate outgrowths of bone joining the s. to the PELVIS in certain animals. **sacro-.**

'sadism, n. [Psych.] An unhealthy development of the sex impulses marked by pleasure in causing physical or other pain to another person, sp. but not necessarily in sex relations. **'sadist,** n. Person given to s. **sa'distic,** a.

'safety, n. Designed to overcome some danger. **s. 'factor.** [Mach.] FACTOR OF SAFETY. **s. glass.** Glass specially made to be less readily broken, sometimes by LAMINATION (*laminated glass*), sometimes by increasing its RESISTANCE to shock by heating till almost soft and then making cold quickly. **s. lamp.** A miner's oil-burning hand-light of such a structure that there is no danger of gas in the air

around taking fire from the flame, in the commonest form this being effected by a cover of very thin wire net, the loss of heat to which keeps the flame from getting out. **'s.-valve,** n. An outlet for steam in a boiler, etc. which is pushed open by the force of the steam when any further increase in this would not be safe.

'sagittal, a. [Zoo.] Being, to do with, or placed in, the middle plane of an animal's body running from end to end and cutting it into right and left halves, or less commonly, any plane parallel to this; to do with the s. suture. **s. 'suture.** The s. joining-line of the two PARIETAL bones in the roof of the head in back-boned animals.

Sagitt'arius, n. [Astron.] The 9th SIGN OF THE ZODIAC.

'sagitatte, a. [Bot.] (Of a leaf) with the stem coming from the point of a deep inlet in the middle of the base so that it is framed by two narrow arms of the leaf pointing down it.

sal, n. (Used in naming chemical and medical substances) SALT, **s. amm'oniac,** [Chem.] AMMONIUM CHLORIDE (NH_4Cl), a white CRYSTALLINE substance used medically, in electric DRY BATTERIES, in printing cotton, etc. **s. vo'latile.** The medical and common name for a complex of a number of CARBONATES of AMMONIUM, a white substance readily giving off NH_3 and used to overcome pain in the head or a tendency to become unconscious by its effect on the nose.

sali-. Salt:— **sa'liferous,** a., **sa'limeter,** n.

sali'cylic acid. [Chem.] $C_6H_4(OH).COOH$, a CRYSTALLINE substance without colour, important medically as an ANTISEPTIC and in producing a number of substances used against colds, nerve pains, RHEU-MATISM, etc.

Sali'entia, n.pl. [Zoo.] An ORDER of AM-PHIBIA having at the stage of full development no tail or GILLS and 4 legs, the back ones being very long and strong and gen. giving the animal great jumping-power. **sali'entian,** n. [Animal] of the S.

sa'lina, n. SALT-PAN or SALT-MARSH.

'saline, 1.a. Made of, having in it, to do with, common salt, or [Med.] a SALT of Mg, Li, K, Na, or other metals of the same group. 2.n. [Med.] A metal salt such as $MgSO_4.7H_2O$ which is used as an APER-IENT. [Biochem.] A s. solution. [Geog., Geol.] SALT-PAN or SALT-MARSH. **s. so'lution.** [Biochem.] A NORMAL SALINE SOLUTION. **sa'linity,** n. The property of being s., the degree to which a liquid, etc. is s.

sali'nometer, n. [Phys.] An instrument for measuring the amount of a salt in a liquid, sp. a form of HYDROMETER used by engineers, which is so scaled as to give straight away the degree to which sea-water etc. is salt.

sa'liva, n. [Zoo.] A liquid produced in the mouths of animals by which food is DISSOLVED or helped to go down the throat more smoothly, and sometimes acted on chemically—in higher animals formed of MUCIN, PTYALIN and water. **'salivant,** n., a. (Medical substance, etc.) causing or increasing the production of s. **'salivary,** a. Producing s., to do with salivation. **salivary gland.** A structure designed for producing s. and sending it into the mouth, sp. one of the great and complex structures, such as the PAROTID GLAND, doing this work in higher animals. **'salivate,** 1.v.i. [Zoo.] Get s. produced, sp. [Med.] in more than normal amount. 2.v.t. [Med.] Make salivate to a greater degree than normal. [Zoo.] Get (a substance needed for some purpose, such as NEST-building) made soft with s. **sali'vation,** n. [Zoo., Med.] Act or process of salivating; PTYALISM. **sa'livous,** a.

'Salk 'vaccine. [Med.] A VACCINE widely used against POLIOMYELITIS, first put forward by Dr. Salk of the U.S.A. in 1955.

'salpinx (salpinges), n. [Zoo.] EUSTACHIAN or FALLOPIAN TUBE. **'salping'ectomy,** n. [Med.] **sal'pingian,** a. **salping(o)-.**

salt, n. [Chem.] Any substance of the sort produced when a metal ATOM or metal-like RADICAL takes the place of one or more H atoms of an ACID, marked by the property of being readily broken up into IONS in water; common s., that is, SODIUM CHLORIDE (NaCl). **s. dome,** s. **plug.** [Geol.] A great mass of solid common s. with an arching top at or near the face of the earth, produced by s. from deep beds moving by degrees to a common point and there working its way up through the beds over it, pushing them out of place in the process. **s. error.** [Chem.] An error in the measure of the pH of a SOLUTION caused by a s. being present. **s. 'glacier.** [Geol.] Stretch of slowly-moving s. forced out from a s. dome over the earth like ice down a mountain, seen only in Persia. **s. lake.** [Geog., Geol.] A body of inland water with no outlet to the sea, gen. in a very dry place, which has become very salt as the effect of giving off more water than it takes in, and is by degrees drying up, the sides above its lowered level being coated with s. **s. marsh.** [Geog., Geol.] A stretch of low flat land which is at certain times covered thinly with salt water, sp. one in a very dry place, getting its water from feeble inland currents and quickly giving it up again, so that for much of the

year it becomes more or less dry, s.-coated earth. **s. pan.** [Geog., Geol.] The s.-coated basin of a dried up s. lake or any other natural hollow in which s. water has undergone the loss of its liquid. **salts,** n.pl. [Med.] Any APERIENT s. or mixed ss. **'salting out.** [Chem.] The process of separating an ORGANIC substance from a SOLUTION of it in water by the addition of a SALT.

'saltant, n. [Biol.] A new form of a SPECIES produced by SALTATION.

sal'tation, n. [Biol.] DISCONTINUOUS VARIATION; a marked change from the normal in a CULTURE of a living thing.

salta'torial, a. [Zoo.] Used in, designed for, to do with, jumping.

'saltatory, a. [Biol.] Of development, marked by jumps, sudden changes, not changing only by slow degrees, as *s. evolution.* [Zoo.] SALTATORIAL. [Med.] Marked by, to do with, a jumping or dancing motion. **s. spasm.** [Med.] A condition in which putting the foot on the floor is the cause of a violent reaction in the muscles of the leg, causing a jump into the air.

'salted, a. [Immunology] (Of animals) having got over any of certain CONTAGIOUS diseases but still having the disease-bodies in the blood so that material for INOCULATION may be got from them.

salt'pet-er, -re, n. POTASSIUM NITRATE; CHILE SALTPETRE.

salts of lemon. [Chem.] The common name for $KH_3C_4O_8.2H_2O$ (*potassium tetroxalate*), a poison used for taking ink-marks out of linen, etc.

'samara, n. [Bot.] A dry fruit not cracking open and having a wing-like expansion for transport by wind, gen. one-seeded, produced by certain trees.

sa'marium, n. Chemical ELEMENT, at. no. 62, at. wt. 150·43, sign Sm, a light grey, hard but readily broken metal of the RARE EARTH GROUP.

'sample, n. A small amount of some substance taken from it as an example, for testing purposes etc., as a s. of ORE.

sana'torium, n. A special sort of hospital, gen. one given up to persons with a disease of a sort needing long care in special conditions, or to those needing rest and building up after some very lowering attack.

'sanat-ory, -ive, aa. [Med.] Making healthy.

sand, n. [Geol.] Loose material formed of small but clearly separate round grains, chiefly of QUARTZ, from about 0·1 to 1 mm. across, produced by the rubbing away of solid stone, and put down in stretches by water or formed into masses by wind. **s. 'culture.** [Bot.] The growth of plants in clean sand mixed with different substances in water, as a way of testing

their chemical needs. **s. dune.** [Geol.,
Geog.] A great round or wall-like mass of
s. formed by the wind acting on a stretch
of it. **'s.-blast, 1.v.i.** and **t.** Get metals,
glass, stone etc., cleaned or marked for
some purpose by driving s. at them with
a great force of air, steam etc. **2.n** A.
mass of sand fired at anything in this way.
'-paper, n. Strong paper with a coating of
s. fixed to one side, used for rubbing
metals, wood, etc., smooth. **'-stone,** n.
[Geol.] Any of a number of sorts of ROCK
made up of s. grains fixed into a solid
mass by some substance such as SiO_2
(*silicon dioxide*), $CaCo_3$ (*calcium carbonate*), etc.

san'guicolous, a. [Zoo.] Living in blood.

'sangui'fication, n. [Zoo.] The forming of
blood; the changing of food-substances
etc. into blood.

san'guineous, a. [Biol.] To do with, having,
blood; blood-coloured, sp. [Bot.]

sangui'niferous, a. [Zoo.] (Of vessels) transporting blood.

san'guivorous, a. [Zoo.] Living on blood.

'sanies, n. [Med.] A thin PUS mixed with
blood, with a disgusting smell, commonly
coming from poisoned wounds, etc.
'sanious, a.

'sanitary, a. [Med.] Of, to do with, living
conditions etc. necessary for keeping
persons healthy, giving as little opening
to disease as possible; (of a place, etc.)
free from conditions in which disease
readily takes root; used, designed, for s.
purposes.

sap, n. [Bot.] The liquid in a plant, sp. the
current of food substances in water moving through the vessels of plants. **s.
'cavity,** [Bot.] The space full of liquid in a
plant CELL. **'-wood** n. The softer coat of
living CELLS forming the outside, that
is the most newly formed part, of the
XYLEM in trees, by which s. is transported
and food stored.

sa'phena, a. [Anat.] A SAPHENOUS VEIN or
nerve. **sa'phenal,** a.

sa'phenous, a. [Anat.] Being, to do with,
placed near, one or the other of the two
chief VEINS near the SURFACE of the leg
in man, the *long* or *internal s. vein* going
from the foot up the inner side of the leg,
the *small, short* or *external s. vein* going
up the back of the leg.

sapo-. Soap.

sapo'naceous, a. To do with, like, soap.
[Bot.] Like wet soap to the touch.

sa'ponifi'cation, n. [Chem.] The HYDROLYSIS
of an ESTER into an ALCOHOL and an ACID,
sp. that of certain FATS with an ALKALI
present so that a SOAP is formed. **s. 'number** or **'value.** (Of a fat or oil) the number
of mg. of KOH (*potassium hydroxide*)
needed for the complete s. of 1 gm.
of the given substance. **sa'ponifier,** n.

sa'ponify, v.t. and i. (Make) undergo s.

'saponin(e), n. [Chem.] Any of a group of
GLUCOSIDES present in certain plants
which may be worked into a mass of small
BUBBLES, like soap, when wet.

'saponite, n. [Mineral.] A non-CRYSTALLINE
SILICATE of Mg and Al present in soft soap-
like masses in pockets in SERPENTINE, etc.

'sapphire, n. [Mineral.] A natural TRANS-
PARENT form of CORUNDUM, deep blue in
colour, used as a jewel stone.

sapr(o)-. DECAY, decayed.

sa'probic, a. [Biol.] (Of very simple ORGAN-
ISMS) living in and on DECAYING plants
or animal substances.

sapro'gen-ic, -ous, aa. [Biol., Biochem.]
Causing PUTREFACTION; to do with
putrefaction, taking place, having
growth, in substances undergoing it,
etc.

'saprolite, n. [Geol.] ROCK which has been
broken up physically and to some degree
chemically without being moved from its
place. **sapro'litic,** a.

sa'prophagous, a. [Zoo.] Using DECAYING
animals or plants as food. **'saprophage,** n.
S. animal.

sa'prophilous, a. [Biol.] (Of an animal or
plant) doing well, able to keep living,
among DECAYING material (for example in
water which is full of it), though not
necessarily limited to such an existence.
'saprophile, n. S. animal or plant.

'saprophyte, n. [Biol.] An animal or plant
living on, and freq. in DECAYING animal
and plant substances, sp. a plant having
its growth in such material and without
the power of PHOTOSYNTHESIS; a BAC-
TERIUM living on dead substances in
the bodies of living plants or animals and
causing no disease. **sapro'phytic,** a.
sapro'phytism, n.

sapr'ozoic, a. SAPROPHAGOUS.

sarc'enchyma, n. [Zoo.] A sort of PAREN-
CHYMA seen in sponges, formed of grain-
like CELLS massed together with little of
the normal jelly-like substance between
them.

sarc(o)-. [Biol.] FLESH. **'sarcoid,** a. [Zoo.].

'sarcocarp, n. [Bot.] The soft part of a stone-
fruit between the stone and the outer skin.

'sarcocyte, n. [Zoo.] The clear ECTOPLASM
coming between that forming the outer
skin and the MYOCYTE in certain PROTO-
ZOA.

'sarcoderm, sarco'derma, n. [Bot.] A soft
coat between any seed and its covering.

Sarco'dina, n.pl. [Zoo.] A CLASS of PROTOZOA
made up of those producing PSEUDO-
PODIA, gen. free-living.

sarco'lemma, n. [Zoo.] The very thin pipe-
like outer cover of a MUSCLE-FIBRE.

sar'cology, n. [Zoo.] That part of the
science of anatomy having to do with the
soft parts, as opp. the bones, of the

body. **sarco'logic(al)**, aa. **sar'cologist**, n.

sar'coma (sar'comata), n. [Med.] A MALIG-
NANT growth of MESODERMAL CELLS,
taking the form of a thick mass of round
or pointed cells with little substance
between them. **sar'coma'tosis**, n. [Med.]
Condition in which a number of ss. are
present. **sar'comatous**, a.

'sarcomere, n. [Zoo.] Any of the units
separated by the division walls across a
muscle FIBRIL.

sar'cophagous, a. [Zoo.] Using meat for
food.

'sarcoplasm, n. [Zoo.] The almost liquid
substance between muscle FIBRILS.
sarco'plasmic, a.

Sarcospo'ridia, n.pl. [Zoo.] An ORDER of long
thin SPOROZOA living in the muscles of
back-boned animals.

'sarcostyle, n. [Zoo.] A muscle FIBRIL.

sarco'testa, n. [Bot.] A thick, softer LAYER
in the coat of a seed.

'sarcous, a. [Zoo.] To do with muscle or
FLESH. **s. 'element**. The dark part in the
middle of a SARCOMERE.

'sardonyx, n. [Mineral.] A form of CHAL-
CEDONY with brown and white bands.

sa'rothrum, n. POLLEN BRUSH.

sar'torius, n. [Zoo.] A long muscle (in
man the longest) in the top part of the
leg by which it may be turned in, as when
seated with the legs across one another.

sas'trugi, n.pl. [Geog.] Waves of hard snow,
sometimes of great size, formed by the
wind on flat, snow-covered stretches, seen
in the north of the U.S.S.R. and in other
places far north or south.

'satellite, 1.n. [Astron.] A smaller natural
body, sp. a PLANET, going round a
greater one. [SPACE RESEARCH] A man-
made body fired up into ORBIT round the
Earth or the Sun by a ROCKET, of which
the first was sent up by the U.S.S.R. in
1957. [Biol.] A structure going with,
placed near, dependent on, another, as:—
[Zoo.] a VEIN by the side of an ARTERY;
[Med.] a smaller crack, wound, growth,
near a chief one; [Bot.] a small part of a
CHROMOSOME joined to one end of the
chief part of it by a thread, 2.a. Being a
s. or having a like relation to some other
thing.

'saturated, a. [Phys.] (Of a substance)
completely full of some other substance
so that it is impossible to take in any
more, sp. completely wet; (of a VAPOUR)
in such a condition that if the liquid producing it is present the amount of gas
given off will be balanced, if there is no
change of TEMPERATURE or PRESSURE
by the amount of gas becoming liquid
again. [Chem.] (Of a SOLUTION) having in
it an amount of a SOLUTE such that if
more is put with it without any change of
temperature or pressure the amount in

solution is not increased; (of a COM-
POUND) having no DOUBLE BOND or
TRIPLE BOND between its ATOMS, so
that it has no power of uniting with a
further atom or atom-group. [Optics]
(Of a colour) unmixed with white or grey.
s. steam. [Eng.] Steam at the same TEM-
PERATURE as the water forming it, as
opp. steam which has undergone further
heating. **s. 'vapour 'pressure.** [Phys.] The
PRESSURE of a s. VAPOUR, that is, of a
vapour in EQUILIBRIUM with its liquid
form. **s. zone.** [Geol.] The part of the
earth's CRUST in which every space is full
of water drained from the upper parts
and unable to go further, because under
this the earth's substance becomes so
tightly massed that there are no openings for the water to make it way through
—ranging from the lower limit of the
CAPILLARY ZONE to some thousands of
feet lower down. **satu'ration**, n. [Phys.,
Chem.] The process of causing to be, or
the condition of being s. [Optics] The
degree of HUE of a CHROMATIC colour, the
degree to which it is unmixed with white
or grey. [Meteor.] The condition of the
air in which as much water VAPOUR is
present as is possible at the given TEM-
PERATURE, any lowering of this producing mist etc. [Mag., Elec.] The condition of a MAGNETIC body in which further
increases in the MAGNETIZING force make
less and less change in the body's MAG-
NETIC FLUX DENSITY. [Elec.] The condition in a THERMIONIC VALVE when all the
ELECTRONS are moving to the ANODE
as quickly as they are given off by the
CATHODE, so that no increase in the
current is caused by increasing the anode
POTENTIAL. **'saturate**, v.t. Make s.
'saturator, n. Any apparatus by which,
or vessel in which, one substance is s.
with another, as used in different processes in industry, etc.

'saturant, n., a. [Phys., Chem.] (Substance)
SATURATING (another).

'Saturn, n. [Astron.] The 6th PLANET from
the sun, at a distance from it of about
886 million miles, having a mass about
95 times that of the earth, a 'year' of
29·46 years, a TEMPERATURE on the
outside of about 150°C, and 9 small
'moons', and noted for being circled by
three bright rings (**Saturn's rings**) one
inside the other. (*See* p. 331.)

'saturnism, n. (Med.) Lead poisoning.

'Sauria, n.pl. [Zoo.] LACERTILIA. **'saurian**,
1.n. Animal of the S. 2.a. Of or like the S.
'sauroid, a.

Saur'opsida, n.pl. [Zoo.] A general name for
birds and most REPTILES taken as a
group, based on certain common properties and structures as opp. those of
fish and MAMMALS, such as the producing

of eggs, having blood CELLS longer than
they are wide, breathing by LUNGS, not
giving milk to the young, the way in
which the head is joined to the back-
bone, etc.

savanna(h), n. [Geog.] An open flat stretch
of green country without trees, sp. in the
south U.S.A.; the band of grass-land
with some small trees which comes
between the thickly wooded country of
great rains on the two sides of the
EQUATOR and the great, dried up, un-
shaded wastes to the North or South.

Sa'vart (or Savart's) wheel. [Acous.] A round
metal plate with a toothed edge touching
a metal tongue, which when turned
round quickly at different rates is made
to give out sounds of different PITCH.

saxi'cavous, a. [Zoo.] Making deep holes in
stones.

'saxicole, saxi'coline, sax'icolous, aa. [Biol.]
(Of animals or plants) living or having
their growth among stones.

Sb, Sign for ANTIMONY.

Sc, Sign for SCANDIUM.

scab, n. [Med.] The dry cover formed over
a wound by the substance sent out from it;
SCABIES. [Bot.] Any of a number of plant
diseases caused by FUNGI or BACTERIA
and marked by s.-like places. **'scabby,** a.
Covered with ss. or s.-like places. **'scabi-
ous,** a. Scabby; having or to do with
SCABIES.

'scabies, n. [Med.] In man, a CONTAGIOUS
skin-disease caused by one of the ACA-
RINA and marked by SCAB-like places on
the skin; in animals, MANGE.

'scabr-ous, -ate, aa. [Biol.] Rough to the
touch, covered with little outgrowths of
some sort, points, SCALES, thick stiff
hairs, etc. **sca'berulous,** a. S. but with
smaller points, etc.

'scala (scalae), n. [Zoo.] Any of the three
twisting, pipe-like divisions of the
COCHLEA of the ear in higher animals, the
s. 'media in the middle, the **s. ves'tibularis**
over this, and the **s. tym'pani** under it.

sca'lariform, a. [Bot.] Having structures or
marks like steps at equal distances, as a
CELL, TRACHEIDE, or vessel with thicker
parts on the walls producing this design.
s. 'thickening. [Bot.] The system of
becoming thicker in parts so as to give a s.
effect, or the design of thicker parts
formed by this process.

scale, 1.n. An instrument for getting the
weight of anything by balancing it
against another weight or against the
force of a spring, etc. [freq. **ss.**); the plate
or vessel of a s. on or in which the thing
whose weight is to be measured is put, or
one or the other vessel of a balance.
[Math., etc.] A space or line marked off
by lines etc. into equal units, used for
measuring size, distance, or degree; a

measuring-instrument such as a rule,
having such a s.; a s. for measuring
distance or size in which the units are
representative of much greater distances,
as on a map; the relation between a unit
of a line s. on a map, etc. and the distance
of which it is representative, or, more
generally, between the size of a copy of
anything and that of the thing copied; a
system of regular steps or stages going
from the lowest degree or example of
something to the highest. [Acous.] A s.
of TONES between two fixed as the limits
of the s., increasing in PITCH by fixed
INTERVALS. 2.v.t. Get marked with a s.;
make the measures of a copy in agreement
with some representative s.; put in the
order of a s. ranging from lower to higher.
s. of 'equal 'temperament. [Acous.]
TEMPERED SCALE. **s. of just into'nation**
or **'temperament.** [Acous.] DIATONIC
SCALE. **'scaled,** a.

scale, n. [Chem., etc.] A thin coating of hard
material, or a small loose or broken-off
bit of such a coating, sp. the coating of
TARTAR formed on teeth or that of SALTS
formed on the inside of a vessel in which
water is regularly heated. [Zoo.] Any of
the thin plates of horn-like or bone-like
material on the outside of the skin of
certain animals, such as fish, or a part
like this. [Bot.] Any small, thin, dry and
leaf-like, or hard and s.-like, part, sp. a s.
leaf. 2.v.t. Take the s. or ss. off anything;
come off in ss., as the skin after certain
diseases. **s. bark, 'scaly bark.** [Bot.] The
hard outer covering of a tree when it is
formed or comes off in irregular plates,
not in one unbroken stretch. **s. hair.** [Bot.]
A hair of flat, s.-like structure. **s. leaf.**
[Bot.] Any leaf which is stronger and gen.
smaller than a normal leaf, designed for
the purpose of covering something, sp. any
of the leaves forming the covering of a
BUD in winter. **'scaled,** a. [Zoo.] Having a
skin covered with ss.; [of certain birds)
having s.-like feathers. **'scaly,** a. Having
a structure like ss., coming off in s.-like
bits, as certain sorts of ROCK, or the skin
after certain diseases. [Biol.] Covered
with, formed of, ss. or s.-like parts

sca'lene, a. [Geom.] (Of a TRIANGLE) having
no two sides or angles equal.

sca'lene, a. [Zoo.] Being or to do with a
scalenus. **sca'lenus,** n. Any of certain
deep muscles going from the back of the
neck to the RIBS (in man three at the
right side and three at the left) by which
the neck may be bent sideways.

scalp, n. [Zoo.] That part of the skin and
muscle etc. covering the bones of the
head under the hair in man, or the like
part of the head in other animals.

'scalpel, n. [Med.] A small straight knife
with a thin pointed blade.

scal′pellum (scalpella), n. [Zoo.] One or the other of two sharp-pointed structures forming part of the mouth in some two-winged insects.

′scanning, n. [Phys.] The motion of a ray of ELECTRONS over something from point to point, again and again, for the purpose of changing light-rays into electric currents (or the other way round) so as to send out (or take in) a picture by TELEVISION. **s. speech.** [Med.] Trouble in talking in which the rate is very slow and words are broken by stops between their parts, a sign of damage to the nerve system. **scan,** v.t. [Phys.] (Of ray) go over from point to point again and again.

′scandium, n. Chemical ELEMENT, at. no. 21, at. wt. 45·10, sign Sc, one of the RARE EARTH METALS.

scape, n. [Bot.] A flower-stem starting at or under the earth, commonly having leaves only in a ring round the base. [Zoo.] A stem-like part, such as the longer base-division of an insect's feeler, the SHAFT of a feather, the lower part of a BALAN-CER. **′scapose,** a. **′scap-oid, -iform,** aa.

′scapho′cephal-y, -ism, nn. [Med.] The condition in which the head is narrow with the join between the PARIETAL bones coming out like the end of a boat, as the effect of bone having been formed there before the right time. **scapho-ce′phalic, scapho′cephalus,** aa.

sca′phognathite, n. [Zoo.] A thin, leaf-like outgrowth of the second MAXILLA of DECAPODA, used for sending water through the breathing-apparatus.

′scaphoid, 1.a. [Biol.] Formed like a boat. 2.n. [Zoo.] The bone at the inner end of the first line of small bones between the arm and the hand or the leg and the foot.

′scapula (scapulae), n. [Zoo.] In man, one or other of the two great, flat 3-sided bones in the upper part of the back, having a connection with the top bone of the arm, or like bone in other animals; any of a number of structures in insects and lower animals giving a suggestion of a s. **′scapular,** 1.a., 2.n. Any of the small feathers on the SHOULDER of a bird. **′scapulo-.**

scar, n. CICATRIX.

scarify, v.t. Make cuts in, sp. [Med.] Make a number of small cuts in the skin to get blood from the smaller blood-vessels. [Engin.] Get the earth or a road broken up with a machine. **′scarifier,** n. [Med.] An instrument with a number of sharp blades worked by a spring, used for scarifying. [Engin.] A machine for scarifying the earth or a road, etc.

′scarious, ′scariose, aa. [Bot.] Thin, dry, and skin-like, gen. brown at the edges.

scarlatina, n. SCARLET FEVER.

′scarlet ′fever. [Med.] An ACUTE, CON-TAGIOUS disease caused by a STREPTO-COCCUS and marked by FEVER, pain in the head and throat, and a mass of small very red points covering the skin, which later comes off in thin, dry bits.

scarp, n. [Geol., Geog.] ESCARPMENT.

′scatter, v.t. and i. Send (the parts of a group or mass) or go in all directions, or put here and there or all over something in no special order, irregularly. [Phys.] Get a group of rays of any sort broken up into rays going in different directions, sp. REFLECT (light, etc.) widely and irregularly; (of a group of rays) become separated and go off in different directions. **′scattered,** a. Having undergone scattering, irregularly placed, broken up and taking different directions. [Bot.] (Of leaves or branches) having no special order, placed here and there at some distance from one another. **′scattering,** n. Sp. [Phys.] The scattering of radio rays as the effect of coming up against something or getting into a place where IONIZATION is irregular, or the scattering of light-rays produced by irregular REFLECTION or by DIFFRACTION.

Scheele's green. [Chem.] A bright green substance made up chiefly $Cu_3(AsO_3)_2.2H_2O$, used in paints and as an INSECTICIDE.

′schema, n. Outline of a system or design; DIAGRAM. **sche′matic,** a. **′-tize,** v.t. Put into the form of a s., give an outline of the system or design of something, sp. using SYMBOLS.

Schick test or **reaction.** [Med.] A test of IMMUNITY to DIPHTHERIA based on the reaction of a person's skin to an INJEC-TION of a small amount of diphtheria poison.

′schiller, n. [Mineral] An IRIDESCENCE seen in certain sorts of ROCK, chiefly PYROXENE and DIALLAGE, produced by s. inclusions. **s. in′clusions.** Small, regularly placed, parallel bodies of a different substance, having the property of DIFFRACTION of light, bedded in a ROCK and causing s. **′schillerized,** a. Having s. **′schilleri′za-tion,** n. The development in ROCK of s. inclusions as the effect of certain changes, for example of a SOLUTION of a certain substance making its way into the spaces between its parts; the condition of having undergone schillerization.

schindy′lesis, n. [Zoo.] A form of join between bones in which a thin plate-like part of one bone goes into a narrow opening in the other. **schindy′letic,** a.

schist, n. [Geol.] Any of a number of sorts of ROCK having a structure of thin parallel plates or leaves and a tendency to become separated into them, formed from older rocks by heat and PRESSURE acting on certain materials, chiefly QUARTZ mixed with some substance forming thin parallel plates, such as MICA.

schizo-. Division; having, produced by, division.

'schizocarp, n. [Bot.] A dry fruit formed of a number of united CARPELS, separating at full growth into its separate one-seeded parts, they themselves not bursting open.

schizo'c(h)roal, a. [Zoo., Geol.] Having a number of simple eyes grouped together into one great eye-structure, said only of certain TRILOBITES or their eyes.

'schizocoel(e), n. [Zoo.] A COELOM which is produced by the division of the MESO-BLAST as opp. ENTEROCOEL. **schizo-'coel-ic, -ous,** aa.

schi'zogamy, n. [Zoo.] The producing, by a division of the body, of one sexed and one unsexed offspring, as in some worms.

schizo'genesis, n. [Zoo.] The producing of offspring by body division. **schizo'genic, schizoge'netic,** aa. **schizo'genous,** a. [Zoo.] To do with s., producing offspring by division. [Biol.] Produced by division, sp. [Bot.] said of spaces formed between CELLS by the division and separating of cell-walls.

schi'zoganthous, a. [Zoo.] (Of birds or their PALATES) having the middle bones united into a long point at the front and the bones at the two sides quite separate from the middle part and from one another.

schi'zogony, n. [Zoo.] The forming of unsexed SPORES by division.

'schizoid, n., a. [Med.] (Person) giving signs of SCHIZOPHRENIA but without having a clearly marked development of the disease.

'schizoly'sigenous, a. [Bot.] (Of a space between CELLS) formed in part by the separating of cell-walls, in part by the destruction of cells.

'Schizomy'cetes, n.pl. BACTERIA.

'schizomy'cosis, n. [Med.] Any disease caused by BACTERIA.

'schizont, n. [Zoo.] In certain SPOROZOA, the animal at the stage when it is about to undergo division into offspring in the body of the HOST.

schizo'pelmous, a. [Zoo.] Having two separate cords of muscle going to the toes, one to the first toe and the other to the rest.

schizo'phrenia, n. [Med.] DEMENTIA PRAE-COX or any disease of the mind having the same sort of effects. **'schizophrene,** n. Person having s. **schizo'phrenic,** a., n.

Schizo'phyta, n.pl. [Bot.] The group of very simple plants, sometimes separated from THALLOPHYTA, having no sexed stage and producing offspring only by division, gen. one-CELLED or formed of thread-like chains of cells, the BACTERIA and the CYANOPHYCEAE.

'schizopod, a. [Zoo.] Said of the LARVA of DECAPODA at the stage when every leg etc. has two branches.

'schizostele, n. [Bot.] Any of the separate threads formed by the division of the PLEROME in plants in which it does not undergo development into a true STELE. **'schizostelic,** a. **'schizostely,** n. The condition of forming ss.

'schizo'zoite, n. [Zoo.] any of the CELLS produced by division from a SCHIZONT.

'schlieren, n.pl. [Mineral.] Lines or places seen in an IGNEOUS ROCK formed of material different from its chief substance but not sharply cut off from it.

'Schumann 'region. [Phys.] That range of very short ULTRA-VIOLET rays of WAVE-LENGTHS between about 2000 and 1200 A.U.

Schwann('s) cell. [Zoo.] Any of the CELLS of which a NEURILEMMA is made up, of which there is one between every two NODES of a MEDULLARY SHEATH.

Schwann('s) sheath. NEURILEMMA.

'Schweitzer's reagent. [Chem.] A liquid formed by the reaction of HN_3 (ammonia) in water with $Cu(OH)_2$ (cupric hydroxide) which has the property of taking CELLULOSE into SOLUTION and is used in making RAYON.

sci'atic, a. [Zoo.] To do with, present in, the part of the body to which the leg is joined: to do with the s. nerve. **s. nerve.** The great nerve going from the body down the back of the leg. **sci'atica,** n. [Med.] Pain in the s. nerve sp. caused by IN-FLAMMATION.

'science, n. Knowledge based on the observation and testing of facts and worked into an ordered system acting as a base for new knowledge and a guide to ways of getting it; such knowledge covering any special field, a branch of general s. **scien'tific,** a. To do with s., sp. (of knowledge or ways of getting it) ordered, controlled, in agreement with tested facts and rules of reasoning, etc. **scien'tifically,** adv. **'scientist,** n. Person whose business is s.

'scintillate, v.i. Give off short, quick, bright bursts of light, said sp. of something such as a jewel from which light keeps being sent back at all different angles. **'scintillating,** a. **scintil'lation,** n. Sp.: [Astron.] The quick changes in the light of a star, giving an effect of scintillation, caused by the REFRACTION of the rays to different degrees in coming through different parts of the air round the earth. [Phys.] The producing by ALPHA RAYS etc. of bright, star-like bursts of light on meeting certain substances; a burst of light so produced.

scio-. Shade:— **sci'ophilous,** a. [Bot.]. **'sciophyte,** n. [Bot.].

'scion, n. [Bot.] A bit of stem or new growth with the power of separate development cut from a plant for planting in the earth or GRAFTING onto another plant.

sci'optic, a. [Optics] To do with IMAGES formed in a dark room.

'scirrhous, a. [Med.] Made hard, sp. by growth of FIBROUS TISSUE.

'scirrhus, n. [Med.] A SCIRRHOUS CARCINOMA. 'scirrho-.

sci'rocco, n. SIROCCO.

'scissile, a. Able to be cut or parted readily, sp. [Bot.].

'sclera, n. [Zoo.] The SCLEROTIC COAT of the eyeball.

sclera'togenous, a. [Zoo.] From which a hard supporting framework of bone, etc. is formed. s. layer. The cord-like structure made up of united SCLEROTOMES at the side of the MEDULLARY TUBE in the EMBRYO of back-boned animals, later forming a cover for the NOTOCHORD.

sclere, n. [Zoo.] Any small, hard, supporting structure, sp. a SPICULE of a sponge.

'sclereid(e), n. [Bot.] Any CELL with hard, thick walls, sp.:— one placed among the other cells of a leaf to give them support; a STONE CELL.

scle'renchyma, n. [Bot.] That material in a plant formed of CELLS having thick walls of wood-forming substance with little or (at full growth) no living cell-substance, designed for supporting and covering the softer parts of the plant. [Zoo.] SCLERODERM. 'scleren'chymatous, a.

scle'riasis, n. [Med.] The becoming hard of a part, sp. of the edge of the eye-cover.

'sclerite, n. [Zoo.] A hard plate, rod etc. of horn or stone-like substance. scle'ritic, a.

scler(o)-. [Biol., Med.] Hard; to do with the SCLEROTIC (and . . .); 'sclerocor'neal, a.

sclero'caulous, a. [Bot.] Having a stiff, hard, dry stem caused by over-development of SCLERENCHYMA, as some plants in very dry places. 'sclero'cauly, n. The condition of being s.

'scleroderm, n. [Zoo.] A hard outer body-covering; (the material forming) the hard supporting framework of CORALS. sclero'dermatous, a. [Zoo.] Having a hard outer covering or supporting structure.

'sclero'derm(i)a, nn. [Med.] A disease marked by the skin becoming increasingly hard, dark, and dry, in certain places or more or less all over, and tightly fixed to the TISSUES under it, sometimes to the point of keeping JOINTS from moving.

'sclerogen, n. [Bot.] The material, made hard with wood substance and MINERALS, forming the walls of STONE CELLS. sclero'genic, scler'ogenous, aa.

'scleroid, a. [Biol.] Having become hard; hard, to do with bones or other hard framework of the body.

scle'roma, n. [Med.] SCLEROSIS, sp. of the skin; a part which has undergone sclerosis.

scle'rometer, n. [Mineral.] Any of a number of instruments for measuring how hard a substance is, gen. by noting the force needed for marking it with, or driving into it, a sharp point.

sclero'phyllous, n. [Bot.] Having hard, stiff, strong leaves, formed chiefly of SCLEREN-CHYMA with little spaces between the CELLS and so being able to do without water for a long time, as plants living in very dry places. sclero'phyll. A s. plant. 'sclero'phylly, n. The condition of being s.

sclero'protein, n. [Biochem.] Any of the group of PROTEINS, not SOLUBLE in water, making up the different hard body-materials such as bone, nails and hair, or present in the form of supporting FIBRES in other materials, for example, COLLAGEN, KERATIN.

scle'rosis, n. [Biol.] The process of becoming, or the condition of having become, thick, hard, chiefly [Bot.] the s. of CELL-walls as the effect of the forming of wood-substance. [Med.] The diseased s. of a given part as the effect of an unnormal increase of FIBROUS material, sp. s. of the walls of the great blood-vessels or of the nerve-system (see MULTIPLE S.). 'sclerose, v.t. and i. (Make) undergo s. 'sclerosed, a. Having undergone s., hard, thick walled.

sclero'testa, n. [Bot.] A hard inner coat of a seed-covering under a SARCOTESTA.

scle'rotic, 1.a. [Bot., Med.] To do with, having undergone, SCLEROSIS. [Zoo.] Being, to do with, the thick, strong, white outer covering of most of the eyeball, the s. coat). 2.n. [Zoo.] The s. coat of the eye. s. 'ossicles or bones. A ring of small bones round the s. of some birds and REPTILES.

scle'rotium (sclerotia), n. [Bot.] A hard mass of HYPHAE. gen. black on the outside, forming a resting-stage from which development may take place very much later in some higher FUNGI. scle'rotial, a. scle'rotioid, a.

'sclerotome, n. [Zoo.] A division-wall separating two MYOTOMES; a mass of MESENCHYMA later undergoing development into a unit of the back-bone.

'scolex (scolices), n. [Zoo.] The 'head' of a CESTODE, that is, the part having the SUCKERS or hooks by which it is fixed to the wall of the INTESTINE of the animal in which it is living. 'scolec-id, -oid, aa. sco'leciform, a.

scoli'osis, n. [Med.] The condition of having the backbone bent sideways scoli'otic, a.

'scolite, n. [Geol.] A pipe-like hole in a ROCK taken to be a FOSSIL worm-hole, probably made by a sea-worm.

'scolopale, n. [Zoo.] The hollow, rod-like middle part of a SCOLOPHORE, which is put in VIBRATION by sound-waves.

'scolophore, n. [Zoo.] A complex nerve-ending in the skin of an insect designed for sensing sound.

'scopa, n. [Zoo.] The POLLEN BRUSH of a bee.

-scope, n. Instrument for the viewing of the named thing, or for the discovery, observation, and sometimes recording of the named effect.

scop(i)-. [Biol.] Brush-like part, SCOPA: 'scopate, a., sco'piferous, a., 'scopiform, a.

sco'polamine, n. [Chem.] An ALKALOID, $C_{17}H_{21}NO_4$, got from the roots of certain plants, which, because of its special SEDATIVE effect on the brain is not only used medically as an ANAESTHETIC etc., but has been of value in getting wrong-doers to give true accounts of their crimes.

'scopula, n. [Zoo.] A brush-like group of hairs, such as a SCOPA or the sticky hairs on the feet of some ARACHNIDA helping them in going up walls, etc.; in sponges, a needle-like SPICULE raying out like a paint-brush at one end. 'scopulate, a. 'scopuliferous, a. scopu'liform, a.

'scopulite, n. [Mineral.] A CRYSTALLITE in the form of a rod with a brush-like structure at the end or a number of such structures down the sides.

-scopy, n. The viewing or observation of, sp. with the help of a -SCOPE. -scopist, n. Person doing -scopy.

scor'butic(al), aa. [Med.] To do with, having, caused by, SCURVY. 'scorbutus, n. SCURVY.

'scoria (scoriae), n. The waste material from the process of getting metals etc. from their ORES, a hard, stone-like, burned-looking mass. [Geol.] (A mass of) rough, dark, burned-looking lava, full of holes, produced by the expansion of gases making their way violently out of liquid BASALT. scori'aceous, a.

'scorify, v.t. Get changed into SCORIA; get (an ORE) tested for gold or silver by scorification. scorifi'cation, n. Sp., in ASSAYING, the process of getting gold or silver from an ORE by heating it to a very high degree with lead in the form of grains and a small amount of BORAX, the gold or silver going into SOLUTION in liquid lead. 'scorifier, n. A vessel of some material which will undergo great heat in which gold and silver ORES are scorified.

'Scorpio, n. [Astron.] the 8th SIGN OF THE ZODIAC.

'scorpioid, a. [Biol.] Like the SCORPIONIDA in some way, gen. in being curved up and back at the end. s. cyme. [Bot.] A CYME of which the branches are first on one side and then on the other of a SYMPODIUM. s. di'chotomy. [Bot.] The

form of forking of a stem in which first the right and then the left branch of the fork goes on to undergo another fork, all these together forming what seems to be a middle stem bent a little this way and that, with a side branch at every turn.

Scorpi'onida, Scorpio'nidea, n.pl. [Zoo.] An ORDER of ARACHNIDA having long narrow bodies ending in a thin SEGMENTED tail with a poisoned STING at the end, which is gen. kept curved up and back, 8-legged, LUNG-breathing animals coming out at night for their food of insects etc.

sco'toma (scotomata), n. [Med.] A dark place in the field of view, freq. so small as to be unnoted in normal seeing, caused by the RETINA or the nerve of the eye not working at some point. '-tous, a.

sco'topia, n. [Zoo., Psych.] The act of seeing in feeble light or at night (see PHOTOPIA). sco'topic, a. To do with s.; (of eyes) designed for, or in adjustment to, ɛ

scour, v.t. Put (natural wool or silk) through a special cleaning process to get out oil, etc. before making into thread. 'scouring, n. The cleaning process used on natural wool etc. (Geog., etc.] The washing away of earth or ROCK by moving water.

'scramble, v.t. [Radio] Get the different FREQUENCIES of sounds being sent out by radio changed in agreement with a certain system, so that if the waves are taken in by any normal radio no clear sounds will be produced, but the radio for which they are designed will be able to get the sounds by changing the frequencies back again. 'scrambler, n. The apparatus by which the FREQUENCIES are changed in scrambling.

scrap, n. Waste or used-up material, sp. metal.

scratch, n. [Acous.] The noise made by the needle rubbing the record when a GRAMOPHONE is playing. s. 'filter. An apparatus used in radio to take away s. when recorded sound is being sent out.

scree, n. [Geol.] A stretch of sharp-edged broken ROCKS at the foot of a slope or mountain, caused by the operation of the sun's heat, or, specially, of FROST, on the solid rock higher up.

screen, 1.n. A thin, wall-like structure used for putting between a thing and something, such as light-rays or a current of air, which it is desired to keep from it; a tray, plate, etc. of thin wire net, or of any material in which small openings have been made or are naturally present, such as metal, cloth, silk, used for separating from the rest those grains of a substance or units of a mass not small enough to go through the holes. [Optics] A flat SURFACE on which a picture may be formed by rays, as in motion-pictures or

TELEVISION. [Phys.] A part of an apparatus designed to keep something which is acting or produced at one point in it, such as light or a MAGNETIC force, from having an effect at another; an EARTHED ELECTRODE in the form of a wire net put between two other electrodes to make the CAPACITANCE between them less. [Printing] A glass plate, or two glass plates put together, covered with thin lines forming a network of small squares, placed between the camera and the thing to be pictured in the process of PHOTO-ENGRAVING. 2.v.t. Get (something) cut off from some effect by the use of a covering s.; put (a substance, etc.) through a hole d s. to take out the greater grains etc. [Optics] Send (a picture), or send a picture of (something) onto a s. **screened,** a. 'screen(ed)-'grid valve. [Phys.] A THERMIONIC VALVE having a s. between the GRID and the ANODE. 'screening, n., a.

screw pro'peller. A PROPELLER of a ship or airplane having two or more blades with a twisting curve fixed onto a turning middle part, and forcing its way through the air or water with a screw-like motion.

scrobe, n. [Zoo.] A narrow, line-like hollow, as that into which the base of a feeler goes in some insects.

scro'biculate, a. [Biol.] Covered with small round holes or hollows.

'scrobicule, scro'bicula, nn. [Zoo.] The smooth part of the hard outer cover round the base of a needle in ECHINOIDEA.

scro'biculus, n. [Biol.] A small round hollow.

'scrofula, n. [Med.] A form of TUBERCULOSIS, commonest in young persons, in which the LYMPHATIC GLANDS are specially attacked, becoming cheese-like in structure and much increased in size. 'scro-fulous, a.

'scrotiform, a. [Biol.] Bag-like.

'scrotum, n. [Zoo.] The bag-like part covering the TESTES of higher animals and man. 'scrotal, a. scroto-.

scrubber, n. Any apparatus used in a gas-works for 'washing' gas, that is sending it through water etc. to take out certain undesired substances. **scrub,** v.t. Put (coal gas, etc.) through a s.

'scruple, n. Unit of APOTHECARIES' WEIGHT = $\frac{1}{3}$ DRACHM or 20 GRAINS.

scum, n. Any substance, sp. a dirty or waste substance, coming to the top of, or forming a coating on, a liquid, e.g. IMPURITIES in liquid metal under the operation of heat, or the covering of green ALGAE seen on small, undrained bodies of inland water.

scurf, n. [Med.] A coating of thin, dry bits of dead substance, covering the skin and coming again when rubbed off, seen in certain diseases or unhealthy conditions,

sp. such a coating on the skin of the head. [Bot.] A s.-like covering of hairs on a leaf. 'scurfy, a.

'scurvy, n. [Med.] A disease caused by need for VITAMIN C, marked by loss of force, a poor condition of the blood, and a tendency for it to come through the blood-vessels in different parts of the body, sp. into the mouth, where the GUMS become soft and sponge-like and the teeth loose.

scute, n. [Zoo.] Any outer plate of bone, horn or other hard material; a SCALE of greater size than those covering the rest of the animal, as on the head of a snake. 'scutal, a. 'scutate, a. [Biol.] Covered with great scales or ss. **scu'ti-ferous, -gerous,** aa.

'scutella (scutellae), n. [Biol.] SCUTELLUM; a very small SCUTE.

'scutellate, a. [Bot.] In form like a somewhat hollow round plate.

scu'tellum, (scutella), n. [Bot.] In the seed of grasses, the flat COTYLEDON specially formed to take in food for the EMBRYO from the ENDOSPERM: [Zoo.] A SCUTE, sp.:—the third plate from the front covering the top of a division of an insect's THORAX; any of the SCALES on the foot of a bird. scu'tellar, a. scu'tellate, a. 'scutel'lation, n. [Zoo.] The condition of being covered with plates or SCALES; the order, grouping, of the scales or plates covering an animal. scu'telliform, a. scutel'ligerous, a.

'scutiform, a. [Biol.] Having the form of a SCALE or plate designed for covering part of the body. [Bot.] PELTATE.

'scutum (scuta), n. [Zoo.] SCUTE, sp. the second and greatest of the plates covering the top of a division of an insect's THORAX.

'scyphate, 'scyphiform, a. [Biol.] Having the form of a cup.

scy'phistoma (scyphistomae), n. [Zoo.] The POLYP stage or form in SCYPHOZOA, in which the animal is small and fixed in one place and in time gives birth by STROBILI-ZATION to the MEDUSA form.

Scypho'zoa, n.pl. [Zoo.] A CLASS of COELEN-TERATA commonly named 'jelly-fish', in which there is no POLYP stage, or the polyp forms, if present, are small, and the MEDUSAE are of great size with TENTACULOCYSTS and gen. no VELUM. 'scypho'zoan, n., a. (Animal) of, like, the S.

'scyphula (scyphulae), n. SCYPHISTOMA.

'scyphus (scyphi), [Bot.] A cup-like structure, sp. the CORONA of a flower or the cup-like expansion of the PODETIUM in LICHENES. scyph'iferous, a. 'scyphose, a. Having an s.

Se, Sign for SELENIUM.

sea, n. [Geog.] The salt water covering parts

of the earth; a division of an OCEAN, or an inland stretch of salt water of great size.
s. bloom. [Bot.] ALGAE of certain sorts FLOATING in masses on or near the top of the sea, sometimes so thickly as to give it a red colour. **s. breeze.** [Meteor.] The more or less regular motion of air from the sea to the land in the daytime in warm weather, caused by the greater heat of the earth warming the air over it so that it goes up and the colder air over the sea comes in to take its place. **s. 'level.** [Geog.] The level to which the s. would come if not moved by TIDES, taken as that half-way between high tide and low tide at any place. **'-plane,** n. An aeroplane which is able to go up from and come down on the water. **'-water,** n. The water of the great ss., made up of 96·4% water with 2·8% common salt, 0·4% $MgCl_2$, 0·2% $MgSO_4$, 0·1% $CaSO_4$ and 0·1% KCl. **'-weed,** n. [Bot.] Any plant living in the sea, sp. a sea ALGA, or such plants taken as a group.

seal, 1.n. Anything, such as a sticky band or a covering of wax, lead etc. put over some opening or join, such as that between a bottle and its cork, to keep it completely shut, safe, air-tight, etc.; any apparatus or adjustment by which gas is kept from getting out of or into, or coming back up, a pipe etc., for example, the putting of the open end of a pipe in water. 2.v.t. Put a s. on (a join, etc.), keep (anything) from getting out of a vessel by the use of a s. (*s.* it *in* the vessel).

seam, n. [Geol., Mining] A thick, more or less level bed of any sort of material which is of value for mining, as a coal s.

se'baceous, a. [Zoo.] To do with, producing, or formed of, fat. [Bot.] Looking like a mass of fat. **s. gland.** [Zoo.] Any of the great number of small skin GLANDS in man and like animals, gen. opening into the hollow where a hair is rooted, by which an oil-like substance is produced which keeps the skin and hair soft.

se'biferous, a. [Zoo.] Transporting oil or some fat-like substance.

sebor'rh(o)ea, n. [Med.] The producing of over-much SEBUM, causing the skin and hair to have a coating of oil.

'sebum, n. [Biochem.] The oil-like substance produced by the SEBACEOUS GLANDS.

'secant, n. [Geom.] (Of an angle) $1 \div$ its COSINE (short form **sec**); a straight line cutting a circle or other curve in two points.

'secodont, a. [Zoo.] Having teeth designed for cutting.

'second, n. A unit of time $= \frac{1}{60}$ minute; a unit of angle-measure $= \frac{1}{60}$ MINUTE, for which the sign is ″.

'secondary, 1.a. Second in order of position or development, or to do with a second stage in a process; second in value, less important; coming later than, sp. as produced by or dependent on, some earlier thing or process; to do with, being, a s. [Elec.] Being or to do with a current produced by INDUCTION, as a *s. current*, a *s.* COIL, etc. [Chem.] Produced by the SUBSTITUTION of two ATOMS or groups, as a *s.* SALT. [Geol.] Old name for MESOZOIC. 2.n. [Optics, Psych., etc.] A s. colour. [Zoo.] Any of the long feathers with a stiff middle structure formed on the second or lower-arm division of a bird's wing; in insects, the back wing. **s. 'accent.** [Phonet.] A STRESS second in force to the chief stress in any word. **s. 'alcohol.** [Chem.] Any of the ALCOHOLS having in them the group :CH.OH, producing KETONES by reaction with O. **s. 'axis.** [Optics] Any straight line going through the middle point of a thin LENS, or through the CENTRE of CURVATURE of a CONCAVE or CONVEX looking-glass, which is not at right angles to it. **s. 'battery.** [Elec.] STORAGE BATTERY. **s. 'body 'cavity.** [Zoo.] COELOM. **s. bow. s. 'rainbow.** [Meteor.] A greater RAINBOW seen outside and not far from a normal one, in which the colours are less strong and go in the opposite order, with red on the inner edge—formed by the light being twice REFLECTED inside the raindrops. **s. bud.** [Bot.] A further BUD produced near and in addition to a normal AXILLARY bud. **s. cell.** [Elec.] STORAGE CELL. **s. cell-wall.** [Bot.] The coat of later material put down on the inside of a CELL-WALL as the cell gets older, gen. having in it more CELLULOSE and less PECTIN than the earlier part of the wall and freq. PITTED. **s. colour.** [Optics, Psych., etc.] Any colour or colour-STIMULUS formed by mixing two PRIMARY COLOURS. **s. de'pression.** [Meteor.] A smaller DEPRESSION going with and freq. moving round a great depression. **s. e'lectron.** In THERMIONICS, any of the ELECTRONS given off by a body as the effect of other electrons falling on it, as opp. these. **s. (electron) e'mission.** The giving off of s. electrons, or the electrons so given off. **s. en'richment.** [Geol.] The forming of VEINS etc. of ORE deep down in the earth as the effect of SOLUTIONS making their way down from the upper parts and undergoing chemical reactions by which solid substances are formed. **s. 'function.** [Psych.] The tendency for every nerve-process which is the cause of an idea in the mind to go on for some time after its effect has been produced, the strong operation of this tendency being looked on as responsible for such qualities as that of being able to keep the mind fixed on one thing, of not being readily turned from one's purpose or moved by new ideas, etc. **s. growth.** [Bot.] Sp., s. thickening. **s. host.** [Biol.] A plant or animal on or in which a PARA-SITE goes through only the LARVA or unsexed stage of its development. **s. ioni'zation.** [Phys.] IONIZATION caused by ELECTRONS produced as a reaction to GAMMA RAYS. **s. 'meristem.** [Bot.] MERISTEM produced by PERMANENT TIS-SUE, for example, PHELLOGEN. **s. 'nucleus.** [Bot.] The NUCLEUS formed by the uniting of the POLAR NUCLEI. **s. 'parasite.** [BIOL.] A PARASITE living on another parasite. **s. perso'nality.** [Psych.] In a person having MULTIPLE PERSONALITY, a personality which is less strong than the chief personality and to some degree controlled by it. **s. 'phloem.** [Bot.] PHLOEM at full development, formed by CAMBIUM and taking the place of the PRIMARY PHLOEM. **s. 'planet.** [Astron.] SATELLITE. **s. radi'ation.** [Phys.] RADIATION produced by a body as the effect of the taking in by it of another (*primary*) radiation of the same sort. **s. ray.** [Phys.] A ray of any secondary radiation. **s. rocks.** [Geol.] Old name for ROCKS of the MESOZOIC ERA. **s. root.** [Bot.] Any side-branch of a root; any root produced in addition to and at a different point from the normal one. **s. sen'sation.** [Psych.] A sense-experience which is produced together with another one by a STIMU-LUS acting only on the sense-apparatus of the second, for example, a sense of colour in connection with hearing certain sounds. **s. sex** (or **'sexual**) **'character.** [Zoo.] Any structure or quality which has no part in the act of sex connection itself but is a mark of sex, being normally present in one sex of an animal and not in the other, for example, the bright feathers of some male birds. **s. spore.** [Bot.] SPORI-DIUM. **s. 'thickening.** [Bot.] The forming of further VASCULAR TISSUE by a CAMBIUM when the development of the plant system is complete, being the process by which the stems and other parts of the plant body become thicker and stronger as opp. PRIMARY GROWTH. **s. 'tissue.** [Bot.] Material produced from s. meristem. **s. 'tremor.** [Geol. etc.] A motion in an EARTHQUAKE which is caused by waves from side to side in the solid material of the earth, coming after the PRELIMINARY TREMOR. **s. tym'panic 'membrane.** [Anat.] A thin MEMBRANE shutting the small round opening from the TYMPANUM of the ear into the COCHLEA. **s. wood, s. 'xylem** [Bot.] XYLEM at full development formed by CAMBIUM

and taking the place of PRIMARY XYLEM. **'secondarily,** adv. *See* PRIMARY.

se'crete, v.t. [Biol.] (Of a CELL or GLAND) get (a certain substance) produced inside itself by acting on material taken in (for example, blood) and send it out again, gen. through its wall or skin, into or out of the plant or animal system. **se'creta,** n.pl. [Zoo., Med.] The substances secreted by a given GLAND or by the body. **se'cretion,** n. The process of secreting; substance secreted. **se'cretive, se'cretory,** aa. Having the property of secreting something.

se'cretin, n. [Zoo.] In back-boned animals, a HORMONE acting on the PANCREAS and LIVER and produced by the operation on the inner coat of the INTESTINES of acid substances coming from the stomach in the process of digestion.

'sectile, a. [Mineral.] (Of a readily crushed substance) able to be cut smoothly with a sharp knife, not going to powder under the blade. [Bot.] Separated into small divisions.

'section, 1.n. The act of cutting through something, separating into parts by cutting; a part or division, natural or made by cutting; a picture of the structure of a thing as it would be seen if cut through on a given plane (a CROSS s., a LONGITUDINAL s., etc.); a very thin cutting of a plant, animal, or MINERAL made ready for the observation of its structure under the MICROSCOPE. [Biol.] A group of SPECIES forming a natural division of a GENUS. 2.v.t. and i. Get cut into ss.; make a s. of in any sense. **'-al,** a. To do with a s.; made up of ss. or parts, sp. of the same form and size.

'sector, n. A part of a circle limited by two RADII and the curve between them; a measuring instrument in the form of a s.

sec'torial, a. [Zoo.] Designed, used, for cutting, as certain teeth.

'secular, a. [Geol., Astron., etc.] (Of processes, changes) taking a very long time, so slow as to have no effect great enough to be noted for hundreds of years. **s. acceler'ation.** [Astron.] A very slow seeming change in the amount of time taken by the moon to go round the earth, making it shorter by about 6 seconds in 100 years, caused by the earth's ORBIT becoming by degrees a truer circle.

'secund, a. [Bot.] Ranged on one side of the stem only, said of flowers or leaves. **se'cundi'florous,** a. Having s. flowers. **'secundly,** adv.

se'cundine, n. [Bot.] The inner coat of an OVULE when two are present. **ss.** [Zoo., Med.] AFTER-BIRTH.

se'dation, n. [Med.] The process of quieting the nerves, stopping pain, sp. by the use of SEDATIVES, or the condition produced by this.

'sedative, n., a. [Med.] A substance used for quieting the nerves, stopping pain.

'sedentary, a. [Zoo.] (Of an animal) living fixed to some support, not moving about from place to place.

'sediment, n. [Chem., etc.] Solid material in powder form which has become separated out of a liquid and gone to the base of the vessel. [Geol.] Solid material put down by water or ice. **sedi'mentary,** a. Forming, having in it, to do with, or formed of, s. **sedimentary rock.** [Geol.] Any ROCK formed from s., sometimes of s. made up of broken rocks, earth, etc. transported and dropped by a current, sometimes of s. produced by chemical reactions, or formed of masses of the hard parts of dead water-animals etc. (one of the three divisions of rock-grouping, *see* IGNEOUS, METAMORPHIC). **'sedimen'tation,** n. [Chem., Geol.] The putting down of s. as the effect of GRAVITY or CENTRIFUGAL force. **sedimentation test.** [Med.] Any test for a disease or for PREGNANCY based on the motion down, like a s., of ERYTHROCYTES or disease-bodies in blood taken from a person and put in a vessel.

seed, 1. n. [Bot.] The small body produced by the FERTILIZED OVULE of a flowering plant, made up of an EMBRYO, freq. with a store of food-material round it, covered by an outer coat; ss. in the mass. [Zoo.] SEMEN. [Chem.] Grain(s) or CRYSTAL(s) of material put into a SOLUTION which is on the point of forming crystals to get the process started. **2.** v.i. [Bot.] (Of a plant) get ss. produced; be dropping ss. to the earth etc. to undergo growth. [Chem.] Undergo CRYSTALLIZATION as the effect of seeding. **3.** v.t. Get ss. planted in (earth, etc.). [Chem.] Put s. into a solution to get crystallization started. [Med.] INOCULATE for science purposes. **s. 'crystal.** [Chem.] A CRYSTAL used for seeding a SOLUTION. **s. leaf, s. lobe.** [Bot.] COTYLEDON. **s. plant,** [Bot.] SPERMATOPHYTE. **s. stalk.** [Bot.] The stem of an OVULE. **s. 'vessel.** [Bot.] Sp., any fruit which is simply a dry and hollow cover for s., as opp. a fruit such as a food fruit, in which the ss. are bedded in, or have round them, a mass of more or less soft substance. **'seeded,** a. Sp.:— [Bot.] (of a plant) at the stage of producing s.; [Med.] having undergone INOCULATION. **'seeding,** n. Sp. [Phys.] the putting of certain ATOMS, such as Na, into a heated gas for the purpose of increasing its electric CONDUCTIVITY. **'-less,** a. [Bot.] (Of a fruit) having no s. in it. **'-ling,** n. [Bot.] A plant produced from a s., sp. a newly-formed plant of this sort.

seep, v.i. (Of liquid) make way slowly through POROUS material. **-age,** n. The process of seeping; (amount of) liquid which has seeped through something, for example, earth.

'Seger cone. [Chem.] A small pointed mass of salt and CLAY becoming soft at a certain degree of heat, used for testing the degree of heat of a FURNACE, sp. in CERAMICS.

'segment, n. A part cut or broken off something; a division. [Biol.] A natural division, any of the parts of which a living thing or one of its structures is formed, sp. a METAMERE, or a division of a leg etc., or one formed in an OVUM in process of development after FERTILIZATION. **seg'ment,** v.t. and i. Get separated, or undergo division, into ss. **seg'mental,** a. To do with, in the form of, a s. or ss. [Zoo.] Sp., present in every s. of a METAMERIC animal; of, to do with, the segmental organs. **seg'mental appa'ratus.** [Zoo.] The BRAIN-STEM. **seg'mental duct.** [Zoo.] In the EMBRYO of a back-boned animal, the DUCT of a segmental organ, later undergoing development into a WOLFFIAN or MÜLLERIAN DUCT. **seg'mental organ.** [Zoo.] NEPHRIDIUM; in the EMBRYO of a back-boned animal, any of the three structures for sending out waste material before the development of the true KIDNEY. **segmen'tation,** n. The process of segmenting or forming ss., sp. in a FERTILIZED OVUM; the condition of being segmented. **segmentation 'cavity.** [Zoo.] The hollow in the middle of a BLASTULA, formed at an early stage in the segmentation of an OVUM. **segmentation 'nucleus.** [Zoo.] The NUCLEUS formed by the uniting of the male and female nuclei when an OVUM is made fertile. **segmentation sphere.** [Zoo.] BLASTULA; BLASOTMERE. **seg'mented,** a. Cut, marked off into, or formed of, ss.

segre'gation, n. The process of becoming, getting, or keeping separated from other things, sp. of the same sort, or from a mass. [Biol.] Sp., the separating again into two different GAMETES, going to the development of two different offspring, of any two ALLELOMORPHS present in a plant or animal, one from its male PARENT and one from its female, this process being one of the bases of MENDEL'S LAW. **'segregate,** v.t. and i. [Make] undergo s. **'segregative,** a.

'seism-ic, -(ic)al, aa. Of, to do with, marked by, noted for, produced by, an EARTHQUAKE or earthquakes. **'seismically,** adv. **seis'micity,** n. The condition or property of being s.; the degree to which a part of the earth is given to having EARTHQUAKES. **'seismogram,** n. A DIAGRAM of a s. motion produced by a seismograph. 'seismograph, n. An instrument recording s. shocks and motions, their form, force and direction. seis'mographer, n. 'seismo'graphic(al), aa. seis'mography, n. The art or process of recording s. shocks, etc.

seis'mology, n. The science of EARTH-QUAKES. seismo'logical, a. seis'mologist, n.

seis'mometer, n. A SEISMOGRAPH with an apparatus for measuring earth motions. seismo'metric(al), aa. seis'momery, n.

'seismonasty, n. [Bot.] The motion of plants in reaction to general physical shocks such as a shake, for example, in some plants a folding of the leaves. seismon'astic, a.

Se'lachii, n.pl. [Zoo.] ELASMOBRANCHII, or that group of them taking in only those at present in existence which have sharp teeth.

se'lectance, n. [Radio] Measure of SELEC-TIVITY.

se'lection, n. The act, process, or property of taking, or giving reaction to, only certain things or parts of a range or group and not others. [Biol.] NATURAL SELECTION, or any process of BREEDING controlled by man which has the like effect of increasing the number of plants or animals with certain qualities and making less the number of those without them, at the same time causing a marked development of these qualities. se'lect, v.t. Take (certain things) from among a number as best for some purpose; (of a chemical substance, an apparatus, etc.) give reaction only to certain things, parts of a range (for example, of radio waves). se'lective, a. To do with, marked by, having the property of s. [Phys.] Sp., (of a process such as the ABSORPTION, EMISSION, or REFLECTION of rays) in which rays of a certain WAVE-LENGTH are the only or chief ones to be taken in or sent out etc., or are taken in etc. to a much greater degree than those of other wave-lengths, as [Optics] the selective ab'sorption of light of a given colour by a certain substance or apparatus. selective radi'ation. [Phys.] RADIATION given off by a heated body of which the distribution is not in agreement with PLANCK'S LAW. s. re'flection. The process or property of REFLECTING certain waves with much less loss of INTENSITY than others. selec'tivity, n. The property of being selective, sp.:—[Radio] The power of an apparatus to take in only waves from any desired station, keeping out all others; [Optics] The property of having a marked degree of selective reflection. se'lector, n. Any apparatus used in engineering, electric systems, radio, the telephone etc., by which the desired one of a number of different connections may be put into effect, for example in the operation of the GEAR-SHIFT in an automobile.

'selenite, n. [Mineral.] A clear, glass-like, uncoloured form of GYPSUM.

se'lenium, n. Chemical ELEMENT, at. no. 34, at. wt. 78·96, sign Se, a non-metal with properties somewhat like those of S, having a number of ALLOTROPIC forms and used in making rubber, red glass, and PHOTOELECTRIC CELLS.

seleno-. Moon. selen'ology, n., selen-'ologist, n.

se'lenodont, n., a. [Zoo.] (an animal) having SELENOID RIDGES on the crushing faces of the MOLARS.

sele'nography, n. [Astron.] The science having to do with the geography of the moon. se'lenograph, n. A map or picture of the moon or any part of it. sele'no-grapher, -graphist, nn. 'seleno-'graphic(al), aa.

'selenoid, a. In form like the new moon.

se'lenotropism, n. [Biol.] The reaction of turning in the direction of the moon's light. se'lenotropic, a.

self-. [Biol.] (Of an act, etc.) done by and to the self. [Mach.] Automatic.

'self-ab'sorption, n. [Phys.] The taking in of a RADIATION by the substance giving it out.

'self-ca'pacitance, n. [Elec.] The CAPACIT-ANCE of any electric CIRCUIT other than that produced by the CONDENSERS in it.

'self-'energy, n. [Phys.] The ENERGY EQUI-VALENT of the mass of a FUNDAMENTAL PARTICLE, based on 1 A.M.U. = 931·8 MEV.

'self-'fertilization, n. [Biol.] The FERTILIZA-TION of a plant or animal by POLLEN or SPERM produced by itself. self-'fertile, a. (Of a plant or animal) having the property of producing offspring by s.-f. 'self-fer'tility, n. self-'fertilize, v.t.

'self-incom'patible, a. [Bot.] SELF-STERILE.

'self-in'duction, n. [Elec.] The producing of a change in the MAGNETIC FIELD round an apparatus transporting an electric current, and so of a change in the ELECTRO-MOTIVE FORCE of this, by an earlier independent change in the current, the change produced in the field acting against the first change and so keeping it from having its full effect straight away. self-in'ductance, n. That property of a CIRCUIT responsible for s.-i., or the measure of this, the unit of which is the HENRY.

'selfing, 'self-polli'nation, nn. [Bot.] SELF-FERTILIZATION. 'self-'pollinated, a.

'self-'sterility, n. [Biol.] In a plant or animal producing male and female sex-CELLS, the property of not being SELF-FERTILE. self-'sterile, a. Having the property of s.-s.

'sella 'turcica, n. [Zoo.] The hollow in the

top side of the SPHENOID bone which is the seat of the PITUITARY GLAND.

se′mantics, n.pl. [Philol.] That part of the science of language which has to do with the senses of words, the history and tendencies etc. of changes and developments in these. **se′mantic,** a. To do with sense or s. **se′mantically,** adv. **se′manticist,** n. Expert in s.

semasi′ology, n. SEMANTICS. **semasio-′logical,** a. **semasi′ologist,** n.

se′matic, a. [Zoo.] Giving a sign of danger, as the bright colours of certain animals with a poisoning bite, etc.

sem(e)i′ology, n. [Philol.] The science of sign-languages. [Med.] SYMPTOM-ATOLOGY. **sem(e)io′logic(al),** aa. **sem(e)i-′ologist,** n.

sem(e)i′otic, a. To do with signs or [Philol.] sign-language or [Med.] SYMPTOMS. **sem(e)i′otics,** n.pl. [Med.] SYMPTOM-ATOLOGY.

′semen, n. [Zoo.] The liquid produced by the sex-apparatus of a male animal and having in it the SPERMATOZOA.

semi-. Half:— -′circle, n., -′circular, a.; in part, or to a certain degree, like but not completely the same as:— ′-′auto′matic, a.,′-′complete, a.,′-′metal, n.,′-′palmate, a.

′semi′caudate, a. [Zoo.] Having only the start of a tail.

′semi′circular ca′nal, [Zoo.] Any of the curved pipe-like parts having to do with the sense of balance in the ear of back-boned animals—in man and higher animals three in number.

′semicon′ductor, n. [Elec.] A material having a high electric RESISTANCE at a normal TEMPERATURE but a very much lower one at a higher temperature, such as Si and THERMISTOR.

′semi′cyclic, a. [Chem.] Half or in part CYCLIC, sp. of COMPOUNDS made up of a chain as well as a ring. **s. bond.** A DOUBLE BOND between a C ATOM in a ring and a C atom in a SIDE-CHAIN, which is not broken by heat but may be damaged by acids.

′semi-di′ameter, n. [Astron.] Half the DIAMETER of a body having a round face, such as the sun and moon, measured as the angle made by joining the ends of the s.-d. to the middle point of the earth, the common unit of measure for such bodies in astronomy.

′semi-′Diesel, n. [Eng.] An engine using the same sort of oil as a DIESEL but less PRESSURE, and firing the CHARGE by sending it into a specially heated vessel or onto a specially heated wall, etc.

′semi-di′urnal, a. Taking place every half-day.

′semi-′floret, -′floscule, nn. [Bot.] A RAY-FLORET of a COMPOSITE FLOWER. **′semi-′floscul-ar, -ous,** aa. Having s.-ff.

′semi′fluid, n., a. (A liquid) so thick as to be almost solid.

′semi′locular, a. [Bot.] (Of an OVARY) having incomplete division walls.

′semi′lunar, a. [Biol.] Formed like a half-moon or a new moon, used sp. of parts of the body of back-boned animals, as the s. VALVES of the heart, the s. CARTILAGE of the knee, the s. *bone* of the part of the arm or front leg nearest the hand or foot.

′semimembra′nosus, n. [Zoo.] A great muscle of the inner and back part of the upper leg having a flat TENDON at its upper end.

′semi′meta′morphosis, n. [Zoo.] INCOM-PLETE METAMORPHOSIS.

′seminal, a. [Biol.] To do with seed or SEMEN. **s. duct.** [Zoo.] Any pipe-like opening through which SPERM is sent out by a male animal. **s. re′ceptacle, s. ′vesicle.** [Zoo.] Vessel in connection with a s. duct in which SPERM is stored in a male animal.

semi′nation, n. [Bot.] The process of the distribution of seeds. [Zoo.] INSEMINA-TION.

semi′niferous, a. [Biol.] Producing seed or SEMEN. **s. ′tubule.** [Zoo.] Any of the long rolled-up pipes in the TESTIS of a back-boned animal in which the development of SPERMATOZOA takes place from the CELLS coating the inside.

′semio′viparous, a. [Zoo.] Giving birth to living young, not eggs—but young at a very incomplete stage of development.

′semi′parasite, n. [Bot.] A PARASITE plant which is not completely without CHLORO-PHYLL and gets only part of its food from its HOST.

′semi′permeable, a. [Chem., Biochem.] Letting liquid, or certain thin liquids, through, but not DISSOLVED substances, used sp. of MEMBRANES.

′semipla′centa, n. [Zoo.] A PLACENTA of which the part formed by the mother does not come away at birth.

′semi-′polar bond. [Chem.] COORDINATE BOND.

′semi-′precious, a. (Of a sort of jewel stone) in the lower range of values of those stones whose position on the HARDNESS SCALE is equal to or over that of the TOPAZ.

′semi′pupa, n. [Zoo.] A resting stage or form between two different LARVA stages in the development of some two-winged insects.

′semi′recondite, a. [Zoo.] Half-covered, as an insect's head by the THORAX.

′semispi′nalis, n. [Zoo.] A thick structure of muscle stretching from the neck down the two sides of the back-bone and made up of parts going from a TRANSVERSE PROCESS of one VERTEBRA to the NEURAL SPINE of a vertebra two or three places higher up.

′semistrepto′stylic, a. [Zoo.] STREPTO-STYLIC to a limited degree.

'semitendi'nosus, n. [Zoo.] A muscle going from the inside to the back of the top part of the leg and having a specially long, round TENDON as its upper end.

Se'mitic, a. [Philol.] Naming or to do with a great and very old family of INFLECTIONAL LANGUAGES, marked specially by the wide use of VOWEL-changes inside a word as a sign of a change of sense or relation, used in EGYPT, PALESTINE, IRAQ and other countries of North Africa and West Asia.

'semitrans'parent, a. (Of a substance) letting light rays through to a degree such that things may be seen through it, but with some DIFFUSION, so that they are not seen very clearly.

'semi'vowel, n. [Phonet.] A sound which is in part a VOWEL and in part a CONSONANT, as that of which the English 'w' is representative.

'semi-'water gas. [Chem.] A gas formed of mixed CO, CO_2, H and N, produced by sending air mixed with steam through heated COKE and used for burning.

'senary, a. Having, formed of, 6 things or parts.

se'nescence, n. [Biol.] That stage in the history of a living thing when its powers are becoming less as it gets nearer the natural end of its existence, the stage of getting old or the condition of being in this stage; in PROTOZOA, the condition in which, after a great number of divisions, the CELLS formed in this way have less power of growth than those of earlier groups, and so become increasingly smaller. se'nescent, a.

'senile, a. [Biol.] In a condition of, caused by, to do with, senility. s. de'mentia. [Med.] A very marked loss of the powers of mind, memory, attention, and control, in the very old. 'senilism, n. [Med.] An unnormal degree of senility, or a condition of senility caused before its time by disease se'nility, n. [Biol.] The condition of loss of powers and destruction of substance which comes about in the very old, or a like stage in the history of a group or sort of living things whose existence is coming to a natural end.

sen'sation, n. [Zoo., Psych.] The power or process of having conscious experiences when events take place in the body, as, for example, when something outside the body has an effect on a SENSE ORGAN; any separate conscious experience of this sort, sp. one forming a unit which it is impossible to get broken up into simpler experiences, as a s. of heat, colour, etc.; the physical process of the transporting of an effect on the body through the nerves to the CENTRAL NERVOUS SYSTEM, or the end-effect produced in the central nervous system, with or without a conscious experience. '-al, a. '-alism, n.

The theory that all knowledge is a development from s., or, more narrowly, that we have no knowledge of anything but ss. '-alist, n.

sense, 1.n. [Zoo., Psych.] Conscious SENSAtion; sense perception; any special sort of sensation, or the power of experiencing it, such as seeing, hearing, smell, taste, touch, pain, etc. [Phys.] Direction. 2.v.t. Be conscious of (an experience), or get knowledge of (a thing), through s. s. 'datum (data). [Psych.] That of which a person is conscious in any separate s. experience, looked on as a unit of sense perception. s. im'pression. [Psych.] A SENSATION or s. datum. s. 'organ. [Zoo., Psych.] Any special apparatus by which an animal is made conscious of a certain sort of effect on the body, as the eye, ear, nose etc. s. per'ception. [Psych.] The act, process, or power of becoming conscious of physical things, sp. outside the body, through the ss., as opp. to, on the one hand, the simple conscious experience of their effects and, on the other, the becoming conscious of non-physical things, such as relations.

'sensible, a. [Zoo., Psych.] Which may be sensed; having the power of sensing; SENSORY; conscious. s. ho'rizon. [Astron.] See HORIZON. sensi'bility, n. [Biol., Psych.] The property of giving reactions to STIMULI or the degree of this property which any living thing has, in general or for named stimuli. [Psych.] A marked tendency to be readily and deeply moved EMOTIONALLY.

sen'siferous, sen'sigerous, aa. [Zoo.] (Of structures, nerves) taking in or transporting sense STIMULI.

'sensile, a. [Zoo., Psych.] SENSORY; having the power of sense experience. [Meteor.] (Of a change in heat or cold) sensed but not great enough to be recorded by a normal instrument.

sen'sill-a, -um, -us, nn. [Zoo.] A small SENSE ORGAN.

'sensitive, a. [Biol., Chem., Phys., Psych., etc.] Giving a reaction to certain STIMULI, substances, operations, forces and so on; giving very ready reactions, very readily changed, moved, damaged; (of instruments) very delicate, recording very small changes, etc. [Med.] Sp. SENSITIZED. [Radio] Having a high degree of sensitivity. s. flame. A gas flame changing in form or size when acted on by sound waves. s. 'volume. [Phys.] The space full of gas between the ANODE and the CATHODE in a GEIGER-MÜLLER COUNTER. '-ness, sensi'tivity, nn. [Biol., Chem., Phys., Psych., Med.] The property of being s. or the degree to which anything in s.; (of an instrument) the amount of change in the reading for a unit amount of whatever is being measured. [Radio] The degree to which a RECEIVER gives a reaction to incoming waves.

'sensitize, v.t. [Chem.] Make (a substance) give a reaction, or a readier reaction, to some other substance, or to some effect (for example, in camera work etc., to the effect of light). [Immunol.] Make the effect of a SERUM on a person or animal greater by putting it into the blood more than once. sensiti'zation, n. 'sensitized, a. 'sensitizer, n. [Chem.] Any substance causing the sensitization of another; any substance other than a CATALYST which when present gets a CATALYTIC reaction started more quickly.

sensi'tometry, n. [Optics] The science or process of measuring the degree to which a camera plate or FILM, or the eye, is acted on by light. sensi'tometer, n. An instrument used for the purpose of s. 'sensito'metric, a.

senso-, sensori-. SENSORY (and ...):— 'sensopa'ralysis, n., 'sensori'muscular, n.

'sensori'motor, a. [Zoo.] To do with or producing sense and motion in reaction to STIMULI, as the s. NERVE-CENTRES.

sen'sorium, n. [Zoo., Psych.] The grey substance of the brain where the NERVE-CENTRES having to do with sense experience are, or, loosely, the brain looked on as the seat of sense-experience; the complete apparatus of sense-experience, the RECEPTORS and the nerve system. sen'sorial a.

'sensory, a. [Zoo., Psych.] To do with the SENSORIUM, sp. of nerves transporting NERVE IMPULSES to it; to do with the senses or sense experience.

'sensum (sensa), n. A SENSE DATUM.

'sentient, a. [Zoo.] Having the property of reaction to STIMULI; having some degree of conscious feeling. 'sentience, n. Sp., the simplest degree of the power of sense experience, the lowest stage of conscious feeling.

'sepal, n. [Bot.] Any of the gen. green and leaf-like units which make up the outer ring of flower-parts forming a cover for the young unopened flower. (See pictures p. 151.) -'ine, '-oid, aa. 'sepalody, n. The changing of other parts of a flower into ss. '-ous, a. Having the named number or sort of ss.

'separable, a. Able to be separated.

separ'ation, n. The act of separating or the condition of being separate, sp. [Bot.] the separating from a plant of a fruit or other body with the power of separate growth. [Geol.] The distance between the two sides or the two upper edges of a FAULT. [Phys.] The s. of one ISOTOPE of an ELEMENT from others with which it is mixed. s. 'factor. [Phys.] (Of U ISOTOPES) the relation of the CONCENTRATION of the

desired isotope after some stage in the process of separating others from it to its concentration before. s. 'layer. [Bot.] ABSCISS LAYER.

'separator, n. Apparatus or machine-part for separating things or keeping them from touching, sp. one used in mining for separating MINERALS of value from waste, or one used in farming for separating the part of milk having in it much butter-fat from the rest.

'sepia, n. [Zoo.] The black ink-like liquid sent out by certain fish of the group DIBRANCHIA in times of danger, used in paints to give a dark brown colour.

'sepsis, n. [Med.] A condition of PUTRE-FACTION in a part of the body caused by taking BACTERIA into the blood through a wound etc. 'septic, a. To do with, in a condition of, s.

'septal, a. See SEPTUM.

'septate, a. See SEPTUM.

'septem'partite, a. [Bot.] (Of leaf) having seven parts with divisions cutting almost to the base.

'septenate, a. [Bot.] With parts in sevens.

sept(i)- 1. Seven. 2. [Med.] SEPSIS, SEPTIC.

septi'c(a)emia, n. [Med.] A general poisoning of the blood, sp. as the effect of taking in BACTERIA into a SEPTIC wound, etc., marked by high FEVER and red places on the skin caused by blood coming through the blood-vessels.

septi'cidal, a. [Bot.] (Of a fruit) opening down the joins between the CARPELS of which it is formed. s. de'hiscence. The form of opening of a s. fruit.

septi'fragal, a. [Bot.] (Of a fruit) opening by the parting of the outer walls from the division walls. s. de'hiscence. The form of opening of a s. fruit.

'septo-, 1. SEPTI-. 2. SEPTUM.

septo'nasal, n. [Zoo.] The middle division-wall of the nose.

'septum (septa), n. [Biol.] A division-wall separating two hollows, two masses of softer substance, etc., as in a fruit, a SHELL, the heart (s. cordis), the nose (s. narium). s. trans'versum. [Zoo.] The DIAPHRAGM. 'septal, a. 'septate, a. Separated into parts by a s. or ss. 'sep'tation, n. The process of becoming or the condition of being septate. 'septo-.

se'quela (sequelae), n. [Med.] An unnormal or diseased condition which is the after-effect of a disease.

se'questrum, n. [Med.] A bit of dead TISSUE or bone which has become separated from a healthy mass.

sé'rac, n. [Geog.] Any of the high points or masses of ice into which a GLACIER is sometimes broken up when it gets to a sharp slope.

'seral, a. [Bot., Geog.] To do with a SERE; (of a plant COMMUNITY) being an in-between stage in a process of development, not a fixed or end-form.

sere, n. [Bot., Geog.] A number of different plant COMMUNITIES coming after one another in a place in the process of its development from first producing plants to producing the fixed selection which comes to be normal to it.

'serial, a. To do with, ranged in, forming part of, a SERIES.

'sericate, se'riceous, aa. [Bot.] Covered with a soft, thick, flat mass of delicate hairs, giving a silk-like look.

'series, n. A number of like things or events ranged in a line or coming after one another, sp. changing by the same amount or in the same way from one to the one after. [Chem.] A group of COMPOUNDS, having a connection of make-up and structure, ranged as a s.; a PERIOD in the PERIODIC TABLE. [Elec.] The form of connection between two or more electric CIRCUITS in which they are placed one after the other so that there is no division of the current going through them (*in s.*). [Geol.] In the grouping of SEDIMENTARY ROCKS, a division of a SYSTEM, made up of the rocks put down in an EPOCH. [Phys.] RADIOACTIVE DISINTEGRATION S. **s. 'winding.** [Elec.] A FIELD WINDING which is in s. with the ARMATURE of the machine of which it is part.

sero-. SERUM or SEROUS (and ...):—

'serology, n. [Med.], **sero'purulent,** a.

'serophyte, n. [Med.] A MICRO-ORGANISM produced in the condition when new SERUM is coming into a wound, as the STREPTOCOCCUS.

se'rosa, n. [Zoo.] A SEROUS MEMBRANE; the FALSE AMNION; the outer skin round the LARVA of an insect.

sero'therapy, 'serothera'peutics, nn. [Med.] The putting into the blood of blood SERUMS having in them ANTIBODIES acting against disease-bodies or the poisons produced by them, as a way of keeping off or overcoming disease.

'serous, a. [Zoo.] Of, to do with, producing, SERUM; (of a liquid) thin, water-like. **s. 'fluid.** Any of the thin water-like liquids present in hollows of the body, sp. those having s. membranes, which probably have something to do with producing the s. fluid. **s. 'membrane.** Any of the delicate skins forming the bag-like inner coats of the chief hollows of the body and covering and supporting the parts inside, the PERITONEUM, PERICARDIUM, etc.

'serpentine, n. [Mineral., Geol.] A natural substance formed chiefly of Mg and Si, of which one sort is ASBESTOS and other sorts, gen. dark green in colour with irregular markings giving the suggestion of a snake's skin, take a high polish and are used for ornaments; ROCK in which s., which is only produced at second-hand in this way, has been formed from other Si substances, such as CHRYSOLITE and PYROXENE.

'Serpek 'process. [Chem.] A process for getting N from the air by the reaction of Al with N forming AlN, which is then broken up by steam, producing NH_3.

'serpulite, 1.n. [Geol.] A FOSSIL worm-pipe. 2.a. Having in it ss. **serpu'litic,** a.

'serra, n. [Zoo.] Any structure having a serrate edge. **'serrate, ser'rated,** aa. (Of an edge) toothed, forming a line of tooth-like parts; (of a part or thing, chiefly [Biol.]) having such an edge, like an instrument used for cutting through wood. [Bot.] Sp. of a leaf, serrated with the teeth sharp and pointing forward (*see* picture p. 223). **se'rration.** n. The condition of being serrated; any of the teeth of a serrated edge. **'serrate-'dentate,** a. Serrated with the edges of the teeth themselves serrated.

ser'ratus, n. [Zoo.] Any of a number of muscles joined to the back-bone or RIBS by separate tooth-like parts.

serri-. SERRATE.

Ser'toli cells. [Zoo.] Any of a number of long CELLS present in the inner coating of the small pipes of the TESTIS to which groups of SPERMATIDS become fixed while undergoing development.

'serum (sera), n. [Zoo.] The water-like part separating from a body-liquid when it goes solid, sp. from the blood; any thin, water-like liquid forming part of the body of an animal. [Med.] Sp., blood s. in which ANTIBODIES have been produced as the effect of disease, used in SEROTHERAPY. **s. 'sickness.** [Med.] The reaction which sometimes takes place about a week after s. has been put into the blood, marked by a low FEVER, pain in the JOINTS, and skin trouble.

'servo'mechanism, 'servo'motor, nn. [Mach.] Any machine apparatus for changing a feeble force into a much greater force, used for the operation of controls etc. in machines of great power.

'servo 'system [Engin.]. In an electric or other machine, any system in which any change from a desired effect has an automatic reaction on the system of such a sort as to put right the error, for example an automatic guiding-apparatus in an airplane.

'sesamoid, 1.a. [Zoo.] Being or to do with a small mass of bone or CARTILAGE formed in a TENDON, sp. where it goes over a JOINT. 2.n. A s. bone or CARTILAGE, as the PATELLA of the knee. **sesa'moidal,** a. S.

sesqui-. One and a half times. [Chem.] Having in it 2 ATOMS of one sort united with 3 of another sort, as *iron sesqui-oxide* Fe$_2$O$_3$.

'**sessile**, a. [Biol.] Fixed to its support by its base; having no stem, as a *s. leaf* or *s. flower*. [Zoo.] Fixed in one place, having no power of moving about; (of an eye in a CRUSTACEAN) without a stem.

set, 1.v.i. [Astron.] (Of a star, etc.) go out of view over the edge of the earth. [Phys., Chem.] (Of a liquid or soft substance) become solid or hard as the effect of chemical change or a change in the degree of heat, as jelly or CEMENT. [Med.] (Of a broken bone) become united into one again by growth. 2.v.t. [Med.] Put the parts of a broken bone together to give them a chance to s.

set, 1.n. A number of things of the same sort which go together for some purpose or from some point of view, forming a complete group, as a *s. of medical instruments*, a *s. of teeth*, the *s. of muscles* controlling some special part, etc.; the direction in which something is placed, turned, curved etc. [Psych.] A condition of adjustment of body and/or mind making ready for, giving a tendency to, a certain sort of act or reaction. [Mech.] A change of form caused by an over-great force or over-frequent use. [Mining] A strong, thick wood frame used to give support to the walls of part of a mine. 2.a. Having undergone setting; fixed in form or direction; unchanging. **s. of 'chromosomes.** [Biol.] A group of CHROMOSOMES handed on to offspring which is formed of one of every sort present in the NUCLEUS of a GAMETE.

'**seta** (setae), n. [Biol.] Any small, thin, stiff, hair-like outgrowth, other than a true hair on animals (*see* HAIR). [Zoo.] Sp., CHAETA. [Bot.] The thin, stiff stem of the SPORE-vessel in BRYOPHYTA; any of certain different long narrow CELLS or cell-structures present in some ALGAE or ASCOMYCETES. **se'taceous**, '**setose**, aa. Having ss.; like a s. **se'tiferous**, **se'tigerous**, aa. '**setiform**, a. '**setule**, '**setula** (setulae), nn. A very small, delicate s. '**setulose**, **-ous**, aa. Having setulae.

'**settling**, n. The SEDIMENTATION of a solid in a liquid as the effect of GRAVITATION. '**settle**, v.i. (Of a solid SUSPENDED in a liquid) undergo s., go down to the base.

'**sewage**, n. The liquid waste in the drains of a town etc. **s. farm.** A farm to which s. is taken for use as MANURE. '**sewer**, n. Great drain-pipe or pipe-like structure forming part of the system of such pipes transporting waste water etc. from the houses of a town '**sewerage, n.** The taking away of liquid house-waste by sewers; the system of sewers in a town, etc.

sex-. 6; SEX.

sex, n. [Biol.] The division of the process

of producing offspring in certain sorts of plants and animals between two groups, 'male' and 'female', different in structure and in the part they take in the operation; one or other of these two groups; the system of different qualities, behaviour, and structure marking off these groups from one another. **s. cell.** GAMETE. **s. 'character.** Any quality, or any structure or process, not only of those which have a part in the producing of offspring, which is special to one s. or the other. **s. 'chromosome.** One or other of the two special sorts of CHROMOSOME (*see* X-CHROMOSOME and Y-CHROMOSOME) by which the sex of an offspring is fixed. **s. de'termination.** The process by which, as the effect of different groupings of the s. chromosomes, an offspring is given its sex. **s. 'differenti'a-tion.** The development of two different ss. in living beings or the condition of having undergone this development; the system of different qualities marking off one s. from the other. **s. gland.** [Zoo.] GONAD. **s. 'hormone.** Any of the HORMONES having a special effect on s. processes or qualities. **s. 'linkage.** The handing on of a certain GENE or the quality dependent on it by a s. chromosome, causing its distribution between male and female offspring to be unequal. **s. mo'saic.** [Zoo.] An animal which is in part male and in part female, having some male and some female qualities or structures at the same time. **s. 'ratio.** [Zoo.] The relation between the number of males and the number of females in a given group, gen. given as the number of males to every 100 females. **s. re'versal. s. transfor'mation.** [Zoo.] The changing of an animal from one s. to the other. **'-less**, a. **s.-'limited**, a. (Of GENES or qualities) limited to plants or animals of one s. or the other. **s.-linked**, a. (Of GENES or qualities) handed on by a s.-chromosome. **-'ology**, n. That branch of biology having to do with s.

'**sextant**, n. An instrument for measuring the ANGULAR distance between two things, sp. a body in the sky and the sky-line, by moving an IMAGE of one of them formed in a looking-glass on a moving arm to the same point as an image of the other seen through clear glass, and measuring the angle between the glasses, used sp. at sea for getting the angular distance of the sun from the earth.

'**sexual**, a. [Biol.] To do with or having sex. **s. di'morphism.** The condition in which the male and female of a sort of plant or animal are markedly different from one another in their outer qualities such as size, colour, etc. **s. 'intercourse.** [Zoo.] COPULATION. **s. se'lection.** [Zoo.] The selection by one sex, sp. the females, of MATES having certain qualities, as a possible force in the development of the sort—those qualities which have the greatest attraction for the opposite sex by degrees becoming general and those which have less attraction going out of existence. '-ly, adv. sexu'ality, n. The property of being s. [Psych.] A person's sex-qualities and behaviour; the quality of having over-strong sex-impulses or a more than normal interest in sex.

'shadow, n. [Optics] The dark space made by a body cutting off the rays from a light-SOURCE, or the dark PROJECTION of the form of this body on a SURFACE from which the rays are cut off, which will be solidly dark and sharply outlined if the source is small in comparison with the distance, but will be made up of a middle dark part with a lighter part round it when the source is great. [Acous.] An effect parallel to the s. produced by the cutting off of light-rays, caused by the cutting off of sound or electric waves by a body in the way.

shaft, n. [Mach.] The rod-like part of an instrument supporting its head, or acting part, for example, the s. of a hammer; a long, straight, gen. solid, rod, supporting turning parts or itself turning, for the purpose of handing on power or motion from one part of a machine to another. [Mining, Engin.] A deep, narrow, straight opening down into the earth, or a like space in a building—for example, for a lift, for letting in air, and so on. [Zoo.] The stiff middle stem of a feather, or sp. the solid part of it away from the base; the straight rod-like part of a long bone of the arm or leg, between the two ball-like ends; the part of a hair other than the root.

shale, n. [Geol.] Stone formed from CLAY and other MUD put down by water (freq. with oils in it produced from the C material of plants and animals which got into it before it got hard), and readily broken into thin plates in a direction parallel to the bed. 'shaly, a. To do with, producing, like, s.

shank, n. [Mach.] The SHAFT of an instrument or that part of it between its head and its hand-part. [Zoo.] SHIN.

shared, a. Common to, used by, joined to, two or more things. s. e'lectron, [Phys.] An ELECTRON common to two ATOMS.

shear, n. [Mech.] Shearing stress; shearing deformation. 'shearing defor'mation. The change of form produced by a shearing stress, for example, as seen in the changing of a four-sided right-angled form into a four-sided form whose sides are still parallel but whose angles are no longer right angles. 'shearing stress. A force

acting on a body in a plane parallel to one of its surfaces in such a way as to give parts of its structure a tendency to a slipping motion over one another, so causing DEFORMATION in which parallel planes are still parallel.

sheath, 1.n. [Mach., Biol.] Any cover like an outer skin or coat going round something. [Bot.] The base of a leaf when it is for some distance folded round the stem. [Zoo.] The outer covering of certain PROTOZOA; the wing-cover of an insect. [Phys.] The outer SHELL of an ATOM when this shell has not its full number of ELECTRONS; in PLASMA PHYSICS, the outer coat of CHARGED PARTICLES between a plasma and the walls of its vessel, the ELECTRODES, or other plasmas. 2. v.t. Be a s. or cover for; get covered with some material designed to keep what is under it from damage. 'sheathed, a. Having a s. '-ing, 1.a. Being a s., acting as a s. 2.n. Sp., material used for sheathing something.

sheet, 1.n. A thin, flat, stretch of anything, as [Geol.] any body of material which is long, wide, thin in comparison, and more or less level, as a s. of ice, a s. of lava, [Metals] a thin plate of metal for use as material (not more than $\frac{1}{4}$ inch thick as said of iron and steel). 2.a. In the form of a s. or ss., as s. rubber, s. metal. s. de'posit. [Geol., Mining] A s. of some MINERAL in the earth. s. e'rosion. [Geol.] The taking away of top SOIL from a stretch of the earth by the wind etc. in a thin regular s., not irregularly here and there. s. 'jointing. [Geol.] Sheeting. s. 'lightning. [Meteor.] LIGHTNING in the form of a sudden lighting of a wide space of sky, caused by an electric DISCHARGE far enough away for its light to have undergone REFLECTION and REFRACTION by clouds etc. in all directions. '-ing, n. [Geol.] A system of parallel cracks in a ROCK mass making division of it into thin ss. one on top of the other.

shell, n. [Bot.] The outer cover of a fruit or seed when very hard, as in a nut. [Zoo.] The outer cover formed of bone-like, horn-like, or CHITINOUS etc. material present in a number of lower animals, for example CRUSTACEA; the thin hard outer cover of an egg, sp. a bird's egg. [Phys., Chem.] Any of the ORBITS of ELECTRONS in an ATOM, pictured as SPHERES one inside the other, and named, starting with the one nearest the NUCLEUS, K-shell, L-shell, M. shell etc., every s. having a fixed number of electrons and a fixed amount of ENERGY. s. gland. s. sac [Zoo.] In some shelled animals, a GLAND producing the material for the s.; a gland in the OVIDUCT of an animal producing the material for the s. of the eggs.

shel'lac, n. [Chem.] LAC after undesired substances have been taken out of it, used in making VARNISH, INSULATING materials, sound records etc., a THERMO-PLASTIC material.

'shell shock, n. [Med.] A diseased condition of the nerves, freq. giving birth to a NEUROSIS, caused in fighting men by war experiences. 'shell-shocked, a. In a condition of s.s.

'sherardize, v.t. To give (a metal, sp. iron or steel) a thin coat of Zn by covering it thinly with powdered Zn and heating to a very high degree in a shut vessel.

shield, n. A plate or SCREEN used for giving cover, keeping something from damage. [Phys.] The ELECTRODE controlling the INTENSITY of a CATHODE RAY BEAM.

shift, 1.n. Change of position, sp. [Geol.] the s. of one side of a FAULT in relation to the other. [Phonet.] A change from one sound to another in the development of a language, sp. in agreement with GRIMM'S LAW. 2.v.i. Undergo a s.

'shima'muski fever. [Med.] An ACUTE disease produced by the bite of a MITE, marked by FEVER, the SWELLING of the neck and other GLANDS, and a dark red RASH.

shin, n. [Zoo.] The front part of the lower division of the leg, the part covering the edge of the TIBIA, in man and 4-legged animals; the tibia of an insect.

shingle, n. [Geog.] A stretch of loose small stones, as freq. seen by the sea.

'shingles, n. HERPES.

S.H.M. SIMPLE HARMONIC MOTION.

shoal, n. [Geog.] A mass of sand or part of the bed of the sea, a river etc., coming up almost to the top of the water, making it much less deep at this point than at places near by.

shock, n. [Med.] A condition of greatly lowered forces marked by loss of colour, quick breathing, and trouble of mind, caused by a great shock to the physical system (such as great loss of blood, sudden and great pain, etc.) or to the mind; ELECTRIC SHOCK. s. ab'sorber. [Engin.] An apparatus, gen. HYDRAULIC, for DAMPING out the effects of shock on VEHICLES by controlling the motion of the SUSPENSION springs. s. tube. [Phys.] A LABORATORY apparatus for producing SUPERSONIC FLOW conditions in a COM-PRESSIBLE FLUID by firing a s. wave down a long, open-ended pipe having fluid air in the lower part of it. s. wave. [Phys.] A wave caused by a s. of great force, in which air-FLOW is changed very suddenly from SUBSONIC to SUPERSONIC, that is, from a VISCOUS to a COMPRES-SIBLE condition, so producing a quick increase in PRESSURE and TEMPERATURE.

'shocked, a. [Med.] In a condition of s.

shoot, n. [Bot.] A part sent out by growth, sp. newly, as the part of a young plant coming out of the earth, a stem with its leaves, a side-branch. [Zoo.] A horn in the first stage of its growth.

'shooting star. [Astron.] METEOR.

shore, n. [Geog.] Land skirting the edge of a body of water, sp. the sea. '-line, n. The outline of the land edging the sea or other great body of water.

short 'circuit. [Elec.] The condition pro-duced when two parts of any electric CIRCUIT are put or come into touch with one another or into connection through a CONDUCTING PATH of very much lower RESISTANCE than the circuit is designed for. short-'circuit, v.t. Make a s.c. in, get changed, cut off, or put into connection, by a s. c.

short-day plant. [Bot.] Plant doing best when it gets daylight for only 12 hours or less.

short-'sighted, a. [Med.] Having MYOPIA. '-ly, adv. '-ness, n.

short wave. [Radio] A radio WAVE whose WAVELENGTH is in the range of 10 to 50 m. 's.-'w., a. [Radio, Med.]. 's.-'w. 'therapy. [Med.] The use of electric waves of from 6 to 30 m. long, having high FREQUENCY, for producing heat in body TISSUES as a way of helping certain conditions.

shot eff'ect, shot noise. [Phys.] A noise produced in the ANODE current of a THERMIONIC VALVE caused by the current being made up of irregular separate bursts as the ELECTRONS get to the anode one after the other.

'shoulder, n. A part giving the suggestion of a man's s., sp. the curve from the neck to the top of the arm. [Zoo.] The part of an animal formed by the bones, their connections, muscles, and covering, joining the arm or front leg to the body. 's. blade. SCAPULA. s. 'girdle. PECTORAL GIRDLE.

'shower, n. [Meteor.] A short and gen. sudden fall of rain limited to a small part of the country, in which the drops are of some size and come down very quickly.

shrub, n. [Bot.] A wood-forming plant which freq. has the look of a small tree but is different from a tree in branching freely from near the earth and having no strong, tall, middle stem.

shunt, 1.n. [Elec.] An apparatus for con-trolling the amount of current going through a CIRCUIT, formed by a wire or other CONDUCTOR put in PARALLEL with it, and said to be 'in s.', which takes off part of the current. 2.a. To do with, having, produced by, a s. s. 'winding. A FIELD WINDING put in s. across the ARMATURE of the machine of which it is part.

'shutter, n. (Of a camera) the part (which may take a number of different forms) by which the opening through which the light comes is covered when not in use, and by the moving of which it is un-covered for the time necessary to take a picture.

'shuttle, n. The boat-like part of a cloth-making machine which goes forward and back taking thread under and over the threads stretched on the frame; any of certain other machine-parts having a like motion or purpose.

Si, Sign for SILICON.

'sial, n. [Geol.] The part of the earth forming the base of the great earth masses, between the upper earth and the lower part at the level of the deep-sea beds, made up chiefly of liquid or solid ROCK having in it much Si and Al.

'sia'loid, n. Like SALIVA. 'sial'orrhoea, n. [Med.] The producing of over-much SALIVA.

'Siamese twins. [Med.] TWINS united to one another at some point of the body.

sib, n. [Anthrop.] A group made up of all persons having one common ANCESTOR. [Zoo.] Sibling. '-ling, n. [Zoo.] Full brother or sister, any of two or more off-spring of the same mother and father in relation to the other(s). '-ship, n. The relation between siblings. [Anthrop.] The condition of being one of a s.

'sibilant, 1.n. [Phonet.] A language sound of the 's' sort, made by forcing out the breath sharply between the tongue and the teeth. 2.a. Said with a sharp sound of breath forced between tongue and teeth.

'siccative, 1.n. A substance having a drying effect, sp. one put into paint to get it dried more quickly. 2.n. Having a drying effect.

'sicula, n. [Geol.] The small pointed body at the end of a GRAPTOLITE forming the starting-point of its branching structure and representative of the animal which gave birth to the COLONY.

side band. [Radio] The band of FRE-QUENCIES on the two sides of the CARRIER FREQUENCY, produced by MODULATION.

side-chain, n. [Chem.] A group of ATOMS joined to a RING in the MOLECULE of a COMPOUND, as when an ALKYL group takes the place of the H in a ring com-pound. 's.-c. 'theory. [Med.] Ehrlich's theory as to the reasons for IMMUNITY, based on the idea that MOLECULES of living substance are in the form of rings with s.-cc., certain of which, named RECEPTORS, have the power of uniting with the molecules of other substances coming into the system.

si'der(e)al, a. [Astron.] To do with the stars; measured by the FIXED STARS. s. day. The time taken by the earth to make one com-plete turn on its AXIS measured from one TRANSIT to another of a FIXED STAR (sp. from one VERNAL EQUINOX to another), which is 3 minutes and 56 seconds shorter than a MEAN SOLAR DAY. s. month. The time, $= 27 \cdot 32166$ days, taken for the moon to go round the earth, measured in relation to the FIXED STARS. s. noon. The point of time when the FIRST POINT of ARIES is on the MERIDIAN at its highest point. s. 'period. The time taken by any PLANET or other body going round another one to come round to the same point again in relation to the FIXED STARS. s. time. Time measured by s. days. s. year. The time taken by the sun in its seeming motion to come back again to the same point in relation to the FIXED STARS, about 20 minutes longer than the TROPICAL YEAR because of the PRECESSION OF THE EQUINOXES.

'siderite, n. [Geol., Mineral.] Natural iron CARBONATE ($FeCO_3$), a CRYSTALLINE substance, gen. light brown in colour, freq. mixed with Mn, Mg, or Ca, an important iron ORE. [Astron., Geol.] A METEORITE formed of nickel and iron. side'ritic, a.

sider(o)-. Iron; star.

si'deroscope, n. [Med.] An instrument for the discovery of small bits of iron or steel in the eye by the use of a MAGNETIC needle.

side'rosis, n. [Med.] A disease of the LUNGS caused by breathing metal dust, common among tin, iron, lead and copper miners and among steel-workers.

'siderostat, n. [Astron.] An instrument formed of a looking-glass moved auto-matically by clockwork so as to send back in a fixed direction, gen. level, light rays from any body in the sky which is under observation.

'side-slip, 1.v.i. (Of an airplane or airship) be slipping sideways and down at an angle at the same time as it is going forward. 2.n. The motion or event of side-slipping.

side wave. [Radio] Any of the different FREQUENCIES making up the SIDE BAND.

'Siemens-'Martin 'process. OPEN-HEARTH PROCESS.

si'enna. n. A yellow-brown form of CLAY becoming orange-red on burning, having in it OXIDES of iron and Mn—used as a colouring substance in paints.

sieve, n. A holed SCREEN for separating greater grains of substance etc. from smaller ones. s. cell. [Bot.] Any of the sort of long, thin-walled, living CELLS without NUCLEI making up a s. tube. s. pit, s. pore. [Bot.] Any of the very small holes in a s. plate. s. plate. [Bot.] A holed part in the side wall or end of a s. tube. s. 'tissue. [Bot.] PHLOEM. s. tube. [Bot.] Any of the long pipe-like structures, made up of a line of s. cells placed end to end and opening into one another through s. plates, present in PHLOEM, and by which food materials are taken to different parts of the plant.

sight, 1.n. [Zoo., Psych.] The process or power of seeing, the sense of which the eye is the instrument. [Mach.] A part of an instrument for guiding the eye in pointing it at something, as the VIEW-FINDER on a camera, or, sp., one or the other of two metal parts on a gun with which anything to be fired at has to be kept in line (the **ss.**). 2.v.t. Get a view of; get (something) in view in a sighting glass or in line with a s.; get (an instrument) pointed in the right direction with the help of a s. or ss.

'sigmoid, a. [Biol.] Curved in two directions like the letter 'S' or half of it. [Zoo., Med.] To do with the s. flexure of the COLON. **s. 'flexure.** [Zoo.] An S-like curve, as of a bird's neck; the s. part of the COLON, nearest to the RECTUM.

sign, n. [Med.] A mark of a disease etc. which is open to observation by a medical man, as opp. a SYMPTOM which may be a private experience, a feeling etc., of which only the ill person has knowledge. [Astron.] Any of the signs of the Zodiac. **signs of the Zodiac.** [Astron.] The 12 equal divisions of the ZODIAC, named after the CONSTELLATIONS which in earlier times had their places there, but which, as the effect of the PRECESSION OF THE EQUINOXES, have now all been moved into the divisions east of the ones having their names—reading from east to west: *Aries, Taurus, Gemini, Cancer, Leo, Virgo, Libra, Scorpio, Sagittarius, Capricornus, Aquarius, Pisces.*

sign 'language. [Philol.] A language using motions of the fingers or hands in place of the voice, as that used by persons without the power of talking or between PRIMITIVE groups living in the same country but having different talking languages.

'signal, 1.n. A sign, sp. one such as a light or sound, an electric current, the motion of an apparatus, etc., designed to give news or orders or to get attention at a distance; in the telegraph, telephone or radio, any electric current designed to have an effect on a RECEIVING apparatus. 2.v.i. Make a s. or ss., give news etc. by ss. 3.a. Used in, to do with, signalling; very marked. **s. colo'ration.** [Zoo.] Special marks by which an animal is seen by another to be of the same sort as itself. **'signaller,** n.

sig'nificant, a. Being a sign; important, (of an error or of the degree to which the

outcome of a test is different from that worked out by theory, etc.) great enough to be important. [Philol.] (Of words, etc.) having, designed to give, a sense. **sig-'nificance,** n. The property of being s.; the sense of a word or sign. **signifi'cation,** n. The act of signifying; significance. **'signify,** v.t. Have as its sense, be a sign of; make clear by sign or word.

'silage, n. Stored plant food for cows, sheep, horses etc. which has been tightly massed in a SILO to undergo FERMENTA-TION, in the process of which ACETIC ACID is produced which keeps it from going bad.

'silent, a. [Phonet.] (Of a letter forming part of a word in writing or print) not sounded, not representative of any sound made in saying the word.

'silica, n. [Chem., Geol.] SiO_2 (*silicon dioxide*), a very hard white substance used in making glass and REFRACTORIES, present naturally in the earth in a CRYSTALLINE form as QUARTZ, sand etc., in a non-crystalline form as OPAL, and in a half-crystalline form as CHALCEDONY. **s. gel.** [Chem.] A form of S in very small grains which is much used for taking up liquids and becomes a GEL in doing so. **s. glass.** FUSED QUARTZ, present naturally in different parts of the earth, and probably having been a METEOR. **s. valve.** [Phys.] A THERMIONIC VALVE made of FUSED s. for use at very high TEMPERATURES.

'silicate, n. [Chem., Mineral.] Any of the SALTS of SILICIC ACID, which make up the greatest group of MINERALS, that is, a substance having in it SiO_3, SiO_4, Si_2O_5, etc., but gen. looked on as formed of SILICA (SiO_2) united with some OXIDE of a metal.

si'liceous, a. Of, to do with, like, having in it, SILICA. [Bot.] (Of plants) living in places where there is much SILICA. **s. 'sinter.** [Geol.] OPAL of a sponge-like structure put down by GEYSERS or warm springs which have come through a s. LAVA.

si'licic acid. [Chem.] Any of a number of feeble ACIDS, the commonest being H_2SiO_3, produced in the form of jelly-like masses by acids acting on ALKALINE SILICATES.

'silicide, n. [Chem.] A substance formed by uniting one metal with Si.

si'licify, v.t. and i. Get or become changed into, or mixed with, SILICA. **si'licified,** a. **si'licifi'cation,** n. The process of silicifying, sp. [Geol.] The process by which SILICA makes its way into or is produced in earlier-formed ROCKS, which it has the effect of keeping together in a hard, solid mass.

'silicle, 'silicule, si'licula, nn. [Bot.] A CAPSULE with the structure of a SILIQUE, but shorter, sometimes as wide as or wider than it is long. si′licular, a.

′silicole, n. [Bot.] A plant living or doing best in places where there is much SILICA, as in sand.

′silicon, n. Chemical ELEMENT, at. no. 14, at. wt. 28·06, sign Si, a non-metal having properties somewhat like those of C, which may be got in two forms, a brown powder or grey CRYSTALS—present in the earth in greater amount than any other element but O. silico-.

′silicone, n. [Chem.] Any of a group of POLYMERIC substances made up of long CHAINS of SiO with HYDROCARBON or FLUOROCARBON groups forming SIDE-CHAINS, the simpler ones being used as LUBRICANTS, the more complex ones as electric INSULATORS, and all having great value as water-REPELLENTS.

sili′cosis, n. [Med.] A disease of the LUNGS caused by breathing SILICA dust.

si′lique, si′liqua, nn. [Bot.] A CAPSULE at least 4 times as long as it is wide, and opening down the two long edges, formed of two CARPELS united longways, with a division down the middle formed by outgrowths from the PLACENTAS supporting two long lines of seeds [Zoo.] A vessel having the form of a s. si′liquiform, a. ′siliquose, a.

silk, n. [Zoo.] The delicate but strong threads produced as a sticky liquid becoming hard in the air by a number of insect LARVAE, sp. silkworms, for the purpose of making coverings for themselves in their resting-stage, and out of which silk cloth is made; threads somewhat like s. produced by other insects or animals for the same or different purposes, for example those forming the BYSSUS in LAMELLIBRANCHIA. ′s.-gland. [Zoo.] A structure (in silkworms, one or the other of two SALIVARY GLANDS of great size) producing the sticky liquid which becomes s. threads. ′silky, a. [Bot.] Covered flatly with small, soft hairs, like s. cloth to the touch. [Zoo.] Having s.-like hairs, feathers, etc.

sill, n. [Geol.] A level or almost level stretch of IGNEOUS ROCK, much wider and longer than it is thick, formed by MAGMA forcing its way between two stretches of SEDIMENTARY ROCK.

′silo, n. An air-tight structure, gen. a tall round building, in which plant-food for animals is put to be changed into SILAGE; a structure for storing grain.

silt, 1.n. [Geol.] Loose material put down by a river, etc. which is of smaller grains than sand.

Si′lurian, a., n. [Geol.] (Of, being, produced in, or to do with) the s. period. S. period. The third, or sometimes the second and third, division of the PALAEOZOIC. s.

′system. The SYSTEM of ROCKS formed at that time. (See p. 559).

si′lundum, n. [Chem. etc.] A very hard substance having in it Si and C, made to be used for electric RESISTORS, etc.

′silver, n. Chemical ELEMENT, at. no. 47, at. wt. 107·88, sign Ag, a NOBLE METAL somewhat soft and very readily worked, used for money and ornaments, the best electric CONDUCTOR. s. glance [Mineral.] Ag_2S (argentite), an important ORE of s. s. ′nitrate. [Chem.] $AgNO_3$, a white, SOLUBLE CRYSTALLINE substance, used medically, in chemical ANALYSIS, and in inks. ′-y, a. Having a look of, of the colour of, s.

′sima, n. [Geol.] The solid part of the outer earth, of greater weight than SIAL, on which the sial and the deep sea-floors are resting, made up of BASIC IGNEOUS ROCK in which the chief substances are Si and Mg.

′simian, a., n. [Zoo.] (To do with or like) a monkey, sp. an ANTHROPOID APE.

′similar, a. Like (to) some other thing or like one another, in a general way, but not completely like. [Geom.] (Of plane forms) the same in form but different in size or position. simil′arity, n. The condition or relation of being s.

si′moom, si′moon, nn. [Meteor., Geog.] A very warm, dry, strong wind full of dust or sand, blowing at times from the sand-wastes of Arabia, Syria, etc., sp. in the spring and summer.

′simple, a. Formed of one substance only, unmixed; not separated into parts, not having divisions, not formed by the uniting of different parts or units, sp. [Bot.] of leaf. s. eye. [Zoo.] An eye with only one LENS, working separately or as a unit of a COMPOUND EYE. s. fruit (s. ′ovary). [Bot.] A fruit (OVARY) formed from one CARPEL. s. har′monic motion. [Phys.] The motion of anything in a straight line from side to side, between limits A and B through a middle point O, with an ACCELERATION in the direction of O which is in PROPORTION to the distance it goes from it, so that it takes the same time to go from A to B as would a point moving at a regular rate round the half-circle of which O is the middle point and AB the DIAMETER. s. ma′chine. [Mech.] Any of the simple structures by which a smaller force may be changed into a greater and on which the development of all machines is said to be based, for example the LEVER, the PULLEY, the wheel, the screw. s. ′microscope. A MICROSCOPE having only one LENS. s. ′tissue. [Bot.] Any TISSUE in which all the CELLS are of the same sort. s. ′umbel. [Bot.] An UMBEL in which the stems of the flowers themselves come from the chief stem (*see* COMPOUND UMBEL).

sim′plicity, n. The property of being simple in any sense. **′simplify,** v.t. Make simple or simpler in any sense.

′simplex, a. Simple, used sp. in electric engineering, telegraph work, etc. for naming apparatus working in only one direction at a time. [Biol.] (Of a POLYPLOID) having the DOMINANT ALLELOMORPH in one of a group of like CHROMOSOMES and the RECESSIVE allelomorph in the others of the group.

′simulate, v.t. [Biol., Med.] Have or put on the look or properties of some other thing, as when one disease has effects very like those of another so that it may be taken for it. **simu′lation,** n. Sp. [Zoo.] MIMICRY.

simul′taneous, a. Taking place, present, at the same time. **s. associ′ation.** [Psych.] The uniting of simple SENSE DATA in one complex PERCEPTION or idea. **s. re′action.** [Chem.] Any of two or more reactions taking place in the same group of substances at the same time.

Sin′anthropus, n. [Anthrop.] The sort of very early man, of the PLEISTOCENE PERIOD, of which the bones came to light in China in 1929, much like PITHECANTHROPUS.

′sinciput, n. [Zoo.] In man and higher animals, the part of the face and head over the eyes, or the upper half of the complete head; in birds, the part of the head from the base of the BEAK to the highest point; the like part of the head in insects.

sine, n. [Geom.] (Of an angle) in a right-angled plane form, ABC, of which B is the right angle, the s. of the angle A (short form sin A) is $\dfrac{CB}{AC}$ and the s. of the angle C is $\dfrac{AB}{AC}$.

′single, a. One only; being one separate thing, not one of two or more grouped together or united in their operation. [Bot.] (Of a flower) having only the normal number of PETALS (*see* DOUBLE). **′s.-′acting,** a. [Mach.] Acting in one direction only. **s.-acting ′engine.** An engine in which the air, gas, oil etc. working the PISTON comes in from one direction only, not first at one end and then at the other. **s. bond.** [Chem.] The connection uniting two MONOVALENT ATOMS or two groups of atoms of which all VALENCIES but one are balanced. **′singly,** adv. One by one.

′sinistral, a. Of, at, in the direction of the left; using the left hand, or the left side of the body, more than the right. **s. shell.** [Zoo.] A SPIRAL SHELL with spirals turning in the opposite direction to the hands of a clock, starting at the point.

sinistr(o)-. SINISTRAL.

sinis′trocular, a. [Med.] Using the left eye more than the right.

′sinistro′gyrate, a. Turned or moving round to the left. **′sinistrogy′ration,** n. A s. turning or motion.

′sinistrorse, a. [Biol.] Twisting in a SPIRAL in the opposite direction to the hands of a clock, (of a SHELL) SINISTRAL.

sink, ′sink-hole, nn. [Geog., Geol.] A round hollow in the earth through which water is drained away forming a current under the earth, caused by the DISSOLVING of certain sorts of ROCK, sp. LIMESTONE, by rain-water.

′sinter, 1. v.i. (Of a powder or earth-like substance, or small bits of a substance) come together into a solid mass as the effect of being heated, but without being made liquid by the heat. **2.**n. Material produced by sintering. [Geol.] SILICEOUS SINTER or any like substance made up of irregular bits united in a solid mass, produced by the EVAPORATION of spring or other waters.

′sinuate, ′sinuous, aa. Waving, curving this way and that, sp. [Bot.] (of a leaf) having an edge waving quite deeply in and out. (*See* p. 223.)

′sinus, n. [Zoo.] A hollow or pocket-like space, sp. any of the air-hollows in the bones of the face in connection with the nose; a wide pipe-like space, without special walls, taking blood, sp. from VEINS, through a part, as in the brain of higher animals or among the muscles and inner parts of lower animals. [Med.] A long narrow hollow going from a place inside the body where PUS is being formed to the outside, and forming an outlet for it. [Bot.] The hollow between two LOBES, as in a leaf. **s. ven′osus.** In the EMBRYO of a back-boned animal, the pipe-like back division of the heart opening into the AURICLE; a like division of the heart in animals without backbones; the hollow inside an auricle, sp. the right auricle. **′-al,** a.

sinu′sitis, n. [Med.] INFLAMMATION of a SINUS of the nose.

′sinusoid, n. [Zoo.] A very small blood SINUS going through the substance of a part, sp. the LIVER, **sinu′soidal,** a. sinusoidal current. [Med.] ALTERNATING current as used medically for helping PARALYSED or feeble muscles.

′siphon, 1.n. An instrument for taking liquid out of a vessel, or from a higher to a lower level, in the form of a pipe bent more or less like a hairpin so that, if one arm is put into an open vessel of liquid and the other arm over the edge with its end lower than the level of the liquid, and the pipe is full of liquid, the liquid in the vessel will be forced through the pipe in an unbroken current. [Zoo.] Any of a number of pipe-like structures in different animals for the intake and/or output of liquid or air, sp. one or other of two such parts formed by the meeting side edges of the MANTEL in BIVALVE MOLLUSCS, by which water is taken into the mouth and breathing-apparatus and sent out again. [Bot.] Any of the pipe-like CELLS ringing a middle cell in the plant-body of certain RHODOPHYCEAE. 2.v.t. Take (liquid) up or in or from one place to another with, or as if with, a s. '-aceous, '-ate, '-eous, aa. [Biol.] Having a s. or ss. '-age, n. The working of a s. si'phonic, a. To do with a s. or siphoning, working in the same way as a s. siphon-.

Siphon'aptera, n.pl. [Zoo.] An ORDER of small insects without wings living at full growth for most of their time on the bodies of birds and higher animals and SUCKING their blood, noted for their great power of jumping.

'siphonet, n. [Zoo.] The HONEYDEW pipe of one of the APHIDIDAE.

siphoni-, siphono-. SIPHON, siphon-like: siphon'iferous, a. [Zoo.] si'phoniform, a.

si'phonium, n. [Zoo.] In some birds, a hard pipe between air spaces in the QUADRATE and the MANDIBLE. si'phonal, a.

Siphon'ophora, n.pl. [Zoo.] An ORDER of HYDROZOA common in warm seas, forming free-moving COLONIES of which the units are specially designed for different purposes such as food-getting and swimming, and freq. ranged round or under a great air-pocket which keeps the colony up in the water—noted for the size and gen. beautiful colouring of the complex animal. sipho'nophoran, 1.a. Of, like, the S. 2.n. An animal of the S.

'siphono'stele, n. [Bot.] A STELE formed of a pipe of PHLOEM outside a pipe of XYLEM with PITH in the middle, as in most FILICALES. 'siphono'stelic, a.

'siphosome, n. [Zoo.] The lower part of a SIPHONOPHORAN, made up of the food-getting and offspring-producing units.

sire, n. The father of an animal, sp. of a horse or dog.

'siren, n. [Acous.] An apparatus producing a very clear and, as used for some purposes (for example, in FOG at sea), a very loud and long note, as the effect of getting a current of air or steam broken by a quickly-turning plate with holes in it, letting the air etc. through in bursts.

Si'renia, n.pl. [Zoo.] An order of MAMMALS living most of the time in water, great animals living on plant food, with thick hair, short necks, front legs wide and flat for swimming and no or RUDIMEN-TARY back legs, and a wide flat tail for guiding them through the water. si'renian, An animal of the S.

si'rocco, n. [Geog., Meteor.] A very warm south wind blowing for days at a time from the Sahara, sp. in spring, and experienced in North Africa, where it is dry and full of dust, and the south of Italy and Spain, where it is less dry but still very damaging to plants.

'sister, a. [Biol.] (Of a CELL or NUCLEUS) produced by the same division of a cell or nucleus as another.

sit(i)o-. Food: si'tology, n., '-'mania, n. [Med.] '-'phobia, n. [Med.]

si'tosterol, n. [Chem.] An ALCOHOL, $C_{29}H_{50}O$, very like CHOLESTEROL, present in grain oil and some other plant foods.

'situs, n. [Biol., Med.] Position. s. in'versus. [Med.] The condition in which an inner part of the body, sp. the heart, is on the opposite side from the normal.

skein, n. [Biol.] SPIREME.

'skeleton, n. A framework without its uniting or covering material, the harder parts of anything from which the soft parts have gone, etc., as a s. CRYSTAL, one whose development has been stopped when little more than its outline was formed. [Zoo.] The complete system of bones, the bone framework, of a back-boned animal; any hard structure or parts, inside or outside the body of an animal, supporting or covering its soft parts. [Bot.] The hard supporting parts seen in certain lower plants such as DIATOMS. 'skeletal, a. Of to do with, in the form of a s. 'skeletal muscle. [Zoo.] STRIATED MUSCLE. skele'togenous, a. [Zoo.] Designed to undergo development into bone or other material of a s. 'skeleto-.

skew, a. Twisted out of a straight line or a right angle, sloping, not turned or placed in what seems to be the natural position; irregular, unbalanced, having undergone greater development on one side than the other, etc. '-ness, n. Condition of being s.

'skia-gram, -graph, nn. RADIOGRAPH (picture).

'skiascope, n. RETINOSCOPE. ski'ascopy, n.

skin, n. S.-like covering of anything. [Zoo.] The outer covering of an animal's body, made up in non-back-boned animals of EPITHELIUM on a BASEMENT MEMBRANE, in back-boned animals of an outside part, or EPIDERMIS, formed of epithelium without nerves or blood-vessels, and of which the outer coats become dead and horn-like, and an inner part, or DERMIS, formed chiefly of CONNECTIVE TISSUE, with nerves and blood-vessels running through it. [Bot.] EPIDERMIS; the outer covering of a fruit or seed.

'skinbound, a. [Med.] Having the skin very tightly fixed to the parts under it as the effect of SCLERODERMA.

skin ef'fect. [Elec.] The effect, increasing

with the FREQUENCY, by which an ALTERNATING electric current is greater near the outside of a wire than farther in, so that the RESISTANCE of the wire, is greater than for a DIRECT current.

skin-'grafting. [Med.] The GRAFTING of small bits of skin onto a wounded place on a person's body. **'skin graft.** A small bit of skin used in s.-g.

'skip 'distance. [Radio] The shortest distance from a radio apparatus at which a SKY WAVE comes back to earth again and may be taken in by other instruments.

skip ef'fect. [Radio] The effect by which the hearing of sounds sent out by a radio apparatus may be impossible for a certain distance round the apparatus though possible farther off, caused by the fact that SKY WAVES going off at less than a certain angle are not sent back by the IONOSPHERE, so that there is a space round the instrument, limited by the SKIP DISTANCE, in which the taking in of such waves from it is impossible.

skull, n. [Zoo.] The bones forming the head of a back-boned animal.

sky wave. [Radio] A radio wave which goes from the instrument sending it out up to the IONOSPHERE and is there turned back to earth.

slag, n. Other materials separated from metals in the process of SMELTING and forming the top part of the liquid ORE, freq. glass-like when cold; more generally, the waste produced in any process of getting metals from ores. [Geol.] SCORIA.

slake, v.t. [Chem., etc.] Put water on QUICKLIME, CaO.s **laked lime.** Ca(OH)$_2$ produced by the slaking of CaO.

slate, n. [Geol.] A smooth, grey-blue, SEDI-MENTARY ROCK in which the chief substances are Si, K, and Al, formed by heat and great force from small-grained materials such as CLAY, SHALE, and SILT, and marked by the property of being readily broken longways into thin regular plates. **'slaty,** a. Like, to do with, having in it, s. slaty **'cleavage.** [Geol.] The property of separating into thin regular plates, like s.

'sleeping 'sickness. [Med.] A serious African disease marked by FEVER, wasting, loss of power, and a half-sleeping condition, caused by PROTOZOA of the GENUS TRYPANOSOMA, which get into the blood from the bite of a fly.

'sleepy 'sickness. [Med.] An EPIDEMIC disease causing ENCEPHALITIS and marked by a great desire for sleep.

sleet, n. [Meteor.] Rain in part turned to ice, or rain and snow falling together.

sleeve, n. [Mach.] A pipe-like cover going over another part, or covering or forming a join between the ends of two pipes or wires, or inside which a connection between two electric wires is made.

slide, 1.n. A slipping motion of one thing over another. [Mach.] A flat part slipping over another and guided to and kept in its place (for example, shutting an opening) by some structure such as an overhanging edge or a hollow gripping its base; a part on which another moves in this way; a sloping, smooth-floored structure for sliding things from one level to another. [Geol.] Any FAULT caused by strong FOLDING, that is, a THRUST or a LAG. [Optics] A plate of glass on which anything is pictured for PROJECTION by an apparatus such as a PROJECTION LANTERN. [Biol., etc.] A thin glass plate on which cuttings of an animal, plant, MINERAL etc. are fixed for observation under a MICROSCOPE. [Phonet.] The changing of a sound into another sound by very small adjustments in the position of the voice apparatus, so that the change is so smooth as to be unnoted by the ear. 2.v.i. Have a s., be moving with a sliding motion. 3.v.t. Make s., put into place, or send from one place to another with a sliding motion. **s. rule.** An instrument for getting a number produced by the MULTIPLICATION or division of two others without working it out in the normal way, in the form of a rule marked with a scale of divisions based on LOGARITHMS but numbered by ANTI-LOGARITHMS, sliding over another marked in the same way, so that by moving the first the desired answer may be got by simple addition or SUBTRACTION.

'slime, n. Very small-grained earth so wet as to be almost liquid; any dirty liquid or almost liquid substance which has the property of coating anything touching it, giving it a disgustingly smooth, wet touch, as water full of DECAYING plant substance. [Metal.] ORE crushed in water to grains so small that they make their way down in it very slowly. **s. plug.** [Bot.] A mass of s. stopping up the holes in a SIEVE TUBE. **s. string.** [Bot.] A cord-like mass of slimy food substance going through a hole in a SIEVE PLATE. **'slimy,** a. Having in it, covered with, s.; wet and smooth like s. **s. 'fungus, s. mo(u)ld.** [Bot.] Plant of the MYXOMYCETES.

sling, n. [Mach.] A cord, chain etc., put under or round something to give it support or for hanging it by, for example that put round a thing to be lifted by a CRANE.

slip, 1.n. [Geol., etc.] Any earth motion changing the places of the parts of a mass of ROCK in relation to one another; the condition produced by a s.; a FAULT or one or other of its parts, or the measure of the distance by which they are separated. [Cryst., Metal.] The process by which a change of form is produced in metal and other CRYSTALS without cracking them, by parts of the crystals moving in relation to one another on certain planes. 2.v.i. Undergo a **s. s. 'bedding.** [Geol.] A structure of STRATA in which they are sloped or curved or bent as the effect of slipping. **s. planes.** [Cryst., Metal.] The special group or groups of planes on which s. takes place in metal and other CRYSTALS.

'slipper ani'malcule. [Zoo.] PARAMECIUM.

slit, 1.n. A long cut or narrow opening, sp.:— [Optics] a narrow right-angled opening with sharp edges, through which light is let into an instrument (for example, a SPECTROSCOPE) or, in a PROJECTOR, sent out; [Astron.] the narrow opening in the roof or wall of an observation room through which the TELESCOPE is pointed at the stars. 2.a. Having a s., having undergone one or more long cuts.

slough, 1. n. [Zoo.] The old outer skin put off by a snake or any other animal which puts off its skin from time to time. [Med.] Mass of dead substance formed in a wound or diseased part and separating from it. [Mining] Material falling in bits from the sides of a mine. 2.v.t. [Zoo.] (Of an animal) put off (its skin). 3.v.i. [Zoo., Med., Mining] Come off as a s. [Med.] (Of wound etc.) get a s. formed.

slow-'motion picture. A motion-picture of which the FILM has gone through the camera very quickly, making a record of more separate positions than is generally done, so that when it is put through the PROJECTOR at a normal rate the pictured motion or event seems to be taking place very slowly.

sludge, n. A soft wet mass of waste as produced in making a deep hole for the discovery of oil, in coal-washing, or from SEWAGE, etc. **'sludger, n.** Any of a number of machines used in different industries for clearing away s.

sluice, 1.n. [Eng.] An apparatus for controlling a current of water in a waterway so that the level may be changed, as in a LOCK, or so that a sudden burst of water may be let through when necessary for the purpose of washing away SILT, working a WATER-WHEEL, etc.; a part of a waterway where a s. is placed; a new waterway made to take water turned from its normal way by a s.; a long box-like structure for washing the gold out of gold-producing earth. 2.v.t. Get cleaned out or cleared away with a strong current of water, sp. from a s. **s. gate.** A s. in the form of a great plate or door-like structure which may be put across a current.

Sm, Sign for SAMARIUM.

small 'calorie. See CALORIE.

small 'circle. The circle in which any plane through a SPHERE other than one going through its middle point is cut by the

sphere, used sp. [Astron., Surveying, etc.] of the sphere of the earth or sky.

small in'testine. [Zoo.] In MAMMALS, birds, and REPTILES, the first of the two chief divisions of the INTESTINE, made up of the DUODENUM, JEJUNUM and ILEUM, which is markedly narrower and freq. very much longer than the rest and the chief seat of those processes of digestion by which the chemicals of value in food are got out of it and taken into the system.

'smallpox, n. VARIOLA.

smear, n. [Bact.] A very thin coat of BACTERIA on a SLIDE or CULTURE. **s. 'culture.** A CULTURE started by putting a s. onto the MEDIUM.

smell, n. [Zoo., Psych.] The sense-experience produced by the effect on special nerve-endings, such as those of the MUCOUS MEMBRANE of the nose in higher animals, of certain gases transported to them, gen. ir very small amounts, by the air; the power of having such sense-experiences; a thing's property of giving off gases causing such sense-experiences.

smelt, v.t. [Metal.] Get metal separated from an ORE, etc. by heating the ore with a FLUX to the point at which it becomes liquid, the liquid waste then separating from the liquid metal and coming to the top of the vessel. **'smelting, n., a.**

smoke, n. [Chem.] A gas, sp. air, with solid PARTICLES of very small size SUSPENDED in it, of which the chief cause is the incomplete burning of coal, gas etc.

smooth muscle. UNSTRIATED MUSCLE.

Sn, Sign for TIN.

Snell's law. [Optics] The law that for a ray of light which is REFRACTED on going from one MEDIUM into another, the SINE of the ANGLE OF INCIDENCE ÷ the sine of the ANGLE OF REFRACTION is a fixed number (named the *index of refraction* of the two media, or of the second if the first is a VACUUM).

snout, n. [Zoo.] The long, forward-pointing sort of nose seen in animals such as the pig.

snow, n. [Meteor.] Small CRYSTALS of ice falling from the sky, gen. in soft little masses, formed from water in the form of gas in the upper air when the degree of cold is under 0°C. **'-drift, n.** [Geol.] S. massed up in one place by the wind, etc. **'-field, n.** [Geog.] A stretch of country covered all the time by s., as on high mountains or in the far North or South. **'-line, n.** [Geog.] The line on a mountain or slope higher than which there is snow at all times of the year—at different distances from sea-level in different parts of the earth. **'-y, a.**

soap, n. [Chem.] An ALKALINE substance made by the reaction of NaOH (*hard s.*) or KOH (*soft s.*) with FATS or FATTY

ACIDS or with RESINS (*resin s.*), by a
process of HYDROLYSIS which gives
GLYCERIN in addition—used with water
for cleaning purposes; any metal salt
of a fatty acid, such as lead s., having
different properties from common s. and
used for different purposes, for example,
as driers in paint.

'social, a. To do with society or the living in
groups of men or other animals; to do
with the science of society among men, or
with conditions dependent on society and
work designed for bettering them. [Zoo.]
(Of animals) living together in groups
with some degree of organization. [Bot.]
(Of plants) naturally forming great
groups covering wide stretches of country.
[Psych.] To do with relations between
persons, based on or coming from a
person's experience with other persons.
s. anthro'pology. That branch of anthropology the chief interest of which is the
organization of early forms of society
among men. s. 'instinct. [Zoo., Psych.]
Any INSTINCT having to do with the
behaviour of an animal as a unit in a
group working together. s. malad'just-
ment. [Psych.] The condition of a person
whose feelings and tendencies are in such
bad adjustment to the society in which
he is living that he is markedly unable to
be happy in or of use to the group. s.
'organism. Society looked on as a living
organization of parts, like a plant or
animal. s. 'parasite. [Zoo.] A different sort
of animal living in a group of s. animals,
and taking its food from them, etc.,
without being of any use to them. s.
'parasitism. [Zoo.] The condition of being
a s. parasite or the condition produced by
a s. parasite. s. psy'chology. That branch
of psychology having to do with the
behaviour and qualities of persons in so
far as these are reactions to or have an
effect on those of other persons, or in
relation to group-living. s. science. Any or
all of the sciences having to do with
society, as SOCIOLOGY, ECONOMICS, etc. s.
'stimulus. [Psych.] Any act or quality of
an animal causing a conscious experience
or a reaction in another animal, sp. man,
s. 'symbi'osis. [Zoo.] The condition in
which an animal of a different sort is
living among a group of s. animals and
the connection is of value to the two
sides.

so'ciety, n. [Zoo.] Any group of animals
living and working together. [Bot.] A
group of plants of one sort forming a unit,
but not a chief unit, of a CONSOCIATION
or ASSOCIATION.

socio-. SOCIAL, SOCIETY.

soci'ology, n. The science of society among
men, covering its history, development,
forms, structure, the organizations and

relations to which it has given birth, etc.
socio'logical, a. soci'ologist, n.

'soda, n. [Chem.] Any of the substances
SODIUM BICARBONATE (*baking s.*), SODIUM
CARBONATE (*washing s.*) and SODIUM
HYDROXIDE (*caustic s.*). s. ash. AN-
HYDROUS SODIUM CARBONATE. s. lake.
[Geol.] A SALT LAKE in which there are
SALTS of SODIUM other than common salt,
chiefly $NaCO_3$. s. lime. [Chem.] A sub-
stance in the form of grains made up of
NaOH and $Ca(OH)_2$ mixed, produced
by the addition of NaOH in water to
CaO, used for taking in water or gas from
the air, or in glass-making. s. 'nitre.
SODIUM NITRATE. s. 'water. Water into
which CO_2 is forced under PRESSURE,
some of the gas making its way out in the
form of BUBBLES when the water is taken
from its bottle etc., used as a drink.

'Soddy-'Fajans law(s). [Phys.] *See* FAJANS
AND SODDY LAWS.

'sodium, n. Chemical ELEMENT, at. no. 11,
at. wt. 22·997, sign Na, a soft, silver-
white ALKALI METAL, very readily
uniting with other substances and giving
a violent reaction with water, necessary
to living things and present in the earth
in great amount but never free. s.
bi'carbonate. $NaHCO_3$, a white CRYSTAL-
LINE substance used in making cakes etc.
and medically as an ANTACID. s. 'carbonate. Na_2CO_3, a clear or white CRYSTAL-
LINE substance, or, in its ANHYDROUS
form, a white powder, with a strong
ALKALINE taste, used for making water
SOFT, and for a great number of other
purposes, such as glass-making, camera
work, etc. s. 'chloride, Common salt,
NaCl. s. hy'droxide. NaOH, a white,
strongly ALKALINE substance, readily
taking up water from the air, used in
making soap, paper etc. s. 'hypo'sulphite.
S. thiosulphate s. 'nitrate. $NaNO_3$,
the natural form of which is named
Chile saltpetre, used for making land
fertile and in the making of HNO_3
(*nitric acid*). s. 'silicate, Na_2SiO_3, *see*
WATER GLASS. s. sulphate. Na_2SO_4, a
white CRYSTALLINE substance, used in a
great number of industries, and medically, in the form $Na_2SO_4.10H_2O$
(*Glauber's salt*), as an APERIENT, very
common in SODA LAKES etc. s. 'thio'sulphate. $Na_2S_2O_3.5H_2O$, a white CRYSTAL-
LINE substance used in camera work and
commonly named '*hypo*'. 's.-cooled
valves. [Engin.] High-quality EXHAUST
VALVES in INTERNAL COMBUSTION
ENGINES, which are kept from over-
heating by putting s. inside the hollow
stems and heads of the valves.

'sodaku, n. [Med.] A disease given to man
by the bite of a rat, caused by a SPIRO-
CHAETE and marked by FEVER.

soft, a. Of water, free from those substances, sp. SALTS of Ca and Mg, which keep soap from forming a LATHER when rubbed in it; of light, or the light effects in a camera picture, DIFFUSED, so that the outlines of things and the limits between light and shade are not sharply marked. [Phys.] Of a VACUUM, not complete; (of an ELECTRON DISCHARGE TUBE etc.) from which not all the air which it is possible to take has been taken. [Phonet.] Of the letter 'c', said like an 's', as in 'face'; of the letter 'g', said like a 'j', as in 'stage'; VOICED. **s. 'chancre.** CHANCROID. **s. fin.** [Zoo.] A FIN supported by s. rays. **s.-'finned,** a. **s. iron.** Iron having little C in it, which does not long keep its MAGNETIC properties after being MAGNETIZED. **s. 'palate.** [Zoo.] In higher animals, the soft back part of the roof of the mouth. **s. ray** [Zoo.] A FIN-RAY made up of short parts joined together which have a little power of motion in relation to one another, so that the ray is not a completely stiff rod. **'soft-rayed,** a. **s. soap.** [Chem.] Any soap of a liquid or almost liquid form, made of K SALTS and liquid FATS. **s. 'solder.** [Metal.] Any ALLOY of lead and tin used as a SOLDER, readily becoming liquid when heated. **s. X-rays.** [Phys.] X-RAYS of the longer WAVE-LENGTHS, which have not as much power of going through substances as those of the shorter wavelengths. **'soften,** v.t. and i. Make or become soft in any sense (see WATER-SOFTENING). **'softener,** n. Any machine, apparatus, or substance used for softening anything, as water, metal, the outlines in a camera picture, etc. **'softening,** a., n. **softening of the brain.** [Med.] A condition in which the brain substance becomes soft as the effect of INFLAMMATION, or the cutting off of the blood from a part through the stopping up of a blood-vessel, causing a loss of the use of those nerves and muscles controlled by the softened part of the brain, or, in GENERAL PARALYSIS OF THE INSANE, of all powers of mind and motion. **'softness,** n. The quality of being s., in any sense. [Metal.] A tendency to be readily changed in form, becoming bent, not broken, under force.

soil, n. [Geol.] The loose earth material on the top of the earth in the upper part of which plants have their growth, formed chiefly of very small grains of ROCK produced by weathering, mixed with dead plant and animal materials, and having air and water in the spaces between. **s. 'binder.** Any plant used for stopping the washing or blowing away of s. by keeping it together with a network of roots or branches running over or

under the earth. **s.-con'ditioning.** The science or process of putting soil into good condition for the growth of plants by physical, chemical and farming operations designed to give it not only desired substances but the right TEXTURE and the power of fighting EROSION. **s. creep.** [Geol.] The slow motion of the upper s. down slopes which goes on all the time as the effect of the opening and shutting of cracks caused by heat and cold, etc. **s. 'flora.** [Bot.] Plants living inside the s., such as certain FUNGI. **s. me'chanics.** The science of the physical properties of s., its structure, motions, etc. **s. so'lution.** [Bot.] The water present in the spaces of the s., which has in it the SALTS forming the food of plants.

sol, n. [Chem.] A liquid COLLOIDAL SOLUTION. **'solate,** v.i. [Chem.] (Of a GEL) become changed into a s. **so'lation,** n.

'solar, a. [Astron.] Of, to do with, produced by, measured in relation to, the sun. [Biol.] Having parts raying out all round. **s. ant'apex.** [Astron.] The point on the CELESTIAL SPHERE opposite the s. apex. **s. 'apex.** [Astron.] That point on the CELESTIAL SPHERE in the direction of which the s. system is moving at the rate of 20 km. a second. **s. cell** [Phys.] A PHOTO-ELECTRIC CELL taking in PHOTONS from the sun's rays and changing the ENERGY into electric power. **s. 'constant.** [Phys.] The amount of RADIANT ENERGY from the sun falling on 1 sq. cm. of the earth in 1 second. **s. 'day.** [Astron.] The time taken by the sun to come round again to the MERIDIAN, on the MEAN measure of which our clock-time is based. **s. month.** [Astron.] $\frac{1}{12}$ of the s. year. **s. motion.** [Astron.] The motion of the s. system in the direction of the s. apex. **s. 'plexus.** [Zoo.] A network of nerves and nerve-connections at the back of the stomach in higher animals. **s. 'system.** [Astron.] The sun and all the bodies moving round it and kept in their places by its attraction, that is, the 9 great PLANETS with their moons together with hundreds of smaller planets and some COMETS and METEORS. **s. time.** [Astron.] The time of day as given by any observation of the true sun, as opp. MEAN SOLAR TIME. **s. year.** [Astron.] TROPICAL YEAR.

'solari'zation, n. The act, process, or effect of solarizing, sp.:—[Bot.] the stopping or slowing for a time of PHOTOSYNTHESIS as the effect of being acted on for a long time by a very strong light; [Photog.] the becoming light of parts normally dark and the other way round in a FILM, etc. as the effect of being overlong in the light. **'solarize,** v.t. Put out in, make undergo the effect of, sunlight.

'**solder,** 1.n. A metal or ALLOY used for uniting other metals by FUSING with them under the operation of heat. 2.v.t. Get (metals) united by the use of s.; get (anything) very tightly united. '**-er.** n. Person whose work is soldering. '**-ing,** a., n. '**soldering iron.** An instrument made of a pointed bit of copper at the end of an iron rod with a hand-part of wood, used for causing s. to become liquid by putting the copper point, heated to a very high degree, against it.

sole, n. [Zoo.] The under side of the foot in higher animals.

so'lenium (solenia), n. STOLON.

so'lenocyte, n. [Zoo.] Any of the great, pipe-like CELLS with CILIA for keeping up an outgoing current in the NEPHRIDIA of certain LARVAE and lower animals, such as worms.

'**solenoid,** n. [Elec.] A wire twisted into a number of equal turns (commonly circles) as if round a pipe, so that there is a pipe-like space going down through the rings, and having the property of acting like a straight MAGNET when an electric current is sent through it. **sole'noidal,** a. Of, to do with, using, produced by, a s.

so'lenostele, n. [Bot.] A form of SIPHONO-STELE having a pipe of PHLOEM inside as well as outside the XYLEM, as in the stems of certain FILICALES.

'**soleus,** n. [Zoo.] A flat muscle in the lower part of the leg in man or of the back leg in four-legged animals.

'**solid,** 1.n. [Phys., Chem.] Any substance of which the MOLECULES have no power of moving freely in relation to one another but are in a condition of VIBRATION in a fixed position, that is, a substance having a fixed form and size and the property of RESISTANCE to any force with a tendency to make a change in these, as opp. a liquid or a gas. [Geom.] Having three DIMENSIONS. 2.a. Being in the condition of a solid, not liquid or gas, not plane or flat; not hollow; DENSE. **s.** '**angle.** [Geom.] The amount of DIVERGENCE at the meeting-point of three DIMENSIONS, as at the point of a CONE, PYRAMID, CUBE etc., sp. [Optics] the angle formed at the middle point of a SPHERE by straight lines from every point of the outline of a space on its SURFACE, measured in STERADIANS. **s. sol.** [Chem.] A COLLOIDAL SOLUTION of a solid in a solid, as that of gold in glass colouring it a deep red. **s. so'lution.** [Phys., Chem.] A SOLUTION in which the SOLVENT and the SOLUTE are in the s. state, as seen in some ALLOYS and in MIXED CRYSTALS. **s. state.** See STATES OF MATTER. **so'lidity,** n. The condition of being s. (in any sense).

so'lidify, v.t. and i. [Phys., Chem.] (Make)

become in a solid condition. **so'lidi'fica-tion,** n. The process of solidifying. **so'lidifier,** n. '**-ing,** a., n. **so'lidifying point.** The TEMPERATURE at which a liquid or gas solidifies under given PRESSURE.

'**solidus curve** or '**solidus,** n. [Phys.,Chem.] A GRAPH giving the relation between changes in the PROPORTIONS of the metals forming a given ALLOY and changes in the TEMPERATURE at which MELTING is started (see LIQUIDUS).

'**solstice,** n. [Astron.] One or other of the two points in the sun's seeming journey through the sky, or of the two times of year (*summer s.* on June 21, *winter s.* on December 22), at which it is farthest from the EQUATOR. **sol'stitial,** a.

'**soluble,** a. [Phys.-Chem.] Having the property of becoming a SOLUTE (*in* a named SOLVENT or, generally, in water). **s. glass.** WATER GLASS. **solu'bility.** n. The property of being s.; the degree to which a substance is s., gen. given as the greatest number of grams of it which may be taken into SOLUTION by 100 grams of its SOLVENT. **solu'bility 'product.** The value of the PRODUCT of the CONCENTRATIONS of the two sorts of IONS formed by an ELECTROLYTE in water etc., when as much as possible has been taken into SOLUTION.

so'lute, n. [Phys.-Chem.] That substance in a SOLUTION whose physical condition is changed into that of the other, or which is present in smaller amount, so that it is looked on as being taken in by the other, for example, in a solution of salt and water, water is the SOLVENT and salt the s.

so'lution, n. The answer to a question, or some way of overcoming a hard point, worked out by Mathematics or reasoning; the process of getting a s. for some question or trouble. [Phys.-Chem.] A mixed substance in which the MOLECULES or IONS of one substance have undergone regular distribution among those of the other so that there is no longer any physical sign that two separate sub-stances are present, sp. a liquid formed by the mixing of a solid with a liquid; the condition of the SOLUTE, which is said to be *in* s. in the SOLVENT; the process of taking, or causing a substance to be taken, into s.

sol'vate, n. [Chem.] A complex formed by solvation. **sol'vation,** n. The regular grouping or uniting of IONS or MOLECULES of a SOLUTE with ions or molecules of its SOLVENT.

'**Solvay 'process.** n. [Chem.] A process used in industry for making SODIUM CARBON-ATE ($Na_2CO_3.10H_2O$) from common salt (NaCl) by acting on it with AMMONIA (NH_3) and CARBON DIOXIDE (CO_2).

solve, v.t. Get a SOLUTION for (a question,

trouble, etc.). **'solvable, a.** Which may be solved.

'solvent, 1.n. [Phys.-Chem.] That substance in a SOLUTION, gen a liquid, which is present in greater amount than the other or whose physical condition is unchanged, so that it is looked on as taking in the other (*see* SOLUTE); a substance having the power of acting as a s. (*for* given substances). 2.a. Being a s. (*for*).

sol'volysis, n. [Chem.] The forming of an ACID and a BASE from a SALT in SOLUTION as the effect of chemical reaction with the SOLVENT. **solvo'lytic, a. 'solvolyze, v.t.** Make (a SALT) undergo s.

'soma (somata), n. [Zoo.] All the parts of an animal other than the GERM-CELLS; the chief part of the body of an animal, taking in its head and tail but not its legs, wings etc. **so'matic, a.** [Biol.] Of, to do with, the parts of a plant or animal other than the GERM-CELLS. [Zoo.] (Of TISSUES, etc.) present in parts of the body other than blood-vessels or the apparatus of digestion, sp. forming the body-wall. [Psych.] Of, to do with, the body only, as opp. the mind or the brain and nerves, which have a connection with mind-processes. **so'matic mu'tation.** [Biol.] A MUTATION caused by a change in CELLS other than GERM-CELLS. **so'matic segre-'gation.** [Bot.] The separating of different sorts of CELLS in plant growth. **so-'matico-.**

'somat(o). Body, SOMATIC.

'somatoblast, n. [Zoo.] A CELL producing SOMATIC CELLS.

'somatocyst, n. [Zoo.] In some SIPHONO-PHORA, an air-space in the NECTOCALYX.

'somatoderm, n. [Zoo.] In an EMBRYO, that part which undergoes development into the body-wall.

'somato'gen-ic, -ous, 'somatoge'netic, aa. [Biol.] Produced from SOMATIC CELLS.

'soma'tology, n. That branch of Anthropology which has to do with the comparison of the structure and development of man's body as seen in different groups and conditions.

'somatophyte, n. [Bot.] A plant whose CELLS for the most part undergo development into special materials, forming a plant-body with a system of parts, as in all higher plants, as opp. an ASOMATOPHYTE.

'somatoplasm, n. [Biol.] The living CELL-substance of SOMATIC cells.

'somatopleure, n. [Zoo.] In the EMBRYOS of higher animals, the outer division of the MESOBLAST, from which the body-wall is formed, **'somato'pleural, a.**

'somite, n. [Zoo.] METAMERE. **'somital, so'mitic, aa.**

som'nambulism, n. [Med.] The condition of a person who gets up and goes about or does other physical acts while still sleeping, so that he has no memory of the event when he comes awake again; a like condition produced by HYPNOSIS. **som'nambulist, n.** A person given to walking etc. in his sleep.

somni-. Sleep; **-'facient, n.** [Med.].

som'niferous, som'nific, aa. [Med.] Sleep-producing.

'somnolent, a. [Med.] Half sleeping, or with a tendency to go to sleep, having trouble in keeping awake. **'somnolence, n.** The condition of being s.

sone, n. [Sonics] A unit of LOUDNESS = that of a simple TONE of which the FREQUENCY is 1000 CYCLES per sec.

'sonic, a. To do with sound, (of instruments) testing or measuring or effecting something by the use of sound-waves. **s. 'cleaning.** The use of very strong sound waves for helping the operation of washing or cleaning dirty materials by the AGITATION or CAVITATION of the cleaning liquid, **s. depth 'finder,** ECHO SOUNDER. **s. 'surgery.** [Med.] The use of ULTRASONIC waves on parts of the body as a way of effecting changes in the tissue at a desired point, which may in the future be of value in certain diseases. **'sonics, n.** The science or TECHNOLOGY of putting sound-waves to work, as in s. DRILLING etc.

'sonolumi'nescence, n. The producing of light in liquids as the effect of CAVITA-TION caused by sound-waves.

so'nometer, n. MONOCHORD.

sopo'rific, n., a. [Med.] (A substance, etc.) causing sleep.

soral, a. [Bot.] To do with a SORUS.

sorbe'facient, n., a. [Med.] (A substance) causing or helping ABSORPTION.

'sorbose, n. [Chem.] An ISOMER of FRUCTOSE.

so'redium (soredia), n. [Bot.] Any of the small outgrowths on LICHENS, formed of a mass of HYPHAE round one or more CELLS of ALGAE, which have the power of separating from the old plant and undergoing development into a new one. **so'redial, so'rediate, a.** Producing ss.

'Sørenson scale. [Chem.] The earliest scale used for measuring pH VALUES.

'sori, n.pl. *See* SORUS.

so'riferous, a. [Bot.] Producing SORI.

so'rosis, n. [Bot.] A COLLECTIVE FRUIT formed from a number of small, tightly-massed flowers together with the part supporting them all.

'sorption, n. [Chem.] General name covering ADSORPTION and ABSORPTION.

'sorus (sori), n. [Bot.] A small massed outgrowth of SPORANGIA produced by a FUNGUS or other lower plant, sp. any of the small dark, round masses formed on the underside of the fertile leaves in FILICALES; in LICHENES, a powder-like

mass of SOREDIA on the plant-body.
so′riferous, aa.

sound, n. [Geog.] A long stretch of water of some size joining two greater bodies of water.

sound, a. [Med.] Healthy, undamaged, working normally.

sound, 1.n. [Zoo., Psych.] The sense-experience of which the ear or some like structure is the instrument. [Phys.] The LONGITUDINAL WAVES moving through some substance, gen. air, by whose operation on the right NERVE-ENDINGS the sense of s. is produced. [Med.] A long, thin, solid rod used for moving round inside hollow places, such as the BLADDER, with a view to the discovery of any unnormal growth, etc. 2.v.t. and i. [Make) give out a s., have an effect on hearing; get knowledge of the condition of something by causing it to give out a s., for example, by giving it a blow. [Med.] Make use of a s. on (a part) for the purpose of observation. **s. ′ab′sorbtion.** [Phys.] The changing of s. energy into some other sort, gen. heat, when it comes up against a body or goes through a MEDIUM. **s. board.** [Acous.] A thin board readily put into VIBRATION by a sounding body, used, for example, in an instrument of music, for making a s. stronger (*see* RESONANCE). **s. box.** [Acous.] That part of a gramophone inside which is the apparatus by which the needle-motions are changed into s. **s. ′camera.** A machine designed for recording s. on a camera FILM to be used in connection with a motion picture etc. **s. ′energy.** The ENERGY transported by s. waves. **s. lo′cator.** [Acous.] An apparatus for fixing the direction from which a s. is coming, used sp. in war for the discovery of the position of airplanes etc. **s. ′ranging.** The process of getting the position and distance of something, sp. guns, from the s. made by it. **s. track.** The space on a motion-picture FILM, parallel to the pictures, where a s. record is fixed. **s. wave.** [Acous.] A WAVE transported by any MEDIUM, solid, liquid or gas, but most commonly produced in air, by which s. is produced (roughly one of from 20 to 20,000 CYCLES per second) [Phys.] Any wave of the same sort as a s. wave, even if outside the limited range of WAVE-LENGTHS by which the ear is acted on. **′-er,** n. An instrument used for taking in telegrams, which makes ss. representative of their sense in place of marks on paper. **′-ing.** 1.a. 2.n. Sp.:— [Geog., Surveying, etc.] The process of measuring how deep the sea or other body of water is at some point, sometimes by simply letting down a weight to the sea-bed on the end of a line and measuring

the line, sometimes by sending a s.-wave to the sea-bed and working out the distance from the time it takes for it to come back; a measure got by sounding. [Meteor.] The process of getting records of the condition of the upper ATMOSPHERE at different points. **′sounding ′balloon.** [Meteor.] A small BALLOON with recording instruments sent up into the ATMOSPHERE and moving freely from place to place, but having some apparatus by which it is made to come back to earth after a certain time, for example, through the loss by degrees of its gas. **′sounding board.** [Acous.] S. board; a board placed over the head or at the back of a person giving a public talk etc., so as to send the s. of his voice back in the direction of his hearers. **′sounding line.** [Geog., Surveying, etc.] A strong cord or wire, marked off into measuring units and having a lead or other weight at the end, used for taking soundings.

source, n. That from which anything comes, the cause or starting-point, sp. [Geog.] of a river, and [Phys.] of WAVES, for example, a *light s.*

South Pole, [Geog.] The point on the earth which is farthest south. **s.p.** [Elec.] (Of a MAGNET) the end which takes up a position pointing south when the magnet has the power of turning freely.

′Southern, a. Of, in, to do with, the south. **S. lights.** AURORA AUSTRALIS.

′Soxhlet appa′ratus. [Chem.] An apparatus for getting a SOLUBLE solid out of a mixed substance by sending a boiling SOLVENT through it over and over again, used sp. for freeing fats.

space charge. [Elec.] The NEGATIVE CHARGE formed in an ELECTRON DISCHARGE TUBE by the electrons sent out by the CATHODE.

space group. [Cryst.] A group of like space lattices. **space ′lattice.** [Cryst.] Any of the regular network designs formed by the ATOMS or unit groups of atoms making up a CRYSTAL.

space ′motion, space ve′locity. [Astron.] The rate and direction of a star's motion in space as worked out from observations of its motion in relation to other bodies in the sky and its motion in the direction of or away from the earth, as given by the SPECTROSCOPE.

space per′ception. [Psych.] The PERCEPTION through any or all of the senses of those properties and relations of things, that is, size, form, distance, position, and direction, by which space is experienced or on which the idea of space as something which may be viewed independently of material things is based.

space probe. *See* PROBE. **space re′search.** [Phys.] The process of getting knowledge of the space between the stars and PLANETS in our GALAXY and others and of these and all other bodies in it—covering Astronomy, Radio-astronomy, PLASMA PHYSICS, and ASTRO-NAUTICS. **'spacecraft, space-ship, space 'vehicle.** VEHICLE used in s. r., sq. ASTRONAUTICS.

space-time, a. To do with the s.-t. continuum. **s.-t. con'tinuum,** [Phys.] The system of four DIMENSIONS, formed by taking time as a fourth dimension of space, which, as the effect of the THEORY of RELATIVITY, has come into use for placing physical events in relation to others

'spadix, n. [Bot.] A flower-SPIKE with a thick middle stem and a SPATHE. **spa-'diceous, 'spadicose,** aa. **spa'diciform.** a.

spal'lation, n. [Phys.] A reaction in which PROTONS and NEUTRONS are taken from a NUCLEUS without FISSION.

span, 1.n. The (measure of the) distance between two limits in time or space, as that between the ends of the thumb and little finger when stretched out, or between the two ends of an arch, the two ends of an airplane, the start and end of an animal's existence, etc. [Engin.] The part of a structure such as an arch, roof, etc., between supports, bridging a space. [Psych.] The amount of material which may be taken in or covered at one time by a given mind-process, for example, attention. 2.v.t. Get (a thing or distance) measured by the s. of the hand or, loosely, in any way; go from end to end of, be bridging (a given space or time).

spar, n. [Mineral.] A general name used in mining and as part of special names (for example, *calc s.,* or CALCITE) for solid MINERALS (other than those formed from metals) which are readily separated into thin, more or less level, plates.

spark, 1.n. [Elec.] A very short burst of light and sound caused by the IONIZATION of the air or another NON-CONDUCTING gas when an electric DISCHARGE takes place in it, as, for example, when an electric current makes a jump from one metal point to another across a narrow space. 2.v.i. Give off electric ss. **s. gap.** [Elec.] A space full of air or other gas between two points in an electric CIRCUIT designed for the producing of a s., for example in a sparking plug. **s. 'generator.** [Elec.] A machine producing ALTER-NATING current which makes use of a s. sent through a s. gap from a CON-DENSER for producing its power. **s. plug.** Sparking plug. **s. 'spectrum.** [Phys.] The SPECTRUM of the light produced when an electric s. is caused between one bit of metal and another, in which lines representative of the IONIZED ATOMS, which are not present in other

sorts of spectra, may be seen. **'-ing,** n. Sp., undesired sparking between two parts of a machine, for example, the BRUSHES and the face of a COMMUTATOR. **'sparking plug.** [Elec.] In an INTERNAL COMBUSTION ENGINE a short, thick, rod-like part, one of a number, screwing etc. into the end of the CYLINDER and having two ELECTRODES with a s. gap between, for producing a s. for firing the gas etc.

'spasm, n. [Med.] A violent, automatic CONTRACTION of a muscle or muscles. **spas'modic,** a. Taking place from time to time, sp. in violent bursts, as some sorts of s. [Med.] Of, to do with, marked by, like, a s. or ss. **spas'modically,** adv.

'spastic, a. [Med.] Of or to do with a SPASM or spasms, sp. caused or marked by a spasm which goes on unbrokenly for a long time; having, to do with, s. paralysis, 2.n. Person having s. paralysis. **s. par'alysis.** A condition in which, as the effect of damage to the brain, the muscles of a part of the body, such as the legs, are locked and unable to be moved.

spathe, n. [Bot.] A great, freq. highly coloured, leaf-like part, coming from the same point on a stem as a flower-SPIKE and arching round and over it, sometimes almost completely covering it. **spa'thaceous, 'spathal,** aa. **'spathed,** a.

'spath-ic, -ose, aa. [Mineral.] Like SPAR.

'spathic 'iron. SIDERITE.

'spathulate, a. [Bot.] SPATULATE.

'spatial, a. To do with space. **'spatio-.**

'spatula, b. [Zoo.] Any structure of spoon-like form. **'spatulate,** a. [Biol.] Spoon-like in form, having a long narrow part ending in a short, wide, flat or somewhat hollow blade, sp. [Bot.] of leaf (*see picture p. 223*).

'spavin, n. A disease of the lower JOINT of the leg in horses, marked by a hard out-growth of bone on the inner side of it.

spawn, 1.n. [Zoo.] A mass of small eggs such as is put out by fish and other water animals. [Bot.] The MYCELIUM of a FUNGUS, sp. a mass of mycelia from food fungi, which is used for starting new growth. 2.v.i. [Zoo.] (Of fish or other water animals) put down or send out eggs or SPERMATOZOA.

spay, v.t. [Zoo.] Take out or make of no use the OVARIES of a female animal so as to put a stop to its producing offspring.

'specialist, n. An expert, sp. a medical man, who has special interest, training, and experience in one part of his field, and gen. keeps his work limited to that, as *a heart s.* **'speci'alty, 'specialty,** nn. Anyone's special branch of knowledge, that in which anyone is a s.

'specialize, 1.v.i. Take a special interest, undergo special training, *in* one limited part of a field, become a SPECIALIST *in* some branch of work or knowledge.

[Biol.] (Of an animal, plant, or part) undergo specialization. 2.v.t. [Biol.] Make undergo specialization. speciali'zation, n. The act or process of specializing or of becoming or causing to become specialized. [Biol.] The process of becoming specialized or the development of specialized parts or qualities; a part or quality which has become specialized. 'specialized, a. Designed for a special purpose; (of knowledge etc.) special, got by specialization; (of a field of knowledge etc.) having undergone division into special branches needing SPECIALISTS. [Biol.] (Of a living thing or a part) having undergone a development in structure such as to give it the properties necessary for some special way of living or some special and limited use, so that it has become very different from the earlier animals or plants or the earlier structure from which it has come down.

speci'ation, n. [Biol.] The process of EVOLUTION by which SPECIES are formed.

'species, n. Sort. [Biol.] The smallest fixed unit in the system of grouping of plants and animals, a division of a GENUS, made up of plants or animals which have in common one or more properties not present in other groups, and which are different from one another only in details which are unimportant in comparison with the ways in which they are the same as one another and unlike other sorts, as is seen by the fact that in natural conditions they have offspring only with one another and that these offspring all have the general properties of the group.

spe'cific, 1.a. To do with, having, or being the special property of, a sort or SPECIES; designed for some special purpose, limited in its operation etc. to certain things; not general, in the sense of being detailed, or clearly pointing to some special thing. [Med.] (Of substances etc.) having a special effect on a certain part of the body or a certain sort of disease; (of a disease) caused by one certain sort of poison, BACTERIUM etc., or producing a special effect on a certain part of the body. [Phys.] (Used in naming a number of CONSTANTS) measured in a special way on which there is agreement, for example, in relation to a fixed STANDARD, or in the form of an amount per unit AREA or VOLUME. 2.n. [Med.] A substance having a special effect against certain diseases or on certain parts of the body. s. ac'tivity. [Phys.] The RATIO between the amount of a RADIOISOTOPE present in an ELEMENT and the amount of the element. s. elec'tronic charge. [Phys.] The number got by the division of the CHARGE on an ELECTRON by its MASS. s. 'gravity.[Phys.]

The relation of the weight of a given measure of a substance to the weight of the same measure of water at 4°C. s. 'gravity 'bottle. [Phys., Chem.] A glass bottle having a long stopper with a pipe-like opening through it, used for measuring amounts of liquid so that the weight of the same amount of given liquids at a given TEMPERATURE may be got, and from that their s. gravities. s. heat. [Phys.] The amount of heat in CALORIES needed for increasing the TEMPERATURE of 1 gram of a given substance by 1°C. s. in'ductive capacity. DIELECTRIC CONSTANT. s. re'sistance. RESISTIVITY. s. ro'tation, s. 'rotary 'power. [Phys., Chem.] A substance's power of OPTICAL ACTIVITY as measured by the angle through which the plane of POLARIZATION of a ray of SODIUM light would be turned by a COLUMN 1 decimetre long of a SOLUTION having in it 1 gram of the substance in every cm^3. s. stain. [Chem. Biochem.] A STAIN colouring certain special structures or substances and not others, or colouring different ones differently so that they are clearly marked off from one another. s. 'volume. [Phys.] The VOLUME of a unit weight of a given substance. spe'cifically, adv. speci'ficity, n. The property of being s.

'specify, v.t. Make quite clear what one is talking about by naming it or giving details. specifi'cation, n. The act of specifying; a statement specifying something, sp. a list of directions for doing or making or building something (freq. 'specifications', as the specifications for a machine).

'specimen, n. A small part or amount of anything, such as a chemical or MINERAL, or a unit of any group, such as a plant or animal, used in science as an example of its sort for observation and testing.

'spectral, a. [Phys., Chem.] Of, to do with, based on, a SPECTRUM. s. distri'bution curve. [Optics] The GRAPH giving the relation between RADIANT ENERGY and WAVE-LENGTH in the light sent out from anything. s. sensi'tivity. [Optics] The different degrees to which a substance giving a reaction to light, sp. one used for coating a camera plate or FILM, is acted on by light of different colours. s. 'series. [Optics] A group of lines in the SPECTRUM of a substance, the WAVE-LENGTHS of which have a regular relation to one another. s. type. [Astron.] A division or group in a system of grouping stars based on the sorts of SPECTRA they give, every division being named by a letter. spectro-.

'spectro'chemistry, n. The branch of chemistry using SPECTRUM ANALYSIS.

'spectrograph, n. [Optics] An instrument for taking camera pictures of SPECTRA; spectrogram. 'spectrogram, n. A camera or other picture of a SPECTRUM. spectro-'graphic, a. spectro'graphically, adv.

'spectro'heliograph, n. [Astron.] An instrument for taking a camera picture of the sun in light of one colour only. spectro-'heliogram, n. A picture of the sun made with a s., in which its markings are seen specially clearly. 'spectrohelio'graphic, a.

'spectro'helioscope, n. [Astron.] An instrument for viewing the sun in light of one colour only.

spec'trometer, n. [Optics] A special SPECTRO-SCOPE used for measuring the WAVE-LENGTHS and the INDICES OF REFRACTION of rays forming a SPECTRUM. spec'tro-metry, n. The art or process of using a s.

'spectropho'tometer, n. [Optics] An instrument for measuring the INTENSITIES of light of different WAVE-LENGTHS in a SPECTRUM. 'spectropho'tometry, n.

'spectroscope, n. [Optics] An instrument for forming and viewing SPECTRA. 'spectro-'scopic(al), a. To do with the s. or with spectroscopy. spectro'scopically, adv. spec'troscopist, n. An expert in spectroscopy or the use of the s. spec'troscopy, n. The observation of SPECTRA and all processes of recording and measuring which go with it.

'spectrum (spectra), n. [Optics] The range of coloured lines or bands, in the order of the WAVE-LENGTHS of the rays by which they are formed, produced on a SCREEN etc. by light which has been broken up into parallel rays of different wave-lengths by being sent through a prism or DIFFRACTION GRATING [Phys., Acous.] A like range of unseen, that is, sound or ELECTRO-MAGNETIC, RAYS in the order of their WAVE-LENGTHS, as an X-ray s. (see CONTINUOUS S. BAND S., LINE S., ABSORP-TION S., EMISSION S, ARC S., SPARK S). s. an'alysis, [Chem.] The ANALYSIS of a complex substance by the observation of the coloured s. produced when light is given out by or sent through it, every substance having a representative s., and the fact of certain lines etc. being present being a sign of certain substances. s. colours. [Optics] Sp., the colours seen in the s. of white light, the chief of which, starting with the shortest WAVE-LENGTH, are VIOLET, blue, green, yellow, orange, and red. 'spectro-.

'specular, a. Smooth and polished so as to give back light-rays like a looking-glass. [Med.] To do with, (of an observation, etc.) done with the help of, a SPECULUM. s. re'flection. [Optics] REFLECTION as by a looking-glass, in which the ANGLE of REFLECTION and the ANGLE of INCIDENCE of every ray are equal and on opposite sides of a line at right angles to their meeting-point with the SURFACE in question, so that any ray seems, after reflection, to be coming from an IMAGE of its starting-point seen in the surface.

'speculate, v.i. [Psych.] Make up or put forward theories or suggestions about something on which there is, or the person forming them has, no or little certain knowledge. specu'lation, n. The act of speculating; a theory or suggestion of this sort. 'speculative, a. To do with, having a tendency to, s.; being a speculation.

'speculum (specula), n. A plate of brightly polished metal made up of $\frac{2}{3}$ copper and $\frac{1}{3}$ tin (s. metal) used as a REFLECTOR in OPTICAL instruments. [Med.] Any of a number of different forms of instrument used for keeping the openings into certain hollow parts of the body, for example, the nose, stretched so that the inside may be looked into.

speech, n. The physical process of giving a knowledge of one's thoughts to others by talk, that is, by a complex system of sounds made by the voice with such control that they, or their groupings, have the clear and fixed quality necessary for the purpose of acting as signs common to a society; the system of sounds used in s., language as produced by the voice and taken in by the ear. s. 'melody, s. tune. [Phonet.] INTONATION, sp. intonation as part of a language, one of the things in which different languages are different. s. sound. [Phonet.] Any of the simplest units of which s. is made up, that is, any sound which is made by using the VOCAL ORGANS in a special, fixed way and is of a sort to be united with other such sounds to make words.

speed, n. Rate of motion of any sort, or of acting; a high s. s. of ro'tation. (Of a turning body) the number of complete ROTATIONS in a unit of time, got by division of the number in a given time by the measure of that time in the units desired. s. 'counter. TACHOMETER. spee'dometer, n. [Mach.] An instrument for measuring rate of motion, sp. a TACHOMETER forming part of an automobile, and so scaled as to give the s. at which the automobile is going at any minute, at the same time recording the distance covered on any journey. '-y, s. Moving or taking place quickly.

'spel(a)ean, a. Of, to do with, living in, CAVES. spel(a)e'ology, n. [Geol., Biol.] The science of CAVES, or of plants and animals living in them. spel(a)e'ologist, n.

'spelter, n. The name given to the lower quality zinc used in industry, which is not quite free from other substances (having in it less than 99·9% zinc).

spent, a. Used up, having had its special power or properties taken from it by use. [Zoo.] (Sp. of fishes or insects) having put out all their eggs or SPERMATOZOA, no longer having any to put out. **s. acid.** [Chem.] Sp., mixed NITRIC ACID (HNO₃) and SULPHURIC ACID (H₂SO₄) which has been used in the process of NITRATION.

sperm, n. [Zool.] SPERMATOZOÖN or SPERMATOZOID; SEMEN.

-sperm, n. Seed, sp. [Bot] used in plant-names based on the form etc. of the seed. **-spermal,** a. Having seeds of the given number or sort, to do with, being, a -sperm.

sperma'ceti, n. [Zoo., Chem.] A white wax-like solid separating from the oil got from the heads and fat of certain CETACEA, and used in making soaps, skin-foods etc.

'spermaduct, n. [Zoo.] A pipe through which SPERMATOZOA are sent out.

'spermaphyte, n. [Bot.] SPERMATOPHYTE. **sperma'phytic,** a.

'spermary, n. [Zoo.] TESTIS.

sperma'tangium, n. [Bot.] The ANTHERIDIUM of certain ALGAE.

sperma'theca, n. [Zoo.] A vessel in female insects and other non back-boned animals into which SPERMATOZOA from the male are taken and stored till needed; a vessel for the same purpose in HERMAPHRODITE animals. **sperma'thecal,** a.

sper'matic, a. [Zoo.] To do with SPERMATOZOA or with a TESTIS, producing, transporting, like, etc., spermatozoa.

'spermatid, n. [Zoo.] A CELL which is produced by the division of a second-stage SPERMATOCYTE and undergoes development into a SPERMATOZOÖN.

sper'matiophore, n. [Bot.] A branch or structure producing SPERMATIA.

sper'matium (spermatia), n. [Bot.] A male germ-cell without the power of moving about, present in RHODOPHYCEAE and in certain FUNGI and LICHENES. **sperma'tiferous,** a. **sper'matio-.**

spermat(o)-. Seed; SPERM.

'spermato'blastic, a. [Zoo.] Producing SPERMATOZOA.

'spermatocyst, n. [Zoo.] A bag-like part having in it SPERMATOZOA.

'spermatocyte, n. [Bot.] A CELL which undergoes development into a SPERMATOZOID. [Zoo.] One or the other of the two cells formed from a SPERMATOGONIUM by the first MEIOTIC division (*primary s.*) or of the two further cells formed from a primary s. by the second meiotic division (*secondary s.*).

'spermato'genesis, n. [Zoo.] The producing of SPERMATOZOA from the SPERMATOGONIUM by way of the first and second groups of SPERMATOCYTES and the SPERMATIDS. **'spermato'genic, 'spermato-ge'netic,** aa.

sperma'togenous, a. [Zoo.] Producing SPERMATOZOA.

'spermato'gonium, n. [Zoo.] The first form of a male GERM-CELL, from which SPERMATOZOA are produced by SPERMATOGENESIS. [Bot.] SPERMOGONIUM. **'spermato'gonial,** a.

'spermatoid, a. [Zoo.] Like SEMEN or like a SPERMATOZOÖN.

'spermatophore, n. [Zoo.] A mass of SPERMATOZOA in a special covering put out by the male of a number of animals. [Bot.] SPERMATIOPHORE.

'Spermato'phyta, n.pl. [Bot.] The greatest DIVISION of plants in existence at the present time, made up of all those producing seeds, marked by a plant-body with a high development of special structures and a clear division into root, stem, leaves and flowers (or other special and complex instruments for REPRODUCTION by the uniting of GERM-CELLS). **'spermatophyte,** n. Any plant of the S. **'spermato'phytic,** a.

'spermatozo(o)id, n. [Bot.] A small free-moving male GERM-CELL in lower plants, gen. freed in water, through which it makes its way by CILIA to a female GERM-CELL, being guided by some attraction or apparatus.

spermato'zoön (spermatozoa), n. Zoo.] The small, free-moving male GERM-CELL of an animal, commonly with a head formed chiefly of NUCLEUS on the end of a long, whip-like tail-part by which motion is effected. **spermato'zoan,** a.

'spermic, a. To do with SPERM or seed, sp. [Bot.] -SPERMOUS.

spermi'duct, n. SPERMADUCT. **spermi'ducal,** a. To do with or near a s.

'spermio'genesis, n. [Zoo.] The changing of a SPERMATID into a SPERMATOZOÖN; SPERMATOGENESIS.

spermo-. SPERM.

'spermocarp, n. [Bot.] An OÖGONIUM after uniting with a male GERM-CELL.

'spermoduct, n. SPERMADUCT.

spermo'gonium (spermogonia), **'spermogone,** nn. [Bot.] A vessel like a bottle, cup, or hollow plate in which SPERMATIA are produced. **'spermogo'niferous,** a. **sper'mogonous,** a.

sperm oil, [Zoo., Chem.] A light yellow oil got, together with SPERMACETE, from the head-hollows and the body-fat of certain CETACEA, used as a LUBRICANT.

sperm'ology, n. [Bot.] The science of seeds. **spermo'logical,** a.

spermo'theca, n. SPERMATHECA.

-spermous, a. [Bot.] Having seeds of the given number or sort.

-spermy, n. [Bot.] The property of being -SPERMOUS.

'sperrylite, n. [Mineral.] A natural substance, $PtAs_2$, of a bright tin-like colour, got from the earth in very small grains, the only natural COMPOUND of Pt which has so far come to light.

sp. gr. = SPECIFIC GRAVITY.

'sphacelate, a. [Med., Bot.] (Of a part of the body or a plant) dead and DECAYING or dried up.

'sphacelous, a. [Med.] To do with, marked by, GANGRENE.

'sphacelus, n. [Med.] Dead substances separating from a SPHACELOUS wound.

sph(a)er(o)-. SPHERE, SPHERICAL.

sphaeren'chyma, n. [Bot.] PARENCHYMA of which the CELLS are ball-like in form.

sphae'ridium (sphaeridia), n. [Zoo.] Any of the small structures formed of a round body on a very short stem present on the outside of the hard covering of some ECHINODERMATA, possibly having to do with the sense of balance.

sphae'r(r)aphide, n. [Bot.] Any of the small round masses of needle-like CRYSTALS present in some plant CELLS.

'sphagnum moss or 'sphagnum, n. [Bot.] (A plant or mass of plants of) a sort of MUSCI which have their growth only in water, where year after year they DECAY, forming PEAT—noted for their sponge-like properties and power of ABSORPTION, which makes them of use for a number of different purposes, some very soft sorts being used for medical dressings.

'sphalerite, n. ZINC BLENDE.

sphe'nethmoid, n. [Zoo.] A bone of the head going round the front part of the brain and forward into the face, taking the place of the ORBITOSPHENOIDS in some AMPHIBIA.

'sphenion, n. [Zoo.] The lower front end of the PARIETAL bone.

'spheno-. [Zoo.] Of the SPHENOID (and ...):— '-man'dibular, a.; '-max'illary, a.; '-pa'rietal, a.; '-'pterygoid, a, etc.

'sphenoid, 1.a. Formed like a WEDGE. [Zoo.] To do with, near, the s. 2.n. [Zoo.] S. bone. [Cryst.] S. crystal. s. bone. [Zoo.] A bone of the middle and lower part of the bone structure of the head in back-boned animals, formed by the uniting of a number of other bones and in man made up of a middle part with two PAIRS of wing-like structures, a smaller pair and a greater pair, at the sides. s. 'crystal. CRYSTAL having four 3-sided faces, meeting in six edges, of which the four side ones are equal to one another and the two end ones are equal and in parallel planes. sphe'noidal, a. S.

sphere, n. [Geom.] A solid or hollow body all points on the limiting SURFACE of which are at the same distance from a middle point, a ball. [Astron.] The sky taken as a s. with the earth as its middle point, half of which is to be seen from the earth, and on which the stars seem to have their places and the different circles etc. used in astronomy as representative of their motions and relations are mapped out. s. of 'action, s. of 'influence. [Phys.] The s. representative of the limits of a force of RADIATION sent out in all directions. 'spheral, 'spheric(al), aa. Having the form of a s., to do with or forming part of a s. 'spherical aber'ration. [Optics] An error in the IMAGE formed by a LENS or a curved MIRROR caused by the rays going to the middle and those going to the edge not coming to quite the same FOCUS. spher'icity, n. The property of being a s.

-sphere, n. A SPHERE. [Astron., Geol.] A SPHERICAL coat round something, or a s. forming one of a number having the same middle point but different sizes so that they come one inside the other. -spheric(al), aa.

'spheroid, n. [Geom.] A form or body like a SPHERE but not completely round, sp. one of a regular form but of which one AXIS is longer than the other, so that it has the look of a ball which has been pulled out or pushed in on two opposite sides. spher'oidal, a. spher'oidal 'jointing. [Geol.] Spheroidal cracks in ROCKS, or the sort of structure produced by spheroidal weathering. spher'oidal state. [Phys.] The condition of a liquid which on being sent onto a highly heated metal plate takes the form of drops rolling about over it without boiling, the effect being caused by a cushion of VAPOUR produced between the liquid and the plate so that they are not in fact touching. spher'oidal 'weathering. [Geol.] The forming of BASALT or like material in a crack between two ROCK masses into a solid s. with a number of separate coats, one outside the other, as the effect of the chemical operation of water running down the crack. spheroi'dicity, n. The condition of being a s.

'spheroidize, v.t. [Metals] Make the steel in an iron ALLOY take the form of more or less round grains by heating the alloy for a long time and then letting it get cold slowly. spheroidi'zation, n.

spher'ome, n. [Bot.] A mass of small round drops of fat in a CELL, or the substance producing them.

sphe'rometer, n. [Phys.] An instrument for measuring the amount of curve of a SURFACE.

'spherula, 'spherule, nn. A little SPHERE or SPHEROID, sp. [Zoo.] A sponge SPICULE of this form. 'spherular, a. 'spherulate, a.

'spherulite, n. [Geol.] A ball-like mass made up of very thin thread-like CRYSTALS going out like rays from a middle point, seen in glass-like VOLCANIC ROCKS and gen. formed of QUARTZ and FELDSPAR. **spheru'litic**, a.

'sphincter, n. [Zoo.] A ring of muscle round an opening or in the wall of a pipe-like part, by which it may be shut or narrowed, as in the ANUS. **'-al**, a. **'-ate**, a. **'sphinctero-**.

'sphygmus, n. [Zoo., Med.] The PULSE. **'sphygmic**, a. **'sphygmoid, sphyg'modic**, aa. PULSE-like, moving with a regular rhythm. **'sphygmogram**, n. [Med.] A record made by a sphygmograph. **'sphygmograph**, n. [Med.] An instrument for recording the motion of the PULSE in the form of a line on paper etc. **sphygmo'graphic**, a. [Med.] To do with a sphygmograph or with sphygmography. **sphyg'mography**, n. [Med.] The use of the sphygmograph; an account of the PULSE. **'sphygmoma'nometer**, n. [Med.] An instrument for measuring BLOOD PRESSURE formed of a bag folded round the arm over an ARTERY into which air is pumped till the blood-current is stopped, the air-pressure being measured by a MANOMETER. **sphyg'mometer**, n. [Med.] Any instrument for measuring the rate and force of the PULSE. **'sphygmophone**, n. [Med.] An instrument for hearing the PULSE.

'spicate, a. [Biol.] Having the form of a SPIKE, having spikes, ranged in spikes, etc.

'spicula (spiculae), 1.n. SPICULE. 2.pl. See SPICULUM.

'spicule, n. A small, gen. hard, pointed or needle-like structure. [Bot.] Any small pointed outgrowth; a small SPIKE; the SHELL of a DIATOM from which the plant has gone. [Zoo.] Any small pointed outgrowth; any of the small hard masses of different forms, made up chiefly of Ca or Si, which give support to the soft parts of a great number of animals without back-bones, such as most sponges. **'spicular**, a. **'spiculate(d)**, aa. **spicu'liferous**, a. **spic'uliform**, a.

'spiculum (spicula), n. [Bot.] Any small sharp point. [Zoo.] Any of a number of small sharp-pointed or rod-like structures for special purposes in different animals, as the SPINES of an ECHINODERM.

'spiegel ('eisen), n. [Metal.] An ALLOY of Fe, Mn and C used in making steel by the BESSEMER PROCESS.

spike, n. A strong sharp point forming a PROJECTION on something, or a pointed bit of metal used for driving into something. [Bot.] A RACEMOSE flower-grouping in which small flowers without stems are ranged on a middle stem, freg. forming a long pointed mass (*see* picture p. 199). **'spikelet**, n. [Bot.] A small s., sp.

one of those made up chiefly of BRACTS with only a small number of flowers, forming a unit of the flower-group in grasses.

spin, 1.n. A quick motion round and round on an AXIS; the motion of an airplane going down in a SPIRAL curve. [Phys.] The possible s. on its axis of any PARTICLE smaller than an ATOM, which may be responsible for some of the ENERGY produced by it and for its having a MAGNETIC MOMENT independently of any CHARGE. 2.v.i. and t. Be or put in quick motion round and round on its axis.

spin, v.t. Get a substance pulled out and formed or twisted into thread, said sp. of the making of thread from natural wool, silk, cotton etc. [Zoo.] (Of an insect, etc.) make (a thread) by sending out a sticky liquid which quickly becomes hard in the air, or make (a structure, for example, for covering itself) of such threads.

'spina (spinae), n. [Zoo.] A small sharp-pointed outgrowth; in insects, an APODEME coming after the FURCA.

'spina 'bifida. [Med.] The condition, present from birth, in which the back-bone has a parting at the lower end and the SPINAL CORD etc. comes out through the opening, causing an elastic SWELLING in the back.

'spinal, a. [Zoo.] Of, to do with, near, the back-bone; to do with, dependent on, the s. cord. **s. anaes'thesia**. The stopping of sense impulses from the lower part of the body from being sent to the brain by the INJECTION of something under the covering of the s. cord, or by disease. **s. 'canal**. [Zoo.] The long, pipe-like hollow through which the s. cord goes, formed by the NEURAL ARCHES. **s. 'column**. [Zoo.] The 'back-bone', the chief support of the body of a higher animal and the seat of the s. cord, a structure formed of a line of VERTEBRAE joined together by locking outgrowths and by LIGAMENTS, and separated by elastic CARTILAGES, in such a way that every vertebra has some degree of motion in relation to those to which it is joined. **s. cord**. [Zoo.] The thick cord of nerve substance, branching from time to time into nerves going left and right, running from the brain down the s. canal, and acting on the one hand as the road by which NERVE IMPULSES are transported to and from the brain, and on the other as the apparatus by which s. reflexes are sent out. **s. nerve**. Any of the nerves rooted in the s. cord and going out in two's, one right and one left, through the openings between the VERTEBRAE, to the skin and muscles of the body, legs, and arms. **s. 'puncture**. [Med.] The process

436

of putting a HYPODERMIC NEEDLE through the outer cover of the s. cord in the lower part of the back to take off some of the CEREBROSPINAL FLUID for the purpose of testing it or making unnormal PRESSURE less. **s. 'reflex.** [Zoo., Psych.] A REFLEX for which the connection is made in the s. cord. **s. shock.** [Med., Zoo.] A condition in which the operation of the s. cord is stopped or limited for a time as the effect of damage to some part of it or to its connections with the brain.

spi'nalis (spinales), n. [Zoo.] Any of a number of muscles making connections between VERTEBRAE by which some part of the backbone is bent or kept straight.

'spinate, a. [Biol.] Having a sharp-pointed PROJECTION or covered with SPINES; having the form of a sharp spine.

'spindle, n. [Mach.] A long pin or rod which is turning or on which something is turned, sp. that by which the thread is tristed and round which it is rolled in a SPINNING machine. [Biol.] Any part or structure giving the suggestion of a rod pointed at the ends, sp. the structure of ACHROMATIN formed between the ASTERS in MITOSIS or MEIOSIS. **s. a'ttachment.** [Biol.] The narrowed part of a CHROMOSOME by which it is joined to the s. **s. 'fibre.** [Biol.] Any of the delicate threads of which the s. seems to be made up.

spine, n. [Bot.] Any small, stiff, rod-like, sharp-pointed part on a leaf or branch formed by a change in its substance or structure at that point, not a separate outgrowth. [Zoo.] Any small, stiff, sharp-pointed part, for example, any of the needle-like outgrowths by which the skin of some animals is covered to keep other animals from touching them, a SPICULE, or a sharp PROJECTION on a bone, etc.; the SPINAL COLUMN; spiny ray. **'-less,** a. [Biol.] Without ss. [Zoo.] Without a back-bone. **spin'escent,** a. [Biol.] Pointed; with a tendency to become hard and s.-like, or to become spinose. **'spinose,** a. [Biol.] Covered, armed, with ss. **spi'nosity,** n. [Biol.] The condition of being spinose. **spi'nous,** a. [Biol.] S.-like; having, covered with, ss. **'spinous 'process.** [Zoo.] Sp.:— NEURAL SPINE; the pointed end on one or other of the greater wings of the SPHENOID; the s. on the head of the TIBIA. **'spiny,** a. Spinous. **spiny fin.** [Zoo.] A FIN supported by spiny rays. **spiny-finned,** a. **spiny ray.** [Zoo.] A FIN-RAY which is completely stiff, without divisions or branches, and pointed at the end.

spin'el(le), n. [Mineral.] Natural $MgAl_2O_4$ or any of a group of substances of like chemical structure, in which the place of the Mg is taken by Zn, Mn, or FERROUS iron and that of the Al by Cr or FERRIC

iron, noted for their different colours and their very hard, pointed CRYSTALS.

spini- [Biol.] SPINE(s):— **spin'iferous,** a., **'spiniform,** a.; [Med., Zoo.] SPINO-.

'spinneret, n. [Zoo.] A structure, gen. one of two, four, or six, in insects or ARACHNIDA by which the thread-forming liquid is sent out in SPINNING. [Mach.] In making RAYON, a metal plate full of small holes through which the CELLULOSE SOLUTION is sent so as to be formed into threads.

spino-. [Med., Zoo.] SPINAL (and ...):— **'-'muscular,** a.,**'-'neural,** a.; [Biol.] SPINI-.

spin'thariscope. n. [Phys.] An apparatus in which a very small bit of a RADIOACTIVE substance is placed in front of a FLUORESCENT SCREEN and viewed through LENSES making clear to the eye the small bursts of light produced by the ALPHA RAYS meeting the screen.

'spinule, n. [Biol.] A very small, sharp-pointed SPINE. **'spinulate(d), 'spinulose,** aa. Having, covered with, ss. **spinu'lation,** n. A covering of SPINES or ss.; the condition of being spinulate. **'spinu'lescent,** a. Somewhat spinulate. **spinu'lescence,** n.

'spiracle, spi'raculum (spiracula), nn. [Zoo.] A breathing-hole sp.:—in insects and other land ARTHROPODA, any of the openings of the breathing-pipes placed in a line down the two sides of the body; in fish, the opening into the mouth in the upper part of the head, a GILL-SLIT whose development has been stopped at an early stage, sometimes having an incomplete gill in it; in CETACEA, the outer opening, or one of the two outer openings, of the nose, placed in the top of the head. **spi'racular,** a. **'spiraculate,** a. **spi'racu'liferous,** a. **spi'raculiform,** a.

'spiral, n., a. (A line or structure) starting at a point and curving regularly round and round, getting by degrees farther and farther from it, sometimes in the same plane or sometimes moving through a number of planes in corkscrew-like turns of equal or increasing size. [Astron.] S. nebula, **s. cell** or **'vessel** or **'tracheide.** [Bot.] Any CELL (or vessel, or TRACHEIDE) having s. thickening in the walls. **s. 'cleavage.** [Zoo.] A system of CLEAVAGE seen in the eggs of a number of lower animals, in which the smaller divisions formed in the top part of the egg are rolled over so as to come opposite the lines of division between the greater divisions of the lower part, this process taking place again at every further division of the different parts, but the direction of turning changing every time, now to the right, now to the left, so that in the end a special and quite regular design of BLASTOMERES is formed. **s. 'flower.** [Bot.] A flower of which the parts are placed in a s. line. **s. 'nebula.** [Astron.] Any NEBULA of the sort which seems through the TELESCOPE to have a structure of ss. and arms, probably made up only of stars without stretches of gas. **s. spring.** [Mach.] A spring formed of a wire twisted into the form of a s. **s. 'thickening.** [Bot.] The addition of new material to the walls of a CELL or XYLEM vessel in the form of a thicker line twisting spirally round them; such a line of new material in the walls of a cell, etc. **s. valve.** [Zoo.] A fold of MUCOUS MEMBRANE going in a s. round the inside of the wall of the INTESTINE in certain fish of lower groups, increasing the SURFACE by which the substances produced by digestion are taken into the system. **'spiralism,** n. [Bot.] The unnatural growth of a normally straight stem into a s. **spir'ality,** n. The condition of being s.; the degree of curve in the turn of a s.

spi'ranthy, n. [Bot.] The twisting of the parts of a flower out of their normal places. **spi'ranthic,** a.

spire, n. [Zoo.] The upper, pointed part of a SPIRAL SHELL, that is, all the structure of turns on top of the first and greatest. [Geol.] A FOSSIL support of an arm of a SPIRIFER.

'spireme, n. [Biol.] The mass of thread-like CHROMOSOMES formed in the NUCLEUS at the start of MITOSIS or MEIOSIS.

'spiricle, n. [Bot.] Any of the thin, thread-like outgrowths of some seed-coats, twisting into SPIRALS when dry.

'spirifer, n. [Zoo., Geol.] A sort of BRACHIO-POD of very early times, of which the two arms inside the SHELL were supported by two SPIRAL BANDS of hard material. **spir'iferous,** a. [Geol.] Having in it FOSSIL ss.

spi'rillum (spirilla), n. [Bot.] A sort of SPIROCHAETE with a very long body and a number of FLAGELLA at the two ends, causing certain diseases of fowls, cows, etc.

spirit, n. [Chem.] The liquid formed chiefly of ETHYL ALCOHOL in water got by the complete DISTILLATION of liquids etc. having alcohol in them, commonly those made from FERMENTED grain or fruit; (used in naming) any of a number of VOLATILE liquids got by distillation from PETROLEUM, wood etc., and used for burning, chiefly in engines (for example, *motor* s.), and as SOLVENTS for fats; (used, chiefly in old chemistry, in naming) any of a number of volatile liquids got by distillation or which are SOLUTIONS of some substance in alcohol. **s. 'level.** LEVEL TUBE. **ss. of salt(s).** (Old name for) HYDROCHLORIC ACID. **ss. of wine.** ETHYL ALCOHOL.

'spirivalve, n., a. [Zoo.] (A GASTROPOD) having a SPIRAL SHELL.

spiro-. SPIRAL. [Med.] Breathing.

'spiroch(a)ete, n. [Med.] Any of a great group of important disease-producing BACTERIA having thread-like SPIRAL bodies all the time in waving motion, responsible for SYPHILIS and certain sorts of FEVER.

'spirograph, n. [Med.] An instrument for recording, in the form of a GRAPH, the motions of breathing. **'spirogram,** n. A record made by a s. **spi'rography,** n.

'spiroid, a. Screw-like in form.

spi'rometer, n. [Med.] An instrument for measuring how much air a person has the power of breathing in or out at one time.

'spironeme, n. [Zoo.] A SPIRAL thread in the stem of certain CILIOPHORA giving it the power of becoming shorter or longer.

spit, n. [Geog.] A narrow, low tongue of land, sp. of sand or loose stones, stretching out into the sea or other body of water.

'splanchnic, a. [Zoo.] To do with the parts inside the body, such as the heart, breathing-apparatus, and all the apparatus of digestion. **splanchno-.**

'splanchnoc(o)el(e), n. [Zoo.] In the EMBRYO of a higher back-boned animal, the space formed between the SOMATOPLEURE and the SPLANCHNOPLEURE which becomes at a later stage the hollow housing the inner parts of the animal.

'splanchnopleure, n. [Zoo.] In an EMBRYO, the inner part of the MESOBLAST, which, separating from the SOMATOPLEURE, undergoes development into the wall of the ALIMENTARY CANAL.

'splayfoot, n. [Zoo.] A wide, flat foot, of which all the underside comes in touch with the earth in walking. [Med.] FLATFOOT, sp. when, in addition, the feet are somewhat turned out. **splay-'footed,** a.

spleen, n. [Zool] A structure formed of a mass of LYMPHOID TISSUE kept together by a thin skin from which division-walls go out to make a framework for the softer substance, placed at the side of the stomach or INTESTINE in most back-boned animals, and playing an important part in the blood system, producing LYMPHOCYTES, storing ERYTHROCYTES to be sent into the blood at need, and causing the destruction of old ones no longer able to do their work. **sple'netic,** **'splenic,** aa. **splenic an'aemia.** [Med.] A CHRONIC disease marked by an increase in the size of the s., ANAEMIA, and LEUCOPENIA, **spleno-.**

'splenial, 1.a. [Zoo.] To do with the SPLENIUS; to do with the s. bone. 2.n. S. bone. **s. bone.** A thin bone on the inner side of the MANDIBLE in some lower back-boned animals.

'splenius, n. [Zoo.] One or the other of two flat muscles coming from the upper back up the back of the neck.

splint, n. [Med.] Any stiff structure, such as a flat rod of wood or metal, used to keep a damaged part of the body, such as a broken bone, unmoving and in place. **s. bone.** [Zoo.] FIBULA; one or other of the two thin bones at the sides of the CANNON BONE in a horse's foot. **'splintage,** n. [Med.] The dressing of a part with a s. or ss.

split, 1.v.i. (Of a structure or substance) become parted or cracked open, sp. from end to end. 2.v.t. Make s., get parted by force without cutting through. [Phys.] Get (a physical structure, sp. the ATOM) separated into the structures of which it is made up. [Chem.] Get (a substance) separated into the substances of which it is made up. 3.n. The process of splitting; a crack or division. 4.a. Having undergone splitting, having a s. **s. person'ality.** [Med., Psych.] DUAL or MULTIPLE PERSONALITY; SCHIZOPHRENIA. **'s.-phase,** a. [Elec.] (Of a machine, etc.) using a PHASE-SPLITTER.

'spodium, n. Bone or animal CHARCOAL, sp. waste from sugar-works, used in producing Ca PHOSPHATES for use in making land fertile.

'spokeshave, n. A sort of plane with the blade placed between two parts for gripping with the two hands, used in forming and smoothing thin, rounded, wood structures, such as the rods of a wheel.

'spondyl(e), **'spondylus,** nn. [Zoo.] VERTEBRA. **spondy'litis,** n. [Med.]. **'spondylous,** a. **spondyl(o)-.**

'spongin, n. [Zoo., Biochem.] The strong, silk-like, PROTEIN material making up the framework of those sponges in common use. **'sponginblast,** **'spongoblast,** nn. A CELL producing s.

spongi(o)-. Sponge, sponge-like.

'spongioblast, n. [Zoo.] Any of the CELLS in the SPINAL CORD of the EMBRYO of backboned animals from which NEUROGLIA cells are produced.

'spong-iose, -ious, 'spongoid, 'spongy, aa. Sponge-like, full of small holes like a sponge. **'spongy 'layer.** [Bot.] The coat of s. parenchyma coming nearest the skin of the under side of a leaf. **'spongy par'enchyma.** [Bot.] PARENCHYMA with great spaces between CELLS and a great number of CHLOROPLASTS, forming a s. layer on the under side of most leaves. **spongi'osity.**

'spongophare, n. [Zoo.] In a RHAGON, the upper part, formed of a network of small spaces.

spon'taneous, a. Produced or taking place as a natural development without the help of man, or as the effect of inner forces without the operation of any outside force, self-caused. **s. com'bustion.** [Phys., Chem.] The taking fire of a substance as the effect of the producing of heat by chemical reactions inside it. **s. de'cay.** [Phys.] The changing of one ELEMENT into another by RADIOACTIVITY. **s. e'mission.** [Phys.] The s. jumping down of an EXCITED ATOM to its lowest ENERGY LEVEL with RADIATION of its energy. **s. gene'ration.** ABIOGENESIS. **s. ig'nition 'temperature.** [Phys.] The TEMPERATURE at which a liquid or gas will take fire in air or O. **spontan'eity,** n. The property of being s., sp., [Biol.] the tendency of sorts of living things to undergo new developments which are seemingly not reactions to living conditions. **'-ly,** adv.

spo'radic, a. Taking place from time to time, or here and there, irregularly, not going on all the time or handed on from place to place, as a *s. disease*; present by itself, not one of a group or number, as *a s. example*. [Bot.] (Of plants) limited to certain places; present over a stretch of country in small widely separated groups. **spo'radically,** adv.

spo'rangial, a. [Bot.] Of, to do with, produced by, a SPORANGIUM, or having or formed of sporangia. **s. sac, s. 'vesicle.** [Bot.] A vessel with very thin walls, produced as an outgrowth from the SPORANGIUM in certain FUNGI, in which the zoöSPORES undergo their later development.

sporangi(o)-. SPORANGIUM, SPORANGIAL: **sporan'giferous,** a., **spo'rangiform,** a., **spor'angiospore,** n.

spo'rangiole, sporangi'olum (sporangiola), nn. [Bot.] A SPORANGIUM of a sort having in it only a small number of SPORES, present with the commoner sort of sporangia in certain FUNGI.

spo'rangio'phore, n. [Bot.] A stem or thread-like part supporting a SPORANGIUM or sporangia.

spo'rangium (sporangia), n. [Bot.] A vessel or walled structure in which SPORES are produced.

spore, n. [Biol.] A very small and simple body, formed of one cell or a group of cells with a wall round it, separating from a plant or PROTOZOAN and having the power of growth into a new one, but never, like a seed or egg, having in it an EMBRYO—produced in very great numbers by all sorts of plants, but sp. FUNGI and BACTERIA, in a number of different ways, and by protozoans by simple cell division, and having the important properties of readily undergoing wide distribution, because of their number and size, and of not readily undergoing destruction, freq. being specially armed against hard conditions by a very thick wall and the power of resting undamaged inside it, without starting development, till conditions are right. **s. ball.** [Bot.]

A round mass of ss. **s. case, s. sac.** A vessel or pocket for ss. **s. group.** [Bot.] A s. formed of a number of CELLS all or some of which undergo independent development like separate ss. **s. 'mother cell.** [Bot.] Any of the CELLS produced by division from an ARCHESPORE which then by MEIOSIS gives birth to four ss. [Zoo.] S.-producing cell. **s. 'tetrad.** [Bot.] The group of 4 ss. produced by a s. mother cell. **sporifi'cation,** n. The forming of ss.

spor(i)-. SPORE: spo'riferous, a.

'**sporidism,** n. [Bot.] A SPORE GROUP.

spo'ridium (sporidia), n. [Bot.] A small SPORE, sp. one produced by ABSTRICTION from a PROMYCELIUM. **sporid'iferous,** a [Bot.] Producing ss.

'**sporo-.** SPORE: -'genesis, spor'ogeny, nn., 'sporoid, a.

'**sporoblast,** n. [Zoo.] A SPORE MOTHER CELL. [Bot.] A unit of a SPORE GROUP.

'**sporocarp, sporo'carpium** (sporocarpia), nn. [Bot.] A structure with a number of CELLS producing SPORES, as seen sp. in RHODOPHYCEA, ASCOMYCETES, MUSCI and some FILICALES.

'**sporocyst,** n. [Zoo.] The strong covering produced round a SPORE in PROTOZOA; a spore covered with a s., as a stage in the history of Protozoa; in some TREMATODA, a stage in which the animal takes a bag-like form, producing, as outgrowths from its inner coat, CELLS which become separated from it and undergo development inside it. **sporo'cystic,** a.

'**sporocyte,** n. [Bot.] A SPORE MOTHER CELL.

'**sporoduct,** n. [Zoo.] In certain Sporozoa, any of the small pipe-like openings in the walls of the covering which the animal takes on in the SPORE-producing stage through which the spores are sent out.

sporo'genic, spor'ogenous, aa. [Biol.] Producing SPORES, producing offspring by spores.

sporo'gonium (sporogonia), n. [Bot.] The SPORE-producing structure or SPOROPHYTE in MUSCI and HEPATICAE, produced by a sex-process and never separating from the mother plant, on which it is almost completely dependent for its food.

'**sporont,** n. [Zoo.] In SPOROZOA, the GERM-CELL-producing form of the animal or stage in its history.

'**sporophore,** n. [Bot.] Any of the structures producing and supporting SPORES in different sorts of FUNGI. **spor'ophorous,** a. [Bot.] To do with a s., producing ss.

'**sporophyll,** n. [Bot.] A leaf, sometimes like a normal leaf, sometimes much changed, producing a SPORE-vessel or spore-vessels.

'**sporophyte,** n. [Bot.] In a plant having ALTERNATION OF GENERATIONS, the

SPORE-producing plant or stage. **sporo-'phytic,** a.

'**sporoplasm,** n. [Zoo.] The PROTOPLASMA of SPORE; a SPOROZOITE.

Sporo'zoa, n.pl. [Zoo.] A CLASS of PROTOZOA of which all are PARASITES and a great number disease-causing, which go through a number of forms, sexed and unsexed, and at one stage in their history undergo SPORULATION. **sporozo'an, -on,** n. Animal of the S. **sporo'zo-an, -ic, -ous,** aa. Of, to do with, like, the S.

sporo'zoite, n. [Zoo.] In certain SPOROZOA, any of the small moving SPORES, freq. like thin curved rods, formed by the division of one of the greater, first-formed spores of the SPOROCYST STAGE.

sport, n. [Biol.] Any plant, animal, or structure markedly different from the normal as the effect of MUTATION.

sporu'lation, n. [Bot.] The forming or freeing of SPORES. [Zoo.] The process in PROTOZOA by which a first-formed spore, after the development of a wall round it, becomes almost completely broken up into smaller spores, which are then freed and undergo development into a different form of the animal. '**sporulate,** v.i. [Bot.] Get SPORES formed or sent out. [Zoo.] Undergo s. '**sporulating,** a.

'**sporule,** n. [Bot.] A small SPORE. '**sporular,** a. **sporu'liferous,** a.

spot, n. MACULA.

'**spotlight,** n. A lighting-apparatus with a LENS designed to give out a narrow parcel of rays so as to send a very bright light onto a limited space. '**-ing,** n. The process of lighting a thing or part of it very much more brightly than the space or things round it by the use of a s.

spot 'welding. WELDING two metal plates together by putting one edge over the other and sending a very strong electric current through them at different points, or 'spots', in place of heating and hammering them all down the join.

spout, 1.v.i. (Of a liquid) come through a small opening with great force so as to keep together in a solid pipe-like form for some distance. [Zoo.] Of CETACEA, send up a s. of water and air on breathing out through the nose at the top of the sea. 2.v.t. Send out a liquid in this way. 3.n. A solid, pipe-like, mass of liquid sent out or up for some distance as the effect of coming with force through an opening.

sprain, 1.n. [Med.] (The condition caused by) a sudden, violent stretching of a JOINT or muscle, damaging the LIGAMENTS, etc. but not putting anything out of place. 2.v.t. Undergo a s. in (a joint or muscle).

spray, 1.n. A mass of small drops of water or other liquid sent into the air, as by a waterfall or waves, or by an apparatus designed for this purpose; an instrument for spraying, sp. [Med.] an ATOMIZER; a liquid used for spraying. 2.v.t. Send a liquid substance onto (something) or about (a place) in the form of s., for example, s. trees with an INSECTICIDE, s. wood etc. with paint to get it coated, s. the inside of the throat, nose etc. with a medical substance; send out (a substance) in the form of s. 'sprayer, n. Any of a number of instruments or apparatuses used for spraying for different purposes.

spring, n. [Med.] Any elastic body or apparatus used for producing a force in some desired direction by going back to its normal form and size when some force keeping it twisted, pulled etc., from the normal is taken off.

spring 'balance. An apparatus for measuring weight by its effect on a SPIRAL steel spring.

'spring 'tide, [Astron.] The increased TIDE caused twice a month at new moon and full moon by the fact that at those times the attraction of the sun and that of the moon are working to the same effect.

'sprocket, n. [Mach.] A tooth-like part, as on the edge of a s. wheel; a s. wheel. **s. wheel.** A wheel with teeth round the edge slipping into the holes of a chain moving round it.

sprue, n. [Med.] A TROPICAL disease of the ALIMENTARY CANAL in which the INTESTINE is unable to take into the blood Ca, fat or sugar, marked by serious INFLAMMATION of the mouth, tongue, and walls of the intestine and by DIARRHEA, and causing ANAEMIA, loss of weight, and a very feeble condition.

spur, n. [Zoo.] A stiff sharp outgrowth, as on the legs of insects or the legs and wings of some birds, sp. that on the leg of a male fowl used in fighting. [Med.] A s.-like outgrowth from a bone or other material of the body. [Bot.] A long, hollow, pointed outgrowth of a flower or flower-part, sp. one storing NECTAR. [Geog., Geol.] A lower side-branch of a mountain or a range of mountains etc., coming out more or less at right angles to it.

'spuriae, n.pl. [Zoo.] The feathers of the BASTARD WING of a bird.

'spurious, a. False, not what it seems to be, sp. [Biol.] (of a part) looking like some named part but in fact different from it in structure. **s. di'ssepiment.** [Bot.] A division-wall in a fruit which is not formed as a division between united CARPELS but by an outgrowth from the wall of one carpel. **s. rad'iation.** [Radio] The sending out of waves outside the range of FREQUENCIES of those designed.

'sputtering, n. [Phys.] The giving off of its substance in small bits, so as to make a coating on the other ELECTRODES or the walls of the vessel, by the CATHODE in a DISCHARGE TUBE. 'sputter, v.i. and t. (Of a CATHODE in a DISCHARGE TUBE) give off its substance or give off (its substance) in this way.

'sputum, n. [Med.] The liquid formed in the nose and upper part of the throat when sent out through the mouth, as in certain unhealthy or diseased conditions.

'squama (squamae), n. [Biol.] A SCALE or scale-like structure, sp. the CALYPTER in insects or a scale-like body on the second division of a feeler in some CRUSTACEA. 'squamate, -ose, aa. Having, formed of, covered with, ss. squa'mation, n. [Zoo.] The order in which the SCALES of an animal are placed. squam'iferous, a. 'squam-iform, -oid, aa.

squa'mosal, 1.a. [Zoo.] Naming or to do with one or the other of two bones of the head in back-boned animals in the same position as the squamous part of the TEMPORAL BONE in man. 2. A squamosal bone; the squamous part of the temporal bone in man. 'squamous, a. [Zoo.] SQUAMATE or SQUAMOID: naming or to do with the flat, upper part of the TEMPORAL BONE in man and higher animals. 'squamous epi'thelium. [Zoo.] PAVEMENT EPITHELIUM.

Squa'mata, n.pl. [Zoo.] An ORDER of REPTILIA made up of LACERTILIA and OPHIDIA.

squa'mella (squamellae), n. [Bot.] PALEA. squa'mellate, a.

'squamula (squamulae), n. [Biol.] A very small SCALE 'squamul-ate, -ose, aa.

square, 1.n. [Maths.] (Of a number, etc.) the second POWER. [Geom.] 4-sided plane form with all its sides equal and all its angles right angles. 2.a. (Naming a unit of measure) being the s. of the given measure, and so forming a unit for measuring AREA, as a 's. cm'. 3.v.t. MULTIPLY (a number etc.) by itself. **s. 'measure.** (System of units for measuring) AREA. **s. root.** Of a given number, the number of which it is the s. **squared,** a. MULTIPLIED by itself, taken to the second POWER, as "x squared" (that is, x^2).

squint, n. [Med.] STRABISMUS.

Sr, Sign for STRONTIUM.

stab 'culture. [Bact.] A CULTURE in the form of a jelly or solid into which the BACTERIA are pushed on a needle or thin wire.

'stabile, a. Unmoving, said sp. [Med.] of ELECTRODES which are kept in one position on the body in sending an electric current through it, or of the current going between such electrodes, opp. LABILE.

sta'bility, n. The property of being stable. [Mech., Elec.] The property of a body or system of forces by which it has a tendency to go back to its normally balanced position or condition of regular motion after having been put out of it by some outside force. as seen in the automatic adjustment of an airplane to air currents, etc. **stabili'zation**, n. The process of stabilizing or the condition of being stabilized, sp. [Bot.] the adjustment of plant growth to conditions in a certain place so that a regular sort of growth is produced there. **'stabilize**, v.t. Make or keep stable, give s. to. **'stabilizer**, n. Sp. [Mech.] Any part or apparatus giving s. to a structure, as the tail plane of an airplane. [Chem.] A NEGATIVE CATALYST; a substance put into a SOLUTION to make it stable. [Elec.] An apparatus for keeping an electric current or e.m.f. fixed or regular independently of changes in the input or output over a certain range. **'stable**, a. Having s., sp.:— [Phys.-Chem.] (Of a substance) not readily changed from one STATE OF MATTER to another; (of an ELEMENT or ATOM) which does not undergo SPONTANEOUS DECAY; (of a solution or system of states) not readily put out of EQUILIBRIUM; [Chem.] (of a complex substance) not readily broken up. **stable equi'librium**. [Mech.] The condition of a body so placed that if given a small push it will (have a tendency to) come back to its earlier position when the impulse is over, that is, of a body whose POTENTIAL ENERGY is as low as possible. **'stable oscill'ation**. [Mech., Elec.] Any OSCILLATION which comes to an end by degrees through loss of ENERGY if not kept up by some outside force.

'stactometer, n. [Med.] A very thin glass pipe or rod for measuring out liquid in drops.

'stadium (stadia), n. [Zoo.] Any clearly marked stage in the existence of an animal, sp. the time between any two ECDYSES.

stage, n. The part of a MICROSCOPE on which the thing to be looked at is placed. [Geol.] A group of ROCKS forming a division of a SERIES and gen. parallel to an AGE in the time-system of geology. **s. mi'crometer**, n. An instrument forming part of the stage of a MICROSCOPE for measuring the size of things put on it.

'stagger, v.t. [Mech., etc.] Put things or parts not in a straight line etc., but first one on one side and then one on the other of some middle structure or line. **'staggered**, a.

'staggers, n. A disease attacking the brain and SPINAL CORD of horses and other animals, causing a loss of control in walking and a tendency for the legs to give way.

'staghorned, a. [Zoo.] Having great branched MANDIBLES, as certain insects.

'stagnant, a. Of a body of water, without currents or outlet, unmoving and gen. dirty with DECAYING plant-substance etc. and covered with an oil-like skin because never cleared out. [Med.] (Of blood or other body-liquid) not moving healthily in a current. **stag'nation**, n. The process of becoming or the condition of being s. [Med.] The stopping or slowing of motion in a body-liquid normally moving.

stain, 1.n. A colouring-substance for a solid such as wood which is thinner than paint and has the effect of a DYE, going into the substance and not simply forming a coating on it; any dye used for colouring things to be viewed under the MICRO-SCOPE, sp. [Biol.] animal or plant substances or very small living things, so as to make clear their structure by colouring TRANSPARENT parts of it, marking out the different parts in different colours or shades, or producing chemical reactions giving signs of certain things and where they are present; an undesired mark of a different colour or with loss of colour, produced on a substance by some colouring material or something acting on it chemically. 2.v.t. Get coloured with a s.; make a s. or ss. on. 3.v.i. Become stained. **'-less**, a. Without any ss. on it, or having the property of not having ss. made on it. **'stainless steel**. A special ALLOY of steel and Cr which, unlike other steel, does not undergo CORROSION in air or as the effect of water or feeble acids.

sta'lactite, n. [Geol.] A finger-like mass of stone hanging from an overhanging ROCK or the roof of a hole in rock, caused by rain-water coming down through a bed of $CaCO_3$, taking it into SOLUTION, and then EVAPORATING on the point of dropping so that the $CaCO_3$ becomes a solid mass, getting longer drop by drop.

'stalagmite, n. [Geol.] An up-pointing mass of $CaCO_3$ on the floor of a hole in ROCK, produced in a like way to a STALACTITE but by water undergoing EVAPORATION after dropping, so that the structure is formed by a process of building up in place of down, freq. seen straight under a stalactite, and sometimes meeting and uniting with it.

stalag'mometry, n. [Phys.] The process of measuring the SURFACE TENSION of a liquid by getting the weight of a drop of it hanging from a thin pipe. **stalag'mo-meter**, n. An instrument used for s.

'stalloy, n. Trade name for a metal made up of steel with a small amount of Si, used in ELECTROMAGNETS because of its low HYSTERESIS losses.

stalk, n. A stem or stem-like part, sp. [Bot.], a long, upright, unbranched stem coming straight from the root and topped by one flower or flower-group, or, in plants, animals, machines, etc., a like structure supporting some part on the end of it. **'s.-eyed,** a. [Zoo.] Having eyes on short ss., as in some CRUSTACEA.

'stamen, n. [Bot.] Any of the parts of a flower producing POLLEN, gen. made up of a delicate stem, the *filament*, with the *anther*, a structure formed of four pollen vessels, at the end (*see* picture p. 151). **'staminal,** a. **'staminate,** a. Sp., having ss. but no CARPELS, that is, being a male flower. **stamin'iferous,** a.

'stamina, a. [Med.] A person's physical power of coming through, not being broken or overcome by, hard conditions, disease etc., a body's general power of keeping on living.

'staminode, stamin'odium (staminodia), nn. [Bot.] A STAMEN whose development is incomplete, producing no POLLEN.

'stammer, 1.v.i. [Med.] Have trouble in going on from one word or part of a word to another in talking, making marked stops between or starting a sound over and over, as the effect of nerve trouble or a PSYCHO-NEUROSIS. 2.n. A condition of stammering.

standard, 1.n. Anything fixed by authority or agreement as an example or rule by comparison with which other things are of the same sort may be measured or tested. 2.a. Being a s. or in agreement with a s. (freq. the same thing as 'normal'). **s. 'atmosphere.** A s. of conditions of the ATMOSPHERE used in judging airplanes, which takes the PRESSURE at sea level as 1013·2 MILLIBARS, the TEMPERATURE as 15°C, and the change in temperature on going up from sea level as 6·5°C per km. **s. cell.** [Elec.] A PRIMARY CELL specially designed to have an e.m.f. which is as little as possible dependent on TEMPERATURE and keeps roughly the same for a very long time, for use as a s. in making electric measuring-instruments etc., the one generally used being the WESTON CELL. **s. devi'ation.** [Statistics] The SQUARE ROOT of the SUM of the SQUARES of the amounts got by the SUBTRACTION of the value of every observation in a group from the ARITHMETICAL MEAN of all their values. **s. so'lution.** [Chem.] A SOLUTION in which the amount of SOLUTE has a given relation to the amount of SOLVENT, sp. a NORMAL SOLUTION. **s. 'specific'ation.** The SPECIFICATION fixed by some authority (international or for a given country) for a machine, instrument, material etc.—in Great Britain by the *British Standards Institute.* **s. 'temperature and 'pressure.** A TEMPERATURE of 0°C and a PRESSURE of 760 mm. Hg, the s. conditions for the comparison of the space taken up by different gases, etc. **s. time.** The time-system used in any

part of the earth which is, by agreement, based on one MERIDIAN fixed as the time meridian for all the places in that part, without taking into account small changes in LONGITUDE which would make the true time different from place to place, for example, in Great Britain and France s. time is time based on the meridian of Greenwich. **'standardize,** v.t. Get a s. for (anything) fixed, or make (examples of anything) in agreement with a fixed s. **'standardized,** a.

'standing wave. STATIONARY WAVE.

'stannate, a. [Chem.] Any SALT of a STANNIC ACID.

'stannic, a. [Chem.] Having in it tin with a VALENCY of 4. **s. 'acid.** [Chem.] Any of a number of ACID substances formed by the reaction of ALKALIS with $SnCl_4$ in water or by that of HNO_3 with the metal tin, and producing s. oxide when highly heated. **s. 'oxide.** SnO_2, a white powder produced by burning tin or heating s. acid, etc.

stannite, n. [Chem.] Any SALT of STANNOUS HYDROXIDE. [Mineral.] A natural steel- or iron-coloured substance formed of tin united with copper, iron, S, and sometimes Zn.

'stannous, a. [Chem.] Having in it tin with a VALENCY of 2. **s. hy'droxide.** $Sn(OH)_2$, a feeble ACID. **s. 'oxide.** SnO, a black, green, or red substance produced by heating s. hydroxide in CO_2, and itself changing into SO_2 when heated.

'stannum, n. The chemical name for tin, Sn.

sta'pedius, n. [Zoo.] A small muscle in connection with the STAPES.

'stapes, n. [Zoo.] The inner one of the three AUDITORY OSSICLES in man and higher animals; in other animals, a small button of CARTILAGE at the inner end of the COLUMELLA AURIS. **sta'pedial,** a.

'staphyl(o)-. [Med.] To do with the UVULA; STAPHYLOCOCCIC.

'Staphylo'coccus (Staphylococci), n. [Bact.] A GENUS of BACTERIA which are frequently seen grouped together irregularly like a mass of small berries on a stem, of which certain sorts are common and important causes of diseases, sp. producing PURULENT INFLAMMATIONS such as ABSCESSES.

staphy'loma, n. [Med.] A pushing forward at any point of the CORNEA or SCLERA of the eye, as in certain diseases. **'staphylo'matic, staphy'lomatous,** aa.

star, n. [Astron.] Any of the great light-giving bodies stationed in the sky, of which the nearest is the sun, as opp. on the one hand to the PLANETS, which do not give out light themselves but only send back the light of the true ss., and, on the other hand, to such light-giving bodies as are only seen moving at a great rate across the sky from time to time, that is, COMETS and METEORS; any of the like bodies at a distance too great to be seen from the earth but of which we may get knowledge by the RADIOTELESCOPE.

starch, n. [Biochem., Chem.] A complex CARBOHYDRATE, $(C_6H_{10}O_5)x$, present in all green plants and stored up in seeds, bulbs etc., a white powder or mass of grains, which is changed into GLUCOSE by HYDROLYSIS, very important as a food material and used in certain processes, such as making pastes or washing linen, for its property of forming a sticky jelly, becoming stiff on getting cold, when mixed with boiling water. **s. gum.** DEXTRIN. **s. sheath.** [Bot.] A coat of CELLS with s. grains in them on the inner side of the CORTEX of a young stem, forming its ENDODERMIS.

Stark ef'fect. [Phys.] The effect by which the lines of its SPECTRUM are made wider or broken up into groups of lines, when a light-giving body is put into a strong ELECTRIC FIELD.

'stasis, n. [Bot.] A stopping of growth [Med.] A stopping or slowing down of the normal current of any body-liquid in a part, sp. of the current of blood through its smaller blood-vessels as the effect of something in the way; a stopping of waste matter in the INTESTINE because of the feeble operation of its muscles or something in the way.

-stasis, n. [Med.] A stopping of the named thing; a causing of the named condition by STASIS.

state, n. Condition. [Phys.] Sp. any of the possible conditions marked by certain amounts of ENERGY, ANGULAR MOMENTUM, and so on, in which an ATOMIC system may be. **s. of matter.** [Phys.] Any of the chief ss., once looked on as only three, solid, liquid, and gas, but among which are now sometimes listed the COLLOIDAL and the PLASMA, in which material substances may be.

'static, 1.a. At rest, unmoving or unchanging. [Phys.] To do with the properties of bodies at rest or of forces which are balanced. [Elec.] To do with, caused by, producing or using, s. electricity, as a s. machine. (*See* DYNAMIC). 2.n. [Radio] Undesired cracking etc. noises given out by a radio RECEIVER as the effect of electric CHARGES in the air. **s. elec'tricity.** [Phys.] An electric CHARGE which is stationed in one place, not moving in the form of a current. **s. length.** [Phys.] The LENGTH of a body as normally measured, without taking into account the THEORY OF RELATIVITY, by which a moving body becomes shorter in the direction of its motion. **s. sense.** [Zoo.] The sense of

balance and position in space. **'statics,** n. [Phys.] The science of balanced forces, producing no motion in the bodies in which they are acting, on which all building is based.

'stationary, n. Not moving, fixed in one place or position or condition of development, etc. **s. air.** [Med.] The amount of air which is normally kept in the LUNGS after breathing out. **s. point.** [Astron.] One or other of the two points in the ORBIT of a PLANET at which it seems for a short time, viewed from the earth, not to be moving, because at that time the earth is moving through an equal angle in the opposite direction. **s. state.** [Phys.] The condition of an ELECTRON when it is at an ENERGY LEVEL, in which condition no energy is given out or taken in by it; the condition of an ATOM all of whose electrons are in a s. state. **s. wave, s. vi'bration.** [Phys.] The sort of VIBRATION, seen in a limited MEDIUM such as a stretched string giving out a sound, in which there are regularly-spaced points where there is no motion, caused by the coming together at those points of equal vibrations moving in opposite directions that is, of one train going forward and another train coming back; like effect caused in radio by two trains of waves of the same FREQUENCY going in opposite directions.

'station 'error. The amount by which the effect of GRAVITY at a place makes its LATITUDE or LONGITUDE as worked out by GEODESY different from that given by astronomy.

sta'tistics, 1.n. sing. The science of working out general laws or working rules of the sort which may be given as, or are based on, relations between numbers (for example, those giving the BIRTH RATE among groups living in different conditions), from a very great number of examples covering a very wide field or a very long time. 2.n.pl. Facts, or numbers representative of these facts, got together or worked out by s. **sta'tistical,** a. To do with, based on, s., given in the form of ss. **sta'tistically,** adv. **statis'tician,** a. An expert in s.

stato-. Fixed.

'statoblast, n. [Zoo.] In some POLYZOA, a BUD produced inside the body in a hard cover which keeps it undamaged through the winter to undergo development into a new animal in the spring.

'statocyst, n. [Zoo.] OTOCYST.

'statocyte, n. [Bot.] A plant CELL having in it one or more STATOLITHS.

'statolith, n. [Zoo.] OTOLITH. [Bot.] A solid grain in a plant CELL, freq. of STARCH, which is free to move under the attraction of the earth when the position of the part of the plant is changed.

'stator, n. [Mach.] In a machine, a fixed part in or round or in connection with which another part is turning, sp. [Elec.] the fixed part of an electric machine as opp. the ROTOR.

'statoscope, n. A specially delicate ALTIMETER recording small changes in the distance of an airplane from the earth.

'status, n. [Med.] Condition (used in naming diseased conditions). s. epi'lepticus. A condition of violent EPILEPTIC CONVULSIONS taking place one after the other without the person's becoming conscious between them. s. lym'phaticus. A condition in which there is an overgrowth of all LYMPHATIC TISSUE causing danger of sudden death, sp. if the person is given an ANAESTHETIC.

stay, n. [Building, Engin.] A rod etc. going from one part to another for the purpose of support or to make the structure stiff, and acting against a pulling force.

'steady, a. Fixed, regular, unmoving or unchanging. s. state. [Phys.] A STATE in which an ATOMIC system may be for some time.

steam, n. [Phys.] Water which has become gas through heating; loosely, the mist produced when s. gives up its heat to the air and becomes changed back into water drops supported for a time by the air. s. 'engine. [Mach.] An engine in which the force produced by the expansion of s. is used for driving a PISTON or turning blades (s. turbine) by which the rest of the machine is put in operation. s. point. [Phys.] The TEMPERATURE at which the greatest VAPOUR PRESSURE of water is equal to the STANDARD ATMOSPHERIC PRESSURE, that is, the normal boiling-point.

'steapsin, n. [Zoo., Biochem.] An ENZYME produced by the PANCREAS and effecting the digestion of fat.

'stearic, a. [Chem.] Of, to do with, like, STEARIN or hard sheep fat. s. acid. [Chem.] A FATTY ACID, $C_{18}H_{36}O_2$, got by HYDROLYSIS from the hard fat of sheep, a white CRYSTALLINE substance becoming a liquid oil at 60°C, used in making waxlights etc. stear(o)-.

'stearin, n. [Chem.] TRISTEARIN; STEARINE.

'stearine, n. [Chem.] A white wax-like solid made up chiefly of STEARIC ACID mixed with PALMITIC ACID, the trade form of stearic acid.

'Stefan's law. [Phys.] The law that the amount of BLACK BODY RADIATION per unit AREA in unit time (S) has a fixed relation to the 4th POWER of the ABSOLUTE TEMPERATURE (T) of the body, that is $S = \sigma T^4$, where the value of σ

(Stefan's constant) $= 5.75 \times 10\text{-}5$ erg. cm^{-2} sec.$^{-1}$ deg.$^{-4}$.

stele, n. [Bot.] The middle part of the root and stem of a plant, that is a stem or root without its CORTEX, formed of XYLEM and PHLOEM, sometimes ringing PITH and freq. ringed by a PERICYCLE, all walled round by the ENDODERMIS. 'stelar, a.

'stellar, a. Of, to do with, a star or the stars; STELLATE. s. 'interfer'ometer. [Astron.] An instrument used in connection with a TELESCOPE for measuring the DIAMETERS of stars of very great size, or other things which no telescope by itself has the power of RESOLVING, by observation of INTERFERENCE FRINGES at the FOCAL POINT of the telescope.

'stellate, a. Like a star, sp. in having pointed divisions or rays ranged round, going out from, a middle part.

'stellite, n. [Metal.] Any of a group of very hard ALLOYS made up of Co, Cr, W, Mo and Fe, used for cutting-instruments, for example, SURGICAL ones, and for covering SURFACES which have to undergo much PRESSURE etc.

'stem, n. [Bot.] Any of the parts of a plant, normally rod-like, giving out BUDS, leaves, and flowers or flower-structures at fixed points and having a growth point at the end—the middle supporting structure of a plant, or any side structure of the same sort; any of the branches of a s., or any of the like smaller structures ending in a leaf or flower. [Zoo., Mach.] Any s.-like part or structure. s. body. [Biol.] The part of a SPINDLE between the two groups of CHROMOSOMES separating in the 4th stage of MEIOSIS or MITOSIS.

stem cor'rection. The putting right in a THERMOMETER of the error caused by the stem not being at the same TEMPERATURE as the bulb.

'stemma, n. OCELLUS.

'stemonous, a. [Bot.] Having the named number or sort of STAMENS.

'stencil, n. Plate of thin metal, stiff card etc., with lettering or a design cut through it so that when it is put over paper and ink etc. brushed over it, the printing or design is produced on the paper.

'steno-. Narrow:— '-'cephaly, n., '-'petalous, a., '-'phyllous, a., etc.

'steno'notal, a. [Zoo.] Of insects, having a very small, sp. a very narrow, THORAX.

'steno'paic, a. Of OPTICAL instruments, using a very small or narrow opening for letting light through, as a PIN-HOLE CAMERA; to do with or using a s. instrument. s. 'spectacles. Dark glasses for the eyes letting light through only a small clear space in the middle.

ste'nosed, a. [Med.] Of a part, marked by STENOSIS.

ste'nosis, n. [Med.] A narrowing of any opening or pipe-like part in the body as the effect of disease. ste'notic, a. To do with or having undergone s.

steno'therm-ic, -al, aa. [Biol.] Living only in a very limited range of TEMPERATURES, able to make adjustment only to small changes in the degree of heat or cold.

'stenter, 1.n. TENTER. 2.v.t. Make (thin cotton material) elastic by stretching in a current of heated air.

step down. v.t. Make (an output, rate etc.) less, sp. [Elec.] make (VOLTAGE) lower. 'step-down, a. [Elec.] Used for lowering VOLTAGE, as a s.-d. TRANSFORMER.

'stepfault. [Geol.] One or the other of two or more parallel FAULTS near together and having the same direction of THROW.

steppe, n. [Geog.] Great flat stretch of grass-land, gen. without trees, said sp. of those in Russia and nearby countries.

step up. v.t. Make an increase in (output, rate, etc.), sp. [Elec.] make VOLTAGE greater. 'step-up, a. [Elec.] Used for increasing VOLTAGE, as a s.-u. TRANSFORMER.

ste'radian, n. [Geom.] The unit of measure of a SOLID ANGLE, being that solid angle produced at the middle point of a ball by a space on the SURFACE of which the measure is equal to the SQUARE of the RADIUS.

'sterco-. (To do with) FAECES: '-'raceous, a.

'sterco'bilin, n. [Biochem.] The brown colouring-substance of FAECES.

'stercome, n. [Zoo.] The mass of brown grains forming the FAECES of some SARCODINIA.

'stercoral, a. [Med.] To do with, caused by, FAECES.

stere, n. Unit of VOLUME in the METRIC SYSTEM = 1 m.³

'stereo-. Solid, taking up space in three directions; STEREOSCOPIC.

'stereo'chemistry, n. That branch of chemistry having to do with the way ATOMS are placed in a MOLECULE, their distribution in space. 'stereo'chemical, a.

'stereo'comparator, n. [Surveying, Astron.] A special STEREOSCOPE used for the comparison of stereoscopic pictures of a stretch of country or sky, taken by a camera with a great distance between its LENSES, with a view to measuring the distances between different points, noting any small change in the position of the stars, etc.

'stereog'nostic, a. [Psych.] To do with the sensing by touch of the size, form, and weight of solid bodies.

'stereo-gram, -graph, nn. A picture giving a STEREOSCOPIC effect, or one designed to be used in a STEREOSCOPE. stereo-'graphic(al), aa.

'stereoi'somerism, n. [Chem.] ISOMERISM caused by different distributions of the ATOMS in the MOLECULE, as when the molecule of one form of a substance has the structure of the molecule of another form as seen in a looking-glass. 'stereo-i'somer, n. 'stereoiso'meric, a.

'stereome, n. [Bot.] A general name for the materials in a plant giving it support or forming its hard frame-work, such as wood.

stere'omer, n. STEREOISOMER.

stere'ometry, n. [Geom.] The measuring of VOLUMES or solid forms.

'stereomi'crometer, n. An instrument fixed to a TELESCOPE for measuring small angles in its field of view.

stereo'phonic, a. [Acous.] Of recorded sound, giving the right effect of the distance and position in space of the SOURCES of the sound as judged by the two ears.

'stereo'planigraph, n. An instrument for making maps from observations made with a STEREOCOMPARATOR.

'stereoplasm, n. [Zoo.] The more solid, sticky, part of living CELL-substance; a hard substance formed in the spaces between the division-walls in some CORALS.

ster'eopsis, n. [Optics] STEREOSCOPIC VISION.

stere'opticon, n. A form of PROJECTION LANTERN giving specially good effects, freq. made up of two such lanterns so that one picture may take the place of another with no sudden change.

'stereoscope, n. An apparatus which, by the use of LENSES or MIRRORS, makes two pictures of the same thing taken from different points of view come together so as to seem like one to the eyes, giving an effect of solid bodies not as pictured on a plane but as seen in deep space. 'stereo-'scopic, a. To do with stereoscopy; of, produced by, the s. stereoscopic 'camera. A camera with two LENSES taking two pictures of the same view from different points at the same time for use with a s. stereo'scopic vision. The natural power of stereoscopy which is the effect of our seeing with two eyes. stere'oscopy, n. The seeing of things as solid, taking up space in three directions, and separated from one another by distances from front to back in the field of view; the science of stereoscopic effects.

'stereo'spondylous, a. [Zoo.] Having the different parts of the units of the backbone united into one solid bone. 'stereo-'spondyly, n. The condition of being s.

'stereo'taxis, n. [Biol.] TAXIS in reaction to the touch of a solid body, as seen in the tendency of certain small animals to get themselves fixed onto things or to make their way into holes or cracks. 'stereo-'tactic, a. stereo'tropism, n. [Biol.]

TROPISM in reaction to the touch of a solid body.

'stereotype, 1.n. A metal plate for printing from, made from a MOULD of whatever is to be printed as first put up in TYPE. 2.v.t. Make ss. of (something to be printed) or get printed by ss. 'stereotyped, a. Produced from ss.; (of behaviour, reactions, or things produced) copying a fixed form, marked by nothing interesting or surprising, the same again and again, automatic. 'stereotypy, n. Printing from ss. [Med.] The doing or saying of the same things over and over by persons of unbalanced mind.

'steric, a. [Chem.] To do with the distribution of ATOMS in space, their positions in the MOLECULE. s. 'hindrance. The effect of certain groups forming part of the MOLECULE in certain ORGANIC substances, in making hard or impossible, by reason of their position and sometimes their size, chemical reactions normal to other groups in the molecule.

ste'rigma (sterigmata), n. [Bot.] In FUNGI, a very small, short stem producing a SPORE or a chain of spores.

'sterile, a. [Biol.] Without the power of producing offspring, fruit or seeds. [Bot.] Of a seed etc., without the power of development. [Med.] Made free from BACTERIA or other living things by sterilization. s. flower. [Bot.] A STAMINATE flower. ste'rility, n. 'sterili'zation, n. [Biol., Med.] The process of sterilizing; the condition of having been sterilized. 'sterilize, v.t. [Biol., Med.] Make s., for example by taking away sex-parts. [Med.] Make s. by heating or the use of chemicals causing the death of BACTERIA etc. 'sterilizer, n. [Med.] An apparatus for freeing anything from BACTERIA etc. by the use of heat, steam, or boiling water.

'sternal, a. [Zoo.] To do with, near, on the same side of the body as, the STERNUM or a STERNITE.

'sternebra (sternebrae), n. [Zoo.] Any of the divisions of which the STERNUM is formed in some back-boned animals.

'sternite, n. [Zoo.] In ARTHROPODA, the hard plate covering the under side of a body-division, or, in insects, the skin of this part, sp. when it is thick and hard.

'sterno-. [Zoo.] Of the STERNUM (and . . .), used chiefly in forming the names of muscles going from the sternum to the other named part:— '-'hyoid, a., n., '-'scapular, a., n., '-'thyroid, a., n.

'sternum (sterna, n. [Zoo.] The chest-bone of a land-living back-boned animal, formed sometimes of one plate of bone, as in birds, but gen. of a number of bones united, which makes connection at its forward or upper end with the CLAVICLES and to which in higher animals the ends of most of the ribs are joined; in ARTHROPODA, the STERNITE.

'steroid, n. [Chem., Biochem.] Any of a number of complex HYDROCARBONS present in living things and having a like structure of C rings to the STEROLS, for example VITAMIN D and the FATTY ACIDS present in BILE.

'sterol, n. [Chem., Biochem.] Any of a group of complex solid ALCOHOLS present in most living things, some of them, for example CHOLESTEROL and ERGOSTEROL, playing an important part in the body-processes of higher animals.

'stetho-. [Med.] Chest.

'stethoscope, n. [Med.] An instrument in the form of a rubber pipe, one end of which is placed on the chest or other part of the body of the person under observation and the other end, gen. forked into two, in the ear or ears of the person making the observation, designed for hearing sounds produced inside the body, for example, by the heart. stetho'scopic(al), aa. ste'thoscopy, n. The art or process of observation with the s.

'sthenic, a. [Med.] Strong, full of force, working strongly, sp. of diseased conditions marked by an over-strong working of the heart, etc. [Psych.] (Of feelings) strong, worked-up, increasing the working of the body's processes and the sense of living force, for example, a feeling of great pleasure, hope, purpose, etc.

'stibine, n. [Chem.] Sb_2H_3 (antimony hydride) a poison gas without colour and with a special smell, burning with a blue-green flame.

'stibium, n. [Chem.] First name for ANTIMONY.

'stibnite, n. [Mineral.] A natural form of Sb_2S_3 (antimony trisulphide), the material from which Sb is chiefly produced, a grey CRYSTALLINE substance with a metal-like look.

-stichons, a. [Biol.] Having the named number of lines of parts etc.

'stigma (stigmas), [Bot.] The part of a CARPEL, gen. a soft or sticky SURFACE at the free end of a STYLE, on which POLLEN grains come to rest and undergo the development by which the male CELL makes its way to the egg cell.

'stigma (stigmata), n. [Zoo.] A small mark or opening, sp. a SPIRACLE or an OCELLUS. [Med.] A small red mark on the skin caused by blood coming through the walls of the small blood-vessels, seen, for example, in persons who take over-much alcohol and in HYSTERIA; any sign or mark of a certain disease or unnormal condition.

'stigmal, stig'matic, aa. [Bot., Zoo., Med.] To do with a STIGMA, having a stigma, stigmas or STIGMATA. stig'matic cell. [Bot.]

Any of the CELLS by which the neck of an ARCHEGONIUM is shut till the development of the egg-cell is completed.

stigma'tiferous, a. [Bot.] **stigmatiform,** a.

stilb, n. [Optics.] A unit of BRIGHTNESS equal to one CANDLE per cm.² at right angles to the rays.

stil'boestrol, n. [Chem., Med.] A CARBOHYDRATE made by chemical processes which has the same effects on the females of higher animals as an OESTROGEN and is used medically.

still, n. A DISTILLING apparatus, sp. one used in distilling alcohol or PETROLEUM.

'still'birth, n. [Med.] The producing, birth, of a dead offspring.

'still-born, a. [Med.] (Of offspring) dead at birth.

stilli'cidium, n. [Med.] The coming away of a liquid drop by drop, as of URINE in certain conditions.

'stilliform, a. In the form of a drop.

Still's disease. [Med.] ACUTE ARTHRITIS all over the body in very young persons.

'stimulant, 1.n. [Med.] A medical substance or other medical STIMULUS having the property of increasing for a time the force or rate of some body process, as a heart s., or sp. of acting on the nerves to give a general feeling of greater force and an impulse to give signs of it in acts and words. 2.a. Being, having the effect of, a s. **'stimulate,** v.t. [Biol., Psych., Med.] Make undergo the operation of a STIMULUS or s., have the effect of a stimulus or s. on (a living substance structure or being). **stimu'lation,** n. **'stimulative, a.**

'stimulus (stimuli), n. [Biol.] Anything acting on and causing a reaction in a living substance, structure, or being, increasing the rate and force of its operation or starting a new operation in it. [Zoo.] Sp., anything acting on a nerve-ending to put in operation a NERVE IMPULSE. [Psych.] Sp., anything giving an impulse to an increased use of body or mind, gen. for a certain purpose. [Bot.] A STINGING HAIR. **s. 'threshold.** [Biol., Psych.] *See* THRESHOLD.

sting, 1.n. [Zoo.] A small sharp-pointed structure, seen chiefly in insects, ARACHNIDS and fish, used for wounding other animals and in some way, for example by connection with a poison vessel, poisoning the wound. [Med.] A sharp sudden pain such as is experienced by man when stung by an insect. 2.v.t. Make a wound in with a s. **'stinging hair.** [Bot.] A hollow hair-like part on a plant producing an IRRITANT liquid which is forced by the broken point into the skin of an animal touching it.

stipe, n. [Bot.] A short thick stem, sp. that of the fruit-body in certain FUNGI, the stem-like part of certain ALGAE, or that

at the base of the leaf in FILICALES. [Zoo.] STIPES.

'stipes (stipites), n. [Zoo.] A short stem such as that supporting the eye in CRUSTACEA; the second division from the base of the MAXILLA in insects.

'stipiform, a. [Biol.] Stem-like.

stipitate, a. [Bot.] Having, or supported on, a STIPE.

'stipple, n. A mass of small points, lines, or other small touches very near together used in place of solid colour to give an effect of shading in printing, painting, etc. **'stippled,** a. Covered with small points or touches of colour, etc.

'stipule, n. [Bot.] One or other of the two outgrowths, gen. leaf-like but sometimes taking other forms, at the base of the leaf stem in a great number of plants. **'stipular,** a. **'stipulate,** a. **'stipuliform,** a.

stirps (stirpes), n. [Bot.] A well-fixed VARIETY of a plant, which does not undergo loss of its special properties when it is CULTIVATED.

'stirrup bone. STAPES.

stock, n. [Biol.] A family-line of plants or animals produced by man from a common ANCESTOR and, as the effect of INBREEDING, forming a group marked off from the rest of its sort by special qualities. [Zoo.] An animal from which a family-line comes; the family-line coming straight down from one animal and formed of itself, its offspring, its offspring's offspring, etc.; a ZOOID produced by a sex-process but producing offspring by some other process, such as BUDDING; a COLONY of ZOOIDS. [Bot.] The chief stem of a plant, or, in GRAFTING, the rooted stem onto which part of another is grafted. [Geol.] A great mass of IGNEOUS ROCK of no special form but gen. roughly like the thick base of a tree, which has been forced up when liquid into the beds of rock over it.

'stoichi'ometry, n. [Chem.] The science of working out EQUIVALENT WEIGHTS, or, more generally, having to do with the uniting of ELEMENTS, and the relations between the properties and the make-up of complex substances. **'stoichio'metric(al),** aa.

Stokes-'Adams syn'drome. [Med.] A condition in which the breathing and PULSE are markedly slow and irregular and there is a tendency suddenly to become unconscious for a time, freq. a sign of HEARTBLOCK.

Stokes'(s) law or rule. [Optics] The law that in FLUORESCENCE the WAVE-LENGTH of the light sent out is gen. longer than that of the light taken in.

'stolon, n. [Bot.] A side stem put out from the base of a plant and running over or sp. under the earth, producing roots and a new plant or, as in the potato, a TUBER. [Zoo.] A short stem-like or pipe-like structure, sp., in ANTHOZOA, POLYZOA etc., such an outgrowth from the body-wall producing BUDS or to which they become fixed, forming the supporting structure of a new COLONY. '-ate, -'iferous, aa.

'stoma (stomata), n. [Biol.] A very small pin-point opening, as of any of a number in animals for different purposes or the opening of a s. in plants. [Bot.] Any of the structures present in the outer skin of plants, sp. leaves and young stems, made up of a small opening ringed by two lip-like CELLS by which it may be opened or narrowed, through which gases are taken in or sent out. '-tal, a. 'stomate, -'tose, '-tous, aa.

'stomach, n. [Zoo.] In back-boned animals, the bag-like expansion of the digestion-pipe into which food goes for the first stage of digestion, having walls with strong muscles, freq. used for crushing the food, and producing liquids by which it is made soft and acted on chemically; in non-back-boned animals, any s.-like expansion or divisions of the digestion-pipe, or, in very simple systems, the simple digestion hollow inside the body. s. pump. [Med.] An apparatus with a long pipe put down the throat for pumping liquids into or out of the s., for example to get it cleared of poison, or to put food in when a person is unable to take it in the normal way, '-al, a. To do with the s. sto'machic, 1.a. Stomachal. [Med.] Being a stomachic. 2.n. A substance with the property of helping the operation·of the s.

sto'matic, a. [Zoo.] To do with the mouth. [Bot.] To do with a STOMA.

'stomat(o)-. (Of) the mouth (and . . .), chiefly [Med.]. 'stoma'titis, n., 'stomato-'gastric, a., etc.

'Stoma'topoda, n.pl. [Zoo.] An ORDER of seaside CRUSTACEA living in holes in the sand, cracks in stones, etc., ranging in size from about 2 to 30 cm., having a flat body with a forward part small in relation to the ABDOMEN, walking-legs and swimming-legs and very strong grippers, eyes on stems, the GILLS on the swimming-legs.

-stomia, -stomy, nn. [Med.] Condition of the mouth.

'stomium, n. [Bot.] The place, formed of thin-walled CELLS, in the wall of the SPORE-vessel in FILICALES where cracking first takes place when the spores are ready to be let out.

stomo'd(a)eum, n. [Zoo.] The part of the forward end of the digestion-pipe in lower animals and in the EMBRYOS of higher where the outer skin is folded in, forming the mouth. stomo'daeal, a. -stomy, n. [Med.] The operation of making an opening into the named part of the body.

stone, a. [Geol.] ROCK when it is in hard solid masses; a bit of s. of small or not very great size. [Bot.] The hard outer covering of the seed inside a DRUPE. [Med.] A CALCULUS, sp. in the KIDNEY or the GALL or URINARY BLADDER; the condition of having ss. in the kidney. S. Age. The earliest of the chief divisions of man's history, when he had stone, but not metal, instruments, covering the EOLITHIC, PALAEOLITHIC and NEO-LITHIC. s. ca'nal. [Zoo.] In ECHINO-DERMATA, a pipe-like part with walls made hard with Ca, joining the MADRE-PORITE to the RING CANAL. s. cell. [Bot.] Any of the short, very thick-walled CELLS of different sizes and forms present sp. in the wood of stems and in fruits and seeds. s. fruit. [Bot.] DRUPE. 'stony, a. S.-like, formed of s., covered with ss., etc.

'stoneware, n. A small-grained pot material, made very hard by firing at great heat, much used in chemical work because of its property of not being damaged by acids.

stool, n. [Med.] The waste put out from the ANUS in a MOTION.

stop, n. [Optics] Any covering structure for stopping light from getting through a part of an OPTICAL instrument or controlling the distribution of the rays, as a plate with a round hole in the middle for limiting the opening through which light goes into a camera or the field of view of an EYEPIECE. [Phonet.] A complete stopping of the breath at some point on its way out through the mouth or nose as part of the process of forming a language sound, saying a word, etc.; a language sound made by letting out the breath after a s., as p, t, k. 'stopped 'con-sonant. [Phonet.] Any of the sounds p, b t, d, k, g, formed with ss. 'stopped 'vowel. [Phonet.] A VOWEL which is cut short suddenly as the effect of a CONSONANT coming after it. 'stopping 'power. [Phys.] The degree to which a material has the property of stopping FUNDAMENTAL PARTICLES from going through it.

'stopcock, n. A VALVE or other stopper for starting, stopping, or controlling a current of water through a pipe, to-gether with the hand-part, if any, used for opening and shutting it, for example, one by which piped water is let into a bath or wash-basin.

'stoppage, n. The act of stopping or condi-tion of being stopped. [Med.] The shutting or stopping up of a pipe in the body, sp. the INTESTINE.

'stopping con'denser. BLOCKING CONDEN-
SER.

'stop watch. A watch, gen. having a scale of
minutes, not hours, and a minute-hand
and second-hand only, which may be
started and stopped as desired for
timing short operations.

'storage 'battery. n.[Elec.]A group of storage
cells in connection, gen. in SERIES, with
one another. 'storage cell. An electric
CELL in which the chemical reaction produced by sending an electric current
through it is changed to its opposite
when it is used for producing an electric
current, so that it comes back to the
same condition as before and may be
given a new CHARGE and used again.

S.T.P.=STANDARD TEMPERATURE AND
PRESSURE.

stra'bismus, n. [Med.] A condition in which
the two eyes are unable to be turned so
that their lines of view come to the same
point, caused by the eye muscles not
working in agreement.   stra'bism-al,
-ic, aa.

strabo-. STRABISMUS:— stra'bometry, n.

stra'botomy, n. [Med.] An operation to
overcome STRABISMUS.

strain, 1.v.t. Get (a cord, muscle, one's
powers, etc.) stretched or forced to the
limit; do damage to by straining. [Mech.]
Make (a body) undergo a change in form,
size, or structure as the effect of an outside force. 2.v.i. Put out all one's force,
go to the very limit of one's powers, in
doing something. 3.n. The act of straining
or the condition of being strained; a
straining force. [Med.] Damage caused by
straining, sp. to the body or mind generally by overtaxing one's powers or feelings, overworking, etc. [Mech.] A change
in the form and/or size, of a body
produced by a STRESS, measured by the
RATIO of the change in size (in
DIMENSION, in AREA or in VOLUME) to the
size before stress. s. 'ageing. [Metal.] The
process by which, with COLD-WORKING,
metals become stronger and harder as
times goes on. s. gauge. An instrument
used for measuring ss. in SURFACES,
made up of a GRID of thin wire having
electric RESISTANCE, which is put onto
the surface, so that any s. in that is taken
up by the grid and may be measured by
the change in its resistance.

strain, v.t. and i. FILTER.

'strain, n. [Biol.] A group of plants or
animals marked by special qualities and
forming a division of a VARIETY, produced
by INBREEDING, as the effect of a natural
attraction for one another, or as that of
control by chance conditions or by man.

strait, n. [Geog.] A narrow stretch of sea
forming a connection between two seas
(freq. ss.).

strand, n. Any of the unit threads, wires, or
like structures forming part of a parcel
of such structures or of a thicker cord,
etc. made by twisting them together.
-ed, a. Made up of ss.

strangu'lation, n. [Med.] The stopping of a
person's breath by gripping the throat
tightly with the hands or a cord etc.;
the shutting of a pipe or other vessel in
the body by narrowing at a point, so that
blood or other material is unable to make
its way through as it does normally.
'strangle, v.t. and i. Put to death, undergo death, by s. 'strangulate, v.t. [Med.]
Make (a blood-vessel etc.) so narrow at
some point that the way through is
stopped. 'strangulated, a. strangulated
'hernia. A HERNIA in which the part
pushed out is so narrowed in forcing its
way through that the blood is unable to
get back through the blood-vessels,
causing the outer part to become
SWOLLEN and hard.

'strata, n.pl. See STRATUM.

'strati-. STRATUM or STRATA.

'stratifi'cation, n. The process of becoming
or the condition of being stratified; a
stratified structure, sp. [Geol.] that seen
in SEDIMENTARY ROCK as the effect of
changes in the sort of material put down,
or of stops in the process, so that one
stretch has time to get hard before a
new one is formed. 'stratified, a. Made up
of, ranged in, STRATA or strata-like
divisions or levels, or, more loosely,
formed of bands of different colours or
substances. stratified epi'thelium. [Zoo.]
A sort of EPITHELIUM having a number of
coats of CELLS of which the outer ones
are flat and hard, the inner full of living
substance. stratified 'thallus. [Bot.] In
LICHENES, a THALLUS with a plate of
ALGAL CELLS between plates of FUNGAL
HYPHAE.

'stratiform, a. STRATIFIED. [Zoo.] Sp., of a
CARTILAGE, bedded in a narrow hollow
in a bone so as to give a smooth level
floor for a TENDON to go over. [Meteor.]
In the form of a STRATUS.

stra'tigraphy, n. [Geol.] That branch of
Geology having to do with the different
STRATA of the outer earth from the point
of view of the order and processes of their
development, the relations of different
groups of ROCKS in time and structure,
and the light on the history of living
things given by the FOSSILS present in
different strata; the order of strata in a
place.   'strati'graphic(al),   aa.   strati-
graphic geology. The science of s.
stra'tigrapher, n.

strato'cumulus, n. [Meteor.] Cloud in the
form of a wide low stretch of separate
dark rolls or round masses very near

together or running into one another, freq. covering all the sky.

'stratose, 'stratous, aa. Made up of STRATA.

'stratosphere, n. [Meteor.] The upper part of the earth's ATMOSPHERE, starting at a distance of roughly 11 km. up (though this may be different from place to place and time to time), a part where the TEMPERATURE is almost the same at any level and no clouds or CONVECTION currents are formed.

'stratum (strata), n. A stretch, bed, or coat of anything forming one of a number of such stretches, one on top of the other, sp. on a level plane; a level division of anything, as *a s. of the sea, a s. of society*. [Geol.] Sp., a more or less level, or clearly at one time level, stretch of SEDIMEN-TARY ROCK in the earth forming one of a number of such stretches coming one on top of the other, from which it is marked off as a natural unit, though freq. itself made up of thinner stretches. [Biol.] A bed of CELLS, sp. one of a number of such beds making up a part.

'stratus (strati), n. [Meteor.] A low, flat, cloud-form,covering a great stretch of sky.

stray, a. [Elec., Radio] Of electric and MAGNETIC effects, not designed, produced in addition to designed effects by some conditions in or near a system, and some-times causing trouble in it.

streak, n. A line or long mark of different colour or structure from the material round it. [Bot.] Any of a number of plant diseases causing ss. of dead substance in leaves, stems etc. [Mineral.] Sp., the colour of a MINERAL in powder form, as seen when it is rubbed with a knife or against some hard substance, freq. different from that of the solid substance and an important sign of its make-up. s. plate. [Mineral.] A plate of hard, white UNGLAZED pot used for rubbing MINERALS on to get their ss.

stream, 1.n. Current, any body of liquid or gas, or any line of PARTICLES, moving in one direction. 2.v.i. Be moving in the form of a current.

'streamline, 1.n. [Phys.] A line of motion in a gas or liquid such that there is never any sudden change in its direction; an outline given to anything designed for moving through air or water such that the s. flow of the current going past it will be unbroken, so as to be acting against its motion as little as possible. 2.v.t. Give (an airplane, ship, automobile etc., or any part) a s. outline. 3.a. To do with, having s. flow or a s. form. s. flow. The motion of a current made up from end to end of ss., that is, in unbroken smooth motion without sudden twists etc.

strength, n. The quality or condition of being strong; the degree to which any-

thing is strong, the measure of its s. [Chem.] (Of a SOLUTION) CONCENTRATION. '-en, v.t. and i. Make or become stronger.

'strepto'coccus (streptococci), n. [Bact.] (Any of) a group of BACTERIA which come in two's or long chains but not in masses, some sorts of which are the cause of serious diseases, as SCARLET FEVER, PUERPERAL FEVER, and INFLAMMATION of the MUCOUS MEMBRANES of the nose and throat, the bones of the ear, etc. 'strepto'coccal, a.

strepto'mycin, n. [Med.] An ANTIBIOTIC produced, like PENICILLIN, from a MOULD and used against a number of diseases, for example TUBERCULOSIS of the brain.

strepto'stylic, a. [Zoo.] Having the QUAD-RATE united with the SQUAMOSAL in such a way that it has the power of moving. strepto'styly, n. [Zoo.] The condition of being s.

stress, 1.n. [Mech.] A force per unit AREA acting on a body from outside and producing a STRAIN, the RATIO of s. to strain being unchanging for that body (*see* MODULUS OF ELASTICITY). [Phonet.] Special force or weight put on a word or part of a word. 2.v.t. [Phonet.] Put. s. on (a word or part), say with s, 'stressed, a. [Phonet.]

'stria (striae), n. A narrow line, mark, band, or hollow, in or on anything, sp. [Biol.]. 'striate, stri'ated, aa. Marked with ss., sp. parallel and being the sign of a STRATIFIED structure. stri'ated 'muscle. [Zoo.] The sort of muscle-sub-stance effecting the motion of parts of the body in reaction to an outside STIMULUS, or, in higher animals, as desired (as against the sort moving automatically and regularly as part of the body's working, *see* UNSTRIATED MUSCLE), made up of long narrow CELLS with the power of pulling themselves into a short thick form very quickly, having more than one NUCLEUS and a delicate outer coat marked by PARALLEL dark ss. (caused by the ALTERNATION of two different substances in the cells), and united by CONNECTIVE TISSUE into parcels with an outer covering of the same tissue running on and forming TENDONS. stri'ation, n. A s.; the fact or condition of being striated; the grouping of the ss. on anything.

strict, a. [Bot.] Stiff and upright, not hanging over or loose, as a stem or flower-group.

'stricture, n. [Med.] A narrowing of some pipe-like part of the body, sp. at one point, caused by a diseased or unnormal condition of itself or parts near it; the narrowed part of a vessel which has undergone s. 'strictured, a.

'stridor, n. [Med.] A rough whistling sound

made in breathing when there is anything stopping up the air-pipes, as in certain diseases. 'stridulous, a. To do with, marked by, s.

stridu'lation, n. [Zoo.] The producing of a sharp, high sound, sp. by insects, by rubbing some part of the body against another, as the edges of the front and back wings, or the back legs against the front wings; the sort of sound produced by s. 'stridulate, v.i. Make a noise by s. 'stridulating, a. stridulating 'organs. The parts of the body used in s., sp. the special apparatus for this purpose on the under side of the body in some insects.

'striga (strigae), n. [Bot.] A stiff, pointed, hair-like SCALE placed flat. [Zoo.] STRIA. 'strigate, a.

'strigil(is), nn. [Zoo.] A comb-like structure for cleaning the feelers etc., seen on the first leg of some insects, as certain bees.

'strigose, a. [Bot.] Covered with hair-like SCALES all pointing one way and rough to the touch. 'strigillose, a. [Bot.] S. but with smaller, more delicate hairs.

strike, n. [Geol.] The direction in a level plane, north to south, east to west, and so on, of a STRATUM, INTRUSION or FAULT, that is, of a line at right angles to the DIP. s. fault. [Geol.] A FAULT whose s. is in the same direction as that of the STRATA etc. cut by it.

string galva'nometer. [Elec.] An instrument for measuring OSCILLATING electric current by the sideways motion produced by it in a thin wire stretched at right angles to the lines of force in a strong MAGNETIC FIELD.

stripe, n. [Biol.] STREAK. striped, a. striped 'muscle. STRIATED MUSCLE.

'strobila (strobilae), n. [Zoo.] A stage or form in the development of some SCYPHOZOA in which the body becomes longer and divisions are formed across it, giving it the look of a number of plates one on top of the other, these divisions later separating off one by one and undergoing development into MEDUSAE; the train of PROGLOTTIDES making up the body of a CESTODE. 'strobilate, v.i. Undergo strobilation. strobi'lation, stro- bili'zation, nn. The process of producing offspring by forming divisions across the body, as in SCYPHOZOA and other COELENTERATES, or putting out a train of PROGLOTTIDES, as in CESTODES.

'strobil(e), n. [Biol.] STROBILA or STROBILUS. strobil'aceous, a. [Biol.] strobil'iferous, a. [Biol.] stro'biliform, 'strobiloid, aa. [Biol.]

'strobilus (strobili), n. [Bot.] A CONE or any cone-like mass of SPOROPHYLLS; a flower SPIKE formed of female flowers covered by thin BRACTS grouped like the parts of a cone.

'stroboscope, a. An instrument for the

observation of things in PERIODIC motion and the measuring of the rate at which they are moving, by lighting them with quick bursts of light in a regular rhythm, so that when the rhythm of the thing under observation is the same, and completely regular, it will be seen at all times in the same position and seem to be unmoving. strobo'scopic, a. strobo- scopic lighting. Lighting using a s. used in camera work for recording the be- haviour of a very quickly moving MECHANISM, for example GEAR-WHEELS.

stroke, n. [Mach.] Blow, as a s. of a hammer; the complete motion in one direction or the other of a PISTON ROD or like part, or the distance covered by such a motion.

'stroma (stromata), n. [Zoo.] The material, gen. CONNECTIVE TISSUE, supporting and forming a framework for the acting CELLS or more complex structures of any apparatus of the body; the delicate TRANS- PARENT framework of an ERYTHROCYTE. [Bot.] In some FUNGI, a thick mass of HYPHAE twisted together in which fruit bodies are bedded or from which they are produced; the thicker substance of a CHLOROPLAST. 'stromal, a. stro'matic, 'stromatous, aa. '-toid, a.

'strontium, n. Chemical ELEMENT, at. no. 38, at. wt. 87·63, sign Sr, a silver-white ALKALINE EARTH METAL somewhat like Ca, very ACTIVE, present naturally in the earth as $SrSO_4$ (celestine). strontium 90. A RADIOACTIVE ISOTOPE of Sr, the chief RADIATION in the FALL-OUT from NUCLEAR BOMBS, with a HALF-LIFE of 25 years—a danger to man because causing bone-TUMOURS if taken in food or drink.

'strophiole, n. [Bot.] CARUNCLE. 'strophio- late, a.

'structural, a. To do with, caused by, structure. [Geol.] Sp., TECTONIC. s. 'colour. Any colour caused by the effect on light of the structure of a SURFACE as opp. colours caused by PIGMENTS, sp. [Zoo.] the blue and green IRIDESCENCE seen in feathers and in the wings of insects. s. 'formula. [Chem.] GRAPHIC FORMULA.

'struma (strumae), n. [Bot.] A cushion-like SWELLING on part of a plant, sp. at one side of the base of the SPORE-vessel in MUSCI. [Med.] A GLANDULAR SWELLING, sp. GOITRE. 'strum'iferous, a. [Bot.] 'strumiform, a. [Bot., Med.] Cushion-like. 'strumose, a. [Med.] STRUMOUS [Bot.] Having a s. or ss. 'strumous, a. [Med.] To do with or having a s.

strut, n. [Engin.] Any supporting part tak- ing the weight of some part of a structure, that is, acted on from end to end by a pushing force.

strychnine, n. [Chem., Med.] A white

CRYSTALLINE ALKALOID, $C_{21}H_{22}N_2O_2$, with very bitter taste, only a little SOLUBLE in water but very soluble in CHLOROFORM and BENZENE, acting strongly on the brain and nerve system and quickly causing death, but used medically in very small amounts as a nerve STIMULANT.

'stuffing-box, n. [Mach.] A hollow cover full of tightly massed material put round the hole through which a moving rod, such as à PISTON, goes into a vessel, to keep material such as water, steam, etc. on one side from getting in or out round the sides of the rod.

stupe'facient, a., n. [Med.] (A substance) causing STUPOR or sleep.

'stupor, n. [Med.] A condition in which a person, though not fully unconscious or sleeping, gives no sign of conscious feeling and little or no reaction to normal STIMULI, and, though not physically without the power of moving, has no impulse to motion. '-ous, a.

'stutter, n., v.i. STAMMER.

St. 'Vitus' dance. [Med.] CHOREA.

sty(e), n. [Med.] A PUSTULE on the edge of the upper or lower EYELID, caused by the poisoning of a SEBACEOUS GLAND by STAPHYLOCOCCI.

style, n. [Bot.] The thin stem-like part of a CARPEL supporting the STIGMA. [Zoo.] Any of a number of small, sharp-pointed, stiff or hard structures in different animals, as those at the end of the feelers or round the ANUS in some insects and CRUSTACEA, those coming up from the base of the cup in some CORALS, or the smaller points on the CINGULUM of a tooth. stylar, a. 'stylate, a. styl'iferous, a.

'stylet, n. [Med.] A long thin PROBE; a wire pushed into a CATHETER or like instrument to make it stiffer, or to keep the opening clear. [Zoo.] Small, stiff, pointed hair.

'stylifer, n. [Zoo.] The structure or part of an animal supporting a STYLE.

'stylo-. [Biol.] Producing a STYLE. [Zoo.] (Muscle, etc.) making a connection between the STYLOID PROCESS of the head and the part named:— '-'glossal, a., '-'glossus, n., '-'hyoid, a., n. '-man-'dibular, a., '-'mastoid, a., etc.

'styloid, a. Like a STYLE in form, sp. [Zoo.] naming outgrowths on certain bones. s. 'process. [Zoo.] A long thin outgrowth from the TEMPORAL BONE of the head in man; the short, pointed outgrowth at the outer end of the ULNA or the RADIUS, or at the upper end of the FIBULA.

'stylolite, n. [Geol.] A small rod-like structure with GROOVES down the sides which is present inside and at right angles to a bed, sp. of LIMESTONE. stylo'lytic, a. To do with a s., made up of or marked by ss.

'stylus, n. [Acous.] A sharp point forming part of an instrument for making marks on a surface, sp. that part of a sound-recording apparatus by which the marks representative of the sound-VIBRATIONS are cut in the wax plate or roll from which gramophone etc. records are made. [Zoo.] STYLE or STYLET; an unbranched sponge SPICULE pointed at one end. [Bot.] STYLE.

'styptic, n., a. [Med.] (A substance) producing CONTRACTION of the blood-vessels and so used for stopping the loss of blood from wounds. 'stypsis, n. The use of a s. or of ss. generally.

sub-. 1. Under in physical position:— -'aqueous, a., -ax'illary, a. [Bot.], -'branchial, a. [Zoo.], -'caudal, a. [Zoo.], -'cortical, a. [Biol.], -'glacial, a. [Geol. etc.], -'lingual, a. [Zoo.], -'nasal, a. [Zoo.], -oc'cipital, a. [Zoo.], -'optic, a. [Zoo.], -'oral, a. [Zoo.], -peri'cardial, a. [Zoo.], -'periton'eal, a. [Zoo.], -'rostral, a. [Zoo.], etc. 2. Under in degree, less than:—-a'cute, a. [Med.], -'audible, a. [Acous.], etc. 3. Almost, very near, in position:— -'basal, a., -'marginal, a., -'tropical, a. 4. Almost, somewhat, in quality or form:— -'alkaline, a. [Chem.], -len'ticular, a., -'ovate, a. [Biol.], -'palm-ate, a. [Biol.], -'sessile, a. [Biol.], etc. 5. Forming a part of a greater or chief thing of the same sort, or being a division of a division:— '-circuit, [Elec.], '-divis-ion, n., '-group, n., '-section, n.; sp., [Biol.] coming in the scale between the more general group whose name is given, and a division of it having a special name, as sub-class, a division between a CLASS and an order:— '-'family, n. [Biol.], '-'genus, n. [Biol.], '-'order, n. [Biol.], '-'phylum, n. [Biol.].

sub'acid, a. [Chem.] Feebly acid. suba'cid-ity, n.

sub'aerial, a. [Geol.] To do with, taking place on, the face of the earth, as opp. under it. [Bot.] Having its growth on or very little higher than the face of the earth.

sub'alpine, a. [Biol.] Living on the high slopes of mountains not much lower than the limit of the trees.

sub'apical, a. Near, almost at, the APEX, sp. [Biol.].

suba'rachnoid, a. [Zoo.] Under the ARACH-NOID, used sp. of the space full of CEREBROSPINAL FLUID between the ARACHNOID and the PIA MATER, and any-thing in connection with this.

sub'arctic, a. [Geog., etc.] Being, placed in, or to do with, the part of the earth out-side and edging the ARCTIC CIRCLE, or having the same sort of weather con-ditions as this.

suba'tomic, a. [Phys., Chem.] To do with

units of substance smaller than ATOMS, or with events taking place inside atoms and the processes and effects dependent on these. **suba′tomics,** n. The science of s. events.

sub′boreal, a. [Meteor.] Very cold but not quite as cold as the ARCTIC.

sub′caudate, a. [Zoo.] Having a small tail-like part which has not undergone development into a tail.

subce′lestial, a. [Astron.] Straight under the ZENITH.

sub′central, a. Not quite in the middle; under the middle point, sp. [Zoo.] under the middle SULCUS of the brain, or under the middle part of a VERTEBRA.

sub′chela (subchelae), n. [Zoo.] A subchelate gripping structure seen in ARTHROPODA.
sub′chelate, a. [Zoo.] Of an arm-like part, having an end-division with the power of folding back and gripping things between it and the part before it; having ss. **sub′cheliform,** a.

sub′clavian, a. [Zoo.] Under the CLAVICLE; to do with the s. artery. **s. ′artery.** The inner end of the chief ARTERY going down the arm or front leg.

sub′coastal, a. [Geog.] Under the sea at the edge of the land.

sub′conscious, 1.a. [Psych.] Said of processes like the normal processes of mind but of which a person is unconscious at the time they are going on in him, though they give signs of themselves by having effects on his behaviour and conscious thought, and he may become conscious of them under expert questioning. 2.n. That part of the mind in which s. processes go on (*the s.*).

sub′costa, n. [Zoo.] The second of the chief NERVURES of an insect's wing.

sub′costal, a. [Zoo.] To do with the SUBCOSTA; under, lower than, the RIBS.

sub′critical, a. [Phys.] (Of FISSILE material) smaller than the CRITICAL SIZE.

′subculture, n. [Biol.] A CULTURE, sp. of BACTERIA or FUNGI, made from an older culture.

subcu′taneous, a. [Zoo.] Under, coming nearest in the body to, the skin, sp. of a back-boned animal. [Med.] Put, or used for putting, under the skin, as a s. INJECTION. **s. ′tissue.** [Zoo.] Sp., loose CONNECTIVE TISSUE, freq. with much fat, under the skin in man and higher animals.

sub′dermal, a. SUBCUTANEOUS.

sub′dural, [Zoo.] Under the DURA MATER or between the dura mater and the ARACHNOID, as the s. *space.*

′suber, n. [Bot.] Cork substance. **′suberous, ′suberose,** aa. Cork-like; having become cork or undergone some degree of SUBERIZATION. **sube′riferous,** a. **su′berification,** n. SUBERIZATION.

su′beric acid. [Chem.] A white CRYSTALLINE

ACID got when cork is acted on by NITRIC and other acids.

′suberin, n. [Bot., Biochem.] A complex, wax-like substance formed from mixed FATTY ACIDS in the walls of cork CELLS, giving them their special property of keeping out water and not readily undergoing DECAY.

′suberi′zation, n. [Bot.] The forming of SUBERIN in the CELL-walls of the outer part of the stem in wood-forming plants, changing it into cork. **′suberize,** v.t. Make undergo s. **′suberized,** a.

sub′fluvial, a. On or under the bed of a river.

subi′mago, n. [Zoo.] A stage or form between the PUPA and the IMAGO in the development of some insects.

′subject, n. Whatever is being talked of or under discussion; person or animal under observation, being given tests, etc., for science purposes, sp. [Med., Psych.]. [Med.] A dead body used for DISSECTION. [Psych.] The self as that which undergoes experience. **sub′jective,** a. To do with the self, forming part of a person's private experience, coloured, caused, or conditioned by a person's special qualities, tendencies, feelings etc., not based simply on knowledge and reasoning common to all men. [Psych.] Sp., (of reactions, etc.) not able to be recorded by physical instruments; not open to observation by persons other than the self; (of things sensed) looked on by the self as present in the body, for example, as opp. colours and sounds; (of sense experiences) ILLUSORY, as when the nerves are so acted on by inner causes as to give the eye the experience of seeing something before it which is not in fact there. **′subjec′tivity,** n.

sub′kingdom, n. [Biol.] In the grouping of plants and animals, a chief branch higher than and made up of PHYLA or, among plants, of DIVISIONS—no longer used in some present-day systems, or used simply as another name for a phylum or division, a different organization having made these the top branches (*see* pp. 560, 562).

sub′lethal, a. [Med.] (Of an amount of a poison, etc.) not enough to be the cause of death.

′sublimate, 1.v.t. [Phys., Chem.] SUBLIME. [Psych.] Get the driving power of the LIBIDO, sp. the sex impulse, or, more loosely, of any strong impulse or feeling, turned to purposes and behaviour other than those natural to it and on a higher plane, for example, s. one's sex desires into a love of art. 2.n. [Chem.] A substance produced by sublimation; CORROSIVE SUBLIMATE. **subli′mation,** n. [Chem., Psych.] The process of SUBLIMING

454

or sublimating. **subli′mational**, a. **′subli-mating**, a.

sub′lime, 1.v.i. [Phys., Chem.] (Of a substance) go from the condition of a solid to that of a gas and/or from that of a gas to that of a solid without becoming liquid. 2.v.t. Make (a substance) s., gen. all the way from a solid to a solid again, for the purpose of getting it free from undesired substances which go off as gas. **sub′limed**, a. **sub′liming**, n.

sub′liminal, a. [Psych.] Lower than the THRESHOLD, that is:— (of a STIMULUS or its effects) not strong enough to be sensed or to get a clear reaction; (of a change in the degree of a stimulus) not great enough to be noted; (of mind processes) not coming into the conscious mind. **s. ′consciousness.** [Psych.] The effect of a s. STIMULUS, which, though not itself consciously experienced, makes some mark on the mind by which experience is in some way conditioned. **s. self.** [Psych.] The part of the self of which a person is unconscious, the workings of the UNCONSCIOUS or SUBCONSCIOUS.

sub′litoral, a. To do with, being, the part of the sea outside low-water mark from the edge to about 180 m. deep. [Bot.] (Of a plant) living not far from the sea but not quite on the edge of it.

′sublux′ation, n. [Med.] The process of twisting or pulling a bone out of its place at a JOINT to some degree, but not completely, or the condition of a bone which has been moved, or of a joint when the bones have been separated, in this way. **sub′luxate**, v.t. Make (a bone, etc.) undergo s.

′submarine, 1.a. Present, acting, living, designed for use, under the top of the sea, in the water or on the sea bed; (of a boat or mine) designed for use under water. 2.n. A s. boat, sp. one designed for attacking ships with TORPEDOES.

submax′illa, n. [Zoo.] The lower bone of the mouth. **′-ry**, a. To do with the s.; placed under the s.

sub′median, a. Being the one nearest in order to the middle one, sp. [Zoo.] of teeth in MOLLUSCA or NERVURES in insects' wings.

sub′mentum, n. [Zoo.] The plate at the base of the lower lip in insects.

sub′merge, sub′merse, vv.t. and i. Put or go completely under water, get completely covered with water. **sub′merged, sub′mersed**, aa. Sp., [Geog., etc.] being under, covered by, a body of water. [Bot.] Submerse. **sub′merse**, a. [Bot.] Living completely covered by water. **sub′mergence, sub′mersion**, nn. The act of submerging or condition of being submerged. **sub′mersible**, a. Able to be used under water, (of a boat, etc.) able to go down and go about under water.

sub′micron, n. [Phys., Chem.] Any PARTICLE between 2×10^{-5} and 5×10^{-7} cm. across, that is, so small as to be seen only with the ULTRAMICROSCOPE. **submi′cronic**, a.

sub′micro′scopic, a. So small as not able to be seen through the common light MICROSCOPE.

submu′cosa, n. [Zoo.] The coat of substance gen. AREOLAR TISSUE, coming under a MUCOUS MEMBRANE. **sub′mucosal**, a.

sub′mucous, a. [Zoo.] Coming under a MUCOUS MEMBRANE.

sub′multiple, n. [Arith.] A number which goes into another number with nothing over, for example 2 is a s. of 10.

sub′normal, a. Lower or less than what is normal. [Psych.] Having less than normal brain power but not quite MORONIC; (less commonly) MENTALLY DEFICIENT.

sub′notochord, n. [Zoo.] In some animals a hard rod under and parallel to the NOTOCHORD.

sub′ocular, 1.a. [Zoo.] Under the eyeball. 2. An arch of CARTILAGE under and supporting the eyeball in some CYCLOSTOMATA. **s. shelf.** An ingrowth of bone supporting the eyeball in some fish.

sub′orbital, n., a. [Zoo.] (In some fish, any of a line of bones) under the eye.

sub′petiol-ar, -ate, aa. [Bot.] (Of a BUD) covered by the base of the PETIOLE.

sub′phrenic, a. [Zoo.] Under the DIAPHRAGM of higher animals.

sub-′Polar ′region. [Geog.] The coldest part of one or other of the TEMPERATE ZONES, whose farthest limit is the limit of tree growth—covered in the North Temperate Zone by CONIFEROUS woods.

sub′radius (subradii), n. [Zoo.] In certain COELENTERATA, a RADIUS of the 4th ORDER, coming between an ADRADIUS and a PERRADIUS or INTERRADIUS.

sub′ramose, a. [Bot.] Branching little.

′subsequent, a. Taking place after, later than, a named time or event. [Geog., Geol.] Formed later than the system of which it is a part, gen. as an outcome of earlier developments. **s. river.** [Geog.] A river draining into a CONSEQUENT RIVER and formed after it by cutting its way through the softer parts of the country in the natural direction of their STRIKE, that is, more or less at right angles to the consequent river and parallel to the slope down which this has made its way.

sub′shell, a. [Phys.] In the ATOM, a division of an ENERGY LEVEL.

sub′sidence, n. [Geog., Geol.] The lowering of the level of a part of the earth in relation to the parts round it as the effect of the parts under it giving way under its weight. [Meteor.] The slow pushing down of great masses of air to the earth, such as takes place in the forming of ANTI-

CYCLONES. **sub′side**, v.i. [Geog., Meteor.] (Of earth or air) become lower, undergo s.

sub′sidiary, a. SECONDARY or AUXILIARY, not the chief.

′subsoil, n. [Geol., Biol.] The bed of loose material between the true SOIL in which plants chiefly have their growth, and the deeper hard ROCK—not so fertile as the true soil because less weathered and having less ORGANIC material in it.

sub′sonic, a. Of a velocity, less than that of sound in air etc.; of any rate of an airplane when the MACH NUMBER is less than 1.

sub′species, n. [Biol.] A division of a SPECIES greater than a RACE, commonly formed of animals or plants separated from others of their species by distance, as the effect of a special adjustment to certain living-places, and so which have been forced to BREED only with one another and have come to breed less readily with those outside the group—but not unable to do so and not different enough in structure to be looked on as a separate species, though sometimes possibly on the way to becoming one. **subspecific**, a.

′substage, n. A part fixed under the STAGE of a MICROSCOPE by which other bits of apparatus, such as a NICOL PRISM, may be kept in place there.

sub′standard, a. Lower in size or quality than some STANDARD.

sub′stantia, n. [Zoo.] (Used as part of a name) substance. **s. ′adaman′tina**. [Zoo.] The hard outer covering of a tooth. **s. e′burnea**. [Zoo.] DENTINE.

sub′stantial, a. To do with substance or with the substance of a thing as opp. its form, etc.

′substantive, a. SUBSTANTIAL. [Chem.] (Of DYES) not needing a MORDANT, opp. ADJECTIVE—used for dyeing cotton and man-made CELLULOSE materials such as RAYON. **s. vari′ation**. [Biol.] A change in the make-up or substance of a plant, animal, or part, as opp. a change in its structure, the number of its parts etc.

sub′stellar point. [Astron.] The point on the earth where it is cut by a line from its middle point to a star, that is, where the star is straight overhead.

substi′tution, n. The putting of one thing in the place of another. [Chem.] The act of substituting a different ATOM or atom-group for one forming part of a MOLECULE, sp. for an atom of H. **s. de′posit**, etc. REPLACEMENT DEPOSIT, etc. **s. ′product**. [Chem.] Any substance produced by s. **sub′stituent**, 1.n. [Chem.] An ATOM or group which has been put in the place of another in a MOLECULE. 2.a. Being a substituent. **′substitute**, 1.v.t. Put something in the place of some other

thing (*substitute* the first *for* the second). 2.n. Anything which has been substituted for, or may be used in place of, another. 3.a. Being a substitute. **′substituted**, a Sp., [Chem.] (of a complex substance) having had some new ATOM etc. substituted for one of its old ones, sp. H.

′substrate, n. [Biochem.] That substance on which an ENZYME has the power of acting.

sub′stratum (substrata), n. The material on which anything is resting, that on which it is based or supported. [Chem., Biol., Bact.] A MEDIUM. [Bot.] The material in which a plant is fixed and has its growth. [Zoo.] The solid material to which an animal is fixed or on which it goes about.

sub′synchronous, a. [Elec.] Having a FREQUENCY which is a SUB-MULTIPLE of the frequency of the driving current.

sub′temperate, a. [Geog.] Of, in, to do with, having the same range of heat and cold as, the less warm parts of the TEMPERATE ZONES.

sub′tend, v.t. [Geom.] (Of a straight line) give opposite to itself (a certain angle), when straight lines are taken from its ends to a given point. [Bot.] Have (a BUD, or a part produced from a bud) in its AXIL, be at the base and on the outside of (a flower, etc.).

subter′ranean, a. [Geog., Geol.] Having its place under the face of the earth, coming from deep down in the earth.

sub′tract, v.t. Take (a part, etc.) *from* something, sp. [Arith. etc.] take (a number or amount) *from* another number or amount. **′-ion**, n. The process of subtracting, for which the sign is ‘ − ’. **′-ive**, a. **subtractive ′colour ′process**. The process used in motion pictures of producing the desired colours in a picture on a SCREEN by sending white light through one, two, or three FILMS, one of which subtracts, completely or to some degree, the red rays, one the blue, and one the green, so that any of these may be taken out or made much less and the different rays may be separated or mixed to give whatever colour is needed; the like process of printing coloured pictures by the use of the three colours COMPLEMENTARY to red, blue, and green, put on one over the other as needed. **sub′tractive ′primary.** In colour printing and camera work the colour COMPLEMENTARY to red (named *minus red*, that is, CYAN), or to blue (named *minus blue*, that is, yellow), or to green (named *minus green*, that is, MAGENTA).

sub′tropic(al), aa. [Geog., etc.] Almost TROPICAL, said of the parts of the TEMPERATE ZONES edging the TORRID ZONE, or of anything special to, or having

a connection with, these parts. **sub-**
'tropics, n.pl. The s. parts of the earth.
'subulate, a. [Bot.] Long and narrow, sloping
to a thin point, said of leaves etc.
suc'cession, n. A number or line of things
coming after one another in time or
place; the act, fact, or condition of
coming after another or one after another.
[Bot.] The s. of different sorts of plants
produced in a place from the start of plant
growth there to the development of a
fixed ASSOCIATION, or the process of slow
change by which this development comes
about. **suc'cessive,** a. Coming one after
another in space or time, sp. straight
away, without spaces or stops between.
suc'cinic acid. [Chem.] A DIBASIC ACID,
$(CH_2COOH)_2$, present in certain plants
and in muscle, used in making DYES.
'succinite, n. [Mineral.] A sort of AMBER
from which SUCCINIC ACID may be got.
suc'cise, a. [Bot.] (Of a part) ending suddenly as if a bit had been cut off.
'succubous, a. [Bot.] Having the leaves so
placed that the top part of every one is
covered by the base of the one over it on
the same side of the stem.
'succulent, a. [Bot.] Soft and thick with
much liquid in its substance, as a s. fruit
or stem.
'succus, n. [Bot.] The liquid part of a plant,
sp. [Med.] as got by crushing for medical
purposes. [Zoo.] The liquid produced by
a GLAND. **s. en'tericus.** [Zoo.] The liquids
produced in the SMALL INTESTINE of back-
boned animals for purposes of digestion.
suck, 1.v.i. Take in something, sp. liquid,
by forming a VACUUM so that it is forced
in by the air, said sp. of taking in liquid
food by using the lips in this way, as a
baby takes in its mother's milk. 2.v.t.
Take in (a liquid) by sucking; make use of
a sucking operation of the mouth or a
SUCKER on (something from which liquid
may be got, as a NIPPLE or a blood-vessel).
'sucker, n. [Mach.] An apparatus producing or working by SUCTION, sp. a pipe
or machine-part into which liquid,
steam or other material is pulled by
suction. [Zoo.] A part designed for
gripping by SUCTION, as those on the
arms of CEPHALOPODA or the TUBE FEET
of ECHINODERMATA; a mouth or other
part designed specially for sucking, or
sometimes for sucking and gripping by
suction at the same time, as in a number
of PARASITES. [Bot.] A new growth of
stem branching from a root or the base of
a stem and going sideways through the
earth at first so as to come up a little
distance away, which has the power of
becoming an independent plant. **'suck-**
ing, a. **sucking disc.** [Zoo.] A SUCKER for
gripping having the form of a soft round
or ring-like outgrowth of the skin, freq.

somewhat hollow on the under side,
which when pushed flat onto something
sends the air from under it and is kept in
place by the weight of the air over it.
sucking stomach. [Zoo.] In some ARTHRO-
PODA, an expansion of the digestion pipe
with strong muscles having the power of
sucking in liquids through the mouth.
'suckle, v.t. [Zoo.] (Of a female animal) give
milk to (its offspring or other young
animal). **'suckling,** n. [Zoo.] A young
animal before it is old enough to do
without its mother's milk.
'sucrase, n. [Chem., Biochem.] INVERTASE.
'sucro-. [Chem.] Having a SUGAR in it.
sucro'clastic, a. [Chem.] (Of an ENZYME)
causing SUGARS to be broken up.
'sucrose, n. [Chem., Biochem.] The common
sugar, $C_{12}H_{22}O_{11}$, got from different
plants and used as food, not commonly
produced by animals—a complex of
GLUCOSE and FRUCTOSE, into which
substances it may be broken up.
'suction, 1.n. [Phys.] The pushing force of
the air or other gas round a body by which
it is forced into any of the space near
it from which the air or gas has been,
completely or in part, taken away;
the forcing of a body, sp. a liquid, into
such a space in this way. 2.a. Producing s.
or working by s. **s. pump.** [Mach.] A
pump in which the water, etc. to be lifted
is pushed into the pipe by the air round
it, as the effect of the taking away of some
air from the pipe itself by the lifting of
the PISTON or bucket. **s. stroke.** [Mach.]
In an INTERNAL COMBUSTION ENGINE,
that motion of the PISTON by which the
mixed gas is pulled into the vessel where,
by a further motion, it is COMPRESSED.
suc'torial, a. [Zoo.] To do with SUCKING,
designed for sucking or as SUCKERS,
having the power of sucking, getting its
food by sucking the blood of other
animals, etc.
'sudor, n. [Zoo.] SWEAT. **'-al,** a. sudo'riferous, a. sudo'rific, n., a. To do with, causing
or increasing, SWEATING. 2.n. [Med.] A
sudorific substance.
'suffix, n. [Philol.] An ending put onto a
word as an INFLECTION, or to make
another word having a connection with it
in sense (which is made clear by the sense
of the ending), as the 's' of *boys* or the
'ly' of *slowly.*
suf'fruticose, s. [Bot.] (Of a plant) with the
part at the base wood-forming and living
on like a tree, while the higher branches
are green and become dead after flowering.
suf'fused, a. Having what is named all
through it, mixed with every part, as s.
with light, colour, blood, etc. **suf'fuse,** v.t.
Go all through the substance of (something). **suf'fusion,** n. Sp., [Med.] The
going of any body-liquid, such as blood

out of its vessels into, among the parts of, the substance round; the condition of any part of the body which has become full of blood or other liquid as the effect of suffusion.

'sugar, n. [Chem.] Any of a group of CRYSTALLINE CARBOHYDRATES which are sweet to the taste and SOLUBLE in water, produced naturally by plants, for example SUCROSE, d-GLUCOSE, FRUCTOSE, and MALTOSE.

sugar of lead. [Chem.] LEAD ACETATE, $(CH_3COO)_2Pb.3H_2O$, which has a sweet taste.

'sugent, su'gescent, aa. SUCTORIAL.

sug'gestion, n. [Psych.] The causing of an idea, belief, impulse, act etc., in a person without any process of reasoning, as the effect of a voiced suggestion, or some act etc. designed to give such a suggestion, by another person, sp. by one having control over the mind of the first person through giving him a conscious or unconscious belief in his power of helping or fear of making him angry etc., as in HYPNOSIS or PSYCHOTHERAPY. sug'gest, v.t. Make the suggestion of (something) to a person. sug'gestible, a. [Psych.] Readily controlled by s.

'sulcal, a. [Zoo.] To do with a SULCUS. [Phonet.] (Of the tongue) with the sides turned up forming a hollow in the top side; (of a sound) said with the tongue in this position, as the letter 'r'.

'sulcate, a. [Biol.] Marked with parallel cracks or long narrow hollows. [Zoo.] Having a SULCUS.

'sulcus (sulci), n. [Zoo.] A hollow line or long narrow hollow in some part of the body, sp. one of those in the brain. 'sulculus, n.

'sulpha drugs. [Med.] SULPHONAMIDES.

'sulpha'nilimide, n. [Chem., Med.] One of the SULPHONAMIDES $NH_2C_6H_4.SO_2NH_2$, causing the destruction of STREPTOCOCCI —the acting part of PRONTOSIL.

'sulpha'pyridine, n. SULPHANILIMIDE united with PYRIDINE.

'sulphate, 1.n. [Chem.] Any SALT or ESTER of SULPHURIC ACID. 2.v.t. [Chem.] Make undergo a reaction with sulphuric acid, make into or get mixed with a s. 'sulphated, a. sul'phation, n. Sp. [Elec.] The forming of a coat of white lead s., $PbSO_4$, on the NEGATIVE plates of STORAGE CELLS, which in time becomes hard and has a bad effect on the working of the cell. sul'phato-.

'sulphide, n. [Chem.] A substance formed by uniting one ELEMENT or group with S; a SALT of H_2S (hydrogen s. or hydrosulphuric acid). sul'phidic, a.

'sulphite, n. [Chem.] Any SALT or ESTER of SULPHUROUS ACID. sul'phito-.

sulph(o)-. SULPHUR, having sulphur in it,

formed of sulphur and what is named: sulpho'chloride, n., 'sulpho'cyanide, n. sulpho'cyanate, n. sulph'oxide, n.

'sulphonal, n. [Chem., Med.] a CRYSTALLINE substance, $(CH_3)_2.C.(SO_2C_2H_5)_2$, without colour, used medically for causing sleep.

sul'phonamide, n. [Chem., Med.] Any of a great and important group of complex chemical substances having in them the group SO_2NH_2 (named the s. group) with strong powers of destruction for different BACTERIA and having very important medical uses, for example SULPHANILAMIDE and M. AND B.

sulpho'nation, n. [Chem.] The process of producing, or changing another substance into, a SULPHONIC ACID. 'sulphonate, v.t. Get SULPHONIC ACID formed by the reaction of H_2SO_4 with ALIPHATIC or AROMATIC COMPOUNDS. 'sulphonated, a. sulphonated oil. An oil which has been made to some degree SOLUBLE in water by REACTION with H_2SO_4.

sul'phonic, a. [Chem.] To do with or having in it the s. group. s. 'acid. Any ACID having in it the s. group. s. group. The MONOVALENT ACID group $SO_2.OH$.

'sulphur, n. Chemical ELEMENT, at. no. 16, at. wt. 32·06, sign S. a non-metal having more than one form, commonly a light-yellow powder burning with a blue flame —widely present in the earth, free or united, necessary to living things, and having a very wide range of uses, for example in making sulphuric acid, matches, DYES, INSECTICIDES, FERTILIZERS, and VULCANIZED rubber, and for medical purposes. s. bac'teria. [Bact.] BACTERIA able to do without O and having the property of acting on substances with s. in them and freeing the s. s. di'oxide. [Chem.] SO_2, a gas without colour and with a strong, cough-causing smell, produced by the burning of s. in air as in VOLCANOES, readily made liquid and gen. used in this form, in making sulphuric acid, in REFRIGERATORS, as a BLEACH, etc. s. tri'oxide. [Chem.] SO_3, a white CRYSTALLINE substance, by the uniting of which with water sulphuric acid is made. sul'phureous, a. Formed of s., having s. in it, like s., sp. [Bot.] in colour. '-etted, a. [Chem.] United or mixed with s. 'sulphur'etted 'hydrogen. HYDROGEN SULPHIDE. sul'phuric, a. [Chem.] Sp., having in it s. with a higher VALENCY. sul'phuric an'hydride. S. trioxide. 'sulphuric acid. [Chem.] H_2SO_4, an oil-like, burning liquid without colour, which DISSOLVES in water with a violent, heat-producing reaction, made by uniting SO_2 with the O of the air and dissolving the SO_3 so produced in water—widely used and very important in industry, for example in making DYES and EXPLOSIVES. **sul'phurous,** a. [Chem.] Sp., having in it s. with a lower VALENCY. **sulphurous acid.** [Chem.] H_2SO_3, a SOLUTION of SO_2 in water.

'sum, n. [Math.] The number or amount got by the simple or ALGEBRAIC addition of two or more numbers or amounts.

sum'mation, n. The process of addition. [Zoo., Psych.] The addition of STIMULI, that is, the producing of a reaction as the effect of two or more different stimuli acting together at the same point, or of like stimuli acting one after the other, when any one of these acting separately would not be enough to get any reaction —a very important process of the nerve-system. **s. tone.** [Acous.] A TONE produced by the operation in the same air-space of two different VIBRATIONS, and having a FREQUENCY equal to the frequencies of the two uniting vibrations put together.

'summer egg. [Zoo.] An egg with a thin SHELL and the property of quick development, produced in spring or summer by some FRESH-WATER animals. (*See* WINTER EGG).

'summer 'solstice. *See* SOLSTICE.

sump, n. [Eng.] A hollow in the earth or under an engine etc., so placed that water or other liquid is drained off into it, for example at the lowest point of a part of a mine, to keep the working part dry.

sun, n. [Astron.] The great, light-giving and heat-giving star about 93 million miles from the earth, 866,000 miles across and of mass 2×10^{27} TONS, made up of a ball-like mass of mixed substances (all of which are present on the earth) in the form of highly heated gases (about 6000°C on the outside), round which the earth and the other PLANETS are moving, and by whose attraction they and all the other bodies making up the system of which our earth is a part are kept in their places; any like body in space outside our system controlling a system of the same sort. **s. 'pillar.** [Meteor.] An upright COLUMN of light seen moving through the s. at sun-up and sun-down, caused by the REFLECTION of sunlight from ice CRYSTALS. **s.-ray 'treatment.** [Med.] ULTRA-VIOLET THERAPY. **'-rise.** n. The coming up of the s. in the morning. **'-shine,** n. [Meteor.] The sun's light when it is strong enough to make a shade. **'sunshine re'corder.** [Meteor.] An apparatus for FOCUSING the sun's rays on a time scale, which is burnt by them and so gives a record of the hours in the day for which the s. was out at the place in question. **'-set,** n. Sun-down. **'-spot,** n. [Astron.] Any of the great dark places, made up of a blue-black middle part with a lighter part round it, coming and going here and there on the face of the s. as seen through the TELESCOPE from time to time, and becoming greatest in number regularly every eleven years—having some connection with MAGNETIC STORMS on the earth. **'-stroke,** n. [Med.] A condition marked by FEVER and COMA caused by the over-heating of the body (for example, by being out in very strong sunlight with the head and neck uncovered) and freq. causing death.

super-. Over in position, higher than, on the upper side of, sp. [Biol.]:— **'-ax'illary,** a. **'-'carpal,** a., **'-'glottal,** a. **'-'sacral,** a., etc.; being the upper of two:— **'-max'illa,** n.; over in degree, very, sp. [Med.] more than normal:— **'-irrita'bility,** n., **'-se'cretion,** n. [Biol.] Being a higher division in the grouping of plants and animals than the one named:— **'-'family.**

'super'acid, a. [Chem.] More than normally acid, said of feeble acids when mixed with certain liquids other than water; (of earth) having a pH-VALUE of between 3·5 and 4. **'supera'cidity.** n.

'super'centrifuge, n. ULTRACENTRIFUGE.

'supercharge, 1.n. A CHARGE greater than normal. 2.v.t. Give a s. to, sp. by the use of a supercharger. **'supercharged,** a. Having a s. [Eng.] (Of an engine) having, working by, a supercharger. **'super-'charger,** n. [Eng.] An apparatus used for pumping or blowing air or gas into an INTERNAL COMBUSTION ENGINE at a PRESSURE higher than that of the ATMOSPHERE, used in airplanes to make up for the loss in air pressure as the machine goes higher, and in automobiles moving at a rate so great as not to get enough air in the normal way.

'super'ciliary, a. [Zoo.] To do with, near, the EYEBROWS, over the eye-hollows.

'super-con'ducting, a. [Elec.] In a condition of SUPER-CONDUCTIVITY.

'super-con'ductive, a. [Elec.] (Of certain metals) undergoing a sudden drop in RESISTANCE and becoming a complete CONDUCTOR of electric current at a TEMPERATURE a little higher than ABSOLUTE ZERO, at which all metals do so. **super'conduc'tivity.** [Elec.] A very high degree of CONDUCTIVITY, sp. that of a superconductor at or under the TEMPERATURE at which its RESISTANCE becomes roughly = O. **supercon'ductor,** n. [Elec.] A s. substance.

super'cool, v.t. [Phys., Chem.] Make (a liquid or gas) colder than the degree at which it normally becomes solid or liquid while still keeping it in the form of a liquid or gas. **super'cooled,** a.

'super'ego, n. [Psych.] That deep-seated part of the mind or self which is at war with the lower impulses coming to the EGO from the ID, causing it pain and regret whenever it gives way to them and does anything out of harmony with the unconscious values or sense of right and wrong which have taken root in the process of its development.

'super'ficial, a. Of, to do with, measuring, or present on, the SURFACE of anything; near the surface, to do with the outer coat or parts of anything, not going deep; (of measures) measuring space of two DIMENSIONS. [Geol.] Sp., said of the loose material, gen. put down by rivers, GLACIERS etc., covering most of the face of the earth, as opp. solid ROCK. 'superfici'ality, n. The condition of being s.

super'ficies, n. SURFACE.

'superf(o)e'tation, n. [Med.] The FERTILIZA-TION of a second OVUM in a women when there is one in process of development from an earlier fertilization.

super'fuse, v.t. SUPERCOOL. 'superfusi-'bility, n. [Chem.] The property of being able to be SUPERCOOLED. super'fusion, n.

super'heat, 1.v.t. [Phys., Chem.] Get a liquid heated to a degree higher than its boiling-point without its changing into VAPOUR; get (steam or other vapour) heated, away from the water etc. by which it was produced, to a degree higher than that at which, at the given PRESSURE, the vapour would be SATURATED if in touch with its liquid. 2.n. [Aeronautics.] The amount by which the gas in a BALLOON is warmer or colder than the air round it. super'heated, a.

super'heterodyne re'ceiver or super'het, n. [Radio] A radio RECEIVER by which the currents produced by incoming waves are changed to currents having a fixed HETERODYNE FREQUENCY greater than an AUDIOFREQUENCY, which are then AMPLI-FIED and DEMODULATED, giving great SELECTIVITY.

superim'pose, v.t. Put (one thing) over, on top of another, as a STRATUM; make an addition which is looked on in this way, as something coming on top of an earlier structure or earlier additions. super-im'posed, a. Sp. [Geol., Geog.] (Of rivers or a river system) taking a form and direction which is not based on the present structure and slopes of the land round, because first formed in super-imposed material sloping etc. differently, which has now been weathered away.

'superimpreg'nation, n. SUPERFOETATION.

su'perior, a. Over, higher in position than, some other thing; upper, being the higher of two, or the highest of more than two, like parts, sp. [Biol.]; over, higher in degree, better, or greater in number or amount, than some other thing or than the normal. [Bot.] (Of the OVARY of a

flower) free from the other flower-rings, seated on a rounded end of the stem with the others ranged round and under it, or at the middle of the base of a cup-like or plate-like end, with them ranged round its edge; (of other rings of a flower or their parts) with the ovary under them, bedded in the expansion at the end of the stem from which they come. s. con-'junction. [Astron.] The position of a PLANET when it is in line with and on the other side of the sun as seen from the earth, or the time when it gets into this position. 'superi'ority, n. The condition of being s.

super'jacent, a. [Geol.] Resting on or over.

super'molecule, n. [Phys., Chem.] A MOLECULE made up of smaller molecules forming a regular structure.

super'natant, a. On the top of a liquid, or (of a part of a ship or other body supported in a liquid) higher than the water line. s. 'liquid. [Chem.] The clear liquid over a SEDIMENT.

super'nova (supernovae), n. [Astron.] A NOVA whose burst into light is specially bright, the complete destruction of the star probably taking place in the process.

super'numerary, a. (Of a part or thing) present in addition to the necessary or [Biol.] normal number of such parts or things.

super'parasite, n. HYPERPARASITE.

super'phosphate, n. [Chem.] Any SALT of PHOSPHORIC ACID, H_3PO_4, which keeps part of the H of the acid, as NaH_2PO_4 or Na_2HPO_4; a substance made up chiefly of SOLUBLE ss. of Ca, sp. $Ca(H_2PO_4)_2$, and $CaSO_4$, produced by the operation of H_2SO_4 on the non-soluble PHOSPHATE $Ca(PO_4)_6$, used in farming for making land fertile, helping plant growth.

super'physical, a. Not a part of the physical system of things, not controlled by physical laws.

super'pose, v.t. Put anything straight over another thing, at a little distance or on top of it. super'posed, a. Sp. [Bot.] (Of a part of a plant) placed higher than and in line with another part. 'superpo'sition, n. super'position 'image. [Zoo.] The complete IMAGE formed by a COMPOUND eye when its structure is such that the images formed by its separate units are superposed.

supersatu'ration, n. [Phys., Chem.] The METASTABLE STATE of a SOLUTION or a SOLVENT, liquid or gas, which has in it more of a SOLUTE than it is normally able to take up at that TEMPERATURE. super-'saturate, v.t. Get (a SOLUTION or SOLVENT) supersaturated. super'saturated, a. In the condition of s.

super'sonic, a. [Phys.] (Of a VELOCITY, for example, that of an airplane) greater than the velocity of sound; in older use, ULTRASONIC, but now gen. limited to the first sense, or when not so limited, used with the word FREQUENCY. **s. 'heterodyne re'ceiver.** [Radio] SUPERHETERODYNE RECEIVER. **super'sonics,** n. The science of s. waves.

'superstructure, n. A structure on the top of another structure, or that part of a structure on top of a base or a given level (in buildings the level of the earth, in ships the level of the highest floor covering all the ship, etc.). [Metal.] The regular design formed in the structure of a solid SOLUTION by the substance in solution, sp. in certain ALLOYS.

'superterr'an-ean, -eous, 'super-terr'ene. aa. On the face of or over the earth.

supi'nation, n. [Zoo.] The motion of the arm by which the soft inner side of the hand is turned forward or, when the arm is outstretched, up (opp. PRONATION); the position of the hand and arm effected by s.; the like motion or position of the leg and foot. [Med.] The condition of being SUPINE. **'supinator,** n. [Zoo.] Any muscle, sp. of the arm, by which s. is effected. **'supinate,** a. [Zoo.] In the position of s.

'supine, a. (Of a person or the position) stretched out flat on the back.

'supplement, 1.n. An addition designed to make something more complete, sp. a separate part put at the end of a book or paper, or going with it, giving anything further which will be of use, such as later facts, further details, a map, an outline, etc., etc. **2.**v.t. (Of an addition or something going with or done in addition to some other thing) make more complete or of greater value, do what is needed for completing some work or process done in part by some other thing; (of a person, etc.) make (something) more complete or of greater effect *by* or *with* some completing or helping addition. **supple-'ment-al, -ary,** aa. Supplementing, being a s. to. **supple'mental air.** [Med.] The (amount of) air which it is still possible to send out of the LUNGS after breathing out with normal force. **supple'mentary angle.** [Geom.] That angle which together with a given one makes an angle of 180°. **'supplemen'tation,** n.

supp'ly, 1.v.t. Give what is necessary for some purpose, as *s.* an engine *with* power, the heart *with* blood. [Zoo.] (Of given nerves and blood-vessels) be the ways by which blood or NERVE IMPULSES are transported to, from, or about (some part or substance of the body). **2.**n. [Elec.] The power or current produced for the use of an electric system or coming into it. **3.**a. [Elec.] To do with supplying or a s., as a *s. station.* **s. point.** [Elec.] A point in an electric power system where a connection may be made for getting power.

supp'ort, n. In camera work, the material, gen. glass, paper, or some CELLULOSE material, which has on it the coating of light-SENSITIVE substance on which a camera picture is produced.

sup'pository, n. [Med.] A small mass of some substance readily becoming liquid when warmed by the body, mixed with medical substances, for pushing into some opening, sp. the RECTUM, VAGINA or URETHRA.

sup'press, v.t. Put a stop to, keep from having an effect or coming to development, sp. [Med.] put a stop to the running of blood from a wound or some like process. **'-ed,** a. Sp. [Biol., Med., Psych.] Having undergone suppression. **'-ion,** n. [Biol.] The stopping of the development of a part normally present, completely or at a very early stage. [Med.] The suppression of some substance normally produced or sent out by the body, through the stopping up of an outlet or the stopping of the process by which the substance is formed, as *suppression of* URINE caused by the KIDNEYS not doing their work. [Psych.] The conscious forcing out of the conscious mind of thoughts, ideas, memories etc., which are unpleasing to it. **'-ive,** a. **'-or,** n. Sp., [Radio., etc] A part or apparatus used for suppressing undesired effects. **suppressor grid.** [Elec., Radio] A GRID put between the SCREEN and ANODE in a THERMIONIC VALVE to keep the SECONDARY ELECTRONS given off by the anode from getting to the other parts of the valve.

'suppurate, v.i. [Med.] (Of a wound or diseased part) make, send out, PUS. **suppu'ration,** n. The process or condition of suppurating. **'suppurant, 'suppurative, 1.**aa. [Med.] Suppurating or with a tendency to s.; causing suppuration. **2.**n. Anything causing suppuration.

'supra-. Higher in position than, on or over, sp. [Zoo.]—: **'-ax'illary,** a. [Bot.], **'-anal,** a., **'-'branchial,** a., **'-'buccal,** a., **'-'caudal,** a., **-cla'vicular,** a., **-'cranial,** a., **'-'hyoid,** a., **'-'labial,** a., **'-'nasal,** a., **-'ocular,** a., **'-'scapular,** a., **'-sphen'oidal,** a., **'-'spinal,** a., **-'temporal,** a. [Zoo.], **'thor'acid,** a. **'-tympanic,** a., etc.; the upper of two or the upper part of something:— **'-'epi-'meron,** n., **'-epi'sternum,** n., **'-max'illa,** n. **'-max'illary,** a.

supra-'angulare, 1.n. [Zoo.] A bone in the lower JAW of snakes, birds etc. coming over the ANGULAR bone. **2.**a. To do with the s.

'supra-au'ricular, a. [Zoo.] (Of certain feathers in birds) over the ear.

'supra'clavicle, 'supra'cleithrum, nn. [Zoo.] A bone of the PECTORAL GIRDLE in fish taking the place of the SCAPULA in higher animals.

'supra'conductivity, 'supracon'ductor, etc. SUPERCONDUCTIVITY, etc.

supra'dorsal, 1.a. [Zoo.] On the back; on the outer side of the back-bone and forming part of it. 2.n. Any of certain s. bones or CARTILAGES present in VERTEBRAE at an early stage of development.

supra'liminal, a. [Psych.] (Of a STIMULUS or of the degree to which one stimulus is stronger than another) great enough to be sensed; (of the effects of stimuli or of events in the mind) conscious.

supra'renal, a. [Zoo.] Placed over or in front of the KIDNEYS; to do with the s. glands. **s. gland, s. body,** or **s. capsule.** A DUCTLESS GLAND (of which there are two in man and higher animals, a greater number in some other animals) at the upper or forward end of the KIDNEY, producing ADRENALIN and other HORMONES playing an important, sometimes necessary, part in the process of living.

'supraspi'natus, n. [Zoo.] A muscle of the upper back in man going to the top of the upper arm.

sur-. SUPER or SUPRA:— **-'anal,** a., **-'angular, -'angu'lase,** nn., aa.

'sural, a. [Zoo.] To do with the back of the lower leg.

'surcharge, n., v.t. SUPERCHARGE. **'surcharged,** a.

'surculus, n. [Bot.] SUCKER. **'surcul'igerous, 'surculose, -ous,** aa.

surd, n. [Maths.] A QUANTITY which it is impossible to give in the form of a complete number or FRACTION, as $\sqrt{2}$ (*the square root of* 2).

'surface, 1.n. The outside of a solid or any of its faces; the limiting face of a body of liquid where it comes in touch with another substance, such as the sides of a vessel or the air over it, sp. the top; the outer coat of anything, the part near and forming the s. 2.a. To do with, at or in, the s. or the part of anything very near it, its outside or outer coat. **s. ac'tivity.** [Chem.] The property or working of a s.-active substance. **s. 'colour.** [Optics] Colour produced by the REFLECTION of light from the s. of a body as opp. the colour produced by light going through a body or the colour of light itself. **s. 'density.** [Phys.] The amount of electric CHARGE on a s. per unit of space. **s. of 'buoyancy.** [Phys.] The plane in which is the CENTRE OF BUOYANCY of anything supported by a liquid. **s. plate.** [Eng.] A hard iron plate whose s. has been made completely flat, used for testing how flat other ss. are **s. 'tension.** [Phys.] That property of LIQUID ss., caused by the fact that MOLECULES in this position are not acted on in all directions by the attraction of other molecules, as those under the s. are, which makes such ss. seem to be formed of a thin, elastic skin, having a tendency to take up as little space as possible (as seen in the forming of drops); the measure of the s. tension of a liquid, equal to the force per cm. etc. acting at right angles to any line across the s. **'s.-'active.** [Chem.] (Of a substance) having an effect on the s. tension when present in a given liquid. **s.-active 'agent.** [Chem.] A s.-active substance which is mixed with a given liquid to give it more wetting or covering power etc., as most DETERGENTS.

'surfaced, a. Having been given a s. of some special sort or material.

surge, 1.n. A sudden, strong wave-like motion or increase of a current in any direction, as a s. of air or water. [Elec.] A sudden short sharp increase in the VOLTAGE of an electric current. 2.v.i. Come with a s. [Elec.] (Of a current) undergo a s., be increased suddenly and sharply and then go back to its normal value.

'surgery, n. That branch of medical science having to do with putting right unhealthy conditions or unnormal structures by physical adjustments and operations, such as the cutting out, training into new positions, stretching, or moving, of parts of the body. **'surgeon,** n. An expert in s. **'surgical,** a. To do with, effected by, using or used in, s. **'surgical 'spirit.** [Med.] METHYLATED SPIRIT with the addition of a little CASTOR OIL and METHYL, SALICYLATE, used chiefly for STERILIZING the skin in operations etc. **'surgically,** adv.

'surplus, n., a. (Amount of something) over, in addition to, the necessary amount for some purpose, more than is needed or used.

'survey, n. A getting together of the facts over a certain field and the organization of them in a system or account, for the purpose of getting more light on some question—as a s. of conditions of work in a given industry etc. [Engin. etc.] The operation of measuring and mapping to scale any part of the earth, fixing its outline, slopes and hollows, the positions and distances of its details in relation to one another, etc., with a view to mapmaking or to engineering work. **sur'vey,** v.t. [Eng.] Make a s. of (country). **sur'veying,** n. [Engin.] The work or science of making ss. of country. **sur'veyor,** n. Expert in surveying, one whose business is surveying.

sur'vive, 1.v.i. Go on living, or keep on being in existence. 2.v.t. S. longer than (some other person or thing); come through (some condition, danger, etc). without being put out of existence.

survival, n. The act or fact of surviving; something from the past still surviving after other things of the same sort have come to an end or new developments have made it of no use, sp. [Zoo., Anthrop., Psych. etc.] a form of behaviour which was natural to man or animal at an early stage but has now no purpose or relation to the way of living. [Philol.] An ending or root-word, etc., which survives in certain words but is no longer used in forming new ones, and the sense of which has gone from common knowledge. **sur'vival of the 'fittest.** [Biol.] The effect produced by NATURAL SELECTION, by which those animals or plants best able to take care of themselves in the conditions of living are the ones which s. **sur'viving,** a. Having survived, still in existence. **sur'vivor,** n. Person or animal which has survived, sp. some danger etc. which others have not survived.

sus'ceptance, n. [Elec.] The RECIPROCAL of REACTANCE, which is equal to $\dfrac{1}{2\pi f L}$ where f is the FREQUENCY of the current and L the INDUCTANCE.

sus'cepti'bility, n. The property of being readily acted on by something, sp. [Biol.] of having a tendency to be attacked by certain PARASITES or diseases. [Elec.] *See* MAGNETIC SUSCEPTIBILITY. **sus'ceptible,** a. Having s. (*to* something).

sus'pended, a. Hanging (*from* a point of support, *by* a thread, etc.); kept from falling down in, kept somewhere between the top and base of, a liquid or a gas as the effect of the VISCOSITY or BUOYANT force of this; stopped for a time. [Phys., Chem.] In a condition of SUSPENSION (*in* a liquid or gas). **s. ani'mation.** [Med.] A death-like condition going on for some minutes or sometimes hours, in which breathing is completely or almost stopped and the operation of the heart so feeble as to seem so. **sus'pend,** v.t. Put into a hanging position; put a stop to for a time.

sus'pension, 1.n. The act of SUSPENDING or the condition of being SUSPENDED. [Phys., Chem.] The condition of a solid broken up into small grains mixed all through and supported by a liquid or gas, but not small enough to be in SOLUTION in it, as dust *in s.* in the air; the condition of a liquid mixed in the same way through another liquid or gas in the form of very small drops; a liquid or gas and a solid or liquid mixed together in this way. [Mach. etc.] A structure designed for hanging something from or supporting it in such a way as to give it the power of moving freely in certain directions, as the s. of a MAGNETIC NEEDLE. 2.a. To do with s., suspended or suspending. **s. bridge.** [Eng.] A bridge whose roadway is SUSPENDED by metal cords etc. from structures at its two ends, in place of resting on arches or other supports. **sus'pensive,** a. Effecting or marked by s. in any sense.

sus'pensor, n. Something from or in which some other thing is hanging, or by which it is supported. [Bot.] In seed-plants and some others, a chain of CELLS forming a sort of stem for the EMBRYO and by its growth forcing it into the ENDOSPERM or other part where food is stored for it; in certain FUNGI, one or other of the two HYPHAE supporting a GAMETANGIUM. **sus'pensory,** a. SUSPENSIVE. [Zoo.] To do with a SUSPENSORIUM.

suspen'sorium, n. [Zoo.] Any structure by which a part is hanging, sp. the bone(s) or CARTILAGE(s) forming the connection between the lower bone of the mouth and the framework of the head.

susten'tacular, a. [Zoo.] Supporting, said sp. of CELLS. **susten'taculum,** n. [Zoo. Med.] A supporting structure.

'suture, 1.n. [Biol.] The line formed by the uniting of two parts or edges, as [Bot.] that where the edges of a CARPEL come together, or [Zoo.] between two META-MERES, two plates of the hard outer covering in insects, two turns of a SHELL, or where two bones with irregular locking edges have become fixed solidly together, as seen sp. in the head of back-boned animals. [Bot.] A line of thinner substance where the bursting open of a fruit will take place. [Med.] The act or process of stitching together the edges of a wound or other material in the body; the join so made, a line of stitches or one stitch of such a line. 2.v.t. [Med.] Get united by stitching. **s. line.** [Zoo.] In AMMONITES, the joining-line between the SHELL-wall and the edge of the SEPTUM. **'sutural,** a. 'sutural bones. [Zoo.] The small bones present between the irregular meeting edges of certain bones in the head of man and monkeys and forming part of the s., the chief part being of FIBROUS TISSUE, the place of which is by degrees taken by a growth of bone.

swab, 1.n. [Med.] A small mass of soft substance such as COTTON WOOL or a sponge, used for cleaning blood from a wound, etc., or putting medical substances onto it; an example of some diseased DISCHARGE taken on a s. from a part of the body, for example, the throat, for testing for BACTERIA. 2.v.t. Get (a part) clean with a s., get dressed *with* some medical substance by using a s.

swamp, n. [Geog., etc.] A stretch of low land, gen. covered with grass or other plant growth, of which the earth is very wet, because of the slow rate of draining, but not under water. 'swampy, a.

swarm, n. [Biol.] A moving mass of insects or other small animals, or of ZOÖSPORES or free-swimming GERM-CELLS, sp. of bees swarming. 2.v.i. [Biol.] Be moving in a mass; (of bees) go together from their old living-place to take up a new one and make a separate society under a new QUEEN, the process by which the old living place is kept from getting overfull as more bees are produced. **s. cell, s. spore.** [Biol.] ZOÖSPORE.

sweat, 1.n. [Zoo.] PERSPIRATION. 2.v.i. PERSPIRE. 3.v.t. [Engin.] Get (metals) heated till soft for the purpose of joining them, sp. get them joined by covering the meeting edges with tin and heating them while pushed together. **s. gland.** [Zoo.] A GLAND producing s., in man present in great numbers in almost all parts of the skin, and formed of a thin pipe-like part going down from an opening in the outer skin to a small bulb-like mass in or under the inner coat. '-ing, n. [Zoo.] The process of giving out s. [Engin.] The process of joining metals by covering the edges with tin and heating. 'sweated joint. [Engin.] A join between two bits of metal made by sweating. 'sweaty, a. Covered with s.; like s.

sweep 'oscillator. [Elec.] A CATHODE RAY TUBE having an apparatus for causing the point of light to move across the SCREEN from time to time, used in TELEVISION.

swell, 1.v.t. and i. (Make) become greater in size, undergo expansion, sp. [Med.] (of a part of the body) become greater than normal as the effect of some damaged or diseased condition causing the TISSUES to become overfull of blood or other liquid. 2.n. [Geog., etc.] A regular wave-motion of the top of the sea without the forming of separate waves. '-ing, n. The process of becoming greater in size, sp. than normal; an expansion, a thicker part of some structure, sp. [Med.] the thick mass or rounded place produced by a swelling of the TISSUES, a swollen place. 'swollen, a. Increased to a size greater than normal, sp. [Med.] having undergone swelling.

swim 'bladder, 'swimming 'bladder. [Zoo.] A bag-like part full of air or gas at the top of the body-hollow in most fish, starting its development as a branch of the ALIMENTARY CANAL and sometimes keeping a connection with it—having as its chief purpose the adjustment of the SPECIFIC GRAVITY of the fish so that it has no trouble in swimming at any level in the water, but in some fish having in addition some use in breathing or hearing.

swimmeret, n. [Zoo.] Any of the branched outgrowths placed in two's on the under side of the body in some CRUSTACEA, sometimes used for swimming, but chiefly for gripping the eggs.

'swimming bell. [Zoo.] NECTOCALYX.

'swimming 'funnel. [Zoo.] In DIBRANCHIA a forward-pointing pipe opening under the back of the neck, through which water is sent out with force from the MANTLE CAVITY pushing the animal suddenly back, and so giving it the power of moving through the water.

'swimming 'ovary. [Zoo.] In certain PARASITIC WORMS, any of the masses of eggs which become separated from the OVARY when their development is complete, moving about loose in the liquid of the body-hollow.

'swimming plate. [Zoo.] CTENE.

swing, 1.n. [Mech.] The motion forward and back between two fixed points of something hanging free, as a weight hanging on a cord, etc., or one such complete motion; a like turning motion (as) of something such as a door fixed at one side or end and free to go through a curve with the other. [Elec.] The process of changing from the highest VOLTAGE in one direction to the highest voltage in the other as in ALTERNATING current, or the amount of this change. 2.v.t. and i. (Make) have a s., get moved or be moving with such a motion.

switch, 1.n. [Engin.] An apparatus of which the chief part is two short rails whose position may be automatically changed, used on a railway for making a connection between one line and another line placed as if branching from it, so that a train on the first line may be turned onto the second and so on. [Elec.] An apparatus for turning electric current from one wire to another, or by which an electric connection is made or broken; the button or other part by moving which a s. is put in operation. 2.v.t. Get (train) changed to another line or (electric current) changed to another CIRCUIT by a s.; put current *on* or *off* by touching a s.

'swivel, n. [Mach.] A connection between two parts (for example, between a hook and a chain) which has a turning motion (as if) on a pin, so that one of the parts may be turned without turning the other.

swollen, a. *See* SWELL.

sy'con-ium, -us, nn. [Bot.] A MULTIPLE FRUIT of which the seeds are walled in by a soft, thick mass formed from a somewhat hollow common RECEPTACLE.

'syenite, n. [Geol.] A sort of COARSE-GRAINED IGNEOUS ROCK of which HORN-BLENDE is an example. **s.-porphyry.** A ROCK formed of the same chemical substances as s. but of MEDIUM GRAIN-size, and having quartz CRYSTALS bedded in a mass of very small ones. (*See* p. 192.)

'**syllable**, n. [Philol.] One or more SPEECH SOUNDS said as a unit and forming a word or a clearly marked division of a word; the letters representative of such a unit, as 'in' and 'come' taken separately or in the word 'income'.

'**syllabus**, n. An outline of the material to be covered in a given time, a number of hours teaching or a group of talks, at a university, etc..

'**Sylvian**, a. [Zoo.] To do with, near, in, the S. fissure. **S. 'fissure.** The deep division in the brain of higher animals separating the FRONTAL LOBE from the TEMPORAL AND PARIETAL LOBES.

'**sylvite**, n. [Mineral.] Natural KCl (*potassium chloride*) present in the earth as CRYSTALLINE masses without colour, sp. near VOLCANOES, important for the producing of POTASH.

sym-. SYN-.

symbi'osis, n. [Biol.] The condition of two different sorts of plants or animals, or a plant and an animal, living together and of use or necessary to one another, or one to the other, sometimes with their bodies in connection, or even united so as to seem one, as in LICHENES (*conjunctive s.*), sometimes physically separate (*disjunctive s.*)—covering PARASITISM and HELOTISM but more frequently used of a relation which is of value to the two. '**symbiont,** '**symbiote,** n.n An animal or plant in a symbiotic relation to another. **symbi'otic(al)**, a. To do with s., living in a condition of s. **symbi'otically,** adv.

'**symbol**, n. Sign, sp. [Math., Phys., Chem.] any letter or letters or other sign used in writing as representative of some thing or operation (*see* CHEMICAL SYMBOL). [Psych.] Any thing, act etc., which has come to be representative of, or to take the place of, another—sp. something representative of, but giving no suggestion of, a desire or impulse of which the person is unconscious, as certain experiences common in DREAMS which to the expert are fixed ss. of unconscious sex desires, etc. **sym'bolic,** a. To do with, marked by, using ss., or being a s. [Philol.] To do with, being, or having, the sort of language system in which a root word undergoes changes of its inner form as signs of the adjustment of its sense to different relations, for example, the change from the present '*do*' to the past '*did*'. **sym'bolically,** adv. '**-ism.** n. The use or theory of ss., or the system of ss. used for any purpose. [Psych.] Sp., the coming of ideas and impulses from the unconscious into the conscious mind, or the producing of behaviour by them, in such a form as to give no sign of the connection between the two. '**-ize,** v.t. Be a s. of; make use of a s. as representative of (*symbolize* something *by* a given s.). '**-iz'ation,** n. Sp., [Psych.] The unconscious process by which symbolism is effected.

'**symmetry,** n. Balance in structure or the grouping of parts, or in relations between numbers (*see* BIRADIAL S., BILATERAL S., RADIAL S., ZONAL s.). [Cryst.] The property of CRYSTALS of having a number of faces of like regular form placed at fixed angles and in a balanced relation to one another, as the effect of the development of their MOLECULAR structure in a regular way in certain fixed directions. **sym'metric(al),** aa. **sym'metrically,** adv.

'**sympa'thetic,** a. [Med., Psych.] Produced as the effect of a like effect on some other part or person, caused by sympathy. [Zoo.] Of, to do with, the s. nervous system. **s. 'nervous 'system.** [Zoo.] AUTONOMIC NERVOUS SYSTEM; that part of the autonomic nervous system having its connections with the backbone between the neck and the SACRUM, and whose chief parts are two parallel chains of GANGLIA running down and under the back-bone, from which NERVE FIBRES go to GLANDS, muscles, blood-vessels of the skin and VISCERA, etc.—freq. having an opposite effect from that produced by the PARASYMPATHETIC nerves, as, for example, in increasing the heart-rate in reaction to pain, danger, etc. **s. re'action.** [Chem.] INDUCED REACTION. **s. vi'bration.** [Phys.] A VIBRATION caused in a body by one in another body and having the same PERIOD. '**sympathize,** v.t. [Med.] (Of a part, sp. an eye) undergo an effect caused by sympathy (*with* a part undergoing a like effect). '**sympathy,** n. [Med.] A relation between parts not very near together or having any straightforward connection with one another such that a change in one has an effect, sp. a like effect, on the other. [Psych.] The fact or process of having some feeling produced in oneself as the effect of the observation or knowledge of the same feeling in another. [Phys., Acous.] The relation between bodies when the VIBRATIONS of one are transported to, and become the cause of vibrations in, the other.

'**sympathin,** n. [Biochem.] A substance present in the SYMPATHETIC NERVOUS SYSTEM having effects like ADRENALIN when sent into the blood, and acting with it.

sym'pathomi'metic, a. [Zoo., Med.] Having the same effects as are produced by STIMULATION of the SYMPATHETIC nerves, said of the operation of ADRENALIN and like substances.

'**Sym'petulae,** n.pl. [Bot.] A great SUBCLASS of DICOTYLEDONS in which the PETALS are united, completely or to some degree. **sym'petalous,** a. [Bot.] Having the PETALS united at the edges.

'symphile, n. [Zoo.] An animal living in a society of others, sp. ants, in harmony, as a friend, but without making any special use of, or being of any special help to them as in SYMBIOSIS. **symp'hil-ic, -ous,** aa. Being as., to do with, having symphily. **'symphily,** n. [Zoo.] The relation between a s. and the society of which it is a part, the condition of living in this way.

sympho'genesis, n. [Bot.] The development of a part by the uniting of two separate parts. **symphoge'netic,** a.

sym'phyllous, a. [Bot.] GAMOPHYLLOUS.

sym'physis, n. [Zoo.] A tight join between two bones (freq. one in which two flat, meeting faces covered with smooth CARTILAGE are kept together by strong FIBRES), such that they have no or only little power of motion in relation to one another, sp. any of certain such joins in the middle line of the body, for example that between the two PUBIC bones (*s. pubis*) or the two halves of the lower mouth-bone in the middle of the chin (*s. mentis*); a joining line between any two structures; a uniting or growth together of parts, sp. bones. **sym'phys-eal, -ial, sym'phytic,** aa. Of, to do with, formed by, marked by, s. **sym'physi'otomy,** n. [Med.] The operation of cutting through the PUBIC s. to make possible the birth of a baby.

'sympie'zometer, n. A form of BAROMETER sometimes used on ships, in which the PRESSURE of the ATMOSPHERE sends a liquid such as oil up in a glass pipe having in it an elastic gas, by the COMPRESSION of which the atmospheric pressure is measured.

sym'plectic, 1.a. [Zoo.] To do with or naming the s. [Geol.] Being or to do with a structure formed by the growth of one MINERAL into another touching it. 2.n. [Zoo.] A bone of the head supporting the QUADRATE in some fish.

'sympodite, n. [Zoo.] PROTOPODITE.

sym'podium, n. [Bot.] A stem formed by a system of stem growth in which the chief stem puts out a branch and itself comes to an end at, or a little after, the fork, the branch then going through the same process, so that the middle stem gets longer by the addition of branch after branch in a more or less straight line, as in SCORPIOID or HELICOID DI-CHOTOMY. **sym'podial,** a. To do with, being, a s., or like a s. in structure.

'symptom, n. [Med.] Any effect on the body or mind, experienced by an ill person or open to observation by a medical man, which is a sign that a disease or unnormal condition is present, giving light on what and/or where it is, etc. **sympto-**

'matic, a. [Med.] Going with, being a s. or representative of, a disease, condition; to do with ss. **'symptoma'tology,** n. [Med.] That branch of medical science which has to do with ss.; the ss. of a disease taken together.

syn-. Together, united:— **'-coty'ledonous,** a., **'-'sepalous,** a.

syn'acm-e, -y, nn. [Bot.] The condition in which the male and female parts of a flower come to full development at the same time.

synaer'esis, n. [Chem.] SYNERESIS.

syn(a)es'thesia, n. [Zoo.] A feeling produced in one part of the body by something acting at another part. [Psych.] The producing together with and as part of an experience caused by the STIMULATION of one of the senses, of a different sort of sense-experience, as in the feeling that certain sounds have certain colours. **'syn(a)es'thetic,** a.

syn'angium, n. [Bot.] A number of SPO-RANGIA united side by side into one, seen in certain FERNS.

sy'nantherous, a. [Bot.] Having the ANTHERS united, forming a pipe.

'synan'thesis, n. [Bot.] The condition of having the flowers and the leaves coming out at the same time. **syn'anthous,** a. [Bot.] Marked by s.; marked by SY-NANTHY.

syn'anthy, n. [Bot.] The joining together of flowers which are normally separate. **syn'anthic,** a.

'synapse, n. [Zoo.] The point where a connection is made between two nerve CELLS for the handing on of NERVE IMPULSES from one to the other, that is, where the AXON of one cell comes in touch with the DENDRITE(s) of another or with some special part of the cell-body.

sy'napsid, a. [Zoo.] (Of the SKULL of a REPTILE) having the deep hollow at the sides, where the muscles for lifting the lower mouth-part come from, all in one, without a division such as is seen in some reptiles.

sy'napsis (synapses), n. [Biol.] The ranging of every two HOMOLOGOUS CHROMOSOMES (one from one PARENT and one from the other) side by side, with homologous points touching, in the first stage of MEIOSIS. [Zoo.] SYNAPSE.

syn'aptene, a. [Biol.] ZYGOTENE.

syn'aptic, a. [Zoo.] Of, at, to do with a SYNAPSE. [Biol.] To do with, marked by, SYNAPSIS, **s. mates.** [Biol.] Any two CHROMOSOMES ranging themselves together in SYNAPSIS. **s. 'nervous 'system.** [Zoo.] A nerve system in which the nerve CELLS are separate, making connections with one another at SYNAPSES.

synar'throsis, n. [Zoo.] A join between bones by which they are fixed together

with no SYNOVIAL CAVITY and no power
of motion in relation to one another, as a
SUTURE.

'syncarp, syn'carpium, nn. [Bot.] A MUL-
TIPLE fruit. syn'carpous, a. [Bot.] To do
with a s.; marked by syncarpy. syn-
'carpy, n. The condition of having the
CARPELS united into a COMPOUND
OVARY.

syn'cerebrum, n. [Zoo.] A second brain
formed by the uniting of one or more of
the lower forward GANGLIA with the
CEREBROGANGLION in some ARTHROPODA.

'synchon'drosis, n. [Zoo.] A SYNARTHROSIS
in which the bones are united by
CARTILAGE.

'synchro-'cyclotron, n. [Phys.] A form of
CYCLOTRON producing short PULSES at
very high ENERGY.

'synchronism, n. The condition or fact or
property of being SYNCHRONOUS.

'synchronize, v.i. and t. Be or make to be,
SYNCHRONOUS with one another (or with
another event or process), or (of machines)
in such adjustment that their operations
are synchronous. 'synchroni'zation, n.
The act or process of synchronizing or the
condition of having been synchronized.
'synchronizer, n. An apparatus for
producing or keeping up the SYN-
CHRONOUS operation of two or more
machines, for example keeping a number
of clocks in time with one another.
'synchronizing, a. To do with, effecting,
synchronization.

'synchronous, a. Taking place at the same
time, changing in the same way at the
same regular times, and (of anything
going on for some time or over and over)
at the same rate, with the same rhythm,
sp. [Phys.] having the same PERIOD and
PHASE.[Elec.] (Of ALTERNATING-CURRENT
machines) in such adjustment as to their
rate of turning that their currents are s.
s. 'con'verter, s. 'generator, s. ma'chine,
s. 'motor, etc. ALTERNATING-CURRENT
electric machines turning at a rate in
step with the current.

'synchroscope, n. [Elec.] An instrument for
seeing if two ALTERNATING electric
CURRENTS are SYNCHRONOUS and if not
to what degree their rates of change are
different.

'synchroton, n. [Phys.] An apparatus for
increasing the rate of motion of ELEC-
TRONS or PROTONS to higher levels even
than the BETATRON, so that their MASS
is markedly increased, using a low-
FREQUENCY MAGNETIC FIELD, as in the
betatron and a high-frequency electric
field, as in the CYCLOTRON.

syn'clastic, a. [Phys.] Curved the same way
in all directions, as the outside of a ball.

'syncline, n. [Geol.] A bent-in fold in
STRATA, that is, a hollow sloping down

from two opposite sides in the direction
of a middle line, opp. an arch (anticline).
syn'clinal, a. To do with, having the
structure of, a s. syncli'norum, n. A s. of
great size, the sides of which are much
bent into smaller ss. and arches.

'syncope, n. [Med.] A sudden complete or
almost complete stopping of breathing
and the motion of the heart for a time,
caused by not enough blood going to the
brain as the effect of nerve trouble,
heart trouble, etc., and causing the
person to become suddenly white, cold
to the touch, and unconscious.

syn'craniate, a. [Zoo.] Having part of the
backbone united into one with the bone
structure of the head.

syn'cryptic, a. [Zoo.] (Of animals) looking
like one another though of different sorts,
as the effect of a common PROTECTIVE
MIMICRY of things round them.

syn'cytium (syncytia), n. [Zoo.] A living
material made up of a stretch or mass of
PROTOPLASM kept together by a PLASMA
MEMBRANE, having a number of NUCLEI
but not separated into CELLS; a cell with
a number of nuclei. syn'cytial, a.

syn'dactyl, a. [Zoo., Med.] Having two or
more fingers or toes fully or in part
united, as a number of birds. '-ism, n.
[Zoo., Med.] The condition of being s.

syn'desis, n. [Biol.] SYNAPSIS. syn'detic, a.
[Biol.] To do with s.; keeping something
together, forming a connection between
parts, sp. [Zoo.]

syn'desm(o)-. LIGAMENT: syndes'mology, n.

syndes'mosis, n. [Zoo.] A SYNARTHROSIS in
which the meeting faces of the bones are
rough and kept together by a LIGAMENT.

'syndrome, n. [Med.] A group of SYMPTOMS
commonly present together, or which,
taken together, are the mark of a certain
disease or condition.

'syne'cology, n. [Biol.] The ECOLOGY of
societies of plants or animals.

syn'ecthran, n. [Zoo.] An undesired insect
of a different sort living in a society of
insects and openly hated and attacked by
them. 'synechthry, n. The relation
between a s. and the society in which it is
living, or, more gen., the living together
of two sorts of animals with profit to
one but against the desire and interest of
the other.

syn'eresis, n. [Chem.] The separating of a
liquid from a GEL naturally, as the effect
of CONTRACTION. [Med.] A like contraction of and separating of liquid from a
CLOT of blood.

'synergetic, syn'ergic, aa. [Zoo., Med.]
Working together, said of parts of the
body such as muscles together effecting a
certain motion, or of HORMONES etc. or
medical substances helping one another's
operation, sp. when their united effect

on the body is greater than that of the two (or more) acting separately. **'syner-gism,** n. [Zoo., Med.] The property or condition of being s. **'synergist,** n. A substance or part, sp. a muscle, s. with another or others.

syn'ergid, syn'ergida (synergidae), nn. [Bot.] In seed plants, one or the other of two small CELLS at the end of the EMBRYO SAC where the MICROPYLE is, and forming with the EGG-CELL the EGG APPARATUS, which seem to be of help in getting the POLLEN TUBE to the egg NUCLEUS. **syn'ergidal,** a.

'syngamy, n. [Biol.] The uniting of two GERM-CELLS for the purpose of producing offspring.

syngen'esious, a. [Bot.] (Of ANTHERS) with their edges united so as to make a hollow pipe; (of STAMENS) having s. anthers.

syn'genesis, n. [Biol.] The producing of offspring by the uniting of male and female CELLS; the current theory that offspring are formed in part from one of the producing cells and in part from the other, not from one or the other only, as in some old theories. **synge'netic,** a. [Biol.] Of, to do with, produced by s. [Geol.] Formed at the same time as the ROCK in which it is bedded, said of an INTRUSION.

syn'karyon, n. [Biol.] A ZYGOTE NUCLEUS formed by the uniting of two PRONUCLEI.

synki'nesis, n. [Mech.] The automatic motion of one part when another part is moved.

syn'odic(al), aa. [Astron.] To do with CONJUNCTION, sp. with the time between one conjunction of two bodies and the conjunction after it. **s. month.** The time between one CONJUNCTION of the moon with the sun and the one after it, that is, between one new moon and another, 29 days 12 hours, 44·34 minutes. **s. period.** (Of any PLANET) the time between two CONJUNCTIONS with the sun.

syn'oecious, a. [Bot.] In seed plants, having male and female flowers in the same CAPITULUM or male and female parts in the same flower; SYNOICOUS. **'-ly,** adv. **'-ness,** a. **syn'oecism,** n. The condition or property of being s.

synoe-'cete, -'kete, nn. [Zoo.] An insect of a different sort living in a society of insects (sp. ants) without being of any use to them, and given no attention, kind or unkind, by them. **syn'oecy,** n. The relation between a s. and the society in which it is living or, more generally, the living together of two sorts of animals with profit to one and no damage to the other.

syn'oicous, a. [Bot.] (Of MUSCI) having ARCHEGONIA and ANTHERIDIA in the same covering.

'synonym, n. [Biol.] A group-name for plants or animals used for a time and still come across, of which the place has been taken among experts by another in better agreement with the facts or with the system of naming.

syn'opsis, n. An outline of the chief points of a book, theory etc., a statement covering some material shortly but so as to give a complete view of it. **syn'optic,** a. To do with, being, a s., giving a complete outline or view of something in short form. **synoptic (weather) chart.** [Meteor.] WEATHER MAP.

syn'otic 'tectum. [Zoo.] The arch of CARTIL-AGE forming the part of the brain-cover at the back and sides of the head between the ears in lower animals and the EMBRYOS of higher.

sy'novia, n. [Zoo.] The MUCINOID liquid present in parts of the body where two moving bones or CARTILAGES, or a bone and a LIGAMENT, etc., come together, designed to make motion smooth and keep them from rubbing on one another. **syn'ovial,** a. **synovial 'cavity,** The hollow inside a CAPSULAR LIGAMENT. **syn'ovial 'fluid.** S. **syn'ovial 'membrane.** The coating of CONNECTIVE TISSUE covered with stretches of flat CELLS present on the inside of a CAPSULAR LIGAMENT, the covering of a TENDON, or other coverings of moving parts, and producing the s. **syno'viparous,** a. Producing s. **syno'vitis,** n. [Med.] INFLAMMATION of a synovial membrane sp. at a JOINT. **syno'vitic,** a. [Med.].

syn'sacrum, n. [Zoo.] The part of the backbone supporting the PELVIC GIRDLE in birds, made up of the SACRAL back-bone divisions united into one with some higher and some lower divisions.

syn'spermous, a. [Bot.] Having a number of seeds united.

'syntax, n. [Philol.] That part of GRAMMAR which has to do with the structure of statements and the relations between words as made clear by position.

syn'technic, a. [Biol.] (Of plants and animals or the relation between them) having some like qualities because of adjustment to like living-conditions, having undergone a parallel development, though in fact of quite different sorts.

synte'nosis, n. [Zoo.] The joining of moving parts by TENDONS, as the divisions of the fingers, etc.

syn'thermal, a. Having the same degree of heat.

'synthesis, n. The putting together of a number of things to make one thing, the process of uniting things into one; something produced by s., a complex of parts. [Chem.] The building up of complex substances from simpler ones. [Philol]. The uniting of a number of ideas in one word, sp. the system of limiting the root sense of a word by INFLECTION. **'synthesize,** v.t. Put together, get united, so as to make one complex thing. **'synthesiz'ation,** n. **syn'thetic,** a. Made by s., to do with s. [Chem.] (Of substances) not produced naturally, made by man by chemical processes, sp. as a copy of some named natural substance, as *s. rubber*, *s.* RESIN. [Philol.] (Of a language) making frequent use of s.

'syntonin, n. [Chem., Biochem.] Any acid ALBUMIN, sp. got from muscle-threads.

'syntony, n. [Radio] Name at one time used for RESONANCE in connection with two or more radio instruments or systems. **syn'tonic,** a. **'syntonize,** v.t. Put (radio instruments or systems) in s. (*with* one another).

syn'tropic, a. [Biol.] (Of like parts) turned, pointing, in the same direction, as the RIBS on one side of the body. **'syntrope,** n. A s. part.

syn'usia, n. [Bot.] A company of plants regularly seen together as part of a greater society of plants living in certain places.

'syphilis, n. [Med.] A very serious CHRONIC disease going through four stages, caused by a SPIROCHAETE and given by one person to another, gen. in the act of sex-connection, or by mother to offspring before birth, marked at the start by CHANCRES, then by BUBOES, then by wet broken places on the skin and deep masses of broken-down TISSUE, and ending, when the disease gets to the brain, in GENERAL PARALYSIS OF THE INSANE.

'syringe, 1.n. A small hand instrument made up of a pipe-like part freq. of glass, or an elastic bulb with a pointed end, having a small opening through which liquid is pulled in by working a little PISTON or crushing the bulb in the hand, and then sent out again in a hard current, used sp. medically, for cleaning wounds, sending a medical liquid into an opening in the body, etc. [Zoo.] SYRINGIUM. 2.v.t. Send a current of liquid onto or into (a part of the body, etc.) with a s., get (wound, etc.) washed with a s.

sy'ringium, n. [Zoo.] A pipe-like apparatus in some insects by which a poisoning or disgusting liquid may be sent out to keep off attackers.

'syrinx (syringes), n. [Zoo.] The apparatus by which a bird makes sounds, a special development at the lower end of the windpipe. **sy'ringeal,** a.

sy'staltic, a. [Zoo.] Undergoing, having the property of, working by expansion and CONTRACTION in turn, as the heart.

'system, n. Any group of things or parts working together to give a united effect, or dependent on one another, or formed by organization into a complex unit, sp. [Biol.], all the different structures specially designed to take part in one complex operation or having one purpose, as the *nerve s.*; an ordered process, way of doing something, or the form, design, or order controlling or produced by such a process, as a s. of branching or branches, sp. [Biol.] a way of grouping and naming the groups of plants and animals. [Zoo., Med.] The body looked on as a s. of working parts. [Zoo.] A COLONY of zoöIDS having a common CLOACA. [Phys., Chem.] An amount of substance forming, or looked on as, a separate body; two or more substances or PHASES together in space, separated from others, and in, or in the process of coming to be in, EQUILIBRIUM. [Elec.] All the apparatus for the distribution of electric power in a certain place. [Geol.] In the grouping of ROCKS by time, the division coming between a GROUP and a SERIES, made up of the rocks formed in a PERIOD. [Cryst]. Any of the divisions, based on the number and relations (that is, the fact of their being equal or unequal and the angles they make with one another) of the AXES round which the faces are ranged, in which CRYSTAL forms are grouped. **'syste'matic,** a. To do with or forming a s., controlled by, in agreement with, a s., putting or put in a regular order, doing or done in an ordered way. [Biol.] To do with systematics. [Med.] To do with or having an effect on all the different parts of one of the body's ss. **syste'matic 'error.** An error which is the same, or of the same sort, and in the same direction (for example, regularly causing some value to be taken as greater or less than it in fact is), in every one of a number of observations, etc. **syste'matically,** adv. **syste'matics,** n. [Biol.] The branch of Biology having to do with the grouping of plants and animals and the naming of the groups. **'systemati'zation,** n. The process of systematizing; something, sp. a statement, writing, etc., systematizing or produced by systematizing. **'systematize,** v.t. Make into a s., give order and design to, put in a systematic form, sp. in writing.

sys'temic, a. [Zoo., Med.] To do with, having an effect on, all the body, the general system. **s. arch.** [Zoo.] In the EMBRYOS of higher back-boned animals and in fish, the chief vessel taking blood from the heart to the body generally. **s. heart.** [Zoo.] In birds and higher back-boned animals, the left half of the heart, by which blood is pumped to all the body but the breathing apparatus, opp. RESPIRATORY HEART. **s. in'fection.** [Bot.]

An INFECTION living on in the PERENNIAL parts of a plant and going from them into the new growth made in the spring.

'systole, n. [Biol.] The stage of CONTRACTION in the heart's motion, when the blood is forced out into the blood-vessels taking it to other parts of the body, or the like stage of contraction in the motion of a CONTRACTILE VACUOLE. sys'tolic, a.

'systrophe, n. [Bot.] The massing of CHLORO-PLASTS which takes place in a very bright light.

'syzygy, n. [Astron.] The point of a PLA-NET'S ORBIT at which it is in CONJUNC-TION OR OPPOSITION. [Zoo.] The joining together so as to be unmoving of two divisions of the arm in CRINOIDEA; the uniting of some PROTOZOANS in long lines.

τ. [Phys.-Chem.] Sign for HALF-LIFE.

Ta, Sign for TANTALUM.

'tabes, n. [Med.] (An old word used at the present day only in names of certain diseases) a wasting away of body substance or a disease marked by this, sp. *t. dor'salis*, LOCOMOTOR ATAXIA caused by the wasting of the nerve substance in the backbone in the later stages of SYPHILIS. ta'betic, 1.a. [Med.] To do with, marked by, having t. 2.n. Person having t., sp. *t. dorsalis*.

tab'escent, a. [Med.] Wasting away. [Bot.] Drying up, becoming brown and dead.

'table, n. Any flat, level structure giving the suggestion of a table-top, as [Mach.] that on which something to be cut out etc. is placed in a machine, or [Geol.] a thick level mass of stone in the earth; a list of things, facts, numbers, etc. so designed that their relations to one another may be seen straight away, for example, in a framework of box-like spaces formed by ruling parallel lines down and across a page, with different headings at the top and side of the chief divisions (e.g. p. 558). [Zoo.] A flat plate of hard bone forming one of two such plates with different bone substance between them, as in the bone structure of the head. '-land, n. [Geog.] A PLATEAU with almost upright or very sharply sloping sides dropping down suddenly to a lower level or the sea. 'tabular, a. Flat-topped and level, table-like; formed of parallel plates or leaves; listed in the form of a t.; to do with, based on, worked out by the use of tt. of facts, measures etc. 'tabulate, v.t. Make a t. of (a group of facts, etc.), get listed in the form of a t.

'tabula (tabulae), n. [Zoo.] A level division-wall going across the pipe-like coverings of certain CORALS and HYDROZOA. 'tabulate, a. Having tt.

'tabu'lare, n. [Zoo.] A bone of the top of the head over the ear in some back-boned animals.

'tache'ometer, ta'chymeter, nn. An instrument used in SURVEYING for measuring quickly the distance of a point by the observation through a TELESCOPE of an upright rod of a given measure placed at that point, the distance being worked out from the measure of the rod as seen in the telescope. tacheo'metric, 'tachy-'metric, aa. To do with a t. or with tacheometry tache'ometry, ta'chymetry, nn. The use or science of the t. or of any like process of measuring distances, etc.

'tachograph, n. A TACHOMETER making a record of its readings; a tachogram. 'tachogram, n. A record made by a t.

tach'ometer, n. [Engin.] An instrument for measuring the number of complete turns per minute of an engine SHAFT.

tacho'metric elec'trometer. [Elec.] An instrument for measuring very small electric currents.

'tach(y)-. Quick.

'tachy'cardia, n. [Med.] Over-quick rhythm of the heart motion. 'tachy'cardiac, a.

'tachy'genesis, n. [Zoo.] A form of development in which certain of the fixed stages normal to like animals are made shorter or are not gone through. 'tachy'genetic, a.

'tachylite, tachylyte, nn. [Geol.] An IGNEOUS ROCK, black and glass-like, formed of BASALT (*see* p. 192).

'tachyp'noea, 'tachyp'nea, nn. [Med.] Very quick breathing.

'tachy'sporous, a. [Bot.] Of a plant, freeing its seeds quickly.

'tactic, a. *See* TAXIS.

'tactile, a. [Zoo., Psych., Bot.] To do with the sense of touch, giving a special reaction to touch; which may be sensed by touch. t. 'corpuscle. [Zoo.] Any of the very small bodies in the skin etc., formed of a group of CELLS together with one or more nerve-endings in a cover, which are instruments of the sense of touch. tac'tility, n. 'tactual, a. [Zoo., Psych.] To do with, caused by, the sense of touch.

'tadpole, n. [Zoo.] The long-tailed, water-breathing later form of the LARVA of SALIENTIA.

'taenia (taeniae), n. [Zoo.] A flat, thin, band-like structure; TAPEWORM. T., n.pl. The GENUS of CESTODA made up of TAPEWORMS. taen'iasis, n. [Med.] The condition of having TAPEWORMS living in the body.

'**tagma** (tagmata), n. [Zoo.] Any of the chief divisions into which the METAMERES are grouped or united in the body of an ARTHROPOD, as the head.

talc, '**talcum,** nn. [Mineral.] Natural $3MgO.4SiO.H_2O$, a somewhat chalk-like or soap-like substance of which there are a number of forms, gen. present in the earth in great masses, used in making soap, paper, powder for the body, and a very hard sort of pot.

tali-. TALO-.

'**talipes,** n. [Med.] Any of a number of conditions of the foot, freq. present from birth and going with a markedly unnormal form, in which, as the effect of the CONTRACTION of one group of muscles or another, only one part of the foot, as the inner or outer side, or the front or back, is placed on the earth in walking. **tali'pedic,** a.

'**tallow,** n. [Chem.] The hard white fat, made up of different GLYCERIDES, got by heating the less delicate fat parts of animals, sp. sheep and cows, and used in making soap, OLEOMARGARINE, etc. '**tallowy,** a.

'**Tallquist** '**method.** [Med.] A way of measuring the amount of HAEMOGLOBIN in the blood by a comparison of the colour of a drop of it on a special paper with a scale of shades of red (**Tallquist scale**) representative of different amounts.

talo-. Of, to do with, the TALUS: '**-'fibular,** a., '**-'tibial,** a.

'**talon,** n. [Zoo.] The sharp, hooked, CLAW, designed for gripping and wounding, of a bird living on other animals; the back CUSP of a three-cusped tooth.

'**talus** (tali), n. [Zoo.] The ANKLE or the ASTRAGALUS in man; like part of a bird's or insect's leg.

'**talus,** n. [Geol.] SCREE.

'**tambour,** n. [Med.] A flat metal cup with a stretched rubber cover moved by the motion of a part of the body, such as a blood-vessel, when put into connection with it by a rubber pipe, and working a pen by which a record of these motions is made.

tamp, v.t. Get (soft material, such as earth) pushed down or into something by hammering it without great force; get (a hole) shut with material, by tamping it in by degrees, said sp. of covering a CHARGE with earth, sand etc. in this way, in BLASTING.

'**tamper,** n. [Phys.] In a REACTOR, the GRAPHITE used for sending back NEUTRONS into the apparatus: in an ATOM BOMB, the metal used for sending back neutrons to the middle.

'**tampon,** n. [Med.] A small tight mass of cotton-wool or like material put into an opening or wound in the body to take up blood or other liquid sent out, or to get the opening stretched.

tan, 1.v.t. Get (Animal skin) made into leather by putting it into a liquid, gen. having in it TANNIN in some form, by physical and chemical uniting with which the outside of the skin is made strong and watertight and kept from being broken up by the chemical operation of the air. 2.n. Any chemical used for tanning skins. '**-ner,** n. Person whose work is tanning. '**-nery,** n. Place where tanning is done. '**-ning,** n. The act or process of tanning skins.

'**tandem,** 1.a. Formed of, having, two things or like parts placed one after the other. 2.adv. Ranged one after the other, not side by side.

'**tangent,** 1.a. Touching, sp. [Geom.] of a straight or curved line or plane touching a curve or plane at one or more points but not cutting it. 2.n. [Geom.] A straight or curved line, or plane, which is t. to a curve or plane; (of an angle) in a right-angled three-sided plane form ABC, of which B is the right angle, the t. of the angle A (short form, **tan A**) is $\dfrac{BC}{AB}$ and the t. of the angle C is $\dfrac{AB}{BC}$. **t. galva'nometer.** [Elec.] A GALVANOMETER having a small freely-moving MAGNETIC NEEDLE in the middle of and at right angles to a great upright COIL, parallel to the MAGNETIC FIELD of the earth, the force of the current going through the coil being in a fixed relation to the t. of the angle through which the needle is turned as the effect of the further magnetic field so produced. **t. point.** In SURVEYING etc., the starting- or ending-point of a curve in a road or railway. **tan'gential,** a. Touching at a point; meeting, acting on, branching off from, something, at an angle other than a right angle. [Geom.] Of, to do with, in the direction of, being, a t.

'**tank,** n. A great open or shut vessel for liquid, as a water-t. from which water is piped in a house, or an oil-t. in an engine. [Biol.] A glass vessel of some size, gen. box-like, in which water-animals or water-plants are kept in water for observation, or CULTURES are produced.

'**tannic,** a. [Chem.] Of, to do with, like, produced from, TANNIN. **t. acid.** TANNIN.

'**tannin,** n. [Chem.] A white, non-CRYSTALLINE, bitter-tasting, very ASTRINGENT, complex substance, readily going into SOLUTION in water, got from plants, sp. the hard outer covering of certain trees, and of great value for TANNING because of its property of driving GELATIN out of solution and uniting with it; any of a group of substances of like chemical structure and properties and wide distribution in plants, used in tanning, ink-making, and as astringents; any other substance, such as certain metal SALTS and certain oils, used as a TAN.

'tantalum, n. Chemical ELEMENT, at. no. 73, at. wt. 180·88, sign Ta, a very hard, light grey metal with a MELTING POINT of 2850°C, readily pulled into threads or hammered into thin plates and on which acids have little effect, used in electric and chemical apparatus and for making hard ALLOYS.

tap, 1.n. A VALVE with a hand-part for opening or shutting it, gen. by turning, for letting water etc. from a pipe, as in a bath. [Engin.] A hard steel screw with cutting edges for making a screw-line inside a pipe, nut, etc. 2.v.t. Take (liquid etc.) from a vessel by making a hole in it, or sp. take liquid, electric current, etc. from (a system of pipes or wires) by making a hole or connection at a point other than that from which it is normally taken, as *t. a telephone wire*, for the purpose of overhearing talk. [Engin.] Make a screw-line inside a pipe, nut, etc. by screwing a t. into it by hand or machine power. **'-ping,** n. Sp.:— [Med.] the process of making an opening into a body-hollow and taking off undesired liquid with a hollow needle; [Elec.] a connection by which a CIRCUIT is tapped. **'-root,** n. [Bot.] A root of which the chief stem is much stronger in growth and greater in size than the side branches it puts out, and which goes straight down into the earth.

tape, n. Linen, steel, or other material in the form of a thin narrow band, such as is used:—[Surveying etc.] for measuring, when marked with a scale; for printing news, price-lists etc. on in a telegraph printing-machine; for recording sound, when the record is not designed to be kept for long. **t.-re'corder.** Instrument for recording sound on a highly MAGNETIC FILM fixed to a moving t. rolling up round a DRUM etc.

'taper, v.t. and i. (Make) get narrower by slow, regular degrees as if coming, or so as to come, to a point at the end, as a rod or leaf; (of an amount, process, etc.) become less by degrees. **'tapered, 'tapering,** aa. Having a tapering form.

ta'petum, n. [Bot.] A coat of CELLS storing food-material round a group of SPORE-producing cells and later becoming broken up so as to give up the material to the spores undergoing development. [Zoo.] A part of an eye by which light is REFLECTED, as in back-boned animals a part of the CHOROID or the RETINA; in back-boned animals, the coat of NERVE FIBRES coming from the CORPUS CAL-

LOSUM and roofing part of the brain. **'tapetal,** a.

'tapeworm, n. [Med.] A CESTODE worm of the sort living at full growth in the INTESTINES of man or other back-boned animals, formed of a head without a mouth but with SUCKERS or hooks by which it is fixed to the intestine, and a long flat body made up of SEGMENTS, through the walls of which food is taken in—these segments producing eggs which gen. go out with the FAECES and undergo the earlier stages of development in the body of some different sort of animal, sp. cows, pigs, and fish, getting into the body of man when the meat of such animals is taken as food.

'tappet, n. [Engin.] A rod-like part slipping forward and back inside a pipe-like cover so as to take a push given it by a CAM at one end to a VALVE at the other, the purpose being to get a straight push on the valve.

tar, n. [Chem.] A thick, dark brown or black sticky liquid formed by the DISTILLATION or coal, wood, and other ORGANIC materials, and made up of a complex of substances, the details of which are dependent on the material from which it is produced.

'target, n. [Phys.] Any ELECTRODE or SURFACE against which ATOMIC rays or PARTICLES (α-RAYS, PROTONS, ELECTRONS, etc.) come at a great rate, for example in a CATHODE RAY TUBE or X-RAY TUBE (in which the t. is the metal plate to which the X-rays are sent out).

'tarnish, 1.n. [Chem.] The change of colour produced on the outside of an uncovered metal, such as silver, caused by some chemical reaction with the air or other touching substance, gen. the forming of a thin coat of an OXIDE etc. 2.v.t. and i. Be the cause of the producing of t. on a metal; (of a metal) have t. produced on it.

'tarsal, tar'sale (tarsalia), nn. [Zoo.] Any of the bones of the TARSUS of the leg in back-boned animals.

'tarso-. Of the TARSUS (and . . .).

'tarsometa'tarsus, n. [Zoo.] The bone formed by the uniting of the METATARSALS with the lowest line of TARSALS in birds.

'tarsus (tarsi), n. [Zoo.] A plate of very solid TISSUE supporting the EYELIDS in man and some other animals; in land-living back-boned animals, the part of the foot, or, in four-legged animals, of the back foot, where it is joined to the leg, or the structure of small bones supporting this part; in some ARTHROPODA, such as insects, the lower end of the leg made up of four or five divisions, **'tarsal,** a.

'tartar, n. [Chem.] A red-brown CRYSTALLINE substance, formed chiefly of $KHC_4H_4O_6$, forming a coating on the sides and base of vessels used in making wine (*see* CREAM OF TARTAR). [Med.] A hard substance by which teeth become coated, made up of PHOSPHATE of LIME and other substances taken from food and mixed with SALIVA. **t. e'metic.** [Chem., Med.] $2(KSbOC_4H_4O_6).H_2O$, a white CRYSTALLINE poison used medically as an EMETIC and for some other purposes, and in DYEING as a MORDANT. **tar'taric,** a. tartaric acid. [Chem.] An ORGANIC acid, $COOH.(CH.OH)_2.COOH$, having four ISOMERIC forms, of which the commonest is got from the t. produced by wine, and used in DYEING, making BAKING POWDER, and for medical purposes. **'tartrate,** n. Any SALT of tartaric acid.

tar'tareous, a. [Bot.] (Of LICHENS) rough and with loose bits coming away on the outside.

taste, n. [Zoo., Psych.] The sense by which certain qualities making substances pleasing or the opposite as food are given, the instruments of which are special nerve-endings, gen. in the outer covering of the SOFT PALATE and sp. the top of the tongue, and the STIMULI for which are SOLUTIONS of certain chemicals acting on these nerve-endings. **t. bud, t. bulb.** Any of the special instruments of t. present in the mouth, somewhat bottle-like structures formed of groups of nerve-CELLS with brush-like endings in an outer cover of supporting cells.

Taung's skull. [Zoo., Anthrop.] The FOSSIL head-bones of a man-like monkey of a group of which we have no other knowledge, unearthed in South Africa.

'Taurus, n. [Astron.] The second SIGN OF THE ZODIAC.

tau'tomerism, n. [Chem.] The condition in which two ISOMERIC substances, readily changed into one another, are united in EQUILIBRIUM into one natural substance, the two forms sometimes being impossible to get separate but forming two different groups of substances by reaction with others. **tau'tomer,** n. [Chem.] A substance formed of two ISOMERIC substances in EQUILIBRIUM; one or other of the two isomeric substances in a tautomer. **tau'tomeral,** a. [Chem.] Tautomeric. [Zoo.] (Of NEURONES) of which the NERVE-FIBRES are part of the white nerve substance on the same side of the SPINAL CORD. **'tauto'meric,** a. [Chem.] To do with, marked by t., being a tautomer. **tau-'tomerize,** v.t. and i. Get or become changed into a tautomer.

'taxidermy, n. The art of making copies of dead animals out of their skins. **taxi-'dermist,** n. Expert in t.

'taxis, n. [Med.] The process of putting into place by hand some part of the body which

is out of place. [Biol.] The motion of a plant, animal, GERM-CELL etc., from one place to another in reaction to a STIMULUS. **'tactic,** a.

-taxis, n. Order, system of placing:— **'phyllo'taxis,** n.; [Biol.] TAXIS.

tax'onomy, n. [Biol.] The science of grouping animals and plants in a system based on their natural relations. **taxo'nomic(al),** aa. **taxo'nomically,** adv. **tax'onomist,** n. Expert in t.

-taxy, n. Order, system of placing:— **'phyllo'taxy,** n.

Tb, Sign for TERBIUM.

T.B. = TUBERCULIN OR TUBERCULOSIS.

Tc, Sign for TECHNETIUM.

Te, Sign for TELLURIUM.

tear, n. [Zoo.] A drop of the salt liquid normally produced in small amount by the LACHRYMAL GLAND to keep the parts of the eye from rubbing one another, but increased to the point of running down the face in drops as the effect of strong, sp. sad, feeling or something getting into the eye. **t. gas.** [Chem.] Any of a number of liquids or gases which DISPERSED in the air have a damaging effect on the eyes, causing so much watering that seeing is for a time impossible—used in war etc.

tear fault. [Geol.] A more or less upright crack in ROCK in which the two sides have been moved only in a HORIZONTAL direction.

tech'netium, n. [Chem.] Chemical ELEMENT, at. wt. about 100, at. no. 43, sign Tc, present in certain ORES of Pt but very infrequently come across—at first named *masurium.*

'technical, a. To do with, special to, some branch of science, learning, art, etc., going into details of expert knowledge in some field; to do with, used in, industry or for some other working purpose, as opp. science. **techni'cality,** n. The property of being t.; a t. detail or word or way of saying something. **'technics,** n.pl. T. details, processes, words, sp. in the arts. **tech'nique,** n. A t. or expert way of doing anything.

'techno-. The science or art of something; TECHNICAL or TECHNOLOGICAL.

tech'nology, n. The science of the processes of industry, science as used in industry or other work. **tech'nological,** a. **tech-'nologist,** n.

tec'tology, n. [Biol.] That part of MORPHOLOGY which has to do only with the units of structure and their sort. **tecto-'logical,** a.

tec'tonic, a. [Biol.] To do with structure. [Geol.] (To do with the ROCK structures and forms) produced by motions of the solid outer part of the earth. **tec'tonics,**

n.pl. [Geol.] The science of t. structures; the t. structures of a place.

tec'torial, a. [Zoo.] Covering, roofing. **t. 'membrane.** The MEMBRANE covering CORTI'S ORGAN.

'tectospon'dylic, tecto'spondylous, aa. [Zoo.] (Of backbone units or the ELASMO-BRANCHS having such backbones) having the middle part CALCIFIED in rings round the NOTOCHORD, one outside the other. **tecto'spondyly,** n. The condition of being t.

'tectrix (tectrices), n. [Zoo.] COVERT. **tec'tricial,** a.

'tectum, n. [Zoo.] A roof-like or covering structure (used sp. in naming parts of the brain, as the **t. mesen'cephali**).

teeth, n.pl. *See* TOOTH.

'teething, v.i. [Med.] The coming of the first teeth in a baby and the effects of this process on the system.

'tegmen (tegmina), n. [Bot.] The inner coat of a seed-covering. [Zoo.] In some CRINOIDEA, a thin, leather-like cover over the top of the cup; in some insects, the thick or hard front wing; in lower back-boned animals and the EMBRYOS of higher, the roof of the framework of the head (**t. cranii**); in higher animals, a thin plate of bone over the MIDDLE EAR (**t. tympani**). **teg'mental,** a.

teg'mentum, a. [Biol.] A covering, sp.:— [Bot.] the outer cover of a leaf-BUD; [Zoo.] the network of FIBRES and GREY MATTER forming the upper part of the MID-BRAIN in higher animals.

'tegula, n. [Zoo.] A small, thin plate covering the join between wing and body in some insects; in two-winged insects, the ALULA. **'tegular,** a.

'tegumen, n. TEGMEN.

'tegument, n. [Biol.] A covering. **tegu'mentary,** a. To do with, being, a t. **tegu'mentary system.** [Bot.] The coat of CELLS forming the outer skin of a plant.

tegu'mentum, n. TEGMENTUM.

'tela, n. [Zoo.] A TISSUE, sp. one of a net-like structure.

'telangi'ectasis, n. [Med.] Expansion of the very small blood-vessels, freq. producing red marks on the skin.

tel'autograph, n. A form of telegraph for the REPRODUCTION of writing, pictures etc. **'telau'tography,** n.

tel(e)-. Produced, working, at a distance, coming from far away.

tele'archics, n.pl. The science of controlling machines, for example, ships or airplanes, from a distance, by radio, sound-waves, light-waves, etc.

te'legony, n. [Zoo.] The idea that a male with which a female has been MATED has some part in offspring produced by the female as the effect of a later MATING with a different male.

'telegraph, 1.n. An apparatus for sending news to a distance by the transporting of electric impulses through wires so as to make signs of some sort representative of numbers and letters. 2.v.i. and t. Send a telegram, send (news) by t. **tele'graphic,** a. **te'legraphist,** n. Trained person working a t. or taking in news sent by it. **te'legraphy,** n. The operation of a t. or the system of telegraphic sending of news.

'telema'nometer, n. [Elec.] An instrument for sending to or recording at a distance the reading of a MANOMETER.

te'lemeter, n. Any instrument for measuring the distance of a thing from the point of observation by an OPTICAL effect of some sort, as a TELESCOPE with a scale giving a measure of the thing seen from which its distance may be worked out. [Elec.] An instrument for reading and telegraphing the measure of electric forces, such as VOLTAGE, to a far-off place and there recording it. **tele'metric,** a. **tele'metry,** n. The TRANSMITTING and re-recording of DATA by radio and ELECTRONIC processes, as in SPACE RESEARCH from a SATELLITE etc., or in industry from an automatic machine; data transmitted and recorded in this way.

telen'cephalon, n. [Zoo.] The forward part of the front division of the brain in back-boned animals. **telen'cephalic,** a.

'teleodont, a. [Zoo.] (Of insects) having MANDIBLES of great size.

tele'ology, n. [Biol.] The view that the reason for any animal, plant, or part being of a certain structure is the use it has, that is, that the existence of animal and plant structures has been caused, and their development guided, by purpose.

'teleophore, n. [Zoo.] GONOTHECA.

Tele'ostei, n.pl. [Zoo.] The group of fishes, taking in much the greater number of the sorts in existence today, having a framework of true bone and no GANOID SCALES, looked on by some authorities as a SUB-CLASS of PISCES, by others as a division of ACTINOPTERYGII, and by others given no place as a separate group. **'teleost,** n., a. (Fish) of the T.

Teleos'tomi, n.pl. [Zoo.] The group of fishes made up of the ACTIONPTERYGII and the CROSSOPTERYGII, at one time looked on as a CLASS or SUB-CLASS, but no longer used in present-day systems of grouping.

te'lepathy, n. [Psych.] The sending of thoughts and experiences from one mind to another without the use of words or physical signs, that is, the causing of an effect by one mind on another in some way other than by sense-experience.

'telephone, 1.n. An apparatus by which talk between two persons at a distance, or the transporting of any sound to a distance, is made possible by the changing of sound-waves at one point into electric impulses going through a wire to the other point, where they are changed back again into sound-waves; any instrument for sending sound to a distance without its being AUDIBLE in the space between. 2.v.i. Make use of a t. for talking to someone, etc. **t. re′ceiver.** The part of a t. to which the ear of a person is put to get the sound of what is being said into the t. transmitter at the other end of the wire, being an instrument for changing electric impulses produced by a changing current into sound-waves—made up of a COIL taking the current, a DIAPHRAGM by whose motions the sound is produced, and a MAGNETIC or electric apparatus for effecting the operation of the one on the other. **t. trans′mitter.** The part of a t. for talking into, and by which the sound-waves are changed into electric current to be transported to some t. receiver by a wire. **tele′phonic,** a. **te′lephony,** n. The science or operation of the t.

tele′photo lens. A LENS made up of a CONCAVE and a CONVEX lens put onto a camera in place of the common one, for increasing the FOCAL LENGTH so as to get clear pictures of things very far away. **tele′photograph,** n. Picture made with a t. l. **′telephoto′graphic,** a. To do with, made by, telephotography. **′telepho′tography,** n. The use of t. ll. for taking camera pictures of far-away things.

′teleprinter, n. In a telegraph system, a machine with lettered keys, like a TYPE-WRITER, by working which a telegram is sent and by which it is automatically printed on paper at the other end.

′telescope, 1.n. [Optics] An instrument for viewing things at a great distance, made up of a long pipe-like structure with a CONVEX LENS (*object lens*) or CONCAVE MIRROR at the outer end, by which the rays from the thing being viewed are formed into a small, very bright IMAGE, and a lens or system of lenses or PRISMS at the other end, where the eye is placed, by which the image is greatly increased in size. (*See* in addition RADIO TELESCOPE.) **2.v.i.** Have parts slipping into one another so that it may be made smaller in size when not in use, as in some pocket etc. tt., whose pipe is made up of two or more of increasingly narrower size. **3.v.t.** Make smaller by getting parts pushed into one another. **tele′scopic.** a. To do with, effected by, like, having powers like, a t.; telescoping, able to be pushed together into smaller size like some tt. [Astron.] Which may be seen only through a t., not to be seen by the

eye without the help of a t. **te′lescopy,** n. The use of, or art of using, tt.

′teleseism, n. An earth shock far from the point where it is recorded. **tele′seismic,** a.

′telether′mometer, n. [Phys.] An apparatus for giving the TEMPERATURE of a point at a distance.

′teletype, n. TELEPRINTER.

te′leuto′sorus, telio′sorus, nn. [Bot.] The fruit of UREDINALES in the TELEUTO-STAGE, a group of TELEUTOSPORES in process of development, together with their supporting structure, forming a small mass under or on the skin of the HOST.

te′leuto′spore, te′leutogonidium, nn. [Bot.] The thick-walled SPORE formed in the fall as the end-stage in the development of UREDINALES, giving birth in the spring to PROMYCELIA. **te′leutospo′riferous,** a.

te′leutostage, ′teliostage, nn. [Bot.] The end, late-summer stage in the development of UREDINALES.

′television, n. The sending onto a SCREEN by radio or other electric apparatus of pictures of something taking place at a distance. **′televise,** v.i. and t. Send out pictures or a picture of (something) by t.

′teliospore, n. TELEUTOSPORE (U.S.A.).

′telium (telia), n. TELEUTOSORUS. **′telial,** a.

tel′lurian, 1.a. Of, to do with, the earth. **2.n.** An apparatus by which the motion of the earth round the sun and the producing of day and night, etc., are made clear.

tell′uric, a. [Chem.] Of, to do with, having in it, TELLURIUM, sp. being a COMPOUND of tellurium in which its VALENCY is high, as **t. acid,** H_2TeO_4.

tel′lurium, n. Chemical ELEMENT, at. no. 52, at. wt. 127·61, sign Te, a metal-like substance with properties like those of S, present in the earth here and there in tin-coloured masses but gen. united with metals, from which it is got in the form of a dark grey powder—used in ALLOYS and in colouring glass.

tell′urous, a. [Chem.] Of, to do with, having in it TELLURIUM, sp. being a COMPOUND of TELLURIUM in which its VALENCY is low, as **t. acid,** H_2TeO_3.

telo-. End.

′teloblast, n. [Zoo.] A great CELL producing a number of smaller cells by BUDDING, as at the growth-point of the EMBRYO in ANNELIDA.

′telocoel(e), n. [Zoo.] The hollow inside the TELENCEPHALON.

telo′dendr(i)on (telodendr(i)a), nn. [Zoo.] Any or all (taken together as a structure) of the branches formed by an AXON at a SYNAPSE.

′teloki′nesis, n. [Biol.] The changes taking place in a CELL in the TELOPHASE.

telo′lecithal, a. [Zoo.] (Of eggs) having the

non-living food material massed together in one half.

'telophase, n. [Biol.] The last stage of MITOSIS or MEIOSIS in which the new NUCLEI are formed and division of the CELL itself takes place.

telosy'napsis, telo'syndesis, nn. [Biol.] The uniting of like CHROMOSOMES end to end in MEIOSIS, opp. PARASYNAPSIS.

telo'taxis, n. [Zoo.] The motions of an animal when they are for a purpose.

'telson, n. [Zoo.] The last division of the body, which is not the same in form as the ring-divisions coming before it, in CRUSTACEA, ARACHNIDA, and the EMBRYOS of insects.

'telum, n. [Zoo.] The end SOMITE of the body of an insect in the later stages of its development, the TELSON being present only in the EMBRYO.

temno'spondylous, a. [Zoo.] (Of a VERTEBRA or an animal having such VERTEBRAE) having the middle bone not united into a solid mass but formed of joined divisions.

'temper, 1.n. The condition of a material in relation to its purpose (for example, of a paste as being stiff, soft, smooth, readily worked), sp. the degree to which steel or a like metal is hard, strong, and elastic, which is dependent on the amount of C in it and the way in which it has been tempered. **2.**v.t. Put (steel) through processes of heating and making cold in oil or water which are designed to make it hard, strong, elastic etc.; give other substances, such as glass, the desired properties by similar processes, or by mixing, working, etc.; make (the effect of something) less strong, sp. by some balancing addition or opposite effect. **'tempered,** a. Having been given desired properties by tempering of some sort; not over-great in degree, balanced, in adjustment to what is needed. **'tempered scale.** [Acous.] Scale of notes in which the FREQUENCY of every note has the same relation to that of the note before it. (freq. **equi-tempered scale**).

'temperament, n. [Psych.] The general tendencies of a person to certain feelings, desires, impulses, ways of behaviour, dependent in part on his natural qualities of mind and feeling, in part on his physical qualities, for example on having nerves which are specially quick or slow in reaction. [Acous.] The system of RATIOS between the FREQUENCIES of the notes in a scale (*see* SCALE OF EQUAL T., SCALE OF JUST T.). **'tempera'mental,** a. [Psych.] Sp., given to frequent, quick, and unreasoning changes of feeling, and to violent outbursts of it. **tempera'mentally,** adv. In t., from the point of view of t.; in a temperamental way.

'temperate, a. Of, in, the middle of a scale,

sp. that between great heat and great cold. [Geog.] Of, to do with, the T. Zone. **T. Zone,** [Geog.] The part of the earth north or south of the TORRID ZONE and limited on the other side by the ARCTIC (*North T.Z.*) or the ANTARCTIC (*South T.Z.*) CIRCLE.

'temperature, n. [Phys.] The degree of heat or cold of a body, as measured on a scale. [Med.] The degree of heat of a person's or animal's body; a higher t. than normal, a sign of disease or something wrong. **t. coeff'icient.** [Phys., Chem., etc.] A fixed number giving the relation between a unit change in t. (gen. 1°C.) and the parallel change in some other property, for example electric RESISTANCE, for a given substance. **t. in'version.** An unnormal increase in the TEMPERATURE of the air going up from the earth, freq. the cause of FOG.

'temple, n. [Zoo.] The upper part of the side of the head, from the eye to over the ear.

'temporal, 1.a. To do with time. [Zoo.] At, to do with, near, the TEMPLE or the t. bone. **2.**n. T. bone. **t. bone.** [Zoo.] A bone at the side of the head in man and some other higher animals, formed by the uniting of a number of parts which are separate in lower forms. **t. lobe.** [Zoo.] The great LOBE of a CEREBRAL HEMISPHERE, under the SYLVIAN FISSURE. **t. muscle.** [Zoo.] A great muscle coming from the hollow in the bone at the side of the head near the eye to the lower mouth bone, which is lifted by it.

tempor'alis, n. TEMPORAL MUSCLE.

temporary, a. Going on, being present or in existence, for only a short time. **t. 'hardness of water.** HARDNESS of water which may be overcome by boiling. **t. 'magnetism.** [Phys.] The property of MAGNETISM which a body such as soft iron has as the effect of being in a MAGNETIC FIELD, but which it no longer has when taken out of the field.

'tempor(o)-. [Zoo.] To do with the TEMPLE (and . . .):—**'temporo-'facial,** a., **'temporomax'illary,** a.

ten'acity, n. TENSILE STRENGTH.

ten'aculum (tenacula), n. [Med.] A thin sharp-pointed instrument with a hooked end, used in operations for lifting blood-vessels etc.

'tendinous, a. Of, to do with, like, a TENDON.

'tendon, n. [Zoo.] A cord or band of strong material made up of parallel white FIBRES massed tightly together, joining a muscle to a bone or other muscle to be moved by it, and united in growth to the covering of the muscle and of the bone. **t. 'reflex.** [Med.] An automatic CONTRACTION of a muscle caused by a blow on its t., used as a test for certain diseases¡

which the normal reaction does not take place.

'tendril, n. [Bot.] A thin, stem-like part, sometimes a special sort of stem, sometimes a changed leaf, with the property of twisting round any possible support, as a stick or cord or a nail in a wall, put out in numbers by CLIMBERS. **'tendrillar,** a. Twisting, t.-like. **'tendrilled,** a. **'tendri'l(l)ous,** a. Having tt.; like a t.

'tenent, a. [Zoo.] Used for fixing to something, gripping, said sp. of a mass of SUCKER-like hairs on the feet of insects.

'tenia, ten'iasis. *See* TAENIA, TAENIASIS.

ten(o)-. TENDON:— **teno'sitis,** n., **ten-'otomy,** n.

tense, 1.a. Stretched tight. [Psych., Med.] In a condition of TENSION, (of a person) with nerves t. as the effect of trouble of mind, fear, or other strong feeling of a like sort. [Phonet.] Said with the tongue and muscles t. 2 v.t. and i. Make or become t., sp. suddenly. **'-ness, 'tensity,** nn.

'tensile, a. [Phys.] Able to be made longer, given an expansion, by a pulling force; of, to do with, TENSION. **t. strength.** (Of a material) power of undergoing a pulling force without giving way, becoming broken, parted; the measure of this power given as the t. force per unit AREA needed to make the material give way. **ten'sility,** n. Sp. [Med.] The condition of a muscle when acting.

ten'simeter, n. [Phys., Chem.] An apparatus for measuring the PRESSURE of a gas, sp. used in getting the TRANSITION POINTS of CRYSTALS.

tensi'ometer, n. [Phys.] An apparatus for measuring TENSION, for example that of wires in an airplane.

'tension, n. Act of stretching; a stretching force; the condition of being pulled or stretched. [Zoo.] Of muscles, sp. the condition of, or force of, or tendency to, CONTRACTION, produced as a reaction to being stretched for some time, or by force put upon a part. [Med., Psych.] Condition or feeling of t., PRESSURE, or STRAIN. [Mach.] A machine-part for producing a desired t. [Mech.] (The measure of) one or the other of two equal and opposite pulling forces acting on a body and causing, or having a tendency to cause, stretching; the condition or change of form produced in a body by such forces. [Phys., Chem.] PRESSURE of a gas, sp. a VAPOUR. [Elec.] The property giving an electric CHARGE the tendency to DISCHARGE, or to go from a body at a higher POTENTIAL to one at a lower; electric potential. **'-al,** a. To do with, produced by, t. **'tensive,** a. (With a tendency to) producing t.

'tensor, n. [Zoo.] A muscle used for stretching a part.

tent, n. [Med.] A small roll or mass of soft material undergoing expansion when wet, used for keeping a wound open or stretching an opening; a small house-like structure put over a person breathing in a special gas, such as O, to keep the gas from getting away.

'tentacle, ten'taculum, nn. [Zoo.] A long, thin, waving and twisting, arm-like or branch-like part, commonly on the head of an animal and one of a number, used as a feeler or gripping instrument and sometimes for other purposes such as swimming or breathing—very different in size and structure in different animals, for example CEPHALOPODS and worms. [Bot.] Any t.-like part, sp. a hair used for taking small insects prisoner in certain plants. **ten'tacular,** a. **ten'tacu'liferous,** a. **ten-'taculiform,** a. **ten'taculoid,** a. **tentaculo-.**

ten'taculocyst, n. [Zoo.] Any of the small instruments of sense on the edge of the umbrella in a number of MEDUSOIDS, formed of very small and much changed TENTACLES, freq. hollow with LITHITES inside.

'tenter, n. A machine or frame for stretching cloth. **'-hook,** n. A hook for fixing material to a t.

'tenth-metre, n. ÅNGSTRÖM UNIT.

ten'tillum (tentilla), n. [Zoo.] A branch of a TENTACLE.

ten'torium (tentoria), n. [Zoo.] An arched fold of the DURA MATER in higher animals, covering the top of the back division of the brain and going over and supporting the back part of the front brain, sometimes completely changed into bone; the inner hard framework of an insect's head. **ten'torial,** a.

'tepal, n. [Bot.] Any of the units of a PERIANTH in which SEPALS and PETALS are no different from one another.

ter-. Three, made up of three, three times etc.:— **termo'lecular,** a.

terat(o)-. [Biol., Med.] TERATOID, to do with strangely unnormal forms: **terat-'ology,** n.

'teratoid, a. [Biol., Med.] (Of animals, sp. man, and their parts) strangely and unnormally formed, markedly and shockingly different from the normal in structure; (of growths) of mixed TISSUES, as a TERATOMA.

tera'toma, n. [Med.] A diseased growth made up of all sorts of body material, such as bone, skin, muscle etc., caused, for example, by some pushing out of place and mixing of TISSUES in the EMBRYO.

'terbium, n. Chemical ELEMENT, at. no. 65, at. wt. 159·2, sign Tb, one of the RARE EARTHS.

'tercine, n. [Bot.] A division of the second coat of an OVULE, at one time taken for a third coat.

tere'bene, n. [Chem., Med.] A substance formed of mixed TERPENES by the operation of H_2SO_4 on TURPENTINE, used medically for coughs.

tere'benthene, n. [Chem.] The chief substance in TURPENTINE.

'terebra, n. [Zoo.] in certain female insects, a pipe for putting down eggs which is designed at the same time for making deep narrow holes in something into which they are dropped, or as an instrument for cutting or STINGING. 'terebrant, 1.a. (Designed for) making deep narrow holes sp. in wood. 2.n. A terebrant insect. 'terebrate, a. Having a t. or other hole-making part; (of a part) terebrant.

'teres, n. [Zoo.] One or the other of two round muscles (t. minor, by which the upper arm is turned out, and t. major, by which it is pulled down and back) going from the SCAPULA to the lower part of the upper bone of the arm.

te'rete, a. [Bot.] Long and round, like a pipe or rod, and narrowing by degrees to a point, as a great number of stems.

'tergite, n. [Zoo.] Thick plate of skin or hard material on the TERGUM in ARTHROPODA.

'tergum, n. [Zoo.] The back of an animal, sp.:— the upper part of a SOMITE in ARTHROPODA; any of the hard plates of the outer covering of CIRRIPEDIA. 'tergal, a.

term, n. A limited time, the time for which anything is fixed to go on; a word or group of words having a clear and limited sense, sp. as special to some branch of art, science, or knowledge; any of the units in a list, SERIES, or statement of a relation, in mathematics—for example,

a, b, and c in $\dfrac{a}{b} = \dfrac{c}{b}$.

'terminal, 1.a. Placed or coming at the end, forming the end part of anything, in time or space, sp. [Bot.] at the end of a stem or branch. 2.n. A part having some special form or purpose at the end of some structure, sp. [Elec.] a metal part at the end of a wire, or on an apparatus, for making a connection with an electric CIRCUIT. t. 'moraine. [Geol., Geog.] The MORAINE put down at the front end of a GLACIER, where MELTING takes place. t. 'threshold. [Psych.] See THRESHOLD. t. ve'locity. [Phys.] The unchanging rate of motion to which a body moving through a gas or liquid under the operation of an unchanging force comes after increasing its rate to this point, for example, a body falling freely in air or water. [Aerodynamics] The greatest rate at which an airplane etc. is able to go, as fixed by its TOTAL DRAG. t. 'voltage. [Elec.] The VOLTAGE at the tt. of an

electric machine where a connection is made to take current from it.

'terminate, v.t. and i. Put an end to, come to an end.

termi'nation, n. End, ending, act of ending, sp. [Philol.] SUFFIX. '-al, a. Sp. [Philol.] Formed or effected by the addition of a t. or tt.

'terminative, a. Ending, limiting, being the end or ending of something.

'terminator, n. [Astron.] The curve forming the inner edge of the moon or other PLANET as seen from the earth when not fully lighted, that is, the line of division between the lighted and the unlighted parts.

termi'nology, n. The body of words special to any science, art, or system, as Biology etc.; the science of naming, or producing systems of t. 'termino'logical, a. 'termino'logically, adv.

'termite, n. [Zoo.] Any insect of the ISOPTERA. termi'tarium, n. The living-place of a COLONY of tt., a complex structure of hard earth, freq. of great size, on top of the earth or in a tree, or sometimes a network of narrow rooms under the earth. 'termital, ter'mitic, aa. ter'mitophile, n. An insect of another sort living among tt. termito-.

'ternary, n. To do with, made up of, three different substances or parts, sp. [Chem.]; ranged in three's, sp. [Biol.]; (of a form, or a system made up of such forms) three-sided, sp. [Cryst.] t. steel. Steel made of Fe and C and one other metal.

'ternate, a. [Bot.] Grouped in three's; having three divisions, sp. (of leaves) made up of three small leaves.

'terpene, n. [Chem.] Any of a group of ISOMERIC substances having the make-up $C_{10}H_{16}$ and a RING structure—liquids without colour and freq. with a pleasing smell, present in the oils of a great number of plants, sp. evergreen trees.

'terra, n. Earth, a word used only in naming certain earth-like substances, as t. cotta, a hard yellow or red substance made of CLAY mixed with sand, potter's waste etc., used for building and ornaments.

'terrace, n. [Geol.] A narrow, level, shelf-like stretch of land, gen. with an almost upright drop from its edge and a wall-like slope at its back, formed on the edge of a body of water as the effect of wasting away or of building-up operations. 'terraced, a.

ter'raneous, a. [Bot.] Rooting in, living on, the earth (as opp. in water, trees, etc.).

ter'raqueous, a. Made up of land and water, sp. [Astron.); present or living on land and in water.

ter'restrial, a. Of, to do with, the earth, used on, or in connection with, the earth, as a t. **telescope** for viewing things at long distances on the earth. [Biol.] Living on the earth (as opp. in water, trees, etc.). [Astron.] (Of a PLANET) of the same sort or size-group as the earth. t. **de′posit.** [Geol.] A DEPOSIT put down on land by the wind, a river, etc., as opp. deposits put down on the edge of the land by the sea. t. **′latitude,** t. **′longitude.** [Geog., etc.] *See* LATITUDE and LONGITUDE. t. **′magnetism.** The MAGNETIC force of the earth, acting inside, on, or near it. t. **poles.** [Geog., etc.] The two opposite points on the earth which are the opposite ends of its AXIS, the NORTH POLE and the SOUTH POLE t. **radi′ation.** [Meteor.] The earth's loss of heat at night by RADIATION to the sky, greatest when there is no cloud and the air is dry. t. **re′fraction.** The REFRACTION of light coming at a sloping angle through the earth's ATMOSPHERE, causing things at a distance to be judged as higher or lower than they in fact are.

ter′ricolous, a. [Biol.] Living on or in the earth.

ter′rigenous, a. [Geol.] Formed of waste from the land, said of parts of the sea-bed.

′territory, n. [Zoo.] A place looked on by some animal or group as its special living and food-getting place, for its use only, from which it makes every attempt to keep away other animals of the same sort.

′tertial, a., n. [Zoo.] TERTIARY.

′tertian, 1.a. [Med.] (Of a FEVER) coming on every third day as t. **malaria.** 2.n. A t. fever.

′tertiary, 1.a. Third in order of position or development, or to do with a third stage. [Zoo.] To do with, being a t. 2.n. [Zoo.] Any of the long feathers on the HUMERUS of a bird's wing. **T.** [Geol.] 1.a. To do with the T. period. 2.n. The T. period. t. **′alcohols.** [Chem.] ALCOHOLS having in them the group COH, as the effect of the CARBON CHAIN having been broken up by OXIDATION. **T. Era** or **Period.** [Geol.] The great division of the earth's history, sometimes taken as an ERA, sometimes as a PERIOD of the CAINOZOIC ERA, from the end of the MEZOZOIC to the coming of man—the time of the development of MAMMALS and present-day plants, and of the forming of high mountains, itself separated into the *Earlier T.* and the *Later T.* (*see p.* 558). t. **cell-wall,** t. **′layer,** or t. **′thickening.** [Bot.] Bands, rings etc. of new material formed on the inside of a SECONDARY CELL-WALL, sp. of a TRACHEID or TRACHEA.

ter′valent, a. TRIVALENT.

′Tesla coil, Tesla trans′former. [Elec.] A TRANSFORMER for HIGH-FREQUENCY ALTERNATING currents, used in radio.

′tesselate(d), a. [Biol.] Marked out in small squares. **tessellated epi′thelium.** [Zoo.] PAVEMENT EPITHELIUM.

′tessera (tesserae), n. A small square or RECTANGLE of stone or like substance put with others to make a design, as in a floor. [Zoo.] A t.-like plate of bone, etc. as on the hard outer coverings of some animals.

test, 1.n. Any process or operation used to make certain of anything, for example, if an apparatus is working properly, or [Med.] if a person has a certain disease, or [Chem.] if a certain substance is present in another, or [Psych.] how much knowledge or what degree of some power of mind a person has. 2.v.t. Give (a thing or person) a t. (*for* the discovery of something). t. **age.** [Psych.] The MENTAL AGE of a person in general or in relation to any special powers, as worked out from his marks in a t. t. **card,** t. **chart.** [Med., Psych.] A card with lines of printed letters of different sizes used for testing eyes. t. **meal.** [Med.] A fixed amount of certain food given to a person before testing the liquids formed by his stomach. t. **′paper.** [Chem.] A paper designed for testing for certain substances in liquids by being IMPREGNATED with some substance which undergoes a change of colour when put into a liquid in which these substances are present, t. **tube.** [Chem.] A thin glass vessel in the form of a pipe shut at one end, in which small amounts of chemical substances are tested, kept separate, etc. t. **type.** [Med., Psych.] The print on a t. card.

test, ′testa (testae), nn. [Zoo.] The hard outside covering of an animal. [Bot.] The strong outer covering of a seed, made up of a number of coats, **test′acean,** 1.n. A RHIZOPOD with a t. 2.a. Of, to do with testaceans. **test′aceous,** a. [Zoo.] To do with, having, a hard outer cover. [Biol.] Brick-red or brown-yellow.

′testicle, ′testis (testes), nn. [Zoo.] The part of the body of a male animal producing SPERMATOZOA. **tes′ticular,** a.

tes′tosterine, n. [Biochem.] A male SEX-HORMONE produced by the TESTES.

tes′tudina-te, -l, aa. [Zoo.] Having a hard covering like CHELONIA.

′tetanus, n. [Zoo.] A condition of violent and long unbroken CONTRACTION in a muscle, such as may be produced by a number of STIMULI, for example electric, coming quickly one after another. [Med.] A disease caused by a BACILLUS and marked by t., sp., and at the start, of the muscles of the mouth, causing great pain and freq. death. **te′tanic,** a. Of, to do with, like, or producing t. **′tetanoid,** a. **′tetani′zation,** n. [Zoo.] The producing of t. in a muscle etc., or the condition produced.

'**tetanize**, v.t. [Zoo.] Make undergo tetanization, be the cause of a condition of t.

'**tetany**, n. [Med.] A condition marked by sharp attacks of TETANUS, sp. of the muscles of the arms and legs, present in a number of diseases.

'**tethelin**, n. [Biochem.] A substance got from the front LOBE of the PITUITARY GLAND which has the property of increasing the rate of growth.

tetr(a)-. 4, having 4 of the named parts:— **tetra'branchiate**, a. [Zoo.], **tetra'carpellary**, a. [Bot.]; [Chem.] Having 4 ATOMS etc. of the named sort:— **tetra'chloride, tetr'oxide.**

tetra'basic, a. [Chem.] Having 4 H ATOMS of which the place may be taken by BASE atoms or groups.

'**tetra'cyclic**, a. [Bot.] Having 4 rings of parts.

'**tetrad**, n. [Chem.] Any ELEMENT with a valency of 4. [Bot.] A group of 4 SPORES produced together and keeping together till development is almost complete. [Biol.] In MEIOSIS the 4 thread-like divisions formed by the uniting of two CHROMOSOMES and then the two parts themselves becoming two.

tetra'dactyl, tetra'dactylous, aa. [Zoo.] Having 4 fingers or toes. **tetra'dactyly**, n. The condition of being t.

tetra'dynamous, a. [Bot.] (Of a flower) having 4 long STAMENS and two short.

'**tetragon**, a. [Geom.] A plane form having 4 straight sides meeting at 4 angles. **te'tragonal**, a. To do with, being a t. [Cryst.] Of the tetragonal system. **te'tragonal 'system**. [Cryst.] The system of CRYSTAL forms having 3 AXES at right angles to one another of which two are equal (*see* p. 99).

'**tetra'hedrite**, n. [Mineral.] A natural SULPHIDE of Cu and S, freq. with other metals, used chiefly for producing copper.

tetra'hedron, n. [Geom.] A solid made up of 4 plane, 3-sided faces. **tetra'hedral**, a. To do with, being a t.

te'tramerous, a. [Biol.] Made up of 4 parts; having parts in groups of 4 or some numbers of times 4.

'**tetra'methylen'e**, n. CYCLOBUTANE.

tetra'morphous, a. [Cryst.] (Of a substance) having 4 different CRYSTALLINE forms.

'**tetraploid**, a. [Biol.] Having 4 times the HAPLOID, that is, twice the normal, number of CHROMOSOMES. **tetra'ploidy**, n. The condition of being t.

Te'trapoda, n.pl. [Zoo.] The group of all back-boned animals but fish, that is, AMPHIBIANS, REPTILES, birds and MAMMALS, all of which have, or at one time had, 4 LIMBS, two front ones and two back ones. '**tetrapod**, n., a. (An animal) of the T.; (an animal, sp. a 4-legged MAMMAL) having 4 feet.

te'trapterous, a. [Zoo.] Having 4 wings.

'**tetra'quetrous**, a. [Bot.] (Of a stem) having 4 sharp angles.

'**tetrarch**, a. [Bot.] Having 4 thick threads or groups of threads of XYLEM running down it.

tetra'somic, a. [Biol.] (Of a TETRAPLOID NUCLEUS, etc.) having 4 of one sort of CHROMOSOME and two of all the others.

'**tetraspo'rangium** (tetrasporangia), n.[Bot.] Vessel producing tetraspores. '**tetraspore**, n. One of the unsexed SPORES of RHODOPHYTA, produced in groups of 4.

te'traster, n. [Zoo.] A form produced in MEIOSIS having 4 ASTRAL points in place of two, caused by POLYSPERMY.

tetra'valent, a. [Chem.] having a VALENCY of 4. **tetra'valence, tetra'valency**, nn.

'**tetrode**, n. [Phys.] A THERMIONIC VALVE with 4 ELECTRODES, such as a SCREENED-GRID VALVE.

'**tetrose**, n. [Chem.] Any of a group of MONOSACCHARIDES with 4 O ATOMS in the MOLECULE.

text, n. The body of a book or other writing as opp. footnotes, headings, pictures, the list of divisions at the front, and so on. '**-book**, n. Teaching-book, book giving an account of some branch of knowledge for learners.

'**textile**, 1.n. Cloth of any sort, or any material made in the same way as cloth by taking threads over and under other threads.

'**texture**, n. That property of a solid substance which is dependent on the size, form, order, and grouping of the smaller parts (grains, threads, etc.) of which it is made up, and the way in which they are united, sp. important in Geology where it is used as one of the properties by which ROCKS are grouped.

Th, Sign for THORIUM.

'**thalamen'cephalon**, n. [Zoo.] The back part of the PROSENCEPHALON joining the CEREBRAL HEMISPHERES to the MESENCEPHALON in the brains of back-boned animals.

'**thalamus**, n. [Bot.] RECEPTACLE. [Zoo.] One or other of two egg-formed masses of GANGLIONS forming the chief division of the upper part of the THALAMENCEPHALON.

tha'lassic, a. To do with the sea, sp. with the smaller bodies of it as opp. the great OCEANS. **tha'lass-, tha'lassi-, tha'lasso-.**

tha'lassophyte, n. [Bot.] Sea ALGA.

tha'lidomide, n. [Med.] A SEDATIVE and ANTI-EMETIC which when taken by a PREGNANT woman may have serious effects on the development of her offspring, causing it to come to birth without arms, for example.

'**thallic**, a. [Chem.] Of, to do with, THALLIUM, having thallium in it, sp. thallium with a VALENCY of 3.

'thallium, n. Chemical ELEMENT, at. no. 81, at. wt. 204·39, sign Te, a silver-white or grey-white metal with properties like lead, used in making certain sorts of glass. thall'iferous, a.

'Thallo'phyta, n.pl. [Bot.] A DIVISION of plants not producing flowers or seeds whose plant-body is one CELL or a THALLUS, of which the chief groups are the FUNGI and ALGAE, and, in most systems of grouping, the BACTERIA and MYXOMYCETES. 'thallophyte, n. A plant of the T. thallo'phytic, a.

'thallus, n. [Bot.] The simple plant-body of THALLOPHYTA, formed of one CELL or of a number ranged in plates or chains, sometimes widely branching and looking somewhat like a seed-plant, but never in fact having true stems, roots, leaves, etc. and freq. without any suggestion of such special divisions. 'thalliform, a. 'thalline, a. Formed of a t.; like a t. 'thalloid, 'thallose, aa.

'thalweg, n. [Geog., Geol.] A line representative of the ups and downs of a river from its starting-point to the sea or other body of water, or joining the lowest points of the hollow cut out by it so as to make clear its general slope.

'thanat(o)-. Death.

'thanatoid, a. [Zoo., Med.] Death-like; causing death, said of animals with poisoned bites, etc.

'thanato'mania, n. [Psych., Med.] A diseased interest in death; an unbalanced desire to be dead, a condition in which there is danger of self-destruction.

'thanato'phobia, n. [Psych.] A diseased fear of death.

thana'tosis, n. [Zoo.] A condition copying death into which some insects are able to put themselves at times of danger, or the act or power of seeming to be dead as a way of keeping safe.

'theatre, n. [Med.] Room in a hospital, etc. where expert attention is given to ill persons, sp. where operations are done (freq. *operating t.*) before learners, other experts, etc.

'theca, n. [Bot.] A bag-like or box-like vessel or cover having in it SPORES or POLLEN, sp. one of those seen on MUSCI or FILICALES. [Zoo.] A cover or covering keeping something delicate from damage, as the DURA MATER, the cover of a TENDON or of a PUPA, or the cup-like or pipe-like structure formed round a number of small animals such as CORALS. 'thecal, a. 'thecate, a. '-phore, n. [Bot.] A structure supporting a t. '-spore, n. [Bot.] A SPORE produced inside a t., an ASCOSPORE. '-'sporous, a. Having the spores inside a t. 'theci-, 'theco-.

'thecium, n. [Zoo.] HYMENIUM in FUNGI or LICHENES.

'thecodont, a. [Zoo.] Having the teeth bedded in hollows in the mouth-bones.

'theelin, n. OESTRIN.

'theine, n. [Chem.] CAFFEINE, a name used chiefly of the caffeine in tea.

'thelium, n. [Zoo.] MAMMILLA; PAPILLA.

'thely-. Female.

'thelyo'toky, n. [Zoo.] PARTHENOGENESIS by which only females are produced. 'thelyo'tokous, a.

Th Em, Sign for THORIUM EMANATION, that is, for THORON.

theme, n. [Philol.] The stem of a word onto which INFLECTIONAL endings are put. the'matic, a. thematic 'vowel. A VOWEL ending the t. but not forming part of the root.

'thenar, n. [Zoo.] The front of the hand; the fat part of the t. at the base of the thumb. 'then-al, -ar, aa.

theo'bromine, n. [Chem., Med.] An ALKALOID, $C_7H_8N_4O_2$, present chiefly in the plant material from which chocolate is made, and in small amounts in tea etc., a white CRYSTALLINE powder with a bitter taste, used medically as a STIMULANT, sp. for the producing of URINE.

the'odolite, n. An instrument for measuring HORIZONTAL or VERTICAL angles between the directions of points at a distance, used in land-measuring, map-making, etc.

theo'mania, n. [Med.] Mind disease in which a person has the belief that he is the Highest Being, or under his special direction.

'theorem, n. A general statement or rule which is seen to be true from reasoning or mathematics.

'theory, n. An account of some general reason for certain facts based on detailed observations and which has enough agreement with the facts to be taken as true for working purposes, or, in mathematics, a system of THEOREMS giving a complete view of some wider question. t. of rela'tivity. *See* RELATIVITY.

theo'retic(al), aa. To do with, based on, given by, theory.

thera'peutic(al), aa. [Med.] To do with, of value in, the medical work of making ill persons well or overcoming the effects of disease. thera'peutic, n. A t. substance. thera'peutics, n. The t. side of medical science or work. 'therapy, n. Therapeutics, or more freq. some special system or branch of it, as in RADIOTHERAPY.

therm, n. [Phys.] A unit of amount of heat, used in Britain for measuring the amount of gas used in a house etc., equal to 100,000 BRITISH THERMAL UNITS or 25,200,000 CALORIES.

'thermal, a. [Phys., Geol., Elec.] Of, to do with, effected by, heat. t. agi'tation.

[Phys.] The motion of the ATOMS or MOLECULES of a body which gives it the form of ENERGY named heat. **t. an'alysis.** [Phys.] The process of working out the relations between TEMPERATURE and changes of structure in metals from the observation of their behaviour from point to point under a regular increase or loss of heat. **t. belt.** [Geog., Meteor.] A clearly marked band round the sides of some river hollows where the plant growth is never damaged, like that higher up or lower down, by FROST, the effect of a COMPRESSION and increase in heat at that level of the air coming down the slopes or mountains. **t. ca'pacity.** [Phys.] (Of a body) the amount of heat needed for increasing its TEMPERATURE by a unit amount, = the SPECIFIC HEAT of the body × its mass. **t. 'conduc'tivity.** [Phys.] A substance's power of transporting heat, given as that amount of heat going in unit time from one face to the other of a plate of it one unit thick, when the faces are one unit square and different from one another in TEMPERATURE by one degree. **t. 'current.** [Aerodynamics, Meteor.] An up-going current of air produced by special heating at one place. **t. dif'fusion.** [Phys., Chem.] In a mixed gas whose TEMPERATURE gets higher by degrees from base to top, the motion of the MOLECULES of greater weight in the direction of less heat and of those of less weight in the direction of greater heat, a tendency sometimes made use of in separating ISOTOPES. **t. dissoci'ation.** [Chem.] DISSOCIATION caused by heat. **t. ef'ficiency.** [Mach.] (Of a heat engine) the relation between the work done by an engine in a given time to the heat (in the form of its MECHANICAL EQUIVALENT) given to it by the steam used or the oil, coal etc. burned. **t. emis'sivity.** Sp. [Bot.] The loss of heat from a leaf to the air or to other parts of the plant. **t. e'quator.** [Geog., Meteor.] A line round the earth through places having the highest MEAN TEMPERATURE for a given time of year; the part of the earth between the north and south limits of the position of the t. equator. **t. 'instrument.** [Elec., etc.] Any instrument whose operation is based on the heating of something by an electric current. **t. meta'morphism.** [Geol.] Chemical changes in the structure of ROCKS caused by heating as the effect of liquid MAGMA coming near or into touch with them. **t. 'neutron.** [Phys., Chem.] The sort of slow-moving NEUTRON whose ENERGY is of the same order of size as the heat energy of the ATOMS or MOLECULES of the substance through which it is moving, by which NUCLEAR FISSION

and other nuclear reactions are caused. **t. ohm.** The unit of t. resistance. **t. re'sistance.** [Elec.] The property in a body acting against the transporting of heat through it. **t. spring.** [Geog., Geol., Med.] A spring of which the water is warmer than the air where it comes out of the earth, as the effect of having come through or from heated parts inside it, freq. with MINERALS in it which make it of value for medical purposes, sp. one warmer than 21°C. **t. value.** [Chem.] Of a chemical reaction, the amount of heat taken in or given out in it.

'therm(a)es'thesia, n. [Med.] The power of sensing heat and cold.

'therm'an(a)esthesia n. [Med.] Loss by the skin of power of sensing heat and cold.

therma'tology, n. [Med.] The science of the medical use of heat, for example the use in certain diseases of waters of THERMAL SPRINGS for bathing etc.

'thermifuge, n. FEBRIFUGE.

'thermion, n. [Phys.] An ELECTRON sent out by a heated substance. **thermi-'onic,** a. Of, to do with, tt. or the producing of tt., effected etc. by tt.; to do with THERMIONICS. **thermionic 'current.** A current formed of tt. having the same direction, such as those produced by a heated CATHODE and moving to the ANODE or to other ELECTRODES. **thermionic e'mission.** The giving off of ELECTRONS from the SURFACE of a CONDUCTOR as the effect of heat. **thermionic tube, thermionic 'vacuum tube,** or **thermionic valve.** A shut glass or metal bulb or pipe-like vessel from which as much gas as possible has been taken, having in it a CATHODE from which, when heated by an electric current to the point of giving off light, ELECTRONS are sent out, an ANODE to which these electrons are kept moving by attraction, and gen. one GRID (but sometimes more) in between, for controlling the number of electrons getting to the anode.

thermi'onics, n. The science of THERMIONIC EMISSION and effects, and of the behaviour and control of ELECTRONS sent out in this way.

'thermistor, n. [Phys.] A SEMI-CONDUCTOR of which the electric RESISTANCE is greatly changed with small changes in TEMPERATURE, and which is for that reason a very delicate instrument for measuring temperature.

'thermit, 'thermite, nn. Trade name, now used generally, for Al in powder form mixed with an OXIDE of some metal with less attraction for O than Al has, so that when fired a violent reaction takes place in which Al_2O_3 is formed with the development of great heat, and the other metal

becomes free, used sp. in INCENDIARY
BOMBS and in WELDING, in what is
named the t. process.
therm(o)-. Heat: 'thermo'genesis, n.;
THERMOELECTRIC: 'thermo'current, n.
thermo'ameter, n. [Elec.] An instrument for
measuring electric current by its heat-
effect in causing the expansion of a
delicate wire in connection with a
pointer.
'**therm(o)anaes'thesia,** n. [Med.] The loss of
the power of sensing heat or cold by
touch.
thermo'barograph, n. [Phys., Meteor.] An
instrument recording at the same time
the TEMPERATURE and PRESSURE of a gas,
sp. of the ATMOSPHERE.
thermo'battery, n. THERMOPILE.
thermo'chemistry, n. [Chem.] The science
of the heat changes in connection with
chemical processes, that is, the amount of
heat taken in or produced by chemical
reactions. **thermo'chemic(al),** aa. **thermo-
'chemist,** n.
thermo'couple, n. [Phys.] A THERMO-
ELECTRIC COUPLE.
'**thermo'dynamics,** n. [Phys.] The science
of the mathematical relations between
heat and WORK or other forms of ENERGY,
and of the general laws controlling
changes in the heat of bodies and effects
producing or produced by heat, of which
the chief are:—**first law of t.** There is a
fixed relation between the amount of heat
used up in any process and the amount of
WORK or some other form of ENERGY
produced, and the other way round, one
CALORIE being equal to $4 \cdot 18 + 10^7$ ERGS.
second law of t. It is impossible for heat to
go of itself from a colder to a warmer
body. **third law of t.** The ENTROPY of any
substance at a TEMPERATURE of ABSOLUTE
ZERO would be ZERO, and gets nearer and
nearer to this as the temperature gets
nearer and nearer to absolute zero, to
which, however, it is impossible for it
ever quite to come.
'**thermoelec'tricity,** n. [Phys.] ELECTRICITY
produced by changing heat into it, as by
a thermoelectric couple. **thermoe'lec-
tric(al),** aa. '**thermoe'lectric 'couple** or
thermoelectric pair. Two wires of different
materials joined to one another at their
ends, by heating one of which joins an
e.m.f. is produced there and an electric
current goes through the CIRCUIT completed by the joined other ends.
'**thermo'electric 'junction.** Join between
the two wires of a thermoelectric couple.
'**thermo'electric power.** The rate at
which the e.m.f. of a thermoelectric
couple CIRCUIT is changed with the
TEMPERATURE of the heated join.
'**thermoelec'trometer,** n. [Elec.] An instrument measuring the heat produced by an

electric current, or the power of the
current as seen from this.
'**thermoe'lectromotive force** or **thermo-
e.m.f.** [Elec.] The ELECTROMOTIVE FORCE
produced at the join between two different metals when heated, as in a
THERMOELECTRIC COUPLE.
'**thermoex'citory,** a. [Zoo.] Causing heat to
be produced in the body.
'**thermogalva'nometer,** n. [Elec.] An instrument measuring electric current by the
effect of a COIL heated by the current on a
THERMOCOUPLE hanging over it.
thermo'genesis, n. The producing of heat
by natural chemical change, sp. [Zoo.]
in the animal body. **thermo'genic,** a.
ther'mogenous, a.
'**thermograph,** n. [Phys., Meteor.] A
THERMOMETER automatically recording
its readings through a stretch of time.
'**thermoin'hibitory,** a. [Zoo., Med.] (Of
nerves) stopping or limiting the producing of heat in the body.
thermo'junction, n. THERMOCOUPLE.
thermo'labile, a. [Chem., Biochem.] (Of a
substance) having a tendency to be
broken up and undergo the loss of its
special properties on being heated.
'**thermolumi'nescence,** n. [Phys., Chem.]
The property or process of the giving out
of light by a body when heated. '**thermolumi'nescent,** a. Having the property of,
or being in a condition of, t.
ther'molysis, n. [Chem.] The process by
which MOLECULES are broken up as the
effect of heat. [Zoo.] The loss of heat by
the body. **thermo'lytic,** a.
'**thermomag'netic,** a. [Phys.] To do with,
produced, working and so on, by heat
and MAGNETISM.
ther'mometer, n. [Phys.] Any of a number
of different sorts of instrument for
measuring TEMPERATURE based on the
fact that the measure of some other
physical property of a substance is
dependent on its degree of heat, changing
regularly as this becomes greater or less—
the commonest form of such an instrument being a glass bulb opening into a
very thin glass pipe shut at the end and
marked with a scale, the bulb and part
of the pipe being full of MERCURY, the
level of which goes up and down the
scale as the bulb becomes warmer or
colder. **thermo'metric(al),** aa. **ther'mometry,** n. The measuring of TEMPERA-
TURE.
thermo'motive, a. [Phys.] Producing, or to
do with producing, motion by heat, as in
heat engines. **thermo'motor,** n. An engine
worked by heat, sp. by heated air.
thermo'nasty, n. [Bot.] The taking up of a
special position by a plant in reaction to
heat, for example the unnatural curving
of a stem as the effect of one-sided

growth caused by an unequal distribution of heat.

'thermo'nuclear reaction. [Phys.] A NUCLEAR reaction caused by heat.

'thermophil(e), thermo'philic, ther'mophilous, aa. [Biol.] Needing, doing well in, heat, or able to undergo great heat without damage.

'thermophone, n. [Acous.] An apparatus for producing sound-waves of changing PRESSURE as the effect of changes in the heat of a thin wire through which an ALTERNATING current is sent, used in telephone RECEIVERS or for testing the ear or some instrument.

'thermophospho'rescence, n. [Phys.] PHOSPHORESCENCE produced by heating a body after it has been acted on by light rays etc.

'thermopile, n. [Phys.] An apparatus made up of a number of THERMOELECTRIC COUPLES, sp. formed of rods of ANTIMONY and BISMUTH, put together in SERIES or in PARALLEL, used for producing electric current or measuring heat sent out in the form of rays.

thermo'plastic, n., a. [Phys., Chem.] (A substance) becoming soft and able to be given different forms when heated, sp. able to undergo this heating process over and over without the loss of its special properties.

thermo'regulator, n. THERMOSTAT.

'thermoscope, n. [Phys.] An instrument giving signs of but not measuring small changes of TEMPERATURE. thermo'scopic(al), aa. Sp. [Zoo.] Designed to give a reaction to changes of TEMPERATURE, as certain special instruments of sense in some CEPHALOPODA.

thermo'setting, a. [Chem.] (Of a substance) at first made soft by heat but then undergoing a chemical change and becoming hard and completely different in structure and properties, so as to be unable to be made soft again by further heat, as certain PLASTICS.

thermo'stable, a. [Biochem.] (Of a structure) able to be heated to a not very high degree without the loss of its special properties.

'thermostat, n., An apparatus based on the expansion of a solid, liquid or gas, sp. the unequal expansion of two metals, by heat, or on the use of a THERMOCOUPLE, for automatically keeping the TEMPERATURE of something at a fixed degree by cutting off the heating (or opposite) process when it gets to this point and starting it again when it goes lower (or higher)—used for example in heating-systems for houses or water, in engines, ice-boxes, INCUBATORS and so on. [Chem.] A vessel or bath of which the TEMPERATURE is kept unchanging. thermo'static, a.

'thermosys'taltic, a. [Zoo.] Of which the CONTRACTION is caused or helped by heat or cold, said of a muscle. 'thermo'-'systalism, n. The CONTRACTION of a muscle caused by becoming warmer or colder.

thermo'taxis, n. [Biol.] TAXIS in reaction to heat. [Zoo., Med.] The process by which body-heat is kept at a regular level, the balancing of the producing and loss of heat by the body. thermo'tactic, a.

thermo'therapy, n. [Med.] The use of heat, for example heated baths etc., for medical purposes.

thermo'tolerant, a. [Bot.] (Of plants) able to go on living in great heat but not doing well. 'thermo'tolerance, n.

ther'motropism, n. [Biol.] TROPISM in reaction to heat. thermo'tropic, a.

'therophyte, n. [Bot.] A plant completing its growth in the warmer part of the year, and living through the cold only in the form of seeds.

'thesis, n. A statement put forward to be supported by argument; the reasoned statement of a new point of view or addition to knowledge supported by independent work in some field, put in the form of a paper or book and produced by a person at a university as one of the conditions of getting a certain degree, such as a Ph.D.

thia-. [Chem.] Having S in the place of the C of the named substance.

'thiamide, n. [Chem.] Any of a group of substances with the same structure as AMIDES but having S in the place of O.

'thiamin, n. [Biochem.] That part of the VITAMIN B complex helping to keep healthy the nerves, muscles and digestion of higher animals, without enough of which man is attacked by BERI-BERI—present in almost all living things and a necessary part of the food of most animals, got chiefly from milk, eggs, plant-seeds, fruit, and green plants.

'thiazole, n. [Chem.] C_3H_3SN, a RING compound with three CH groups, a liquid without colour and with a smell and other properties very like those of PYRIDINE, used in forming DYE substances and, united with a SULPHONAMIDE, for medical purposes. (See p. 392.)

'thickening, n. [Biol.] New material formed on or in something, such as and sp. the wall of a VESSEL, making it thicker, or a thicker part formed in this way. t. 'fibre. [Bot.] Any of the bands of t. seen twisting round the walls of plant-CELLS or VESSELS.

'thickness, n. The third DIMENSION of a solid, the other two being LENGTH and BREADTH; more loosely, measure from side to side in any direction as opp. measure from end to end; the property or condition of being thick in any sense; measure of t., the degree to which a thing is thick.

thigh, n. FEMUR.

thigmo′taxis, n. STEREOTAXIS. **thigmo-′tactic,** a.

thig′motropism, n. STEREOTROPISM. **thigmo′tropic,** a.

′thinner, n. Any liquid, but most commonly TURPENTINE or WHITE SPIRIT, added to paint to make it thinner, but not necessarily a SOLVENT for it.

′thio-. [Chem.] Having S in the place of the O of the named substance. **′t.-′aldehyde,** n., **′t.-′ether,** n., **′-car′bonic,** a.

thio-′acid, n. [Chem.] An acid in which the place of the OH in the group –CO(OH) is taken by SH.

′thio-′alcohol, n. MERCAPTAN.

′thio′cyan-ate, -ide, nn. [Chem.] Any substance having in it the group –CNS.

′Thiokol, n. Trade name for any of a group of POLYMERS with rubber-like properties, not damaged by oil, not attacked by SOLVENTS, and able to be VULCANIZED.

′thionyl, n. [Chem.] The group SO, acting for the purpose of uniting with other substances as a unit with a VALENCY of 2.

′thiophen(e), n. [Chem.] C_4H_4S, a RING COMPOUND with four CH groups—a liquid without colour present in COAL TAR and having properties very like BENZENE. **thio′phenic,** a. (*See* p. 392.)

thio′sulphate, n. [Chem.] Any substance having in it the group –S_2O_3.

third ′eyelid. NICTITATING MEMBRANE.

third quarter of the moon. *See* MOON.

thix′otropy, n. [Chem.] The property of certain GELS of becoming liquid on shaking and solid again when at rest. **thixo′tropic,** a.

′Thomson ef′fect. n. [Phys.] The producing of a DIFFERENCE OF POTENTIAL between two parts of a wire as the effect of a difference in the degree to which they are heated.

′thorax, n. [Zoo.] In higher animals, the part of the body between the neck and the stomach, in which are the heart and breathing-apparatus and to which are joined the arms or front legs, the front part of which in man is named the chest; in ARTHROPODA, the middle of the three chief divisions of the body, supporting the legs and wings (if any), sometimes united with the first division, the head, but clearly marked off from the third division, the ABDOMEN; a like front part of the body, sometimes forming one with the head, sometimes coming between it and the back division, in other animals, such as certain worms. **tho′racic,** a. **tho′racic duct.** The chief of the system of LYMPH vessels in higher animals, running down the t. **tho′racic ′index.** [An-

throp., Med.] The RATIO between the measure of the t. from back to front at its thickest part and its measure from side to side. **thoraco-**.

′thoraco′plasty, n. [Med.]The operation of taking out parts of the RIBS so as to take all air from a diseased LUNG to keep it from working and give it a chance of getting better.

′thoride, n. [Chem.] Name given to any of the RADIOACTIVE ISOTOPES of Th.

′thorium, n. Chemical ELEMENT, at. no. 90, at. wt. 232·12, sign Th, a dark grey, RADIOACTIVE metal. **t. eman′ation.** THORON.

thorn, n. [Bot.] A short, hard, sharp-pointed structure on a stem produced by a special development of a leaf or branch BUD.

′thoron, n. [Chem.] A RADIOACTIVE gas produced at one stage in the radio-active changes of THORIUM, an ISOTOPE of RADON with a HALF-LIFE of 54·5 seconds.

thread, n. [Mach.] The RIDGE going round and round a screw or round the wall of a pipe etc. designed to take a screw, or any such ridge twisting round the outside of a solid pipe-like part or the inside of a hollow one.

thread cell. [Zoo.] NEMATOCYST.

′threadworm, n. [Zoo.] A NEMATODE worm.

′three-′colour process. In camera work or printing, any process producing all other colours by the use of three PRIMARY colours, as in the SUBTRACTIVE COLOUR PROCESS.

′three-e′lectrode valve. TRIODE.

′three-′phase, a. [Elec.] (Of an ALTERNATING-current electric system) using, made up of, 3 CIRCUITS whose currents are different in PHASE by one-third of a CYCLE.

′threshold, n. [Zoo., Psych., Phys.] The lowest degree of a given physical force or condition by which a certain effect may be produced, sp. the least amount of a STIMULUS necessary for producing a nerve, muscle, or sense reaction (**′stimulus t.**); the least amount of change in a given force or condition, sp. a stimulus, by which a change in the effect or reaction is produced (**′difference t.**); the degree of a given force or condition, sp. a stimulus, producing the greatest possible effect, no further increase or change in the effect being produced by increasing the force etc. over this point (**′terminal t.**). **t. ′frequency.** [Phys.] The smallest FREQUENCY of light needed for producing a PHOTOELECTRIC effect on coming against a given metal.

thrill, n. [Med.] An unnormal VIBRATION of the breathing- or blood-system which may be noted by feeling the body with the hand.

throat, n. [Bot.] The opening of a pipe-like part, sp. of a COROLLA or CALYX of which the parts are united edge to edge.

throb, 1.v.i. [Med.] PULSATE, sp. of a part of the body in which, as the effect of a wound or some diseased condition, the pulsating of the blood-vessels is strong enough to give pain. 2. A PULSATION.

'thromb-ase, -in, nn. [Biochem.] A substance produced in blood when blood-vessels are damaged which, by uniting with FIBRINOGEN to make FIBRIN, is responsible for changing liquid blood into a jelly.

thromb(o)-. [Med.] To do with, causing etc., a THROMBUS, or THROMBOSIS:— **thrombo'genic,** a., **'thromboid,** a.

'thrombocyte, n. [Zoo.] A very small grey body of a sort present in great numbers in the blood of higher animals, which has the property of being readily broken up, freeing THROMBOPLASTIN for the process of changing liquid blood into jelly.

'thrombogen, n. [Biochem.] The substance in the blood which is changed into THROMBIN by the operation of THROMBO-PLASTIN.

thrombo'kinase, n. THROMBOPLASTIN.

thrombo'plastin, n. [Biochem.] A KINASE in the blood and TISSUES changing THROM-BOGEN into THROMBIN when Ca salts are present.

throm'bosis, n. [Med.] The forming of a THROMBUS in a blood-vessel, stopping, or with a tendency to stopping, it up. [Zoo.] The becoming jelly-like or solid of the blood or any body-liquid. **'thrombosed,** a. Having a THROMBUS, having undergone t. **throm'botic,** a.

'thrombus, n. [Med.] A small mass of jellied blood formed in a blood-vessel or the heart as the effect of disease.

'throttle, 1.v.t. [Eng.] Make (a current of steam, gas, etc.) less by the use of a t. valve, or make the rate of (an engine) slower in this way. 2.n. T. valve; t. lever. **t. 'lever.** A LEVER by moving which a t. valve is put into operation. **t. 'valve.** A VALVE by which a current of steam etc. in an engine is made less or shut off.

throw, 1.v.t. Get (a vessel, etc.) formed on a potter's wheel. [Mach.] Give a pull or other motion to (a LEVER or SWITCH) to put parts of a machine, an electric CIRCUIT, etc. into or out of connection. 2.n. [Mach.] Act of throwing a LEVER etc.; the range of motion of a part moving, or which may be moved, forward and back. [Geol.] The amount by which the material on the two sides of a FAULT has been moved in an up-and-down direction, or by which any body of ROCK has been moved up (up-

throw) or down (**downthrow**) by a fault.

'thrum-eyed, a. [Bot.] (Of a flower) with a short STYLE and long STAMENS coming up to or out of the opening of a pipe-like COROLLA.

thrush, n. A disease of the feet of animals such as the horse, marked by INFLAM-MATION and the producing of PUS.

thrust, n. [Mech.] A pushing force; a t. of one part of a thing or structure on another part, sp. an outgoing side-ways force, as of an arch against a supporting wall, or the force producing a geological t. [Geol.] a t. fault. **t. fault.** A FAULT in which the material on one side has been pushed up and over that on the other.

'thulium, n. Chemical ELEMENT, at. no. 69, at. wt. 169·4, sign Tu, one of the RARE EARTH METALS.

'thunder, n. [Meteor.] The noise coming after a burst of LIGHTNING, caused by the sudden heating and expansion of the air near the electric DISCHARGE, producing violent wave-motions. **'t.-cloud.** A cloud marked by strong up-currents of air in which drops of water become electrically CHARGED and from which, when their united POTENTIAL becomes high enough, an electric DISCHARGE takes place causing LIGHTNING and t. **'t.-storm.** n. A violent rain with t. and LIGHTNING.

'thymol, n. [Chem.] A PHENOL, $C_{10}H_{14}O$, in the form of white CRYSTALS with a pleasing smell, present in a great number of plant oils, used as an ANTISEPTIC.

'thymus, n. [Zoo.] A DUCTLESS GLAND of uncertain purpose in the neck or chest of back-boned animals, in man and higher animals wasting away when development is complete, possibly having something to do with growth. **'thymic,** a. **thym(o)-.**

'thyratron, n. [Phys.] A TRIODE having in it a gas, such as Hg, A, He or Ne, at low PRESSURE, and letting a strong current through when a small VOLTAGE is put on the GRID.

thyre(o)-, thyro-, Of, to do with, the THYROID GLAND (and . . .).

'thyroid, 1.n. [Zoo.] The t. gland. 2.a. Of to do with, produced by, near, the t. **t. 'body, t. gland.** An ENDOCRINE GLAND in the front of the neck in back-boned animals producing THYROXIN. **t. 'cartilage.** The greatest of the CARTILAGES of the LARYNX, forming a V whose point comes at the front of the throat, pushing it out into the round mass named the 'Adam's apple'.

thy'roxin(e), n. [Biochem.] A HORMONE, $C_{15}H_{11}O_4NI_4$, produced by the THYROID, which has the property of increasing the rate of OXIDATION in the body and an important connection with growth and development, the outcome of being without it, or without enough of it, being CRETINISM or MYXEDEMA.

'thyrsus, n. [Bot.] A form of mixed flower-grouping in which the chief stem is RACEMOSE, and the thickly massed side branches CYMOSE 'thyrsoid, a.

Ti, Sign for TITANIUM.

'tiber, tibre, n. [Med.] The number of units by measure of a SOLUTE in one unit of a STANDARD SOLUTION.

'tibia, n. [Zoo.] In four-legged back-boned animals and man, the inner and gen. greater of the two long bones of the lower (back) leg between the knee and the foot; in insects, the 4th division (starting from the base) of the leg. 'tibial, a. tibio-.

tibi'ale, n. [Zoo.] That bone of the upper line of TARSALS which is in line with the TIBIA.

'tibio'fibula, n. [Zoo.] A bone of the leg in certain animals representative of the united TIBIA and FIBULA.

tibio'tarsus, n. [Zoo.] A bone in the leg of birds representative of the TIBIA united with some of the TARSALS.

tic, n. [Med.] A frequent, quick, automatic motion of the muscles, sp. of the face, which is outside a person's control. t. 'douloureux. NEURALGIA in the nerves of the face, marked by sudden attacks of sharp pain causing a t.

tick, n. [Zoo.] Any of the greater-sized of the two chief sorts of ACARINA, all of them blood-SUCKERS on man or other animals and some of them transporters of important diseases.

tide, n. [Astron., Geog.] The regular in-coming (flood t.) and outgoing (ebb t.) of the sea in relation to the land twice every LUNAR day (24 hours 51 minutes) as the effect of a lifting of its level caused by the attraction of the moon, and to some degree of the sun. See SPRING T., NEAP T. 'tidal, a. To do with, produced by, having, tt., as a tidal river. tidal air. [Med.] The amount of air (500 c.c.) taken into and sent out of the body in a normal act of breathing. tidal range. [Geog.] The lift of the level of the water between its highest point (high t.) and its lowest (low t.) at a place. tidal stream. A sea current produced by and changing with the tt. tidal wave. [Geog.] BORE; a very great wave sent onto the land by an earth-shock.

tie, n. [Engin. etc.] A rod etc. going between and keeping together two parts of a structure, and acted on by a pulling force.

till, n. [Geol.] BOULDER CLAY. '-ite, n. Very old and hard t.

'timbre, n. [Acous.] QUALITY. [Phonet.] The QUALITY [Acous.] of a SPEECH SOUND.

time and 'motion study. Detailed observation of the motions used and the time

taken by a workman in doing certain work—gen. with a view to the discovery of the best way of doing it and the training needed.

'time-'constant, n. [Elec.] In a REACTOR or a CONDENSER, the time taken for the current or CHARGE to undergo $1 - \dfrac{1}{2 \cdot 71828}$ of the complete change caused in it by a change in the VOLTAGE given to it.

tin, n. Chemical ELEMENT, at no. 50, at. wt. 118·7, sign Sn, a soft, silver-white metal not acted on by air or water in normal conditions, but changing as the effect of cold into a grey, readily powdering ALLOTROPIC form (grey tin)—used chiefly for coating or mixing with other metals, sp. iron and steel. t. plague. The change of white t. into grey t. as the effect of cold. t. plate. Iron or steel in the form of thin plates coated with t. by being put into a bath of the metal made liquid by heat. t. py'rites. [Mineral.] STANNITE. '-stone, n. CASSITERITE.

'tincal, n. [Mineral.] The natural BORAX substance got from SALT LAKES.

'tinc'torial, a. Giving colour, to do with colour or colouring processes such as DYEING.

'tincture, n. [Med.] A SOLUTION of a medical (gen. plant) substance in ALCOHOL or in alcohol and ETHER.

'tinea, n. [Med.] RINGWORM.

tin'nitus, n. [Med.] A sense of whistling or other noise in the ears caused by some condition or disease acting on the nerves of the ear.

tin'tometer, n. [Chem., etc.] Trade name for a special instrument for the comparison of colours of liquids, etc.

'tintype, n. FERROTYPE.

tire, n. TYRE.

'tissue, n. [Biol.] A mass of animal or plan CELLS, commonly of the same or of one or two sorts, united by their walls or by some substance between them into one of the materials, gen. designed for a special purpose, forming the plant or animal body, as skin t., muscle t., nerve t. t. 'culture. The growth or keeping in a living condition in liquids designed for this purpose, gen. in a glass vessel, of bits of t. taken from an animal or plant; a liquid having in it living t. taken from an animal or plant for observation and testing. t. respi'ration. See RESPIRATION.

'titanata, n. [Chem.] Any SALT or ESTER of TITANIC ACID.

ti'tanic, a. [Chem.] Of, having in it, TITANIUM. t. acid. Any of a number of feeble acids formed from TiO_2, sp. $Ti(OH)_4$ or H_2TiO_3.

'titanite, n. [Mineral.] A natural hard CRYSTALLINE substance formed chiefly of SILICATE of Ca and Ti with some iron etc., ranging from dark brown to yellow in colour, used sometimes as a jewel stone.

ti'tanium, n. Chemical ELEMENT, at. no. 22, at. wt. 47·90, sign Ti, a metal somewhat like iron, but of less weight and higher MELTING-point, used for mixing with other metals, sp. aluminium and steel, and, united with other substances, in DYEING and paint-making etc. **t. 'oxide.** TiO₂, a white substance used as a PIGMENT and for producing TITANATES.

ti'tration, n. [Chem.] The measuring of the amount of a substance, A, in a SOLUTION by the addition to a measured amount of the solution of the smallest amount of a second liquid, B, measured from a BURETTE, necessary for a complete reaction, as seen from a certain effect, gen. a change of colour. **ti'trate,** v.t. Get measured etc. by t. **titri'metric,** a. **ti'trimetry,** n. ANALYSIS by t.

Tl, Sign for THALLIUM.

Tm. One of the two signs used for THULIUM, the other being **Tu.**

τ meson. [Phys.] A MESON of weight 1000 times that of an ELECTRON.

Tn, Sign for THORON.

T.N.T. or **TNT.** TRINITROTOLUENE.

to'copheral, n. [Biochem., Chem.] VITAMIN E, or any of the complex ALCOHOLS of which it is made up.

'toilet, n. [Med.] The cleaning and dressing of the wound after an operation.

'tolerance, n. [Med.] The power of undergoing a given effect, such as a shock, or of taking into the system a poisoning substance etc., without serious damage; the degree of this power, given, for example, as the amount of a certain substance which may be taken into the system by the person in question without serious damage. [Bot.] A plant's power of living without serious damage through certain conditions or attacks of disease. [Mach.] The limits between which the size of a machine part designed for working with other parts may be different without making such working impossible. **'tolerant,** a. [Med., Bot.] Having a certain degree of t. for a given effect, disease or substance, sp. [Med.] through having got used to it (*tolerant of*); (of a plant) having t. for hard conditions generally. **'tolerate,** v.t. [Med.] Be tolerant of (some substance etc.) **toler'ation,** n.

'toluene, 'toluol, nn. [Chem.] C₆H₅CH₃, a readily-burning liquid, without colour and with a special smell, present in coal TAR, used as a SOLVENT and in making DYES, TRINITROTOLUENE, and other, sp. medical, substances.

-tomy, n. [Med.] The operation of cutting out or cutting into the named part.

ton, n. Unit of weight = 2240 pounds or 1014·047 kilograms (*long t.*, used n Britain for coal), or 2000 pounds, or 907·20 kilograms (*short t.*, used generally in the U.S.A., and in Britain for metals). *See* TONNE.

tone, n. [Acous.] A sound produced by one regular VIBRATION of the air at a fixed rate (freq. *pure tone*); any sound formed of a complex of tt., as a note in music; TONALITY; the INTERVAL between any t. and the one coming after it in a music scale. [Philol., Phonet.] The PITCH or change in pitch of the voice in saying something, sp. when used as a sign of feeling or sense; any of the fixed tt. or families of tt. used in a t. language. [Zoo., Med.] The condition of being somewhat tight and elastic normal to a living TISSUE, sp. the condition of some CONTRACTION present in healthy muscle at rest by which the parts of the body are kept in position. [Med.] (Of the system or any of its parts) the condition of being in good working order, ready with quick and strong reactions, which is dependent on the healthy and regular working of chemical and nerve processes going on all the time (*see* TONUS). [Bot.] A condition of healthy balance in the reactions of a plant to light, heat, and water. [Psych.] The general feeling colouring a person's reactions at some time, such as a tendency to pleasure or the opposite, FEELING TONE. **t. language.** [Philol.] A language using a system of different fixed tt. to give different senses to words which in other ways have the same sound, as Chinese. **'tonal,** a. [Acous.] Of, to do with, a t. or tt. or with tonality. **to'nality,** n. [Acous.] The quality by which one t. is sensed as different from another. **'t.-deaf,** a. [Psych.] (Of a person) not having the power of sensing the tonality of notes in music, that is, of hearing different tt. as different. **'t.-'deafness,** n.

tongs, n. Any of a number of two-legged, gen. scissors-like instruments with ends formed for gripping, used for taking up bits of heated substance, lifting or transporting delicate bits of material, and a great number of other special purposes in the LABORATORY, in industry, and in medical work.

tongue, n. [Zoo.] In back-boned animals a soft, flat-topped, muscled, moving structure fixed to the floor of the mouth, which is the chief instrument of taste, used in addition for helping to get food crushed and sent down the throat, and, in man, for forming the sounds used in talking; in lower animals, sp. insects, a mouth-part like a t. in structure or use. [Mach.] A part giving a suggestion of a t. in form, or in the fact that it is a more or less flat

PROJECTION designed to be slipped into a hole or between two other lip-like parts, etc. **t. de′pressor.** [Med.] A spoon-like instrument for pushing down the t. for the purpose of looking into the mouth or throat. **′t.-tie,** n. [Med.] A condition in which the motion of the t. is limited because the fold of skin joining it to the mouth on the under side is not long enough or not freely moving. **′t.-tied,** a. [Med.] Having t.-tie and so without the power of talking clearly.

′tonic, 1.a. [Acous.] To do with, in relation to, a TONE. [Philol.] Of or to do with TONES or TONE LANGUAGES. [Phonet.] (Of a sound) VOICED; (of a word or part of a word) said with special force or PITCH. [Zoo., Med., Bot.] Of, to do with, producing, a condition of tone or TONUS. [Med.] Marked by a long, unbroken, unnormally hard CONTRACTION of the muscles, as a *t.* SPASM. 2.n. [Acous.] The key note of a system of TONES, in relation to which they are grouped in a music scale. [Med.] A medical substance helping to put right the TONE of the body or any part when its working has become slow and feeble. **to′nicity,** n. [Zoo., Med.] The condition of having TONE or TONUS.

tonne, n. Measure of weight = 1000 kg. or 0·9842 TON, other name *metric ton.*

to′nometer, n. [Acous.] An instrument for measuring the FREQUENCY of notes of music. [Med.] Any instrument for measuring the TENSION or PRESSURE of anything in the body, as the tension of the eyeball or the pressure of a gas in the blood. [Chem.] An apparatus for measuring the pressure of a VAPOUR. **tono′metric,** a. **to′nometry,** n.

′tonoplast, n. [Bot.] The skin of PROTOPLASM round a VACUOLE.

′tonsil, n. [Zoo.] A mass of LYMPHOID substance with deep cracks into which the MUCOUS MEMBRANE covering it is folded, in the mouth or throat of higher animals, sp. one or other of the two at the openings of the PHARYNX (*the tt.*) probably an apparatus for the destruction of disease BACTERIA. **′tonsillar,** a. **′tonsil-′lectomy,** n. [Med.] **′tonsil′litis,** n. [Med.].

′tonus, n. [Zoo., Med.] A condition (of some TISSUE or part) of being in operation all the time, for example that unending reaction to unending small NERVE IMPULSES by which the normal TONE of STRIATED MUSCLE is kept up. [Med.] An unnormal condition of TONIC SPASM.

ton′variator, n. [Acous.] A sound RESONATOR of which the note may be changed, used for the comparison of notes in music.

tooth (teeth), n. [Zoo.] In back-bone animals, any of the hard, gen. sharp, parts fixed inside the mouth for the separating and crushing of food and freq. used as instruments of attack, in higher animals having root-like parts planted in hollows in the JAW-BONES and top parts of different form for different purposes—made up of a middle soft part with nerves and blood-vessels, inside a hard body of DENTINE coated in part with ENAMEL and in part with CEMENT; in other animals, any hard gen. horn-like structure in or about the mouth having a like purpose. [Zoo., Mach., etc.] Any small, hard part giving the suggestion of a t., sp. a COG. [Bot.] Any small, pointed PROJECTION on the edge of a leaf etc.

′topaz, n. [Mineral.] A natural SILICATE and FLUORIDE of Al, a yellow or blue CRYSTALLINE and freq. glass-like substance used as a jewel stone.

′tophus (tophi), n. [Med.] Any of the stone-like masses of SODIUM URATE formed round the JOINTS, CARTILAGES (sp. of the ear) etc. in persons having GOUT. **toph′aceous,** a. To do with, like, tt., having or formed of hard sand-like grains.

′topical, a. [Med.] To do with a certain part of or place on the body.

topo′chemical, a. [Chem.] (Of a chemical reaction) taking place only at a special, limited place in a body, as the face of a solid or the grains of a COLLOID; to do with t. reactions. **topo′chemistry,** n.

to′pography, n. [Geog., Surveying, etc.] (An account of) the SURFACE details, natural and man-made, of a stretch of country, the positions, forms, distances from one another, different levels, etc., of its parts and the structures to be seen on it; the science or process of mapping out the t. of places. [Med.] An account or view of) the system of parts making up the body or a division of it, from the point of view of their relations of form, size, position, etc., as CEREBRAL *t.* [Psych.] The system of different divisions or levels looked on as making up the mind in certain schools of thought, as the unconscious, the SUBCONSCIOUS, etc., or the ID, the EGO, and the SUPEREGO. **to′pographer,** n. [Geog., etc.] Person whose business is t. **′topo′graphic(al),** aa. **′topo′graphic ado′lescence.** [Geog.] The stage in the development of a stretch of country when its chief rivers have been formed, cutting deep and narrow hollows through it, but before the parts between them have been cut through by branch rivers or much changed in their outlines. **′topo′graphic an′atomy.** [Med.] T., or the science of any part from the point of view of its placing, or the mapping of places in the body where something takes place. **′topo′graphic ′infancy.** [Geog.] The stage in the development of a stretch of country when its hollows are still full of water but before clear-cut rivers have made their way through the softer substance of the parts round. **'topo'graphic map.** [Geog. etc.] A map in greater detail than a general geography map, giving not only rivers, mountains, towns, different levels, etc., but roads, railways, woods, bridges, the streets of towns, etc. **'topo'graphic ma'turity.** [Geog.] The stage in the history of a stretch of country in which the development of its river-system is complete and much of the high land has been wasted away into lower slopes. **'topo-'graphic old age.** [Geog.] The stage in the development of a stretch of country in which, as the effect of wasting away, it has come almost to BASE LEVEL.

'toponym, n. A name given to something by science, for example to a part of the body or a plant or animal, based on its position, or the place from which it comes.

'topotype, n. [Zoo.] An example of a sort of animal got from the same place as that from which the TYPE was got. **topo-'typic(al),** aa.

'topset beds. [Geol.] The almost level top beds put down in a DELTA starting at its inland edge.

tor, n. [Geog.] A great mass of ROCK, gen. GRANITE, by itself, which has been weathered to a very sharply outlined form, freq. with almost upright sides.

'toric lens. [Optics] A simple LENS used in eye-glasses which is in-curved equally in all directions, like part of the inner side of a hollow ball, on the side near the eye, and out-curved unequally, like part of the outer side of a pipe bent into a curve, on the other.

tor'nado, n. [Meteor.] A very violent WHIRLWIND, looking like an upright V-formed cloud, covering only a small space but moving quickly over the earth for a time and causing great destruction by pulling up trees and buildings into the near-VACUUM produced at its middle—special to places where heated air with much water in it and cold dry air come together; in W. Africa a very violent wind and THUNDER-STORM on a wide front caused by like conditions, coming gen. between the wet and the dry times of the year.

'toroid, 1.a. In the form of a solid pipe bent into a circle. 2.n. [Elec.] A TRANSFORMER in which the current-transporting wire is twisted like the thread of a screw round a t. middle part. **to'roidal,** a. T. or to do with a t. **to'roidal 'winding.** [Elec.] The sort of WINDING seen in a t.

tor'pedo, n. A pipe-like vessel pointed at the two ends, having EXPLOSIVE in the head, an engine driving it at a great rate in the body, and a guiding-apparatus in the

tail, for firing, sp. under water, at one ship by another.

'torpid, a. [Zoo., Med.] (Of an animal or person) in a condition of having no or little power of moving, acting, or feeling, with the mind and senses giving no or very slow and incomplete reactions; (of a part) not working or working very slowly, very hard to get a reaction from. **tor-'pidity,** n. **'torpify,** v.t. Make t. **'torpor,** n. The condition of being t., sp. that of a person t. in body and mind.

torque, n. [Mech.] A turning or twisting effect or MOMENT, two equal and opposite parallel forces acting on a body and causing, or with a tendency to cause, ROTATION—equal to one of these forces MULTIPLIED by the PERPENDICULAR distance between their lines of action, measured in FOOT-POUNDS.

'torques, n. [Zoo.] A collar-like ring of hair, feathers, or skin round the neck. **'torquate, tor'quated,** aa. Having a t.

Torri'cellian 'vacuum. [Phys.] The space with nothing in it over the Hg in a BAROMETER, produced by getting the pipe full of Hg and then turning it upside-down and putting the open end in an open vessel of the liquid.

'Torri'celli's law. [Phys.] The law that the rate at which liquid comes out of a hole in a vessel is the same as that of a body after falling a distance equal to that from the top of the liquid to the hole.

'torrid, a. [Geog.] Dried up with the heat of the sun, very warm and dry; of, to do with, the T. Zone. **T. Zone.** [Geog.] The part of the earth between $23° 30'$ N. and $23° 30'$ S. with the EQUATOR through the middle, where there is great heat all through the year because of its position in relation to the sun.

'torsion, n. A process or condition of twisting or turning. [Mech.] The STRAIN or STRESS produced in any body by a twisting force, a TORQUE, sp. in a rod, wire, or thread. **t. 'balance.** [Phys.] A delicate instrument for measuring very small forces, such as those of electric attraction, by their effect in moving a small rod hanging by the middle from a thin wire or thread, the t. of which, caused by any turning motion of the rod, is generally measured by the REFLECTION of a ray of light to a scale from a small looking-glass in the end of the rod, which gives the amount of the force which is balanced by this t. **t. head.** A turning part with a scale, at the top of a t. balance, from which the wire is hanging and by turning which t. may be produced in it. **'torsional, 'torsile,** aa. Of, to do with, produced by or producing t.

'torso, n. [Med., etc.] Man's body without the arms, legs, or head, that is the middle part of the body to which these structures are joined.

'torticollis, n. [Med.] A condition in which the neck is twisted into an unnatural position as the effect of RHEUMATISM or of some disease of the part of the backbone supporting the neck, causing the unnormal CONTRACTION of some of the neck muscles.

'torticone, n. [Zoo.] A SPIRAL SHELL.

'tortuose, 'tortuous, aa. Bent or curving first in one direction, then in the opposite, sp. [Bot.].

'torulose, a. [Bot.] Having small, rounded outgrowths or thick places, sp. MONILIFORM.

'torulus (toruli), n. [Zoo.] The hollow in which an insect's feeler is planted.

'torus (tori, n. [Bot.] The RECEPTACLE of a flower; the thicker part of the cover of a BORDERED PIT. [Zoo.] A RIDGE or fold, sp. that supporting the hook-like outgrowths in POLYCHAETA. [Anat.] A smoothly rounded outgrowth.

'total, 1.a. Complete, taking all together, taking everything in. 2.n. The number or amount given by the addition of all the numbers or amounts of a group. t. ab'sorption coefficient or 'factor. [Optics] EXTINCTION COEFFICIENT. t. e'clipse. [Astron.] An ECLIPSE of the sun by the moon coming between it and the earth when the moon is near enough to the earth for its UMBRA to be falling on it. t. heat. [Phys., Eng.] The amount of heat needed for changing a unit mass of a liquid at one TEMPERATURE (in ENGINEERING, 1 pound of water at 0°C.) into SATURATED VAPOUR at any other given temperature (in engineering, the boiling-point as dependent on the PRESSURE in the boiler). to'tality, n. The condition of being t. or a t.; all of a number of things taken together. [Astron.] The condition or time in an ECLIPSE when the cutting off of the light is complete.

'toti-. Completely:— '-'palmate, a. [Zoo.].

to'tipotent, a. [Zoo.] (Of a BLASTOMERE) having the power of development into a complete animal.

'touchstone, n. [Mineral.] A sort of black or grey FLINT-like stone used for testing the degree to which gold and silver are free from other metals by the colour of the mark they make when rubbed across it.

'touchwood, n. [Bot.] Wood which has been attacked by FUNGI to the point of being so DECAYED as to go to bits at a touch and to take fire very readily when dry.

'tourmaline, n. [Mineral.] Any of a group of natural SILICATES of B and Al united with Fl and different amounts of Mg, Fe, or an ALKALINE EARTH METAL—CRYSTALLINE substances of almost all colours, some clear and valued as jewels,

and all having marked PIEZOELECTRIC, PYROELECTRIC, and DICHROIC properties.

'tourma'linic, a. 'tourmalini'zation, n. [Geol.] The processes, effected by PNEUMATOLYSIS, by which other MINERALS become changed into t. in the earth. 'tourmalinize, v.t. Make (a substance) undergo tourmalinization.

'toughness, n. [Metal.] The property of being strong, not readily bent or changed in form, on the one hand, and not readily broken, on the other. tough, a. Having t.

'tourniquet, n. [Med.] An apparatus formed of a band or thick bit of material put round or over a part and twisted or screwed down tight so as to put a stop to loss of blood from a wound by shutting a cut ARTERY.

tox'(a)emia, n. [Med.] A diseased condition caused by taking into the blood poisons produced by BACTERIA at some damaged or diseased point in the body (see SEPTICAEMIA). tox'(a)emic, a.

toxi-. TOXIN or TOXIC: 'toxicoid, a., tox-'iferous, a.

'toxic, a. [Med.] Of, to do with, produced or poisoned by, a poison or TOXIN; poisoning, acting as a poison (to). 'toxicant, a., n. Poisoning (substance). toxi'cation, n. The process of poisoning or the condition of being poisoned. tox'icity. n. The quality of being toxicant or the degree to which a substance, etc. is toxicant; the sort and amount of a TOXIN produced by a given BACTERIUM etc.

'toxic(o)-. To do with, caused by, poison. toxico'genic, a. toxi'cology, n. The branch of medical science having to do with poisons. toxico'logic(al), aa. toxi'cologist, n.

'toxin(e), n. [Biochem., Med.] Any poison produced by a plant or animal, sp. by BACTERIA acting on food or in the body of an animal; any t. having the property of causing the forming of an ANTITOXIN in the blood of an animal attacked by it.

'toxoid, n. [Med.] A TOXIN which has gone through a process causing the loss of its poisoning properties but still has the power of causing the forming of ANTITOXINS when put into the blood of an animal, used in IMMUNIZATION.

'toxophil(e), a. [Med.] (Of a substance or RECEPTOR—see SIDE-CHAIN THEORY) having the property of uniting with TOXINS.

'toxophore, n. [Biochem.] The poison-group of a TOXIN MOLECULE.

tra'becula (trabeculae), n. [Bot.] A rod-like CELL or line of cells bridging a space between other cells or across a hollow; a thick cord-like fold or band coming out from something, sp. one of those seen on the inner side of the wall of a SPORANGIUM or across the PERISTOME teeth in MUSCI. [Zoo.] A rod-like structure or a FIBROUS band or plate forming part of the inner framework of a part, as in the heart and the SPLEEN; in the brain of the EMBRYO of a back-boned animal, one or other of two somewhat curved rods of CARTILAGE in front of and later uniting with the PARACHORDALS. **tra'becular,** a. **tra'beculate,** a.

trace, 1.n. A present mark, print, effect, etc. made by something which at one time was present or took place, sp. as now acting as a sign of this earlier event or condition; a line made by a recording instrument representative of and recording some motion or effect. [Zoo., Psych.] The after-effect of a nerve-reaction on living-substance, by which the same reaction is more readily produced another time, making learning possible and forming the physical parallel of memory, conscious or unconscious. [Bot.] *See* LEAF TRACE, BRANCH TRACE. [Chem.] A very small amount of a substance present in another substance, sp. one so small as to be unable to be measured. 2.v.t. Make a line recording (some motion, etc.), as does an instrument recording the motion of the heart; go over in detail the way taken by something moving or the steps in any development, sp. make the discovery of these by working them out from point to point forward or back. **t. 'element.** [Biochem.] A chemical ELEMENT of which only a t. or little more is needed to keep a plant or animal healthy, but that little it is impossible to do without. **'-able,** a. Which may be traced. **'tracer,** n. Sp., anything used for tracing the way taken by something, as a substance giving off smoke or flame put into a BULLET etc. for the purpose of outlining its flight, or an ISOTOPE used in the tracer method. **tracer 'method.** [Zoo., Med.] The system of tracing a substance through its motions and chemical changes in the body by the addition to it of an ISOTOPE having properties which give special chances for the observation or testing of its behaviour (*see* RADIO-ACTIVE TRACING). **'tracing,** n. Sp., a record of something in the form of a line made by an instrument on paper etc.

tra'chea (tracheae), n. [Bot.] A long water-transporting pipe running down the wood-substance of plants, formed of a line of CELLS placed end to end of which the end-walls have been, completely or in part, broken down, and the side-walls have become thick and PITTED, and from which the living cell-substance has, at full development, gone; a unit cell of a t., shorter and wider than a TRACHEID, with walls somewhat less thick and more

PITS. [Zoo.] A breathing-TUBE, sp.:- in land-living back-boned animals, the 'wind-pipe' or first part of the breathing apparatus running down the front of the neck and branching into the two chief BRONCHI; in insects, any of the chief air-pipes branching through the body and taking in air through openings in the sides of it. **tra'cheal,** a. [Biol.] **tra'cheal gill.** [Zoo.] In some water-living insect LARVAE a thin-walled pipe-like or leaf-like part on the outside of the back part of the body, taking gases through its walls from the water to the tt. inside the body with which it has a connection, and the other way round. **'tracheate,** a. [Zoo.] Breathing by tt., as insects. **trache'ation,** n. [Zoo.] The distribution and position of the tt. in the wings of an insect before the forming of the VEINS.

'tracheid(e), n. [Bot.] A long, narrow, pipe-like, non-living CELL with narrowed shut ends and thick walls, in touch with other vessels through PITS, present in wood, sp. that of evergreen trees, for giving support and transporting water. **tra'cheidal,** a. **tra'cheidal cells.** T.-like CELLS IN TRANSFUSION TISSUE.

'trachelate, a. [Biol.] Neck-like.

'trachel(o)-. [Zoo.] Neck, sp. of UTERUS; throat or TRACHEA.

trach'enchyma, n. Substance of TRACHEA of plant.

trache(o)-. [Zoo., Med.] (Of, to do with) the TRACHEA or tracheae (and ...):— **trache'itis,** n., **trache'otomy,** n.

'tracheole, n. [Zoo.] Any of the smaller, more delicate branches of the TRACHEAE of insects, through whose thin walls the exchange of O and CO_2 with other parts of the body takes place.

'tracheo'phyta, n.pl. [Bot.] All the sorts of plants in which water is transported in vessels.

tra'choma, n. [Med.] A serious CONTAGIOUS disease of the inner coating of the EYELIDS, marked by the forming of small hard grain-like outgrowths with the destruction of nerve-endings at those points, sometimes causing the loss, in part or completely, of the power of seeing. **tra'chomatous,** a.

'trachy-. [Biol.] Rough:— **'-'carpous,** a. [Bot.], **'-'glossate,** a. [Zoo.]; [Geol.] (Formed of) TRACHYTE (and ...):— **'-'andesite,** n., **'-'basalt,** n.

'trachyte, n. [Geol.] A sort of IGNEOUS ROCK (*see* p. 192), the ORTHOCLASE making up the chief part of which is generally in the form of more or less parallel flat rods, and mixed with small amounts of BIOTITE and other coloured SILICATES. **tra'chytic,** a. Of, having in it, like, t., sp. having a like structure of more or less parallel rods.

track, n. TRACE, in the form of a line of marks outlining the way something has gone, sp. a line of footprints, wheelprints, and so on, made on the earth etc. by something moving over it; a line specially made for something moving to go in or on, as that in a sound record, or the line of rails for a train. 2.v.t. Go after (something) guided by its t., get a knowledge of the way taken by something by the observation of its t. ′**tracking.** [Acous.] The process by which the needle of a RECORD PLAYER etc. keeps to the t. on a sound record; the needle's power of tracking.

tract, n. [Zoo.] A system of parts all having a connection and to do with the same purpose, as the DIGESTIVE t., sp. a group of NERVE FIBRES, gen. in the brain or SPINAL CORD, all starting and ending together

′**traction,** n. The act or power of pulling, as of an engine or muscle, or the condition of being pulled; the grip of a body, as a wheel or cord, on a SURFACE over which it is moving, keeping it from slipping— caused by FRICTION, and dependent on the surfaces, or one or the other surface, not being quite smooth. **t.** ′**engine.** A steam-engine with great wheels worked by an engine on top of the boiler, used in road-making or for pulling great weights on roads or across country. ′**-al,** a. ′**tractive,** a. Of, to do with, used in, pulling. **traction pull.** The pull, in POUNDS, of a railway engine.

′**tractor,** 1.n. [Mach.] An automobile used in farm work for pulling carts, ploughs, etc., used in place of horses in the fields; a t. propeller. 2.a. Pulling. **t. propellor.** In an airplane, a PROPELLER placed at the front so that the airplane is pulled forward by it, as opp. a PUSHER.

trade wind. [Meteor.] Any of the dry winds blowing regularly in the direction of the EQUATOR in the parts of the earth up to 30° north or south of it, from the northeast in the north part and from the southeast in the south part, caused by the effect of the turning-motion of the earth on the current of air all the time moving to the equator from colder parts.

′**traffic engi′neering.** The science of roadbuilding and design, taking special account of the need to keep VEHICLES moving with as little loss of time as possible and to make as small as possible the danger of smashes or of running into persons walking.

′**tragus,** n. [Zoo.] The rounded, back-pointing outgrowth at the front of the outer opening of the ear in higher animals.

trail, n. [Astron.] Any of the long bright lines seen sometimes at the back of a great METEOR: a line made on a camera plate by letting the IMAGE of a star go across it as opp. keeping it at one point by moving the plate.

′**trailer,** n. Any cart or other wheeled thing pulled by a TRACTOR or another cart etc.

train, n. [Mach.] A complete system of moving parts for transporting motion from one end of it to the other, as that putting the hands of a clock in connection with the chief spring. [Radio] A group of radio WAVES coming one after the other for a limited time.

tra′jectory, n. [Phys.] The curved way taken by a body moving through space under the operation of the attraction of the earth or the sun etc., as the t. of a PLANET or of something fired from a gun.

′**trama,** n. [Bot.] In an AGARIC, the somewhat loose network of HYPHAE forming the middle part of a GILL.

′**trammel,** n. An instrument for forming ELLIPSES on paper, etc.; BEAM COMPASS (freq. **tt.** or *a pair of tt.*); any of a number of measuring-instruments used in the adjustment of machines.

trance, n. [Med.] A sleep-like condition, as that produced by deep HYPNOSIS, in which there is some power of sense and motion but no memory when the person has come back to normal of what he did or said at that time.

′**tranquillize,** v.t. [Med.] Make (worked up person or nerves) quiet. ′**tranquillizer,** n. Sp. medical substance.

trans-. Across, through, over, further than; on the other side of (some named place or point on a scale).

trans-′**compound,** *trans-***form,** *trans-***position.** [Chem.] *See* CIS-TRANS ISOMERISM.

′**transcon′ductance,** n. [Elec.] The amount of the increase of the current in one part of an electric CIRCUIT for every unit increase in the e.m.f. put into it at some other point, of which MUTUAL CONDUCTANCE is a special example.

trans′crystalline, a. [Crystal., etc.] Going through the CRYSTALS themselves, not between them (said of cracks in metal etc.), opp. INTERCRYSTALLINE. **t.** ′**failure.** T. cracking, the normal sort of cracking in metals.

trans′current, a. Going across, from side to side of, something.

trans′ducer, n. [Acous., Elec., Mach.] An apparatus worked by power from one thing and handing it on, in the same or in some other form, to another thing, as the part of a telephone system where electric power is changed into sound.

′**transect,** n. [Bot.] A band marked off across a stretch of plant-growth, for example, through a wood, for observation and recording of details about the different sorts of plants making it up etc.

tran′sect, v.t. Get (something) cut across, make a division through (something).

'**transfer,** 1.v.t. Get (something) moved or changed *from* one place *to* another. 2.n. Act of tranferring; a change of place, as [Med.] of a pain from one part of the body to another. [Photog.] A camera picture which has been transferred from one SUPPORT to another by transferring the light-sensitive coating on which it has been made, gen. on thin paper. **t. of 'training.** [Psych.] The development of some power of mind or body by the training of some other power having some connection with it. **t. 'printing.** The t. of designs to vessels etc. of pot material by printing from thin paper prints taken from inked printing plates. **t. 'process.** [Photog.] Any process of making tt. '**transference,** n. Act of transferring, sp. [Psych.] the direction of old, sp. unconscious, feelings and desires to a new thing or person, as in PSYCHOANALYSIS the development of a feeling of love or hate for the medical man based on the feelings of the person in his care for the father and/or mother whose place he is taking in the SUBCONSCIOUS mind.

'**transference number.** [Phys., Chem.] In ELECTROLYSIS, that amount of all the current which is transported by any one sort of ION.

trans'form, v.t. Make undergo a complete change of form, condition, or structure, sp. [Phys.] get (one form of ENERGY) changed into another form of energy, [Elec.] get (a current) changed in VOLTAGE. '**transfor'mation,** n. Sp.:— [Phys.] RADIOACTIVE change; [Zoo.] METAMORPHOSIS; [Metal.] A change in the make-up of a solid ALLOY. '**transfor'mation 'constant.** [Phys.] DECAY CONSTANT. '**transfor'mation 'theory.** [Biol.] The old theory that it was possible for one form of living thing to become changed into some completely different form, as a plant into an animal.

trans'former, n. [Elec.] An apparatus by which the VOLTAGE of an ALTERNATING CURRENT is made higher (*step-up t.*) or lower (*step-down t.*) without changing its FREQUENCY, made up of two COILS, one of a small number of turns of thick wire and the other of a great number of turns of thin wire, a current going through the first of these causing an INDUCTION current of higher voltage in the second,and one going through the second, an induction current of lower voltage in the first.

trans'formism, n. [Biol.] The process of change from one sort to another put forward in the TRANSFORMATION THEORY; belief in the transformation theory.

trans'fuse, 1.v.t. Put (a liquid) from one vessel into another; get a liquid or gas ~ixed all through another. [Med.] Do the act or operation of transfusion. 2.v.i. (Of a liquid) go all through something or from one place to another. **trans'fusion,** n. Sp., [Med.] the operation of putting the blood of one animal or person into the blood-vessels of another, or of putting some other liquid into the blood current. **trans'fusive,** a. Which may be transfused or has a tendency to t.; to do with transfusion, sp. [Med.]. **transfusion cell.** [Bot.] A CELL with walls through which liquids go. **transfusion 'tissue.** [Bot.] Plant material made up chiefly of non-living transfusion cells, as in the leaves of certain evergreens.

trans'gression, n. [Geol.] UNCONFORMABILITY; the covering of land by water on a great scale, causing UNCONFORMABLE beds of material to be put down on older beds. **trans'gressive,** a. [Geol.] Pushing over the top of other material by degrees, causing UNCONFORMABILITY.

'**transient,** 1.a. In existence, taking place, for only a short time. 2.n. Anything t., sp. not part of a regular process or development. [Acous.] A t. sound. [Elec.] A sudden short change in a current caused by a sudden and irregular increase of VOLTAGE, etc. '**transience,** n.

tran'silient, 1.a. [Zoo.] Joining parts of the brain which have other parts in between, said of nerves. [Biol.] (Of changes) sudden, as that producing a SPORT.

'**transillumi'nation,** n. [Med.] The process of sending light through the walls of a hollow part of the body to see what their condition is.

tran'sistor, n. [Radio] An apparatus using a very small plate of GERMANIUM CRYSTAL with three ELECTRODES in place of a THERMIONIC VALVE, sp. for AMPLIFYING radio SIGNALS, so making possible a very much smaller form of radio RECEIVER.

'**transit,** 1.n. The act or condition of journeying or being transported, sp. across, through, or over something. [Astron.] The seeming motion of a body in the sky across the MERIDIAN of the place of observation, caused by the turning motion of the earth; the motion of one body in the sky across the face of another as seen from the earth, for example of a PLANET across the sun. [Surveying] A t. theodolite. 2.v.t. [Astron., Surveying] Get a t. telescope or t. theodolite turned over in an upright plane. [Astron.] (Of a body in the sky) make a t., go across the field of view or the face of another body. **t. 'instrument, t. 'telescope.** [Astron.] A TELESCOPE supported at the middle on a level east-to-west AXIS round which it may be turned in the plane of the MERIDIAN, used for the observation of the times of t. of stars. **t. the'odolite.** [Surveying] A THEODOLITE with a

TELESCOPE able to be transited.
tran′sition, n. A change, or the process of change, from one condition or stage to another. **t. ′elements**. [Chem.] The ELEMENTS such as Fe, Co, Ni, coming in the middle of any of the two-line groups going across the PERIODIC TABLE, which are different from one another chiefly in the degree to which the inner SHELL of ELECTRONS is complete, and so have a number of like properties. **t. point, t. ′temperature**. [Phys.-Chem.] The TEMPERATURE at which one PHASE of a substance is changed into another or at which the two are in EQUILIBRIUM, sp. of the change from one CRYSTALLINE form of a substance to another. **t. ′region**. [Bot.] That part of a young plant where root structure becomes changed into the structure of an up-forcing stem. **trans′itional**, a. Of, to do with, produced in the process of, being, a t. **transitional epi′thelium**. [Zoo.] A sort of EPITHELIUM such as that covering the inside of the BLADDER and like parts in back-boned animals, formed of only three or four coats of CELLS, new growth being effected by the MITOSIS of the cells of the lowest coat.

′transitory, a. Going on or present for only a short time.

trans′lation, n. [Mech.] A motion of a body in which all points of it are moving at the same rate in the same direction. **trans′lational, trans′latory**, aa.

translo′cation, n. [Biol.] The moving of part of a CHROMOSOME to another chromosome, or to a different place in the same one. [Bot.] The transport of food substances in water from one part of a plant, such as the leaves, to the parts needing them. **translo′catory**, a.

trans′lucent, trans′lucid, aa.(Of a substance, etc.) letting light through, but with such irregular changes in the direction of the rays that it is not possible to see things clearly through it, as a mist, waxed paper, etc.

trans′median, a. [Zoo.] (Of muscles) going across the middle plane of the body.

′transmi′gration, n. A motion across or through something to a new place, sp. [Med.] the going of LEUCOCYTES through the walls of blood-vessels.

trans′mission, n. The act or process of transmitting something. [Mach.] The apparatus by which motion is transmitted from the engine of an automobile to the rod turning the wheels. [Optics] The power of t., measured by the RATIO of the amount of light transmitted by something, as a plate of glass etc., to the amount falling on it. [Elec.] Sp., the transporting of electric power over a distance. **t. coe′fficient, t. ′ratio**. [Optics]

T. t. dyna′mometer. An apparatus for measuring the power of a machine at work without using or wasting any of this power. **t. ef′ficiency**. [Elec.] In electric and radio systems etc., the RATIO of the output to the intake of power. **t. loss**. [Elec.] The loss of power in a radio wave or electric current in the process of t. **t. unit**. [Elec.] Old name for DECIBEL. **trans′missible**, a. Which may be transmitted. **trans′missive**, a. (Designed for) transmitting something; transmissible. **transmis′sivity**, n. Property or power of transmitting. **trans′mit**, v.t. and i. Send, give (to some other thing), let through, get handed on, sp. an effect or property, such as force, light, motion, feeling, or the qualities handed on to a living thing by those producing it. [Radio] Send out news etc. by radio waves. **trans′mittance**, n. T. or the power of t., sp. [Optics]. **trans′mitted**, a. **trans′mitter**, n. Sp.:—[Elec.] Any apparatus which transmits electric current or power into a system, sp. the part of a telephone for talking into, where sound waves are changed into electric waves, or the instrument by which telegrams are sent; [Radio] A transmitting apparatus or station, sp. that part of the first by which electric current is changed into radio waves.

′transmis′someter, n. [Phys.] An instrument for measuring the amount of light or other ENERGY which a body lets through.

′transmu′tation, n. The changing of one thing into another, sp.:— [Biol.] of one SPECIES into another; [Phys.-Chem.] of one ELEMENT into another, naturally, as in RADIOACTIVITY, or by firing NEUTRONS etc. at a substance and so causing a reaction by which the NUCLEI of its ATOMS are changed. **trans′mute**, v.t. Make (something) undergo t. (into something).

trans′parent, a. (Of a substance, etc.) letting light-rays through in a regular way, so that things may be clearly seen through it, as glass. **trans′parency**, n. The quality of being t.; a camera picture on glass or other t. substance designed to be seen by light coming through it.

′transpi′ration, n. [Biol.] The act or process of transpiring. **trans′piratory**, a. Of, to do with, t. **trans′pire**, 1.v.i. [Biol.] (Of an animal, plant, or part) give off something in the form of a gas through the skin, sp. [Bot.] give off WATER VAPOUR, chiefly through the STOMATA of the leaves, a process helping to keep the food-current moving through the plant; (of liquid etc.) be given off through the skin in the form of gas. [Phys.] (Of a gas) go through a POROUS substance or go in a current through a long narrow pipe. 2.v.t. Give off in the form of a gas.

trans'plant, v.t. Get (a plant) uprooted from its place and planted again in another. [Zoo., Med.] Take out a part of the body of an animal and put it in the body of another animal, or in a different place in the same animal, to undergo growth there, as in GRAFTING, but used of parts, such as teeth, with which the uniting of TISSUE does not necessarily take place.

'transport 'number. TRANSFERENCE NUMBER.

trans'pose, v.t. Get the places of (two things) exchanged, make a change in the order of things, as t. letters in a word. [Elec.] Take (telegraph or telephone wires) across one another at regular points, so that the left wire becomes the right, etc., to overcome the effects of INDUCTION. transpo'sition, n. Act of transposing or condition of being transposed, sp. [Med.] of a part of the body placed at a different point, gen. on the opposite side, from the normal. transpo'sitional, a.

'transpy'loric. [Med.] (Of a level plane or line through man's body) cutting the PYLORUS.

'transudate, n. [Med.] A transuded substance, sp. a thin liquid, formed almost completely of the liquid part of blood, coming through the walls of blood-vessels as the effect of their stopping up at some point. transu'dation, n. The process of transuding; a t. transu'datory, a. tran'sude, 1.v.i. (Of a liquid) come slowly through the small holes in a MEMBRANE or a body-material such as the skin. 2.v.t. Be sent out through (a material etc., such as skin); make (a liquid) t.

'transur'anic, a. [Chem.] (Of an ELEMENT) having a greater at. no. than URANIUM; to do with the group of t. elements, all of which are man-made by TRANSMUTATION.

trans'versal, a. [Biol.] TRANSVERSE.

trans'verse, a. Being across or between from side to side, in a direction at right angles to longways; wider than it is long. t. 'colon. [Zoo.] That part of the COLON in man which goes across the body from right to left. t. 'magnet. [Phys.] A plate of iron or steel longer than it is wide which has been MAGNETIZED so that the POLES are at the opposite sides, in place of, as normally, at the opposite ends. t. 'process. [Zoo.] In back-boned animals, a sideways outgrowth of a VERTEBRA—in man etc., one or the other of two coming out left and right from the NEURAL ARCH and supporting the end of a RIB, in lower animals, a PARA-POPHYSIS. t. wave. [Phys.] A wave in which the VIBRATIONS are at right angles to the direction in which the wave is moving. trans'versely, adv. Sp. [Bot.] of the named longer-than-wide form,

but joined to the plant by one of its longer sides, not, as commonly, by one end. trans'verso-. [Biol.] T. (and . . .); transversely. [Zoo.] (Of, to do with) a t. process (and . . .).

trans'versus, n. [Zoo.] Any of a number of small TRANSVERSE muscles.

trap, n. Any of a number of parts, sp. in water-systems, letting one sort of thing go through and keeping back another, as a *steam t.* in an engine by which water formed from steam is let out without letting any steam out; in a drain-pipe from a basin etc., a bent part keeping a certain amount of water in it so that gas from the lower drains is unable to come up the pipe.

trap for'mation. [Geol.] The forming of land into a step-like structure caused by the unequal weathering of beds, very frequently seen where country has been overrun by one coat after another of LAVA. trap or trap rock or trap'pean rock. Old name for solid LAVA or other sorts of ROCK with a tendency to t. f., now used as a common name for a great number of FINE-GRAINED, dark-coloured, IGNEOUS ROCKS. trapp'ean, a. To do with t. f., or of or like trap rock.

tra'pezium, n. [Geom.] (In England) a plane form made up of 4 straight sides of which only two are parallel; (U.S.A.) a TRAPEZ-OID in the English sense. [Zoo.] The first bone of the second line of CARPAL bones; a parcel of FIBRES going across the lower part of the PONS VAROLII. t. effect. [Phys.] The effect produced in a CATHODE RAY TUBE when the VOLTAGES on the DE-FLECTOR PLATES are unbalanced, causing the outline on the screen to take the form of a t. in place of a square. tra-'peziform, a. Like a t. in form.

tra'pezius, n. [Zoo.] One or other of the two great flat 3-sided muscles in the neck and upper part of the back by which the arm or front leg is lifted.

'trapezo'hedron, n. [Geom., Cryst.] A solid form of which the faces are TRAPEZIUMS. 'trapezo'hedral, a.

'trapezoid, 1.n. [Geom.] (In England) a 4-sided plane form with no two sides parallel; (U.S.A.) a TRAPEZIUM in the English sense. 2.a. Formed like a t. or TRAPEZIUM. trape'zoidal, a.

'trauma (traumata), n. [Med.] A wound or other violent damage to any part of the body; a damaging shock to the mind (freq. *psychic t.*). trau'matic, a. [Med., Bot.] To do with or caused by a t. of any sort or, in plants, by physical damage. 'traumatism, n. [Med.] The unhealthy condition of the system caused by a t. [Bot.] The condition of being damaged. 'traumatize, v.t. [Med.] Make a wound in, do damage to, for example in an

operation. **trauma'tology, trauma'tosis,**
n. [Med.] n. Traumatism.

'traumato'nasty, n. [Bot.] The curving of a
part of a plant after being wounded.

trau'matropism, n. [Bot.] TROPISM in
reaction to a wound, TRAUMATONASTY
'trauma'tropic, a.

traumo'tax-is, -y, nn. [Biol.] The motions of
CELLS or NUCLEI as the effect of wounding.

'travel, v.i. Go from place to place. [Mach.]
(Of a moving part) go in its motion (a
certain distance or in a certain direction).
'traveller, n. [Mach.] A moving part or
apparatus used for transporting some
other thing. **'travelling,** a. Sp., (of an
instrument etc.) moving, or able to be
moved or taken from place to place.

'traverse, 1.v.t. Go over or be across (a
distance, etc.). 2.n. [Mach.] A part going
across; a side-to-side motion of a part.
[Surveying] T. survey, **t. 'survey.** [Sur-
veying] A map of a road, bit of country,
etc. in which the curves are paralleled
by measured straight lines joined end to
end at measured angles from turning-
point to turning-point. **'traversing,** n. The
making of t. surveys.

'travertine, n. [Mineral.] Natural CRYSTAL-
LINE $CaCO_3$, put down by spring waters,
sp. warm springs, of which some sorts are
very solid and beautifully banded with
colour, others somewhat sponge-like in
structure—used in building.

tread, n. [Mach.] That part of the wheel of a
carriage, engine, automobile etc., which
comes in touch with the earth or a rail
of a railway etc. line.

treat, v.t. Make (a substance) undergo some
process, the operation of some other
substance, etc. [Med.] Give (a person)
medical attention (*for* some disease or
condition); make use of medical processes
or substances to get the better of (a
disease or condition) or make (a wound)
well. **'-ment,** n. [Med.] Act or process of
treating a disease or ill person, sp. the
way of doing this, the processes and
substances used for this purpose.

tree, n. [Bot.] A tall (roughly from 10 to
200 feet), PERENNIAL, wood-forming plant
having a clearly marked, thick middle
stem for at least some part of its growth,
and gen. not branching before a point
some feet up from the earth, as opp. a
SHRUB.

'trefoil, n., a. [Bot.] (Flower or leaf) having
3 leaves or deep-cut divisions round a
common middle.

treg(a)-. [Elec.] 10^{12} times: **'tregadyne,** n.,
tregohm, n.

'Trema'toda, n.pl. [Zoo.] A CLASS of PLATY-
HELMINTHES, with a hard skin covering
the body, a forked INTESTINE, and one or
more SUCKERS for fixing themselves in
place, all of which are PARASITES going

through a complex process of development and living their last stage in the
LIVER, intestine, blood-vessels, or LUNGS
of a back-boned animal, sometimes
causing serious disease. **'trematode,** n., a.
(Animal) of, like, the T.

'tremble, v.i. Be moved by a shaking motion.
be shaking, sp. of a person as the effect of
disease or great cold, or of some strong
feeling such as fear. **'trembler,** n. [Elec.]
A part in quick motion to and from an
ELECTROMAGNET so as to keep starting
and stopping an electric CIRCUIT, as in an
electric bell. **'trembling,** n., a.

'tremelloid, 'tremullose, aa. [Bot.] Jelly-like.

'tremor, n. A shaking motion, as a not very
violent shaking of the earth, sp. [Med.]
an automatic shaking of the body or a
part of it caused by loss of control of the
muscles, seen in persons who are very
old, or moved by very strong feeling, and
in certain diseases.

trench 'fever. [Med.] A disease caused by a
VIRUS transported by LICE, common in
the armies of the 1914-18 war, marked
by attacks of FEVER coming back from
time to time and pains in the head, back,
arms, and legs. **trench foot.** [Med.] A
condition of the feet marked by hard,
thick, red places sometimes becoming
GANGRENOUS, caused by their being
cold and wet for a long time, common in
armies fighting under such conditions.
trench mouth. [Med.] A disease of the
throat and mouth caused by a BACILLUS,
or sometimes by not getting enough
VITAMIN C, common in armies in the field.

tre'pan, 1.v.t. TREPHINE. 2.n. An instrument for trepanning, the place of which
has now been taken by the trephine.
trepa'nation, n.

tre'phine, 1.v.t. [Med.] Take a round bit of
bone out of (the SKULL) for the purpose of
making the PRESSURE on the brain less
or doing an operation on the brain; take
out a round bit from some other part,
for example, from the eye in GLAUCOMA.
2.n. A medical instrument for cutting out
a round bit, sp. one of pipe-like form with
a toothed cutting-edge for trephining the
skull.

tri-. 3, having 3 of the parts or things
named:— **-'androus,** a., **-'coty'ledonous,**
a., **-'cyclic,** a. [Chem.], **-'flagellate,** a,
-'lateral, a., **-'linear,** a., **-'lobate,** a.
-'locular, a., **-'nodal,** a. **-'polar,** a.
Sp. [Biol.], **-'septate,** a., **-'sporous,** a.
etc.

tri'actinal, tri'actine, aa. [Zoo.] Having
3 rays, said sp. of sponge SPICULES.

'triad, n. A group of 3. [Chem.] An ATOM,
group, or substance with a VALENCY
of 3.

'triangle, n. [Geom.] A plane form with
3 straight sides meeting in 3 angles. **t. of**

forces. [Mech.] A t. whose sides are representative in measure and direction of 3 forces balancing one another at a point; the rule that if 3 forces acting at a point are in balance, a t. may be formed of 3 lines representative of their measures and directions, taken in order—and the other way round. **tri'angular,** a. Having the form of a t.

tri'angulate, 1.a. Made up of, marked with, TRIANGLES. 2.v.t. Get land measured by TRIANGULATION.

tri'angu'lation, n. [Surveying etc.] The system or operation of measuring great stretches of land by starting from a measured base-line, forming a TRIANGLE on that with the third angle at a given point some distance away, measuring the base angles with a THEODOLITE and so getting the measure of the sides, and then using one of these as the base of a further triangle, and so on; the network of triangles into which a stretch of land is marked out for the purpose of t.

'triarch, a. [Bot.] Made up of 3 parallel parcels of wood substance, as the middle part of some roots.

'Trias, n. [Geol.] The PERIOD in the earth's history forming the first division of the MESOZOIC ERA from about 200 to 170 million years back; the SYSTEM OF ROCKS of that time, in which SANDSTONE is common. **Tri'assic,** 1.a., 2.n. The T. period (*see* p. 558).

tri'basic, a. [Chem.] (Of an ACID) having 3 H ATOMS of which the place may be taken by metal atoms, and so forming 3 sorts of SALTS.

tribe, n. [Biol.] Name given sometimes to a SUB-ORDER or a division of a sub-order greater than a FAMILY, but gen. to one or the other parallel divisions of a family.

'tribo-. [Phys.] To do with or caused by rubbing: **'-e'lectric,** a., **'-elec'tricity,** n., **'-fluor'escence,** n., etc.

'tribolumi'nescence, n. [Phys.] The giving out of light by certain CRYSTALS, as sugar, when rubbed together or crushed. **tribolumi'nescent,** a.

tri'bometer, n. [Phys.] An instrument for measuring the force needed for pushing a given body over another, that is, the amount of FRICTION between them.

'tribo'phospho'rescence, n. [Phys.] TRIBOLUMINESCENCE in which light is given out for some time after the rubbing has come to an end.

'tributary, n. [Geol.] A river joining and sending its waters into a greater river.

'triceps, n. [Zoo.] A muscle with 3 heads, sp. the great muscle at the back of the upper arm. **tri'cipital,** a. [Zoo.] Of a part, sp. a muscle, having 3 heads or starting-points by which it is joined: to do with a t.

tri'chiasis, n. [Med.] A turning-in of the hairs round the eye, causing it to become INFLAMED etc. by rubbing.

trichi'niasis, trichi'nosis, nn. [Med.] A serious disease caused by getting certain hair-like NEMATODE worms from pig-meat into the INTESTINE and from there into the muscles.

'trichite, n. [Geol.] A thin thread-like or hair-like CRYSTAL, such as is seen freq. in groups in LAVA. [Bot.] The sort of long, thin, needle-like crystal which in theory is the chief unit of structure of STARCH grains in plants. [Zoo.] A hair-like sponge-SPICULE.

'trich(o)-. (A) hair:— **'trichoid,** a., **'trich-ology,** n.

tricho'carpous, a. [Bot.] Having fruit covered with hair.

'trichocyst, n. [Zoo.] Any of certain very small hair-like bodies present under the skin of some CILIOPHORA and able to be pushed out, possibly for gripping.

tri'chogenous, a. [Zoo.] Hair-producing, said sp. of the CELLS under the skin of insects and other ARTHROPODA by which the hair-like or hard, needle-like structures covering the body are produced.

'trichogyne, n. [Bot.] A hair-like part at the end of the part producing female GERM-CELLS in some ALGAE and FUNGI, helping to take in the male gamete. **'tricho'gyn-ial, -ic,** aa.

'trichome, n. [Bot.] Any hair-like outgrowth from the skin of a plant. **tri'chomic,** a.

'trichophore, n. [Bot.] The CELL or group of cells producing a TRICHOGYNE. [Zoo.] Any of the bag-like parts from which the stiff short 'hairs' on the skin of CHAETO-PODA come.

Trich'optera, n.pl. [Zoo.] An ORDER of ENDOPTERYGOTE insects with bodies and wings covered with hair, living in inland water in the LARVA stage inside a pipe-like cover which they get coated with bits of stick, stone, sand, leaves etc.

tri'chosis, n. [Zoo.] The distribution of the hair on an animal. [Med.] Any diseased condition of the hair.

tri'chotomy, n. Division into 3 parts, branches, groups. **tricho'tomic, tri-'chotomous,** aa. Sp., [Bot.] having 3 equal or almost equal branches coming from the same part of the stem.

-trichous, a. [Zoo.] Having hair of the sort named.

tri'chroism, n. [Phys.] The property seen in some CRYSTALS of being of 3 different colours when viewed in different directions.

'trichro'matic, a. To do with, having, formed of, using, 3 colours. **'trichro-mat, -mate,** nn. [Psych.] A person who may be made to see all colours in his experience by the use together of 3 STIMULI, red, blue, and green, but is not able to see all colours with less than these three stimuli, that is, a person whose power of seeing colour is normal. **t. 'process.** THREE-COLOUR PROCESS. **t. 'theory (of 'colour 'vision).** [Zoo., Psych.] The theory that the seeing apparatus has 3 different structures for giving a reaction to the 3 different STIMULI of red, green, and blue light, all other colours being produced by the uniting of the sense-effects produced by these three. **tri'chromatism,** n. The condition of a trichromat.

'trichur'iasis, n. [Med.] Disease caused by certain NEMATODE worms, of whip-like form, narrowing from a round base to a hair-like end, in the INTESTINE.

'trickle charge. [Elec.] A CHARGE produced by a trickle charger. **'trickle 'charger.** [Elec.] An apparatus for CHARGING a STORAGE BATTERY with a very small current going in all the time.

tri'clinic, a. [Cryst.] Having 3 unequal AXES of which no two are at right angles. **t. 'system.** The division in the grouping of CRYSTALS which is made up of t. crystals.

tri'colour, a. TRICHROMATIC.

tri'cuspid, a. 3-pointed, sp. [Zoo.]. [Zoo.] To do with the t. valve. **t. valve.** [Zoo.] The t. VALVE between the two divisions of the heart on the right-hand side in MAMMALS. **'-ate,** a. T., sp. [Bot.] of a leaf.

tri'cyanide, n. [Chem.] A substance formed of one ELEMENT or RADICAL united with 3 CYANOGEN (C_2N_2) groups.

tri'ennial, a. Coming about once in every three years. [Bot.] Going on for three years.

'trifid, a. Having 3 narrow points, sp. [Bot.] (of a leaf etc.) cut about halfway to the base into 3 finger-like divisions.

tri'foliate(d), aa. [Bot.] Having 3 leaves or leaf-like parts coming from the same point; (of a complex leaf) made up of 3 small leaves (see picture p. 223).

tri'furcate(d), aa. With 3 forks or branches.

tri'gamma, n. [Zoo.] The 3-branched fork formed by the VEINS of the wing in LEPIDOPTERA.

'trigamous, a. [Bot.] Having male, female, and two-sexed flowers in the same CAPITULUM.

tri'geminal, a. [Zoo.] 3-branched, or ranged in 3 lines; to do with the t. nerve. **t nerve.** The 5TH CRANIAL NERVE, having three chief branches, one going to the eye, for seeing, one to the upper mouth-bone for feeling pain, etc., and one to the muscles by which the lower mouth-bone is worked.

'trigger, n. The part of a gun which is pulled by the finger to make it go off; any of a number of things by which processes over which they have no further control are put in motion, as [Chem.] the substance which gives the start to a CHAIN REACTION.

'trigon, n. A 3-angled form, a TRIANGLE. [Zoo.] The cutting part formed of 3 points of an upper MOLAR tooth.

'trigonal, a. To do with, being in the form of, a TRIANGLE. [Zoo.] To do with the TRIGON or TRIGONE. [Cryst.] HEXAGONAL with three equal AXES. **t. system.** [Cryst.] The CRYSTAL group formed of t. crystals. looked on by some authorities as a separate system (**t. system**) by others as a division (**t. class**) of the HEXAGONAL SYSTEM (see p. 99).

'trigone, tri'gonium, nn. [Zoo.] A roughly 3-sided, 3-angled space, sp. that on the inner side of the BLADDER between the openings of the URETERS and the URETHRA.

'trigo'nometry, n. The branch of mathematics having to do with the relations between the sides and angles of TRIANGLES. **trigono'metric(al),** aa. **'trigono-'metric(al) 'ratios** [Geom.] The 6 RATIOS between any two sides of a right-angled TRIANGLE, whose value is dependent on one or the other of the other two angles, that is, SINE, TANGENT, COSINE, COTANGENT, SECANT, COSECANT.

tri'hydrate, n. [Chem.] A substance in which 3 MOLECULES of water are united with one molecule of some other substance.

tri'hydric, a. [Chem.] Having in it 3 HO groups, sp. with every one united to a different C ATOM.

trill, 1.n. [Phonet.] A quick VIBRATION of one part of the mouth against another, for example of the tongue against the front part of the roof of the mouth, or of the lips against one another, in forming SPEECH sounds. 2.v.t. Get (a sound) formed, say, with a t. **trilled,** a. Formed with a t., as a *trilled 'r'*.

'trillion, n. In England, 1,000,000 BILLION; in U.S.A., 1,000 billion.

'Trilo'bita, n.pl. [Zoo.] A CLASS of ARTHROPODA from $\frac{4}{5}$ cm. to 10 cm. long, which were common in the early part of the PALAEOZOIC and went out of existence near its end, having a flat body about half as wide as its middle point as it is long, curving regularly to almost pointed ends, and marked on the under-side into 3 long divisions, a head with a wide, CRESCENT-like cover, united in one with the back-covering and having two eyes on its top side, delicate legs with two branches, and freely-moving THORAX divisions freq. giving the animal the power of rolling itself into a ball. **tri'lobite,** n., a. (Animal) of the T. **trilo'bitic,** a.

tri'meric, a. [Chem.] (Of a COMPOUND) made up of the same substances in the same amounts in relation to one another as another compound, but having 3 times

its MOLECULAR WEIGHT, said of substances produced by POLYMERIZATION.
'trimer, n. A substance t. with another.
'trimerous, a. [Bot.] (With parts) in groups of 3 or some number of times 3.
'tri'methylene, n. CYCLOPROPANE,
'tri'metric 'system. [Cryst.] ORTHORHOMBIC SYSTEM.
'trimon'oecious, a. [Bot.] TRIGAMOUS.
tri'morphism. [Chem., Cryst.] A substance's power of forming 3 different sorts of CRYSTALS. [Biol.] The existence of 3 different forms of one SPECIES of animal or plant. [Bot.] The producing by one plant of 3 different forms of a certain part, sp. a flower. tri'morphic, a. Sp., [Biol.]. tri'morphous, a. Sp., [Chem.] Cryst.].
tri'nitr(o)-. [Chem.] Having 3 NO₂ groups, sp. in place of H.
tri'nitro'phenol, n. PICRIC ACID.
'trinitro'toluene, n. [Chem.] C₇H₅(NO₂)₃, a yellow CRYSTALLINE solid with great EXPLOSIVE power, made by the reaction of TOLUENE with NITRIC ACID (HNO₃) and SULPHURIC ACID (H₂SO₄).
tri'nomial, a. [Biol.] (Of names) formed of 3 words, or (of systems) using t. names.
'triode, n. [Phys.] A THERMIONIC VALVE having a CATHODE, an ANODE, and a GRID for controlling the current of ELECTRONS going from the first to the second.
tri'(o)ecious, a. [Bot.] (Of a sort of plant) producing male, female, and two-sexed flowers on different plants.
'triose, n.[Chem.] Any SUGAR having three O ATOMS in the MOLECULE, that is, of the simplest sort.
tri'partite, a. Made up of 3 parts, having 3 divisions. [Bot.] (Of a leaf) with 3 divisions separated almost to the base.
tri'phenyl'methane, n. [Chem.] CH.(C₆H₅)₃, a CRYSTALLINE substance without colour from which are produced an important group of DYES (t. dyes).
triple, 1.a. 3 times as great, as much; having 3 parts, ranged in 3's, etc. 2.v.t. Make 3 times as great in number or amount. t. bond. [Chem.] A connection between two ATOMS having a VALENCY of 3 using unnecessarily all 3 units of uniting power, so that it is possible for the two still to take on 4 ATOMS of some substance with a valency of 1, or two with a valency of 2. t. (-ex'pansion) 'engine. [Engin.] A steam engine in which the steam undergoes expansion in 3 stages, going first into a vessel where the PRESSURE is high, then into one where it is lower, and then into one where it is low. t. point. [Phys.-Chem.] A point representative of the TEMPERATURE and PRESSURE at which the solid, gas, and liquid forms of a substance are in EQUILIBRIUM. trip'licity, n. tripli-, triplo-.

'triplet, n. A group of 3 like things present together, sp. grouped or united in some way, as [Phys.] 3 lines in a SPECTRUM which are very near together or united into one. [Zoo.] Any one of 3 offspring, sp. babies, produced at a birth.
'triplex, a. Having, made up of, 3 like parts, done in 3 stages. T. glass. Trade name for glass made up of 3 plates so as to make it very hard to get broken.
'triplicate, 1.a. Of which there are 3 same things, parts, copies, etc. 2.n. Any one of 3 like things, copies, examples. 3.v.t. Make 3 copies, examples, of. tripli'cation, n. 'triplicative, a.
triplo'blastic, a. [Zoo.] Having in the EMBRYO 3 different coats of CELLS, the outer (ectoderm), the inner (endoderm) and the middle one (mesoderm), from which the different parts of the body are produced by further development, as all METAZOA but COELENTERATES.
'triploid, a. [Biol.] Having 3 times the HAPLOID number of CHROMOSOMES.
'tripod, n. A 3-legged support, as for a camera. 'tripodal, a. T.-like, having 3 leg-like or feet-like parts, sp. [Zoo.] (of a bone) having 3 points or outgrowths.
tri'quetrous, a. Having 3 sharp edges or angles, sp. [Bot.] (of a stem) having 3 hollowed sides meeting in 3 sharp edges.
tri'radia-l, -te, aa. [Biol.] Having 3 rays, or parts raying out from a middle point.
tri'sect, v.t. Make division of into 3 parts, sp. 3 equal parts. tri'sected, a. tri'section, n.
tri'serial, a. [Biol.] Ranged in 3 groups or lines. [Bot.] (Of a flower) having only 3 rings of flower-parts.
'trismus, n. [Med.] A condition in which the upper and lower parts of the mouth are locked together, sp. by an unbroken CONTRACTION of the muscles, as in TETANUS.
tri'somic, a. [Biol.] (Of a NUCLEUS or living thing) DIPLOID for all CHROMOSOMES but one sort, of which 3 are present. 'trisome, n. A t. being or NUCLEUS.
tri'stearin, n. [Chem., Biochem.] A white solid formed by the reaction of GLYCERINE and STEARIC ACID, present in plant and animal fats, sp. in the harder sorts.
'tristichous, a. [Biol.] Ranged in 3 lines, sp. [Bot.] 3 upright lines.
tritan'omaly, n. [Optics., Psych.] A form of DEFECTIVE COLOUR VISION in which a person, though normal in being a TRICHROMAT, sees the blue part of the SPECTRUM more feebly than a normal person.
'tritan'opia, n. [Optics, Psych.] An uncommon form of DICHROMATISM in which a person is unable to see different CHROMATIC colours in the blue and yellow

part of the SPECTRUM—earlier named '*blue-yellow blindness*'.

'tritium, n. [Chem.] A RADIOACTIVE ISOTOPE of H of mass 3, sign T, produced by the BOMBARDMENT of DEUTERONS by DEUTERONS.

trito'cerebr-on, -um, n. [Zoo.] In insects and CRUSTACEA, the united GANGLIA of the third division of the head, forming a part of the 'brain'. 'trito'cerebral, a.

'triton, n. [Chem.] The NUCLEUS of the TRITIUM ATOM, made up of one PROTON and two NEUTRONS, used in the HYDROGEN BOMB.

'tritor, n. [Zoo.] The crushing face of a tooth.

tritu'bercular, a. [Zoo.] (Of teeth) having 3 rounded points. tritu'berculy, n. [Zoo.] The condition of being t. or having t. teeth; a theory of the development of MOLAR teeth in higher animals by the addition of first one and then two more points to the one point of the earliest forms, and then the moving of these 3 chief points to different positions and the growth of new points etc. to give them their present complex form.

'tritural, a. [Zoo.] (Of a part, as a tooth) designed for crushing.

tritu'rate, 1.v.t. [Chem.] Get rubbed or crushed to the smallest-grained powder, sp. under a liquid. 2.n. A triturated substance, sp. one used for medical purposes. 'triturable, a. Able to be triturated. tritu'ration, n. Process of triturating. [Med.] A t. 'triturator, n. Sp. an apparatus for triturating medical substances.

tri'valent, a. [Chem.] Having a VALENCY of 3.

'trocar, n. [Med.] A rod-like, sharp-pointed instrument, used for putting through the wall of a hollow part of the body to make an outlet for liquid, or slipped through a pipe which it is desired to put into a wound or part for draining it, and slipped out again when the pipe has been worked into position.

'trochal, a. [Zoo.] Wheel-like in form.

'trochanter, n. [Zoo.] In back-boned animals, an outgrowth on the top end of the long bone of the upper part of the leg, of which there are generally two (in man, the *greater t.* and the *lesser t.*), though sometimes only one and sometimes 3, to which muscles used in moving the leg in different directions are fixed; the second division from the base of an insect's leg. tro'chanteric, a.

'trochate, a. [Zoo.] Wheel-like in form; TROCHIFEROUS.

'Trochel'minthes, n.pl. A PHYLUM of METAZOA made up of very small water animals without body divisions, moving by the use of CILIA.

'Trochidae, n.pl. [Zoo.] A FAMILY of GASTROPODA living in the sea and having a SHELL twisting regularly from a flat

base to a pointed top, looking like a pointed hat on the animal's back when it is moving. 'trochid, n., a. (Animal) of the T.

troch'iferous, a. [Zoo.] Having a round, flat, wheel-like part.

'trochlea, n. [Zoo.] Any part giving the suggestion of a PULLEY, such as an opening or narrow hollow in a bone through which a TENDON goes, sp. at the lower end of the long bone of the upper arm (or front leg) and the leg. (or back leg). 'trochlear, a. trochlear 'muscle. [Zoo.] In back-boned animals, the upper of the two eye-muscles near the nose, the TENDON of which goes through a ring of LIGAMENT (the *t. of the orbit*) in the upper back part of the eye-hollow. trochlear nerve. [Zoo.] In back-boned animals, the 4th nerve of the head, going to the trochlear muscle.

troch(o)-. [Zoo.] Wheel-like.

'trochoid, 1.a. [Zoo.] Wheel-like in form; of, to do with, like, the TROCHIDAE or their SHELL; (having the power of) turning on a middle point, line, or PIVOT, like a wheel. 2.n. [Geom.] The curve made by any point on the edge of a circle rolling like a wheel on a flat pane. tro'choidal, a. [Geom.].

'trocho-phore, -sphere, nn. [Zoo.] The sort of small free-swimming LARVA, gen. egg-like in form, common among water worms, molluscs etc., marked by a band of CILIA going round the middle of the body in front of the mouth, and another group of cilia at the upper end forming an instrument of sense.

'trochus, n. [Zoo.] The inner, more forward, of the two rings of CILIA in ROTIFERA.

'troglodite, n. [Anthrop.] CAVE DWELLER.

'trolley, n. A wheeled cart or box running on an overhead rail; a wheel or other apparatus running on an overhead electric wire and taking current, which is sent on to street electric transport through a long rod etc.

'trona, n. [Mineral.] URAD.

tro'peic, a. [Zoo.] CARINATE.

trophal'laxis, n. [Zoo.] The exchange of food between animals, as in societies of insects between the LARVAE or young and the others, or between an animal of a different sort and those forming the society in which it is living as a friend.

troph'amnion, n. [Zoo.] In the eggs of some insects, a coat of PROTOPLASM round the part where development is taking place, from which the young animal gets food.

'trophi, n.pl. [Zoo.] The mouth-parts in insects and ROTIFERA.

'trophic, a. [Biol.] To do with the use of food by the system of an animal, with growth and development as dependent on food.

troph(o)-. [Biol.] Food, the building up of living things by food.

'trophoblast, n. [Zoo.] The special outer coat of the CHORION of a higher animal, coming in touch with the PLACENTA and uniting the EMBRYO to it, freq. causing destruction of the outer skin of the placenta so as to take food from the mother to the EMBRYO.

'trophocyte, n. [Zoo.] Any of the great CELLS of the FAT BODY in insects.

'trophoderm, n. [Zoo.] TROPHOBLAST.

'trophodisc, n. [Zoo.] A mass of food-storing CELLS round eggs or SPERMATOZOA.

tropho'geneic, a. [Biol.] (Of special forms, properties) caused by special food, by taking food different in quality or amount from that taken by other forms, opp. BLASTOGENIC.

'tropho'nema (trophonemata), n. [Zoo.] In CHONDRICHTHYES which give birth to living young, any of the thread-like outgrowths on the inside of the UTERUS producing a liquid food for the EMBRYO.

tropho'nucleus, n. [Zoo.] In PROTOZOA such as TRYPANOSOMES, the true NUCLEUS, looked on as controlling food processes and growth, as opp. the KINETONUCLEUS.

'trophophore, n. [Zoo.] In sponges, a group of CELLS which later undergoes development into a GEMMULE.

'trophoplasm, n. [Biol.] That part of the substance of a CELL which has to do chiefly with making use of or storing food, as opp. IDIOPLASM.

'trophoplast, n. [Bot.] PLASTID.

'trophosome, n. [Zoo.] All the units of a COLONY of HYDROZOA which have to do with food, taken together.

'trophosphere, n. TROPHOBLAST.

tropho'spongia, n. [Zoo.] The sponge-like MUCOUS MEMBRANE between the TROPHOBLAST and the wall of the UTERUS.

'tropho'taxis, n. [Biol.] TAXIS in reaction to food, a form of CHEMOTAXIS.

'tropho'tropism, n. [Biol.] TROPISM in reaction to food, a form of CHEMOTROPISM.

tropho'zoite, n. [Zoo.] A SPOROZOAN at the stage of full development.

tropho'zooid, n. [Zoo.] A food-getting ZOÖID in a colony of free-swimming TUNICATES.

-trophy, n. [Biol., Med.] Growth, the taking in of food so as to make growth.

-tropia, n. [Med.] A condition in which the AXES of the eyes are turned in the way named.

'tropic, 1.n. [Astron.] One or other of the two small circles of the CELESTIAL SPHERE parallel to the CELESTIAL EQUATOR and 23° 27′ north (**T. of Cancer**) or south (**T. of Capricorn**) of it, marking the limit of the sun's DECLINATION north or south. [Geog.] The two circles having the same

relation to the earth's EQUATOR and given the same names (**the tt.**, sp. that band of the earth between the tt.). 2.a. Tropical. **'tropical,** a. Of, to do with, like, the tt. **'tropical month.** [Astron.] The MEAN time taken by the moon to go from a point on the ECLIPTIC back to the same point again, 27 days, 7 hours, 43 minutes, 4·7 seconds. **'tropical rain 'forest.** [Geog.] The sort of great, wet, evergreen wood seen in tropical countries which have much rainfall and no dry time of year, in which, because of the heat and water, growth is very thick, and the competition between plants to get to the sunlight makes the trees and CLIMBERS go up very high. **'tropical year.** The time of 365 days 5 hours 48 minutes 45·51 seconds between the sun's being at the VERNAL EQUINOX and its being there again, 20 minutes 23·5 seconds shorter than the generally used SIDERAL YEAR because of the PRECESSION OF THE EQUINOXES.

'tropic, tro'pistic, aa. [Biol.] Of, to do with, caused by TROPISM.

-tropic, a. [Biol.] Turning, changing, having TROPISM of the named sort or in reaction to the named thing.

'tropic 'acid. [Chem.] $C_9H_{10}O_3$, a white CRYSTALLINE solid with acid properties produced from ATROPINE.

'tropism, n. [Biol.] An automatic change in the position or direction of a plant, animal, or part, in reaction to something outside itself, a turning, sloping, curving, etc. to (**positive t.**) or away from (**negative t.**) something acting on it from outside; in man, sp. a REFLEX causing a motion of all the body.

'tropopause, n. [Meteor.] The meeting-level of the TROPOSPHERE and the STRATOSPHERE, the distance of which from the earth is different at different points, ranging from about 18 km. at the EQUATOR to 10 km. at the POLES.

tro'pophilous, a. [Bot.] (Of a plant) with the property of adjustment to heat and cold, wet and dry, so as to be able to go on living healthily in places which have very different weather conditions at different times of the year, as trees which put off their leaves at regular cold or dry times.

'trophophyte, n. [Bot.] A TROPOPHILOUS plant.

'troposphere, n. [Meteor.] That part of the ATMOSPHERE between the earth and the STRATOSPHERE, where the TEMPERATURE normally gets lower as we go up and there is much cloud and much motion of air-currents caused by unequal heating— the seat of the weather.

-tropous, a. [Bot.] Turning, curved, in the way named.

-tropy, n. [Biol.] TROPISM. [Bot.] The property of being -TROPOUS.

trough, n. Any of a number of box-like open vessels for liquids, used for different purposes in mining, industry etc., sp. one of long narrow form, not very deep, and with out-sloping sides; the hollow between the highest points of two ADJACENT water waves, or of other waves of like form. [Chem.] PNEUMATIC T. [Elec.] The vessel of a t. battery. [Geol.] Any long, narrow, t.-like hollow. [Meteor.] A long stretch of low ATMOSPHERIC PRESSURE running out into other parts from a greater and wider stretch, gen. given its full name, **t. of low pressure. t. 'battery.** [Elec.] An electric BATTERY of which the CELLS are not separate but are formed by divisions across a long vessel. **t. fault.** [Geol.] The structure formed by two parallel FAULTS sloping down to one another so that a long narrow hollow is formed between them.

'Trouton's law, Trouton's rule. [Chem.] The law that there is a fixed relation between the LATENT HEAT OF VAPORIZATION of a liquid per GRAM-MOLECULE, measured in CALORIES, and its ABSOLUTE boiling-point, and that this is roughly the same for most liquids.

troy weight, n. An old English system of units of weight, still in use for gold, silver, and medical substances, in which the chief units are the **pound troy** of 12 troy ounces, **the ounce troy,** of 20 pennyweights, and the **pennyweight** of 24 GRAINS or 1·5552 grams.

true, a. [Geog., Surveying, etc.] (Of a direction) based on the direction of the earth's AXIS and not on that of the MAGNETIC POLES, as *t. north.* **t. a'nomaly.** [Astron.] *See* ANOMALY. **t. rib.** [Zoo.] Any of those RIBS which are joined straight to the STERNUM by their CARTILAGE ends, in man the seven from the top, right and left. **t. 'vocal cords.** *See* VOCAL CORDS.

'truncate, 1.v.t. Get the end or point of something cut off, make shorter or give a square end to in this way. [Math., Cryst.] Get an angle or angles or an edge or edges of some solid plane-sided form cut off, forming a plane. 2.a. Truncated. **trun'cated,** a. Having undergone truncation, cut short. [Geom., Cryst.] With its angle(s) or edge(s) changed into planes, sp. in a regular way. [Biol.] Having the look of having been truncated, ending suddenly as if by the loss of its point, said sp. of a leaf. **trun'cato-.** [Biol.] Truncately; t. and ...

'truncus arteri'osus. [Zoo.] The great blood-vessel at the front of the heart in non-AMNIOTE back-boned animals and the EMBRYOS of amniotes, through which the blood is forced from the VENTRICLE.

trunk, n. The chief stem of anything branching, as of a blood-vessel, or sp. [Bot.] the thick, strong, tall, chief stem of a tree. [Zoo.] That middle part of the body of an animal, sp. man, to which the head, arms, and legs are joined, the body without these parts; the THORAX of an insect; the PROBOSCIS of PROBOSCIDEA.

'trunnion, n. [Mach.] One or the other of two short rods coming out, gen. at right angles, on opposite sides of a great gun, TELESCOPE, etc., by which it may be turned on the line joining them as on an AXLE, so as to be pointing lower or higher.

truss, n. [Eng.] A stiff framework of long rod-like parts for supporting a weight such as a roof or bridge, so designed that a force acting at one point is balanced by the complex forces of the structure and any change of form is impossible so long as every part is unbroken. [Med.] An apparatus used for putting force on a part to keep it in place, sp. one in the form of a leather etc. band going round the lower part of the body with expansions at the front ends for supporting a HERNIA.

'tryma, n. [Bot.] A nut-like DRUPE of which the outer and middle coats are formed into a hard cover separate from the rest, and the inner is dry with a division wall through the middle.

'Trypano'soma, n.pl. [Zoo.] A GENUS of PROTOZOA with a thin waving band, an expansion of the front FLAGELLUM, all down one side of the body for swimming purposes—PARASITIC at full development in man and other higher animals, to which they are given by certain insects, and causing serious diseases, for example SLEEPING SICKNESS. **'trypano'somal,** a. **'trypano'some,** n. [Zoo.] Animal of the T. **'trypanosom'iasis,** n. [Med.] The condition of having trypanosomes in the body or any of the diseases caused by this, sp. SLEEPING SICKNESS. **trypan(o)-.** [Med.] Of, to do with, caused by, trypanosomes.

'trypsin, n. [Biochem.] An ENZYME produced by the PANCREAS of back-boned animals which is of help in getting PROTEINS broken up in the INTESTINE; any of a number of like enzymes in other animals or parts and in plants. **tryp'sinogen,** n. The substance produced in the PANCREAS from which t. is formed by reaction with ENTEROKINASE. **'tryptic,** a. Of, to do with, t.

Tu, One of the two signs used for THULIUM, the other being **Tm.**

tube, n. A pipe of any form, straight, curved, or twisted etc., sp. one of small size or some material other than metal, as glass or rubber, or a vessel in the form of a straight pipe shut at one end (and able to be corked etc. at the other). [Biol.] The t.-like part of any ring of flower-parts which are united edge-to-edge for some distance up from the base, sp. of a COROLLA. [Radio, Elec., etc.] VALVE. t. **foot.** [Zoo.] In ECHINODERMATA, any of the hollow, t.-like outgrowths in connection with the inner system of water-pipes, used for breathing and other purposes, such as walking or gripping, food-getting, or as feelers. **t. of force.** [Phys.] The pipe-like form produced in theory by the lines of electric or MAGNETIC force going out to the edge of the FIELD from every point on a small circle or other shut curve on the outside of an electrically or MAGNETICALLY CHARGED body. **'tubal,** a. To do with a t. or tt., sp. [Zoo., Med.] with a FALLOPIAN TUBE. **'tubate, 'tubular,** aa. T.-like in form; having, formed of, tt. or a t. **tubi-.**

'tuber, n. [Bot.] A short, thick, almost ball-like root (*root t.*) or stem going down into the earth (*stem t.*), made up chiefly of stored food material, as in the potato plant. [Med., Zoo.] A rounded outgrowth or SWELLING. **'-'iferous,** a. [Bot.]. **'-oid,** a. **'-ose, '-ous,** aa. Covered with rounded or knot-like PROJECTIONS. [Bot.] Formed of, producing, tt.; like a t.

'tubercle, n. [Biol., Med.] A small rounded expansion or outgrowth, natural or diseased, as on a root or tooth or the skin of certain REPTILES, or a small TUBEROSITY on a bone. [Zoo.] The outgrowth at the end of a RIB which is joined to the TRANSVERSE PROCESS of a back-bone unit. [Med.] Any of the small, grey, grain-like bodies, made up of a mass of CELLS, gen. with dead ones in the middle, formed inside a part of the body or on the skin in TUBERCULOSIS. **t. ba'cillus.** [Med.] The BACILLUS causing TUBERCULOSIS. **'tubercled,** a. **tu'bercular,** a. Of, to do with, having, marked by, like, tt. [Med.] Loosely, TUBERCULOUS, **tu'berculate(d),** aa. **tubercu'lation,** n. The forming or growth of tt.; the order in which tt. are placed.

tu'berculid(e), n. [Med.] A diseased place on the skin caused by poisons from the TUBERCLE BACILLUS.

tu'berculin(e), n. [Med.] Any of a number of substances produced from TUBERCLE BACILLI for use in testing for or fighting TUBERCULOSIS. **t. test.** Sp., the HYPODERMIC INJECTION of t. to see if an animal has, or has had, TUBERCULOSIS, INFLAMMATION being produced where the disease is or has been present.

tu'bercu'losis, n. [Med.] The serious disease caused by the TUBERCLE BACILLUS and marked by the forming of TUBERCLES, FEVER, and wasting, in man very commonly attacking the LUNGS, but freq.

the LYMPH GLANDS or the bones, and possibly almost any of the inner parts of the body. **tu'berculous,** a. [Med.] To do with, like, having, caused by, t. or the TUBERCLE BACILLUS.

tube'rosity, n. [Bot., Med.] The condition of being TUBEROUS. [Zoo.] A rounded outgrowth on a bone, to which a muscle or LIGAMENT is fixed, as those on the head of the long bone of the upper arm or front leg.

'tuberous, a. *See* TUBER.

tu'bicolpus, a. [Zoo.] Forming and living in a pipe-like structure, as certain worms.

'tubing, n. Material in the form of a TUBE, as *rubber t.*

'tubular, a. *See* TUBE.

'tubule, n. A small TUBE. **'tubulate(d),** aa. TUBE-like or having a tube or t. **'tubu-'liferous,** a. **'tubuli'form,** a. **'tubul-ose, -ous,** aa. **tubuli-.**

'tubuli'florous, a. [Bot.] Having COMPOSITE FLOWERS of which all the units are pipe-like.

'tubulus (tubuli), n. [Biol.] TUBULE. [Bot.] The neck or opening of a bottle-like ASCOCARP; in some FUNGI, a pipe-like part with a HYMENIUM on the inside. [Zoo.] A pipe-like OVIPOSITOR. **'tubulo-.** Pipe-like and . . . [Med.] FISTULOUS.

tufa, n. [Geol.] A freq. sponge-like but sometimes solidly massed stone, made up chiefly of $CaCO_3$, put down by springs or other inland waters (freq. *calcareous t.*). **tu'faceous,** a.

tuff, n. [Geol.] A solid stone or looser mass made up of the small bits of burned material sent out by a VOLCANO. **tuf-'faceous,** a.

tuft, n. [Biol.] A separate, somewhat stiff mass of hairs, feathers, branches, etc. such as the crest of a bird, or a group of like plants massed together at the base, such as a *t. of grass.* **'tufted,** a. Sp. [Bot.] (of plants) grouping themselves in tt.

'tular'(a)emia, n. [Med.] A disease of rats etc. given to man by them or taken to him by flies etc., marked by FEVER and SWELLING of the LYMPHATICS, and sometimes by other effects like those of TYPHOID.

'tumefy, v.t. and i. [Med.] (Make) SWELL. **tume'facient,** a. [Med.] Producing SWELLING. **tume'faction,** n. The process of tumefying or condition of being tumid; a tumefied part. **tu'mescence, a.** A tendency to t., or the condition of becoming or being to some degree tumid. **tum-'escent,** a. **'tumid,** a. Tumified. **tu'midity,** n.

'tumo(u)r, n. [Med.] A SWELLING or unnormal increase in size of a part; most commonly, a mass of new TISSUE formed by unnormal growth from normal body materials which may be not in itself diseased, but is unnecessary, out of place, and gen. unlimited in growth, using up food materials to no purpose, and causing trouble and pain by pushing against other parts. '-ous, a.

'tumulus, n. [Anthrop.] A high mass of earth or stone covering the last resting-place, freq. a stone building, of important dead of very early times.

'tundra, n. [Geog.] Any of the great flat or somewhat waving stretches of country without trees, but thickly covered with low plant growth in summer, in the far north of the earth, chiefly edging the ARCTIC CIRCLE, where roots are able to go only about 5 cm. down into the earth because at that level it is hard with ice all the year round.

tune, 1.n. [Acous.] (Of sounds) a condition of harmony or agreement in PITCH; (of VIBRATING wires, instruments of music, etc.) the condition of being in such adjustment as to give out sounds which are in t. with one another or with a given system of pitches. [Radio, Elec.] (Of radio or electric waves or the apparatus producing them) harmony or agreement in FREQUENCY, sp. the condition of being in RESONANCE. [Phonet.] See SPEECH MELODY. 2.v.t. [Acous.] Put (a sound or instrument) in t. (with another). [Radio, Elec.] Make the necessary adjustments in the CAPACITY and/or INDUCTANCE of an electric CIRCUIT to give it a desired FREQUENCY, sp. to put it in RESONANCE with an incoming current or system of radio waves. tuned, a. tuned 'circuit. [Elec.] A CIRCUIT made up of a COIL and a CONDENSER so tuned as to take in very readily, or, on the other hand, to keep out, current of a given FREQUENCY. 'tuning, n. Sp., [Radio] the tuning of a radio RE-CEIVER to the FREQUENCY of waves from a desired station, etc. tuning in. [Radio] The adjustment of a radio RECEIVER to get the best possible reaction to waves from a given station. tuning out. [Radio] The opposite operation to tuning in, that is, adjustment to keep out undesired waves.

'tungsten, n. [Chem.] The name given to WOLFRAM up to 1949, and still used in addition, sign W. 'tungstic, a. 'tungstic ochre. Tungstite. 'tungstite, n. [Mineral.] Natural WO₃, a yellow or yellow-green earth-like substance. 'tungsto-.

'tunic, n. [Biol.] A natural covering, as of a seed. 'tunica, n. A t., sp. [Zoo.] a soft covering, as a MEMBRANE or the MANTLE of a MOLLUSC, etc. '-ary, a. [Zoo.] '-ate, 1.a. [Bot.] Having a t., or having or made up of a number of coats on top of one another. [Zoo.] Covered with a t.; of, to do with, like, the TUNICATA. 2.n. Animal of the TUNICATA. '-ated, a. TUNICATE.

Tuni'cata, n.pl. UROCHORDA.

'tunicin, n. [Biochem.] A jelly-like substance, like the CELLULOSE of plants, present in the outer covering of URO-CHORDA.

Turbell'aria, n.pl. [Zoo.] A CLASS of PLATY-HELMINTHES which are small, soft-bodied, covered with CILIA, and flat and leaf-like in form, with no body-hollow and a mouth on the under side opening straight into a simple or branched INTESTINE, almost all free-swimming, non-PARASITIC, and living in water.

'turbid, a. (Of a liquid) not clear, clouded with a powdered solid etc. turbi'dimeter, n. [Phys.-Chem.] An instrument for the comparison of the turbidity of liquids by a comparison of the amount of light coming through them. '-i'metric, a. '-'imetry, n. The use of the turbidimeter. tur'bidity, n.

'turbinal, 1.a. [Zoo.] Twisted into a SPIRAL. 2.n. A t. bone or CARTILAGE, sp. one of those in the walls of the nose in back-boned animals, supporting the MUCOUS MEMBRANE.

'turbinate, a. [Bot.] Round and flat at the top and narrowing (almost) to a point at the base, by which it is fixed. [Zoo.] TURBINAL; (of a SHELL) SPIRAL with a wide base narrowing sharply to a pointed top.

'turbine, n. [Eng.] An engine in which the power is produced by the turning of a thick rod as the effect of a current of water, steam, air etc. driving against the blades of, or through sloping openings cut into, a wheel-like structure fixed to it. 'turbo-. Worked by a t. 'turbo-'jet 'engine. An INTERNAL COMBUSTION engine having tt. which are turned by the push of the heated gas forced out between their blades.

'turbulence, n. [Phys.] An irregular motion of a current of liquid or gas, marked by sudden twists and EDDIES. 'turbulent, a. In a condition of t. turbulent flow. T.

'turgid, a. [Biol., Med.] Full, with walls stretched, in a condition of SWELLING or TURGOR. 'turgidity, n.

tur'gescence, n. [Biol.] The process of becoming TURGID; TURGOR. tur'gescent, a.

'turgor, n. [Biol.] The condition normal to living CELLS, of being stretched by the substance inside them, sp. [Bot.] the stiff quality given to the parts of a healthy plant by the expansion of its cells with the right amount of water, without which they go soft and without support. t. 'pressure. [Bot.] The force of the water inside it on the walls of a plant CELL.

'turio(n), nn. [Bot.] A SCALY young BUD put out by a stem running under the earth; in some water-plants, a fat, food-storing bud, which comes away from the plant in the fall and undergoes development into a new plant in the spring. **turion′iferous**, a.

′turpentine, n. [Chem.] An ESSENTIAL OIL formed of mixed TERPENES, got by DISTILLATION of the oil-RESIN produced by a number of evergreen trees—an uncoloured, readily fired liquid going solid in the air, used chiefly as a SOLVENT and thinner for paints, polishes etc. (freq. *oil of t.*); any of the resins from which t. is made.

′turquoise, n. [Mineral.] A sky-blue or blue-green OPAQUE jewel stone formed of a HYDROUS aluminium PHOSPHATE mixed with a little copper.

′turreted, a. [Zoo.] (Of SHELLS) twisting round and round from the base to a high point.

tusk, n. [Zoo.] A very long, freq. curved, tooth of great size, gen. one of two, which comes outside the mouth and is used for fighting or as a sort of spade, etc.

′tuyère, n. [Eng.] A short pipe, gen. of copper, through which air is forced into a BLAST-FURNACE, as in making iron.

′Twaddell′s hy′drometer. [Chem.] A form of HYDROMETER for measuring the SPECIFIC GRAVITY of liquids of greater weight than water, sp. acids. **Twaddell scale.** The scale used on T.h., so designed that $1 + \dfrac{\text{the reading on the scale}}{200}$ = the SPECIFIC GRAVITY of the liquid in question, sign °Tw. **Twaddell**, n. T.h.; Twaddell scale.

′twilight, n. [Astron.] The half-light coming to earth between the time when the sun is 18° lower than the HORIZON and its coming up, or between its going down and its becoming 18° lower than the horizon, caused by REFLECTION of the sun's rays from the upper ATMOSPHERE. **t. sleep.** [Med.] A half-conscious condition produced by MORPHINE and SCOPOLAMINE, sp. in a woman who is giving birth, to make her unconscious of pain and with no memory of the process. **t. ′vision.** [Zoo., Psych.] SCOTOPIA.

twin, n. One or the other of two like things which go, or are joined, together. [Zoo., Med.] One or the other of two offspring produced at a birth, sometimes from the same egg (**i′dentical tt.**), sometimes from two different eggs (**fra′ternal tt.**), sp. by an animal such as man, commonly producing only one. [Cryst.] T. crystal. **t. ′crystal.** [Cryst.] A CRYSTAL formed by the growth together of two (**simple t.**) or more (**re′peated** or **′multiple t.**) like crystals in such a way as to make a regular form, the parts of one being placed in a looking-glass relation to those of the other, so that the two together make a balanced structure. **′twinning**, n. [Cryst.] The

forming of t. crystals. **′twinning ′axis.** [Cryst.] The AXIS round which one of two CRYSTALS in a t. crystal seems to have been turned to make it opposite in position to the other. **′twinning law.** [Cryst.] A rule representative of the system by which twinning takes place in a given substance. **′twinning plane.** [Cryst.] The plane to which the twinning axis is at right angles.

′twining, n., a. [Bot.] Of a plant-stem, (the process of) twisting itself round and round things in corkscrew turns, for support. **twine**, v.t. Go round things in this way.

′two-′colour ′process. Any process in colour-printing or making coloured camera-pictures in which only two colours are used for producing all others, in place of three as in the THREE-COLOUR PROCESS (which *see*).

′two-′cycle ′engine, ′two-stroke ′engine. [Eng.] An INTERNAL COMBUSTION ENGINE with a two-stroke cycle. **two-stroke cycle.** [Eng.] A complete working motion of a PISTON in an INTERNAL COMBUSTION ENGINE which is made up of only two stages, firing taking place on the upper side of the piston and a VALVE letting in new gas on the under side while the piston is at the top, and the intake making its way up to the top through the CRANKCASE, and the burned gas its way out through another valve, when the piston is at its lowest point, the motion of the piston itself opening and shutting the valves in question.

′two-di′mensional, a. Having measure in two directions only, plane.

′two-e′lectrode valve. DIODE.

′two-′fluid ′theory. [Elec.] The old theory that NEGATIVE and POSITIVE ELECTRICITY are two separate FLUIDS balancing out one another's effects when present together.

′two-′phase, a. [Elec.] (Of ALTERNATING-CURRENT systems or the power etc. produced by them) using two currents different in PHASE.

′twyere, n. TUYÈRE.

′tylose, ty′losis, nn. [Bot.] A hollow expansion of the wall of a PIT going into a transporting VESSEL, stopping it up, common in HEARTWOOD. [Zoo.] Any irregular growth of a CELL or cells into the hollow of another. [Med.] A thick, hard place formed on the skin as the effect of rubbing etc. **ty′lotic**, a.

tym′panic, a. [Zoo.] To do with, near, the TYMPANUM or the t. bone. **t. bone.** In higher animals, a bone of the head supporting the t. membrane. **t. ′bulla.** In some animals, a rounded, hollow expansion of the t. bone going round the outer part of the t. cavity. **t. ′cavity.** The hollow of the MIDDLE EAR. **t. 'membrane.** A thin stretched skin covering the outer opening of the MIDDLE EAR and put into motion by sound waves.

'tympa'nites, 'tympany, nn.[Med.] METEOR-ISM. **tym'panic, 'tympan'itic,** aa. [Med.] Of, to do with, marked by, t.; giving out a hollow sound when given a blow, as the ABDOMEN in t.

'tympanum, n. [Zoo.] In higher animals, the MIDDLE EAR or the TYMPANIC MEMBRANE; in insects a thin, stretched skin covering or forming part of a hearing-apparatus, as on the legs of some insects. **'tympano-.**

'Tyndall eff'ect. [Optics] The sending of light rays in all directions by small grains of material in their way, for example dust in the air.

Tyndalli'zation, n. FRACTIONAL STERILIZA-TION.

'Tyndall 'meter. [Chem.] An apparatus for measuring the amount of SUSPENDED material in a liquid by the amount of light sent out sideways from the BEAM formed when light is sent through the liquid. **tyndall'imetry,** n. [Chem.] The measuring of the CONCENTRATION of SUSPENSIONS by the use of the T.m.

type, n. A form of structure common to a group, a representative form or example. [Biol.] An animal or plant having the properties of structure and operation common to a group, and on which a grouping is based; an animal- or plant-group looked on as representative of the greater group of which it is a division. **'typical,** a. Of, to do with, a t., representative (*of* a group). **'typify,** v.t. Be representative of (a group). **t. 'specimen.** The plant or animal on which the first account of a SPECIES was based, by observation of which a new group came to be formed.

type, n. The squares of metal or wood, or any one of them, on which letters, numbers, etc. are CAST for printing from; the print made from t.. **t. 'metal.** An ALLOY of lead, ANTIMONY and tin used for making t. because it undergoes a small expansion on getting cold, which gives CASTS made from it specially sharp, clear edges.

typhil'itis, n. [Med.] INFLAMMATION of the CAECUM—the name at one time given to APPENDICITIS.

'typhlosole. n. [Zoo.] A longways fold of the inner wall of the INTESTINE in some lower animals, giving a greater SURFACE for taking food substances into the system.

'typhoid, 1.a. [Med.] Of, to do with, like, TYPHUS or t. fever. 2.n. An INFECTIOUS disease caused by a BACILLUS taken into the system in food or water, marked by INFLAMMATION and sometimes PERFORA-

TION of the INTESTINES, unbroken FEVER, expansion of the SPLEEN, and at one stage small red places on the chest and front of the body. **t. state.** The conditions specially marked in t., sp. the great loss of force, when seen in other diseases. **t. fever. T.**

ty'phoon, n. [Meteor.] A very violent CYCLONE of limited range taking place over the seas near China.

'typhus, n. [Med.] A serious CONTAGIOUS disease taken from person to person by LICE, marked by long unbroken FEVER, a very feeble condition of body and mind, and the covering of the body with small red places.

'typonym, n. [Biol.] A name based on the name of a type SPECIMEN or SPECIES, not on its properties.

tyre, n. The band going round a wheel, on which it comes against the road etc., sp. the PNEUMATIC t. used today on bicycles and automobiles for cushioning the motion.

U, Sign for URANIUM.

'udder, n. [Zoo.] The MAMMA of animals such as the cow and horse.

u'dell, n. [Chem.] Open-ended pot vessel with a narrow neck at one end like a bottle, used in SUBLIMATION, sp. of I.

u'dometer, n. [Meteor.] An instrument measuring rainfall.

-ula, -ule, nn. A small one of whatever is named, **-ular,** a. **-ulate,** a.

ul(a)-. [Med.] The GUMS: **u'litis,** n.

'Ulbricht sphere, Ulbricht globe pho'to-meter. INTEGRATING SPHERE.

'ulcer, n. [Med.] A diseased place on the skin or a MUCOUS MEMBRANE where destruction of the substance is taking place, making an open, PUS-forming wound, gen. caused by BACTERIA etc. attacking the outside, not by developments in deeper substance. **'-ate,** v.t. and i. (Make) undergo ulceration, **'-ated,** a. **ulcer'ation,** n. The process of forming an u. or uu. or the condition of undergoing this process; an u. or ulcerated place. **'-ative,** a. Ulcerous or causing ulceration. **'-ous,** a. **'ulcero-.**

u'letic, a. [Med.] To do with the GUMS.

'ulna, n. [Zoo.] The back one of the two bones of the lower front leg in 4-legged animals or the arm in man (that is, the one on the inside when the front of the hand is facing forward). **'ulnar,** a. **ulno-.**

ul'nare (ulnaria), n. [Zoo.] That one of the

small bones at the join between arm and hand or front leg and foot which is in line with and nearest to the ULNA.

-ulose, - ulous, aa. Marked by, having, or with a tendency to have, the thing named.

u'lotrichous, a. [Zoo., Anthrop.] Having wool-like or tightly twisted hair.

-ulum, -ulus, nn. A small one of whatever is named.

'ultimate, a. Last, furthest, sp. being the end effect or outcome or part of a process. [Mech.] (Of a STRESS, etc.) that which is needed to get a given substance broken, or the greatest which a substance will undergo without being broken. [Phys., Chem., etc.] Unable to undergo further division, simple, as *u.* PARTICLES; to do with the ELEMENTS of which a substance is made up, as *u.* ANALYSIS, **u. lines.** [Chem.] RAIES ULTIMES. **u. 'tensile stress.** [Metal] In testing a metal for TENSILE STRENGTH, the degree of force at which it gives way DIVIDED by the AREA of a CROSS-SECTION at the start of the test.

'ultra-. Farther off in space than, on the other side of; greater in degree than, or higher than, on the further side of, on a scale; greater or smaller than the thing named but of the same sort, as **'ultra-'microbe,** a MICROBE so small as not to be seen through a MICROSCOPE; (before names of instruments) more than normally delicate, used for more detailed observation or measuring, or for producing smaller effects, than the common instrument of that name, as an **'ultra-'micrometer** (*see* MICROMETER).

'ultra'atomic, a. [Phys., Chem.] Of, to do with, PARTICLES smaller than ATOMS.

'ultra'basic, a. [Geol.] (Of ROCKS) having in them only from 35% to 45% of SiO2 with a great amount of material formed of Fe and Mg.

'ultra'centrifuge, n. [Phys.-Chem.] A CENTRIFUGE turning at a very great rate for separating very small bits from a substance.

'ultra'filter, n. [Chem.] A FILTER with specially small holes keeping back the solid part of a COLLOIDAL SOLUTION when this is forced through it. **'ultra'fil-'tration,** n. The separating of the solid grains from a COLLOIDAL SOLUTION by forcing it through an u. or a SEMI-PERMEABLE MEMBRANE.

'ultra-'mafic, a. [Geol.] (Of IGNEOUS ROCKS) having an uncommonly great amount of substances formed of iron, Mg, and Si but no FELDSPAR. **'ultra'mafite,** n. Any of the group of u. ROCKS.

'ultrama'rine, n. A blue colouring-substance made by powdering LAPIS LAZULI, or, more commonly at the present day, a copy of this produced chemically by heating KAOLIN with S, C, Na2CO4 and sometimes Na2SO4.

'ultra'microscope, n. [Optics] An apparatus made up of a MICROSCOPE together with a light and LENSES sending a very strong pencil of light onto a dark body, sp. through a liquid, by which it is possible to see bodies, sp. COLLOIDAL grains, so small as not to be seen through a common microscope.

ultra'phonic, a. ULTRASONIC.

ultra'photic, a. ULTRA-VIOLET or INFRA-RED.

ultra'red, a. INFRA-RED.

'ultrashort waves. [Radio] ELECTRO-MAGNETIC waves of WAVELENGTH less than 10 metres.

'ultra'sonic, a. [Phys.] (Of WAVES) of the same sort as sound-waves but having a FREQUENCY greater than that of those by which man's hearing is acted on, that is, greater than about 20,000 CYCLES per sec. **'ultra'sonics,** n. The science of u. WAVES.

'ultra-violet rays. [Phys., Med.] Those WAVES in the range of ELECTRO-MAGNETIC waves coming between the shortest seen by the eye and the longest X-RAY, that is, of WAVE-LENGTH between 3900 and 50 A.U., which, though unseen, may be recorded by their effects on a camera plate—important for their effects on the body (in which, by acting on ERGOSTEROL, they are the producers of VITAMIN D), and for causing FLUORESCENCE in certain substances. **u.-v. r. 'therapy.** [Med.] The use of u.-v. rr. medically against skin troubles etc.

'umbel, n. [Bot.] A sort of RACEME in which the chief stem makes no growth between the flowers so that they come from about the same point, forming a flat or arched flower-head with the first-formed flowers on the outside, the latest in the middle (*see* picture, page 199). **'-ar,** a. **'-late,** a. **um'bellifer,** n. A plant flowering in uu. **umbel'liferous,** a. **um'belliform,** a. **um-'bellule,** n. Any of the small uu. of an u. whose stems are ended not by flowers but again by uu. (*compound u.*).

'umber, n. A sort of yellow-brown earth turning red-brown when strongly heated, formed chiefly of natural OXIDES of iron and Mn, used as a colouring-substance in paint.

umbi'licus (umbilici), n. [Zoo.] In higher animals, the little hollow, in man low down on the front of the body, marking the place where the umbilical cord was joined before being cut or broken off at birth; the hollow forming the middle point round which the pipe-like SHELL is twisted in certain GASTROPODS; a small hollow on the stem of a feather at the

start of the VANE; any small hollow like
an u. [Bot.] HILUM. **um′bilical,** a. **umbilical cord.** [Zoo.] The cord or stem by
which the offspring of a higher animal is
joined in the body of the mother to the
PLACENTA, having in it the blood-vessels
taking blood from one to the other and
some part of the YOLK-SAC and the
ALLANTOIS. [Bot.] FUNICLE. **umbilical
′vesicle.** [Zoo.] In the EMBRYOS of higher
animals, the YOLK-SAC, or that part of it
which is outside the embryo and in connection with it through the u. cord.
um′bilicate(d), aa. [Biol., Med.] Having
an u. or u.-like hollow, sp. in the middle.
umbili′cation, n. The condition of being
umbilicate; an u.-like hollow. **um′bili-
form,** a. [Biol.] Formed like an u.
′umbo (umbos or umbones), n. [Biol.] A
small rounded or round-pointed outgrowth, sp. [Bot.] at the middle of the
upper side of a PILEUS, [Zoo.] on a VALVE
of a two-valved SHELL and being the
first-formed part of it. **′-nal,** a. **′-nate,** a.
′umbra, n. [Optics] A part of space from
which light is completely cut off, a
complete shade. [Astron.] The pointed,
darkest, middle part of a shade made by a
third body coming between a light-
giving body and another, where the light
is completely cut off. (See PENUMBRA).
′umbral, a.
um′brella, n. [Zoo.] A bell-like or flat
umbrella-like structure, sp. that forming
the chief part of the body in most
MEDUSAE, and by regular CONTRACTIONS
of its hollow side moving the animal
through the water.
′umlaut, n. [Philol.] The effect on a VOWEL
of another vowel which at one time came
after it in a word but is generally no
longer present, or a special vowel-sound
given to a letter because of this, as the
German *ä* or *ae*, representative of old *ai*;
the sign ·· put over a letter to give it the
u sound in German.
′uncate, a. UNCINATE.
un′certainty ′principle. [Phys.] The rule
that, because of the WAVE properties of
all moving PARTICLES, it is never possible
to give the true position and the true
MOMENTUM for any particle, for example,
an ELECTRON, at the same point of time,
and the nearer right we are about one of
these the less right we are about the
other.
un′ciferous, a. [Biol.] Having hooks or
hook-like structures.
′unciform, a. [Biol.] Formed like a hook.
′uncinate, a. [Biol.] Hook-like, hooked at
the end.
un′cinus (uncini), n. [Zoo.] A small hooked
or hook-like structure, sp. any of those
very small hard hooks produced on
TORI in certain worms, or any of the

hooked side-teeth on the RADULA of a
GASTROPOD.
′uncon′ditioned, a. [Psych.] Of a reaction or
STIMULUS, natural, taking place or acting
without any process of conditioning or
learning.
uncon′formable, a. [Geol.] Marked by
UNCONFORMITY. **′unconforma′bility,** n.
UNCONFORMITY.
uncon′formity, n. [Geol.] The condition of,
or relation between, beds of ROCK of
which one is on top of the other but was
not put down on it when this was new,
but only later, after a process of EROSION,
so that (a) the two beds are not as near in
time as they are in space, and are not
representative of an unbroken chain of
events, and (b) they are frequently
sloping in different directions and at
different angles, and their meeting
SURFACE is not plane but very irregular;
the meeting surface between two such
beds.
un′conscious, 1.a. [Psych.] (Of mind processes) of which the person in whom they
are working, and on whose behaviour they
frequently have a very strong effect, is not
only u. but is unable to become conscious
by looking inside himself, though he may
be given a knowledge of them by PSYCHO-
ANALYSIS. 2.n. The u. processes taken
together, the u. part of the mind, covering
the roots of INSTINCT and RACIAL memory
together with very strong REPRESSIONS
formed in very early years and the mind-
forces responsible for all repression.
′-ness, n.
′uncus (unci), n. [Zoo.] A hook-like structure, sp. the head of any of the food-
crushing parts in the MASTAX of ROTI-
FERA, or a hooked part near the sex-
apparatus on the underside of some male
insects.
′undercarriage, n. In an airplane, the part
under the body, which has wheels etc. on
which the plane is supported when on land
and which is gen. folded up when in the
air.
′underclay, n. [Geol.] A bed of CLAY coming
under a bed of coal, representative of the
earth in which the trees forming the coal
were rooted.
under′hung, a. [Zoo.] (Of the lower JAW)
coming further forward than the upper
jaw, sp. with the lower teeth slipping
over the upper teeth.
′undershot, a. [Zoo.] UNDERHUNG. [Mach.]
(Of a water-wheel) turned by water
running under it and meeting the curved
blades with which it is edged.
′undershrub, n. [Bot.] A SHRUB of which
only the base structure of branches goes
on living through the winter, etc., all
the flowering parts falling away.
′undertow, n. [Geog., etc.] The outgoing

current under the water produced by waves rolling onto the edge of the land.

'underwing, n. [Zoo.] The back wing of an insect, which is covered, when folded, by the front wing.

'undine, n. [Med.] A small bottle ending in a curved, pointed, pipe-like neck, for dropping medical liquids into the eye.

'undulant, a. UNDULATING. u. 'fever. [Med.] One or the other of two diseases marked by a regular coming and going of FEVER, with expansion of the SPLEEN and pain and swelling of the JOINTS, caused by two like BACTERIA, one attacking goats, the other cows, and got by man from the milk of these animals.

'undulate, 1.v.i. Be moving (from place to place or in one place) with a WAVE MOTION; have a wave-like form or outline, be curved in and out or up and down. 2.a. Undulating, sp. in form. [Bot.] Having an u. edge with not very deep curves. 'undulated, a. U. 'undulating, a. undulating 'membrane. [Zoo.] VIBRATILE MEMBRANE. undu'lation, n. Undulating motion or form; a unit wave or VIBRATION. undu'latory, a.

'ungual, a. [Zoo.] To do with, like, having, a nail, CLAW or HOOF. [Med.] To do with the finger or toe nails.

'unguent, un'guentum, nn. [Med.] Any medical substance in the form of a soft paste or wax for rubbing into the skin.

'unguis (ungues), n. [Zoo.] A nail, CLAW or hook, sp. in insects. [Bot.] The stem-like base part of some PETALS. un'guinal, a. [Bot.] To do with uu. or an u.

'ungula (ungulae), n. [Zoo.] HOOF. 'ungulate, 1.a. Having uu. 2.n. Animal of the UNGULATA.

Ungu'lata, n.pl. [Zoo.] The group, taking in the ARTIODACTYLA, the PERISSODACTYLA, the PROBOSCIDEA, the HYRACOIDEA, and other ORDERS no longer in existence (sometimes listed as an order with these as SUB-ORDERS, but not in the latest systems), made up of HOOVED MAMMALS living on plants or grass and in great groups, gen. in flat open country, over which their feet are designed for running, and having flat-topped teeth and never more than 4 back toes, for example, horses, sheep, goats.

'unguligrade, a. [Zoo.] Walking on the HOOVED ends of the toes, as the horse or cow.

uni-. One, MONO:— -'branchiate, a., -'ciliate, a., -'florous, a., -'locular, a., '-mo'lecular, a., -'nucleate, a., -'petalous, a., -'septate, a.

uni'axial, a. [Cryst.] Having only one OPTIC AXIS. [Biol.] Having only one AXIS of development, not branching.

uni'cellular, a. [Biol.] Made up of only one CELL.

'unicorn shell. [Zoo.] The sort of SHELL, seen on a number of sea animals, which has on one lip of its opening a markedly long, narrow, pointed outgrowth.

uni'cuspid, a. [Zoo.] (Of a tooth) having only one point.

unidi'rectional, a. [Elec., Radio, etc.] Working or going only or chiefly in one direction, as a u. ANTENNA. u. 'current. DIRECT current.

'unify, v.t. and i. Get or become united, made into one. 'unified, a. unified field theory. A general mathematical theory of ELECTRIC and MAGNETIC FIELDS, put forward by Einstein, covering ELECTROMAGNETIC and GRAVITATIONAL theories as special examples of a general law.

uni'filar, a. [Phys.] Having, using, only one thread or wire.

'uniflow 'engine. [Engin.] A steam-engine in which the steam comes in at one end and goes out through outlets in the middle opened by the PISTON, so that its direction is unchanging.

uni'foliolate, a. [Bot.] (Of leaves) COMPOUND but of which all but one of the parts undergo no development, so that it seems to be simple.

'uniform, a. The same at all points or all times, completely regular, unchanging. uni'formity, n. The condition of being u.

uni'frequent, a. [Phys.] Of one FREQUENCY only.

uni'jugate, a. [Bot.] Of leaves, made up of two small leaves on opposite sides of the stem.

uni'lateral, a. Coming from one side or direction only. [Biol.] (Having parts, for example, flowers) all on one side or turned to one side. [Phys.] Letting electric current through in one direction only.

'union, n. The process of uniting or the condition of being united; a complex thing produced by u. [Med.] The growth together of material or parts after being separated by cutting etc. [Mach.] Any of a number of structures for uniting others, forming a connection between them, for example between a pipe and an engine.

uni'ovular, a. [Biol.] Producing, produced by, to do with, only one egg, sp. [Zoo.] of IDENTICAL TWINS.

u'niparous, a. [Zoo.] Producing only one offspring at a birth. [Bot.] Producing only one branch at every branching.

uni'planar, a. [Mech.] To do with, taking place in, one plane, as u. motion.

uni'polar, a. Having, produced by, or acting by, one POLE only. [Elec.] HOMOPOLAR. [Zoo.] Of NERVE-CELLS having NERVE FIBRES only at one end. unipo'larity, n.

uni'ramous, a. [Zoo.] Of the legs, etc. of CRUSTACEA, not forked.

uni′seri-al, -ate, aa. [Biol.] Ranged in one line or stretch, only one unit wide or deep.

uni′sexual, a. [Bot.] Of one sex only, male or female, not the two together. [Biol.] Having the male and female parts in separate flowers. **unisexu′ality,** n.

′unit, 1.n. Any fixed amount or value used for measuring anything, sp. one forming part of a system of measures, as a centimetre, a second, a pound, a DYNE, etc.; any of the like parts making up a complex thing or into which it may be separated, sp. any of the smallest of such parts, of which no further division is possible; a UNITY; the number 1. 2.a. To do with, being formed by or forming, a u.; measuring 1 u. only, of whatever system is being used. **u. ′character.** [Biol.] A quality which is handed on to off-spring as an independent u., that is, an ALLELOMORPH. **u. ′factor.** [Biol.] A FACTOR by which a u. character is handed on. **u. (mag′netic) pole.** [Elec. etc.] A MAGNETIC POLE which at a distance of 1 cm. from another magnetic pole, of opposite sign but the same power, has an attraction for it of 1 DYNE.

′unitary, a. Of, to do with, units; forming a unit, without division. **u. field ′theory.** UNIFIED FIELD THEORY.

′unity, n. The condition of being one without division, or of being united; the number 1.

uni′valent, a. [Biol.] One only, not having or uniting with another like it, said sp. of those CHROMOSOMES separating from the rest in the first MEIOTIC division. [Chem.] Having a VALENCY of 1.

′univalve, n., a. [Zoo.] (A SHELL) which is all one, not formed of two separate parts joined together.

uni′variant, a. [Phys.-Chem.] Having one DEGREE OF FREEDOM.

uni′versal, a. To do with all, unlimited; general, covering everything. [Mach.] (Of an instrument or part) which may be used for most or all purposes of the sort in question, for example, by having the power of adjustment to different sizes and forms of the things with which it is used. **u. ′donor.** [Med.] A person whose blood is of such a BLOOD GROUP that it may safely be put into that of any other person. **u. joint.** [Mach.] A joining-part between the ends of two rods etc. which lets one of them have the power of turning in any direction inside certain limits, used sp. in automobiles for taking the power of the engine to the back wheels. **u. re′cipient.** [Med.] A person whose blood is of such a BLOOD GROUP that blood from any other person may safely be put into him. **u. shunt.** [Elec.] An apparatus formed of a number of different SHUNTS to which connections may be made for GALVANOMETERS of different RESIST-ANCES. **u. time.** A system of time fixed by international agreement, being the same as GREENWICH MEAN TIME but measured from 0 hours to 24, starting at 12 p.m.

′universe, n. Everything in existence taken together and looked on as one system; any seemingly independent great field of existence or thought. [Astron.] The system of all physical bodies in space, today generally looked on as limited in size but undergoing expansion; that part of the u. in the range of our observation, the great group or system of stars of which the sun's system is a part; any great and seemingly independent system of stars such as our u. **u. of ′discourse.** The range of existence etc. with which a given system of thought and discussion has to do.

′unknown (′quantity). [Math.] Any value of which knowledge is not given and which has to be worked out from other values.

un′paired, a. [Zoo.] (Of parts) of which there is only one, not forming one of two parts such as are frequently balanced by one another on opposite sides of the body, and so, gen., placed in the middle plane of the body.

un′satisfied, a. [Chem.] (Of a unit of VALENCY of an ELEMENT in a COMPOUND or a VALENCY BOND) not used, not taken up, free for uniting with another element or group, for example in CO the C has two u. valencies.

un′saturated, a. [Chem.] (Of a COMPOUND) having a DOUBLE or TRIPLE BOND between certain of its ATOMS, gen. C atoms, so that it has the power of forming new compounds by the addition of further atoms or groups; (of a SOLUTION) not having in it as much of the SOLUTE as it is possible for it to take at that TEMPERA-TURE; (of a VAPOUR) able to be made colder or to undergo greater COMPRESSION without forming a liquid.

un′stable, a. Readily changing, not fixed or regular. [Psych.] Marked by INSTABILITY. [Phys.-Chem.] (Of a substance) readily changing from one STATE OF MATTER to another; (of an ELEMENT or ATOM) RADIO-ACTIVE; (of a complex substance) very readily broken up into the substances of which it is formed, or very readily under-going reactions with other substances. **u. equi′librium.** [Mech.] The condition of a body so placed that if given a small push it will make a complete change of position before coming to rest again. **u. ′oscilla-tion.** [Phys.] Any OSCILLATION, of a body, electric current, or any other thing, which goes on increasing in range.

unstri′ated, a. Smooth, not formed of or marked with bands of different colour or substance etc., **unstri′ated ′muscle.** [Zoo.] The muscle substance made up chiefly of long UNINUCLEATE CELLS pointed at the two ends, with no dark lines going across it and gen. in the form of flat stretches, present in the walls of blood-vessels, the INTESTINE etc., and acting automatically under the control of the SYMPATHETIC NERVOUS SYSTEM—much slower in CONTRACTION than STRIATED MUSCLE, and with a marked power of keeping up a contraction for a long time.

un'striped, a. UNSTRIATED, sp. of muscle.

unsymm'etric(al), aa. Not SYMMETRICAL. [Chem., Bot., Elec.] ASYMMETRIC.

un'voiced, a. [Phonet.] VOICELESS, sp. having undergone a change from VOICED to voiceless.

'upcast, 1.a. [Mining, Geol.] Going in an up direction. 2.n. [Mining] A SHAFT taking a current of used air out of a mine. [Geol.] UPTHROW.

up'heaval, n. [Geol.] A violent uplifting of part of the earth from inside, causing FAULTS, overturning, and general damage to the earlier structure.

'upland, 1.n. [Geog.] The higher land of a stretch of country (freq. *uu.*), or a bit of high, but not mountain, country, sp. far inland. 2.a. Of, to do with, present in, high land.

Upper, a. [Geol.] (Before names of divisions of time, ROCK SYSTEMS, etc.) later, the later part of, as the **U. Carboniferous** (*see* p. 559).

'upthrow, n. [Geol.] The side of a FAULT on which beds have been moved up, or the amount by which they have been moved in an up direction.

'upthrust, n. A force acting in an up direction, sp. [Geol.] an uplifting of part of the outer earth.

ur'(a)emia, n. [Med.] A condition caused by disease of the KIDNEYS in which poisons normally sent out in the URINE get into the blood, causing pain in the head, VOMITING, CONVULSIONS and COMA. **ur'(a)emic,** a.

'uranate, n. [Chem.] Any SALT of URANIC ACID.

u'ranic, a. [Chem.] Of, to do with, formed from, producing, URANIUM, having in it uranium, sp. of higher VALENCY. **u. acid.** H_2UO_4, a yellow powder.

ur'aninite, n. [Mineral.] A natural substance formed chiefly from a URANATE of URANYL but with some lead, Th, Ra, and other metals, sometimes in the form of black, or, less frequently, grey or white, CRYSTALS, but sometimes a non-CRYS-TALLINE black mass, and then named *pitchblende.*

u'ranism, n. [Med.] HOMOSEXUALITY in a man together with a strong feeling against the opposite sex.

'uranite, n. [Mineral.] A general name for the natural PHOSPHATES of U and copper

(*copper u.*) and of U and Ca (*lime u.*); URANINITE.

u'ranium. n. Chemical ELEMENT, at. no. 92, at. wt. 238·07, sign U, a RADIO-ACTIVE, hard, white metal made up of a mixed group of ISOTOPES of at. wts. 238, 235, and 234, the first of these (U238) having a HALF-LIFE of $4·5 \times 10^9$ years. **u.-ac'tinium series.** [Phys., Chem.] A RADIOACTIVE SERIES starting with U235 and sending with lead 207. **u.-'radium series.** A RADIOACTIVE SERIES starting with U238 and ending with lead 206.

'urano-. 1. [Astron.] The sky and the stars:— **uran'ography,** n., **uran'ometry,** n., **uran'ology,** n. 2, [Med.] The PALATE:— **'urano-'plasty,** n., **'uranoscope,** n.

U'ranus, n. [Astron.] The 7th PLANET in order from the sun, at a distance of about 1783 million miles from it, having a mass about 14·6 times that of the earth, a 'year' of 84 years, and four 'moons'—the first planet of which the discovery was made by a TELESCOPE (in 1871).

'uranyl, n. [Chem.] The group $-UO_2$.

ur'ao, n. [Mineral.] A natural, gen. CRYSTAL-LINE substance, $Na_2CO_3.NaHCO_3.2H_2O$, of a light grey or yellow-white colour, put down by some SODA LAKES and springs.

'urate, n. [Chem.] Any SALT of URIC ACID. **ur'atic,** a. Having in it, to do with, a u. or uu. **urat-.**

'urce'ol-ar, -ate, aa. [Biol.] Formed like a round bottle with a narrow neck or mouth. **'urce'olus,** n. An u. structure, sp. the u. or pipe-like covering of certain ROTIFERA.

u'rea, n. [Chem.] $NH_2.CO.NH_2$, the chief solid substance in the URINE of man and other back-boned animals, being the waste material from the digestion of PRO-TEINS—CRYSTALLINE and very SOLUBLE in water. **u.-for'maldehyde 'resin.** Any of a group of clear RESINS made by CON-DENSING u. with FORMALDEHYDE and used importantly in the making of PLASTICS (**u.- formaldehyde 'plastics**). **u'real,** a. **ure'ameter,** n. [Biochem., Med.] An instrument for measuring the amount of u. in URINE. **ureo-.**

'urease, n. [Biochem.] An ENZYME present in the seeds of certain plants, and in a great number of BACTERIA, which has the effect of helping in the HYDROLYSIS of UREA and is used medically for measuring the amount of urea in the blood.

U'redi'nales, n.pl. [Bot.] An ORDER or group of BASIDIOMYCETES which are PARASITIC under the skin of plants, sometimes in different plants at different stages, and whose SPORES are produced in small masses by which the skin of stems and leaves is broken, so that they become marked with hard, thick, orange-brown places where the spore-fruit is bursting through. 'ure'dineal, 'ure'dineous, aa. 'ure'dinio-, u'red(o)-.

ure'dinium (uredinia), n. UREDOSORUS.

ure'diniospore, u'rediospore, u'redospore, nn. [Bot.] Any of the thin-walled, orange-brown summer SPORES produced by the UREDINALES in UREDOSORI, and giving birth to MYCELLIA.

u'redo'sorus (uredosori), n. [Bot.] Any of the masses of UREDOSPORES and HYPHAE formed by the UREDINALES and marking the skin of the plant on which they are living with small, orange-brown, thick places.

u'redostage, n. [Bot.] The stage in the history of the UREDINALES at which UREDOSPORES are formed.

'ureide, n. [Chem.] Any of the substances formed by the uniting of UREA with an ORGANIC acid.

u'remia, n. URAEMIA.

ureo'telic, a. [Zoo.] (Of animals) having UREA as that chief part of their URINE by which undesired N is taken out of the body (see URICOTELIC).

u'resis, n. [Zoo.] URINATION.

u'reter, n. [Zoo.] The pipe by which URINE is taken from the KIDNEY to the BLADDER in higher back-boned animals or to the CLOACA in fish, etc. u'reteral, a. u'reter(o)-.

'urethan(e), n. [Chem., Med.] A SOLUBLE and CRYSTALLINE substance without colour, $H_2N.CO.OC_2H_5$, used medically as a HYPNOTIC and SEDATIVE; any other ESTER of CORBAMIC ACID.

u'rethra, n. [Zoo.] The pipe by which URINE is sent from the BLADDER to the outside in higher back-boned animals, and by which, in males, the SPERM is sent out as well. u'rethro-.

u'retic, 1.a. [Med.] Of, to do with, URINE, sp. URINATIVE. 2.n. A URINATIVE substance.

'-urgy, n. The art or science of working the named thing.

-uria, n. [Med.] Condition of the URINE:— al'buminuria, n., 'glucosuria, n., etc.

'uric 'acid. [Biochem.] $C_5H_4N_4O_3$, a substance of which only a small amount is present in the URINE of man and most higher animals, but which is the chief waste substance produced by the digestion of PROTEINS in birds and non-back-boned land animals—a white powder which is almost INSOLUBLE, the forming of hard masses of which in the body is the cause of GOUT and other troubles.

'urico'telic, a. [Zoo.] (Of animals) having URIC ACID as that chief part of their URINE by which undesired N is taken out of the body (see UREOTELIC).

'urine, n. [Zoo.] The waste material produced and sent out of the body by the KIDNEYS, which in man and higher animals is a liquid formed chiefly of UREA, in birds, snakes, and non-back-boned animals, a solid or almost solid substance formed chiefly of URIC ACID. 'urinary, a. Of, to do with, producing, present in, u. 'urinary 'bladder, 'urinary sac. A bag-like part in which u. coming from the KIDNEYS is stored until the impulse comes to send it out of the body. 'urinary tract. All the apparatus having to do with the producing and sending out of u. from the uriniferous tubules to the URETHRA. 'urinate, v.i. Send out u. uri'nation, n. 'urinative, n., a., Sp. [Med.] (Substance) causing or increasing urination. uri'niferous, a. uriniferous 'tubule. Any of the mass of small pipes in a KIDNEY by which u. is produced and sent on into the chief hollow, from which it goes into the urinary bladder. uri'niparous, a. uri'nometer, n. [Med.] An instrument for measuring the SPECIFIC GRAVITY of u. 'urinous, a. urin-, urini-, urino-.

'urite, n. [Zoo.] Any of the divisions of the ABDOMEN in ARTHROPODA.

urn, n. [Bot.] The SPORE-vessel in MUSCI. [Biol.] A u.-shaped vessel. 'u-shaped, a. Having the form of a round-based vessel so curved as to be narrowest at the top and base and widest about half-way between.

uro-. 1. [Zoo., Med.] (Of, to do with) URINE or the URINARY TRACT (and . . .), or the process of sending out urine:— '-cys'titis, n. [Med.], -'genic, u'rogenous, aa., -'genital, a., [Zoo.] u'rology, n. [Med.], u'rologist, n. [Med.], u'roscopy, n. [Med.] etc. 2. [Zoo.] Tail.

'uro'bilin, n. [Biochem.] STERCOBILIN, $C_{33}H_{44}O_6N_4$, as a part of UROCHROME, normally present in the URINE in only very small amounts and chiefly in the form of a substance, 'urobil'inogen, changing into it when acids are present. '-'(a)emia, n. [Med.] The condition in which u. is present in the blood. '-'uria, n. [Med.] The condition in which there is over-much u. in the URINE.

'urochord, 1.n. [Zoo.] The NOTOCHORD when limited to the tail end, as in the LARVAE and sometimes in the complete stage of UROCHORDA; an animal of the UROCHORDA. 2.a. Of, to do with, the u. or UROCHORDA, sp. having the notochord limited to the tail end. uro'chordal, a. U.

'Uro'chorda, 'Urochor'data, nn.pl. [Zoo.] A SUB-PHYLUM of CHORDATA (or in some systems a CLASS of ACRANIA) living in the sea, freq. having a NOTOCHORD only in the LARVA stage and then only in the tail, the animal at full development being DEGENERATE, with a much simpler nerve-system than the larva, and no brain, COELOM or body-divisions, breathing by GILL-SLITS and gen. having a thick outer covering formed chiefly of TUNICIN.

'urochrome, n. [Biochem.] The chief colouring-substance of the URINE, giving it its normal yellow colour, made up of UROBILIN and AMINO ACIDS.

'urocoel, n. [Zoo.] A part for sending out waste substances from the body in MOLLUSCA.

'urocyst, n. [Zoo.] The URINARY SAC.

uro'daeum, n. [Zoo.] The part of the CLOACA into which the GENITAL and URINARY pipes go, sp. in birds and REPTILES (*see* COPRODAEUM).

Uro'dela, n.pl. [Zoo.] An ORDER of AMPHIBIA with a very long body, 4 legs, and a tail at all stages of development. uro'delan, n., a. (Animal) of the U. uro'delous, a. Sp., having a tail at full growth as well as in earlier stages.

'urohyal, n. [Zoo.] A middle bone or bit of the bone-structure in the HYOID ARCH of a fish or bird.

'urolith, n. [Med.] A CALCULUS formed in the URINE in the body.

'uromere, n. [Zoo.] URITE.

'uropa'tagium, n. [Zoo.] The skin stretching between the upper part of the back legs of CHIROPTERA; one or the other of two small hard plates near the ANUS of an insect.

'uropod, n. [Zoo.] Any of the legs or other outgrowths on the ABDOMEN in CRUSTACEA, sp. one on the tail part greater in size or different in structure from the rest.

uro'pygium (uropygia), 'uropyge, nn. [Zoo.] The short, thick tail-end of a bird's body to which the tail feathers are fixed. uro'pygial, a. uropygial gland. A great GLAND on the back of a bird at the start of the tail feathers, producing the oil-like substance with which a bird keeps its feathers clean and smooth, and, in water-birds, water-tight.

uro'rubin, n. [Biochem., Med.] A red colouring-substance present in URINE in unnormal conditions.

u'roscopy, n. [Med.] The observation and testing of URINE to see if a person has a certain disease or not.

uro'sternite, n. [Zoo.] The plate on the under side of a URITE in ARTHROPODA.

uro'sthenic, a. [Zoo.] Having a strong tail designed for forcing the body through the water.

'urostyle, n. [Zoo.] The tail part of the backbone in AMPHIBIA and fishes, where it has no divisions.

uro'toxic, a. [Zoo., Med.] Of, to do with, the poisoning properties of URINE. uro'tox'icity, n. [Zoo., Med.] The poisoning properties of URINE. uro'toxin, n. [Med.] Any poisoning substance present in URINE. uro'toxy, n. A unit for measuring

urotoxicity, being the amount needed for causing the death of an animal of weight 1 kilogram.

uro'tropine, n. [Chem.] HEXAMETHYLENE-TETRAMINE.

'Urtica, n.pl. [Bot.] A GENUS of DICOTY-LEDONOUS plants of which the flowers are small, green, and without PETALS, and the fruit is an ACHENE, noted for the STINGING hairs with which their leaves are covered.

'urticant, 1.a. [Biol., Med.] With the property of poisoning the skin when touched, causing it to become red etc., as the STINGS of plants or animals or certain substances. 2.n. A u. substance.

urti'caria, n. [Med.] A skin disease marked by small, burning SWELLINGS with red skin all round them, which there is a strong desire to keep rubbing, and which come up and go down suddenly, sometimes caused by food, sometimes by insects, plants or medical substances.

'Ustilagi'nales, n.pl. [Bot.] An ORDER of BASIDIOMYCETES which are PARASITIC on a number of plants, sp. grasses, noted for producing small masses of black and freq. dust-like SPORES, sometimes on the leaves, sometimes on the flowers and sometimes in the seeds, and causing great destruction, most importantly to food grains.

'uterine, a. [Zoo.] Of, to do with, the UTERUS.

'uterus, n. [Zoo.] The complex part of a female MAMMAL (of which in animals other than man there are gen. two), in which the development of offspring to the point of birth takes place, walled with UNSTRIATED MUSCLE and coated inside with a GLANDULAR MEMBRANE producing food for the young in the early stages; in lower animals, the lower part of an OVIDUCT, or sp. any expansion or branch of an oviduct in which eggs or young undergo development. [Bot.] The PERIDIUM in some FUNGI. u. mascu'linus. [Zoo.] In male MAMMALS, a small bag-like part in the PROSTATE GLAND which is probably representative of the structure which in the female has undergone development into the u. 'utero-.

'utricle, n. [Biol.] A little, bag-like, hollow part, for example one of those seen on the leaves of some water-plants in which small animals are taken prisoner. [Bot.] A dry, gen, one-seeded, fruit in a thin, dry, hollow cover, or such a cover itself, [Zoo.] In back-boned animals, the hollow of the INNER EAR into which the SEMI-CIRCULAR CANALS go.

u'tricular, a. Bag-like. [Zoo.] Of, to do with, the UTRICULUS. u'triculo-. [Zoo.] (Of the) UTRICLE or UTRICULUS (and . . .).

u'triculus, n. [Zoo.] The UTRICLE of the ear. u. pros'taticus. UTERUS MASCULINUS.

'uva, n. [Bot.] A BERRY formed from a SUPERIOR OVARY, such as that from which most wine is made. 'uval, a.

'uvea, n. [Zoo.] The coloured back coat of the IRIS of the eye. [Med.] Uveal tract. 'uveal, a. uveal tract. [Med.] The u. together with the rest of the IRIS, the CHOROID, and the CILIARY BODY.

'uvula, n. [Zoo.] The soft finger-like body hanging from the back of the roof of the mouth. 'uvular, a. Sp. [Phonet.] (Of a sound) said with the use of the u., for example, by a quick motion of the u. against the back of the tongue. 2.n. [Phonet.] A uvular sound.

V, Sign for VANADIUM.

v, Sign for VELOCITY; in THERMODYNAMICS etc., sign for the VOLUME of a gas.

v-, [Chem.] Sign for VICINAL.

'vaccine, n. [Med.] A liquid made from that taken from the VESICLES produced in VACCINIA, and having in it the living vaccinia VIRUS, for use in vaccination; more widely, any liquid having in it disease BACTERIA or viruses, sp. dead or made feeble by some process, or of a sort, such as the vaccinia virus, causing effects like to but less serious than those of the disease against which it is used, for use in vaccination. v. lymph. Liquid taken from VACCINIA VESICLES used in making v. v. point. A little pointed rod of bone, etc., used in earlier days for taking up the v. lymph and on which it was dried. 'vaccinable, a. Giving the desired reaction to vaccination, able to be vaccinated with good effect. 'vaccinal, a. Of, to do with, v. or vaccination. 'vaccinate, v.t. INOCULATE (person or animal) with a v., sp. with the VACCINIA VIRUS sgainst VARIOLA by the special proces. of wounding the skin on the arm or leg and putting the v. on the wound. vacci'nation, n. 'vaccinee, n. Person undergoing vaccination. 'vaccino-.

vac'cinia, n. [Med.] A disease of cows like VARIOLA but much less serious, which if given to man by VACCINATION is responsible for the development of ANTIBODIES keeping him from getting VARIOLA. vac'cinial, a.

'vacuole, n. [Biol.] A hollow in the PROTOPLASM of a CELL, gen. very small in animal cells but in plants freq. taking up most of the cell, having in it a water-like liquid. 'vacuolar, a. vacuolar 'membrane. The skin of PROTOPLASM forming the wall of a v. 'vacuolate(d), aa. 'vacuol(iz)'ation, nn. The development of vv.

'vacuome, n. [Biol.] A system of VACUOLES in a CELL.

'vacuum, 1.n. [Phys.] A space with no substance whatever in it (absolute v.); a space from which as much air or other gas as possible (a high v.) or somewhat less than this (a partial or low v.) has been taken. 2.a. Of, to do with, having in it, producing or produced by, a v.; (of an instrument or process) worked by SUCTION. v. bottle, v. flask. A bottle or vessel for keeping drink or food warm or cold designed in the same way as the DEWAR FLASK. v. 'crystalli'zation. [Chem.] The CRYSTALLIZATION of a liquid in a v. at a TEMPERATURE lower than its boiling-point at normal PRESSURE. v. distillation. [Chem.] DISTILLATION in a v. or near v., by which the boiling-point is lowered, used for substances which become broken up when heated to a high degree and so are hard or impossible to DISTIL in the normal way. v. fil'ter. [Chem.] A FILTER in which some degree of a v. is produced on the outlet side, so that material is pushed through at a greater rate than normal. v. gauge. An instrument for measuring the degree of a v. v. pump. An instrument for pumping air or other gas out of a vessel or shut space; PULSOMETER. v. tube, v. valve. [Phys.] A vessel or bulb having two or more ELECTRODES coming into it, and in which a high v. has been produced so as to make possible an electric current between them, sp. a THERMIONIC VALVE.

'vadose, a. [Geol.] To do with or caused by water at or near the face of the earth, higher than GROUND WATER.

'vagal, a. See VAGUS.

va'gina, n. [Zoo.] The pipe-like part going from the UTERUS to the outside in the females of higher animals, sometimes one of two; a pipe-like cover. [Bot.] An expansion of a leaf-base going round the stem. 'vaginal, a. Sp., to do with the female v. 'vaginate, vagin'iferous, aa. [Biol.] Having a pipe-like cover round it, or round part of it.

vagi'nicolous, a. [Zoo.] Building a pipe-like cover round itself and living in it, as some PROTOZOA.

'vagini'pennate, a. [Zoo.] Having wings with coverings, as COLEOPTERA.

va'ginula, n. [Biol.] A small pipe-like cover, sp. [Bot.] round the base of the stem of the CAPSULE in BRYOPHYTA.

'vagus, n. [Zoo.] One or the other of the two CRANIAL NERVES of back-boned animals (the 10th in the system of numbering), branching to the stomach and other parts of the apparatus of digestion and to the heart and LUNGS or GILLS (freq. v. nerve). 'vagal, a.

'valence, n. [Chem.] VALENCY; unit of valency; VALENCY BOND. v. e'lectron, v. shell. See VALENCY.

'**valency,** n. [Chem.] The power of an ATOM or group of uniting with others, measured as the number of H atoms with which it may, in fact or in theory, be united, or whose place in a complex substance it is able to take. **v. bond.** The connection by which two ATOMS in a MOLECULE are united, of which the chief forms are the COVALENT BOND, the COÖRDINATE BOND, and the ELECTROVALENT BOND (*see* in addition DOUBLE BOND and TRIPLE BOND). **v. e'lectron.** Any of the ELECTRONS in the v. shell of an ATOM, which are chiefly responsible for its chemical and physical properties. **v. 'formula.** A CHEMICAL FORMULA in which points or short lines are put between SYMBOLS to make clear if the v. bond between the substances is SINGLE, DOUBLE, or TRIPLE, as HC:CH or H—C≡C—H for ACETYLENE (C_2H_2). **v. shell.** The outer ring of ELECTRONS of an ATOM, looked on in present-day theory as made up, when complete, of 8 electrons, but as being incomplete in most ELEMENTS, a fact which gives atoms of different elements the power of uniting with one another by the taking in and giving up of electrons between these rings, forming v. bonds.

va'leric acid, [Chem.] Any of four FATTY ACIDS, $C_4H_9CO_2H$, **valeric,** a. Of, to do with v.a. **valer(o)-.** (*See* p. 557).)

'**valetudi'narian,** n. [Med.] A delicate person needing regular medical care and unable to do much, sp. one whose chief interest is his feeble or unhealthy condition. **'-ism,** n. The condition of being a v.

'**valgus,** 1.a. [Med.] (Of legs) arched out (or in) in the middle so that the knees are farther away from one another than normal or so near as to be in one another's way; (of a person) having v. legs. 2.n. The sort of TALIPES seen in a v. person (freq. *talipes v.*); a condition in which the arch of the foot is so low that the inner side is flat on the earth in walking.

vall'ecula, (valleculae), n. [Biol.] GROOVE. **vall'ecular,** a. **valle'culate,** a.

'**valley,** n. [Geog.] Any long hollow or stretch of flat land between mountains or slopes, sometimes cut out by a river and sloping more or less regularly down in the direction of the sea or some other water basin, sometimes produced by motions of the earth. **v. train.** The stones and sand etc. put down in a v. by water coming from a GLACIER. **v. winds.** [Meteor.] The regular currents of air blowing up the sides of a v. in the day time and down at night when the weather is clear, caused by the heating of the higher slopes of the v. by the sun to a greater degree than its lower part.

'**value,** n. [Optics] In the MUNSELL COLOUR SYSTEM, the quality of LIGHTNESS as judged by the eye. **vv.** [Photog.] The degree to which the shades of a black-and-white camera picture are representative of the vv. of the colours in the view pictured, and give the right relations between them.

'**valva,** n. [Zoo.] VALVE.

'**valval, 'valvar,** aa. *See* VALVE.

'**valvate,** a. [Biol.] Having a VALVE or valves, sp. [Bot.] of a fruit etc. opening by the lifting of a door-like cover or side parts. [Bot.] (Of PETALS, SEPALS or leaves in a BUD) meeting at the edges but not going over one another at all. **v. de'hiscence.** [Bot.] The system of opening of a v. fruit or ANTHER, **v. aesti'vation (ver'nation).** [Bot.] The ranging of PETALS and SEPALS in a flower-BUD (or of leaves in a leaf-bud) with their edges meeting.

valve, n. [Mach.] Any automatic or other apparatus forming part of a pipe or other vessel, by which the pipe etc. may be opened or shut, completely or to some degree, by the operation of some moving part (sometimes working like a door, sometimes slipping or rolling into place) —for the purpose of letting through in one direction only, or of controlling or keeping back as desired, a current of liquid or gas, or a mass of loose solid material; the moving part of a v., by whose change of position the v. is shut or opened. [Zoo.] Any structure, gen. a muscle or a fold or folds of MEMBRANE, by which a pipe or like vessel, or an outlet in any part of the body is opened or shut, freq. automatically, so as to let through liquid etc. in one direction only; a v.-like fold or membrane; any of the separate parts, freq. so joined as to have the power of moving in relation to one another, forming the SHELL in certain water CRUSTACEA; any of the plates or pipe-like parts forming the covering of the OVIPOSITOR or other outer sex-parts in certain insects. [Bot.] Any of the parts into which a seed-cover of the sort bursting open when the seeds are ready becomes separated; the cover of certain ANTHERS, which comes off when the POLLEN is ready to be let out; one or the other of the two box-and-cover-like halves of the outer covering of a DIATOM. [Elec., Radio] Any apparatus which lets electric current through in one direction only, used chiefly as a RECTIFIER; in Great Britain but not commonly in U.S.A., any VACUUM TUBE or GAS-DISCHARGE TUBE used for any purpose. '**valval, 'valvar,** aa. Valvular, **valval view.** [Bot.] A view of a DIATOM in which one or other of the vv. is facing the eye, as opp. ZONAL VIEW. **'-less,** a. Without a v., sp. [Mach.] of an engine in which the

PISTON itself does the work of a v., opening and shutting the outlet and inlet in its motion. **val'viferous,** a. [Biol.] **'valviform,** a. [Biol.] **'valvular,** a. [Biol.] Of, to do with, like, a v. or vv., sp. [Med.] to do with by the vv. of the heart; having, opening by, acting as, a v.

'valvula, n. [Zoo.] A small VALVE or valve-like fold controlling the inlet or outlet of liquid etc. **'valvulate,** a.

'vanadate, n. [Chem.] A SALT or ESTER of VANADIC ACID.

va'nadic, a. [Chem.] Of, to do with, having in it, VANADIUM, said sp. of a complex substance in which vanadium has one of its higher VALENCIES. **v. 'acid.** Any of a number of ACIDS formed from V_2O_5 (VANADIUM PENTOXIDE), as H_3VO_4, gen. not in existence as free substances but forming VANADATES.

va'nadious, 'vanadous, aa. [Chem.] Of, to do with, having in it, VANADIUM, sp. said of a complex substance in which vanadium has one of its lower VALENCIES.

va'nadium, n. Chemical ELEMENT, at. no. 23, at. wt. 50·95, sign V, a very hard white metal used chiefly for mixing with steel. **vanado-.**

'van de 'Graaff generator. [Elec.] An apparatus for the development of very high VOLTAGES made up of a band of material going round two PULLEYS, near one of which it gets a high CHARGE from an electric machine which is taken on by it to the other and there sent out into a vessel which, taking in charge after charge, becomes very highly charged—used as an ACCELERATOR for CHARGED PARTICLES.

'van der 'Waals' force(s). [Phys.] The force of attraction between MOLECULES or ATOMS of all substances.

vane, n. Any thin, flat blade of wood or metal fixed to a turning rod so as to be turned by a current of air or water, as the vv. of a PROPELLER. [Zoo.] The wide, flat or waving soft part of a feather, that is, the BARBS with their outgrowths, as opp. the stiff supporting structure from which they come.

van 't Hoff's law. [Chem.] The law that the OSMOTIC PRESSURE of a SOLUTION having in it little of the SOLVENT is the same as that of the same amount of the solvent would be if it were in the form of a gas at the same degree of heat as the solution and taking up the same space.

'vapour, n. Any liquid or gas clouding the air, as mist, steam, smoke. [Phys.] A gas, sp. the gas form of any substance which is normally a liquid or solid; a gas at a TEMPERATURE lower than its CRITICAL TEMPERATURE, that is one which may be made liquid by an increase in PRESSURE only, without making it colder. **v.**

'density. [Phys.] The weight of a unit measure of a gas given in relation to that of the same measure of H, or sometimes O or air, at the same TEMPERATURE and PRESSURE. **v. 'pressure, v. 'tension.** The PRESSURE of a v., sp. SATURATED v. pressure. **'vaporable,** a. Which may be vaporized. **vapor'imeter,** n. An instrument for measuring v. pressure or VOLUME, used sp. in measuring: 1. the amount of alcohol in mixed alcohol and water, and 2. the vaporizing power of oils. **'vapori'zation,** n. The process of vaporizing. **'vaporize,** v.t. and i. [Phys.-Chem.] (Make) become changed from a solid or liquid condition into a mist or gas, give off part of its substance in the form of mist or gas. **'vaporizer,** n. Any instrument or apparatus for turning a liquid or solid into a v., sp.:— [Med.] an ATOMIZER; [Engin.] a part of an INTERNAL COMBUSTION ENGINE in which the PETROLEUM or like oil used in driving it is vaporized for burning. **'vaporous,** a. Giving off v., formed of v., v.-like.

'variable, 1.a. Changing, sp. readily and frequently, or able to be changed. [Elec.] (Of instruments) of which some property, such as CAPACITY, rate, INDUCTANCE etc., may be changed to any degree between given wide limits, as a v. CONDENSER. 2.n. [Math.] A value which is different in different conditions. **v. re'sistor, v. re'sistance.** [Elec.] RHEOSTAT. **v. star.** [Astron.] Any of those stars whose BRIGHTNESS as seen from the earth is not fixed, but changing between two limits—some in a regular rhythm, with fixed times of anything from an hour or two to 20 months or more, some seemingly irregularly. **varia'bility,** n. The condition of being v. or the degree to which a thing is v. [Chem.] The number of DEGREES OF FREEDOM of a system.

'variance, n. The fact, property, or condition of changing or of being different, sp. from what is regular or normal; amount by which a thing is changed or by which two things, for example two values for the same thing got in two different ways, are different, not in agreement. [Chem.] VARIABILITY.

'variant, 1.a. Different, sp. from what is general, regular, normal. [Biol.] Being, to do with, a v. 2.n. A v. thing, sp. [Biol.] an animal or plant which is a little different from its TYPE, but not different enough to put it in a different SPECIES.

vari'ation, n. Change, act or fact of changing; fact of being somewhat different from what is regular or normal; amount or degree of v. [Astron.] A change in the AVERAGE motion or direction of a PLANET caused by a change in its distance from, and so its attraction by, another. [Phys.]

DECLINATION (gen. *magnetic v.*). [Biol.] The v. of a plant or animal in structure or physical properties from its group, sp. its SPECIES, or of offspring from the plants or animals producing them; a plant or animal marked by v. **v. of 'latitude.** [Astron.] A small regular change in the LATITUDE of any place caused by a small move of the AXIS on which the earth is turning and other more complex effects. **vv.** [Biol.] The points in which the offspring of the same plants or animals, or in which animals or plants of the same group, are different from one another. **'-al, a.**

'varicated, a. [Med.] Having, marked by, a VARIX or varices.

'vari'cation, n. [Med.] The forming of a VARIX or varices; the condition of having a varix or varices; the form of a varix or the way in which varices are grouped.

vari'cella, n. [Med.] A CONTAGIOUS disease chiefly attacking the young and not in itself serious, marked by outbursts of PAPULES and VESICLES in one place after another, commonly limited to the chest, face, back, and the upper parts of the arms and legs. **vari'celloid,** a.

vari'cellate, a. [Zoo.] (Of a SHELL) having small or not very sharply marked VARICES.

'varices, n.pl. *See* VARIX.

'varicose, a. [Med.] (Of VEINS, or less frequently ARTERIES or LYMPHATICS) having become unnormally long, SWOLLEN and twisted, a condition caused by the stretching of the walls by the force of the blood and commonest in the veins of the legs, sp. of women as the effect of producing offspring; to do with, marked or caused by, for use in connection with, v. veins. [Bot.] (Of a leaf VEIN or any hollow, thread-like part) unnormally SWOLLEN. **v. 'ulcer.** [Med.] An open wound formed by the bursting of a v. VEIN under the skin, sp. of the leg. **'varicosed,** a. (Of animal or plant VEINS or the parts having them) v. **vari'cosis,** n. [Med.] The forming of v. VEINS etc.; varicosity. **vari'cosity,** n. [Med.] The condition of being v.; a v. VEIN or part. **varico-.**

'variegated, a. Marked with different colours, sp. in irregular masses.

va'riety, n. [Biol.] A group of plants or animals forming part of a SPECIES but marked off as a separate division of it by having in common certain properties which are different from the TYPE but clearly developments from it, and which are regularly handed on to their offspring when produced by BREEDING with one another—the effect of special living-conditions together with long INBREEDING. [Mineral.] Any of the somewhat different forms which may be taken by the same MINERAL as to the effect of dif-

ferent conditions of development or of being mixed with small amounts of other substances.

va'riola, n. [Med.] A serious INFECTIOUS disease caused by a VIRUS, freq. causing death, and marked by the development of a thick mass of PAPULES, chiefly on the arms, legs and face, which later become VESICLES, and last, PUSTULES forming thick SCABS, which come off, gen. marking the skin for ever with small hollows. **va'riolar, va'riolous,** aa. **'variolate,** 1.a. Having marks on the skin like those made by v. 2.vt. Make undergo variolation, **'variolated,** a. Having undergone variolation or had v.; variolate. **vario-'lation, varioli'zation,** n. INOCULATION with the v. VIRUS—an earlier process, the place of which has now been taken by VACCINATION. **'varioloid,** a.1., 2.n. A less serious form of v. sometimes attacking persons who have undergone VACCINATION or have had v.

'variole, n. [Biol.] A small hollow, as [Med.] one made on the skin by a VARIOLA. [Geol.] Any of the small round bodies bedded in VARIOLITE.

'variolite, n. [Geol.] Any of different sorts of small-grained BASIC ROCK having bedded in them small, more or less white, round bodies made up of a mass of FELDSPAR needles raying out from a middle point. **vario'litic,** a.

'vari'ometer, n. [Radio] A VARIABLE INDUCTOR made up of two COILS, gen. one inside the other, of which the inner may be turned round its middle point so as to make a change in their MUTUAL INDUCTANCE.

'varix (varices), n. [Med.] A VARICOSE VEIN, ARTERY, or LYMPHATIC. [Zoo.] Any of the high RIDGES across the turns of certain SPIRAL SHELLS, representative of an earlier position of the outer edge of the opening.

'varnish, n. A SOLUTION of a RESIN in SPIRITS or oil (gen. quick-drying) used as a coating for paint to keep it from damage and give it a polished look. **'varnished,** a. [Bot.] Having a bright, polished look, as some leaves.

varve, n. [Geol.] A thick coat of sand and earth material, marked by a regular change from less smooth at the base to very smooth at the top, put down in one year (from summer to summer) on the bed of a body of inland water by rivers draining from GLACIERS, or from the ice in the end stage of an ICE AGE—of great use in Geology for the purpose of v. analysis, by which, for example, the CHRONOLOGY of the PLEISTOCENE Ice Age has been worked out. **v. an'alysis.** The observation of the vv. on the beds of bodies of water such as the Baltic Sea for the purpose of getting a picture of the time and order of past events in the land's history. **v. clay.** The sort of CLAY made up of vv. forming the beds of certain inland waters. **varved,** a. Made up of vv., put down in clearly marked beds of one year's growth.

vas (vasa), n. [Zoo.] A small vessel or pipe transporting liquid. **v. 'deferens.** A pipe by which SPERM is sent out from a TESTICLE to the outside or to some other part—in man and higher animals, to the PENIS. **'vasa effe'rentia.** Mass of very small vv. going from a TESTICLE to the v. deferens. **'vasa va'sorum.** In back-boned animals, very small blood-vessels forming a network in the walls of the greater ones, sometimes coming from a branch of the same vessel, sometimes from one near by.

'vascular, a. [Biol.] To do with, made up of, having, vessels for transporting liquid, sp. blood or SAP. **v. an'asto'mosis.** [Bot.] A small v. bundle going across between the chief v. bundles of a stem or root and making a connection between them. **v. 'area.** [Zoo.] In the eggs of AMNIOTE back-boned animals, the part of the YOLK-SAC where the development of the blood-vessels has its start. **v. 'bundle.** [Bot.] Any of the separate cord-like or band-like v. structures running long-ways down the stems and roots and into the leaves of plants and taking liquids up and down, made up of XYLEM and PHLOEM side by side or one inside the other, with FIBROUS supporting CELLS here and there, and sometimes all round them, and, in most DICOTYLEDONS and GYMNOSPERMS (but not in MONOCOTYLEDONS), with CAMBIUM between the xylem and phloem, making possible further growth—ranged in different ways in different plants, sometimes all through the stem substance, sometimes in a ring or rings round the edge, with PITH in the middle. **v. 'cryptogam.** [Bot.] A CRYPTOGAM having v. tissue, as FILICALES. **v. 'cylinder.** [Bot.] STELE. **v. plant.** [Bot.] Any of the higher sorts of plants having special v. tissue for the distribution of food and water, as all seed plants. **v. strand.** V. bundle. **v. ray.** [Bot.] Any of the upright plates of PARENCHYMA going from the middle to the edge of a stem or root, through XYLEM and PHLOEM, and transporting liquids across it, seen as a narrow raying line when the stem etc. is cut across. **v. 'system.** [Zoo.] The system of vessels by which blood and LYMPH are transported through the body; WATER-VASCULAR SYSTEM. [Bot.] The v. material of a higher plant, forming a system for the distribution of water and food-material to all

parts of, and acting as a support for, it. **v. 'tissue.** [Bot.] Any material designed for transporting liquids in plants, but sp. the complex of XYLEM and PHLOEM as seen in v. bundles, of which a v. system is made up. **'vascu'larity,** n. [Biol.] The condition of being v. **'vasculari'zation,** n. [Biol.] The process of becoming v., sp. [Med.] the forming and branching out of very small blood-vessels. **'vasculature,** n. [Zoo.] The system of blood-vessels of an animal or part, or the way in which these are ranged. **'vasculo-.**

vas'culiform, a. [Bot.] Formed like a little plant-pot.

'Vaseline, n. [Med.] Trade name for the jelly-like or butter-like forms of PETROLATUM, used medically as an OINTMENT or ointment BASE.

vasi'factive, a. VASOFORMATIVE.

va'siferous, a. [Biol.] Having a pipe-like part or parts.

'vasiform, a. [Biol.] Acting as, having the form of, a pipe or other transporting vessel.

vaso-. [Zoo.] Of, to do with, blood-vessels; VASOMOTOR. [Med.] Of, to do with, the VAS DEFERENS.

'vasocon'strictor, n., a. [Zoo., Med.] (A nerve, a medical substance, etc.) causing vasoconstriction. **'vasocon'striction,** n. A narrowing of blood-vessels, sp. ARTERIES, by the operation of the UNSTRIATED MUSCLE in their walls.

vaso'dentine, n. [Zoo.] A sort of DENTINE full of small blood-vessels, present sp. in the teeth of lower back-boned animals.

'vasodi'lator, n., a. [Zoo., Med.] (A nerve, medical substance, etc.) causing vasodilatation. **'vasodila'tation, 'vasodi'lation,** nn. The expansion or RELAXATION of blood-vessels, sp. ARTERIES, by the operation of the UNSTRIATED MUSCLE of their walls, or by the stopping of VASOCONSTRICTION.

vaso'formative, a. [Zoo.] Forming, or to do with the forming of, blood or blood-vessels.

vaso'ganglion, n. [Zoo.] A knot of blood-vessels, sp. a RED BODY.

'vasohyper'tonic, a., n. VASOCONSTRICTOR.

'vasohypo'tonic, a., n. VASODILATOR.

'vasoin'hibitory, a. [Zoo., Med.] Slowing down or stopping the operation of VASOMOTOR nerves, sp. VASOCONSTRICTORS. **'vasoin'hibitor,** n. Anything, such as a medical substance, having a v. effect.

vaso'motion, n. [Zoo.] The expansion and narrowing of blood-vessels, sp. ARTERIES, for the purpose of controlling the amount of blood going through them. **vaso'motor,** a. Causing, to do with, v., said sp. of the nerves going to the muscles in the walls of the blood-vessels.

'vasopa'resis, n. [Med.] The loss of the

power of operation in the VASOMOTOR nerves.

'vaso'pressin, n. [Biochem.] The HORMONE produced by the back part of the PITUITARY GLAND, which has the effect of narrowing the small blood-vessels, so increasing the BLOOD PRESSURE.

'vaso'pressor, n. [Med.] A substance causing an increase in the BLOOD PRESSURE.

'vaso'sensory, a. [Zoo.] (Of nerves or effects) effecting or to do with the sense-reactions of blood-vessels.

'vaso'tonic, a. [Zoo.] Of, to do with, causing, increasing, the TONUS of the muscles of blood-vessels.

'vaso'tonin, n. [Biochem.] Any of certain substances produced in the blood when it becomes jelly-like by which VASOCONSTRICTION is caused.

'vaso'trophic, a. [Zoo.] To do with giving food to blood-vessels.

vat, n. A great open vessel for liquid, such as is used in making paper, wine, etc., or in DYEING. v. dye, v. dye stuffs. [Chem.] A group of DYES which are themselves not SOLUBLE, used for DYEING by first changing them into soluble but uncoloured COMPOUNDS and mixing with liquid ALKALIS, from which liquid the coloured dye is formed again, on cloth wetted with it, by a straightforward reaction with the O of the air, so that no MORDANT is needed.

vault, n. Any structure like an arched roof, sp. [Zoo.], the top of the head, etc.

'vector, n. [Biol.] An animal, gen. an insect, transporting disease BACTERIA or other PARASITES from one plant or animal to another. [Math.] A QUANTITY which is made up of an amount moving in a direction and so may be given in the form of a straight line, of which the measure is representative of the amount and the direction of the direction (for example VELOCITY).

veer, v.i. [Meteor.] (Of wind) have the direction from which it is coming changed in the same direction as the hands of a clock, for example, from west to northwest, opp. BACK. '-ing, a., n.

'vegetable, 1.n. A plant. 2.a. To do with, of, produced from, plants. v. 'kingdom. [Biol.] The group of living things made up of all plants, the highest group in the system of grouping in Botany, of which the chief divisions are SUB-KINGDOMS (see p. 560). v. pole. VEGETAL POLE.

'vegetal, a. VEGETABLE. v. pole. [Zoo.] That point on an egg straight opposite the ANIMAL POLE, furthest from the NUCLEUS and gen. where there is most YOLK, the process of division is slower, and the BLASTOMERES are of greater size than those produced round the animal pole.

vege'tation, n. [Bot., Geog.] Plant growth,

plants as forming a cover for the earth, all the growth of plants in a given place.

'vegetative, a. [Biol.] Having the power of growth, or (of earth etc.) of supporting plant growth; of, to do with growth, sp. with the general processes of growth and living, or the apparatuses of these, as opp. the producing of offspring; of, to do with, like, plants; of, to do with, v. reproduction. v. cone. [Bot.] The round-pointed MERISTEMATIC end of a stem where growth takes place. v. 'functions. [Zoo.] The automatic necessary processes of the body controlled by the v. nervous system, such as digestion and blood-distribution. v. 'multipli'cation, v. 'propa'gation, v. 'repro'duction. [Zoo.] The producing of offspring by any process other than a sex process, sp. BUDDING. [Bot.] The producing of new plants by the rooting and development of some part of a plant body, as a bulb, a cutting, a RHIZOME, etc. v. 'nervous 'system. [Zoo.] AUTONOMIC or SYMPATHETIC NERVOUS SYSTEM. v. pole. VEGETAL POLE.

'vegetism, n. [Biol.] The property or condition of being VEGETATIVE.

'vehicle, n. Any such thing as a carriage, cart, automobile, airplane etc., in or on which things or persons are transported from place to place; a substance in which another substance is SUSPENDED etc. for use, for example, colouring material in oil to make paint, medical substances in fat to make OINTMENT etc.

veil, n. [Biol.] VELUM.

vein, n. [Zoo.] Any of the blood-vessels taking blood back to the heart from the very small hair-like blood-vessels bedded in the different parts of the body, in higher animals having thinner walls than ARTERIES and freq. VALVES at different points to keep the blood from going back; a NERVURE of an insect's wing. [Bot.] Any of the VASCULAR BUNDLES forming the supporting framework of a leaf. [Geol., Mining] An irregular mass of some MINERAL, freq. one of value, which has been formed in a crack in a bed of ROCK by CRYSTALLIZATION from heated or cold liquids running into it. 'veined, a. Having vv. of any sort; marked with v.-like lines. '-stone, n. [Geol.] Any material of the sort formed in vv., gen. of simple chemical make-up and of markedly SYMMETRICAL CRYSTAL structure and freq. without Si, having separated from the more complex substances making up the masses of IGNEOUS ROCK—a form in which metals of value are freq. present. [Mining] A v. or, loosely, any other mass of material of value under the earth; the waste material present in a v. as opp. the ORE. '-ous, 'venous, aa.

[Biol.] To do with, having, vv. **'venous blood.** [Zoo.] The blood present in vv., which has gone through the CAPILLARIES, where it has given up O and become full of CO$_2$, and now has to go through the breathing-apparatus to give out the CO$_2$ and take in more O—marked in higher animals by its dark red colour as opp. the bright red of the blood in the ARTERIES.

ve'lamen (velamena), n. [Zoo.] VELUM. [Bot.] A thick silver-coloured coat, formed of a structure of dead CELLS full of air, which has the property of taking in water like a sponge, seen on the outside of the AERIAL ROOTS of certain plants. **vela'mentous,** a. To do with, like, having a v. **vela'mentum,** n. [Zoo.] V.

'velar, a. 1.n. VELUM, sp. [Phonet.] that of the roof of the mouth in man. 2.a. [Phonet.] Formed with the tongue touching or near the v. **ve'laric,** a.

ve'larium (velaria), n. [Zoo.] In certain SCYPHOZOA, the thin waving band round the edge of the UMBRELLA, like the VELUM of HYDROZOA but different in having pipe-like hollows with an ENDODERMIC inner coat running through it.

'velate, a. *See* VELUM.

'veliger, n. [Zoo.] The second LARVA stage of most MOLLUSCS, coming after the TROCHOPHORE, in which the VELUM is present together with some of the parts (such as the FOOT and the SHELL) of the animal as it will be at full development.

ve'locity, n. The rate at which any process or motion goes on, sp. a high rate. [Mech.] Rate of motion in a given direction, measured in units of distance per unit of time. **v. 'constant.** [Chem.] The v. of a chemical reaction, given as the number of GRAM-MOLECULES in a litre which are changed in 1 second, when the mass of every substance taking part in it = 1 unit. **v. head.** [Phys.] The ENERGY per unit weight of a current of liquid or gas produced by its v. **v. of es'cape.** [Astron.,etc.] The smallest v. a moving body would have to have to take it out of range of the attraction of a greater body or system on or near which it is, for example, the smallest v. necessary to let a star get away from a group kept together by attraction, or a gas or other body get out of the field of attraction of the earth or other PLANET, and go off into outer space. **v. of light.** [Phys.] The unchanging rate of motion of light in a VACUUM, used as a measure of comparison for very high vv., about 29·979 thousand million cm. or 186,326 MILES per sec., sign *c.* **v. of propa'gation** [Elec.] The rate at which an electric wave goes down a wire, which is the same as the v. of light. **v. 'ratio.** [Mech.] (Of a machine such as, or

based on the operation of, a PULLEY, LEVER etc.) the RATIO of the distance through which the point at which the pushing or pulling force starting the operation is moved in a given time to the distance through which the weight to be lifted etc. is moved in the same time.

'velum (vela), n. [Biol.] A thin MEMBRANE acting as a cover or division and giving the suggestion of a curtain, sp.:— [Bot.] in young AGARICS, a network of HYPHAE covering all or part of the top and stem of the plant-body, broken in the process of growth and becoming in the older plant the ANNULUS or the VOLVA; in MUSCI, the CALYPTRA; in ASCOMYCETES, a thin skin covering a SPORE vessel; [Zoo.] in higher animals, the loose, soft part at the back of the roof of the mouth; in some CILIOPHORA, a thin skin edging the mouth; in sponges, a membrane narrowing the opening of a water-pipe; in HYDROZOA, a band of membrane sloping in and forming a sort of shelf round the edge of the UMBRELLA; a collar-like CONTRACTILE band, freq. with curtain-like side expansions, supporting the ring of CILIA in front of the mouth in a VELIGER and forming a swimming apparatus. **'velar.** a. **'velate,** a.

ve'lutinous, a. [Biol.] Covered thickly with very short, soft, upright hairs, very smooth and soft to the touch.

'velvet, n. [Zoo.] The soft, very VASCULAR, VELUTINOUS skin covering and giving food to ANTLERS in process of growth, and rubbed off by the animal when their development is complete.

'vena (venae), n. [Zoo.] VEIN. **v. 'cava** (venae cavae). Any of the three chief blood-vessels taking the blood back from the different parts of the body to the right side of the heart.

ve'nation, n. [Biol.] The VEIN system of a part, the veins themselves taken together or the structure formed by them, their order and distribution, sp. of a leaf or an insect's wing.

'venda 'vales, n. [Geog., Meteor.] Strong, irregularly violent, south-west winds blowing on the east side of Spain and in the Straits of Gibraltar, sp. in winter, and causing much rain.

ven'eno-. [Zoo., Med.] To do with, producing, VENOM (and . . .):— **'-sa'livary,** a.

ve'nereal, a. [Med., Psych.] To do with, caused by, COPULATION; of, to do with, diseases given by one person to another in the process of copulation.

vene'section, n. [Med.] The process of letting blood from a VEIN by cutting it, used to give help in certain conditions.

'venom, n. [Zoo., Med.] Any poison produced by an animal, for example, a snake

or an insect, and used for poisoning other
animals in biting or in some other way
wounding them. **'-ous**, a. [Zoo.] (Of
animals) having a poisoning apparatus,
having the power of poisoning other
animals by biting them, etc. **'venomo-.**
'venomo'salivary gland. A SALIVARY
GLAND producing poison.

'venose, a. [Biol.] Full of VEINS, clearly
marked with veins, sp., of a leaf, having
thick veins; having v.-like markings.
ve'nosity, n. [Biol.] The condition of
being v. [Med.] A condition in which the
VEINS are over-full of blood; a condition
in which the blood in the ARTERIES is like
VENOUS BLOOD.

'venous, a. See VEIN.

vent, n. An opening or pipe for the outlet
or inlet of gas or liquid. [Zoo.] The outlet
of the ANUS or CLOACA in back-boned
animals. [Geol.] The pipe-like hollow
coming up through a VOLCANO from the
deeper parts of the earth to the basin at
the top; the mass of ASHES or solid LAVA
stopping up the v. of a volcano which is
no longer, or only from time to time, in
operation. **'v.-hole**, n. A v. for gas or
liquid.

'venter, n. [Zoo.] The ABDOMEN, or the
hollow inside it, or its front or under
side in man and other back-boned
animals; a rounded expansion like the
outcurved lower part of the abdomen, for
example, the thickest part of a muscle.
[Bot.] The rounded expansion forming the
base part of an ARCHEGONIUM and housing one egg-CELL.

'ventifact, n. [Geol.] A small stone which
has been given form and polish by driving
sand transported by the wind.

'ventilate, v.t. Send good air through (a
building, mine, etc.) to take the place of
bad or used air sent out at the same time,
keep air moving in and out of (a building
etc.) so that it is kept good for breathing,
or (of windows, pipes, etc.) be the
instrument by which this is done; send a
current of cold air through a motor etc.
to keep it from getting overheated, or be
the apparatus by which this is done.
'ventilating, a. **ventilating 'tissue.** [Bot.]
The system of air-spaces in a plant by
which air is kept moving through it.
venti'lation, n. The act of ventilating or
the condition of being ventilated. **'venti-
lator**, n. Any apparatus or structure
designed for ventilating.

'ventral, a. [Biol.] Of, to do with, like, near,
the VENTER. [Zoo.] Being, to do with, on
or near the under side, or, in man, the
front side, of the body. [Bot.] (To do with,
on, the side of a flower-part) facing the
middle line of a plant; on, to do with,
being, the side of a leaf facing the stem;
on, to do with, being, the lower side of a

flat plant-body or part other than a leaf
(opp. DORSAL). **v. a'orta.** [Zoo.] In fish the
great branching ARTERY taking the
blood from the heart to the breathing-
apparatus. **v. ca'nal cell.** [Bot.] A small,
unwalled CELL in the VENTER of an
ARCHEGONIUM between the neck and the
egg-cell, **v. fin.** [Zoo.] PELVIC FIN, sp. in
U.S.A.; ANAL FIN. **v. root.** [Zoo.] That
part of a SPINAL NERVE-ROOT made up of
MOTOR FIBRES. **v. 'suture.** [Bot.] The
line down which the OVULES are placed
in a CARPEL, looked on as the joining
line of the two edges of an infolded leaf of
which the carpel is a development.
'ventrally, adv. **ventri-, ventro-.** [Zoo.,
Med.] (To do with) the ABDOMEN (and
. . .):—**ven'troscopy**, n.; v. (and . . .):—
'ventro'lateral, a.

'ventricle, n. [Zoo.] A hollow in a part of the
body, sp.:— in back-boned animals and
MOLLUSCS, the division of the heart into
which blood is taken from the AURICLE(s)
and by the thickly-muscled walls of which
it is pumped out again into the ARTERIES
—in birds and MAMMALS one of two, the
right v. sending blood to the breathing-
apparatus, the *left v.* to the other parts
of the body; any of the system of spaces
full of CEREBROSPINAL FLUID in the
brain of back-boned animals in connection with one another and with the
hollow down the middle of the SPINAL
CORD, in man 4 in number; one or other
of the two hollows in the LARYNX between the true and the false VOCAL
CORDS; in birds, the GIZZARD; in ARTHRO-
PODA, the second and middle part of the
ALIMENTARY CANAL. **ven'tricular**, a.
VENTRICOSE. [Zoo.] To do with a v.;
to do with the stomach or with the
VENTRAL wall of the ABDOMEN. **ven-
'triculo-.**

'ventricose, a. [Biol.] Rounded out, thicker,
in the middle or on one side. **v. shell.**
[Zoo.] A SHELL of which the VALVES or
WHORLS are markedly rounded out in
the middle. **ventri'cosity**, n.

ven'triculus, n. [Zoo.] The stomach or, in
certain animals with a complex stomach,
the chief division of it, in birds, the
GIZZARD; a VENTRICLE.

ventro'dorsal, a. [Biol.] Going from the
VENTRAL side to the DORSAL side, sp.
[Zoo.].

Ven'turi tube (or pipe). [Phys.] An apparatus formed of two pipe-like parts with
wide round openings at one end and
narrowing down to small round openings joined by a very short narrow pipe
(named the **Venturi throat**) at the other,
used for making a connection between
two divisions of a wider pipe so that
the rate of motion of a current of
liquid or gas going through it will be

greatly increased through the throat, and by BERNOUILLI'S PRINCIPLE, the PRESSURE will be made less, giving a way of working out the rate in the chief pipe from the change in pressure. **Venturi 'meter.** An instrument based on the V.t. for measuring the rate of a current of liquid or gas through a shut pipe.

'venule, n. [Biol.] Any of the small branches of the VEINS in animals, or sp. in leaves or the wings of insects. **'venular,** a. **'venul-ose, -ous,** aa.

'Venus, n. [Astron.] The brightest of the PLANETS in the sun's system, second in order of distance from the sun (about 67,000,000 miles) about $\frac{4}{5}$ the size of the earth, taking about 225 days to go round the sun, and having no moons.

vera'nillo, n. [Geog., Meteor.] In the TROPICS of America, a regular short space of dry weather in the middle of the wet time of year.

ve'rano, n. [Geog., Meteor.] The long dry time of year in the TROPICS of America.

'verbal, a. Of, to do with, words, sp. as opp. facts; given in words. [Psych.] To do with the use of language, the power of talking. **v. be'haviour.** [Psych.] Those reactions of the body whose outcome is the making of signs or the saying or writing of words. **v. 'image.** [Psych.] An IMAGE in the mind of the form or sound or feeling of saying a word. **'verbalism,** n. [Psych.] A tendency to make use of words in one's thought-processes without giving attention to the facts and relations of which they are representative.

ver'bigeration, n. [Med.] The saying over and over of the same sounds or words without sense, as in some unbalanced conditions of mind.

Ver'det's constant. [Phys.] A measure, changing with the TEMPERATURE, of the ROTATION produced in PLANE-POLARIZED light by a MAGNETIC FIELD round it (*see* FARADAY EFFECT).

'verdigris, n. [Chem.] The green or blue substance formed on copper and brass when acted on by air, chiefly a BASIC CARBONATE of copper; copper ACETATE, or a substance made up of different basic copper acetates, used in DYEING and medically in powders and OINTMENTS for skin troubles.

ve'ridical, a. [Psych.] (Of a DREAM or other mind-IMAGE) in agreement with a fact or event, sp., in PSYCHIC RESEARCH, giving a true picture of something at a distance or in the future etc., of which the person having the experience has no normal knowledge.

'verifiable, a. Which may be VERIFIED, is not outside the range of knowledge, or of tests to make clear if it is true or false. **'ver'ifia'bility,** n.

verifi'cation, n. The act of verifying, or the condition of being verified; the fact(s) by agreement with which something is verified. **'verifi'cative, 'verifi'catory,** aa. **'verify,** v.t. Get, by the use of tests or by the discovery or producing of facts, such support for (a statement, idea, theory etc.) as to make it clear that it is true, or (of facts etc.) give such support.

'Vermes, n.pl. [Zoo.] An old group-name used at one time for all non-back-boned animals but ARTHROPODA, later for a group made up of worm-like animals, and now no longer in use.

vermi-. [Zoo., Med.] Worm:— **'-cide,** n., **ver'mivorous,** a.

vermian, a. [Zoo.] Of worms, worm-like; to do with the VERMIS.

ver'micular, a. [Biol.] Worm-like in form or motion; marked with waving lines or bands like those made by a w. on the earth.

'ver'miculate(d), aa. [Biol.] VERMICULAR; full of worms, being lived on, undergoing damage or destruction, by worms. **'vermicu'lation,** n. Worm-like motion, sp. PERISTALSIS; a system of VERMICULAR marking; the condition of being full of worms.

'vermicule, n. [Zoo.] A small worm-like structure or animal, as certain SPOROZOA in their free-moving stage.

ver'miculite, n. [Mineral.] Any of a group of natural SILICATES, produced generally by some chemical change in MICA, which when heated undergo expansion, their leaves separating and forming into long worm-like structures.

'vermiform, n. Worm-like in form. **v. ap'pendix.** [Zoo.] In some higher animals, a thin pipe some inches long, with no opening at the end, opening into the CAECUM at the joining-point of the LARGE and SMALL INTESTINES, a VESTIGIAL end-part of the caecum, having in it much LYMPHOID TISSUE. **v. 'process.** [Zoo.] V. appendix; VERMIS.

'vermifuge, n. [Med.] A substance causing the destruction of worms in, or driving them out of, the INTESTINES. **vermi-'fugal,** a.

ver'milion, n. [Chem.] A bright red form of HgS used as a colouring-substance in paints.

'vermin, n.pl. [Med.] A general name for insects PARASITIC on, or living on the bodies of, man and other animals. **'-'ation,** n. Verminosis; the development and producing of worms in the INTESTINE. **'-'osis,** n. The condition of being verminous and its unhealthy effects. **'-ous,** a. To do with, caused by, v. or worms; having v. on the body or worms in the INTESTINE.

'vermis, n. [Zoo.] In man and higher animals, ringed part of the chief division

of the CEREBELLUM; in birds and REP-TILIA, the chief division of the cerebellum.
'**vernal**, a. To do with, taking place in, the spring of the year. **v. 'equinox.** *See* EQUINOX.
'**vernalization**, n. [Bot.] Putting seeds through a process of wetting a little to get growth started and then, when the first sign of development is seen, keeping them very cold for some weeks before planting, by which process the time between the planting and the flowering of certain plants is made shorter—used sp. for causing grains normally not pro-ducing seed the same year if put in in the spring to do so, so that there is no need for planting them in the fall, as is generally done.
ver'nation, n. [Bot.] The way in which leaves are folded or rolled up in the BUD.
'**vernier**, n. A short scale slipping on a great one, such as a rule, so that it may be moved to the point of any reading, and having divisions which are some FRAC-TION (gen. $\frac{9}{10}$) of the smallest divisions of the great scale, so that the reading of this, when it comes at a point between two marks, may be given to a degree smaller than is marked on it by noting the posi-tion where the marks on the two scales are in line and working it out from this (gen. by simply noting the number of v. divisions between this point and the point of the reading).
'**veronal**, n. [Med.] Trade name for BARBITAL for use in producing sleep.
'**verricule**, n. [Zoo.] A small brush-like group of almost parallel upright hairs, threads, etc. **verr'iculate**, a.
'**ver'ruca** (verrucae), n. [Med.] A WART. [Biol.] A small, solid, rounded outgrowth on the skin of an animal or on a THALLUS. '**verru'cate(d)**, '**verrucose**, '**verrucous**, aa. **verru'cosity**, n. The condition of being verrucose. [Med.] A v. **ve'rruculose**, a. Covered with small vv. **verruci-**.
'**versatile**, a. [Bot.] (Of an ANTHER, etc.) fixed to its stem at only one point so as to have the power of turning freely in the wind, etc. [Zoo.] Able to be turned forward or back, as the toes of a bird, or moved up and down and from side to side, as the feelers of an insect.
'**versicolour(ed)**, **versi'colorous**, aa. [Biol.] (Sp. of like parts) not all of the same colour; changing colour as it gets older.
'**versiform**, a. [Biol.] (Sp. of like parts) not all of the same form; changing in form as it gets older.
'**version**, n. [Med.] A condition of a part, sp. the UTERUS, in which it is turned in a direction other than the normal one without being bent; the operation of turning a baby round in the uterus so that it is in the right position for birth.

'**vertebra** (vertebrae), n. [Zoo.] Any of the small bones or CARTILAGES, or in some lower animals, groups of separate bones, forming the units of which the back-bone is made up; any of the v.-like small bones of a ray in certain ECHINODERMS. '**ver-tebral**, a. Of, to do with, having, vv. or a vertebral column, made up of vv. '**vertebral 'column**. The back-bone (*see* SPINAL COLUMN). '**vertebrate**, 1.a. Having a back-bone; of, to do with, the VERTE-BRATA. 2.n. Vertebrate animal. **verte-'bration**, n. The condition of being made up of vv. or divisions like vv., or the process of forming vv. **vertebr(a)-**, **vertebro-**.
Verte'brata, n.pl. [Zoo.] The SUB-PHYLUM of CHORDATA made up of all animals having a SKULL covering a more or less complex brain, a head in which are placed special instruments of sense, and an inner frame-work of bone or CARTILAGE, together with, in all but a small number of forms at an early stage of development, a back-bone—fish, birds, AMPHIBIA, REPTILES, and MAMMALS.
'**vertex**, n. The top or highest point of any-thing, sp. [Zoo.] the highest point of the head in a back-boned animal, or the upper part of the front of the head, be-tween the eyes, in insects. [Astron.] ZENITH. [Geom.] In any plane or solid form, the top point; the end-point or meeting-point of a line or lines.
'**vertical**, n. Upright, going or pointing straight up and down; to do with, at, a VERTEX, sp. [Zoo.] the vertex of the head. [Bot.] In the direction of the AXIS, long-ways. **v. angle.** [Astron., Surveying] ANGLE OF ELEVATION. **v. circle.** [Astron.] Any great circle of the CELESTIAL SPHERE whose plane is at right angles to the plane of the HORIZON, sp. one in which the ALTITUDE of a star is measured. [Sur-veying] The round plate for measuring v. angles forming part of a THEODOLITE. **v. 'index**. In CRANIOMETRY, the RATIO of the v. measure of the SKULL to its measure from front to back. '**vertically**, adv.
'**verticil**, n. [Bot.] A circle of like parts at the same level on a stem etc., for example, a circle of leaves or any of the rings of parts making up a flower. **verti'cillate**, a. Having vv., ranged in vv.
'**verticil'laster**, n. [Bot.] A flower-grouping looking like one thick mass of flowers but formed of two massed DICHASIA on opposite sides of the stem.
'**vertigo**, n. [Med.] A feeling as if one's head were turning round and round or other things were circling round one, causing a loss of balance or making it hard to keep from falling. **ver'tiginous**, a. Having a feel-ing of v., of, like, producing, v.
ver'timeter, n. An instrument measuring

small changes in air PRESSURE, used in airplanes for measuring the rate at which the plane is going up.

'**vesica**, n. [Zoo., Med.] BLADDER, sp. the URINARY BLADDER. '**vesical**, a.

'**vesicant**, '**vesica'tory**, nn., aa. [Med.] (Any substance) causing VESICLES on the skin (for example, a **v. gas**, used in war), sp. (one) used for this purpose as a COUNTER-IRRITANT. '**vesicate**, 1.v.i. (Of the skin or a part) have a VESICLE or vesicles produced on it. 2.v.t. (Of a substance, etc.) be the cause of vesicles being produced on (the skin, etc.). '**vesicated**, a. Having VESICLES. **vesi-'cation**, n. The process of vesicating or the condition of being vesicated, a VESICLE or vesicated place on the skin.

'**vesicle**, n. [Zoo.] A small round hollow or bag-like part, sp. one full of liquid or gas; a small, round hollow outgrowth on the outside of a SHELL or CORAL; any of the 3 hollow divisions of the brain in the EMBRYO of a back-boned animal which undergo development into the 3 chief parts of the brain at full growth. [Med.] A place on the skin where the outer coat is pushed up into the form of a v. by the forming under it of a thin, water-like liquid, as the effect of a burn, or of rubbing, or of some disease. [Bot.] A small air-hole in the substance of a plant; any small, rounded, thin-walled hollow produced on a leaf etc. by the separating and expansion of the outer skin, as the effect of damage or disease. [Geol.] Any of the small round holes common inside solid LAVAS as the effect of the expansion of gases in them while still liquid. **ve'sicular**, a. [Biol., Med., Geol.] Of, to do with, being, like, a v.; vesiculate. [Med.] To do with the ALVEOLI of the LUNGS. **ve'sicular 'breathing**. [Med.] Normal breathing, in which the air comes freely through the ALVEOLI. **ve'sicular gland**. [Bot.] A GLAND under the outer skin of a leaf, fruit etc., producing an ESSENTIAL OIL. **vesicular 'murmur**. [Med.] A soft sound coming through a hearing instrument put against the chest whenever air is breathed in normally, probably produced by the sudden expansion of the ALVEOLI in taking in air. **ve'siculate**, a. [Biol., Med.] Having the form of a v.; having, marked by, covered with, vv. **ve'sicu'lation, n.** [Biol., Med.] The forming of vv. or the condition of having vv. **ve'siculose, ve'siculous**, aa. **ve'sicul(a)-, ve'siculo-**. [Biol., Med.] Sp., of, to do with, a SEMINAL v. or vv.:— **ve'sicu'lectomy,** n., **ve'sicu'litis,** n.

vesico-. BLADDER.

ve'sicula (vesiculae), n. [Zoo.] A VESICLE. **v. semi'nalis** (vesiculae semi'nales). A SEMINAL VESICLE.

'**vespertine**, a. [Bot.] (Of a flower) opening at nightfall. [Zoo.] Moving about, sp. in the air, in the half-light between sundown and night, or before sun-up.

'**vessel**, n. [Zoo.] Any pipe for transporting liquid, such as those through which the blood goes. [Bot.] TRACHEA. **v. 'element, v. 'segment**. [Bot.] Any of the CELLS making up a v.

'**vestibule**, n. [Zoo.] A smaller space opening into a greater one or joining two greater spaces, sp.:— the chief hollow of the BONY LABYRINTH of the INNER EAR in back-boned animals, or the parts inside this; in some PROTOZOA a small, somewhat pipe-like hollow with the mouth at its base; in back-boned animals, the part of the inside of the mouth which is outside the teeth; in female MAMMALS, the space between the inner lips of the VULVA framing the opening of the URETHRA. **ves'tibular**, a. Sp., to do with the v. of the ear. **ves'tibulate**, a. Having or like a v. **ves'tibulitis**, n. [Med.] INFLAMMATION of the v. of the ear, causing FEVER, VERTIGO, NAUSEA, and in the end complete loss of hearing. **ves'tibulo.-**

'**vestige**, n. Some small part still present of something which in its full form is no longer in existence. [Biol.] A part which in the process of time has become small, incomplete in structure, without the power of working, and of no use to a plant or animal, but which at an earlier stage in the growth of the plant or animal, or an earlier stage in the history of its sort, was fully formed and had a purpose. **ves'tigial**, a. To do with, being, a v.

'**vestiture**, n. [Biol.] A covering on the skin, as hair, feathers, SCALES, etc.

'**veterinary**, a. [Med.] To do with v. medicine. **v. 'medicine**. Medical work in connection with animals other than man, sp. those used by man, as horses, cows, sheep, dogs, etc. **v. 'surgeon**. Person trained in v. medicine. '**veteri'narian**, n. V. surgeon.

vex'illum, n. [Bot.] The great upper back PETAL in a PAPILIONACEOUS flower. [Zoo.] The VANE of a feather. **vex'iliary**, a. To do with, being, a v. '**vexillate**, n.

'**viable**, a. [Med.] (Of FOETUS) able to come to birth and go on living outside the mother's body; (of offspring) living at birth and with no damage or unnormal structure such as would make it impossible for it to go on living. [Biol.] Having the power of normal development (said of seeds or SPORES etc.).

'**viaduct**, n. [Engin.] A bridging structure which takes a road or railway over some wide natural hollow or road etc., made up of a number of arches or other supports.

vi'braculum (vibracula), n. [Zoo.] Any of the long, moving, whip-like or needle-like structures produced by certain PROTOZOAN COLONIES, by the special development of some of their units, as a way of arming themselves against danger. **vi'bracular,** a. **vi'braculoid,** a.

vi'brate, v.t. and i. (Make) have a shaking motion; (make) have a regular, sp. quick, motion in a straight or curved line, forward and back through a middle point between fixed limits. **'vibrancy,** n. The property or condition of being vibrant. **'vibrant,** a. Vibrating. **'vibratile,** a. Vibrating, having the power of vibrating, able to v. or be vibrated, designed to v., sp. [Biol.]. **vibratile 'membrane.** [Zoo.] In certain PROTOZOA, a thin, flat vibratile band down one side of the animal by the motion of which it makes its way through the water. **'vibrating,** a. **vi'bration,** n. The act of vibrating or condition of being in vibrating motion; vibrating motion or one unit of this, being a complete motion from a middle point out to one limit, then back through the middle point to the other, and back to the starting-point again—or, sometimes, one-half such a motion, that is, from middle point to one limit and back again. **vi'brational,** a. **vi'brator,** n. Any of various sorts of instrument, gen. electric, for producing an effect by vibrating, for example one used for producing high-VOLTAGE ALTERNATING CURRENT from a BATTERY for a radio in an automobile, or a vibrating apparatus used medically for MASSAGING the body. **'vibratory,** a. Vibrating, or causing, marked by, having the power of, to do with, vibration.

'vibrio, n. [Bact., Med.] Any of the BACTERIA of the GENUS *Vibrio* having short, stiff bodies, freq. curved like an 'S' or half an 'S', and gen. only one long, tail-like FLAGELLUM for swimming, among which is the sort causing CHOLERA.

vi'brissa (vibrissae), n. [Zoo.] Any of the stiff hairs seen on the face, for example near the nose and mouth or round the eyes, in MAMMALS, freq. acting as instruments of touch.

vibro-. Of, to do with, VIBRATION, acting by vibration, etc.

'vibrograph, n. An instrument for measuring and recording the VIBRATIONS of a structure, machine etc.

vi'brometer, n. VIBROGRAPH. [Med.] An instrument for causing quick VIBRATION of the TYMPANIC MEMBRANE, used in some diseases of the ear.

'vibro'taxis, n. [Biol.] TAXIS in reaction to VIBRATIONS of the air, earth etc., near-by.

'vibro'tropism, n. [Biol.] TROPISM in reaction to vibrations of the air, earth etc., near-by.

vi'carious, a. [Med.] (Of a DISCHARGE) taking the place of the regular or normal discharge named, or coming from a place different from that of the normal discharge.

'vicinal, a. [Cryst., Mineral.] (Of CRYSTAL faces) unnormal, present in addition to the regular ones, which are almost in the same planes and to which they are joined. [Chem.] SUBSTITUTED on C ATOMS in the 1, 2, 3, or 1, 2, 3, 4, positions in the BENZENE or NAPHTHALENE RING.

'Victor 'Meyer appa'ratus. [Phys.] An apparatus for measuring VAPOUR DENSITIES, in which a certain amount of a substance is dropped into a heated bulb and the air pushed out of the bulb by the vapour produced is measured.

'video, a. [Phys.] To do with, used in sending, TELEVISION pictures. **v. 'frequency.** The rate of ALTERNATION of any of the currents used in sending TELEVISION pictures, the range being from 0 to about 2 million CYCLES per second.

'view-finder, n. The part of a camera which, by the use of a LENS of very short FOCAL LENGTH, gives to the eye a small picture of the view in front of the camera which, if the picture is taken, will be recorded on the FILM etc.

vill'itis, n. INFLAMMATION of the CORONET in horses.

'villose, 'villous, aa. [Bot.] Covered with long, straight, delicate, separate hairs. [Zoo.] Covered with VILLI. **vil'losity,** n.

'villus (villi), n. [Zoo.] A very small hair-like or finger-like outgrowth, sp.:- in back-boned animals, any of those covering the inside of the small INTESTINE and by which food is taken into the system, formed of a LACTEAL with muscle and CAPILLARIES round it, all covered by EPITHELIUM; in MAMMALS, any of such outgrowths forming part of the PLACENTA, produced by the CHORION and going into the wall of the UTERUS. [Bot.] Any of the straight, soft hairs on a VILLOUS plant.

'vimen (vimina), n. [Bot.] A long, thin, readily bent stem or branch. **'vimineous,** a. Sp., producing vv.

vi'nasse, n. [Chem.] The liquid which is over after the DISTILLATION of alcohol from sugar and wine, from which POTASH (K_2CO_3) and AMMONIA (NH_3) are got.

'vinculum (vincula), n. [Zoo.] A thin FIBROUS band joining parts of the body, as that joining the two chief TENDONS of the foot in birds.

'vinegar, n. [Chem.] The liquid made up chiefly of from 3% to 6% of ACETIC ACID produced by the FERMENTATION of alcohol got from fruit or grain, as wine, beer, etc.—used for giving taste to food or for keeping it from going bad.

'vinous, a. Of, to do with, like wine, sp. [Bot.] of the colour of red wine.

'vinyl, a. [Chem.] Having in it the v. group. **v. group.** The MONOVALENT RADICAL $CH_2:CH-$, important in the making of PLASTICS, etc. because of the ready POLYMERIZATION of a number of substances in which it is present. **v. 'resins.** RESINS made from **v. 'chloride** ($CH_2:CH.Cl$) and **v. 'acetate** ($CH_3.COOCH.CH_3$), having a wide range of uses as PLASTICS.

'violet, n. [Phys.] The colour produced by v. rays, seen at the opposite end of the SPECTRUM from red. **v. ray.** A ray of the shortest WAVE-LENGTH in the range of those light-rays which may be seen.

vi'rescence, n. [Bot.] The turning green of parts of plants which are not normally green, such as PETALS, as the effect of disease; the green condition so produced. vi'rescent, a.

'virgate, a. [Bot.] Rod-like, long, thin, stiff and branching little.

'virgin, (Of ELEMENTS) natural, not produced by processes of industry, present in the earth as itself not in the form of a complex substance; (of an oil, metal, etc.) as first got from its plant, ORE, etc., produced by the first stage in the process of getting it ready for marketing.

'Virgo, n. [Astron.] The 6th SIGN OF THE ZODIAC.

'virile, n. [Zoo., Med.] To do with, having the properties and powers of a man at full development, sp. that of having offspring. **v. 'member.** PENIS. **vi'rility, n.**

viri'lescence, n. [Zoo., Med.] The increasing VIRILISM freq. seen in female animals as they get old. viri'lescent, a.

'virilism, n. [Med.] The having or development of male qualities of body and mind, other than sex parts and powers, in a female, sp. as caused by disease of the SUPRARENAL GLANDS.

vi'rosis, n. [Med., Bot.] Any disease caused by a VIRUS.

'virtual, a. Having the effect of what is named, though not in fact what the name says, true in an 'as if' sense. **v. 'focus.** [Optics] The point at which lines representative of rays REFLECTED or REFRACTED to the eye come together if taken far enough back, and from which the rays themselves seem to come, producing a v. image. **v. 'image.** [Optics] A picture produced on the eye by REFLECTED or REFRACTED rays, which would not be formed on a SCREEN at the point where it seems to be in space, for example, a thing seen in a plane looking-glass. **v. 'value.** [Elec.] ROOT-MEAN-SQUARE VALUE. **v. volts** or **'amperes.** The measure of the v. value in VOLTS or AMPERES.

'virulent, a. [Bot., Med.] (Of poisons or disease-BACTERIA, etc.) having great power of destruction, against which the natural fighting powers of the animal or plant system attacked have little or no effect; (of diseases) marked by quick development and serious effects, very freq. causing death. **'virulence, n.** The property of being v.; the degree of power which a BACTERIUM, etc. has of causing disease.

'virus, n. [Biol., Med.] TOXIN; any disease-causing MICRO-ORGANISM, sp. a FILTER-PASSER.

'viscera, n.pl. [Zoo.] See VISCUS, sp. the INTESTINES. **'visceral, a.** Of, to do with, in or among, the v. or a VISCUS. **'visceral arch.** Any of the supporting structures of bone or CARTILAGE, in form like an upside-down arch, in the walls of the mouth and PHARYNX in back-boned animals, the first two of which are the MANDIBULAR and HYOID ARCHES, and the rest (VESTIGIAL in air-breathing animals) the BRANCHIAL ARCHES of fish; any of the divisions between the mouth and the first GILL-SLIT and between the gill-slits themselves, which are supported by the visceral arches. **'visceral bar.** The curved rod of bone or CARTILAGE forming the right or left half of a visceral arch, the two halves meeting at the lower end. **'visceral cleft.** Any of the hollows or GILL-SLITS between the visceral arches. **'viscero-.** (To do with) v. or a VISCUS, visceral and (. . .).

'viscero'cranium, n. [Zoo.] The part of the framework of the head formed of the JAWS and VISCERAL ARCHES. (See NEURO-CRANIUM.)

'viscerop'tosis, n. [Med.] The dropping of the INTESTINES and other VISCERA to an unnormally low position in the body, chiefly as the effect of a feeble condition of the muscles of the ABDOMEN and PELVIS. **'viscerop'totic, a.**

'viscid, a. (Of a liquid) very thick or sticky, not running readily; sticky, giving out, covered with, a v. substance, sp. [Biol.] of leaves, seeds etc. **vis'cidity, n.**

vis'cometer, visco'simeter, nn. [Phys.] Any of different sorts of instrument for measuring the VISCOSITY of liquids.

'viscose, 1.a. VISCOUS; of, to do with, the substance v. 2.n. A very thick, sticky, orange-brown liquid made by acting on CELLULOSE with NaOH (*sodium hydroxide*) and CS_2 (*carbon disulphide*), used in making RAYON.

vis'cosity, n. The property of being VISCID. [Phys.] That property of a liquid or gas working against the completely free motion of one part of it over another, the effect of attraction between its MOLECULES. **'viscous, a.** (Of a liquid) having a marked degree of v., VISCID. [Phys.] Having the property of v.

'viscus (viscera), n. [Zoo.] Any of the working-parts inside the great inner hollows of the body, as the heart, lungs, intestines etc.

'visi'bility, n. The property of being visible. [Meteor.] The distance away at which things may be seen as dependent on the amount of light or sp. of mist in the air, given on a scale from 0 at 50 m. or less to 9 at 50 km.; the degree to which the air is clear of mist etc. **v. curve.** [Optics] A scale giving the relations between the WAVELENGTH and the LUMINOSITY of light, that of greatest luminosity having a wave-length of 5550 Å and the colour bright green. **'visible,** a. Which may be seen. **visible ho'rizon.** The line seemingly marking the meeting-place of earth and sky as seen from a given point.

'vision, n. [Zoo., Psych.] The sense of seeing, the instrument of which is the eye and the STIMULUS of which is light; the process of seeing. [Med., Psych.] A HALLUCINA-TION in which the sense taking part is v., something seemingly seen by the physical eye which is not in fact before it.

'visual, a. Of, to do with, experienced by, used in, the sense or process of seeing; which may be seen. **v. a'cuity.** [Psych.] The power of the eye, different in dif-ferent persons, of sensing small spaces between points very near together in space, and so of seeing small details. **v.'angle.** The angle formed by two straight lines from the ends of anything in the v. field meeting at the eye. **v. a'phasia.** [Med.] A condition in which a person is unable to give any sense to seen words of which he normally has knowledge. **v.'axis.** The straight line going from the point on which the eye is fixed to the CENTRE of ROTATION of the eye, not necessarily the same as the OPTIC AXIS. **v. field.** All the space, with all the things in it, which may be seen by the eyes at a given time with-out moving them. **v. plane.** The plane in which are the v. axes of the two eyes. **v. 'purple, v. red.** [Zoo., Biochem.] A deep red or blue-red complex colouring-substance present in the RODS of the eye in man and higher back-boned animals, and in like parts of other eyes, which gives the power of seeing in a feeble light. **v. sensi'tivity.** [Zoo., Psych.] The RATIO of the amount of light given out by a body as recorded by a given eye to all the RADIANT ENERGY given out by it. **v. 'yellow.** [Zoo., Chem.] A yellow substance into which v. purple is changed by the operation of strong light.

visuo-. VISION; VISUAL (and . . .).

vital, a. [Biol.] Living, or of, to do with, necessary to, living processes or living things; (of a part) the wounding or destruction of which puts an end to an animal's or plant's existence. **v. ca-'pacity,** [Zoo., Med.] The breathing-power of the LUNGS, measured by the number of cm.^{3} of air which they are able to send out after taking in as full a breath as possible. **v. force.** [Biol.] The ENERGY responsible for the process of living, that by which a plant or animal keeps on living, sp. when looked on as something different from the chemical and physical energy which are used and produced in living processes. **v. 'func-tions.** [Zoo., Med.] Those processes of the body the stopping of which puts an end straight away to the existence of a living thing—as breathing, the distribution of the blood, digestion, etc. **v. 'principle.** The non-material force on which living is taken to be dependent by some schools of thought, for example VITALISM. **v. stain.** [Biol.] A STAIN which may be used for colouring living substance without causing its death. **v. 'staining.** [Biol.] The STAINING of living CELLS etc., which may be done while they are still in a living thing by putting a v. stain into its system, or, after they are taken from it, by putting them into a v. stain. **v. sta'tistics.** STATISTICS having to do with the number of births, deaths, persons getting married, persons having diseases, etc., in a given place over a given time.

'vitally, adv. **vi'tality,** n. The property or condition of being v.; power of living, of fighting hard conditions, disease etc., so as to keep on living, and (of sorts) pro-ducing offspring. [Med., Psych.] (Of a person) force, ENERGY, the quality of taking pleasure in acting and not readily becoming tired.

'vitalism, n. [Biol.] The theory or belief that a non-material force is responsible for and acting in all living things; the belief, commoner than the first at the present day, that the development of living processes and the behaviour of living things are not completely covered by the laws of chemistry and physics, and that to some degree living substance and living beings are not controlled by these but free to do things which are not part of the material chain of cause and effect, opp. MECHANISM. **'vitalist,** n. **vital'istic,** a. Of, to do with, v.

'vitamin, n. [Biochem.] Any of a number of different complex ORGANIC substances which have to be got by animals (and by some plants, though most green plants are independent of ready-made organic complexes, since they have the power of making them from INORGANIC materials) from their food, though only in very small amounts, if they are to keep healthy.

v. A. A yellow oil present in butter, milk, the yellow of eggs, green leaves, oranges, and LIVER-oil, sp. of fish, necessary to man and certain other animals, the effects of not having (enough of) it being NYCTALOPIA, the stopping of growth in the young, the forming of hard, rough skin, and in the end death. **v. B. (complex).** A group of vv. present together in YEAST and other foods and earlier taken for one v.—of very wide distribution, for example, in YEAST, eggs, milk, grain, and most fruit and green plants, and some or all of which are necessary to man and a great number of other living things, among the most important being B_1 (*see* THIAMIN), B_2 (*see* RIBOFLAVIN), B_6 (*see* PYRIDOXINE, PANTOTHENIC ACID and NICOTINIC ACID). **v. C.** A v. necessary to man and monkeys, present in meat, fish, fruit, sp. of the orange family, and most green plant food, but broken up when heated, the effects of not having enough of it being SCURVY, HAEMORRHAGE and serious changes in the bone substance. **v. D.** Any of a number of STEROLS present with v. A. in plant-food and fish-LIVER oils and produced from ERGOSTEROL in milk and other foods, and in the skin of man, by the operation of the ULTRA-VIOLET RAYS in sunlight, having to do with the forming of CALCIUM PHOSPHATE in bone, and without which young persons get RICKETS and the bones of older ones, sp. PREGNANT women, become soft. **v. E.** A v. present in the oils of seeds, sp. grain-seeds, and in most leaves, and necessary to a number of higher animals, its effect being on the power of producing offspring in male and female, and on milk-producing in the female. **v. F.** The American name for v. B_1. **v. G.** The American name for v. B_2. **v. H.** A v. present in YEAST, LIVER, eggs, potatoes, with the property of increasing the growth of yeast and BACTERIA, a part of the v. B complex, now gen. named 'biotin'. **v. K.** A yellow substance present in plant oils and other plant substances and necessary to man for the COAGULATION of the blood, but of which some is made for him by BACTERIA in the INTESTINES. **v. P.** A v. present in fruits of the orange family and necessary to man, the effect of not getting it being loss of blood from the MUCOUS MEMBRANES and other serious troubles. **'-ize,** v.t. Get a v. into (food) by some process, for example by letting the food be acted on by ULTRA-VIOLET rays. **'vitami'nology,** n.

vitel'larium, n. [Zoo.] A VITELLINE GLAND, sp. a special part of the OVARY in PLATY-HELMINTHES and ROTIFERA, producing the food material of the egg, by which the OVUM is coated. **vitel'larian,** a.

'vitellary, a. [Zoo.] VITELLINE.

'vitelli-. (To do with) the YOLK of an egg:— **'vitel'liferous,** a., **'vitel'ligenous,** a.

'vitellin, n. [Biochem.] A PROTEIN present in egg-YOLK.

'vitelline, a. [Zoo.] Of, to do with, like, the YOLK of an egg. [Biol.] Yellow. **v. duct.** [Zoo.] The pipe-like part taking food from the YOLK-SAC to the INTESTINE of the EMBRYO. **v. gland.** [Zoo.] A GLAND producing YOLK. **v. 'membrane.** [Zoo.] A skin formed round an egg-CELL, seen in a fowl's egg round the YOLK—in insects freq. not formed till the egg has been FERTILIZED. **vi'tello-.**

vi'tello-in'testinal duct. VITELLINE DUCT.

vi'tellus, n. [Zoo.] YOLK.

vit'rella (vitrellae), n. [Zoo.] RETINOPHORE.

'vitreo-. VITREOUS.

'vitreo'dentine, n. [Zoo.] A specially hard form of DENTINE.

'vitreous, a. Of, to do with, produced from, like, glass; of, to do with, the v. humour. **v. elec'tricity.** Old name for POSITIVE ELECTRICITY, because it was of the sort produced by rubbing glass with silk. **v. 'humo(u)r.** [Zoo.] The jelly-like substance in the space between the LENS and the RETINA in the eye of back-boned animals.

'vitrify, v.t. and i. Get or become changed into glass or a glass-like condition as the effect of great heat. **'vitri'faction, 'vitri-fi'cation,** nn. **vitri'fiable,** a. Which may be vitrified. **'vitrified,** a.

'vitriform, a. Glass-like.

'vitriol, n. [Chem.] SULPHURIC ACID (H_2SO_4), (named sometimes *oil of v.*); any of certain glass-like SULPHATES of metals, named from their colours **blue v.,** $CuSO_4.5H_2O$, **green v.,** $FeSO_4.7H_2O$, **white v.,** $ZnSO_4.7H_2O$. **vitri'olic,** a.

vitro, See IN V.

'vitro-. Glass, glass-like.

'vitta (vittae), n. [Bot.] Any of the long narrow, pipe-like oil vessels in the walls of the fruits of some UMBELLIFEROUS plants. [Biol.] A narrow band of different colour or structure. **'vittate,** a. [Bot.] Having vv. [Biol.] Banded longways.

'vivifi'cation, n. [Zoo.] The changing of the materials got from food into living substance by the body.

vi'viparous, a. [Zoo.] Giving birth to offspring which are living and well forward in development when they come from the body of the mother, as opp. dropping eggs from which the young come later. [Bot.] (Of a plant) producing among or in the place of flowers, small plants or BULBILS with the power of becoming new plants when separated off; (of seeds) starting GERMINATION before being dropped from the plant.

vivi'parity, n. [Zoo.] The property of being

VIVIPAROUS; the process of producing from the body living offspring as opp. eggs.

vi'vipary, n. [Bot.] The property of producing SHOOTS or BULBILS among or in place of flowers; the GERMINATION of a seed before it becomes separated from the plant producing it.

vivi'section, n. The act of cutting up living animals or doing operations or tests on them, for the purpose of observation in the interests of medical etc. science. **'-ist,** n. Person doing or supporting v.

'vivo. See IN V.

'vocal, a. [Zoo.] To do with the voice. [Phonet.] VOICED; to do with, being, a VOWEL sound. **v. bands, v. cords.** [Zoo.] In air-breathing back-boned animals, four folds of the inner coat of the LARYNX, going from back to front, two on the right wall and two on the left, the VIBRATION by the breath of the lower and thinner PAIR (the *true v. cords*) producing the voice, the upper and thicker pair, which in fact have no v. use, being named the *false v. cords*. **v. 'cavities.** [Zoo.] The hollows of the mouth and upper part of the throat, which have an effect on the sound-waves produced by the true v. cords. **v. chink.** [Zoo.] GLOTTIS. **v. folds, v. 'ligaments.** The true v. cords. **v. 'fremitus.** [Med.] The motion of the chest-wall in talking, as noted by a hand placed on it.

'vocalize, v.t. [Philol.] Get (a CONSONANT sound) changed into a VOWEL, say as a vowel. [Phonet.] VOICE.

voice, 1.n. [Phonet.] The TONE produced by narrowing and then opening the space between the true VOCAL CORDS so as to get the outgoing breath-current broken up into a very quick train of VIBRATIONS. 2.v.t. [Phonet.] Say (a given sound) using the vocal cords to get the air-current broken up so as to give it v., as in saying '*b*', in place of keeping the vocal cords away from one another, as in saying '*p*'. **voiced,** a. Sounded with v. **'-less,** a. Sounded without v.

'volar, a. [Zoo.] To do with the inner side of the hand or the under side of the foot.

'volatile, a. (Of a substance) readily going from a solid or sp. a liquid condition into that of a gas, having a high VAPOUR PRESSURE. **v. oil.** [Chem.] Sp., ESSENTIAL OIL. **vola'tility,** n. **vo'latilize,** 1.v.i. (Of a liquid or solid) be v., go off in the form of gas, sp. at a TEMPERATURE lower than boiling-point. 2.v.t. Make (a liquid or solid) volatilize.

'volcanism, vulcanism, nn. [Geol.] The forming of VOLCANOES, or the effects produced on the earth by volcanoes themselves.

vol'cano, n. [Geol.] An opening from which steam, liquid ROCK (*lava*), gases, etc. are sent out from the heated inner parts of the earth, sp. a mountain made up of such materials gone solid, with a basin-like hollow (*crater*) at the top and a pipe-like hole down its middle through which such material makes its way, sometimes quietly and regularly, sometimes in violent EXPLOSIONS from time to time, sending masses of volcanic ash high into the air and causing great destruction all round it. **vol'canic, a. volcanic ash.** The solid material sent out from a v. by the EXPLOSIVE force of heated gases, ranging in size from dust to great stones, some of them formed of masses of lava which have gone solid while in the air. **volcanic belt.** [Geog., Geol.] A stretch of the earth in which vv. are commoner than in most parts, freq. so ranged that they are more or less in a line on the face of the earth. **volcanic bomb.** A ball-like, sometimes hollow, mass of lava sent out from a v. by EXPLOSION, rounded in its journey through the air, and having become solid in this form. **volcanic cloud.** A rolling mass of water-VAPOUR and dust hanging over a v. in operation. **volcanic glass.** Natural glass produced as the effect of lava becoming cold so quickly that there is no time for CRYSTALLIZATION. **volcanic mud.** The wet sticky mass formed by the mixing of volcanic dust and small bits of volcanic ash with water, as seen running down the sides of a v. like lava, or on the beds of waters into which the dust and ash have been dropped. **volcanic neck.** See NECK. **volcanic rock.** ROCK produced by liquid lava becoming solid, or volcanic ash becoming massed together, on, or in cracks very near, the face of the earth; any rock having the sort of structure produced by MAGMA becoming cold quickly, that is, formed of very small CRYSTALS freq. with much glass among them, seen only in rocks formed from volcanic lava or from magma running in very thin stretches into beds of other rock not far from the face of the earth. **volcanic vent.** See VENT. **volcanic wind.** [Meteor.] A wind produced by a volcanic outburst, caused by the heating of the air over it.

vo'lition, n. [Psych.] The property of the mind which has to do with desire and purpose and the effecting of these by acting; a conscious decision to do something, together with the feeling of having power to get the body acting as desired. **'-al,** a. **vo'litional 'tremor.** [Med.] A shaking of the body in certain diseases, produced by attempting an act.

volt, n. [Elec.] The PRACTICAL UNIT of ELECTROMOTIVE force, being that POTENTIAL DIFFERENCE between the ends of a wire of RESISTANCE = 1 OHM by which a current of 1 AMPERE is produced, = 10⁸ C.G.S. ELECTROMAGNETIC units. **v.-'ampere**, n. The unit used for measuring the power of an ALTERNATING CURRENT, = 1 v. × 1 ampere. **'-age**, n. The measure of ELECTROMOTIVE FORCE or POTENTIAL DIFFERENCE given in vv.

'Volta eff'ect. [Elec.] The producing of a DIFFERENCE OF POTENTIAL between two bits of different sorts of metal when touching. **Volta's law.** [Elec.] The law that when a number of bits of different metals are placed touching one another, as in a VOLTAIC PILE, the DIFFERENCE OF POTENTIAL between the free ends of the line is equal to the differences of potential at every join put together.

vol'taic, a. [Elec.] Of, to do with, producing or produced by, electric current, or to do with the science of this, sp. v. current. **v. cell.** PRIMARY CELL. **v. 'couple.** Two substances, gen. metals, between which an electric current is produced when they are put together into an ELECTROLYTE. **v. 'current.** Electric current produced by a chemical reaction. **v. elec'tricity.** Electric force in the form of a current. **v. pile.** A STORAGE BATTERY formed of a number of round plates of the same two different metals put one on top of another, first one metal and then the other, with a plate of cloth wetted with an ELECTROYTE between them. **v. 'series.** A list of chemical ELEMENTS in such order that if any two of them are used together as ELECTRONES, the first in the list will be the NEGATIVE one.

volt'ameter, n. [Elec.] An instrument formed of an ELECTROLYTIC CELL for measuring the amount of electric current going through a CIRCUIT by the amount of material fired at, or put down on, the CATHODE in a given time.

'voltmeter, n. [Elec.] Any instrument for measuring the VOLTAGE of a CIRCUIT by recording in VOLTS the POTENTIAL DIFFERENCE between two points in the circuit to which the v. is joined in PARALLEL.

'voluble, a. [Bot.] Having the property of curving itself round and round things in corkscrew form for support.

'volume, n. [Phys.] The (measure of the) amount of space taken up by a body or substance, used as a measure of the size of the body or the amount of the substance—given in CUBIC units, for example, cm³. [Acous.] LOUDNESS or [Radio etc.] the power of an electric current used for producing sound-waves, as conditioning the loudness of the sound. **v. elas'ticity.** [Phys.] The RATIO of the force producing a change of v. in anything to the change of v. produced. **vo'lumeter**, n. [Phys.] An

instrument for measuring the v. of a gas or liquid, or of a solid by the amount of liquid of which it takes the place. **volu-'metric(al)**, aa. Of, to do with, the measuring of v. **volu'metric an'alysis.** [Chem.] The discovery of the amount of a substance present in a SOLUTION by the use of a fixed v. of a STANDARD solution of some testing substance producing a reaction when mixed with the solution in question.

vo'luminous, a. Taking up much space.

'voluntary, a. [Zoo., Psych.] To do with, under the control of, VOLITION, not automatic—caused or effected by a purpose formed in the mind. **v. 'muscle.** STRIATED MUSCLE.

'volute, 1.n. A complete turn of a SPIRAL, for example, [Zoo.] one complete turn of a spiral SHELL. 2.a. Twisted like a corkscrew.

vo'lution, n. A rolling, turning or twisting motion or form, or one roll, turn, or twist, sp. [Zoo.] a VOLUTE.

'volva, n. [Bot.] The VELUM of an AGARIC, sp. when, after it has been broken through, it takes the form of a cup-like part round the base of the PILEUS. **'volvate**, a.

'volvulus, n. [Med.] A twist in some part of the INTESTINES shutting or narrowing the pipe so that material is unable to get through.

'vomer, n. [Zoo.] One of two opposite bones of the front of the head in back-boned animals, forming at their forward ends part of the middle division of the nose. **'-ine**, a. **vo'mero-.**

'vomero'nasal, a. [Zoo.] To do with the VOMERS and the hollows of the nose.

'vomica, n. [Med.] A hollow space formed by the destruction of substance, sp. in the LUNGS; a mass of PUS in the lungs or other breathing-parts which may be sent out through the mouth.

'vomit, 1.v.t. and i. [Med.] Send up, gen. with a violent impulse (what is in the stomach), through the mouth. 2.n. The material vomited. **'-ory**, **'-ive** nn., aa. (Substance, etc.) causing vomiting. **vomitu'rition**, n. Frequent violent attempts at vomiting without sending anything up; quiet vomiting of small amounts without any violent motion of the stomach.

von 'Baer's law. [Biol.] The law on which the RECAPITULATION THEORY is based, that different sorts of plants and animals are in the EMBRYO stage like one another and only become markedly different in the process of development.

-vorous, a. [Zoo.] Using as food, living (chiefly) on, what is named. **-vore**, n. Animal which is -vorous.

'vortex (vortices), n. [Phys.] A mass of liquid

or gas having a quick circling motion round its middle, at which there is a tendency for a VACUUM to be formed so that other bodies coming near are pulled into it, sp. such a mass forming part of a greater mass having a different motion. 'vortical, a. Of to do with, a v.; like a v. in motion or form; (of motion) circling. vor'ticity, n. The condition of being in vortical motion.

'vowel, n. [Phonet.] Any sound used in talking in the making of which the breath is not stopped at any point after it comes from the VOCAL CAVITIES, so that it has the RESONANCE given by their form; any letter representative of such a sound, as a, e, i, o, u.

vug(g), vugh, nn. [Mining] A small hollow in a body of MINERAL, frequently having CRYSTALS of a different substance on its sides.

'vulcanite, n. [Chem.] Hard rubber produced by VULCANIZATION. [Geol.] Any IGNEOUS ROCK of very small-grain structure, such as is produced from LAVA.

vulcani'zation, n. [Chem.] The process of making natural rubber harder, stronger, more elastic, by getting it to take in S— in one process by heating the rubber and S together, in another by acting on plates of cold rubber with S_2Cl_2. 'vulcanize, v.t. Make (natural rubber) undergo v.

'vulva, n. [Zoo.] The outer structure or opening of the sex-apparatus of a female back-boned animal; the outer opening of the egg-pipe in non-backboned animals, such as insects. 'vulvar, vulvo-.

W, [Chem.] Sign for WOLFRAM (tungsten).

'wadi, n. [Geog.] A water-way in the Sahara and other dry wastes of that part of the earth which is dry for most of the year.

'waist, n. [Zoo.] The narrowed part of man's body between the RIBS and the HIPS; the greatly narrowed part of the ABDOMEN of certain insects, such as flies and bees.

'Wallace's line. [Zoo.] The line of division between the ORIENTAL REGION and the AUSTRALASIAN REGION, going southwest through the islands between Malaya and Australia, east of the Philippines, and between Celebes and Borneo.

Wall'erian de'generation. [Med.] The DEGENERATION of the end-part of a NERVE FIBRE when separated from the rest by a cut, or by a crushed part.

'wandering cell. [Zoo.] A LEUCOCYTE, sp. one which has gone from the blood into the substance of a part.

'warbling, n. [Radio] A process of quickly changing the FREQUENCY of an electric current back and forward between certain limits, used in sending out radio waves or testing MICROPHONES.

warm-'blooded, a. [Zoo.] Having a fixed normal degree of body heat which is higher, gen. much higher, than that of the air outside the body and independent of it.

warm front. [Meteor.] The sloping line of division between a mass of warm air pushing forward over the face of the earth and the colder air over which it is moving, that is, the forward edge of such a motion, gen. having cloud and rain in front of it.

'warning color'ation. [Zoo.] APOSEMATIC COLORATION.

warp, n. In cloth, the long-ways threads which are fixed on the frame in making it, and under and over which the threads of the WEFT are taken at right-angles.

warp, v.t. and i. (Make) become twisted or curved out of the right form as the effect of some one-sided expansion or CONTRACTION of its substance caused by heat, wet, etc., as a structure made of young wood, or a gramophone record stored in an over-warm place.

wart, n. [Biol.] A small, quite hard, round-topped outgrowth on the skin, sp. [Bot.] one caused by a FUNGUS disease, or [Med.] one formed by the overgrowth of PAPILLAE or PRICKLE CELLS, freq. forming a somewhat dark, thick, horn-like outer skin.

'washer, n. [Mach.] A thin flat ring of metal, leather etc., used generally for edging some rod-like part for different purposes, for example, put under a nut to give wider PRESSURE and keep it from cutting into something, or round the lip of a bottle stopper or the join between pipes so as to make a tight join, etc.

'washing 'soda. $Na_2CO_3.10H_2O$ (sodium carbonate), so named because used for putting in water to make it SOFT for cleaning purposes.

'Wassermann re'action, Wassermann test. [Med.] A blood reaction used as a test for SYPHILIS, based on the fact that the blood of a person having syphilis will give no reaction to a HAEMOLYSIN because of COMPLEMENT FIXATION by syphilis ANTIBODIES.

'water, n. [Chem.] The substance H_2O, produced by the burning of H in O, the liquid form of which has in it a small amount of HEAVY WATER and some POLYMERS such as H_4O_2—the commonest and most important SOLVENT, in its natural liquid form only free from DISSOLVED substances when it is falling as rain, marked by the property of expansion when it becomes colder than

4°C. (at which the weight of 1 cm³=1 gram) and by the forming of ice at 0°C., normal boiling-point 100°C. [Med.] Loosely, any of the w.-like liquids produced by the body, as in the eyes or the mouth, sp. URINE and the AMNIOTIC FLUID. [Jewels] The degree to which a jewel stone is clear, or a PEARL bright. **w. 'balance.** [Bot.] The relation between the w. taken in by a plant and the w. given out by it. **w. 'blister.** [Med.] A VESICLE which has only a clear, w.-like liquid in it, no PUS or blood. **w. bloom.** [Bot.] A green coating coming suddenly on the top of a body of FRESH w., made up chiefly of a great mass of CYANO-PHYCEAE. **w. 'culture.** [Bot.] The growth of plants with their roots in w. having in it a measured amount of a salt or salts, used as a way of testing for the sorts and amounts of salts needed by them. **w. e'quivalent.** [Phys.] THERMAL CAPACITY. **w. gap.** [Geog.] A deep narrow way cut by a river through hard ROCK in a line of mountains. **w. gas.** [Chem., etc.] A gas for burning formed of mixed H and CO and produced by forcing steam over COKE heated till it is red. **w. gland.** [Bot.] A structure of CELLS in the inner substance of a leaf, under a w. STOMA, for controlling the amount of w. given out by it. **w. glass.** [Chem.] Na_2SiO_3 (*sodium silicate*), or K_2SiO_3 (*potassium silicate*), or the two together, in w., or in the form of a powder or glass-like mass for putting in w., forming a sticky liquid with the property of becoming hard, used for pasting things together, uniting substances into a hard mass, coating things to keep out air, etc. (for example eggs for storing), in soap-making, and for a great number of other purposes. **w. 'hemisphere.** [Geog.] That half of the earth made up chiefly of w. of which New Zealand is almost at the middle. **w. of consti'tution.** [Phys.-Chem.] W. forming part of a MOLECULE of a complex substance which it is very hard or impossible to take away without getting the molecule broken up. **w. of 'crystalli'zation, w. of hy'dration.** [Phys.-Chem.] W. forming part of a MOLECULE of a substance which has been produced by CRYSTALLIZATION from a w. SOLUTION, and which may be got away by heating, gen. with the loss of the substance's CRYSTAL structure. **w. on the brain.** [Med.] HYDROCEPHALUS. **w. on the knee.** [Med.] The forming of a w.-like liquid causing INFLAMMATION inside the knee-JOINT, as the effect of a blow, etc **w. pore.** [Bot.] STOMA, sp. one of those at the ends of the leaf VEINS in certain plants. [Zoo.] The opening to the outside of a w. tube. **w. 'power.** [Mach.] The force of moving w., for example of a river, waterfall, etc., as

used for driving machines or producing electric power. **w. 'softening.** [Chem.] The process of taking Ca and Mg and other SALTS out of HARD water by chemical reactions. **w. table.** [Geol.] The upper limit of that part of the earth in which every space in its substance is full of w., an irregular level, in places coming to the top of the earth and forming the bed of a body of w., but gen. some distance down, and, though becoming higher in wet weather and lower in dry, ranging only between certain fixed limits, the lowest of which is named *the permanent w. table.* **w. tube.** [Engin.] A pipe through which w. goes in an engine, steam-boiler, etc. [Zoo.] Any one of the system of branching and CILIATED pipes with openings to the outside, sometimes through SOLENO-CYTES, by which certain non-back-boned animals send out the liquid waste from digestion. **'w.-tube 'boiler.** [Engin.] A boiler in which the w. to be changed into steam is sent through a great number of pipes heated by fire or hot gases round them and all going into greater vessels, so that steam unmixed with w. is very quickly produced. **w. 'turbine.** [Mach.] A TURBINE worked by w. **w. 'vapour.** [Phys., Chem.] W. in the form of gas, sp. when formed at a degree of heat lower than boiling-point and [Meteor.] present in the ATMOSPHERE. **w. wheel.** [Mach.] A wheel for driving machines which is turned by the force or weight of w., for example a w. turbine, or an upright wheel turned slowly by the weight of w. falling at one point into buckets hanging round the edge, or by the force of it driving against blades. **'w.-cooled, a.** [Engin. etc.] Kept from getting overheated by cold w., gen. running in pipes etc. through it, or in a hollow wall round it. **'-course.** [Geog.] A river or any running w., or a dry bed at one time hollowed out for itself by running w. **'w.-gauge, n.** [Engin. etc.] An instrument for measuring air-PRESSURE by its effect on water in a glass pipe; w. pressure given as the long measure of a COLUMN of w. producing it; a glass tube, gen. upright but sometimes sloping, in connection at its lower end with the w. vessel in a boiler and at its upper end with the steam vessel, from the level of the w. in which the level of the w. in the boiler may be seen. **'w.-parting, n.** Watershed. **'-proof. a.** Not letting w. through, coated with some substance to give it this property, said sp. of materials, not structures. **'-shed, n.** [Geog., etc.] The high land down the opposite slopes of which ww. go to different rivers, seas etc., the line of division between two river-systems. **'w.-softener, n.** An apparatus for w.

softening. **'-spout,** n. [Meteor.] A TORNADO at sea, marked by the forming of an upright solid body of w., pulled up from the sea by the middle VACUUM, between the sea and the point of the cloud. **'-tight,** a. (Of a structure) able to keep out w., without cracks or openings through which w. might come. **w.-'vascular system.** [Zoo.] In ECHINODERMATA the system of pipes in the body-hollow through which w. goes from the sea and a w.-like substance from the body-hollow into the TUBE-FEET, causing and controlling their operation, and in addition probably sending out liquid waste and having some part in breathing; a like system of pipes in other non-backboned animals, sp. worms, for sending out liquid waste. **'-wall,** n. [Eng.] A structure of pipes between the wall of a FURNACE and the fire, through which cold w. is sent to keep the heat of the fire from damaging the wall.

waterbrash, n. [Med.] A sudden coming into the mouth of water-like liquid from the SALIVARY GLANDS, sometimes a sign of a DUODENAL ULCER.

watt, n. [Elec.] The unit of electric power, = that producing 1 JOULE or 107 ERGS of work per second, or that of a current of 1 AMPERE with an ELECTROMOTIVE FORCE of 1 VOLT in operation for 1 second. **'-age,** n. The electric power of an apparatus given in ww. **w.-'hour,** n. The unit of electric work commonly used in marketing electric power, = the work done by 1 w. in 1 hour. **'-meter,** n. An instrument for measuring electric power in ww.

'wattle, n. [Zoo.] A loose, soft, freq. brightly coloured, fold of skin, hanging under the mouth or from the throat of a bird, snake, etc.

wave, n. [Phys.] One unit of a w. motion, that is, any of the like groups of events which, coming one after another, equally spaced in time, make up a w. motion, for example, any of the RIDGES formed on a liquid by a w. motion produced by the VIBRATION of its PARTICLES as the effect of some impulse (given, for example, by the wind or a ship). (*See* ELECTRIC W., ELECTROMAGNETIC W., RADIO W., LONGITUDINAL W., TRANSVERSE W., STATIONARY W.). **w. bundle.** [Phys.] A group of ww. forming a unit, such as that given off by an ELECTRON in changing from one ENERGY LEVEL to another. **w. 'filter.** [Radio] An apparatus for cutting out any part or parts of a complex of electric ww. **w. front.** [Phys.] The SURFACE formed at any point of time by all the most forward points in a w. motion, or by a cut across such a motion taking in all the points at that stage which have the same position in parallel ww. and are moving in the same direction.

w. me'chanics. [Phys.] A theory based on the QUANTUM THEORY which makes use of the mathematics of w.-motion to make clear the behaviour of ELEMENTARY PARTICLES. **w. 'motion.** [Phys.] The moving on through space of a substance of ENERGY in the form of VIBRATIONS, by the starting up of such vibrations at one point of the space (or in one PARTICLE of the substance) after another, in a given direction or directions, as seen in ww. on water (formed of water particles in vibration), in sound ww. (formed of air MOLECULES in vibration), in ELECTROMAGNETIC ww. (such as light ww. where the vibrations are PERIODIC motions of an ELECTRIC and a MAGNETIC FIELD at right-angles to one another), and so on. **w. 'number.** The number of ww. in a w.-length.

$$= \frac{\text{number of waves per sec.}}{\text{rate of w. motion}} \text{ or } \frac{1}{\text{w.-length}}.$$

w. path. The line or lines of direction of a w. or w. train. **w. 'theory of light.** The theory that light goes from place to place by a w. motion, at one time said to take place in the ETHER but now looked on as ELECTROMAGNETIC and needing no MEDIUM. **w. 'theory of 'matter.** W. mechanics. **w. train.** A line of ww. coming in groups with stops between them. **'-band,** n. [Radio] Any of the ranges of w.-lengths used in radio, forming a limited part of the complete range of RADIO WAVES. **w.-guide,** n. [Radio] Metal pipe through which ELECTROMAGNETIC WAVES of very high FREQUENCY are guided, used sp. in RADAR. **'w.-form, 'w.-shape.** nn. The line or curve made by the GRAPH of a w. **'w.-length,** n. The distance between any point in a w. and the point having the same position in the one coming before or after it in a w. motion,

$$= \frac{\text{rate of w. motion}}{\text{number of waves per sec}}.$$

'-mark, n. [Geol.] RIPPLE MARK. **'-'meter,** n. [Radio.] An instrument for measuring w.-lengths.

wax, n. [Chem.] Any of a group of non-CRYSTALLINE solid substances, not SOLUBLE in water and becoming soft at summer heat, produced by plants and animals, specially bees, and made up chiefly of ESTERS of MONOHYDRIC ALCOHOLS, as opp. FATS; any of a number of other substances got from plants and animals which have w.-like properties but are chiefly esters of FATTY ACIDS; any of a number of w.-like substances made up of HYDROCARBONS and got from MINERALS, as PARAFFIN WAX. [Biol.] Any w.-like substance produced by a plant or animal, sp. bees-wax, or that produced in the pipe-like part opening into the outer ear in man and higher animals. **'waxy,** a. W.-like.

weak, a. Not strong, sp.:— [Phys.] (of colours) having low SATURATION; [Chem.] (of SOLUTIONS) having little of the SOLUTE in comparison with the amount of the SOLVENT; [Phonet.] (of STRESS) small; (of words or parts of words) said with little or no stress. **w. e'lectrolyte.** [Chem.] An ELECTROLYTE which undergoes little IONIZATION.

weal, n. WHEAL.

wean, v.t. [Zoo., Med.] Put a stop to the giving of its mother's milk to (a baby or young animal) when it is old enough to take other food.

'weather 'forecast. [Meteor.] A statement as to the probable weather in the near future made at a WEATHER STATION and based on science, given out to the public by newspaper or radio.

'weather-glass, n. [Meteor.] Any instrument for giving the condition of the ATMO-SPHERE, sp. the changes of PRESSURE, as a guide to the weather.

'weather map. [Meteor.] A map on which are marked the chief weather conditions, such as ATMOSPHERIC PRESSURE, TEM-PERATURE, amount of water in the air, the direction and rate of the wind, the amount of cloud, etc., at different points over a wide stretch of country at a given time, produced in WEATHER STATIONS generally every twelve hours and used in working out WEATHER FORECASTS.

'weather 'station. [Meteor.] A station where observations of weather and ATMO-SPHERIC conditions are made and re-corded, and gen. from which WEATHER FORECASTS are given out.

'weathering, n. [Geol.] The processes of chemical and physical change caused in ROCK open to the operation of air, rain, ice, snow, the sun's rays, and so on. **'weathered,** a. Having undergone w.

web, n. (A stretch of) any net-like material or any material made, like cloth, by taking threads over and under other threads at right angles, sp. when soft and thin. [Zoo.] The net-like structure of silk threads made by certain ARACHNIDA for the purpose of taking prisoner flies and other insects for food, or any of the like structures made by other insects; the VANE of a bird's feather; the thin soft skin stretched between the toes of swimming birds and AMPHIBIA, or at the base of and between the fingers and toes in man. **'webbed,** a. Sp., [Zoo.] (of feet) having toes united by a w. most of the way down, as swimming birds. **'webbing,** n. W. as a material. **'-foot,** n. [Zoo.] A webbed foot, **'webby,** a. Of, to do with, like, covered with, a w. or ww.

'weber, n. [Elec.] A unit of MAGNETIC FLUX $= 10^8$ MAXWELLS.

'Weber's law, 'Weber-'Fechner law. FECH-NER'S LAW.

wedge, 1.n. Anything in the form of a w. [Mech.] A bit of wood, metal, etc. having 5 plane faces, two of them being three-sided and equal, two others RECTANGULAR and equal and sloping together to a thin edge, used for driving into wood or stone to get it parted, into a space between two things or parts (for example a door and its frame, to keep them, or one of them, from moving), under a weight which has to be lifted from the floor etc., and so on—one of the SIMPLE MACHINES. 2.v.t. Get fixed with or as with a w. so that motion is impossible. **w. bone.** [Zoo.] A w.-formed bone, sp. any of the INTERCENTRA of this form seen in certain LACERTILIA. **w. of high 'pressure.** [Meteor.] A w.-formed RIDGE OF HIGH PRESSURE, that is, one in which the ISOBARS are in the form of a 'V'. **w. pho'tometer.** [Phys., Astron.] An instru-ment for the comparison of INTENSITY of light, for example, from two stars, by sending the light through a w. of glass.

weed, n. [Bot.] Any WILD plant of no use to man which makes its way into farm fields and gardens where it is not desired.

weep, v.i. Give out water or other liquid in drops, sp. [Med.] of a damaged or diseased place on the skin which is kept wet by a water-like liquid coming out, or [Bot.] of the hard stem of a tree, or of the green stem of a plant when touched.

weft, n. In cloth or cloth-making, the threads which are taken at right angles through the WARP.

'Wegener's hy'pothesis. [Geol.] The theory, not generally supported by experts, that all the great land masses were at one time one mass from which they became broken off, slowly moving on their base of SIMA to their present positions, and that they are still moving.

weight, 1.n. [Phys.] The force of the earth's attraction acting on a body, dependent on its MASS and its distance from the earth and commonly used as the measure of mass and given in units of mass, such as the pound or gram, the effect of the distance being the same for all masses. [Math.] In judging or working out AVERAGES from a number of observations, for example in STATISTICS or in Astron-omy and Physics, a number given to a relation or observation representative of the number of examples of it, or of the degree to which it is probably true. 2.v.t. [Math.] Make use of ww. in judging (observations or statistics) or in getting (averages) based on these. **'weighted average, 'weighted mean.** An AVERAGE got by MULTIPLYING every number in the group to be averaged by the w.

given to it and then DIVIDING the amount got by addition of these by the amount got by addition of the ww.

weir, n. A wall put across a river to keep the water high on the side from which it is coming.

'Weismannism, n. [Biol.] NEO-DARWINISM as put forward by the German biology expert Q. WEISMANN. **Weis'mannian,** a.

weld, v.t. Get (two plates, rods or other bodies of metal, sp. iron and steel) joined by heating them at the meeting-place till they are united by running together or are soft enough to be united by hammering or force. (*See* ARC-WELD-ING, OXY-ACETYLENE WELDING, RESIST-ANCE WELDING).

'Weldon 'process. [Chem.] A process for making Cl gas from HCl and MnO_2, in which the used material is made to give further Cl by reaction with $Ca(OH)_2$ and then again with HCl. **Weldon mud.** The half-liquid mass produced by the operation of $Ca(OH)_2$ on the used material over from the first part of the W.p.

well, n. [Eng.] A pipe-like hole walled with brick etc. taken deep into the earth for the purpose of getting down to a store of water, oil, or gas, and pumping it up, or, in a simple water w., pulling it up in a bucket; a like deep hole made for draining water away from the top of the earth, or going down to solid ROCK as a vessel in which the supports of some structure, such as a bridge, are rooted. [Mach. etc.] A low or deep, gen. walled, hollow space in a machine or other structure. **'w.-head.** The top of a water or oil w., or a structure put up over it.

wen, n. [Med.] A small BENIGN TUMOUR, sp. a SEBACIOUS CYST, on the skin, gen. on the face, head, or neck, causing no pain.

'Weston cell. [Elec.] A STANDARD CELL of VOLTAGE 1·0183 at 20°C., formed of a Cd ANODE coated with solid $CdSO_4$ and an Hg CATHODE coated with Hg_2SO_4, in a SATURATED SOLUTION of $CdSO_4$.

Westphal 'balance. [Phys.] A form of scales for getting the loss of weight of a body in water, formed of an arm from the end of which the body is hanging into the liquid, with a scale on which a weight is moved for balancing the loss, used for measuring the SPECIFIC GRAVITY of liquids or solids.

wet, a. (Of processes, apparatuses, and tests in chemistry and industry) using water or other liquids, done with liquids.

wet-and-dry-bulb hy'grometer. [Meteor.] PSYCHROMETER.

wetta'bility, n. [Phys., Chem.] The degree to which a solid is made wet by a liquid, measured by the force of ADHESION between the two.

'whalebone, n. [Zoo.] The horn-like substance forming the great plates with comb-like inner edges hanging from the upper mouth-bones inside the mouths of those CETACEA having no teeth, and acting as a sort of net to keep back from the water going into and out of the mouth the small animals used as food.

whale oil. [Chem.] An oil got from the BLUBBER of CETACEA, used in making soap etc.

w(h)eal, n. [Med.] A flat, white or light red, SWELLING suddenly produced on the skin and gen. going away quite quickly, seen in URTICARIA and as the effect of certain insect bites or plant stings.

'Wheatstone bridge. [Elec.] An electric CIRCUIT formed of 4 RESISTANCES (one of which is to be measured), a CELL, and a GALVANOMETER, so put together that the RATIO of one resistance to another may be changed till two of them are balanced by the other two and there is no current going through the galvanometer, when the resistance to be measured may be worked out.

wheel ani'malcule. [Zoo.] A ROTIFER.

wheel 'organ. [Zoo.] The CILIATED ring or round part at the front of a ROTIFER; a ciliated wheel-like part of the mouth in CEPHALOCHORDA which keeps a current of water from the outside coming into the mouth.

'whirlpool, n. [Geog.] A part of the sea, a river etc., where the water is circling round and round, forming a hollow in the middle into which anything on the water near it is pulled, caused by some specially irregular form of the sea or river bed, or by the meeting of currents from different directions.

'whirlwind, n. [Meteor.] A more or less upright body of air of limited size circling round and round a middle line and all the time moving into the middle and up, sp. one moving over the earth and pulling up dust, sand, etc. into the part of low PRESSURE at its middle, common over sand wastes in very warm countries.

'whisper, 1.n. [Phonet.] SPEECH without TONE produced by keeping the inner GLOTTIS shut and the VOCAL CORDS un-moving and sending the breath through the outer glottis, the sound being caused by the FRICTION of the air against its walls; whispering voice. 2.v.t. Say (a speech sound) with whispering voice. **'whispered,** a. **'whispering voice.** The quality given to a SPEECH sound by producing it in the outer GLOTTIS with the inner glottis shut.

white 'arsenic. [Chem.] As_2O_3 (*arsenic trioxide*), the most important substance made from As, a white powder, a violent poison used for the destruction of rats etc.

white (blood) cell. [Zoo.] LEUCOCYTE.

white damp. [Mining] Poison gas made up chiefly of CO (*carbon monoxide*) in the air of a mine, an after-effect of incompletely burned-out fires, gas EXPLOSIONS, etc.

White Dwarf. [Astron.] Any of a small number of not very bright stars of such great DENSITY that the theory is that they are made up of ATOMIC NUCLEI without any ELECTRONS.

white 'fibre. [Zoo.] Any of the white, waving, unbranched, inelastic FIBRES grouped together in parcels in CONNECTIVE TISSUE.

white 'iron. A sort of hard, silver-coloured PIG-IRON or CAST IRON in which most of the C is in the form of Fe_3C.

white lead. [Chem.] BASIC CARBONATE of lead, $2PbCO_3.Pb(OH)_2$, a white powder very widely used as a PIGMENT in paints.

white light. [Phys.] Light made up of rays of all the WAVE-LENGTHS producing seen light, that is, light which may be broken up into a SPECTRUM ranging through all the colours from red to VIOLET.

white 'matter. [Zoo.] That substance in the brain and SPINAL CORD of back-boned animals which is chiefly made up of MEDULLATED NERVE FIBRES and so white in colour, present outside the GREY MATTER and making the connections between different parts of the nerve system.

white 'metal. Any of a number of white ALLOYS of lead or tin, sp. one formed of more than half tin with different amounts of lead, copper, Sb, and sometimes Zn, used for a number of purposes, most importantly for BEARINGS.

white 'mica. [Geol., Mineral.] MUSCOVITE.

white radi'ation. [Phys.] Any RADIATION, even if not of seen light, which, like white light, may be broken up into rays covering the range of FREQUENCIES between two limits.

white spirit. A liquid made by DISTILLING PETROLEUM, used in making and in thinning paints and VARNISHES.

white trap. [Geol.] A sort of ROCK made by the reaction of liquid DOLERITE with the CO_2 produced by it on running into beds with much C in them.

white 'vitriol. [Chem., Mineral.] A substance in the form of CRYSTALS without colour, sometimes present naturally in the earth, being $ZnSO_4$ (*zinc sulphate*) united with 7 MOLECULES of water, used medically and in DYEING, VARNISH-making, etc.

white yolk. [Zoo.] The lighter yellow substance forming the middle part of the YOLK of a bird's egg and of which thin coats are present between the thick coats of deep yellow substance going round this. **w.y. spheres.** Very small round structures seen in w.y.

'whitlow, n. [Med.] PARONYCHIA.

whole, 1.a. Complete. 2.n. A complete thing or group having all its parts or units; that which, though it may have parts or divisions, is so united in structure, properties, effects etc. that it may be looked on as one thing without thought of its make-up. **w. 'number.** [Arith.] INTEGER.

'whooping-'cough, n. [Med.] PERTUSSIS.

whorl, n. [Bot.] VERTICIL. [Zoo.] One turn of a SPIRAL SHELL.

'wide-'screen 'process. In moving pictures, any of a number of processes for taking pictures on a FILM much wider than the 35mm. normally used which will be sharp and clear to the very edge, used for sending a picture onto a very wide SCREEN to give an effect of great space and range. (*See* ANAMORPHOTA LENS.)

'Widal('s) test. [Med.] A test for TYPHOID FEVER in which a drop of a person's blood-SERUM is put into a liquid having in it typhoid BACTERIA, the massing together of which after a certain time is a sign that the disease was present in the blood-serum.

'Wiedemann-Franz law. [Phys.] The law that the relation between the power of transporting heat and the power of transporting electric current is the same for all metals at a given TEMPERATURE, that is, the greater the one, the greater the other in all metals.

Wien's dis'placement law. [Phys.] The law that the WAVE-LENGTH of the MONOCHROMATIC RADIATION of greatest power from a BLACK BODY gets smaller as the ABSOLUTE TEMPERATURE gets greater.

wild, a. [Biol.] (Of a plant or animal) not CULTIVATED or DOMESTICATED, being of a sort produced without the help or care of man, living, having growth, in natural conditions.

will, n. [Psych.] The mind's power of conscious purpose, decision, to do something, that is, of VOLITION.

'willow leaf. [Astron.] NODULE.

'Wilson 'chamber. [Phys.] CLOUD CHAMBER.

'wilt, 1.v.i. [Bot.] (Of a plant, leaf, or stem) become soft and undergo a stopping of growth because the loss of water is not made up by intake, as in very dry weather. **'wilting 'coef'ficient.** The PERCENTAGE of water present in the earth when plants rooted in it undergo wilting.

'Wimshurst ma'chine, n. [Elec.] An electric machine for producing an electric CHARGE by INDUCTION and storing it, made up of two round glass plates facing one another on the same AXIS very near together, and going round in opposite directions, with bits of metal round their edges which keep coming against BRUSHES by which the charge is taken off and transported to LEYDEN JARS.

winch, n. [Mach.] A machine for pulling or lifting things by turning a cord or chain round a DRUM, worked by hand or machine-power.

wind, n. [Meteor.] A natural current of air on a great scale, moving over the earth in any direction, sp. one more or less parallel to the earth (as opp. an up or down 'current'), caused by unequal heating and the tendency of air to go from places of higher to places of lower PRESSURE. [Med.] FLATULENCE. **w. cone.** [Meteor etc.] A short pipe of cloth narrowing to a point and kept open at the great end by a ring, fixed to the top of a strong thick rod going high into the air, and so designed that its angle with a level plane gives an idea of the rate of the w. at the same time as its angle with an upright one gives the wind's direction—used sp. on air-fields. **w. dis'persal.** [Bot.] The distribution of seeds etc. by the w. **w. gap.** [Geog.] A WATER GAP which no longer has water running through it. **w. rose.** [Meteor.] A design of straight lines of different sizes coming from different directions to a small circle, the lines being representative of the direction and sometimes the force of the ww. to be looked for at a given place at a given time of year and the degree to which they are frequent, and the circle having in it a number giving the PERCENTAGE of times without any w. at all—used as a guide by airmen. **w. scale.** [Meteor.] A system of words or numbers representative of the force of the w., as the *Beaufort Scale* covering the range of rates of from 1 to over 75 miles an hour by the numbers 1–12. **w. sock.** W. cone. **w. vane.** An apparatus put up on top of a building etc. for marking the direction of the w., gen. made up of a fixed frame with arms pointing north, south, east, and west, with a level pointer freely moved by the w. over it. **'w.-borne,** a. [Geol., Bot.] Transported by the w. **'-mill,** n. A structure for working a machine, having a number of raying flat blades placed OBLIQUELY round a middle rod which is kept turning round by the force of the w. on the blades; a building of earlier times with such a four-armed structure where grain was crushed. **'-pipe,** n. [Zoo.] TRACHEA. **w.-'tunnel.** A great pipe-like structure through which air may be sent at a fixed rate to see its effects on an airplane or other structure (gen. used on a small-scale copy of one).

'winding, n. The process of turning, or turning something, round and round, sp. some part working a machine (as *w. a*

watch to get it going), or of putting wire, thread etc. on something by taking it round and round it. [Elec.] The current-transporting material in an electric machine when it is in the form of a COIL going round something, as in a DYNAMO or TRANSFORMER (*see* ARMATURE W., FIELD W.); the way in which the w. goes from one part to another of an electric apparatus (*see* SERIES W., SHUNT W.).

'windlass, n. [Mach.] WINCH, sp. a hand-turned one for pulling up water from a WELL or used in old sailing ships.

'window, n. [Phys.] Any opening or bit of material used for letting through certain rays but not others.

wing, n. [Zoo.] An 'arm' or front leg which has undergone development into an instrument of flight (though it may not be of any value for that purpose, as in certain birds) by the growth of feathers or a stretch of skin joining the 'fingers', seen only in birds, CHIROPTERA and PTERODACTYLS; the thin, strong MEMBRANE (one of 2 or 4) forming the flying instrument of an insect; any w.-like expansion, for example, of a bone. [Bot.] ALA. [Airplanes] The right or left half of a supporting PLANE.

'winter egg. [Zoo.] An egg with a thick cover produced in the fall by some non-backboned animals living in inland water, and not undergoing development till the spring (*see* SUMMER EGG).

'winter 'solstice. [Astron.] *See* SOLSTICE.

wired 'wireless. [Radio] The system of sending ELECTROMAGNETIC waves of RADIOFREQUENCY over wires, used for telephoning long distances.

'wireless, n. Radio.

'wisdom tooth. [Zoo.] The upper or lower, right or left, back tooth in man, which undergoes development long after the rest, gen. in the 17th year or later.

'withers, n.pl. [Zoo.] The high sloping part of the back between the SHOULDER-bones in the horse, sheep, cow, and like animals. sp. the horse.

'Wolffian 'body. [Zoo.] The MESONEPHROS of a back-boned animal. **'Wolffian duct.** The pipe-like part draining the W.b., becoming the URETER or UROGENITAL DUCT in lower animals, and the VAS DEFERENS in higher males, but coming to almost nothing in the female of birds, REPTILES and MAMMALS. **'Wolffian ridges.** Short RIDGES running long-ways on the two sides of some EMBRYOS which are the starting-points for the development of the legs.

'wolfram, n. [Chem.] Chemical ELEMENT, at. no. 74, at. wt. 183·92, sign W, a hard grey metal with the highest MELTING POINT (3370°C.) of any metal, used for the wires in electric bulbs, in making very hard steel, and for other purposes—named 'tungsten' up to 1949. [Mineral.] WOLFRAMITE.

'wolframite, n. [Mineral.] Natural (FeMn)WO₄ (*iron manganese tungstate*) a brown-black or grey-black CRYSTALLINE substance from which W is produced.

'Wollaston 'prism. [Optics] A PRISM of some BIREFRINGENT material made up of two equal right-angled prisms with their long faces joined together and so cut that a ray of light going through them is PLANE-POLARIZED into two rays whose VIBRATIONS are at right angles to one another.

womb, n. UTERUS.

wood, n. [Bot., Chem.] XYLEM, which is made up chiefly of COMPOUNDS or LIGNIN and CELLULOSE mixed with some INORGANIC substances. w. 'alcohol, w. 'spirit, [Chem.] METHYL ALCOHOL. w. 'fibre. [Bot.] A long, pointed, dead CELL with specially thick, hard walls, present in w. and acting only as a support, not as a water-pipe. w. 'naphtha. [Chem.] A substance formed chiefly of w. alcohol got by the DESTRUCTIVE DISTILLATION of wood. w. 'opal. [Mineral.] A sort of OPAL formed by the SILICIFICATION of bits of wood bedded in SEDIMENTARY ROCK, in which the structure of the wood whose place has been taken may sometimes be clearly seen. w. ray. [Bot.] XYLEM RAY. w. 'sugar. [Chem.] XYLOSE. w. tin. [Mineral.] A form of CASSITERITE having a FIBROUS structure and a brown colour giving the suggestion of w. '-en, a. Made of w. -'y, a. W.-like. [Bot.] Having a marked amount of w. in its substance or (of a CELL) made hard by the forming of LIGNIN in its walls.

Wood's 'metal. An ALLOY of 50–68% Bi with lead, tin, and Cd, becoming liquid at 71°C. and used where this property is of value for opening VALVES to overcome the danger of overheating (as in boilers) or fire (as in an automatic water-system to keep buildings from burning).

woof, n. WEFT.

wool, n. [Zoo.] An outgrowth of the skin of animals which is hair-like but different from hair in that the separate threads have a cover of very small scales and have in their substance a special fat—naturally shorter than hair, which may be present on the same animal as part of the same coat, and with the property of twisting up, seen chiefly on sheep; the w.-like coat of hair seen on some insects. [Bot.] A thick mass of soft, short, gen. white, hairs, covering a leaf or stem. 'woollen, a. Made of w. 'woolly, a. Of, like, covered with, w.

work, n. [Phys.] The output of ENERGY taking place when the point at which a force is acting is moved in the direction in which it is acting—measured by the force × the distance of the motion, or the turning-force × the angle through which it is moved, and the common units of which are:- [Mech.] The ERG and the FOOT-POUND, and [Elec.] the JOULE. w. 'function. [Phys.] (Of a metal) the amount of ENERGY which has to be given to those of its free ELECTRONS having the greatest energy to give them the power of getting away from the metal.

work, v.t. Get (a material) into a desired condition or form by pushing and pulling it, sp. a metal by hammering and/or rolling it. w-.'hardening. The process causing metal to become harder and stronger as the effect of getting its CRYSTALS broken into smaller ones and changed in position by hammering, rolling, etc.; (of a metal) the undergoing of this process, gen. effected by COLD-WORKING.

'worker, n. [Zoo.] Among insects living in societies, such as ants and bees, any of those, forming the great mass of the group, which are without sex-powers and do all the work of building, food-getting, etc.—gen. females of incomplete sex-development.

'working hy'pothesis. A theory or rule used as a guide for tests and observations because it seems to be of use in that way, though not strongly enough supported by reasoning or current knowledge or in clear enough relation to theories which are so supported, to have, so far, a place in a reasoned account of things.

'working 'substance. [Mech.] The substance used in a machine, gen. a liquid or gas, by the expansion etc. of which the machine-parts are put in operation, sp. the substance in a HEAT ENGINE which first takes in and then gives out heat ENERGY.

worm, n. [Zoo.] A loose general name for a great number of different sorts of non-back-boned animals having in common the properties of being long and thin and having no legs or other outgrowths, such as the common earthworm. [Mach.] The short, turning, screw structure forming part of a w. gear. w. gear. [Mach.] A machine-part for handing on motion, formed of a w. put sideways to the edge of a toothed wheel so that the threads on the w. come one after the other against the teeth of the wheel and keep it turning. w. wheel. The toothed wheel worked by the w. in the w. gear.

wort, n. [Biol.] A liquid made from MALT used in making CULTURES of BACTERIA, etc.

Woulfe 'bottle, Woulfe jar. [Chem.] A glass bottle with two or more necks used for washing gases.

wound, n. [Med., Bot.] Any unnatural hole or parting in a TISSUE, made for example by cutting or disease. **w. cork.** [Bot.] A coating of cork formed under and round ww. in plants to keep damaging substances, disease bodies etc., from getting in. **w. 'hormone.** [Biol.] Any HORMONE which has the power of helping the growth of new TISSUE or any other adjustment of the processes of a plant or animal necessary to overcome the damage of a w.

wrist, n. [Zoo.] CARPUS, sp. in man. **'w.-drop,** n. [Med.] PARALYSIS of the muscles lifting the hand, so that it is impossible to put it, facing down, in a straight line with the outstretched arm, commonly caused by lead-poisoning.

writer's cramp. [Med.] A sudden CRAMP of the finger muscles coming on whenever writing is attempted, caused by overuse of them in writing.

wrought iron, n. Iron with almost no C or other substances in it but mixed with between 1% and 2% of SLAG, forming long, thread-like structures which make it very strong, though it is softer than steel and readily hammered out and WELDED.

'wryneck, n. [Med.] TORTICOLLIS.

X, [Chem.] Sign for an ELECTRONEGATIVE ATOM or group; one of the two signs for XENON, the other being Xe.

'xanthate, n. [Chem.] Any SALT or ESTER of XANTHIC ACID.

'xanthein, n. [Bot., Chem.] A SOLUBLE yellow colouring-substance in plants.

'xanthic, a. [Chem.] Of, to do with, XANTHIN or XANTHINE; to do with x. acid. **x. acid.** [Chem.] $CS(OC_2H_5)SH$, an oil without colour, or any of the group of like THIO-ACIDS.

'xanthene, n. [Chem.] A white CRYSTALLINE RING COMPOUND formed of 3 HC groups and one O ATOM, important for the number of substances which may be produced from it. **x. dyes.** [Chem.] A group of yellow and orange-red DYES having a ring-structure of 4 HC groups, one CO group, and one O ATOM, looked on as produced from x.

'xanthin, n. [Chem.] An INSOLUBLE yellow colouring-substance got from yellow flowers.

'xanthine, n. [Biochem.] A white substance $C_5H_4N_4O_2$, present in the muscles, LIVER, PANCREAS, and, in small amounts, in URINE, produced in the digestion of PROTEINS and forming URIC ACID by reaction with O.

'xanth(o)-. Yellow:- **xantho'carpous,** a., **'xanthodont,** a.

Xan'thochroi, n.pl. [Anthrop.] A division of the CAUCASIAN branch of man made up of the light-haired, white-skinned men of North Europe.

'xantho'chroia, 'xantho'derma, nn. [Med.] An unnatural yellow colouring of the skin.

xan'thochroism, n. [Zoo.] A condition in which yellow takes the place of some or all other colours normally present, as in the skin of certain fish or the feathers of certain birds.

'xantho'chromia, n. [Med.] An unnatural yellow colouring of the skin or any other body substance, sp. the CEREBROSPINAL FLUID.

xan'thochroous, a. [Med.] To do with or having XANTHOCHROIA.

'xanthoderm, n. [Anthrop.] Person of the yellow-skinned branch of man.

xantho'melanous, a. [Anthrop.] Having a yellow skin and black hair.

'xanthophore, n. [Zoo.] A CELL of the outer covering in some fish, CRUSTACEA, etc. producing a yellow colouring-substance.

'xanthophyll, n. [Biochem.] $C_{40}H_{56}O_2$, a yellow colouring-subtance present in plants, gen. together with CAROTENE, the two together forming part of CHLOROPHYLL and being responsible for the yellow colour of falling leaves etc., produced when the chlorophyll has been broken up.

'xanthoplast, n. [Zoo.] Any of the yellow CHROMATOPHORES present in some MASTIGOPHORA.

xan'thopsia, n. [Med.] A condition in which the eye sees everything as yellow, as sometimes in JAUNDICE.

xan'thopsin, n. [Biochem.] A colouring-substance present in the eyes of insects flying by night.

xan'thopterin, n. [Biochem.] The yellow-colouring substance present in the wings of some LEPIDOPTERA.

'xanthous, a. [Anthrop.] Yellow-skinned or to do with the yellow-skinned branch of man.

X-'body. [Bot.] A grain of PROTEIN-like substance formed in a plant-CELL attacked by a VIRUS.

X-'chromosome, n. [Biol.] One of the two sorts of CHROMOSOME by which the sex of offspring is controlled, of which all the SOMATIC CELLS and young GAMETES of one of the sexes (named *the homogametic sex*—in man, it is the female) have two, and the gametes at full development have one, and the somatic cells and only half the gametes of the other (named the *heterogametic sex*) have one, the uniting of two X cc. giving birth to offspring of the homogametic sex (*See* Y-CHROMOSOME.)

Xe, Sign for XENON.

ʹxenia, n. [Bot.] In CROSS-FERTILIZATION, the effect of the POLLEN on the form, colour etc. of fruit or seed produced from it, so that properties of the male are seen in the first stage of development, and not, as normally, only in the plant produced.

xeno-. Different, strange, other than normal; of a different family or sort.

ʹxenoblast, n. [Cryst.] A CRYSTAL not having its natural form because forced into a different one by others round it.

ʹxenocryst, n. [Geol.] A CRYSTAL or grain of a different substance bedded in IGNEOUS ROCK as the effect of overrunning by it when liquid.

xeʹnogamy, n. [Bot.] CROSS-POLLINATION. **xeʹnogamous,** a.

ʹxenolith, n. [Geol.] A small body of ROCK bedded in IGNEOUS ROCK of a different sort as the effect of overrunning by it when liquid.

xenoʹmorphic, a. [Geol.] (Of ROCK structure) in which the MINERALS have not been able to take their normal CRYSTAL form because there has not been room enough for free growth; (of minerals) irregular, unnormal in their crystal structure for this reason.

ʹxenon, n. Chemical ELEMENT, at. no. 54, at. wt. 131·3, sign Xe, or, less commonly, X, one of the INERT GASES, present in the air in very small amount.

xenoʹphya, n.pl. [Zoo.] Bits of material from outside, not made by the animal itself, used in forming the hard outer cover or framework of certain PROTOZOA, sponges, etc.

ʹxerarch, a. [Bot.] (Of a plant SUCCESSION) starting in very dry conditions and going on to more balanced conditions halfway between dry and wet.

ʹxeric, a. [Bot.] (Of plants) XEROPHYTIC; (of a place or conditions) in which the earth and air are very dry, so that a plant gets little water and the loss from normal stems and leaves is at a very quick rate.

xero-. Dry.

xeroʹderm(i)a, n. [Med.] A skin disease in which the skin becomes very dry and rough, rubbing off in thin bits.

xeʹrography, n. A non-chemical process of taking camera pictures in which the camera plate is given an electric CHARGE, which is taken away by light falling on it, so that when the plate is dusted with charged powder a picture is formed.

xeroʹmorphic, a. [Bot.] (Of plants or their parts) having properties of structure like that of a XEROPHYTE, though not necessarily its power of putting up with very dry conditions. **xeroʹmorphy,** n. **ʹxeromorph,** n. A x. plant.

xeʹrophilous, a. [Bot.] (Of plants) living under very dry conditions, doing best with little water.

xerophʹthalmia, n. [Med.] A dry condition of the CONJUNCTIVA, the effect of not getting enough VITAMIN A in the food.

ʹxerophyte, n. [Bot.] A plant with the power of putting up with very dry conditions, going without water for a long time, as the effect of being able to become almost completely dried up without undergoing destruction, or of having special properties of structure by which water is stored or its loss controlled (for example, leaves with a very thick skin or a coating of hairs, or which are of narrow, sometimes needle-like, form so that the SURFACE is small, etc.). **xeroʹphytic,** a.

ʹxerosere, n. [Bot.] A plant SUCCESSION starting on dry land.

xeroʹstomia, n. [Med.] An unnormally dry condition of the mouth.

ʹxiphihumeʹralis, n. [Zoo.] In some backboned animals, a muscle going from the upper bone of the front leg to the XIPHISTERNUM.

xiphiʹsternum, n. [Zoo.] The pointed back end or (in man) lowest part of the chestbone, gen. made of CARTILAGE.

ʹxiphoid, a. In the form of a band with the sides curving or bent suddenly to a point, like certain sorts of fighting-blade. [Zoo.] To do with the XIPHISTERNUM. **x. ʹcartilage.** The XIPHISTERNUM when it is formed of CARTILAGE. **x. ʹprocess.** XIPHISTERNUM.

xiphoʹphyllous, a. [Bot.] Having XIPHOID leaves.

Xiphoʹsura, n.pl. [Zoo.] An ORDER of sea ARACHNIDA of much greater size than most land forms, marked by a CARAPACE in the form of a half-circle and a long, stiff, pointed, tail-part, animals living chiefly on the sea-bed near the land, and going down into the sand for their food, noted for the fact that present-day forms are almost no different from the earliest representative of the group.

X-ray, n. [Phys.] An ELECTROMAGNETIC WAVE of the range of WAVE-LENGTHS ·01 to 50 A.U., produced when CATHODE RAYS come up against a solid substance, and having the properties of IONIZING gases through which they go, of going through solid substances which do not let light through, and of acting on camera plates, FLUORESCENT SCREENS, etc. in the same way as light, the last two powers making them of special value for taking camera pictures of parts inside the body for medical purposes, etc. **X-r. anʹalysis.** [Cryst.] The observation of the ATOMIC structure of CRYSTALS by the use of X-rr., based on the fact that the planes of the ATOMS forming a crystal have the same effect on X-rr. as a DIF-

FRACTION GRATING. **X-r. 'photograph.** A picture of the inside of something, sp. the body, made by sending X-rr. through it to a camera PLATE etc., giving a design in which DENSER material, such as bone, takes the form of dark masses. **X-r. pho'tography.** The taking of X-r. photographs. **X-r. spec'trometer.** [Phys.] An instrument for measuring the WAVE-LENGTHS of X-rr. by their angles of DIFFRACTION on meeting a CRYSTAL of a given substance. **X-r. 'spectrum.** [Phys.] (A picture of the lines representative of) the system of WAVE-LENGTHS of the X-rr. given out by a substance when BOMBARDED by CATHODE RAYS. **X-r. tube.** [Phys.] A VACUUM TUBE designed for producing X-rr., having a CATHODE by which ELECTRONS are sent out in great numbers and go at a great rate to an ANODE (named in this connection an *anticathode* or *target*) of special material, gen. W, from which X-rr. are sent out as an effect of this. **X-radi'ation,** n. The sending out of X-rr., or X-rr. sent out.

X-unit or **X.U.,** n. [Phys.] A unit of WAVE-LENGTH $= 10^{-11}$ cm., used chiefly for giving the wave-lengths of X-RAYS.

'xylan, n. [Chem.] A yellow, sticky substance which may be broken up to give XYLOSE, present in wood, gen. in connection with CELLULOSE.

'xylem, n. [Bot.] The wood of a plant, a material designed for transporting water and liquid food material through the plant and giving it support, made up of VESSELS, WOOD FIBRES, TRACHEIDS, and PARENCHYMA of which the CELL-walls are to some degree LIGNIFIED, formed first from the PROCAMBIUM (*primary x.*) and later produced by the CAMBIUM (*secondary x.*). **x. ray.** [Bot.] That part of a VASCULAR RAY which goes through the x.

'xylene, 'xylol, nn. [Chem.] $C_6H_4(CH_3)_2$, an oil-like liquid present in coal or wood TAR and having 3 ISOMERIC forms present together.

xylo-. Wood:— **'xyloid,** a., **xy'lophagous,** a., **'xylophage,** n. [Chem.] XYLENE; XYLOSE.

'xylocarp, n. [Bot.] A hard, wood-like fruit.

'xylochrome, n. [Bot.] A mixed colouring-substance produced by wood-CELLS before their death and giving its dark colour to HEARTWOOD.

'xylogen, n. [Bot.] XYLEM in process of development.

xy'lology, n. [Bot.] The science of the structure of wood.

xy'lometer, n. An instrument for measuring the DENSITY of wood.

'xylonite, n. Trade name for a CELLULOID-like material used for camera FILMS, etc.

xy'lophilous, a. [Bot.] Having its growth on wood, as certain FUNGI. [Zoo.] Living in or on wood, as certain insect LARVAE etc.

'xylose, n. [Chem.] A white PENTOSE present in a great number of plants, $C_5H_{10}O_5$.

xylo'stroma, (xlyostromata), n. [Bot.] The thick, cloth-like MYCELIUM of certain wood-attacking FUNGI.

Y, Sign for YTTRIUM.

Y-'alloy, Y-'metal, nn. An ALLOY of Al with copper, Mg, Si, nickel and iron, becoming stronger and harder with time after being heated to 500°C. and then put suddenly into cold water.

yard, n. British unit of long measure $= 3$ feet or 91·4399 cm.

yarn, n. Thread for making into cloth, etc.

yaw, n. Of a ship or airplane, give an undesigned turn so that its nose is pointing away from the line of motion desired, be unable to keep going straight as the effect of the push of the wind or water, machine trouble, etc.

yaws, n. [Med.] A CONTAGIOUS skin-disease of very warm countries, caused by a SPIROCHAETE and marked by the forming of bright or dirty red SWELLINGS like those of SYPHILIS, chiefly on the face, toes, and sex parts, sometimes, like syphilis again, later attacking the bones. **yaw,** n. Any of the SWELLINGS formed in y.

Yb, Sign for YTTERBIUM.

Y-'chromosome, n. [Biol.] The SEX-CHROMOSOME present only in the HETERO-GAMETIC SEX, gen. smaller than the X-CHROMOSOME and with a much smaller number of GENES, and having the opposite effect to the X-chromosome, all offspring produced by the uniting of Y GAMETES with X gametes being of the Y sex.

year, n. [Astron.] The time taken by the earth to make one complete journey round the sun, the measure of which is different by minutes when taken in different ways (*see* ANOMALISTIC YEAR, SIDEREAL YEAR, TROPICAL YEAR) but which is fixed for general purposes as 365·2425 MEAN SOLAR DAYS; the y. as used in the CALENDAR, taken as 365 days in three yy. out of every four and as 366 days every fourth y. (named *leap year*).

yeast, n. [Bot.] A substance formed of a mass of any of certain very small one-CELLED FUNGI, most of which are of the ASCOMYCETES, with the important property of producing ENZYMES, causing sugars to be broken up into ALCOHOL and CO_2—seen as a yellow-white coating on the top or as a mass at the base of liquids got from sweet fruits or grain which have been kept for some time, and of great value in making bread and alcohol drinks (sp. beer) and medically for its PROTEINS and VITAMINS; any of the plants or sorts of plant making up y.

'yellow 'fever. [Med.] An ACUTE disease common in the TROPICS, sp. South America, the West Indies, and West Africa, marked by FEVER, VOMITING, INFLAMMATION of the LIVER and KIDNEYS, and loss of blood from the skin and stomach, caused by a FILTER-PASSER given to man by the bite of a flying insect, freq. causing death.

'yellow 'fibre. [Zoo.] Any of the straight, thick, branching, very elastic, yellow FIBRES seen by themselves in a certain sort of CONNECTIVE TISSUE (see WHITE FIBRE). yellow fibro'cartilage. A sort of FIBROCARTILAGE formed chiefly of y. ff.

'yellow snow. [Bot.] Snow covered with a growth of yellow ALGAE, seen sometimes on very high mountains and near the SOUTH POLE.

'yellow spot. [Zoo.] MACULA LUTEA.

yellow 'vision. [Med.] XANTHROPSIA.

yield, n. Output, amount of anything produced by any process.

yield point. [Metal] The TENSION at which a wire, rod etc., of metal goes on stretching without any increase in the force acting on it, and under which, or any higher tension, it after a time gives way completely.

yolk, n. [Zoo.] The store of food-material for the EMBRYO in the OVUM of an animal, made up of NUCLEO-PROTEINS, fat etc.—seen in a bird's egg as a yellow ball in the middle, but different in its distribution and amount in different animals. y. duct. VITELLINE DUCT. y. gland. VITELLARIUM. y. plug. A mass of y.-CELLS stopping up part of the BLASTO-PHORE in some back-boned animals. y. sac. The part like a round bag full of y. hanging from the EMBRYO in a great number of back-boned animals, such as birds and snakes, and opening into its INTESTINE through the y. stalk. y. stalk. The hollow stem joining the y. sac to the EMBRYO.

'Young-'Helmholtz 'theory of 'colour vision. [Zoo., Psych.] TRICHROMATIC THEORY OF COLOUR VISION.

Young's 'modulus. [Phys.] The degree of ELASTICITY of a stretched wire or rod, equal to the RATIO of the stretching force per unit AREA across the wire to the amount by which every unit LENGTH is increased.

Yt, Sign for YTTRIUM.

yt'terbium, n. Chemical ELEMENT, at. no. 70. at. wt. 173·04, sign Yb, gen. looked on as a RARE EARTH METAL. ytt'erbic, a.

'yttrium, n. Chemical ELEMENT, at. no. 39, at. wt. 88·92, sign Y or Yt, gen. looked on as a RARE EARTH METAL. 'yttric, a. 'yttro-.

Z, [Chem.] Sign for ATOMIC NUMBER. [Elec.] Sign for IMPEDANCE.

za'lambodont, a. [Zoo.] (Of INSECTIVORA) having the crushing teeth narrow and with RIDGES in the form of a V.

Zamboni('s) pile. DRY PILE.

'Z-'chromosome, n. [Biol.] Name sometimes used in place of Y-CHROMOSOME when it is the female sex in which it is present.

'Zeeman ef'fect. [Phys.] The division of the lines of a LINE SPECTRUM into groups of lines when the substance or body producing the light is in a strong MAGNETIC FIELD, an effect which may be used as a key to the ATOMIC structure of a substance or for measuring the magnetic field round a star.

'zein, n. [Chem.] A PROLAMINE got from the American Indian CEREAL, *Zea mays.*

'zenith, n. [Astron.] The point on the CELESTIAL SPHERE which is straight over the point of observation on the earth, opp. the NADIR. z. 'distance. The distance of a body in the sky from the z., measured by the angle made at the point of observation by straight lines from the body and the z.

'Zenker's de'generation. [Med.] A form of DEGENERATION marked by the forming of a jelly-like or wax-like substance in STRIATED MUSCLE in certain diseases, sp. TYPHOID FEVER.

'zeolite, n. [Mineral.] Any of a group of natural SILICATES of Al with Na, K, Ca or Ba united with much water, which is readily given up on heating without loss of CRYSTALLINE structure, and as readily taken back from the air, present chiefly in GEODES in IGNEOUS ROCK. z. 'process. A process for SOFTENING water by the use of man-made zz. with Na or K in them, based on their ready exchange of these metals for the Ca in the water.

'Zernicke 'microscope. PHASE-CONTRAST MICROSCOPE.

'zero, n. The number 0; the starting-point on any measuring-scale, sp. on scales of heat, the fixed point (in the CENTIGRADE and other systems (the point at which water becomes ice) from which degrees go up or down, the lower readings having the sign — in front of them, as −1°C.= one degree under z. (*See* ABSOLUTE Z., PHYSIOLOGICAL Z.) **z. 'method.** NULL METHOD. **'z.-point 'energy.** [Phys.] The ENERGY of MOLECULES or atoms at a TEMPERATURE of ABSOLUTE ZERO. **'z.-point vi'bration.** [Phys.] The motion of ATOMS or MOLECULES which is independent of heat and gives them their z.-point energy. **z. po'tential.** [Elec.] The electric POTENTIAL of the earth, by comparison with which other potentials are measured; in a DISCHARGE TUBE with more than two ELECTRODES, the potential of the CATHODE. **z.-'valent.** [Chem.] (Of ELEMENTS or ATOMS) having no power of uniting with other elements or atoms

zinc, n. Chemical ELEMENT, at. no. 30, at. wt. 65·38, sign Zn, a hard, blue-white metal not readily acted on by air, used as a coating for steel, in printing, in a great number of ALLOYS, and commonly in electric CELLS. **z. blende.** [Mineral.] Natural ZnS (*z. sulphide*), one of the chief substances from which the metal is got.

'zincate, n. [Chem.] Any SALT of $Zn(OH)_2$ (*zinc hydroxide*), that is, any substance having in it the group $-ZnO_2$.

'zircon, n. [Mineral.] A stone made up chiefly of $ZrSiO_4$ (*silicate of zirconium*), of wide distribution and different colours, sometimes clear and sometimes valued as a jewel stone, sp. the uncoloured sort.

zir'conium, n. Chemical ELEMENT, at. no. 40, at. wt. 91·22, sign Zr, an uncommon metal present naturally in the earth only united with other substances, sometimes taking the form of a black powder, sometimes of a metal somewhat like iron but white in colour, noted for its powers of keeping free from CORROSION—used in ALLOYS, sp. for ELECTRONIC VALVES and NUCLEAR REACTORS.

Zn, Sign for zinc.

zo'(a)ea, n. [Zoo.] An early LARVAL form of certain DECAPODA, in which the development of the head and the front part of the body are well forward and the divisions of the ABDOMEN are marked, but the back part of the body is thin and with no or only small and incomplete legs etc. **'-form,** a. Looking like a z.

'Zoan'tharia, n.pl. [Zoo.] An order of ANTHOZOA having 6 or more than 8 TENTACLES, which are generally unbranched.

zo'arium (zoaria), n. [Zoo.] The unit animals of a POLYZOAN COLONY taken together. **zo'arial,** a.

'zodiac, n. [Astron.] The circling band of the sky, about 18° wide, with the line of the sun's motion down the middle and

the lines of motion of the moon and all the PLANETS falling inside its limits, cut up into 12 equal divisions from side to side, the signs of the z. (*see* SIGN). **zo'diacal,** a. **zodiacal light.** [Astron.] A feeble light seen (most clearly in the TROPICS) before sun-up and after sun-down, taking up a 3-sided space of sky, with its base on the sky-line and its point in the direction of the sun's motion —caused by the REFLECTION of the sun's rays, but from what is still open to argument.

'zoetrope, n. An old-time apparatus for amusement in which pictures on the inside of a turning, pipe-like structure are seen through narrow openings in its wall and give the effect of a motion picture; name given to early processes of making coloured motion pictures.

'zoic, a. [Zoo.] To do with animals, (of times, etc.) marked by the existence of animals or signs of it. **-zoic.** 1.a. [Biol.] Living, having growth, in or on what is named. 2.a., n. [Geol., etc.] (To do with) an ERA or the group of ROCKS formed in it.

'zoid, n. [Biol.] ZOÖSPORE; ZOOID. **-zoid,** n.

'Zöllner ill'usion. [Psych.] An example of error in judging space relations in which the eye sees as sloping together two lines which are in fact parallel but have a number of short lines going across them at a sharp angle in opposite directions (Zöllner's lines).

'zona, n. [Zoo.] ZONE. **z. pel'lucida, z. 'radiata.** The thick, clear, more or less elastic coat of the OVUM of a MAMMAL, outside the VITELLINE MEMBRANE.

'zonal, a. Of, to do with, a ZONE, having the form of a zone, ranged or living in zones. **z. 'index.** [Geol.] The name of the special FOSSIL representative of a ZONE as used for naming that zone. **z. 'symmetry.** [Zoo.] METAMERISM. **z. view.** [Bot.] (Of a DIATOM) the view of it in which the joining-line of the two halves is seen, opp. VALVAL VIEW. **'zonally,** adv.

'zonary, a. ZONAL. **z. pla'centa.** [Zoo.] A PLACENTA in which the VILLI are ranged in a band round the EMBRYO, seen sp. in CARNIVORA and PROBISCIDEA. **z. placen'tation.** [Zoo.] The condition in which the PLACENTA is a z. placenta.

'zonate, a. Marked with rings or bands going round it, or ranged in such rings or bands, sp. [Biol.]. [Bot.] (Of TETRASPORES) ranged in one line. **zon'ation,** n. The condition of being z., or the forming of rings or bands of different colour or quality, or the way in which such bands are ranged. [Biogeog.] The distribution of plants or animals in clearly limited parts of the earth.

zone, n. Any space or part—of the earth, the sky, the body or any other structure or SURFACE—having more or less clearly-marked limits, sp. one of band-like form. [Biol.] A band of different colour or structure, freq. one going round something. [Biogeog.] A z. of country marked by certain chief sorts of animals and/or plants, or made up of one sort of plant growth, etc.; any of the great divisions of the earth based on the sorts of animals and plants present there. [Geog.] Any of the five great divisions of the earth based on TEMPERATURE conditions, circling the earth between fixed LATITUDES (*see* TORRID Z., TEMPERATE Z., and FRIGID Z.). [Geol.] A part of the structure of the solid outer coat of the earth marked by some special property, make-up, and so on (for example, the SATURATED z.), sp. a division of a STAGE of ROCKS made up of a group of STRATA in which some special FOSSIL or fossil material is markedly present, the name of which is given to the z. [Chem.] A part of a HETEROGENEOUS substance where the MOLECULES are all pointing in the same direction. [Cryst.] A group of CRYSTAL faces whose lines of INTERSECTION are all parallel to a line going through the middle of the crystal (the **z. axis**), and the lines at right angles to which are all in the same plane (the **z. plane**). [Zoo. Psych.] In the eye of man, any of the divisions of the RETINA said by some experts to have different powers of seeing colour. **zz. of 'audi'bility** [Acous.] Zz. outside the AREA to the limits of which a very loud sound, such as that produced by an EXPLOSION is sent in the normal way, and separated from it by zz. where no sound is produced, in which it again becomes AUDIBLE as the effect of REFLECTION of the sound-waves from the upper ATMOSPHERE. **z. plate.** [Optics] A glass plate with a number of OPAQUE rings at different distances from the middle, so designed as to have the effect of a LENS. **z. 'television.** A TELEVISION system in which different parts of the picture are sent separately to the RECEIVER and put together again there. **z. time.** The system of time used in ships' clocks to get GREENWICH MEAN TIME wherever they are, based on the division of the earth into 24 zz. of 15°, or one hour, so numbered that the addition of this number to the time in any z. gives the time as it then is at Greenwich. **'zoned,** a. Having, ringed by, ranged in, zz. **'zoning,** n. The forming of, or separating into or condition of distribution in, zz. [Mineral.] A ROCK structure of bands of different colours or properties round a common middle point, caused by the addition one after the other of coats of somewhat different CRYSTALLINE mat-

erials. **zon(o)-.** Z., ZONAL, ZONALLY.
'zonula cili'aris. [Zool.] ZONULE OF ZINN.
'zonule, n. A small ZONE. **z. of Zinn.** The MEMBRANE joining the CRYSTALLINE LENS of the eye of a back-boned animal to the CHOROID, and keeping it in place.
zoo-. Animal, to do with animals.
'zoöbi'otic, a. [Biol.] Living as a PARASITE on, or in SYMBIOSIS with, an animal.
'zoöchlo'rella (zoöchlorellae), n. [Biol.] Any of a sort of green ALGAE living SYMBIOTICALLY in the body-substance of certain animals, such as COELENTERATA and sponges, and colouring it green.
'zoö'chlor-ic, -ous, aa. [Bot.] (Of seeds or SPORES) undergoing distribution by animals.
zoö'coenocyte, n. [Bot.] The COENOCYTIC ZOÖSPORE of certain green ALGAE.
'zoöcyst, n. SPOROCYST.
zoö'cytium, n. [Zoo.] The common jelly-like and freq. branched support of a COLONY of certain CILIOPHORA.
zoö'dendrium (zoodendria), n. [Zoo.] The tree-like branched stem supporting the units of the COLONY in certain CILIOPHORA.
zo(o)'ecium, n. [Zoo.] The body-wall of a unit of a POLYZOAN COLONY. **zo(o)'ecial,** a.
'zoöga'mete, n. [Biol.] A GAMETE having the power of moving from place to place.
zo'ogamy, n. [Zoo.] The producing of off-spring by a sex-process.
zoö'genesis, n. The coming into being of animals on the earth, and their development into different sorts.
zo'ogenous, a. [Med.] (Of diseases) caused by animals, starting in animals.
'zoöge'ography, n. [Zoo.] The science of the distribution of animals on the earth.
'zoö'gloea, n. [Bot.] A mass of BACTERIA bedded in a sticky or jelly-like substance formed by the taking in of water by the CELL walls, a regular stage of development in certain sorts. **zoö'gloeal,** a.
'zoögoni'dangium (zoögonidangia), n. Unsexed ORGAN producing ZOÖGONIDIA.
'zoögo'nid, 'zoögonidium (zoogonidia), nn. [Bot.] ZoÖSPORE.
zo'ogonous, a. [Zoo.] VIVIPAROUS.
'zooid, 1.a. [Biol.] Animal-like; like, but not having quite the full properties of a separate, independent and self-supporting animal. 2.n. [Biol.] A CELL or SPORE with the power of moving from place to place, as a ZOÖSPORE or SPERMATOZOÖN. [Zoo.] A more or less independent form produced in some way other than by a normal sex-process, sp. one of those forming a stage between sex-produced forms in the development of animals having ALTERNATION OF GENERATIONS, for example, a MEDUSA; any of the units making up a COMPOUND ANIMAL, as seen in PROTOZOA, COELENTERATA, etc., for

example a CORAL POLYP—sometimes limited to those whose only business is the producing of offspring, as BLASTOSTYLES.

'zoö-'lith, -'lite, nn. [Geol.] A FOSSIL animal.

zo'ology, n. A general name for all branches of the science of animals. **zoö'logical,** a. To do with animals or with z. **zo'ologist,** n.

'zooming, n. The process of sending an airplane (or, of an airplane, of going) suddenly higher at a sharper angle than it would be lifted by the engine in normal flight, by using the stored-up force of its forward MOMENTUM. **zoom.** v.t. and i. (Make) undergo this process.

zoö'philia, zo'ophilism, zo'ophily, nn. [Psych.] Love for animals, sp. an unnormal degree of it causing unhealthy impulses, etc.

zo'ophilous, a. [Bot.] (Of plants) POLLINATED by animals other than insects.

zoö'phobia, n. [Med.] An unnormal fear of (certain) animals.

'zoöphyte, n. [Zoo.] Any animal which is plant-like in looks or other properties, such as those of being fixed in one place, of having a branching, tree-like growth, and of producing offspring at some stage by BUDDING, for example, sponges, ANTHOZOA, and HYDROZOA. **zoö'phytic,** a.

zoö'plankton, n. [Zoo.] Animal PLANKTON.

'zoösperm, n. [Biol.] Any swimming SPORE, sexed or unsexed.

'zoöspore, n. [Bot.] An unsexed, uncovered SPORE with one or more CILIA by the motion of which it goes through the water, seen in certain ALGAE and lower FUNGI. [Zoo.] Any of the small swimming SPORES, moving like an AMOEBA or by the motion of CILIA, produced in PROTOZOA by SPORULATION. **'zoöspor'angium,** n. [Bot.] The vessel in which zz. are produced.

zoö'thecium, n. [Zoo.] ZOÖCYTIUM. **zoö'thecial,** a.

zo'otomy, n. [Zoo.] The science of the ANATOMY of animals, sp. of animals other than man.

zoö'toxin, n. [Med., etc.] Any poison produced by an animal, for example by a snake.

zoö'trophic, a. [Biol.] HETEROTROPHIC or HOLOZOIC.

'zoöxan'thella (zoöxanthellae), n. [Biol.] Any of the small yellow or brown one-CELLED ALGAE living SYMBIOTICALLY in certain RADIOLARIANS and colouring their substance.

zoö'xanthin, n. [Biochem.] A yellow colouring-substance present in birds' feathers.

'zoster, n. [Med.] HERPES.

Zr, Sign for ZIRCONIUM.

'zwitterion, n. [Chem.] A complex ION

having two CHARGES, a + and a − charge.

zyga'pophysis (zygapophyses), n. [Zoo.] Any of the outgrowths of the NEURAL ARCH, gen. 4 in number, two at the front and two at the back, by which a VERTEBRA is joined to those coming before and after it. **'zygapo'physeal,** a.

'zyg(o)-. [Biol.] PAIRED, having to do with a PAIR; ZYGOSIS.

zygo'dactyl(e), zygo'dactylous, aa. (Of birds) having two toes pointing forward and two pointing back. **zygo'dactylism,** n.

'zygodont, zygo'dontous, aa. [Zoo.] Having MOLAR teeth of which the 4 CUSPS are united in twos.

zy'goma, n. [Zoo.] The arch of bone at the front or side of the head under the eye in higher back-boned animals. **'zygo'matic,** a. **zygomatic arch.** The z. **'zygo'matico-.**

zygo'morph-ic, -ous, aa. [Biol.] Having BILATERAL SYMMETRY. **'zygo'morphism, 'zygo'morphy,** nn.

'Zygomy'cetes, n.pl. [Bot.] A division of PHYCOMYCETES made up of plants in which the offspring are ZYGOSPORES produced by the coming together of complete GAMETANGIA without the separating of their CELLS into independent GAMETES—generally SAPROPHYTIC but some PARASITIC.

zygo'nema, n. [Biol.] The AMPHITENE STAGE of MEIOSIS.

'zygophore, n. [Bot.] A HYPHA supporting a GAMETANGIUM in ZYGOMYCETES.

'zygophyte, a. [Bot.] A plant producing ZYGOSPORES.

zy'gosis, n. [Biol.] The uniting of two GAMETES, sp. two gametes of like size and form producing a ZYGOSPORE.

'zygo-sperm, -spore, nn. [Bot.] A SPORE formed by the uniting of two GAMETES of like size and form, gen. a thick-walled resting spore, seen sp. in ALGAE and FUNGI. [Zoo.] ZYGOTE.

'zygospor'angium, n. [Bot.] A vessel in which ZYGOSPORES are formed.

zygo'sporophore, n. [Bot.] ZYGOPHORE.

zygo'taxis, n. [Bot.] The attraction between two ZYGOPHORES by which the uniting of the GAMETANGIA is made possible.

'zygote, n. [Biol.] Any CELL formed by the uniting of two sex-cells, a newly-FERTILIZED egg-cell; the plant or animal produced by a z. **zy'gotic,** a. **'zygoto-.**

'zygotene, a. [Biol.] AMPHITENE.

zygo'zoöspore, n. [Bot.] A ZYGOSPORE with the power of moving from place to place.

'zymase, n. [Biochem.] The old name for a complex of ENZYMES present in YEAST by which alcohol and CO_2 are produced from sugars.

'zymic, a. To do with FERMENTATION.

'zymin, n. ENZYME.

zym(o)-. [Chem., Biol., Med.] FERMENTA-
TION or FERMENT: **'zymo'genesis,** n.
zy'mology, n., **zy'mometer,** n.

'zymogen, n. [Biol., Biochem.] A substance
from which an ENZYME is produced in a
plant or animal by the operation of a
KINASE.

zymo'genic, a. [Chem., Biol.] Producing
FERMENTATION; to do with a ZYMOGEN.

zy'molysis, n. [Biochem.] The operation of
ENZYMES or the changes produced by it.

'zymoscope, n. [Biochem.] An apparatus for
measuring the FERMENTING power of a
YEAST by measuring the amount of CO_2
produced from a given amount of sugar.

zy'mosis, n. [Chem., Biochem.] FERMENTA-
TION. [Med.] The operation of BACTERIA,
seemingly FERMENTATION or some very
like process, taking place in INFECTIOUS
diseases. **zy'motic,** 1.a. Of, to do with,
caused by or causing Z. or an INFECTIOUS
disease. 2.n. [Med.] A zymotic disease.

zy'musterol, n. [Biochem.] A STEROL very
like ERGOSTEROL, got from YEAST.

COMMON SHORT FORMS in Chemistry, Physics, etc.

A	ampere	**e.m.f.**	electromotive force
Å	ångström	**e.m.u.**	electromagnetic unit
abs.	absolute	**eqn.**	equation
a.c.	alternating current	**equiv.**	equivalent
amp	ampere	**e.s.u.**	electrostatic unit
anhyd.	anhydrous	**eV**	electronvolt
approx.	approximate(ly)	**expt.**	experiment(al)
aq.	aqueous		
atm	atmosphere (unit of pressure), atmospheric	**°F**	degree(s) Fahrenheit
		F	farad
		fig.	figure (diagram)
at.wt.	atomic weight	**f.p.**	freezing-point
		ft	foot
b	bar (unit)	**ft-lb.**	foot-pound
b.h.p.	brake horse-power		
b.p.	boiling-point	**G**	gauss
Btu	British Thermal Unit	**g**	gramme(s)
		gal	gallon
°C	degree(s) Celsius (or Centigrade)	**giga-**	$\times 10^9$
		gr	grain(s)
cal	calorie or calories		
calc.	calculated	**H**	henry
c.	cubic	**h**	hour
c.c.	cubic centimetre	**hp**	horse-power
cd	candela	**Hz**	hertz
c.d.	current density		
centi-	$\times 10^{-2}$	**i.h.p.**	indicated horse-power
c.g.	centre of gravity	**in**	inch
cm	centimetre	**in²**	square inch
cm²	square centimetre	**in³**	cubic inch
cm³	cubic centimetre	**insol.**	insoluble
coeff.	coefficient	**i.r.**	infra-red
conc.	concentrated		
concn.	concentration	**J**	joule
const.	constant		
corr.	corrected	**°K**	degree(s) Kelvin
crit.	critical	**kc**	kilocycle
cryst.	crystalline	**kcal**	kilocalorie
c/s	cycle per second	**kcps, kc/s**	kilocycles per second
cu.	cubic	**kgf**	kilogramme (force)
cwt	hundredweight	**kg**	kilogramme (mass)
		kilo-	$\times 10^3$
d.c.	direct current		
deci-	$\times 10^{-1}$	**l**	litre
decomp.	decomposition	**L**	lambert
deg.	degree	**lat.ht.**	latent heat
dil.	dilute	**lbf**	pound or pounds (force)
dist.	distilled		
dyn	dyne	**lb**	pound or pounds (mass)
e.h.p.	effective horsepower	**liq.**	liquid

COMMON SHORT FORMS in Chemistry, Physics, etc.

lm	lumen
lx	lux
M	molar concentration
M	molecular weight
m.	mile
m	metre
m²	square metre
m³	cubic metre
max.	maximum
mega-	×10⁶
mg	milligramme(s)
micro-	×10⁻⁶
milli-	×10⁻³
min.	minimum
mol.	molecule, molecular
mol. wt.	molecular weight
m.p.	melting-point
N	newton
N., or N-	normal (solution)
obs.	observed
oz.	ounce
P	poise
p.d.	potential difference
pdl	poundal
ppt.	precipitate
recryst.	recrystallized
rev/min	revolutions per minute

r.h.	relative humidity
r.m.s. or **R.M.S.**	root mean square
s	second
sb	stilb
sec.	second
sol.	soluble
soln.	solution
sp.	specific
sp.gr.	specific gravity
sp.ht.	specific heat
sp. vol.	specific volume
sq.	square (measure, as 'square inch')
s.t.p.	standard temperature and pressure
temp.	temperature
u.v.	ultra-violet
V or v	volt(s) or voltage
vac.	vacuum
v.d.	vapour density
v.p.	vapour pressure
vol.	volume
W	watt
Wb	weber
Wh	watt-hour)
wt.	weight
yd	yard

THE CHEMICAL ELEMENTS—Atomic Weights and Numbers

Element	Symbol	Atomic Number	Atomic Weight	Valency
actinium	Ac	89	227	–
aluminium	Al	13	26·98	3
americium	Am	95	243	–
antimony	Sb	51	121·75	3,5
argon	A	18	39·95	0
arsenic	As	33	74·92	3,5
astatine	At	85	210	–
barium	Ba	56	137·34	2
berkelium	Bk	97	249	–
beryllium	Be	4	9·01	2
bismuth	Bi	83	208·98	3,5
boron	B	5	10·81	3
bromine	Br	35	79·91	1,3,5,7
cadmium	Cd	48	112·40	2
calcium	Ca	20	40·08	2
californium	Cf	98	251	–
carbon	C	6	12·01	2,4
cerium	Ce	58	140·12	3,4
cesium	Cs	55	132·91	1
chlorine	Cl	17	35·45	1,3,5,7
chromium	Cr	24	51·99	2,3,6
cobalt	Co	27	58·93	2,3
columbium, *see* niobium				
copper	Cu	29	63·54	1,2
curium	Cm	96	247	–
dysprosium	Dy	66	162·5	3
einsteinium	Es	99	254	–
erbium	Er	68	167·26	3
europium	Eu	63	151·96	2,3
fermium	Fm	100	253	–
fluorine	F	9	18·99	1
francium	Fr	87	223	1
gadolinium	Gd	64	157·25	3
gallium	Ga	31	69·72	2,3
germanium	Ge	32	72·59	4
gold	Au	79	196·97	1,3
hafnium	Hf	72	178·49	4
helium	He	2	4·0	0
holmium	Ho	67	164·93	3
hydrogen	H	1	1·00	1
indium	In	49	114·82	3
iodine	I	53	126·90	1,3,5,7
iridium	Ir	77	192·2	3,4
iron	Fe	26	55·85	2,3
krypton	Kr	36	83·80	0
lanthanum	La	57	138·91	3
lead	Pb	82	207·19	2,4

THE CHEMICAL ELEMENTS Atomic Weights and Numbers

Element	Symbol	Atomic Number	Atomic Weight	Valency
lithium	Li	3	6·94	1
lutetium	Lu	71	174·97	3
magnesium	Mg	12	24·31	2
manganese	Mn	25	54·94	2,3,4,6,7
mendelevium	Md	101	256	–
mercury	Hg	80	200·59	1,2
molybdenum	Mo	42	95·94	3,4,5,6
neodymium	Nd	60	144·27	3
neon	Ne	10	20·18	0
neptunium	Np	93	237	–
nickel	Ni	28	58·71	2,3
niobium (columbium)	Nb	41	92·91	3,4,5
nitrogen	N	7	14·01	3,5
nobelium	No	102	254	–
osmium	Os	76	190·2	2,3,4,6,8
oxygen	O	8	15·99	2
palladium	Pd	46	106·4	2,3,4
phosphorus	P	15	30·97	3,5
platinum	Pt	78	195·09	2,4
plutonium	Pu	94	242	–
polonium	Po	84	210	–
potassium	K	19	39·10	1
praseodymium	Pr	59	140·91	3
promethium	Pm	61	147	3
protactinium	Pa	91	231	–
radium	Ra	88	226	2
radon	Rn	86	222	0
rhenium	Re	75	186·22	4,6,7
rhodium	Rh	45	102·91	3,4
rubidium	Rb	37	85·47	1
ruthenium	Ru	44	101·07	3,4,6,8
samarium	Sm	62	150·35	2,3
scandium	Sc	21	44·97	3
selenium	Se	34	78·96	2,4,6
silicon	Si	14	28·09	4
silver	Ag	47	107·87	1
sodium	Na	11	22·98	1
strontium	Sr	38	87·62	2
sulphur	S	16	32·06	2,4,6
tantalum	Ta	73	180·95	5
technetium	Tc	43	99	–
tellurium	Te	52	127·60	2,4,6
terbium	Tb	65	158·92	3
thallium	Tl	81	204·37	1,3
thorium	Th	90	232·04	4
thulium	Tm	69	168·93	3
tin	Sn	50	118·69	2,4

THE CHEMICAL ELEMENTS Atomic Weights and Numbers

Element	Symbol	Atomic Number	Atomic Weight	Valency
titanium	Ti	22	47·90	3,4
tungsten (wolfram)	W	74	183·85	6
uranium	U	92	238·03	4,6
vanadium	V	23	50·94	2,3,4,5
xenon	Xe	54	131·30	0
ytterbium	Yb	70	173·04	3
yttrium	Y	39	88·91	3
zinc	Zn	30	65·37	2
zirconium	Zr	40	91·22	4

THE GREEK LETTERS WITH THEIR ENGLISH PARALLELS

A	α	alpha	a		N	ν	nu	n
B	β	beta	b		Ξ	ξ	xi	x
Γ	γ	gamma	g		O	o	omicron	o (short)
Δ	δ	delta	d		Π	π	pi	p
E	ϵ	epsilon	e (short)		P	ρ	rho	r
Z	ζ	zeta	z		Σ	σ	sigma	s
H	η	eta	e (long)		T	τ	tau	t
Θ	θ	theta	th		Υ	υ	upsilon	u
I	ι	iota	i		Φ	φ	phi	ph
K	κ	kappa	k		X	χ	chi	ch
Λ	λ	lambda	l		Ψ	ψ	psi	ps
M	μ	mu	m		Ω	ω	omega	o (long)

ROMAN NUMBERS

I	1	XX	20	CCCC	400
II	2	XXV	25	D	500
III	3	XXX	30	DC	600
IV	4	XXXV	35	DCC	700
V	5	XL	40	DCCC	800
VI	6	XLV	45	DCCCC	900
VII	7	L	50	M	1,000
VIII	8	LV	55	MC	1,100
IX	9	LX	60	MCC	1,200
X	10	LXV	65	MCCC	1,300
XI	11	LXX	70	MCCCC	1,400
XII	12	LXXV	75	MD	1,500
XIII	13	LXXX	80	MDC	1,600
XIV	14	LXXXV	85	MDCC	1,700
XV	15	XC	90	MDCCC	1,800
XVI	16	XCV	95	MDCCCC	1,900
XVII	17	C	100	MM	2,000
XVIII	18	CC	200	$\bar{V}$	5,000
XIX	19	CCC	300	$\bar{M}$	1,000,000

PERIODIC TABLE OF ELEMENTS

(for Atomic Weights, see table, page **550**)

	Group 0	A Group 1 B	A Group 2 B	A Group 3 B	A Group 4 B
I		hydrogen (H) 1			
II	helium (He) 2	lithium (Li) 3	beryllium (Be) 4	boron (B) 5	carbon (C) 6
III	neon (Ne) 10	sodium (Na) 11	magnesium (Mg) 12	aluminium (Al) 13	silicon (Si) 14
A IV B	argon (A) 18	potassium (K) 19 29 copper (Cu)	calcium (Ca) 20 30 zinc (Zn)	scandium (Sc) 21 31 gallium (Ga)	titaneum (Ti) 22 32 germanium (Ge)
A V B	krypton (Kr) 36	rubidium (Rb) 37 47 silver (Ag)	strontium (Sr) 38 48 cadmium (Cd)	yttrium (Y) 39 49 indium (In)	zircon (Zr) 40 50 tin (Sn)
A VI B	xenon (Xe) 54	caesium (Cs) 55 79 gold (Au)	barium (Ba) 56 80 mercury (Hg)	rare earths* 81 thallium (Tl)	hafnium (Hf) 72 82 lead (Pb)
VII	radon (Rn) 86		radium (Ra) 88	actinides†	

* Rare Earth Series: lanthanum (La) 57, cerium (Ce) 58, praseodymium (Pr) 59, neodymium (Nd) 60, illinium (Il) 61, samarium (Sm) 62, europium (Eu) 63, gadolinium (Gd) 64, terbium (Tb) 65, dysprosium (Dy) 66, holmium (Ho) 67, erbium (Er) 68, thulium (Tm) 69, ytterbium (Yb) 70, lutecium (Lu) 71.

† Actinide Series: actinium (Ac) 89, thorium (Th) 90, protactinium (Pa) 91, uranium (U) 92, neptunium (Np) 93, plutonium (Pu) 94, americium (Am) 95, curium (Cm) 96, berkelium (Bk) 97, californium (Cf) 98, einsteinium (Es) 99, fermium (Fm) 100, mendelevium (Md) 101, nobelium (No) 102.

A Group 5 B	A Group 6 B	A Group 7 B	Group 8
nitrogen (N) 7	oxygen (O) 8	fluorine (F) 9	
phosphorus (P) 15	sulphur (S) 16	chlorine (Cl) 17	
vanadium (V) 23 33 arsenic (As)	chromium (Cr) 24 34 selenium (Se)	manganese (Mn) 25 35 bromine (Br)	iron (Fe) 26. cobalt (Co) 27 nickel (Ni) 28
columbium (Cb) 41 51 antimony (Sb)	molybdenum (Mo) 42 52 tellurium (Te)	technetium (Tc) 43 53 iodine (I)	ruthenium (Ru) 44 palladium (Pd) 46 rhodium (Rd) 45
tantalum (Ta) 73 83 bismuth (Bi)	tungsten (W) 74 84 polonium (Po)	rhenium (Re) 75	osmium (Os) 76 platinum (Pt) 78 iridium (Ir) 77

HOMOLOGOUS SERIES OF ORGANIC CHAIN COMPOUNDS

Group	General formula	One carbon atom	Two carbon atoms
paraffins	RH	methane CH_4	ethane C_2H_6
alkyl halides	RX	methyl halide CH_3X	ethyl halide C_2H_5X
alcohols	ROH	methyl alcohol CH_3OH	ethyl alcohol C_2H_5OH
acids	$RC\overset{\displaystyle O}{\underset{OH}{<}}$	formic acid $HC\overset{\displaystyle O}{\underset{OH}{<}}$	acetic acid $CH_3C\overset{\displaystyle O}{\underset{OH}{<}}$
aldehydes	$RC\overset{\displaystyle O}{\underset{H}{<}}$	formaldehyde $HC\overset{\displaystyle O}{\underset{H}{<}}$	acetaldehyde $CH_3C\overset{\displaystyle O}{\underset{H}{<}}$
amides	$RC\overset{\displaystyle O}{\underset{NH_2}{<}}$	formamide $HC\overset{\displaystyle O}{\underset{NH_2}{<}}$	acetamide $CH_3C\overset{\displaystyle O}{\underset{NH_2}{<}}$
amines	RNH_2	methylamine CH_3NH_2	ethylamine $C_2H_5NH_2$
nitro compounds	RNO_2	nitromethane CH_3NO_2	nitroethane $C_2H_5NO_2$

Three carbon atoms	Four carbon atoms	Five carbon atoms	Six carbon atoms
propane C_3H_8	butane C_4H_{10}	pentane C_5H_{12}	hexane C_6H_{14}
propyl halide C_3H_7X	butyl halide C_4H_9X	amyl halide $C_5H_{11}X$	hexyl halide $C_6H_{13}X$
propyl alcohol C_3H_7OH	butyl alcohol C_4H_9OH	amyl alcohol $C_5H_{11}OH$	hexyl alcohol $C_6H_{13}OH$
propionic acid $$C_2H_5C\overset{\displaystyle O}{\underset{\displaystyle OH}{}}$$	butyric acid $$C_3H_7C\overset{\displaystyle O}{\underset{\displaystyle OH}{}}$$	valeric acid $$C_4H_9C\overset{\displaystyle O}{\underset{\displaystyle OH}{}}$$	caproic acid $$C_5H_{11}C\overset{\displaystyle O}{\underset{\displaystyle OH}{}}$$
propionaldehyde $$C_2H_5C\overset{\displaystyle O}{\underset{\displaystyle H}{}}$$	butyraldehyde $$C_3H_7C\overset{\displaystyle O}{\underset{\displaystyle H}{}}$$	valeraldehyde $$C_4H_9C\overset{\displaystyle O}{\underset{\displaystyle H}{}}$$	caproic aldehyde $$C_5H_{11}C\overset{\displaystyle O}{\underset{\displaystyle H}{}}$$
propionamide $$C_2H_5C\overset{\displaystyle O}{\underset{\displaystyle NH_2}{}}$$	butyramide $$C_3H_7C\overset{\displaystyle O}{\underset{\displaystyle NH_2}{}}$$	valeramide $$C_4H_9C\overset{\displaystyle O}{\underset{\displaystyle NH_2}{}}$$	hexylamide $$C_5H_{11}C\overset{\displaystyle O}{\underset{\displaystyle NH_2}{}}$$
propylamine $C_3H_7NH_2$	butylamine $C_4H_9NH_2$	amylamine $C_5H_{11}NH_2$	hexylamine $C_6H_{13}NH_2$
nitropropane $C_3H_7NO_2$	nitrobutane $C_4H_9NO_2$	nitropentane $C_5H_{11}NO_2$	nitrobexane $C_6H_{13}NO_2$

GEOLOGICAL TIME-TABLE

Time Interval (Millions of Years)	Period or Epoch and Rock System	Era	Biological and Geological Events
	Recent	Quaternary	Start of society. Development of man.
1 million years back	Pleistocene or Glacial		Earliest man.
10 — 10	Pliocene	Tertiary	Greatest development of mammals.
25 — 15	Miocene		Increase of mammals.
40 — 15	Oligocene		Start of present-day mammals.
60 — 20	Eocene		Earliest form of horse. Alps and Himalayas formed.
70 — 30	Palaeocene		The earliest forms of mammals.
135 — 65	Cretaceous	Mesozoic	Great reptiles come to an end. Andes and Pyrenees formed.
180 — 45	Jurassic		Grasses and flowering plants. Great winged and other reptiles. Sierra Nevada and Atlas mountains formed.
220 — 40	Triassic		Great development of reptiles and ammonites. Gymnosperms chief plants.

GEOLOGICAL TIME-TABLE

Time Interval (Millions of Years)	Period or Epoch and Rock System	Era	Biological and Geological Events
50 ⎱ 270	Permian	Palaeozoic	Sea vertebrates become common. Trilobites come to an end. Appalachian mountains formed.
80 ⎱ 350	Upper Carboniferous (Pennsylvanian)		First great reptiles and amphibians. Great development of Archegoniatae.
	Lower Carboniferous (Mississippian)		First fossil winged insects. Coal beds formed.
50 ⎱ 400	Devonian		Fish in great number. Earliest land plants. Coal beds put down.
40 ⎱ 440	Silurian		The oldest amphibians—the first air-breathing animals.
60 ⎱ 500	Ordovician		Sea animals in great number of most invertebrate sorts. The earliest fish.
100 ⎱ 600	Cambrian		Trilobites the chief sort of living things. Musci.
400 ⎱ 1000	Proterozoic	Pre-Cambrian	The earliest forms of living things of which we have signs—Protozoa, sponges, Algae, worms.
2000 ⎱ 3000	Archaeozoic		Mountain-building and sea-forming time.—The start of living things.
3000 ⎱ 6000	Azoic		Before the start of living things.

559

THE CHIEF GROUPS IN THE CLASSIFICATION OF PLANTS

The Vegetable Kingdom				
Sub-Kingdom	Division (or Phylum)	Class	Sub-Class	Order
Thallophyta	Schizophyta	Schizomycetes (Bacteria)		
	Myxophyta	Myxomycetes		
	Algae	Bacillario- phyceae (Diatoms)		
		Cyanophyceae		
		Chlorophyceae		
		Phaeophyceae		
		Rhodophyceae		
	Fungi	Phycomycetes		
		Ascomycetes		
		Basidiomycetes		Ustilagines
				Uredinales
	Lichenes	Ascolichenes		
		....		
		....		
Archegoniatae	Bryophyta	Hepaticae Musci		
	Pteridophyta			Psilotales
				Lycopodiales
				Equisetales
				Filicales

Sub-Kingdom	Division (or Phylum)	Class	Sub-Class	Order
Spermatophyta	Gymnospermae	Coniferae		Coniferales Ginkgoales
				Cycadales
	Angiospermae	Monocotyle-dones		
		Dicotyledones	Monochlamy-deae	
			Polypetalae	
			Sympetalae	

THE CHIEF GROUPS IN THE CLASSIFICATION OF ANIMALS

The Animal Kingdom					
Sub-Kingdom	Phylum	Sub-Phylum	Class	Sub-Class	Order
Protozoa	Protozoa		Mastigophora		
			Sarcodina		
			Ciliophora		
			Sporozoa		
Parazoa	Porifera				
Metazoa	Coelenterata	Cnidaria	Hydrozoa		
			Scyphozoa		
			Anthozoa		
		Ctenophora			
	Platy-helminthes		Turbellaria		
			Trematoda		
			Cestoda		
	Nemertinea				
	Nematoda				
	Trochel-minthes		Rotifera		
	Annelida		Chaetopoda	Polychaeta	
				Oligochaeta	
			Archiannelida		
			Hirudinea		
	Arthropoda	Crustaceae	Branchiopoda		Cladocera
			Copepoda		
			Cirripedia		
			Malacostraca	Eucarida	Decapoda
				Peracarida	Amphipoda
					Isopoda
		Myriapoda			

562

Sub-Kingdom	Phylum	Sub-Phylum	Class	Sub-Class	Order
Metazoa *contd.*	Arthropoda *contd.*	Insecta	Apterygota		
			Pterygota	Endopterygota	Aphaniptera
					Coleoptera
					Diptera
					Hymenoptera
					Trichoptera
				Exopterygota	Anopleura
					Dermaptera
					Ephemeroptera
					Hemiptera
					Isoptera
					Mallophaga
					Odonata
					Orthoptera
		Arachnida			Scorpionida
					Araneida
					Acarina
	Mollusca		Lamellibranchia		
			Gastropoda		
			Cephalopoda	Dibranchia	Decapoda
	Brachyiopoda				
	Polyzoa				
	Echinodermata		Asteroidea		
			Echinoidea		
			Holothuroidea		
			Ophiuroidea		
			Crinoidea		
	Chordata	Hemichorda			

Sub-Kingdom	Phylum	Sub-Phylum	Class	Sub-Class	Order
Metazoa *contd.*	Chordata *contd.*	Urochorda	Ascidaceae		
		Cephalo-chorda			
		Vertebrata	Cyclostomata		
			Elasmo-branchii	Holocephali	
			Pisces	Ganoidei	
				Teleostei	
				Crossopterygii	Dipnoi
			Amphibia		Apoda
					Urodela
					Salientia
			Reptilia		Chelonia
					Loricata
					Rhyncho-cephalia
					Squamata
			Aves		
			Mammalia	Prototheria	Monotremata
				Metatheria	Marsupalia
				Eutheria	Edentata
					Sirenia
					Cetaceae
					Proboscidea
					Hyracoidea
					Artiodactyla
					Perissodac-tyla
					Rodentia
					Carnivora
					Insectivora
					Chiroptera
					Primates

BRITISH WEIGHTS AND MEASURES

Linear measure (unit is the inch)

1 inch	=	2·54 centimetres
12 inches	=1 foot	=3·05 decimetres
3 feet	=1 yard	=9·144 decimetres
5½ yards	=1 rod, pole or perch	=5·029 metres
40 poles	=1 furlong (220 yards)	=2·012 hectometres
8 furlongs	=1 mile (1760 yards)	=1·61 kilometres

Square measure (unit is the square inch)

1 square inch	=	6·452 square centimetres
144 square inches	=1 square foot	=9·290 square decimetres
9 square feet	=1 square yard	=0·836 square metre
30¼ square yards	=1 square rod, pole or perch	=25·292 square metres
40 square poles	=1 rood	=10·116 square decametres
4 roods	=1 acre	=40·47 square decametres
640 acres	=1 square mile	=2·590 square kilometres

Cubic measure (unit is the cubic inch)

1 cubic inch	=	16·387 cubic centimetres
1728 cubic inches	=1 cubic foot	=28·318 cubic decimetres
27 cubic feet	=1 cubic yard	=0·765 cubic metres

Troy weight

1 grain	=	0·065 grams
24 grains	=1 pennyweight	=1·555 grams
20 pennyweights	=1 ounce	=31·104 grams

Avoirdupois weight (unit is the ounce)

1 dram	=	1·772 grams
16 drams	=1 ounce	=28·350 grams
16 ounces	=1 pound	=453·592 grams
14 pounds	=1 stone	=6·35 kilograms
28 pounds	=1 quarter	=12·7 kilograms
4 quarters	=1 hundredweight	=50·8 kilograms
20 hundredweights	=1 ton	=1·016 tonnes

Liquid measure (unit is the pint)

1 gill	=	0·142 litre
4 gills	=1 pint	=0·568 litre
2 pints	=1 quart	=1·136 litres
4 quarts	=1 gallon	=4·546 litres

Dry measure (unit is the peck)

1 peck	=	9·092 litres
4 pecks	=1 bushel	=3·637 decalitres
4 bushels	=1 quarter	=2·909 hectolitres

THE METRIC SYSTEM
Linear measure (unit is the metre)

10 millimetres	= 1 centimetre	= 0·393 inch
10 centimetres	= 1 decimetre	Move decimal point
10 decimetres	= 1 metre	one place to the right
10 metres	= 1 decametre	for every later unit.
10 decametres	= 1 hectometre	
10 hectometres	= 1 kilometre	
10 kilometres	= 1 myriametre	

Square measure (unit is the are = 100 square metres)

10 centiares	= 1 deciare	= 11·960 square yards
10 deciares	= 1 are	Move decimal point
10 ares	= 1 decare	two places to the right
10 decares	= 1 hectare	for every later unit.

(Unit is the square metre)

100 square millimetres	= 1 square centimetre	= 0·155 square inch
100 square centimetres	= 1 square decimetre	Move decimal point
100 square decimetres	= 1 square metre	two places to the right
100 square metres	= 1 square decametre	for every later unit.
100 square decametres	= 1 square hectometre	
100 square hecto-metres	= 1 square kilometre	

Liquid measure (unit is the litre)

10 centilitres	= 1 decilitre	= 0·176 pint
10 decilitres	= 1 litre	Move decimal point
10 litres	= 1 decalitre	one place to the right
10 decalitres	= 1 hectolitre	for every later unit.
10 hectolitres	= 1 kilolitre	
10 kilolitres	= 1 myrialitre	

Mass (unit is the gram)

10 milligram	= 1 centigram	= 0·000353 ounce
10 centigram	= 1 decigram	Move decimal point
10 decigram	= 1 gram	one place to the right
10 gram	= 1 decagram	for every later unit.
10 decagram	= 1 hectogram	
10 hectogram	= 1 kilogram	
10 kilogram	= 1 myriagram	
10 myriagram	= 1 quintal	
10 quintals	= 1 millier or tonne	

CONVERSION FACTORS
Length

inches to centimetres	multiply by	2·54
centimetres to inches		0·394
feet to centimetres		30·48
centimetres to feet		0·033
metres to feet		3·280
feet to metres		0·305
yards to metres		0·914
metres to yards		1·094
rods to metres		5·029
metres to rods		0·199
furlongs to kilometres		0·201
kilometres to furlongs		4·971
miles to kilometres		1·609
kilometres to miles		0·621

Area

square inches to square centimetres	6·452
square centimetres to square inches	0·155
square feet to square metres	0·092
square metres to square feet	10·763
square yards to square metres	0·836
square metres to square yards	1·196
acres to hectares	0·405
hectares to acres	2·471
square miles to square kilometres	2·590
square kilometres to square miles	0·386

Volume

cubic inches to cubic centimetres	16·387
cubic centimetres to cubic inches	0·061
cubic feet to cubic metres	0·028
cubic metres to cubic feet	35·315
cubic yards to cubic metres	0·765
cubic metres to cubic yards	1·308

Velocity

feet per second to metres per second	0·305
metres per second to feet per second	3·281
feet per second to kilometres per hour	1·097
kilometres per hour to feet per second	0·911
miles per hour to metres per second	0·447
metres per second to miles per hour	2·237
miles per hour to kilometres per hour	1·609
kilometres per hour to miles per hour	0·621

CONVERSION FACTORS

Mass

graines to gram	multiply by 0·065
gram to graines	15·432
ounces to gram	28·350
kilogram to ounces	35·274
pounds to kilogram	0·454
kilogram to pounds	2·205
hundredweights to kilogram	50·802
tonnes to hundredweights	19·684
tons to tonnes	1·016
tonnes to tons	0·984